environment

THE SCIENCE BEHIND THE STORIES

P9-CFE-251

environment

THE SCIENCE BEHIND THE STORIES

SECOND CANADIAN EDITION

JAY WITHGOTT

SCOTT BRENNAN

BARBARA MURCK
University of Toronto Mississauga

PEARSON

Toronto

Vice-President, Editorial Director: Gary Bennett
Senior Acquisitions Editor: Lisa Rahn
Senior Marketing Manager: Kim Ukrainec
Senior Developmental Editor: Darryl Kamo
Project Managers: Marissa Lok, Rachel Thompson
Manufacturing Manager: Susan Johnson
Production Editor: Heidi Allgair
Copy Editor: Sally Peyrefitte

Proofreader: Tara Tovell
Compositor: Element
Permissions Researcher: Derek Capitaine
Art Director: Julia Hall
Cover and Interior Designer: Miguel Acevedo
Cover Image: Cover photo © Edward Burtynsky, courtesy
Nicholas Metivier, Toronto

Credits and acknowledgments of material borrowed from other sources and reproduced, with permission, in this textbook appear on the appropriate page within the text or on page CR-1.

Original edition published by Pearson Education, Inc., Upper Saddle River, New Jersey, USA. Copyright © 2013 Pearson Education, Inc. This edition is authorized for sale only in Canada.

If you purchased this book outside the United States or Canada, you should be aware that it has been imported without the approval of the publisher or the author.

Copyright © 2013 Pearson Canada Inc. All rights reserved. Manufactured in the United States of America. This publication is protected by copyright and permission should be obtained from the publisher prior to any prohibited reproduction, storage in a retrieval system, or transmission in any form or by any means, electronic, mechanical, photocopying, recording, or likewise. To obtain permission(s) to use material from this work, please submit a written request to Pearson Canada Inc., Permissions Department, 26 Prince Andrew Place, Don Mills, Ontario, M3C 2T8, or fax your request to 416-447-3126, or submit a request to Permissions Requests at **www.pearsoncanada.ca**.

10 9 8 7 6 5 4 3 2 1 [CKV]

Library and Archives Canada Cataloguing in Publication

Withgott, Jay
    Environment : the science behind the stories / Jay Withgott, Scott Brennan, Barbara Murck.–2nd Canadian ed.

Includes bibliographical references and index.
ISBN 978-0-321-73936-0

1. Environmental sciences–Textbooks. I. Brennan, Scott R II. Murck, Barbara W. (Barbara Winifred), 1954- III. Title.

GE105.W58 2012   363.7   C2011-906804-4

Environmental Statement

This book is carefully crafted to minimize environmental impact. Pearson Canada is proud to report that the materials used to manufacture this book originated from sources committed to sustainable forestry practices, tree harvesting, and associated land management. The binding, cover, and paper come from facilities that minimize waste, energy usage, and the use of harmful chemicals.

Equally important, Pearson Canada closes the loop by recycling every out-of-date text returned to our warehouse. We pulp the books, and the pulp is used to produce other items such as paper coffee cups or shopping bags.

The future holds great promise for reducing our impact on Earth's environment, and Pearson Canada is proud to be leading the way in this initiative. From production of the book to putting a copy in your hands, we strive to publish the best books with the most up-to-date and accurate content, and to do so in ways that minimize our impact on Earth.

PEARSON

ISBN 978-0-321-73936-0

Brief Contents

Contents

4 EVOLUTION, BIODIVERSITY, AND POPULATION ECOLOGY 89

CENTRAL CASE
STRIKING GOLD IN A COSTA RICAN CLOUD FOREST 90

7 SOIL RESOURCES   179

10 FORESTS AND FOREST MANAGEMENT   286

CENTRAL CASE
BATTLING OVER THE LAST BIG TREES AT CLAYOQUOT SOUND   287

11 MINERAL RESOURCES AND MINING 316

12 FRESHWATER SYSTEMS AND WATER RESOURCES 339

13 MARINE AND COASTAL SYSTEMS AND FISHERIES   373

14 ATMOSPHERIC SCIENCE AND AIR POLLUTION   405

CENTRAL CASE
THE RAIN AND THE BIG NICKEL   406

16 FOSSIL FUELS: ENERGY USE AND IMPACTS   486

18 MANAGING OUR WASTE   561

19 ENVIRONMENTAL HEALTH AND HAZARDS   593

22 ENVIRONMENTAL POLICY: DECISION MAKING AND PROBLEM SOLVING 688

23 STRATEGIES FOR SUSTAINABILITY 722

Preface

To the Student

This is a unique time in human history. Within your lifetime, our global society must chart a promising course for a sustainable future, or its future will be at risk. The stakes could not be higher, and the path we take will depend largely on how we choose to interact with our environment.

Today we live long lives enriched with astonishing technologies, in societies more free, just, and equitable than ever before. We enjoy wealth on a scale our ancestors could not have dreamed. Yet we have purchased these things at a price. By tapping into Earth's resources and ecological services, we are depleting our planet's bank account and running up its credit card balance. Never before has Earth had so many people making so many demands upon it. We are altering the land, air, water, nutrient cycles, biodiversity, and climate, rapidly and fundamentally. More than ever before, the future of our society rests with how we treat the world around us.

In this book you will learn a lot about environmental problems, but you will also learn about the truly innovative ways that people solve these problems. Sometimes environmental problems can seem overwhelming, but every challenge also represents an opportunity. Now is the time for innovation and creativity and for the fresh perspective that a new generation offers. You and your fellow students are *key* to achieving a sustainable future for our civilization. Your decisions, actions, discoveries, and entrepreneurial spirt will make all the difference.

Environmental science helps show us how Earth's systems function and how we influence these systems. It gives us a big-picture understanding of the world and our place within it. Studying environmental science helps us to comprehend the problems we create, and it can help us to find solutions for those problems. This is not just another course in your university or college program; it relates to everything that is around you, and it will resonate for the rest of your life.

Environmental science is part of the basic literacy of the twenty-first century. The more you learn about it, the better off you will be, so please allow yourself to become engaged with this book, this course, and this subject matter. It is important not only for your own life, but for all of us. Your ideas and energy *will* make a difference, and will help to shape the future of our environment and our society.

To the Professor

The complaint we most frequently hear from students in environmental science courses is that the deluge of environmental problems seems overwhelming. In the face of so many problems, students often come to feel that there is no hope or that there is little they can personally do to make a difference. We aimed to counter this impression by drawing out innovative solutions that have worked, are being implemented, or can be tried in the future. We do not paint an unrealistically rosy picture of the challenges which lie ahead, but we portray dilemmas as opportunities and try to instill hope and to encourage action.

Both the original *Environment: The Science Behind the Stories* and the Canadian editions of the book have grown from our professional experiences in teaching, research, and writing. Jay Withgott has synthesized and presented science to a wide readership. His experience in distilling and making accessible the fruits of scientific inquiry shaped the book's content and the presentation of its material. Scott Brennan has taught environmental science to thousands of undergraduates and developed an intimate feeling for what works in the classroom. His knowledge and experience have shaped the book's pedagogical approach. Barbara Murck brings to this strong team more than 20 years of experience teaching environmental science and Earth science to undergraduates at the University of Toronto, and 15 books published in related fields. She is an award-winning lecturer who has worked on finding practical solutions to environmental problems from Toronto to Niger to Vietnam.

We sincerely hope that our efforts will come close to being worthy of the immense importance of our subject matter. We invite you to let us know how well we have achieved our goals and where you feel we have fallen short. We are committed to continual improvement and value your feedback, as does the team at Pearson Canada. Please feel free to write and send comments or suggestions to Barbara Murck at barbara.murck@utoronto.ca and to Lisa Rahn of the Pearson editorial team at lisa.rahn@pearsoned.com.

Jay Withgott, Scott Brennan, and Barbara Murck

The Canadian Edition

When we embarked upon writing a first Canadian edition of *Environment: The Science Behind the Stories*, we endeavoured to produce a book that represents a truly Canadian perspective of environmental science while maintaining the powerful teaching and learning tools of the American edition. We wanted to tell students about the great, sometimes groundbreaking, work done by Canadian environmental scientists. We wanted to celebrate our environmental heroes and heroines, achievements, and history and to familiarize students with the people, locations, and events of that history with examples from coast to coast to coast.

During these first years of the Canadian edition, we have enjoyed receiving feedback and suggestions from adopters and reviewers across Canada. You, our users, have told us that you appreciate the truly Canadian focus of the book, as well as the balanced approach and the integration of science with policy. You like the rigour and the breadth and depth of coverage and value our efforts to represent environmental issues from all corners of this vast country and around the world. You also welcome the clarity and liveliness of the writing and the visual program.

What's New in the Second Canadian Edition?

For the second Canadian edition we maintain all of the aforementioned strengths, while enhancing the Canadian content, clarifying the overall structure, and updating the book as a whole. We responded to your suggestions for new examples, additions, and, where needed, conceptual reorganization. You will discover many new and updated graphs, photos, and tables, as well as new end-of-chapter questions.

In this edition, we have reworked Chapter 2 (Matter, Energy, and the Physical Environment) to provide a more coherent introduction to the basics of environmental science and to Planet Earth as the substrate for all environmental processes. We introduce the concept of ecosystems earlier (in Chapter 3). We dedicate an entire chapter to soils (Chapter 7, Soil Resources) with material on agriculture and food now grouped more effectively in Chapter 8 (Agriculture, Food, and Biotechnology). The new edition also offers a brand new chapter, Mineral Resources and Mining (Chapter 11), filling a content gap from the first edition in an area that is crucial for the Canadian environment and economy.

In the second Canadian edition, 19 out of the 23 "Central Cases" have a Canadian focus. Several cases are new, including "A Different Way of Doing Business" in Chapter 23, "Mining for . . . Cell Phones?" in Chapter 11, "Saving the Polar Bear: What Will It Take?" in Chapter 9, and "The Retreat of the Athabasca" in Chapter 15. These cases present the stories that our students *need* to know if we are to move forward in our search for environmental solutions, rather than repeating the mistakes of the past.

This edition showcases numerous new "The Science Behind the Story" features, including examples of exciting and innovative work by Canadian scientists. One example is "Tip Jets and NADW off the Coast of Greenland" (in Chapter 13, Marine and Coastal Systems and Fisheries), which profiles the contributions of physicist Kent Moore to our understanding of the formation of North Atlantic Deep Water. Most chapters now contain just one "The Science Behind the Story"—but don't worry, the pieces you enjoyed in the first edition are not gone; they have joined the library of information and learning tools available on the companion website at www.myenvironmentplace.ca.

Roots: The Language of Environmental Science

A brand new feature in the second Canadian edition is "Roots," which introduces students to the origins of some of the scientific terminology they need to know to be conversant in the language of environmental science. Learning the origins of words and their relationships to other familiar words can help students remember the terms more easily and expand their scientific vocabulary more effectively.

roots

PHOTOSYNTHESIS

The term **photosynthesis** is a combination of two Greek roots, *phos*, meaning "light," and *syntithenai*, meaning "to put together." The word thus nicely describes the chemical process of photosynthesis, in which light energy is used to recombine molecules to make sugars. You will find the prefix *photo-* in many terms that are important in environmental science, and it always indicates the involvement of light.

Canadian Environmental Perspectives

At the end of each chapter, we introduce Canadians who have contributed in a wide variety of ways to our understanding of the environment. Some of the individuals profiled are famous; others are regular people making everyday contributions to environmental knowledge and management. Some are scientists; a number are not. Some are controversial. Some work in the private sector, some in the public sector, some in nonprofits, and some in academia. Our goal is to inspire young environmental scientists to realize that there are *many* different ways of approaching the study of the environment. We also wanted to explore the differences between environmentalism and environmental science more fully, to help students understand that these are fundamentally distinct approaches but that they can and do often inform one another.

Integrated Central Cases

Telling compelling stories about real people and real places is the best way to capture students' interest. Narratives with concrete detail also help teach abstract concepts because they give students a tangible framework with which to incorporate new ideas. We integrate each chapter's "Central Case" into the main text, weaving information and elaboration throughout the chapter. In this way, the concrete realities of the people and places of the central case study demonstrate the topics we cover. Students and instructors using the book have lauded this approach, and we hope it can continue to bring about a new level of effectiveness in environmental science education.

The Athabasca Glacier has retreated about 1.5 km since 1844. Markers show the annual retreat of the end, or toe, of the glacier.

CENTRAL CASE:
THE RETREAT OF THE ATHABASCA

"Warming of the climate system is unequivocal."
—INTERGOVERNMENTAL PANEL ON CLIMATE CHANGE, *FOURTH ASSESSMENT REPORT*

"We're in a giant car heading towards a brick wall and everyone's arguing about where they're going to sit."
—DAVID SUZUKI

The Athabasca Glacier is one of six valley glaciers that flow like huge rivers of ice from the Columbia Icefield, which straddles the border between Jasper and Banff National Parks. The Columbia Icefield, which sits among some of the highest peaks in the Canadian Rockies, is a remnant of the massive glacial ice that covered much of Canada during the Pleistocene glaciation. The Athabasca Glacier itself is about 6 km long and between 90 and 300 m in thickness.

Glaciers, although they consist of solid ice, flow (very slowly) under the influence of gravity. There are two main mechanisms for glacial flow. The first involves *internal deformation* of the crystals of ice. This is something like what would happen if you were to press down and slightly sideways on a deck of cards: the cards would slide past one another. Similarly, the ice crystals in the glacier slide translationally along internal planes of weakness. The second main flow mechanism is called *basal sliding*. This happens when a layer of meltwater lubricates the contact between the glacial ice and the underlying rock. Both mechanisms are probably at work in the Athabasca Glacier, which is moving downslope at a rate of a few centimetres per day.

Glaciers also grow and shrink in both volume and area, driven by changes in temperature and precipitation. When more snow falls than can melt in a year, the snow becomes compressed by additional snowfall and

CANADIAN ENVIRONMENTAL PERSPECTIVES

Eira Thomas

Eira Thomas has been dubbed Canada's "Queen of Diamonds."

- **Exploration geologist**
- Former **CEO** and **President** of Stornoway Diamond Corp.
- One of *Canada's Top 40 Under 40*, 2004

Eira Thomas began her career as a geologist earlier than most. At eight years old, she and her sister began to accompany their geologist father on summer expeditions to mineral exploration camps outside Yellowknife, Northwest Territories. Later, as an undergraduate at the University of Toronto, Thomas was attracted to the cross-disciplinary nature of geology. "I wasn't one of those individuals who went to university knowing exactly what I wanted to do. I was interested in science. I chose geology because it was more of a generalist science, encompassing physics and chemistry and biology."

After graduation, Thomas returned to the Northwest Territories to work with Aber Resources, the exploration company started by her father. In 1994 and 1995 (aged 26), she led the team of exploration geologists that discovered the site that would eventually become Diavik Diamond Mine. (A photo of the Diavik Mine opens the chapter on environmental ethics and economics.) Only the second producing diamond mine in Canada, Diavik went into production in 2003 and is one of the highest-grade diamond deposits in the world.

Thomas served as vice president of exploration for Aber for two years. Until August, 2011 she was president and CEO of Stornoway Diamond Corp. and remains actively involved with many other business-related ventures (mining in 2011, she was the recipient of Canada's Top 40 Under 40" award.

However, field geology remains her passion. "I spent a lot of time travelling around with my father, prospecting in the North.... It's a pretty infectious type of business, especially when you're a child and you're out prospecting along and looking for things. It's the ultimate treasure-hunting career." Thomas is also devoted to Canada's North. She believes strongly that diamond development is important for long-term economic growth and social development in the North, where unemployment is often extremely high. She was instrumental in establishing a partnership with Nunavut Tunngavik, an

Aboriginal organization set up to ensure that promises made under the Nunavut Land Claims Agreement are carried out. Mining in Canada's North takes place in environmentally sensitive locations. Says Thomas, "Diamond mining requires no chemicals and has a limited impact on the landscape. We leave a very small footprint and don't need any infrastructure. You can fly out a week's worth of production in a suitcase."

"There is something magical about the North, and we are very involved with the local communities with regard to training initiatives. I spoke with an elder and he explained how he wanted his grandson to go to university. But he also needs to find a reason for his grandson to come back home."
—Eira Thomas

Thinking About Environmental Perspectives

Eira Thomas feels strongly that mining is important for the economic and social prosperity of Canada's North. Many Aboriginal leaders agree. But mining can be highly disruptive to the environment. What kinds of steps should mining companies be required to take to ensure a proper balance between environmental costs and economic or social benefits? What role should Aboriginal leaders and organizations play in making decisions regarding exploration and mining on traditional lands?

The Science Behind the Story

Our goal is not simply to present students with facts, but to engage them in the scientific process of testing and discovery. To do this, we feature "The Science Behind the Story" boxes, which expand upon particular studies, guiding readers through details of the research. In this way we show not merely *what* scientists discovered, but *how* they discovered it. Instructors and students confirm that this feature enhances comprehension of chapter material and deepens understanding of the scientific process itself—a key component of effective citizenship in today's science-driven world.

THE SCIENCE BEHIND THE STORY

Tip Jets and NADW off the coast of Greenland

Dr. Kent Moore of the University of Toronto in a research plane over the North Atlantic.

The formation of North Atlantic Deep Water (NADW), in which extremely cold water sinks in the northern part of the Atlantic to join the deep oceanic circulation, is an integral part of the global thermohaline circulation. It is also crucial for keeping the northern Atlantic basin connected to the rest of the global circulation system. If NADW formation were suppressed, the warm Gulf Stream current—responsible for the relatively mild climate of northeastern North America and Western Europe—could be cut off from entering the North Atlantic, with devastating climatic consequences for this region and globally.

Given its importance, it is surprising to learn that ocean water sinks to form NADW only under extremely specific conditions, and these conditions occur in just a handful of geographic locations in the North Atlantic. What's more, as Professor Kent Moore from the University of Toronto and his colleagues have discovered, the sinking of cold ocean water is also dependent upon highly specialized conditions in the atmosphere off the coast of Greenland.

To investigate the conditions under which NADW forms, Dr. Moore deploys scientific buoys in the North Atlantic, which measure the temperature and other characteristics of ocean water (yes, pretty much like the buoys in the first part of the movie *The Day After Tomorrow*). With data from these buoys, he is able to pinpoint the exact locations where ocean water

becomes cold and dense enough to sink, becoming NADW.

Dr. Moore, an atmospheric physicist, and colleagues have also investigated the role of the atmosphere in oceanic circulation in this part of the Atlantic. They do this by comparing satellite imagery and buoy data to information they collect by flying aboard a research plane equipped with scientific instruments for measuring a wide variety of atmospheric conditions. The aircraft, a modified four-engine passenger jet, is nicknamed FAAM (Facility for Airborne Atmospheric Measurements).

The scientists have discovered that the topography of Greenland plays a fundamental role in oceanic circulation in the North Atlantic, and specifically determines the locations where NADW circulation can be triggered. High-speed wind events, with wind speeds greater than 25 m/sec, are common near the southern end of Greenland, which acts as a massive topographic barrier. The topographic barrier funnels and directs the winds in one direction or another, forming very narrow

high-speed wind streams over the adjacent ocean. These events are called *tip jets* (or *reverse tip jets*, depending on the direction of flow) and Dr. Moore describes the experience of flying through one of these high-speed wind streams as "rough."

What Dr. Moore and his colleagues have discovered, in particular, is that tip jets and related wind events are intimately associated with the formation of NADW. The high-speed winds have the effect of drawing warmth away from surface ocean water, cooling it sufficiently to increase its density and trigger sinking. The locations where this occurs are extremely localized because of the narrow channeling of winds that must pass either around or over the topographic barriers formed by the coast of Greenland.

Given the importance of NADW and the thermohaline circulation system in regulating climate, particularly around the North Atlantic, Professor Moore agrees that there is much fundamental research that needs to be carried out to improve our understanding of these atmospheric and oceanic processes and connections.

Extremely focused, high-speed wind events called tip jets, like this one off Cape Farewell on the southern coast of Greenland, are crucial in the formation of North Atlantic Deep Water because they draw heat away from surface water. In this figure, based on satellite imagery from February 2007, wind speeds are shown in metres per second.

Weighing the Issues

Students need critical-thinking skills to navigate the grey areas at the juncture of science, policy, and ethics. We aim to develop these skills with "Weighing the Issues" questions in each chapter. These serve as stopping points for students to absorb and to reflect upon what they have read, to wrestle with some of the complex dilemmas in environmental science, and to engage in spirited classroom discussion.

weighing the issues

COASTAL DEVELOPMENT

A developer wants to build a large marina on an estuary in your coastal town. The marina would boost the town's economy but eliminate its salt marshes. As a homeowner living adjacent to the marshes, how would you respond?

End-of-Chapter Features

Each chapter concludes with features that facilitate review and develop critical-thinking skills. "Reviewing Objectives"

summarizes each chapter's main points and relates them to the learning objectives presented at the chapter's opening, enabling students to confirm that they have understood the most crucial concepts. "Testing Your Comprehension" questions provide concise study questions targeted to main topics in each chapter, while "Thinking It Through" questions encourage broader creative thinking aimed at finding solutions. "Interpreting Graphs and Data" uses figures from recent scientific studies to help students build quantitative and analytical skills in reading graphs and making sense of data. "Calculating Footprints," now available on the companion website at www.myenvironmentplace.ca, enables students to calculate the environmental impacts of their own choices and then see how individual impacts scale up to impacts at the societal level.

The Teaching and Learning Package

We have prepared an excellent supplements package to accompany the text.

For the Student

www.myenvironmentplace.ca Created specifically for this text, this site features review exercises that provide automatic feedback, activities to expand understanding of environmental science, an electronic version of this text, and resources for further exploration. Available 24/7, this personal study portal allows students to access the online materials they need to succeed in their courses.

Study on the Go At the end of each chapter, you will find a unique QR code providing access to *Study on the Go*, an unprecedented mobile integration between text and online content. Students link to Pearson's unique *Study on the Go* content directly from their smartphones, allowing them to study whenever and wherever they wish! Go to one of the sites below to see how you can download an app to your smartphone for free. Once the app is installed, your phone will scan the code and link to a website containing Pearson's *Study on the Go* content, including popular study tools such as Quizzes and more, which can be accessed anytime.

ScanLife
http://getscanlife.com/

NeoReader
http://get.neoreader.com/

QuickMark
http://www.quickmark.com.tw/

For the Professor

Instructor's Resource CD ROM (ISBN 978-0-321-77525-2)
This aid provides quick and easy access to a wealth of valuable teaching tools, including an Instructor's Manual, TestGen Test Bank, Test Item File, PowerPoint Slides, and Image Library. Please do not hesitate to contact your Pearson campus representative if you are missing any resources or are uncertain how to access any of the instructor resources.

Instructor's Manual (ISBN 978-0-321-78457-5)
The Instructor's Manual includes lecture outlines, teaching notes which integrate material from the chapter, discussions of "Weighing the Issues" and "The Science Behind the Story" features, suggestions for supplementary print and online resource material, and solutions to end-of-chapter questions and problems.

TestGen Test Generator (ISBN 978-0-321-77523-8)
Pearson TestGen is a special computerized test file that enables instructors to view and edit existing questions, add questions, generate tests, and print tests in a variety of formats. This test bank contains approximately 1400 questions and includes multiple-choice, short-answer, graphing, and scenario based items. For all questions, we identify a suggested answer, an associated learning objective, and a difficulty level of easy, moderate, or difficult. The Pearson TestGen is compatible with Windows or MacIntosh systems.

PowerPoint Slides (ISBN 978-0-321-77521-4)
Our colourful electronic slides are available in Microsoft PowerPoint®. The slides highlight, illuminate, and build on key concepts in the text.

Image Library (ISBN 978-0-321-78282-3)
The Image Library is an impressive resource to help instructors create vibrant lecture presentations. Almost every figure and table from the text is provided in electronic format and is organized by chapter for convenience. These images can be imported easily into Microsoft PowerPoint to create new presentations or to add to existing ones.

Technology Specialists
Pearson's Technology Specialists work with faculty and campus course designers to ensure that Pearson technology products, assessment tools, and online course materials are tailored to meet your specific needs. This highly qualified team is dedicated to helping schools take full advantage of a wide range of educational resources by helping to integrate a variety of instructional materials and media formats. Your local Pearson Canada sales representative can provide you with more details on this service program.

CourseSmart
CourseSmart goes beyond traditional expectations, providing instant online access to the textbooks and course materials you need in an environmentally friendly format. You can save time and hassle with a digital eTextbook that allows you to search for the most relevant content at the very moment you need it. Whether it's evaluating textbooks or creating lecture notes to help students with difficult concepts, CourseSmart can make life a little easier. See how when you visit www.coursesmart.com.

Acknowledgements

A textbook is the product of *many* more minds and hearts than one might guess from the names on the cover. All three of us have been exceedingly fortunate to be supported and guided, through this and previous editions of the book, by a tremendous publishing team and a small army of experts in environmental science who have generously shared their time and expertise. Although we alone, as authors, bear responsibility for any inaccuracies, the strengths of this book result from the collective labour and dedication of innumerable people.

As the author of the Canadian edition I am extremely grateful to the team at Pearson Canada for its support, advice, and professionalism throughout the development of both Canadian editions. Special thanks go to Gary Bennett, Vice President, Editorial Director. Many thanks also to Sherry Zweig, Senior Sales Representative, who first got me involved with this project and with Pearson Canada.

I especially want to thank Darryl Kamo, Senior Developmental Editor, for his expert advice, feedback, and encouragement throughout the writing and development of this second Canadian edition, but especially for his patience. Darryl, thanks for giving me so much leeway and for believing all of my excuses. I told you I would make it! I also wish to extend special thanks to Michelle Sartor, Editor-in-Chief; Lisa Rahn, Senior Acquisitions Editor; Kim Ukrainec, Senior Marketing Manager; Heidi Allgair, Associate Director, Full Service; Marissa Lok and Rachel Thomson, Project Managers; and Sally Peyrefitte, Copy Editor; Derek Capitaine, Photo Researcher; for their dedication to quality and for overseeing this Canadian edition's journey into print.

I would also like to thank Carolyn Winsborough, a Ph.D. candidate from the University of Toronto, who helped to research words for the new "Roots" feature. Lastly, for the second Canadian edition I would like to thank my ever-patient family, who happily put up with a perpetually temporary office on the dining room table, as well as my colleagues, friends, and generations of students at the University of Toronto Mississauga.

We dedicate this book to today's students, who will shape tomorrow's world.

(for Jay Withgott and Scott Brennan) Barbara Murck

Reviewers

We have been guided in our efforts by extensive input from colleagues across Canada who have served as reviewers and advisors for the both Canadian editions, in addition to the contributions of many reviewers for the U.S. editions. The participation of so many learned and thoughtful experts has improved the book in countless ways and has made this edition much stronger. If the thoughtfulness and thoroughness of these reviewers are any indication, we feel confident that the teaching of environmental science is in excellent hands!

Sarah Boon, *University of Lethbridge*
John Buschek, *Carleton University*
Varun Gupta, *University of Toronto Mississauga*
Walter A. Illman, *University of Waterloo*
Dalton Irwin, *Natural Resources*
Robert K. Loney, *Trent University*
Paul McMillan, *Capilano University*
Scott Munro, *University of Toronto Mississauga*
Ann-Lise Norman, *University of Calgary*
Maxwell Ofosuhene, *Trinity Western University*
Mary Olaveson, *University of Ontario Institute of Technology*
Brian O'Neill, *Holland College*
David F. Scott, *University of British Columbia Okanagan*
Piotr Trela, *Memorial University*
Stephen Turnbull, *University of New Brunswick*
Frank Williams, *Langara College*

Jay H. Withgott is a science and environmental writer with a background in scientific research and teaching. He holds degrees from Yale University, the University of Arkansas, and the University of Arizona. As a researcher, he has published scientific papers on topics in ecology, evolution, animal behaviour, and conservation biology in journals including *Proceedings of the National Academy of Sciences, Proceedings of the Royal Society of London B, Evolution*, and *Animal Behavior*. He has taught university-level laboratory courses in ecology, ornithology, vertebrate diversity, anatomy, and general biology. Jay has authored articles for a variety of journals and magazines including *Science, New Scientist, BioScience, Smithsonian, Current Biology, Conservation in Practice*, and *Natural History*. He combines his scientific expertise with his past experience as a reporter and editor for daily newspapers to make science accessible and engaging for general audiences. Jay lives with his wife, biologist Susan Masta, in Portland, Oregon.

Barbara Murck has taught environmental and Earth science at the University of Toronto Mississauga for more than 20 years. Her academic background is in geology, with degrees from Princeton University and the University of Toronto. Barb has worked on a wide variety of environmental management projects in the developing world, from Africa to Asia, mainly as an expert on training and curriculum development. She has published numerous books on topics ranging from physical geology to environmental science to sustainability. She was honoured with the University of Toronto President's Teaching Award in 2010. She lives with her family, including the world's best cat and dog, in a 110-year-old house in Southern Ontario. When not at work, she is likely to be found hiking the Bruce Trail. She greatly appreciates having had the opportunity to influence the lives and learning of thousands of students over the years.

Scott Brennan has taught environmental science, ecology, resource policy, and journalism at Western Washington University and at Walla Walla Community College. He has also worked as a journalist, photographer, and consultant.

About the cover . . .

"We've never stopped taking things from nature. Even the act of taking from the earth is natural since we are not outside of nature. What is different today is the scale. Current society is searching for a way to come to terms with that taking from the earth. Recycling is one way we can put a stop to a certain amount of damage to the earth. This material comes from and collects around urban centres in large recycling yards. These yards are like secondary mines."

"The 'Urban Mines' photographs are a testament to Burtynsky's ability to balance the form and content of his images. He avoids emphasizing content to the point where his photographs might become *reportage*, but includes enough information so that they are more than mere exercises in formalism."

extracts from the book: *Manufactured Landscapes* essay: *Seeing the Big Picture* by Lori Pauli—National Gallery of Canada.

environment

THE SCIENCE BEHIND THE STORIES

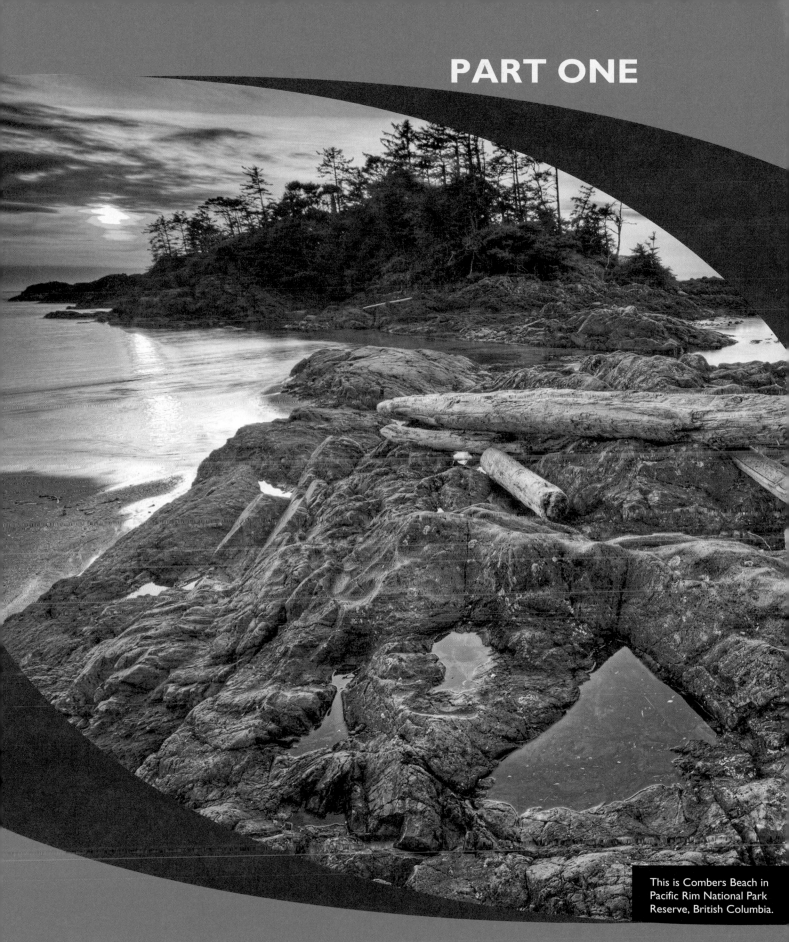

PART ONE

This is Combers Beach in Pacific Rim National Park Reserve, British Columbia.

FOUNDATIONS OF ENVIRONMENTAL SCIENCE

An Introduction to Environmental Science

Earth is like an island.

Upon successfully completing this chapter, you will be able to

- Define the term *environment*
- Describe natural resources and explain their importance to human life
- Characterize the interdisciplinary nature of environmental science

- Understand the scientific method and how science operates
- Diagnose and illustrate some of the pressures on the global environment
- Articulate the concepts of sustainability and sustainable development

Crescent Earth, in the first photo of the whole planet.

CENTRAL CASE:
EARTH FROM SPACE: THE POWER OF AN IMAGE

"The two-word definition of sustainability is 'one planet.'"
—MATHIS WACKERNAGEL, ECOLOGICAL ECONOMIST AND CO-DEVELOPER OF THE ECOLOGICAL FOOTPRINT CONCEPT

"We're not the first to discover this, but we'd like to confirm, from the crew of *Apollo 17*, that the world is round."
—EUGENE CERNAN, *APOLLO 17* COMMANDER

*C*onsider the following: Prior to November 9, 1967, no one had *ever seen* a photograph of the whole planet Earth, because no such thing existed.

Those of us who were alive back in 1967 were not completely clueless. We knew that Earth is a planet, surrounded by space. We knew that Earth is round (although visual confirmation of this fact still made a considerable impact on *Apollo 17* astronauts a few years later). Yet a simple photograph of Earth—floating in space, blue and shining and covered by clouds, vegetation, and a whole lot of water—managed to take everyone by surprise and changed both society and history in the process.

Actually, the very first photographs of the whole Earth, taken in 1967, were not the ones that eventually caught the imagination of the general public. The 1967 photographs were taken by automated camera from the unmanned *Apollo 4* spacecraft, the first spacecraft to get far enough away from Earth to photograph the entire planet. Only part of the planet was in sunlight, so the photographs show only a "crescent" Earth (see photo). Not long after, on December 24, 1968, *Apollo 8* astronauts took the first hand-held photographs showing Earth rising over the horizon of the Moon (the closing photo of this book). The crew did a live radio broadcast that day, during which astronaut James Lovell commented, "The Earth from here is a grand oasis in the big vastness of space."[1]

It was not until 1972 that the *Apollo 17* mission put astronauts in a position to photograph the entire *illuminated* planet Earth. The result was the famous Blue Marble[2] image, a version of which opens this chapter. The photograph was beautiful, its impact stunning, even unsettling. The original image was oriented with Antarctica at the top of the globe and an "upside-down" Africa in the middle. The unfamiliar perspective caused consternation among those who had never stopped to consider that the convention of orienting maps with north at the top is completely arbitrary.

The Blue Marble photograph is widely credited with kick-starting the modern environmental movement. Just five years elapsed between the first whole-Earth photographs in 1967 and the last ones to be recorded by human hands. (Since 1972, no manned space flight has been far enough away for the planet to be photographed in its entirety by astronauts.) In that five-year period was the summer of love, and war—the Vietnam War, the Six Days War, the Cold War. The Beatles sang on the first live international satellite television production. Canada celebrated the hundredth year of Confederation. Neil Armstrong became the first person to walk on the Moon. Civil rights activist Martin Luther King, Jr., died; so did J. Robert Oppenheimer, the "father of the atomic bomb." The first hand-held calculator was sold (for almost $400).

Society changed dramatically during those five years, and it was a period of dawning awareness and public involvement in environmental issues. The first major oil spill happened in 1967, when the *Torrey Canyon* ran aground near England with 120 000 tonnes of crude oil on board. The first hints of trouble began to surface (literally) from hazardous chemicals stored underground at Love Canal, New York. Within a few years the site would be infamous, leading to the first declaration of an environmental state of emergency in the United States and making a grassroots hero of local activist Lois Gibbs. Books on environmental topics began to appear on bestseller lists, including *Limits to Growth,*[3] *The Population Bomb,*[4] *Small Is Beautiful,*[5] and their predecessor, *Silent Spring.*[6] The 1970s opened with the signing of the first federal environmental legislation, the United States' *Environmental Protection Act* (1970). The first Earth Day was held (1970). Greenpeace was founded (1971). The *United Nations Environment Programme* was established (1972).

British astronomer Sir Frederick Hoyle is reputed to have said, in 1948, "Once a photograph of the Earth, taken from outside, is available—once the sheer isolation of the Earth becomes known—a new idea as powerful as any in history will be let loose." To what extent were these and subsequent milestones in environmental history descended from the first glimpses of our planet from space, with all of its fragility and limitations? We will never know with certainty, but the Blue Marble is considered to be one of the most influential photographs in history—possibly the most widely distributed image of all time—and it remains an iconic symbol of the modern environmental movement.

Our Island, Earth

Viewed from space, our home planet appears suspended against a vast inky-black backdrop. Although few of us will ever witness that sight directly, photographs taken from space convey a sense that Earth is small, isolated, and fragile. From an astronaut's perspective it is apparent that Earth and its natural systems are not unlimited. As our population, our technological powers, and our consumption of resources increase, so does our ability to alter our planet and damage the very systems that keep us alive.

Our environment is more than just our surroundings

A photograph of Earth reveals a great deal, but it does not adequately convey the complexity of our environment. Our **environment** is more than water, land, and air; it is the sum total of our surroundings. It includes all of Earth's **biotic** components, or living things, as well as the **abiotic** components, or nonliving things, with which we interact. Our environment has abiotic constituents—the continents, oceans, clouds, rivers, and icecaps that you can see in the photo of Earth from space. It also has biotic con-

roots

ENVIRONMENT

The term **environment** dates from the 1600s. It has the same roots as the Old French verb *environer* (now *environner*), meaning "to encircle" or "to surround." The root word is *viron*, meaning "circle," originating from the verb *virer*, "to turn." Adding the prefix *en-*, meaning "in," creates the literal definition of *environ*, which is "in circle." The suffix *-ment* comes from the Latin *-mentum*, which was used to convert a verb into a noun.

stituents—the animals, plants, forests, soils, and people that occupy the landscape. In a more inclusive sense, it also encompasses the built environment—the structures, urban centres, and living spaces humans have created. In its *most* inclusive sense, our environment includes the complex webs of scientific, ethical, political, economic, and social relationships and institutions that shape our daily lives.

Environment

People commonly use the term *environment* in a narrower sense—of a nonhuman or "natural" world apart from human society. This connotation is unfortunate, because it masks the important fact that humans exist within the environment and are a part of the interactions that characterize it. As one of many species, we share with others a fundamental dependence on a healthy, functioning planet. The limitations of language make it all too easy to speak of "people and nature," or "society and the environment," as though they were separate and did not interact. However, the fundamental insight of environmental science is that we are part of the natural world, and our interactions with its other parts matter a great deal.

Why is it important that we give careful consideration to the meaning of the term *environment*? Back in 1970, when the federal government passed Canada's first environmental legislation, the environmental awareness of most North Americans was limited. If they thought about it at all, most people would have equated *environment* with *wilderness*, although this oversimplification was changing as public consciousness of environmental issues grew. Wilderness preservation is still an important concern, but our understanding of the environment, our impacts on it, and its role in our health and daily lives has broadened dramatically.

Today our definition of *environment* must be sufficiently comprehensive to include its legal, social, economic, and scientific aspects. Consequently, the mandate of **Environment Canada** is equally comprehensive:[7] to preserve and enhance the quality of Canada's natural environment, conserve our renewable resources, and protect our water resources. International relations, politics, ethics, business management, economics, social equity, engineering, law enforcement—all of these now play a role in managing and protecting the environment.

To accomplish this, our environmental leaders and policymakers need to know what they are talking about. As a community, we must constantly improve and refine our basic scientific understanding of water, air, land and soils, wildlife, weather and climate, and the dynamic interactions among all the components of which ecosystems are composed. That is where *environmental science*—the central focus of this book—comes in.

Environmental science explores interactions between humans and the physical and biological world

Appreciating how we interact with our environment is crucial for a well-informed view of our place in the world and for a mature awareness that we are one species among many on a planet full of life. Understanding our relationship with the environment is vital because we are altering the natural systems we need, in ways we do not yet fully comprehend.

We depend utterly on our environment for air, water, food, shelter, and everything else essential for living. However, our actions modify our environment, whether we intend them to or not. Many of these actions have enriched our lives, bringing us longer life spans, better health, and greater material wealth, mobility, and leisure time; however, many of them have damaged the natural systems that sustain us. Such impacts as air and water pollution, soil erosion, and species extinction compromise the well-being of living organisms, pose risks to human life, and threaten our ability to build a society that will survive and thrive in the long term. The natural environment was functioning long before the human species appeared, and we would be wise to do our best to maintain its integrity and keep its key elements in place.

Environmental science is the study of how the natural world works, how our environment affects us, and how we affect our environment. We need to understand our interactions with—and our role in—the environment. Such knowledge is the essential first step toward devising solutions to our most pressing environmental problems.

Many environmental scientists are taking this step, trying to apply their knowledge to develop solutions to the many environmental challenges we face. Part 1 of this book provides an introduction to the abiotic and biotic components of our environment, and to the basic concepts and principles of science as applied to the study of the environment.

It can be daunting to reflect on the magnitude of environmental dilemmas that confront us today. We will examine these challenges and issues in Part 2, starting with a look at the human population itself and how it has grown and changed over time.

Fortunately, with these problems also come countless opportunities for devising creative solutions. Right now, global conditions are changing more quickly than ever. Right now, through science, we as a civilization are gaining knowledge more rapidly than ever. And right now, the window of opportunity for acting to solve problems is still open. With such bountiful challenges and opportunities, this particular moment in history is an exciting time to be studying environmental science. This book will show you how to apply your knowledge of environmental science to begin an exploration of solutions for our current challenges.

Natural resources are vital to our survival

Islands are finite, and their inhabitants must cope with limitations in the material resources. On our island, Earth, human beings, like all living things, ultimately face environmental constraints. Specifically, there are limits to many of our **natural resources**, the various substances and energy sources we need to survive. We can view the renewability of natural resources as a continuum from the most to the least renewable (**FIGURE 1.1**).

Natural resources that are replenishable over short periods are **renewable natural resources**. Some renewable resources, such as sunlight, wind, and wave energy, are perpetually renewed and essentially inexhaustible. Others renew themselves more slowly, and they may become nonrenewable if we use them at a rate that exceeds the rate at which they are renewed or replenished. Populations of animals and plants that we harvest from the wild may be renewable if we do not overharvest them but may vanish if we do.

Renewable resources such as groundwater and soil can be harvested according to principles similar to those that govern living resources. However, the rate of regeneration of such resources is limited by the rates of physical processes, such as the infiltration of groundwater to replenish an aquifer, or the physical and chemical weathering of rock to produce soil. Because these rates can be quite slow—it can take up to 10 000 years for soil formation to occur in cold climates like those of northern Canada, for example—it may take a very long time for these resources, once damaged or depleted, to be replenished.

Resource management is strategic decision making and planning aimed at balancing the use of a resource with its protection and preservation. The basic premise of renewable resource management—for both living and nonliving resources—is to balance the *rate of withdrawal* from the stock with the *rate of renewal* or *regeneration*. The **stock** is the harvestable portion of the resource. If the stock is being harvested or withdrawn at a faster rate than it can be replenished—faster than trees can be seeded and grow to maturity or faster than fish can be born and grow to a harvestable age or faster than precipitation can infiltrate to replenish the groundwater—then the stock will eventually be depleted. Renewable resources are sometimes called *stock-and-flow resources*, highlighting the importance of this balance in their management.

FIGURE 1.1
Natural resources lie along a continuum from perpetually renewable to nonrenewable. Perpetually renewable or inexhaustible resources, such as sunlight, will always be there for us. Nonrenewable resources, such as oil and coal, exist in limited amounts that cannot be renewed on a humanly accessible time scale and could one day be gone. Other resources, such as timber, groundwater, soils, and food crops, can be renewed if we are careful not to deplete them or damage them.

Renewable natural resources
- Sunlight
- Wind energy
- Wave energy
- Geothermal energy

- Agricultural crops
- Fresh water
- Forest products
- Soils

Nonrenewable natural resources
- Crude oil
- Natural gas
- Coal
- Copper, aluminum, and other metals

In contrast, **nonrenewable natural resources**, like fossil fuels and mineral deposits, are in finite supply and are depletable, because they are formed *much* more slowly than we use them; it can take 100 million years for natural geological processes to form an ore deposit or a petroleum deposit. Once we use them up, they are no longer available because they will not be replenished on a humanly accessible time scale. Simply by withdrawing from the stock we are depleting the resource. These resources lie at the other end of the continuum in **FIGURE 1.1**.

Our civilization depends on numerous minerals: Iron is mined and processed to make steel. Copper is used in pipes, electrical wires, and a variety of other applications. Aluminum is extracted via bauxite ore and used in packaging and other end products. Lead is used in batteries, to shield medical patients from radiation, and in many other ways. Zinc, tungsten, phosphate, uranium, gold, silver—the list goes on and on. Although we rely on these resources, we do not manage their extraction in the way we manage renewable natural resources. Like fossil fuels, minerals are nonrenewable resources that are *mined* rather than *harvested.* Therefore, the mining industry benefits by extracting as much as it can as fast as it can and then, once extraction becomes too inefficient to be profitable, moving on to new sites. From a consumer's perspective, the management of nonrenewable mineral resources demands conservation, reuse, and recycling.

Still other resources are *truly* nonrenewable and non-replenishable: once an atom has been split to release its nuclear energy, it will never return to its original state; once a species has become extinct, it will never return to life.

We need to manage the resources we take from the natural world carefully and effectively, because many of them are limited or may become so. Resource managers are guided in their decision making by available research in the natural sciences, but their decisions are also influenced by political, economic, and social factors. A key question in managing resources is whether to focus narrowly on the resource of interest or to look more broadly at the environmental system of which the resource is a part. Taking a broader view can often help avoid damaging the system and can thereby help sustain the availability of the resource in the long term.

Preserving natural resources is an important consideration for the future, but it also speaks to the past and to our shared history as Canadians. Our economy, our identity, and even our national symbols have always been closely linked to the abundant physical resources of our environment. In recent years, however, the consumption of natural resources has increased greatly—in Canada and throughout the world—driven by rising affluence and the growth of the largest global human population in history.

Human population growth has shaped our resource use

For nearly all of human history, only a few million people populated Earth at any one time. Although past populations cannot be calculated precisely, **FIGURE 1.2** gives some idea of how recently and suddenly our population has grown, surpassing 7 billion people in 2011.[8]

Four significant periods of societal change appear to have triggered remarkable increases in population size, concomitant with greatly increased environmental impacts. The first happened as many as 2.5 million years ago during the *paleolithic* (or *Old Stone Age*) *period*, when early humans gained control of fire and began to shape and use stones as tools with which to modify their environment.

The second was the transition from a nomadic, hunter-gatherer lifestyle to a settled, agricultural way of life. This change began to occur around 10 000 to 12 000 years ago, and it is formally known as the *neolithic period* or *Agricultural Revolution*.

The third major societal change, known as the *Industrial Revolution*, began in the mid-1700s and entailed a shift from rural life, animal-powered agriculture, and manufacturing by craftspeople, to an urban society powered by fossil fuels. Life improved in many ways as a result of the Industrial Revolution, but it also marked the beginning of industrial-scale pollution and many other environmental and social problems that had not previously been experienced. Air quality declined dramatically as a result of the new reliance on coal. Water quality declined, and so did the urban landscape, as a result of the gathering of people into densely populated city centres. Workplace health and safety, too, underwent a dramatic decline as factories were hastily erected and expanded. In many respects, the modern environmental movement had its roots in the efforts taken by concerned citizens during the Industrial Revolution to ensure a cleaner, safer environment for working and living.

Today we are in the midst of a fourth transition, which some have labelled the modern *Medical–Technological Revolution*. Advances in medicine and sanitation, the explosion of communication technologies, and the shift to modern agricultural practices collectively known as the Green Revolution have allowed more people to live longer, healthier lives. However, as in the Industrial Revolution, we are facing new environmental challenges as a result of the technological advancements. For example, new approaches to food production could bring an end to hunger but have the potential for environmental and health impacts that are beyond our current understanding.

Each major societal transition introduced technological advancements that made life easier and resources

(a) World population growth

(b) Urban society

FIGURE 1.2 For almost all of human history, the world's population was low and relatively stable. It increased significantly as a result of the Agricultural Revolution and then as a result of the Industrial Revolution **(a)**. Our skyrocketing population has given rise to congested urban areas, such as this city **(b)**.

more available, effectively increasing the carrying capacity of the environment for humans and allowing the human population to increase dramatically. The modern Medical–Technological Revolution is still ongoing, and the ultimate impacts on population and the environment are as yet unknown. Much future human well-being will depend on the urban environment and the creation of sustainable, liveable cities for growing human populations around the world.

Resource consumption exerts social and environmental impacts

Population growth affects resource use and availability, and it is unquestionably at the root of many environmental problems. However, patterns and habits of resource consumption are also to blame. The Industrial Revolution enhanced the material affluence of many of the world's people, raising standards of living by raising consumption. It led to an increase in population, but the new technologies (e.g., coal-fired steam engines) and increased levels of consumption also increased pressures on the environment. We can expect that the same will be true of the Medical–Technological Revolution.

One approach to this relationship represents our total impact (I) on the environment as the product of population (P), affluence (A), and technology (T), as follows:

$$I = P \times A \times T$$

This "IPAT" model shows that impact is a function not only of population but also of affluence (which stands in for "level of consumption") and technology. An increase in the *number of people* (P) has impacts on the global

environment, but we must also concern ourselves with the impacts of *increased consumption* of natural resources and manufactured goods by the world's people (A), and the impacts of *new technologies* (T) on the environment, sometimes in ways that we can just barely imagine.

Carrying capacity and the "tragedy of the commons" When we think about Earth's limited resources and the capacity of the planet to support a growing human population, it is useful to consider the idea of carrying capacity. **Carrying capacity** is a measure of the ability of a system to support life. Environmental scientists quantify carrying capacity in terms of the number of individuals of a particular species that can be sustained by the biological productivity of a given area of land. When the carrying capacity of the land (or water) system is exceeded—that is, when there are simply too many individuals for the system to support—one of two things will typically happen: either the population of that species will decline or collapse, or the system itself will be altered, damaged, or depleted.

Ecologist Garrett Hardin of the University of California, Santa Barbara, illustrated this process while disputing the economic theory that the unregulated exercise of individual self-interest serves the public good. According to Hardin's best-known essay, "The Tragedy of the Commons," published in the journal *Science* in 1968,[9] resources that are open to unregulated exploitation inevitably become overused and, as a result, are damaged or depleted.

Hardin based his argument on the scenario of a public pasture, or "commons" that is open to unregulated grazing. He argued that each person who puts animals to graze on the commons will be motivated by selfish interests to increase the number of his or her animals in the pasture. Because no single person owns the pasture, no one has the incentive to limit the number of grazing animals or to expend money or effort to care for the pasture. This is known as the **tragedy of the commons**: each individual withdraws whatever benefits are available from the common property as quickly as possible, until the resource becomes overused and depleted. Ultimately, the carrying capacity of the pasture will be exceeded, and its food production capacity will collapse.

In some situations, private ownership may address this problem. In China, for example, private land ownership—illegal for many decades, under Communism—has recently become possible in some rural areas. These limited experiments with private ownership have shown that landowners tend to be better environmental stewards than are short-term tenants, primarily because they are willing to make long-term investments in land management. In other cases, people who share a common resource may voluntarily organize and cooperate in enforcing its responsible use. In other cases the dilemma may require government regulation of the use of resources held in common by the public, from forests to air to freshwater. Each approach has its own strengths and weaknesses.

Calculating our ecological footprint   As global affluence has increased, human society has consumed more and more of the planet's limited resources. We can quantify resource consumption by using the concept of the "ecological footprint," developed in the 1990s

---

weighing the issues

THE TRAGEDY OF THE COMMONS

Imagine you make your living by fishing. You are free to boat anywhere and set out as many traps as you like, and fish have been abundant. Limits and regulations are rarely enforced. However, the fishing grounds are getting crowded. Catches begin to decline, leaving you and all the others with catches too meagre to support your families. Some call for dividing the waters and selling access to individuals plot by plot. Others urge the fishers to team up, set quotas among themselves, and prevent newcomers from entering the market. Still others implore the government to get involved and pass laws regulating the size of the catch.

What do you think is the best way to combat this tragedy of the commons and save the fishery?

---

by environmental scientists Mathis Wackernagel and William Rees, working together at the University of British Columbia. The **ecological footprint** is a tool that can be used to express the environmental impact of an individual or a population. It is calculated in terms of the area of land and water required to provide the raw materials that person or population consumes, and to absorb or recycle the wastes produced. The footprint calculation gives the total surface area "used" by a given person or population, including direct and indirect impacts. The ecological footprint is essentially the *inverse* of carrying capacity—it is a measure of the land (and water) required to sustain an individual, rather than the number of individuals that can be sustained by an area of land (or water). The capacity of a terrestrial or aquatic system to be biologically productive and to absorb waste, especially carbon dioxide, is called **biocapacity**. When a population exceeds or overshoots the carrying capacity or biocapacity of a system, the system will be at risk of permanent damage.

Researchers calculate that our species is now using 39% more resources than are available on a sustainable basis from all the land on the planet. That is, we are exceeding the biocapacity of the planet, and depleting renewable resources 39% faster than they are being replenished. This is like drawing the principal out of a bank account, rather than living off the interest. Furthermore, people from wealthy nations have much larger ecological footprints than do people from poorer nations. The ecological footprint of an average Canadian is approximately 7.6 hectares—roughly two to four city blocks.[10] Yet, if we could divide up all the productive, habitable land of this planet equally among the 7 billion people who are now alive, each person would receive less than one city block. If all of the world's people consumed resources at the rate of North Americans, we would need the equivalent of at least two additional planet Earths to meet our resource needs.

Footprint calculations vary dramatically—you will probably even find some variations among the footprint calculation exercises in this book. This is because the calculation depends heavily on how certain components are defined. For example, different approaches to the ecological footprint calculation use different methodologies to account for the surface area of the oceans (which clearly does not have the same significance as land area does for humans, as "living space" or even "biologically productive space"). Sometimes these differences can become political; for example, various energy sources— fossil fuels, nuclear energy, hydroelectric power—have very different environmental impacts. How should the impacts of different energy sources be accounted for in footprint calculations? When is one impact "more negative" than another? The Global Footprint Network[11] is an international nongovernmental organization that is working toward standardizing ecological footprint calculations worldwide. This should make the calculations more robust and their application to questions of environmental impact and sustainability more effective.

Environmental science can help us avoid mistakes made in the past

There is historical evidence that civilizations can crumble when pressures from population and consumption overwhelm resource availability (see "The Science Behind the Story: The Lesson of Rapa Nui"). Many great civilizations have fallen after depleting resources or damaging their environment. The Greek and Roman empires show evidence of this, as do the civilizations of the Maya, the Anasazi, and other New World peoples. Plato wrote of the deforestation and environmental degradation accompanying ancient Greek cities, and today further evidence is accumulating from research by archeologists, historians, and paleoecologists, who study past societies and landscapes. The arid deserts of today's Near Eastern and Middle Eastern countries were far more lushly vegetated when the great ancient civilizations thrived there.

Researchers have now learned enough about ancient civilizations and their demise that scientist and author Jared Diamond—in his 2005 book, *Collapse*—could hypothesize why civilizations succeed and persist, or fail and collapse.[12] Diamond identified five critical factors that determine the survival of civilizations: climate change, hostile neighbours, trade partners, environmental problems, and, finally, the society's response to environmental problems. It is interesting to note that only one of these factors—the response to environmental problems—is wholly controllable, and it is this factor that has been the crucial determinant of survival. Success and persistence, it turns out, depend largely on how societies interact with their environments.

Today we are confronted with news and predictions of environmental catastrophes on a regular basis, but it can be difficult to assess the reliability of such reports. It is even harder to evaluate the causes and effects of environmental change. Perhaps most difficult is to devise solutions to environmental problems. Studying environmental science will outfit you with the tools to evaluate information on environmental change and think critically and creatively about possible actions to take in response. Let us examine this broad field we call environmental science, and then explore the process and methods of science in general.

The Nature of Environmental Science

Environmental scientists aim to comprehend how Earth's natural systems function, how humans are influenced by those systems, and how we are influencing those systems. In addition, many environmental scientists are motivated by a desire to develop solutions to environmental quandaries. The solutions themselves (such as new technologies, policy decisions, or resource management strategies) are applications of environmental science. The study of such applications and their consequences is also part of environmental science.

Environmental science is an interdisciplinary pursuit

Studying and addressing environmental problems is a complex endeavour that requires expertise from many disciplines, including ecology, geology, chemistry, biology, economics, political science, demography, ethics, and many others. Environmental science is thus an **interdisciplinary field**—one that employs concepts and techniques from numerous disciplines and brings research results from these disciplines together into a broad synthesis (**FIGURE 1.3**). Traditional disciplines are valuable because their scholars delve deeply into topics, uncovering new

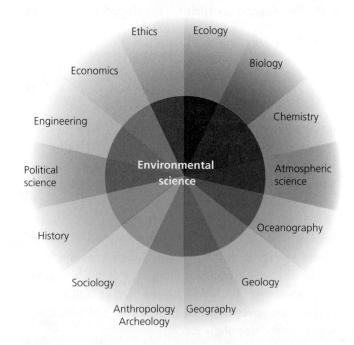

FIGURE 1.3
Environmental science is a highly interdisciplinary pursuit, involving input from many different established fields of study across the natural sciences and social sciences.

knowledge and developing expertise in particular areas. Interdisciplinary fields are valuable because their practitioners take specialized knowledge from different disciplines, consolidate it, synthesize it, and apply it in a broad context to serve the multifaceted interests of society.

Environmental science is especially broad because it encompasses not only the natural sciences (disciplines that study the natural world) but also the social sciences (disciplines that study human interactions and institutions). The natural sciences provide us with the means to gain accurate information about our environment and to interpret it reasonably. Addressing environmental problems, however, also involves weighing values and understanding human behaviour, and this requires the social sciences. Most environmental science programs focus predominantly on the natural sciences as they pertain to environmental issues. In contrast, programs heavily incorporating the social sciences often prefer the use of the term *environmental studies* to describe their academic umbrella. Whichever approach we take, these fields reflect many diverse perspectives and sources of knowledge.

Just as an interdisciplinary approach to studying issues can help us better understand them, an integrated approach to addressing problems can produce effective and lasting solutions. For example, consider how the Canadian mining industry is approaching the problem of *acid drainage*, which can occur wherever sulphur is present at a mine site. Sulphur is a very common constituent of coal and metal ores, both of which are important to the Canadian economy. If sulphur-bearing waste rock at a mine site interacts with rain or surface water, sulphuric acid is formed; if it is not contained, the acid can enter local streams, where it is devastating to affected ecosystems. To solve a problem involving acid drainage, a mining company would need to consult a biologist or an ecologist regarding the impacts of the acid on local plants and animals. A hydrologist would be helpful, to understand the flow of water at the site. A mining engineer could help decide how best to contain and isolate the waste rock piles. The company would want to consult with a chemist about the nature and behaviour of the acidic solution and how it interacts with rocks and soils. Someone skilled at management would also be helpful, to act as a liaison between the scientists and the mine management team. Canadian mining companies routinely make use of teams like this in their efforts to control acid drainage.

People differ in their perception of environmental problems

Environmental science arose in the latter half of the twentieth century, as people sought to better understand environmental problems and their origins. However, the perception of what constitutes an environmental problem may vary from one person or group of people to another, or from one context or situation to another. A person's age, gender, class, race, nationality, employment, and educational background can all affect whether he or she considers a given environmental change to be a "problem."

For instance, people today are more likely to view the spraying of the pesticide DDT as a problem than people did in the 1950s, because today more is known about the health risks from pesticides (**FIGURE 1.4**). However, a person living today in a malaria-infested village in Africa or India may still welcome the use of DDT if it kills mosquitoes that transmit malaria, because malaria is viewed as a more immediate health threat. Thus, an African and a North American who have each knowledgeably assessed the pros and cons may, because of differences in their circumstances, differ in their judgment of the severity of DDT as an environmental problem.

People also vary in their awareness of problems. For example, in many cultures women are responsible for collecting water and fuelwood. As a result, they are often the first to perceive environmental degradation affecting

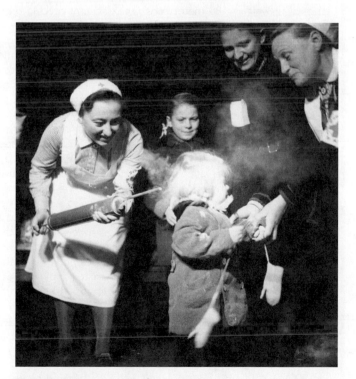

FIGURE 1.4
How a person or society defines an environmental problem can vary with time and circumstance. In 1945, health hazards from the pesticide DDT were not yet known, so children were doused with the chemical to treat head lice. Today, knowing of its toxicity to people and wildlife, developed nations have banned DDT. However, in some countries where malaria is a threat, DDT is still used as an effective means of eradicating mosquitoes, which transmit the disease.

THE SCIENCE BEHIND THE STORY

The Lesson of Rapa Nui

These immense moai (statues) are on Easter Island.

Rapa Nui (Easter Island) is one of the most remote islands on the globe. When European explorers reached the island in 1722, they found a barren landscape populated by fewer than 2000 people, living a marginal existence in caves. The desolate island featured gigantic statues of carved stone, evidence that a sophisticated civilization had once lived there. How could people without wheels or ropes, on an island without trees, have moved statues 10 m high, weighing 80 metric tons? The answer lies in the fact that the island did not always lack trees, and its people were not always without rope.

Scientists have determined that the island was once lushly forested, supporting a prosperous society of 6000 to 30 000 people. This once-flourishing civilization exceeded the carrying capacity of the island by overusing resources and cutting down trees, destroying itself in a downward spiral of starvation and conflict. Today, Rapa Nui stands as a demonstration of what can happen when a population consumes too much of the limited resources that support it.

To solve the mystery of the island's past, scientists have used various methods. British scientist John Flenley excavated sediments from the bottoms of the island's volcanic crater lakes, examining ancient grains of pollen to reconstruct changes in vegetation over time. Flenley and other researchers found that when Polynesian people first arrived (between 300 C.E. and 900 C.E.), the island was covered with a species of palm tree related to the tall, thick-trunked Chilean wine palm.

The palms would have provided fuelwood, building material for houses and

canoes, fruit, and fibre—and, presumably, logs to move the stone statues. Scientists have tested hypotheses about how the islanders moved their monoliths, recreating the feat by using great quantities of rope, with tree trunks as rollers or sleds. The only likely source of rope on the island is the fibrous inner bark of the *hauhau* tree, a species that today is near extinction.

At least 21 other species of plants (including trees) that were once common on the island are now completely gone. Around 750 C.E., tree populations began to decline, and ferns and grasses became more common. By 950 C.E., the trees were largely gone. Around 1400 C.E., pollen levels plummeted, indicating a dearth of vegetation. The same sequence occurred two centuries later at two other sites, more remote from village areas. Evidence now supports the hypothesis that people gradually denuded the island.

With the trees gone, soil would have eroded away—confirmed by sediment that accumulated in Rapa Nui's lakes. Faster runoff of rainwater would have meant less freshwater available for drinking. Erosion would have degraded agricultural lands, lowering crop yields. Reduced agricultural production would have led to starvation and population decline.

Analyses by ornithologist David Steadman show that at least 6 species of land birds and 25 species of seabirds nested on Rapa Nui and were eaten by islanders. Today, no native land birds and only one type of seabird are left. Early islanders also feasted on porpoises, fish, sharks, turtles, octopi, and shellfish. Analyses of islanders' diets in the later years indicate that little seafood was consumed. With the trees gone, islanders could not build the great double-canoes their ancestors used for fishing. Europeans who visited in the eighteenth century observed only a few old small canoes and flimsy rafts made of reeds.

As resources declined, the islanders' main domesticated food animal, the chicken, became more valuable. Archeologists found that later islanders kept chickens in stone fortresses designed to prevent theft. The once prosperous and peaceful civilization fell into clan warfare, revealed by

The haunting statues of Rapa Nui (Easter Island) were erected by a sophisticated civilization that collapsed after depleting its resource base and devastating its island environment.

unearthed weapons made of hard volcanic rock and skeletons with head wounds.

Canadian economists Scott Taylor and James Brander took a different approach to investigating what happened at Rapa Nui.[13] They developed a computer model of the interplay between renewable resources and population. The model is based on standard ecological *predator–prey models*, with people in the role of predator, and resources as their prey. This scenario generates "feast-and-famine" cycles of rising and falling population and resource stocks. The researchers speculate that such cycles may account for the decline and eventual collapse of other civilizations as a result of rapid population growth and consequent resource degradation.

Is the story of Rapa Nui as unique and isolated as the island itself, or does it hold lessons for our world today? Earth may be vastly larger and richer in resources than was Rapa Nui, but the human population is also much larger. The islanders must have seen that they were depleting their resources, but they could not stop. Perhaps we can learn from them, and act wisely to conserve the resources on our island, Earth.

these resources. In most societies, information about environmental health risks tends to reach wealthy people more readily than poor people. Thus, who you are, where you live, what you do, your income, your gender, and your socioeconomic status can have a huge effect on how you perceive your environment, how you react to change, and what impact those changes may have on how you live your life.

Environmental science is not the same as environmentalism

Although many environmental scientists are interested in solving problems, it is incorrect to confuse environmental science with environmentalism or environmental activism. They are *not* the same. *Environmental science* is the pursuit of knowledge about the workings of the environment and our interactions with it. **Environmentalism** is a social movement dedicated to protecting the natural world—and, by extension, humans—from undesirable changes brought about by human choices (**FIGURE 1.5**). Although environmental scientists study many of the same issues environmentalists care about, as scientists they attempt to maintain an objective approach in their work. Remaining as free as possible from personal or ideological bias—and open to whatever conclusions the data demand—is a hallmark of the effective scientist.

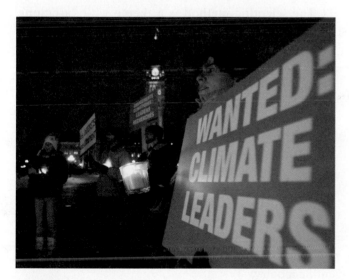

FIGURE 1.5
Environmental scientists play roles very different from those of the environmental activists shown here. Some scientists do become activists to promote what they feel are workable solutions to environmental problems. However, those who do so generally try to keep their advocacy separate from their scientific work. This photograph shows Greenpeace activists protesting on Parliament Hill in Ottawa. Greenpeace is an international organization of environmental activists that was founded in Vancouver in 1971.

In each chapter of this book you will find *Canadian Environmental Perspectives*, offering brief profiles of Canadian environmental scientists as well as individuals in non-scientific professions who contribute to the understanding, protection, management, and sustainable use of the natural environment. These people play a wide range of roles, from policy maker to activist, artist, journalist, hunter, or animal rescuer. Many of them are scientists *and* writers, or scientists *and* filmmakers or gardeners or politicians or musicians—and, yes, many of them are also environmentalists. All these people have made a difference, one way or another. All of them rely on and contribute to our knowledge, as well as to our intuitive appreciation of the natural environment. Environmental science is *distinct* from philosophy, law, commerce, religion, politics, art, and activism, but is it necessarily *exclusive* of these human undertakings? You will have to judge this for yourself, but you can count on this book to help you make a more informed judgment of what you read, hear, and experience in your encounters with the natural environment.

The *Canadian Environmental Perspective* presented in this chapter highlights David Suzuki—scientist, activist, and environmentalist. Admired by many, but controversial for his activist stance on environmental issues, Suzuki exemplifies what a multifaceted undertaking it can be to work on behalf of the environment in today's world.

The Nature of Science

Science is a systematic process for learning about the world and testing our understanding of it. The term *science* is also commonly used to refer to the accumulated body of knowledge that arises from this dynamic process of observation, testing, and discovery.

Science

The word *science* originates from the Latin word *scientia*, meaning "knowledge," and the Latin verb *scire*, meaning "to know." The latter probably originally meant "to separate or distinguish one thing from another," pointing to the role of classification in science over the ages.

Knowledge gained from science can be applied to societal problems. Among the most important applications of science are its use in developing new technologies, and its use in informing policy and management decisions (**FIGURE 1.6**). These pragmatic applications in themselves are not science, but they must be informed by science in order to be effective. Many scientists are motivated simply by a desire to know how the world works, and others are motivated by the potential

roots
SCIENCE

The word **science** originates from the Latin word *scientia*, meaning "knowledge," and the Latin verb *scire*, meaning "to know." The latter probably originally meant "to separate or distinguish one thing from another," pointing to the role of classification in science over the ages.

for developing useful applications and solutions to problems.

Environmental science is a dynamic yet systematic means of studying the world, and it is also the body of knowledge accumulated from this process. Like science in general, environmental science informs its practical applications and often is motivated by them.

Why does science matter? The late American astronomer Carl Sagan wrote the following in his 1995 treatise *The Demon-Haunted World: Science as a Candle in the Dark:*

> *We've arranged a global civilization in which the most crucial elements—transportation, communications, and all other industries; agriculture, medicine, education, entertainment, protecting the environment; and even the key democratic institution of voting—profoundly depend on science and technology.*[14]

Sagan and many others have argued that science is essential if we hope to develop solutions to the problems—environmental and otherwise—that we face today. We might go a step further and suggest that the *democratization* of science—making the science of our world accessible and understandable to as many people as possible—is also essential if we are to make informed decisions about the management of this planet.

Scientists test ideas by critically examining evidence

How can we tell whether warnings of impending environmental catastrophes—or any other claims, for that matter—are based on scientific thinking? Scientists examine ideas about how the world works by designing tests to determine whether these ideas are supported by evidence. If a particular statement or explanation is testable and resists repeated attempts to disprove it, scientists are likely to accept it as a useful explanation. Scientific inquiry is thus an incremental approach to the truth.

The scientific method is a key element of science

Scientists generally follow a process called the **scientific method**. A technique for testing ideas with observations, it involves several assumptions and a series of interrelated steps. There is nothing mysterious about the scientific method; it is merely a formalized version of the procedure any of us might naturally take, using common sense, to answer a question.

The scientific method is a theme with variations, however, and scientists pursue their work in many different ways. Because science is an active, creative, imaginative process, an innovative scientist may find good reason to stray from the traditional scientific method when a particular situation demands it. Scientists from different fields approach their work differently because they deal with dissimilar types of information. A natural scientist, such as a chemist, will conduct research quite differently from a social scientist, such as a sociologist. Because environmental science includes both natural and social sciences, in our discussion here we use the term *science* in its broad sense, to include both. Despite their many differences, scientists of all persuasions broadly agree on the fundamental elements of scientific inquiry.

The scientific method relies on the following assumptions:

■ The universe functions in accordance with fixed natural laws that do not change from time to time or from place to place.

FIGURE 1.6
Scientific knowledge can be applied in policy and management decisions and in technology. Prescribed burning, shown here, is a management practice to restore healthy forests and is informed by scientific research into forest ecology.

- All events arise from some cause and, in turn, lead to other events.
- We can use our senses and reasoning abilities to detect and describe natural laws that underlie the cause-and-effect relationships we observe in nature.

As practised by individual researchers or research teams, the scientific method (**FIGURE 1.7**) typically consists of the steps outlined below.

Make observations   Advances in science typically begin with the observation of a phenomenon that the scientist wants to explain. Observations set the scientific method in motion and function throughout the process.

Ask questions   Scientists are naturally curious about the world and love to ask questions. Why are certain plants or animals less common today than they once were? Are storms becoming more severe, or flooding more frequent? Why? What causes excessive growth of algae in local ponds? Do the impacts of pesticides on fish or frogs mean that people could be affected in the same ways? All of these are questions environmental scientists have asked and attempted to answer.

Develop a hypothesis   Scientists attempt to answer their questions by devising explanations that can be tested. A **hypothesis** is an educated guess that explains a phenomenon or answers a scientific question. For example, a scientist investigating the question of why algae are growing excessively in local ponds might observe chemical fertilizers being applied on farm fields nearby. The scientist might then state a hypothesis as follows: "Agricultural fertilizers running into ponds cause the algae in the ponds to increase." Sometimes this takes the form of a *null hypothesis*, a statement that the scientist is expecting no relationship between variables, such as between fertilizer and algal growth in a pond.

Make predictions   The scientist next uses the hypothesis to generate **predictions**, which are specific statements that can be directly and unequivocally tested. In our algae example, a prediction might be: "If agricultural fertilizers are added to a pond, the quantity of algae in the pond will increase." A null hypothesis can also lead to predictions; for example, the scientist might predict that adding agricultural fertilizer to a pond will cause no change in the amount of algae growing in the pond.

Test the predictions   Predictions are tested one at a time by gathering evidence that could potentially refute the prediction and thus disprove the hypothesis. The strongest form of evidence comes from experimentation. An **experiment** is an activity designed to test the validity of a hypothesis. It involves manipulating **variables**, conditions that can change. For example, a scientist could test the hypothesis linking algal growth to fertilizer by selecting two identical ponds and adding fertilizer to one while leaving the other in its natural state. In this example, fertilizer input is an *independent variable*, a variable the scientist manipulates, whereas the quantity of algae that results is the *dependent variable*, one that depends on the fertilizer input. If the two ponds are identical except for a single independent variable (fertilizer input), then any differences that arise between the ponds can be attributed to that variable. Such an experiment is known as a *controlled experiment* because the scientist controls for the effects of all variables except the one being tested—the dependent variable. In our example, the pond left unfertilized serves as a **control**, an unmanipulated point of comparison for the manipulated or treated pond. Whenever possible, it is best to reproduce an experiment;

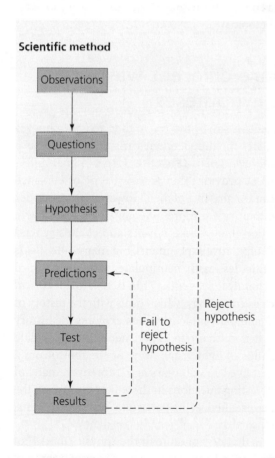

Scientific method

FIGURE 1.7
The scientific method is the observation-based hypothesis-testing approach that scientists use to learn how the world works. This diagram is a simplified generalization that, although useful for instructive purposes, cannot convey the true dynamic and creative nature of science. Moreover, researchers from different disciplines may pursue their work in ways that legitimately vary from this model.

that is, to stage multiple tests of the same comparison of control and treatment. Our scientist could perform a *replicated experiment* on, say, 10 pairs of ponds, adding fertilizer to one of the ponds in each pair.

Experiments can establish *causal relationships*, showing that changes in an independent variable cause changes in a dependent variable. However, experiments are not the only means of testing a hypothesis. Sometimes a hypothesis can be convincingly addressed through *correlation*—that is, searching for relationships and patterns among variables.

Suppose our scientist surveys 50 ponds, 20 of which are fed by fertilizer runoff from nearby farm fields and 30 of which are not. Let us also say he or she finds seven times as much algal growth in the fertilized ponds as in the unfertilized ponds. The scientist would conclude that algal growth is correlated with fertilizer input—that is, that one tends to increase along with the other.

Although this type of evidence is weaker than the causal demonstration that controlled experiments can provide, sometimes it is the best approach, or the only feasible one. For example, in studying the effects of global climate change, we could hardly run an experiment that involved adding carbon dioxide to 10 treatment planets and comparing the result to 10 control planets.

Analyze and interpret results   Scientists record **data**, or information, from their studies. They particularly value *quantitative* data, information expressed numerically, because numbers provide precision and are easy to compare. The scientist running the fertilization experiment, for instance, might quantify the area of water surface covered by algae in each pond, or measure the dry weight of algae in a certain volume of water taken from each pond. Even with the precision that numbers provide, however, a scientist's results may not be clear-cut. Experimental data may differ from control data only slightly, or different replicates may yield different results. The scientist must therefore analyze the data by using statistical tests. With these mathematical methods, scientists can determine objectively and precisely the strength and reliability of patterns they find. If the results are unreliable or cannot be replicated, it may be necessary to attempt a different kind of test.

Some research, especially in the social sciences, involves information that is *qualitative*, or not expressible in terms of numbers. Research involving historical texts, personal interviews, surveys, detailed examination of case studies, or descriptive observations of behaviour can include qualitative data on which statistical analyses may not be possible. Such studies are still scientific in the broad sense, because their data can be interpreted systematically by using other accepted methods of analysis.

If experiments disprove a hypothesis, the scientist will reject the hypothesis and may develop a new one to replace it. If experiments fail to disprove the hypothesis, this outcome lends support to the hypothesis but does not *prove* it is correct. The scientist may choose to generate new predictions to test the hypothesis in a different way and further assess its likelihood of being true. Thus, the scientific method loops back on itself, often giving rise to repeated rounds of hypothesis revision, prediction, and testing (see **FIGURE 1.7**).

If repeated tests fail to disprove a particular hypothesis, and evidence in its favour is accumulating, the researcher may eventually conclude that the idea is well supported. Ideally, a scientist would want to test all possible explanations for the question of interest. For instance, our scientist might propose an additional hypothesis that algae increase in fertilized ponds because numbers of fish or invertebrate animals that eat algae decrease. It is possible, of course, that both hypotheses could be correct and that each may explain some portion of the initial observation that local ponds were experiencing algal blooms.

There are different ways to test hypotheses

An experiment in which the researcher actively chooses and manipulates the independent variable is known as a *manipulative experiment* (**FIGURE 1.8A**). A manipulative experiment provides the strongest type of evidence a scientist can obtain. In practice, however, some modes of scientific inquiry are more amenable to manipulative experimentation than others. Physics and chemistry tend to involve manipulative experiments, but many other fields deal with entities less easily manipulated than are physical forces and chemical reagents. This is true of *historical sciences*, such as cosmology, which deals with the history of the universe, and paleontology, which explores the history of past life. It is difficult to experimentally manipulate a star thousands of light years away, or the tooth from a mastodon that lived 15 000 years ago. Moreover, many of the most interesting questions in these fields centre on the causes and consequences of particular historical events, rather than the behaviour of general constants.

Disciplines that do not quite fit the "physics model" of science sometimes rely on *natural experiments* rather than manipulative ones (**FIGURE 1.8B**). For instance, an evolutionary biologist might want to test whether animal species isolated on oceanic islands tend to evolve large body sizes over time. The biologist cannot run a manipulative experiment by placing animals on islands and continents and waiting long enough for evolution to do its work. However,

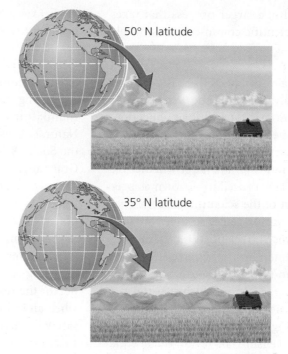

50° N latitude

35° N latitude

FIGURE 1.8
A researcher wanting to test how temperature affects the growth of a crop might run a manipulative experiment in which the crop is grown in two identical greenhouses: one kept at 20°C and the other kept at 25°C **(a)**. Alternatively, the researcher might run a natural experiment in which he or she compares the growth of the crop in two fields at different latitudes: a cool northerly location and a warm southerly one **(b)**. Because it would be difficult to hold all variables besides temperature constant, the researcher might want to collect data on a number of northern and southern fields and correlate temperature and crop growth using statistical methods.

20°C

25°C

(a) Manipulative experiment

(b) Natural experiment, or correlational study

this is exactly what nature has already done. The biologist might test the idea by comparing pairs of closely related species, in which one of each pair lives on an island and the other on a continental mainland, or one is a modern species and the other an ancient, fossilized relative. The experiment has in essence been conducted naturally, and it is up to the scientist to interpret the results.

In many disciplines, both manipulative and natural experimentation are used. For example, an ecologist wanting to measure the importance of a certain insect in pollinating the flowers of a given crop plant might fit some flowers with a device to keep the insects out while leaving other flowers accessible, and later measure the fruit output of each group. Other questions that involve large spatial scales or long time scales may instead require natural experiments.

The social sciences generally involve less experimentation than the natural sciences, depending more on careful observation and statistical interpretation of patterns in data. For example, a sociologist studying how people from different cultures conceive of the notion of wilderness might conduct a survey and analyze responses to the questions, looking for similarities and differences among respondents. Such analyses may be either quantitative or qualitative, depending on the nature of the data and the researchers' particular questions and approaches.

Descriptive observational studies and natural experiments can show correlation between variables, but they cannot demonstrate that one variable *causes* change in another, as manipulative experiments can. Not all variables are controlled for in a natural experiment, so a single result could give rise to several interpretations. However, correlative studies, when done well, can make for very convincing science, and they preserve the real-world complexity that manipulative experiments often sacrifice. Moreover, sometimes correlation is all we have. Because large-scale manipulations are difficult, some of the most important questions in environmental science tend to be addressed with correlative data.

The large scale and complexity of many questions in environmental science also mean that few studies, manipulative or correlative, come up with neat and absolute results. As such, scientists are not always able to give policymakers and society definitive answers to questions. Even when science is able to provide answers, deciding upon the optimal social response to a problem can still be very difficult.

The scientific process does not stop with the scientific method

Individual researchers or teams of researchers follow the scientific method as they investigate questions that interest them. However, scientific work takes place within the context of a community of peers, and to have any impact, a researcher's work must be published and made accessible to this community. Thus, the scientific method is embedded within a larger process that takes place at the level of the scientific community as a whole (**FIGURE 1.9**).

Peer review   When a researcher's work is done and the results have been analyzed, he or she writes up the findings and submits them to a journal for publication. Several other scientists specializing in the topic of the paper examine the manuscript, provide comments and criticism (generally anonymously), and judge whether the work merits publication. This procedure, known as **peer review**, is an essential part of the scientific process. Peer review is a valuable guard against faulty science contaminating the literature on which all scientists rely. However, because scientists are human and may have their own personal biases and agendas, politics can sometimes creep into the review process. Fortunately, just as the vast majority of individual scientists strive to remain accurate and objective in conducting their research, the scientific community does its best to ensure fair review of all work.

Conference presentations   Scientists frequently present their work at professional conferences, where they interact with colleagues and receive comments informally on their research. Feedback from colleagues can help improve the quality of a scientist's work before it is submitted for publication.

Grants and funding   Research scientists spend large portions of their time writing grant applications requesting money to fund their research from private foundations or government agencies, such as the Natural Sciences and Engineering Research Council or the Social Sciences and Humanities Research Council. Grant applications undergo peer review just as scientific papers do, and competition for funding is often intense. Scientists' reliance on funding sources can also lead to potential conflicts of interest. A scientist who obtains data showing his or her funding source in an unfavourable light may be reluctant to publish the results for fear of losing funding—or, worse yet, may be tempted to doctor the results. This situation can arise, for instance, when an industry funds research to test its products for safety or environmental impact. Most scientists do not succumb to these pressures, but some funding sources have been known to influence scientists toward certain results. This is why as a student or an informed citizen, when critically assessing a scientific study, you should always try to find out where the researchers obtained funding.

FIGURE 1.9
The scientific method (inner box) followed by individual researchers or research teams exists within the context of the overall process of science at the level of the scientific community (outer box). This process includes peer review and publication of research, acquisition of funding, and the development of theory through the cumulative work of many researchers.

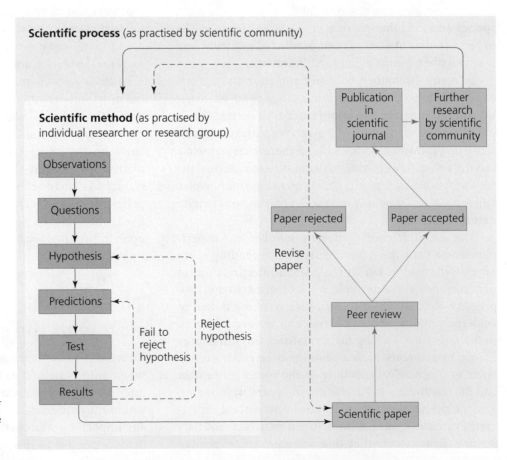

weighing the issues

FOLLOW THE MONEY

Let us say that you are a research scientist and are interested in studying the impacts of chemicals released by pulp-and-paper mills on nearby freshwater lakes. Obtaining research funding has been difficult; then a representative from a large pulp-and-paper company contacts you. The company also is interested in the impacts of its chemical effluents on nearby water bodies, and it would like to fund your research project. What are the pros and cons of this offer?

Repeatability   Sound science is based on doubt rather than certainty and on repeatability rather than one-time occurrences. Even when a hypothesis appears to explain observed phenomena, scientists are inherently wary of accepting it. The careful scientist will test a hypothesis repeatedly in various ways before submitting the findings for publication. Following publication, other scientists usually will attempt to reproduce the results in their own experiments and analyses.

Theories   If a hypothesis survives repeated testing by numerous research teams and continues to predict experimental outcomes and observations accurately, it may potentially be incorporated into a theory. A **theory** is a widely accepted, well-tested explanation of one or more cause-and-effect relationships, which has been extensively validated by extensive research. Whereas a hypothesis is a simple explanatory statement that may be refuted by a single experiment, a theory consolidates many related hypotheses that have been tested and supported by a large body of experimental and observational data.

Note that scientific use of the word *theory* differs from popular usage of the word. In everyday language, when we say something is "just a theory," we are suggesting it is a speculative idea without much substance. Scientists, however, mean just the opposite when they use the term; to them, a theory is a conceptual framework that effectively explains a phenomenon and has undergone extensive and rigorous testing, such that confidence in it is extremely strong. For example, Darwin's *theory of evolution by natural selection* has been supported and elaborated upon by many thousands of studies over 150 years of intensive research. Such research has shown repeatedly and in great detail how plants and animals change over generations, or evolve, to express characteristics that best promote survival and reproduction. Because of its strong support and explanatory power, the evolutionary theory is the central unifying principle of modern biology.

Science may go through "paradigm shifts"

Results obtained by the scientific method may sometimes later be reinterpreted to show that earlier interpretations were incorrect. Science goes through periodic revolutions, or dramatic upheavals in thought, in which one scientific *paradigm*, or dominant view, is abandoned for another. For example, before the sixteenth century, scientists believed that Earth was at the centre of the universe. They made accurate measurements of the movement of the planets, then applied elaborate corrections that seemed to be needed in order to explain their measurements from a geocentric (Earth-centred) viewpoint. Nicolaus Copernicus eventually disproved the geocentric model of the solar system by demonstrating that placing the Sun at the centre of the solar system explained the planetary data and observations much better. A similar paradigm shift occurred in the 1960s, when geologists accepted the theory of plate tectonics because evidence for the movement of continents and the action of tectonic plates had accumulated and had become overwhelmingly convincing.

Understanding how science works is vital to assessing how scientific ideas and interpretations change through time, with new information. This process is especially relevant in environmental science, a young field that is changing rapidly as we gather vast amounts of new information, as human impacts on the planet multiply, and as lessons from the consequences of our actions become apparent. Because so much remains unstudied and undone, and because so many issues we cannot foresee are likely to arise in the future, environmental science will remain an exciting frontier for you to explore as a student and as an informed citizen throughout your life.

Sustainability and the Future of Our World

Throughout this book you will see examples of environmental scientists asking questions, developing hypotheses, conducting experiments, gathering and analyzing data, and drawing conclusions about environmental processes and the causes and consequences of environmental change. Environmental scientists who aim to understand the condition of our environment and the consequences of our impacts are studying the most centrally important issues of our time. New technologies and new scientific approaches have made it easier than ever before to monitor these changes (see "The Science Behind the Story: Mission to Planet Earth"). You will also see, throughout this book, profiles of environmental leaders who are attempting to translate the scientific understanding of environmental change into political, social, and economic actions to protect our environment.

Population and consumption lie at the root of many environmental impacts

We modify our environment in diverse ways, but the steep and sudden rise in human population has amplified nearly all our impacts. Our numbers have nearly quadrupled in the past 100 years, reaching 7 billion in 2012. We add about 80 million people to the planet each year—more than 200 000 per day. Today, the rate of population growth is slowing, but our absolute numbers continue to increase and shape our interactions with one another and with our environment.

Our consumption of resources has risen even faster than our population growth. The rise in affluence has been a positive development for humanity, and our conversion of the planet's natural capital has made life more pleasant for us so far. However, like rising population, rising per capita consumption amplifies the demands we make on our environment.

Moreover, affluence and consumption have not grown equally for all the world's citizens. Today, the 20 wealthiest nations boast 40 times the income of the 20 poorest nations—twice the gap that existed four decades ago. The ecological footprint of the average citizen of a developed nation, such as Canada or the United States, is considerably larger than that of the average resident of a developing country (**FIGURE 1.10**).

We face many environmental challenges

The dramatic growth in human population and consumption is due in part to our successful efforts to expand and intensify the production of food. Since the origins of agriculture and the Industrial Revolution, new technologies have enabled us to grow increasingly more food per unit of land. These advances in agriculture must be counted as one of humanity's great achievements, but they have come at some cost. We have converted nearly half the planet's land surface for agriculture; our extensive use of chemical fertilizers and pesticides negatively affects organisms and alters natural systems; and

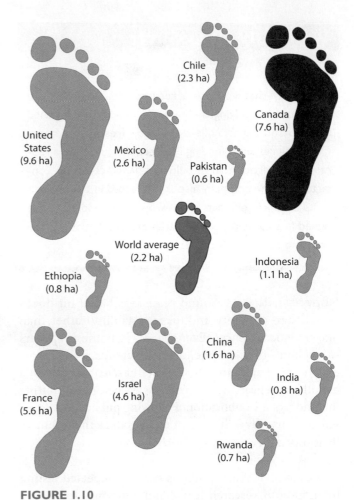

FIGURE 1.10

The citizens of some nations have larger ecological footprints than others. Shown here are ecological footprints for average citizens of several developed and developing nations, as of 2003.
Source: Data from Global Footprint Network, 2006.

erosion, climate change, and poorly managed irrigation are destroying 5 million to 7 million hectares of productive cropland each year.

Meanwhile, pollution from our farms, industries, households, and individual actions dirties our land, water, and air (**FIGURE 1.11**). Outdoor air pollution, indoor air pollution, and water pollution contribute to the deaths of millions of people each year. Environmental toxicologists are chronicling the impacts on people and wildlife of the many synthetic chemicals and other pollutants we emit into the environment.

Perhaps our most pressing pollution challenge may be to address the looming spectre of global climate change. Scientists have firmly concluded that human activity is altering the composition of the atmosphere and that these changes are affecting Earth's climate. Since the start of the Industrial Revolution, atmospheric carbon dioxide concentrations have risen to a level not present in hundreds of thousands—likely millions—of years. This increase has resulted from our reliance on burning

FIGURE 1.11
Indoor and outdoor air pollution contribute to millions of premature deaths each year. Environmental scientists and policymakers are working to reduce these problems in a variety of ways.

Table 1.1   Main Findings of the Millennium Ecosystem Assessment

- Over the past 50 years, humans have changed ecosystems more rapidly and extensively than in any comparable period of time in human history, largely to meet rapidly growing demands for food, freshwater, timber, fibre, and fuel. This has resulted in a substantial and largely irreversible loss in the diversity of life on Earth.

- The changes made to ecosystems have contributed to substantial net gains in human well-being and economic development, but these gains have been achieved at growing costs. These costs include the degradation of ecosystems and the services they provide for us, and the exacerbation of poverty for some groups of people.

- This degradation could grow significantly worse during the first half of this century.

- The challenge of reversing the degradation of ecosystems while meeting increasing demands for their services can be partially overcome, but doing so will involve significantly changing many policies, institutions, and practises.

Source: Adapted from Millennium Ecosystem Assessment, *Synthesis Report, 2005.*

fossil fuels to power our civilization. Carbon dioxide and several other gases absorb heat and warm Earth's surface. The anthropogenic enhancement of this process is likely responsible for glacial melting, sea-level rise, impacts on wildlife and crops, and increased episodes of destructive weather. Atmospheric carbon dioxide also contributes to the acidification of ocean water.

The combined impact of human actions, such as climate change, overharvesting, pollution, the introduction of non-native species, and particularly habitat alteration, has driven many aquatic and terrestrial species out of large parts of their ranges and toward the brink of extinction. Today Earth's *biological diversity*, or **biodiversity**, the cumulative number and diversity of living things, is declining dramatically. Many biologists say we are already in a mass extinction event comparable to only five others documented in all of Earth's history. Biologist Edward O. Wilson has warned that the loss of biodiversity is our most serious and threatening environmental dilemma, because it is not the kind of problem that responsible human action can remedy. The extinction of species is irreversible; once a species has become extinct, it is lost forever.

Solutions to environmental problems must be global and sustainable

The nature of virtually all these environmental issues is being changed by the set of ongoing phenomena commonly dubbed *globalization*. Our increased global interconnectedness in trade, politics, and the movement of people and other species poses many challenging problems, but it also sets the stage for novel and effective solutions.

The most comprehensive scientific assessment of the present condition of the world's ecological systems and their ability to continue supporting our civilization was completed in 2005, when more than 2000 of the world's leading environmental scientists from nearly 100 nations completed the *Millennium Ecosystem Assessment*. The four main findings of this exhaustive project are summarized in **TABLE 1.1**. The Assessment makes clear that our degradation of the world's environmental systems is having negative impacts on all of us but that with care and diligence we can still turn many of these trends around.

Our energy choices will influence our future immensely

Our reliance on fossil fuels to power our civilization has intensified virtually every negative impact we have on the environment, from habitat alteration to air pollution to climate change. Fossil fuels have also brought us the material affluence we enjoy. By taking advantage of the richly concentrated energy in coal, oil, and natural gas, we have been able to power the machinery of the Industrial Revolution, produce the chemicals that boosted agricultural yields, run the vehicles and transportation networks of our mobile society, and manufacture and distribute our countless consumer products. It is little exaggeration to say that the lives we live today are a result of the availability of fossil fuels.

However, in extracting fossil fuels, we are splurging on a one-time bonanza. Scientists calculate that we have

THE SCIENCE BEHIND THE STORY

Mission to Planet Earth: Monitoring Environmental Change

Ellesmere Island National Park Reserve is the most northerly park on Earth.

Science begins with observation. One of the most significant legacies of the space program is the ability to observe Earth from afar. The development of this ability changed our perspective on this planet permanently, leading to a new sense of respect, care, and concern for the environment that continues to grow as a social priority.

Since the last hand-held photograph of the whole planet was taken in 1972 by Apollo 17 astronauts, scientists and technologists have dramatically improved their ability to capture and interpret a wide variety of images of this planet. Hand-held photography continues to provide an important part of the data returned by manned space missions (you can see many of these photographs archived at NASA's website, www.nasa.gov). Today, satellites and the sophisticated instrumentation they carry provide us with the opportunity to observe, study, monitor change, and gather an unprecedented amount of information about the planet, through technologies and processes that are collectively referred to as *remote sensing*.

By the early 1980s, NASA scientists and administrators had faced the reality that they were unlikely to obtain the necessary funding to return to the Moon any time in the near future. Instead, they began to turn their attention to another nearby planetary object: Earth. They called the new scientific approach *Earth system science*

and defined as its goal "to obtain a scientific understanding of the entire Earth system on a global scale by describing how its component parts and their interactions have evolved, how they function, and how they may be expected to continue to evolve on all timescales."[15] The observation and interpretation of environmental change was fundamental to this new scientific approach, right from the beginning.

To achieve the goals of Earth system science, scientists began to use technologies that had been developed for other purposes—space exploration, communications, even warfare—to observe Earth and its component parts over time, and they called the new endeavour *Mission to Planet Earth*. The scientific results of this mission have been and continue to be spectacular. Satellites and remote detection and measuring technologies have provided a massive amount of information about the environment, how it changes over time, and how human activity affects it—information with a depth and

breadth that would have been unimaginable back when those first whole-planet photographs were taken. The photo of Ellesmere Island National Park Reserve (top left), acquired in August 2003 by the Advanced Spaceborne Thermal Emission and Reflection Radiometer (ASTER) aboard NASA's *Terra* satellite, shows a tidewater glacier in Greely Fjord, situated in the southwestern corner of the Reserve. Icebergs floating in the fjord are chunks that have broken off the glacier. The corrugated surface on the glacier near its terminus (or end) is a network of crevasses. The strong linear features running through the glacier are flow lines. The dark blue features are melt ponds; they are darker than the ice and absorb more sunlight, thus melting more ice. A great deal of what environmental scientists now know about this planet as a coherent system, how its various parts interact, and how it is changing and evolving has been based on information derived from the Mission to Planet Earth.

This satellite image shows Lake Athabasca, the dark, irregular patch straddling the border between Alberta (west) and Saskatchewan (east), and numerous active summer forest fires (indicated by red dots). A large smoke plume stretches across Saskatchewan and into Manitoba, to the east. This image was acquired by the Moderate Resolution Imaging Spectroradiometer aboard the Terra satellite in July 2002.

depleted half the world's oil supplies and that we are in for a rude awakening very soon, once the supply begins to decline while the demand continues to rise. Coal and natural gas are also nonrenewable and available in limited supply, although we are likely farther from reaching the limits of those resources. The search is now on for alternative sources of energy that will allow us to maintain an acceptable standard of living while minimizing the environmental impacts of energy use. How we handle the imminent crisis of fossil fuel depletion and the search for replacements will largely determine the nature of our lives in the twenty-first century.

Fortunately, potential solutions abound

We cannot, of course, live without exerting *any* impact on Earth's systems. We face trade offs with many environmental issues, and the challenge is to develop solutions that increase our quality of life while minimizing harm to the environment that supports us. Fortunately, many workable solutions are at hand, and we can achieve many more potential solutions with further effort.

In response to agricultural problems, scientists and others have developed and promoted soil conservation, high-efficiency irrigation, and organic agriculture. In addition, technological advances and new laws have greatly reduced the pollution emitted by industry and automobiles in wealthier countries. Canadian scientists have been at the forefront of many of these technological advances and have made fundamental contributions to global environmental management theories and to our current understanding of the human–environment rela-

FIGURE 1.13
Our dependence on fossil fuels has caused a wide array of environmental impacts. Although fossil fuels have powered our civilization since the Industrial Revolution, many renewable energy sources exist, such as solar energy, which can be collected with panels like these. Such alternative energy sources could be further developed for sustainable use now and in the future.

tionship. Amid ample reasons for concern about the state of global biodiversity, advances in conservation biology are enabling scientists and policymakers in many cases to work together to protect habitat, slow extinction, and safeguard endangered species (**FIGURE 1.12**).

Recycling is helping to relieve our waste disposal problems, and alternative renewable energy sources are being developed to take the place of fossil fuels (**FIGURE 1.13**). These are but a few of the many solutions we will explore in the course of this book, and we will examine some of the new structures, programs, processes, and technologies that are emerging in support of these solutions.

Are things getting better, or worse?

Despite the myriad challenges we face, some people maintain that the general conditions of human life and the environment are getting better, not worse.

Furthermore, some people maintain that we will find ways to make Earth's natural resources meet all our needs indefinitely and that human ingenuity will see us through any difficulty. Such views are sometimes characterized as *cornucopian*. (In Greek mythology, *cornucopia*—literally "horn of plenty"—is the name for a magical goat's horn that overflowed with limitless grain, fruit, and flowers.) In contrast, people who predict doom and disaster for the world because of our impact upon it have been called *Cassandras*, after the mythical princess of Troy with the gift of prophecy, whose dire predictions were not believed.

FIGURE 1.12
Human activities are pushing many organisms toward extinction. Efforts to save endangered species and reduce biodiversity loss include many approaches, but all require that adequate areas of appropriate habitat be preserved in the wild. The habitat of polar bears, for example, is increasingly threatened by global climate change.

At least three questions are worth asking each time you are confronted with seemingly conflicting statements from Cassandras and cornucopians:

1. Do the impacts being debated pertain only to humans or also to other organisms and natural systems?
2. Are the debaters thinking in the short term or the long term?
3. Are they considering all costs and benefits relevant for the question at hand, or only some?

As you proceed through this book and encounter many contentious issues, consider how a person's perception of them may be influenced by these three factors.

Sustainability involves meeting environmental, social, and economic goals

The primary challenge in our increasingly populated world is how to live within our planet's means, such that Earth and its resources can sustain us, and the rest of Earth's biota, for the foreseeable future. This is the challenge of **sustainability**, a guiding principle of modern environmental science. Sustainability means leaving our children and grandchildren a world as rich and full as the world we live in now. It means not depleting Earth's natural capital, so that after we are gone our descendants will enjoy the use of resources, as we have. It means developing solutions that are able to work in the long term. Sustainability requires maintaining fully functioning ecological systems, because we cannot sustain human civilization without sustaining the natural systems that nourish it.

Environmental protection is often cast as being in opposition to the economic and social needs of human society, but environmental scientists have long recognized that our civilization cannot exist without a functional natural environment. In recent years, people of all persuasions have increasingly realized the connection between environmental quality and human quality of life. Moreover, we now recognize that often it is society's poorer people who suffer the most from environmental degradation. This realization has led advocates of environmental protection, economic development, and social justice to begin working together toward common goals. This cooperative approach has given rise to the modern drive for sustainable development.

Economists employ the term *development* to describe the use of natural resources for economic advancement (as opposed to simple subsistence, or survival). Construction of homes, schools, hospitals, power plants, factories, and transportation networks are all examples of development. **Sustainable development** is the use of renewable and nonrenewable resources in a manner that satisfies our current needs without compromising future availability of resources. The United Nations has defined sustainable development as development that " . . . meets the needs of the present without sacrificing the ability of future generations to meet their needs."[16] This definition is taken from the United Nations–sponsored *Brundtland Commission* (named after its chair, Norwegian prime minister Gro Harlem Brundtland), which published an influential 1987 report entitled *Our Common Future*.

Prior to the Brundtland Report, people aware of human impact on the environment might have thought *sustainable development* to be an oxymoron—a phrase that contradicts itself. Although development involves making purposeful changes intended to improve the quality of human life, environmental advocates have long pointed out that development often so degrades the natural environment that it threatens the very improvements for human life that were intended. Conversely, many people remain under the impression that protecting the environment is incompatible with serving people's economic needs.

Fortunately, sustainable development efforts by governments, businesses, industries, organizations, and individuals everywhere—from students on campus to international representatives at the United Nations—are beginning to alter these perceptions. These efforts are generating sustainable solutions that meet environmental, economic, and social goals simultaneously, satisfying the so-called "triple bottom line."

Sustainability and the triple bottom line demand that our current human population limit its environmental impact while also promoting economic well-being and social equity. These aims require us to make an ethical commitment to our fellow citizens and to future generations. They also require that we apply knowledge from the sciences to help us devise ways to limit our impact and maintain the functioning environmental systems on which all life depends.

"Will we develop in a sustainable way?" may well be the single most important question in the world today. Environmental science holds one crucial key to addressing it: Because so much remains unstudied and undone, and because it is so central to our modern world, environmental science will remain an exciting frontier for you to explore as a student and as an informed citizen throughout your life.

CANADIAN ENVIRONMENTAL PERSPECTIVES

David Suzuki

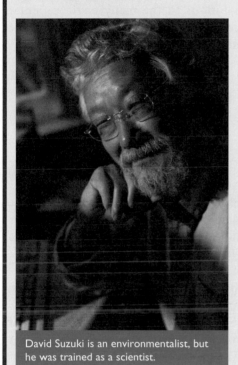

David Suzuki is an environmentalist, but he was trained as a scientist.

- ◼ **Zoologist, geneticist**, and **professor** University of British Columbia, Sustainable Development Research Institute
- ◼ **Environmentalist** and **activist**
- ◼ **Writer** *The Sacred Balance: Rediscovering Our Place in Nature*
- ◼ **Radio and TV broadcast journalist** *Quirks & Quarks* and *The Nature of Things*

What remains to be said about a man who has been called "Canada's environmental conscience"? He has a long list of honorary degrees. He is a Companion of the Order of Canada, placed fifth in the Canadian Broadcasting Corporation's "Greatest Canadian" contest, and has received scores of major environmental and journalism awards. He was the subject of the acclaimed 2010 documentary *Force of Nature: The David Suzuki Movie*. We see him on TV often, exhorting us not to air condition our homes to the point at which penguins would be comfortable.

What we sometimes forget is that before he was a journalist, writer, activist, or TV broadcaster, David Suzuki was a scientist.[17] He completed a degree in biology in 1958, spent that summer working as a fish biologist for the Department of Lands and Forests in Ontario, and then went on to graduate school in zoology at the University of Chicago. By 1962 Suzuki had accepted an appointment in the Department of Genetics at the University of Alberta, moving a year later to a faculty position at the University of British Columbia.

When Suzuki started out as a young professor teaching genetics—a science he adored for its precision and the promise it held for society—he encountered questions at the intersection between science and ethics. Specifically, he learned how genetics had been used by the Nazis and others with an interest in institutionalizing racism.[18] Suzuki's own family had had property seized and been placed in internment camps by the Government of Canada during the Second World War. "Once a Jap, always a Jap," a Member of Parliament said at the time,[19] echoing the belief that treachery and untrustworthiness were genetically encoded into anyone of Japanese descent.

This history makes Suzuki a perfect starting point for a discussion about the difference between environmentalism and environmental science. They are different—but not entirely separate. Ideally, science informs and responds to political and social influences, without being overly influenced by them. David Suzuki has consciously given up "doing" science on an everyday basis, freeing himself to focus on the more political side of science. Today he is much better known for his activism and journalism than for his science. On the rapidly developing field of biotechnology, so close to his own scientific background, he comments:

There is absolutely no reason to suppose that biologists know enough to anticipate the ecological and health ramifications of a revolutionary technology such as genetic engineering. Governments must resist the economic pressures and show leadership and concern for the long-term health of people and nature. And scientists involved in this exciting area should learn from history and welcome free and open discussion about ecological, health, and social implications of their work.[20]

Science is a human endeavour; it can never be entirely free of political or social influence. We want our leaders to incorporate scientific understanding into their social decisions, but there is no foolproof way to ensure that science is not misused to serve political ends. By becoming aware of the complex relationships among science, society, and politics, we can work to ensure that an appropriate balance is maintained.

"We must reinvent a future free of blinders so that we can choose from real options."
—David Suzuki

Thinking About Environmental Perspectives

David Suzuki is no stranger to controversy. Throughout much of his career he has faced criticism for speaking out on environmental issues. Is it acceptable, in your view, for a scientist also to be an activist, or a spokesperson, for a cause? To what extent, if at all, does environmental activism compromise a person's ability to function as a scientist? If a scientist uncovers something in the course of doing research that may be of importance to the general public, is it appropriate for him or her to speak out about this discovery? Or does the act of speaking out compromise objectivity as a scientist?

Conclusion

Finding effective ways of living peacefully, healthfully, and sustainably on our diverse and complex planet will require a thorough scientific understanding of both natural and social systems. Environmental science helps us understand our intricate relationship with the environment and informs our attempts to solve and prevent environmental problems.

Identifying a problem is the first step in devising a solution to it. Many of the trends detailed in this book may cause us worry, but others give us reason to hope. One often-heard criticism of environmental science courses and books is that they emphasize the negative. Recognizing the validity of this criticism, in this book we attempt to balance the discussion of environmental problems with a corresponding focus on potential solutions. Solving environmental problems can move us toward health, longevity, peace, and prosperity. Science in general, and environmental science in particular, can aid us in our efforts to develop balanced and workable solutions to the many environmental dilemmas we face today and to create a better world for ourselves and our children.

REVIEWING OBJECTIVES

You should now be able to:

Define the term *environment*

- Our environment consists of everything around us, including living and nonliving things.
- Humans are a part of the environment and are not separate from it.

Describe natural resources and explain their importance to human life

- Resources from nature are essential to human life and civilization.
- Some resources are inexhaustible or perpetually renewable, others are nonrenewable, and still others are renewable if we are careful not to exploit them at too fast a rate.
- Hardin articulated the concept of carrying capacity, the number of individuals who can be sustained by a given area of productive land. Wackernagel and Rees pioneered the idea of the ecological footprint, a measure of the amount of productive land it would take to support an individual at a certain level of consumption.

Characterize the interdisciplinary nature of environmental science

- Environmental science uses the approaches and insights of numerous disciplines from the natural sciences and the social sciences.

Understand the scientific method and how science operates

- Science is a process of using observations to test ideas.

- The scientific method consists of a series of steps, including making observations, formulating questions, stating a hypothesis, generating predictions, testing predictions, and analyzing the results obtained from the tests.
- The scientific method has many variations, and there are many different ways to test questions scientifically.
- Scientific research occurs within a larger process that includes peer review of work, journal publication, and interaction with colleagues.

Diagnose and illustrate some of the pressures on the global environment

- The increasing human population and increasing per capita consumption exacerbate human impacts on the environment.
- Human activities, such as industrial agriculture and the use of fossil fuels for energy, are having diverse environmental impacts, including resource depletion, air and water pollution, habitat destruction, and the diminishment of biodiversity.

Articulate the concepts of sustainability and sustainable development

- Sustainability means living within the planet's means, such that Earth's resources can sustain us—and other species—for the foreseeable future.
- Sustainable development means pursuing environmental, economic, and social goals in a coordinated way, and it is the most important pursuit in our society today.

TESTING YOUR COMPREHENSION

1. What do renewable resources and nonrenewable resources have in common? How are they different? Identify two renewable and two nonrenewable resources.
2. How did the Agricultural Revolution affect human population size and the environment? How did the Industrial Revolution affect human population size and the environment? Explain your answers.
3. What is the tragedy of the commons? Explain how the concept might apply to an unregulated industry that is a source of water pollution.
4. What is environmental science? Name several disciplines involved in environmental science.
5. What are the two meanings of the word *science*? Name three applications of science.
6. Describe the scientific method. What is the typical sequence of steps?
7. Explain the difference between a manipulative experiment and a natural experiment.
8. What needs to occur before a researcher's results are published? Why is this important?
9. Give examples of three major environmental problems in the world today, along with their causes.
10. How would you define the term "sustainable development"?

THINKING IT THROUGH

1. Many resources are renewable if we use them in moderation but can become nonrenewable if we overexploit them. Order the following resources on a continuum of renewability (see **FIGURE 1.1**), from most renewable to least renewable: soils, timber, freshwater, food crops, and biodiversity. What factors influenced your decision? For each of these resources, what might constitute overexploitation, and what might constitute sustainable use?
2. Why do you think the inhabitants of Rapa Nui did not or could not stop themselves from stripping their island of all its trees? Do you see similarities between the history of Rapa Nui and the modern history of our society? Why, or why not?
3. What environmental problem do *you* feel most acutely yourself ? Do you think there are people in the world who do not view your issue as an environmental problem? Who might they be, and why might they take a different view?
4. If the human population were to stabilize tomorrow and never surpass 7 billion people, would that solve our environmental problems? Which types of problems might be alleviated, and which might continue to become worse?
5. Consider the historic expansion of agriculture and our ability to feed increasing numbers of people, as described in this chapter. Now ask yourself, "Are things getting better or worse?" Ask this question from four points of view: (1) the human perspective, (2) the perspective of other organisms, (3) a short-term perspective, and (4) a long-term perspective. Do your answers to this question change? If so, how?
6. You have become the head of a major funding agency that disburses funding to researchers pursuing work in environmental science. You must give your staff several priorities to determine what types of scientific research to fund. What environmental problems would you most like to see addressed with research? Describe the research you think would need to be completed so that workable solutions to these problems could be developed. Would more than science be needed to develop sustainable solutions?
7. If you were an environmental scientist, and were asked to provide an assessment of a complex environmental situation, what kinds of experts would you call upon? Think about the various specialists and team members who might be needed to contribute their expertise to the following situations: the construction of a new hydroelectric dam; the proposed draining of a wetland to build a new subdivision; a proposal to permit moose hunting in a national park; or the management of a large oil spill just offshore from a pristine beach.

INTERPRETING GRAPHS AND DATA

Environmental scientists study phenomena that range in size from individual molecules to the entire Earth and that occur over time periods lasting from fractions of a second to billions of years. To simultaneously and meaningfully represent data covering so many orders of magnitude, scientists have devised a variety of mathematical and graphical techniques, such as exponential notation and logarithmic scales. Below are two graphical representations *of the same data*, representing the growth of a hypothetical population from an initial size of 10 individuals at a rate of increase of approximately 2.3% per generation. The graph in part (a) uses a conventional linear scale for the population size; the graph in part (b) uses a logarithmic scale.

1. Using the graph in part (a), what would you say was the population size after 200 generations? (Twenty-five years is a pretty standard length of time to use

for one generation.) After 400? After 600? After 800? How would you answer the same questions by using the graph in part (b)? What impression does the graph in part (a) give about population change for the first 600 generations? What impression does the graph in part (b) give?

2. Compare these graphs to **FIGURE 1.2A**. What does the human population appear to be doing between 10 000 B.P. and 2000 B.P.?

3. The size of a population that is growing by a constant rate of increase will plot as a straight line on a logarithmically scaled graph like the one in part (b), but if the annual rate of increase changes, the line will curve. Do you think the data for the human population over the past 12 000 years would plot as a straight line on a logarithmically scaled graph? If not, when and why do you think the line would bend?

(a) Linear scale   **(b) Logarithmic scale**

Hypothetical population growth curves **(a)** and **(b)**, assuming an initial size of 10 and a constant rate of increase of approximately 2.3% per generation.

CHAPTER ENDNOTES

1. NASA, The *Apollo 8* Christmas Eve Broadcast, http://nssdc.gsfc.nasa.gov/planetary/lunar/apollo8_xmas.html

2. Information about the Blue Marble and other photographs of Earth from space can be obtained from NASA's Earth Observatory website, http://earthobservatory.nasa.gov/Newsroom/BlueMarble/BlueMarble_history.html

3. Meadows, D., D. L. Meadows, J. Randers, and W. W. Behrens III (1972) *Limits to Growth*, New York, Universe Books.

4. Ehrlich, P. R. (1968) *The Population Bomb*, Sierra Club-Ballantine Books.

5. Schumacher, E. F. (1973) *Small Is Beautiful: Economics as If People Mattered*, New York, Harper & Row.

6. Carson, R. (1962) *Silent Spring*, Houghton Mifflin.
7. Environment Canada, www.ec.gc.ca
8. The United Nations officially marked the "Day of Seven Billion" on October 31, 2011.
9. Hardin, G. (1968). The Tragedy of the Commons, *Science*, Vol. 162, No. 3859, pp. 1243–1248.
10. Based on the assumption that an average city block is roughly 2–4 ha.
11. Global Footprint Network, www.footprintstandards. org
12. Diamond, J. (2005) *Collapse: How Societies Choose to Fail or Succeed*, Penguin Books.
13. Brander, J. A., M. S. Taylor (1998) The Simple Economics of Easter Island: A Ricardo-Malthus Model of Renewable Resource Use, *The American Economic Review*, Vol. 88, No. 1, pp. 119–138.
14. Sagan, C. (1995) *The Demon-Haunted World: Science as a Candle in the Dark*, Random House/Ballantine Books.
15. Earth System Science Committee (1986) *Earth System Science: A Program for Global Change*, NASA Advisory Council.
16. Brundtland, G. H. (1987) *Report of the World Commission on Environment and Development*: Our Common Future, Oxford University Press.
17. Based partly on information from the website of the David Suzuki Foundation, www.davidsuzuki.org/About_us/Dr_David_Suzuki/
18. Suzuki, David, Biotechnology: A Geneticist's Personal Perspective, www.davidsuzukifoundation. org/files/General/DTSbiotech.pdf
19. Ibid, p. 5.
20. Ibid, p. 23.

MyEnvironmentPlace

Visit **www.myenvironmentplace.ca** to access online resources that complement your textbook. MyEnvironmentPlace inlcudes

- an eText version of the book
- animations on key topics
- videos
- self-grading practice quizzes
- and more!

Follow the registration instruction on the Student Access Code Card included with this text. If your book does not have a Student Access Code Card, you can purchase access to it at **www.myenvironmentplace.c**a.

Matter, Energy, and the Physical Environment

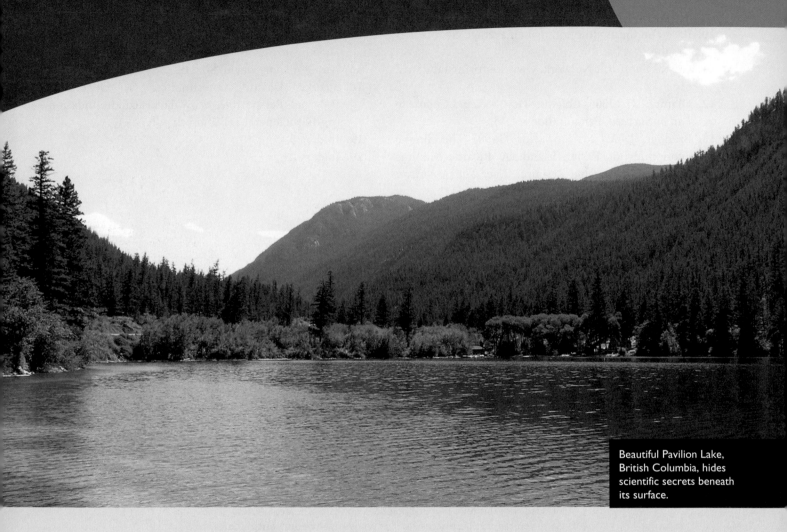

Beautiful Pavilion Lake, British Columbia, hides scientific secrets beneath its surface.

Upon successfully completing this chapter, you will be able to

- Outline some fundamental principles of matter and energy
- Summarize the basic types of matter that are the building blocks for all materials on Earth
- Differentiate among various types of energy and their roles in environmental systems
- Describe how photosynthesis and cellular respiration turn energy into matter and back again
- Explain how plate tectonics and the rock cycle shape the landscape around us and Earth beneath our feet
- Summarize the main hypotheses for the origin of life

A diver examines a microbialite in Pavilion Lake.

CANADA

Hudson Bay

Ontario

Toronto

UNITED STATES

CENTRAL CASE:
THE UNUSUAL MICROBIALITES OF PAVILION LAKE

"Life exists in the universe only because the carbon atom possesses certain exceptional properties."
—SIR JAMES JEANS, ASTRONOMER, PHYSICIST, AND MATHEMATICIAN

"The universe, that vast assemblage of every thing that exists, presents only matter and motion: the whole offers to our contemplation an immense, uninterrupted succession of causes and effects."
— PAUL-HENRI THIRY, BARON D'HOLBACH, FRENCH-GERMAN PHILOSOPHER (1770)

Pavilion Lake is a beautiful, clear blue-green lake that is protected as part of the Marble Canyon Provincial Park system in British Columbia. The lake holds traditional spiritual significance for the Pavilion First Nations Indian Band. In recent years, a group of scientists from NASA's Ames Research Center also has taken an interest in some of the unique characteristics of the lake. The feature of greatest scientific interest is the presence in the lake of *microbialites*—reeflike sedimentary structures composed of calcium carbonate (a combination of calcium, carbon, and oxygen) of organic derivation. Some of these structures are visible as light-blue patches in the lake, as shown in the chapter-opening photo. Microbialites that occur in freshwater environments are less well known scientifically than the much more common oceanic reefs, also composed of calcium carbonate.

Researchers such as Chris McKay and Darlene Lim, from the University of British Columbia and NASA Ames Research Center, are interested in learning about the biological origins of the Pavilion Lake freshwater microbialites and the geobiological conditions that control their *morphology*, or physical form (photo, above). The widely varying morphologies of the Pavilion Lake microbialites, which range from chimney-

Geobiologist Darlene Lim collects a sample.

pressure and light levels at these depths differ substantially. These differences in the physical environment influence the biological processes by which the structures are formed.

Understanding how life-supporting environments originated on Earth depends to a great extent on understanding the formation of carbonate rocks. The formation of carbonates early in Earth history was a crucial step in the chemical evolution of our atmosphere, and it is an integral part of the history of chemical interaction among the various parts of Earth's physical and biological environment.

Pavilion Lake has been identified as one of three possible terrestrial analogues for the formation of carbonate structures on Mars. (The others are Lake Alchichica, Mexico, and Pyramid Lake, Nevada.) Scientific models predict that if Mars once had a thick CO_2-rich atmosphere, like that of early Earth, there should be carbonate rocks present at or near the surface of the planet, as there are on Earth. However, scientists have detected only trace levels of carbonate in Martian soil, and no massive carbonate outcrops have been identified on the surface. Where, then, are the missing carbonates?

The study of terrestrial carbonates like the microbialites of Pavilion Lake may help scientists answer questions like these. In the process, they hope to develop a deeper understanding of early physical environments and life on Earth.[1]

shaped to cone-, leaf-, and dome-shaped, appear to be related to depth. The structures occur in water depths ranging from 5 cm to 30 m, and conditions of

Matter

Examine any environmental issue—whether it is a question of basic science or an application to human–environment interactions—and you will likely discover chemistry playing a central role. Chemistry helps us understand how the land, oceans, atmosphere, and life on Earth—indeed, Earth itself as a planet—came to be as they are now. The study of chemistry shows us how various components of our environment combine, separate, and recombine in different forms, as well as what drives these transformations.

In environmental science, chemistry is central to understanding how pollutants such as sulphur dioxide and nitric oxide cause acid rain; how compounds such as carbon dioxide and methane contribute to atmospheric and climatic change; how organisms acquire food and energy from their surroundings; how soil fertility supports food production for both humans and animals; and how pesticides and other artificial compounds we release into the environment affect the health of wildlife and people. Chemistry is essential in managing water pollution, sewage treatment, atmospheric ozone depletion, hazardous waste and its disposal, and just about any energy-related issue. Moreover, countless applications of chemistry can help us find solutions for current environmental problems.

To begin to appreciate the complex chemistry involved in environmental science, and to understand how the Earth system supports life, we must begin with the fundamentals: We will look first at matter and then move on to consider energy.

Matter cannot be created or destroyed

All of the material in the universe that has mass and occupies space, whether solid, liquid, or gaseous, is termed **matter**. Matter may be transformed from one type of substance into others, but it cannot be created or destroyed. This principle is referred to as the *law of conservation of matter*. In environmental science, this principle helps us understand that the amount of matter stays constant as it is recycled in nutrient cycles and ecosystems. It also makes clear that we cannot simply wish away matter (such as waste and pollution) that we want to eliminate. Any piece of garbage or drop of spilled oil (**FIGURE 2.1**) or billow of smokestack pollution or canister of nuclear waste that we dispose of will not simply disappear. Instead, we will need to take responsible steps to mitigate its impacts.

Atoms, isotopes, and ions are chemical building blocks

All matter is composed of elements. An **element** is a fundamental type of matter, a chemical substance with a given set of properties, that cannot be broken down into substances with other properties. Chemists recognize 92 elements occurring in nature, as well as more than 20 others that have been artificially created. Elements that are especially abundant in living organisms include carbon, nitrogen, hydrogen, and oxygen (**TABLE 2.1**). Each element has its own abbreviation, or chemical symbol. The *Periodic Table of the Elements* (see **APPENDIX C**)

Table 2.1	Earth's Most Abundant Chemical Elements, by Mass		
Earth's crust	**Oceans**	**Air**	**Organisms**
Oxygen (O), 49.5%	Oxygen (O), 85.8%	Nitrogen (N), 78.1%	Oxygen (O), 65.0%
Silicon (Si), 25.7%	Hydrogen (H), 10.8%	Oxygen (O), 21.0%	Carbon (C), 18.5%
Aluminum (Al), 7.4%	Chlorine (Cl), 1.9%	Argon (Ar), 0.9%	Hydrogen (H), 9.5%
Iron (Fe), 4.7%	Sodium (Na), 1.1%	Other, <0.1%	Nitrogen (N), 3.3%
Calcium (Ca), 3.6%	Other, 0.4%		Calcium (Ca), 1.5%
Sodium (Na), 2.8%			Phosphorus (P), 1.0%
Potassium (K), 2.6%			Potassium (K), 0.4%
Magnesium (Mg), 2.1%			Sulphur (S), 0.3%
Other, 1.6%			Other, 0.5%

Potential Pathways for Oil to Reach Bottom Sediments

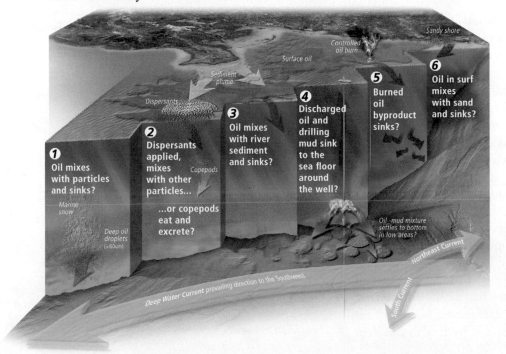

FIGURE 2.1

Matter never just disappears, as much as we might sometimes wish it. In this case, oil that was spilled in the Gulf of Mexico in 2010 has moved around and changed its form, along all of the pathways shown here. All of the oil ended up somewhere—in the rocks and sediments at the bottom of the gulf, or mixed with sediment on the shore, or dispersed in the water, or ingested by marine organisms, or volatilized into the air.

THE SCIENCE BEHIND THE STORY

How Isotopes Reveal Secrets of Earth and Life

Dr. Keith Hobson works with Environment Canada and the University of Saskatchewan.

Isotopes are one of the most powerful instruments in the environmental scientist's toolkit. They enable scientists to date ancient materials, reconstruct past climates, and study the lifestyles of prehistoric humans. They also allow researchers to work out photosynthetic pathways, measure animals' diets and health, and trace flows of materials through organisms and ecosystems.

Researchers studying the past often use radiocarbon dating. Carbon's most abundant isotope is ^{12}C, but ^{13}C and ^{14}C also occur in nature. Carbon-14 is

a **radioactive isotope**, which means that it decays spontaneously. It occurs in organisms at the same low concentration that it occurs in the atmosphere. Once an organism dies, no new ^{14}C is incorporated into its structure, and the radioactive decay process gradually reduces its store of ^{14}C, converting these atoms to ^{14}N (nitrogen-14).

The decay is slow and steady, acting like a clock. Scientists can date ancient organic materials by measuring the percent of carbon that is ^{14}C and matching this value against the clocklike progression of decay. In this way, archaeologists and palaeontologists have dated prehistoric human remains; charcoal, grain, and shells found at ancient campfires; and bones and frozen tissues of recently extinct animals, such as mammoths. The most recent ice age has been dated from ^{14}C analysis of trees overrun by glacial ice sheets. Other radioactive isotopes that decay more slowly are used to establish timelines for much older rocks and minerals.

Researchers interested in present-day processes often use **stable isotope**

analysis. Unlike radioactive isotopes, stable isotopes occur in nature in constant ratios, and they do not decay radioactively. For instance, nitrogen occurs as 99.63% nitrogen-14 and 0.37% nitrogen-15. These ratios, or *isotopic signatures*, of various environmental materials and processes are diagnostic—almost like fingerprints. For example, organisms tend to retain ^{15}N in their tissues but readily excrete ^{14}N. As a result, animals higher in the food chain show isotopic signatures biased toward ^{15}N, as do animals that are starving.

Keith Hobson, an ecologist with the Prairie and Northern Wildlife Research Centre, Canadian Wildlife Service of Environment Canada, and the University of Saskatchewan, used nitrogen signatures to analyze the diets of seabirds and marine mammals, showing that geese fast while nesting, and to trace artificial contaminants in food chains.

Hobson and other scientists have also used stable isotopes for ecological studies. When animals eat plants, they incorporate the plants' isotopic signa-

---

summarizes information on the elements in a comprehensive and elegant way.

Elements are composed of **atoms**, the smallest components that maintain the chemical properties of that element (**FIGURE 2.2**). Every atom has a nucleus consisting of *protons* (positively charged particles) and *neutrons* (particles with no electric charge). The atoms of each element have a defined number of protons, referred to as the element's *atomic number*. (Elemental carbon, for instance, has six protons in its nucleus; thus, its atomic number is 6.) An atom's nucleus is surrounded by negatively charged particles known as *electrons*, which balance the positive charge of the protons.

All atoms of a given element contain the same number of protons, but not necessarily the same number of neutrons. Atoms of the same element with differing numbers of neutrons are called **isotopes** (**FIGURE 2.2A**). The atomic number of carbon is 6, so all isotopes of carbon have six protons (if they had a different number of protons, they wouldn't be carbon). But different numbers of neutrons are possible, leading to different

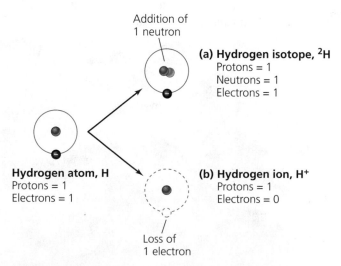

Addition of 1 neutron

(a) Hydrogen isotope, ^2H
Protons = 1
Neutrons = 1
Electrons = 1

Hydrogen atom, H
Protons = 1
Electrons = 1

(b) Hydrogen ion, H^+
Protons = 1
Electrons = 0

Loss of 1 electron

FIGURE 2.2
Hydrogen is an element; it contains 1 proton + 0 neutron (mass number = 1). Deuterium **(a)**, an isotope of hydrogen, contains 1 proton + 1 neutron, and thus has greater mass than a typical hydrogen atom. Because deuterium has 1 proton, it is still a form of hydrogen. If a hydrogen atom loses its one electron **(b)**, it gains a positive charge and becomes a hydrogen ion, H^+.

tures into their own tissues, and this signature passes up the food chain. Grasses have higher ratios of ^{13}C to ^{12}C than oak trees do, for instance, whereas cacti have intermediate ratios. As a result, carbon isotope studies can tell ecologists what an animal has been eating. Similarly, archaeologists have used isotopic signatures in human bone to determine when ancient people switched from a hunter-gatherer diet to an agricultural one.

Researchers also use isotopes to track movements of birds and other animals that migrate thousands of kilometers. This is possible because isotopic signatures in rainfall vary systematically across large geographic regions. This signature gets passed from rainwater to plants and from plants to animals, leaving a fingerprint of geographic origin in an animal's tissues. Hobson and colleagues used a combination of isotopic data from hydrogen and carbon to pinpoint the geographic origins of monarch butterflies that had migrated to Mexico, providing important information for their conservation (see map).

Stable isotope analysis is used to study many different environmental materials and processes today, and there remains much more we can learn from the use of these subtle chemical clues.

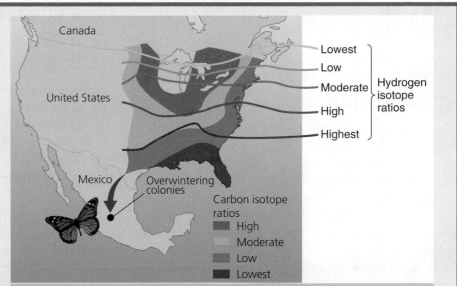

Plants in different geographic areas have different carbon and hydrogen isotopic ratios, which caterpillars incorporate into their tissues when they eat the plants. When the caterpillars metamorphose into butterflies and migrate, they carry these isotopic signatures with them. This map of isotopic ratios across eastern North America, produced from measurements of monarch butterflies, shows decreasing ratios of ^{13}C to ^{12}C from north to south (coloured bands) and increasing ratios of ^2H to ^1H from north to south (grey lines). By measuring carbon and hydrogen isotopic ratios in monarchs wintering in Mexico and matching the numbers against this map, researchers were able to pinpoint the geographic origin of many of the butterflies.

Source: Wassenaar, Wassenaar, L. I., and K. A. Hobson (1998). Proceedings of the National Academy of Sciences of the USA 95:15436–15439.

mass numbers for the various isotopes of carbon. Isotopes are denoted by their mass number, followed by their elemental symbol. For example, ^{14}C (carbon-14) is an isotope of carbon that has 8 neutrons and 6 protons in the nucleus, rather than the more common 6 neutrons and 6 protons of ^{12}C (carbon-12).

Because they differ slightly in mass, isotopes also differ slightly in their behaviour. This fact has turned out to be very useful for researchers. Scientists have been able to use isotopes to study a number of phenomena that help illuminate the history of Earth's physical environment. Researchers also have used them to study the flow of nutrients within and among organisms and the movement of organisms from one geographic location to another (see "The Science Behind the Story: How Isotopes Reveal Secrets of Earth and Life.").

Some isotopes are *radioactive* and decay spontaneously, changing their chemical identity as they shed subatomic particles and emit high-energy radiation. These radioisotopes decay into lighter radioisotopes, until they eventually become stable isotopes. Each radio-

isotope decays at a rate determined by its **half-life**, the amount of time it takes for half of the atoms to give off radiation and decay. Each radioisotope has its own characteristic half-life, and the half-lives of various radioisotopes range from fractions of a second to billions of years. For example, the naturally occurring radioisotope uranium-235 (^{235}U) is the principal source of energy for commercial nuclear power. With a half-life of about 700 million years, ^{235}U decays into a series of daughter isotopes, eventually forming lead-207 (^{207}Pb).

In addition to having stable or radioactive isotopic variants, involving differences in the nucleus, atoms also may gain or lose electrons from their outer shells. In so doing, they become **ions**, electrically charged atoms or combinations of atoms (**FIGURE 2.2B**). Ions are denoted by their elemental symbol followed by their ionic charge. For instance, Ca^{2+} is a calcium atom that has lost two electrons and so has a positive charge of 2 (mussels and clams use this common ion to form shells). Ions that form when an atom loses electrons, and therefore carry a positive charge, are called *cations*. Ions that form when an atom gains electrons, and therefore carry a negative charge, are called *anions*.

Atoms bond to form molecules and compounds

Atoms can link chemically to form **molecules**, combinations of two or more atoms. Molecules may contain one element or several. Common molecules that contain only a single element include oxygen (O_2) and nitrogen (N_2), both of which are abundant in air. A molecule composed of atoms of two or more different elements is called a **compound**. Water is a compound; it is composed of two hydrogen atoms bonded to one oxygen atom, denoted by the chemical formula H_2O. Another common compound is carbon dioxide, consisting of one carbon atom bonded to two oxygen atoms; its chemical formula is CO_2.

Atoms **bond**, or combine chemically, because of an attraction for one another's electrons. The strength of this attraction varies among elements, so atoms may be held together in different ways according to whether and how they share or transfer electrons.

When atoms in a molecule share electrons, they generate a *covalent bond*. For instance, two atoms of hydrogen bond to form hydrogen gas, H_2, by sharing electrons equally. Atoms in some covalent bonds share electrons unequally, with one atom exerting a greater pull. Such is the case with water, in which oxygen attracts electrons more strongly than does hydrogen. If the strength of attraction is sufficiently unequal, an electron may actually be transferred from one atom to another. Such a transfer creates oppositely charged ions that are said to form *ionic bonds*. Compounds formed in this manner are called *ionic compounds*, or *salts*. Ordinary table salt (NaCl) contains ionic bonds between positively charged sodium cations (Na^+), each of which donates an electron, and negatively charged chloride anions (Cl^-), each of which receives an electron.

Elements, molecules, and compounds can also come together in mixtures without chemically bonding or reacting. Such a mixture of two or more substances is called a **solution**, a term most often applied to liquids but also applicable to gases and solids. Crude oil, for example, is a heavy liquid mixture of many kinds of molecules that consist primarily of carbon and hydrogen atoms. Many other types of atoms are mixed into the solution or bonded to the carbon and hydrogen. Air in the atmosphere is also a solution, composed of molecules of nitrogen (N_2), oxygen (O_2), water (H_2O), carbon dioxide (CO_2), methane (CH_4), ozone (O_3), and many others. Blood, ocean water, mud, plant sap, most minerals, and metal alloys such as brass are all solutions.

The chemical structure of the water molecule facilitates life

Water dominates Earth's surface, covering over 70% of the globe, and its abundance is a primary reason why Earth is hospitable to life. Scientists think life originated in water and stayed there for 3 billion years before moving onto land. Today every land-dwelling creature remains tied to water for its existence.

The water molecule's amazing capacity to support life results from its unique chemical properties. As mentioned previously, the oxygen atom in a water molecule attracts electrons more strongly than do the two hydrogen atoms, resulting in a polar molecule in which the oxygen end has a partial negative charge and the hydrogen end has a partial positive charge. Because of this, water molecules can adhere to one another in a special type of interaction called a *hydrogen bond*, in which the oxygen atom of one water molecule is weakly attracted to the hydrogen atoms of another (**FIGURE 2.3**).

These loose connections among molecules give water several properties important in supporting life and stabilizing Earth's climate (**FIGURE 2.4**):

■ Water remains liquid over a wide range of temperatures. At Earth's surface, water exists in liquid form from 0 °C all the way to 100 °C. This means that water-based biological processes can occur in a very wide range of environmental conditions.

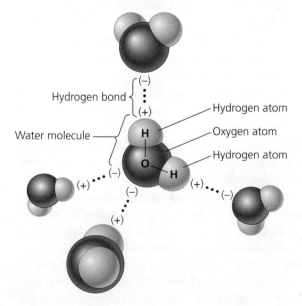

FIGURE 2.3
Water is a unique compound that has several properties crucial for life. Shown here, hydrogen bonds give water cohesion by enabling water molecules to adhere loosely to one another.

Ice

Liquid water

(a) Why ice floats on water

Sodium ion surrounded by negatively charged regions of water molecules

Water molecule

Chloride ion surrounded by positively charged regions of water molecules

Salt (sodium chloride, Na⁺Cl⁻)

(b) Water as a solvent; how water dissolves salt

FIGURE 2.4

(a) Ice floats on water because solid ice is less dense than liquid water. This is an unusual property of H_2O—it is far more common for the solid form of a material to be denser than the liquid form.
(b) Water can dissolve many chemicals, especially polar and ionic compounds. Seawater holds sodium and chloride ions, among others, in solution.

■ Water exhibits strong cohesion. (Think of how water holds together in drops and how the drops on a surface join together when you touch them to one another.) This facilitates the transport of chemicals, such as nutrients and waste, in plants and animals and in the physical environment.

■ Water has a high heat capacity, which means that water can absorb a large amount of heat with only small changes in its temperature (it takes additional energy to break the hydrogen bonds). This quality helps stabilize systems against change, whether those systems are organisms, ponds, lakes, or climate systems.

■ Water molecules in ice are farther apart than in liquid water (**FIGURE 2.4A**). This means that ice is less dense than liquid water—the reverse of most other compounds, which become denser as they

freeze. In ice, each molecule is connected to neighbouring molecules by stable hydrogen bonds, forming a spacious crystal lattice. In liquid water, hydrogen bonds frequently break and re-form, and the molecules are closer together and less well organized. This property explains why ice floats on water. Floating ice has an insulating effect that can prevent water bodies from freezing solid in winter.

■ Fresh water reaches its maximum density at 4°C; water cooled to this temperature increases in density, but when cooled below this temperature it becomes gradually less dense. This means that surface water cooled below 4°C by winter air will tend to remain at the surface, promoting the formation of ice and further insulating deeper waters from the frigid air.

■ Water molecules bond well with other polar molecules because the positive end of one molecule bonds readily to the negative end of another. As a result, water can hold in solution, or dissolve, many other molecules, including chemicals necessary for life (**FIGURE 2.4B**). It follows that most biologically important solutions involve water, and we sometimes informally refer to water as the "universal solvent," meaning that it is able to dissolve most things.

■ Another important characteristic of water is its transparency to light; without this feature there would be no photosynthesis, which is an ultimate source of energy for almost all organisms living in water.

Hydrogen ions control acidity

In any *aqueous solution* (a solution in which water is present as a solvent), a small number of water molecules *dissociate*, or split apart, each forming a hydrogen ion (H^+) and a hydroxide ion (OH^-). The product of hydrogen and hydroxide ion concentrations is always the same; as the concentration of one increases, the concentration of the other decreases. Pure water contains equal numbers of these ions, and we refer to it as *neutral*. Most aqueous solutions, however, contain different concentrations of these two ions. Solutions in which the H^+ concentration is greater than the OH^- concentration are called *acidic*; the stronger the acid, the more readily dissociation occurs and H^+ ions are released. Solutions in which the OH^- concentration is greater than the H^+ concentration are called *basic*.

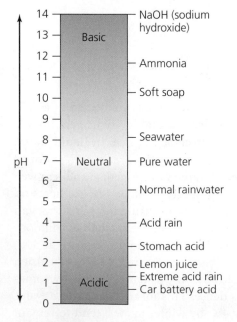

FIGURE 2.5
The pH scale measures how acidic or basic a solution is. The pH of pure water is 7, the midpoint of the scale. Acidic solutions have higher hydrogen ion concentrations and lower pH, whereas basic solutions have lower hydrogen ion concentrations and higher pH.

The **pH** scale (**FIGURE 2.5**) quantifies the acidity or basicity of solutions. The scale runs from 0 to 14; pure water (neutral) has a hydrogen ion activity of 10^{-7} and it is said to have a pH of 7. Solutions with pH less than 7 are acidic; those with pH greater than 7 are basic. The pH scale is logarithmic, so each step on the scale represents a tenfold difference in hydrogen ion concentration. Thus, a substance with pH of 6 contains 10 times as many hydrogen ions as a substance with pH of 7, and a substance with pH of 5 contains 100 times as many hydrogen ions as one with pH of 7. **FIGURE 2.5** shows the pH for a number of common substances. For example, normal rainwater is slightly acidic, but industrial air pollution has intensified the acidity of precipitation. As a result, the pH of rain in parts of south-central Canada and the northeastern and midwestern United States now frequently dips to 4 or lower.

Matter is composed of organic and inorganic compounds

Beyond their need for water, living things also depend on organic compounds, which they create and of which they are composed. **Organic compounds** consist of carbon atoms (and generally hydrogen atoms) joined by covalent bonds, often with other elements, such as nitrogen, oxygen, sulphur, and phosphorus. Carbon's unusual ability to build elaborate molecules has resulted in millions of different organic compounds, many of which are highly complex.

Chemists differentiate organic compounds from **inorganic compounds**, which also are fundamentally important in the support of life. (Water is one example of a crucial inorganic compound.) Some inorganic compounds may contain carbon, but they are not organic because they lack the carbon–carbon bonds that are characteristic of organic compounds. It is important to remember that in scientific terminology, *organic* doesn't

weighing the issues
WHAT DOES *ORGANIC* MEAN?

Do you think it is important for the general public to understand the difference between the scientific usage of the term *organic* and the more general usage, where it often means "environmentally friendly" or "pesticide-free"? Should there be legal guidelines governing the use of terms like *organic* on products available on store shelves?

H—C—H   H—C—C—H

(a) Methane, CH$_4$ **(b) Ethane, C$_2$H$_6$**   **(c) Naphthalene, C$_{10}$H$_8$**
(a polycyclic aromatic
hydrocarbon)

FIGURE 2.6
The simplest hydrocarbon is methane **(a)**. Many hydrocarbons consist of linear chains of carbon atoms with hydrogen atoms attached; the shortest of these is ethane **(b)**. Volatile hydrocarbons with multiple rings, such as naphthalene **(c)**, are called polycyclic aromatic hydrocarbons (PAHs).

mean "natural" or "environmentally friendly" or "pesticide-free," as we have come to use it in everyday language. The term *organic* doesn't even imply that a compound is or was once alive—it simply refers to the presence of carbon–carbon bonding in the chemical compound.

Most biological materials are composed of organic compounds called **hydrocarbons**, which consist primarily of carbon and hydrogen (although other elements may enter the compounds, often as impurities). The simplest hydrocarbon is **methane (CH$_4$)**, the key component of natural gas; it has one carbon atom bonded to four hydrogen atoms (**FIGURE 2.6A**). Adding another carbon atom and two more hydrogen atoms gives us ethane (C$_2$H$_6$), the next-simplest hydrocarbon (**FIGURE 2.6B**). The smallest (and therefore lightest-weight) hydrocarbons exist in a gaseous state at normal temperatures and pressures. Larger (and therefore heavier) hydrocarbons are liquids, and those with more than 20 carbon atoms are normally solids.

Some hydrocarbons pose health hazards to wildlife and people. For example, the polycyclic aromatic hydrocarbons, or PAHs (**FIGURE 2.6C**), are volatile molecules with a structure of multiple carbon rings. These toxic compounds can evaporate from spilled oil and gasoline, and they can mix with water. The eggs and young of fish and other aquatic creatures, such as beluga whales, are often most at risk (see "Central Case: The Plight of the St. Lawrence Belugas," in the chapter on environmental systems and ecosystems). PAHs also occur in particulate form in various combustion products, including cigarette smoke, wood smoke, and charred meat.

Macromolecules are building blocks of life

Organic compounds sometimes combine to form long chains of repeated molecules. Some of these chains, called *polymers*, play key roles as building blocks of life. Three types of polymers are essential to life: proteins, nucleic acids, and carbohydrates. Lipids, not considered to be polymers, are also fundamental to life. These four important types of molecules are referred to as *macromolecules* because of their large size.

Proteins consist of long chains of organic molecules called *amino acids* (**FIGURE 2.7A**). Organisms combine up to 20 different types of amino acids into long chains to build proteins (**FIGURE 2.7B**), with parts of the chain exposed and others hidden inside complex folds (**FIGURE 2.7C**). The folding pattern affects the protein's function because the position of each chemical group helps determine how it interacts with other molecules. Some proteins help produce tissues, such as skin, hair, muscles, and tendons, and provide structural support

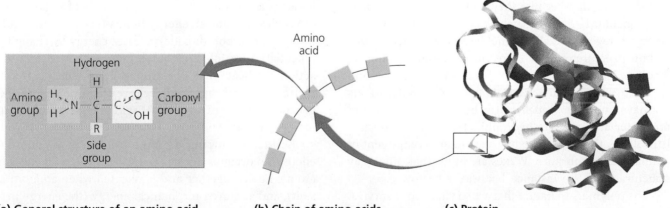

(a) General structure of an amino acid   **(b) Chain of amino acids**   **(c) Protein**

FIGURE 2.7   Proteins are polymers that are vital for life. They are made up of long chains of amino acids **(a, b)** that form complex convoluted shapes **(c)**, which help determine their functions.

for the organism. Some help store energy, and others transport substances. Some act in the immune system to defend the organism against foreign attackers. Still others act as hormones, molecules that serve as chemical messengers within an organism. Finally, proteins can serve as enzymes, molecules that catalyze, or promote, certain chemical reactions, such as digestion.

Nucleic acids direct the production of proteins. The two nucleic acids—**deoxyribonucleic acid (DNA)** and **ribonucleic acid (RNA)**—carry the hereditary information for organisms and are responsible for passing traits from parents to offspring. Nucleic acids are composed of nucleotides, structural units made of a sugar molecule, a phosphate group, and a nitrogenous base. In DNA, the nucleotides link together in a double strand, like a ladder, that is twisted into a spiral. Hereditary information is encoded in the sequencing of the nucleotides that form the rungs of the ladder. Regions of DNA coding for particular proteins that perform particular functions (that is, segments of the ladder) are called **genes**. RNA molecules use this genetic information to direct the order in which amino acids assemble to build proteins, in turn influencing the structure, growth, and maintenance of the organism.

Carbohydrates, a third type of biologically important macromolecule, consist of atoms of carbon, hydrogen, and oxygen. Glucose ($C_6H_{12}O_6$), a simple sugar, is one of the most common and important carbohydrates, providing energy that fuels plant and animal cells. Glucose also serves as a building block for complex carbohydrates, such as starch. Plants use starch to store energy, and animals eat plants to acquire starch. Both plants and animals use complex carbohydrates to build structure. Insects and crustaceans form hard shells from the carbohydrate chitin. Cellulose, the most abundant organic compound on Earth, is a complex carbohydrate found in the cell walls of leaves, bark, stems, and roots.

A fourth important type of macromolecule is the chemically diverse group of compounds called **lipids**, classified together because they do not dissolve in water. These include fats and oils, which are convenient forms of energy storage, especially for mobile animals. Their hydrocarbon structures somewhat resemble gasoline, a similarity echoed in their function: to effectively store energy and release it when burned. Phospholipids are similar to fats but have one water-repellent (or hydrophobic) side and one water-attracting (or hydrophilic) side. This characteristic allows them to make up the primary component of animal cell membranes. Waxes are lipids that often play structural roles (for instance, beeswax in beehives).

The polymers in nature that are so vital to our survival have inspired chemists to create innumerable types of synthetic (human-made) polymers, which we call **plastics**. Polyethylene, polypropylene, polyurethane, and polystyrene are just a few of the many synthetic polymers in our manufactured products today (known by brand names such as Nylon, Teflon, and Kevlar). Plastics, many of them derived from hydrocarbons in petroleum, are all around us in our everyday lives, from furniture to food containers to fibre optics to fleece jackets.

We value synthetic polymers because they are versatile, and they resist chemical breakdown. Although plastics make our lives easier, the waste and pollution they create when we discard them is long-lasting as well. In future chapters we will see how pollutants that resist breakdown can cause problems for wildlife and human health, for water quality, for marine animals, and for waste management. Fortunately, chemists, policymakers, and citizens are finding more ways to design and use less-polluting substances and to recycle materials effectively.

Energy

Matter is the building material, and energy is the driver of Earth's environmental processes. Energy is involved in nearly every biological, chemical, and physical process. But what, exactly, is energy? **Energy** is the capacity to change the position, physical composition, or temperature of matter—in other words, a force that can accomplish work.

Scientists differentiate between two types of energy: **potential energy**, energy of position; and **kinetic energy**, energy of motion. Consider river water held behind a dam. By preventing water from moving downstream, the dam causes the water to accumulate potential energy. When the dam gates are opened, the potential energy is converted to kinetic energy, in the form of water's motion as it rushes downstream.

Such energy transfers take place at the atomic level every time a chemical bond is broken or formed. Chemical energy is potential energy held in the bonds between atoms. Converting a molecule with high-energy bonds (such as the carbon–carbon bonds of sugars) into molecules with lower-energy bonds (such as the bonds in water or carbon dioxide) releases energy by changing potential energy into kinetic energy and produces motion, action, or heat. Just as automobile engines split the hydrocarbons of gasoline to release chemical energy and generate movement, our bodies split glucose molecules in food for the same purpose (**FIGURE 2.8**).

Besides occurring as chemical energy, potential energy can occur as nuclear energy (the energy that holds atomic nuclei together and is released when an atom is split), and as stored mechanical energy (the energy in a compressed spring, the water behind the dam, or a tree bending in the wind). Kinetic energy also takes a variety of forms. These include thermal energy, light energy,

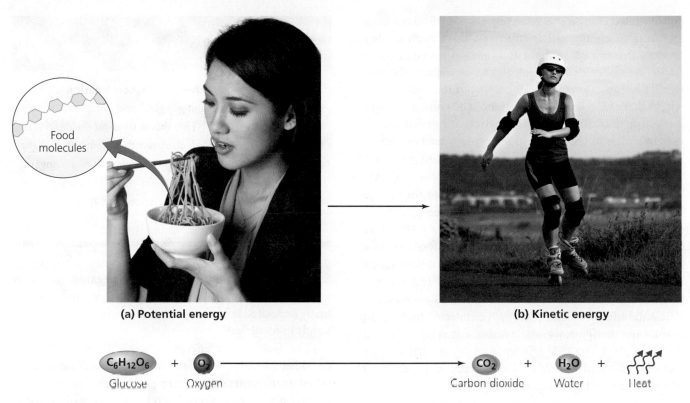

(a) Potential energy   (b) Kinetic energy

$C_6H_{12}O_6$ + O_2 ⟶ CO_2 + H_2O + Heat
Glucose   Oxygen   Carbon dioxide   Water   Heat

FIGURE 2.8   Energy is released when potential energy is converted to kinetic energy. Potential energy stored in sugars, such as glucose, in the food we eat **(a)**, combined with oxygen, becomes kinetic energy when we exercise **(b)**, releasing carbon dioxide, water, and heat as by products.

electrical energy, and sound energy, all of which involve movement of electrons, atoms, molecules, or objects.

Energy is always conserved but can change in quality

Although energy can change from one form to another, it cannot be created or destroyed. The total energy in the universe remains constant and thus is said to be conserved. Scientists call this principle the *first law of thermodynamics*. The potential energy of the water behind a dam will equal the kinetic energy of its eventual movement down the riverbed. Similarly, burning converts the potential energy in a log of firewood to an equal amount of energy produced as heat and light. We obtain energy from the food we eat, which we expend in exercise, put toward the body's maintenance, or store as fat; we do not somehow create additional energy or end up with less than the food gives us. Any individual system can temporarily increase or decrease in energy, but the total amount in the universe remains constant.

Although the overall energy will be conserved in any energy transfer, the *second law of thermodynamics* states that the nature of the energy will change from a more-ordered state to a less-ordered state, if no force counteracts this tendency. That is, systems tend to move toward increasing disorder (termed *entropy*). For instance, after death every organism undergoes decomposition and loses its structure. A log of firewood—the highly organized and structurally complex product of many years of slow tree growth—transforms in the campfire to a residue of carbon ash, smoke, and gases such as carbon dioxide and water vapour, as well as the light and the heat of the flame. With the help of oxygen, the complex biological polymers that make up the wood are converted into a disorganized assortment of rudimentary molecules and into heat and light energy.

The nature of any given energy source helps determine how easily humans can harness it. Sources such as fossil fuels and the fuels used in nuclear power plants contain

weighing the issues

ENERGY AVAILABILITY AND ENERGY POLICY

Contrast the ease of harnessing concentrated energy, such as that of petroleum, with the ease of harnessing highly diffuse energy, such as that of heat from the oceans. How do you think these differences have affected our society's energy policy and energy sources through the years?

concentrated energy; it is relatively easy to withdraw large amounts of energy efficiently from these high-quality sources. In contrast, sunlight and the heat stored in ocean water are more diffuse energy sources. Each day the world's oceans absorb heat energy from the Sun equivalent to that of 250 billion barrels (about 40 trillion litres) of oil—more than 3000 times as much as our global society uses in a year. But because this energy is spread out across such vast spaces, it is difficult to harness effectively.

In every transfer of energy, some energy is lost—not destroyed, but converted into a less-usable form. The inefficiency of some of the most common energy conversions that power our society can be surprising. When we burn gasoline in an automobile engine, only about 16% of the energy released is used to power the automobile's movement; the rest is converted to heat and escapes without being used. Incandescent light bulbs are even less efficient; only 5% of their energy is converted to the light that we use them for, while the rest is lost as heat. Viewed in this context, the 15% efficiency of some current solar technologies and 7% to 15% efficiency of geothermal power plants look pretty good.

Light energy from the Sun powers most living systems

The energy that powers Earth's environmental systems comes primarily from the Sun. The Sun releases radiation from large portions of the electromagnetic spectrum, although our atmosphere filters much of this out, and we see only a small part of this radiation as visible light (**FIGURE 2.9**).

Most of the Sun's energy is reflected or absorbed and re-emitted by the atmosphere, land, or water. Solar energy drives our weather and climate patterns, including winds and ocean currents. A small amount (less than 1% of the total) powers plant growth, and a still smaller amount flows from plants into the organisms that eat them and

roots
PHOTOSYNTHESIS

The term **photosynthesis** is a combination of two Greek roots, *phos*, meaning "light," and *syntithenai*, meaning "to put together." The word thus nicely describes the chemical process of photosynthesis, in which light energy is used to recombine molecules to make sugars. You will find the prefix *photo-* in many terms that are important in environmental science, and it always indicates the involvement of light.

the organisms that decompose dead organic matter. A minuscule amount of energy, relatively speaking, is eventually deposited below ground in the form of the chemical bonds in fossil fuels.

The Sun's light energy is used directly by some organisms to produce their own food. Such organisms, called **autotrophs** or **primary producers**, include green plants, algae, and cyanobacteria (a type of bacteria named for their characteristic blue-green, or cyan, colour.) *Photoautotrophs* turn light energy from the Sun into chemical energy via the process of **photosynthesis** (**FIGURE 2.10**). In photosynthesis, sunlight powers a series of chemical reactions that convert carbon dioxide and water into sugars, transforming low-quality energy from the Sun into high-quality energy the organism can use.

Photosynthesis is a complex process, but the overall reaction can be summarized with the following equation:

PHOTOSYNTHESIS: $6CO_2 + 12H_2O +$ the Sun's energy $\rightarrow$
$$C_6H_{12}O_6 \text{ (sugar)} + 6O_2 + 6H_2O$$

The numbers preceding each molecular formula indicate how many molecules of each type are involved in the reaction. Note that the sums of the numbers on each side of the equation for each element are equal; that is,

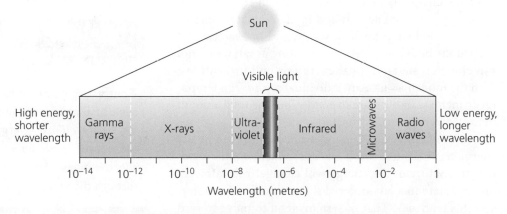

FIGURE 2.9 The Sun emits radiation from many portions of the electromagnetic spectrum. Visible light makes up only a small portion of this energy. Some radiation that reaches our planet is reflected back; some is absorbed by air, land, and water; and a small amount powers photosynthesis.

Sun

Visible light

High energy, shorter wavelength | Gamma rays | X-rays | Ultra-violet | Infrared | Microwaves | Radio waves | Low energy, longer wavelength

10^{-14} 10^{-12} 10^{-10} 10^{-8} 10^{-6} 10^{-4} 10^{-2} 1

Wavelength (metres)

FIGURE 2.10
In photosynthesis, autotrophs such as plants, algae, and cyanobacteria use sunlight to convert carbon dioxide and water into sugars and oxygen. This diagram summarizes the complex sets of chemical reactions involved. In the light reactions, water is converted to oxygen in the presence of sunlight, creating high-energy molecules (ATP and NADPH). These help drive reactions in the Calvin cycle, in which carbon dioxide is used to produce sugars.

there are 6 C, 24 H, and 24 O on each side. This illustrates how chemical equations are balanced, with each atom recycled and matter conserved. No atoms are lost; they are simply rearranged into different molecules. Note also that water appears on both sides of the equation. The reason is that for every 12 water molecules that are dissociated in the process, 6 water molecules are newly created. We can streamline the equation by showing only the net loss of 6 water molecules:

PHOTOSYNTHESIS: $6CO_2 + 6H_2O$ + the Sun's energy →
$$C_6H_{12}O_6 \text{ (sugar)} + 6O_2 + 6O_2$$

Thus in photosynthesis, water, carbon dioxide, and light energy from the Sun are transformed to produce sugar (glucose) and oxygen. To accomplish this, green plants draw up water from the ground through their roots, absorb carbon dioxide from the air through their leaves, and harness sunlight. With these ingredients, they create sugars for their growth and maintenance and release oxygen as a by-product.

Animals, in turn, depend on oxygen and sugars from photosynthesis (**FIGURE 2.11**). Animals survive by being **consumers**, or **heterotrophs**, organisms that gain their energy by feeding on other organisms. They eat plants (thus becoming *primary consumers*), or they eat animals that have eaten plants (thus becoming *secondary consumers*), and they take in oxygen. It is thought that animals appeared on Earth's surface only after the planet's atmosphere had been supplied with oxygen by cyanobacteria, the earliest autotrophs.

Utilizing the chemical energy created during photosynthesis requires a process called **cellular respiration**. To release the chemical energy of glucose, cells use the reactivity of oxygen to convert glucose back into its original starting materials; in other words, respiration can be thought of a "reverse photosynthesis"; it oxidizes glucose to produce carbon dioxide and water. The net

FIGURE 2.11
When an animal such as this deer eats the leaves of a plant, it consumes the sugars the plant produced through photosynthesis and gains energy from those sugars.

equation for cellular respiration is thus the exact opposite of that for photosynthesis:

RESPIRATION: $C_6H_{12}O_6$ (sugar) $+ 6O_2 \rightarrow$
$$6CO_2 + 6H_2O + energy$$

The energy gained per glucose molecule in respiration is only two-thirds of the energy input per glucose molecule in photosynthesis—a prime example of the second law of thermodynamics. Cellular respiration is a continuous process that occurs in all living things; it is essential to life. It occurs both in the autotrophs that create sugars and in the heterotrophs that eat them.

Geothermal energy also powers Earth's systems

Although the Sun is Earth's primary power source, it is not the only one. A minor additional source is the gravitational pull of the Moon, which causes ocean tides. A more significant additional energy source is **geothermal energy**—heat that emanates from Earth's interior.

Geothermal energy is powered primarily by radioactivity. When we think of radioactivity, nuclear power plants and atomic weapons may come to mind, but it is a natural phenomenon that involves the release of radiation by radioisotopes as their nuclei spontaneously decay. Radiation from naturally occurring radioisotopes deep inside Earth heats the inside of the planet, and this heat gradually makes its way to the surface. This internal heat energy drives geological processes, heats magma that erupts from volcanoes, and warms groundwater and thermal hot springs (**FIGURE 2.12**). Geothermal heat

FIGURE 2.12
These thermal pools at Rabbitkettle Hot Springs in Nahanni National Park Reserve, Northwest Territories, are heated year-round by geothermal energy from deep below the ground. The bright colours on the rocks are colonies of bacteria that thrive in the hot, mineral-laden water.

(a) Hydrothermal vent

(b) Giant tubeworms

FIGURE 2.13
Hydrothermal vents on the ocean floor **(a)** send spouts of hot, mineral-rich water into the cold blackness of the deep sea. Specialized biological communities thrive in these unusual conditions. Odd creatures such as these giant tubeworms **(b)** survive thanks to bacteria that produce food from hydrogen sulphide by the process of chemosynthesis.

from within the planet is now being harnessed for commercial power, especially in locations where it is particularly concentrated at the surface.

Long before humans came along, geothermal energy was powering other biological communities. In certain locations on the ocean's floor, jets of geothermally heated water—essentially underwater geysers—gush into the icy-cold depths. One of the amazing scientific discoveries of recent decades was the realization that these heated-water, or *hydrothermal*, vents can host entire communities of organisms that thrive in the extreme high-temperature, high-pressure conditions. Gigantic clams, immense tubeworms, and odd mussels, shrimps, crabs, and fish all flourish in the seemingly hostile environment near scalding water that shoots out of tall chimneys of encrusted minerals (**FIGURE 2.13**).

These locations are so deep underwater that they completely lack sunlight, so their communities cannot fuel themselves through photosynthesis. Instead, bacteria in deep-sea vents use the chemical-bond energy of hydrogen sulphide (H_2S) to transform inorganic carbon into organic carbon compounds in a process called **chemosynthesis**. There are many types of chemosynthesis, but note how this particular reaction closely resembles the photosynthesis reaction:

CHEMOSYNTHESIS: $CO_2 + 6H_2O + 3H_2S \rightarrow$
$$C_6H_{12}O_6 \text{ (sugar)} + 3H_2SO_4$$

The two processes use different energy sources, but each combines water and carbon dioxide to produce a sugar and a by-product, and each produces potential energy that is later released during cellular respiration. Energy from chemosynthesis passes through the deep-sea-vent animal community as heterotrophs such as clams, mussels, and shrimp gain nutrition from *chemoautotrophic* bacteria (which use the oxidation of chemicals like hydrogen sulphide, as shown in the equation on the previous page, as a source of energy to generate organic matter). Seafloor hydrothermal vent communities excited scientists not only because they were novel and unexpected, but also because, like the Pavilion Lake microbialites, they may hold clues to the early Earth and might even help us answer the question of how life itself originated.

Geological Systems: The Physical Basis for the Environment

If we want to understand how our planet functions, a good way to start is to examine the rock, soil, and sediment beneath our feet. The physical processes that take place at and below Earth's surface shape the landscape around us and lay the foundation for most environmental systems and for life. Understanding the physical nature of our planet also benefits our society, for without the study of Earth's rocks and the processes that shape them, we would have no energy from geothermal sources or from fossil fuels. We are constantly drawing on resources and processes from beneath the surface of our planet and putting them to use in our everyday lives.

Our planet is dynamic, and this dynamism motivates *geology*, the study of Earth's physical features, processes, and history. A human lifetime is just a blink of an eye in the long course of geologic time, and Earth as we currently experience it is merely a snapshot in our changing planet's long history. We can begin to grasp this long-term dynamism as we consider two processes of fundamental importance—plate tectonics and the rock cycle.

Earth consists of layers

Most geological processes take place near Earth's surface, but our planet consists of multiple layers (**FIGURE 2.14**). At the planet's center is a dense **core** consisting mostly of iron, solid in the inner core and molten in the outer core. Surrounding the core is a thick layer of rock called the **mantle**. A portion of the upper mantle, called the *asthenosphere*, contains softer rock, which is close to its melting temperature and actually molten in some areas.

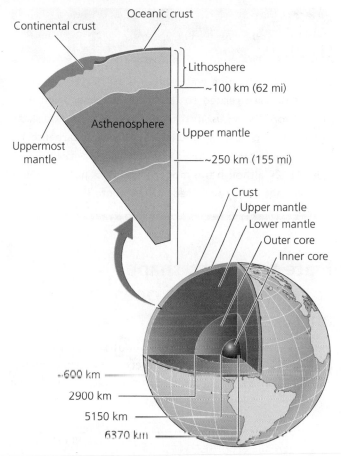

FIGURE 2.14

Earth's three primary layers—core, mantle, and crust—are themselves layered. The inner core of solid iron is surrounded by an outer core of molten iron. The rocky mantle has several layers (not shown here), including the relatively soft asthenosphere in the upper part. The lithosphere consists of the uppermost mantle (above the asthenosphere) and the crust. The crust is of two major types: dense, thin oceanic crust; and less-dense, thicker continental crust.

The harder rock above the asthenosphere is what we know as the **lithosphere**. The lithosphere includes the uppermost mantle and the **crust**, the thin, brittle, low-density layer of rock that covers Earth's surface, and on which we live.

The intense heat from inside rises from core to mantle to crust, and eventually dissipates at the surface. In regions where the crust is particularly thin or the heat flow is high, we can harness geothermal energy by drilling boreholes into the crust. The heat from the inner layers of Earth also drives convection currents in the mantle, pushing the mantle rock upward (as it warms) and downward (as it cools), like a gigantic conveyor belt system. As the mantle material moves, it drags large plates of brittle lithosphere along its surface. This movement of lithospheric plates is known as **plate tectonics**, a process of extraordinary importance to our planet.

roots

TECTONICS

The term **tectonics** was used in the 1600s to refer to things that are related to "building." It comes from the Latin word *tectonicus*, in turn from the Greek *tektonikos* (pertaining to building) and *tekton* (builder or carpenter). The word began to be used in a geological context in the late 1800s, although the modern theory of plate tectonics was not widely accepted until well into the 1960s.

Plate tectonics shapes the geography of oceans and continents

Our planet's surface consists of about 15 major tectonic plates, which fit together like pieces of a jigsaw puzzle (**FIGURE 2.15**). Imagine peeling an orange and then placing the pieces of peel back onto the fruit; the ragged pieces of peel are like the lithospheric plates that form Earth's surface. However, the plates are even thinner relative to the planet's size—more like the skin of an apple or the glass of a lightbulb. The lithospheric plates move at rates of roughly 2 to 10 cm per year. This slow movement has influenced Earth's climate and life's evolution throughout our planet's history as the continents combined, separated, and recombined in various configurations. By studying ancient rock formations throughout the world, geologists have determined that at least twice in Earth's history all landmasses were joined together in a "supercontinent," before splitting and moving apart from one another once again.

There are three main types of plate boundaries

The processes that occur at the boundaries between plates have major consequences. We can categorize these boundaries into three types: divergent, transform, and convergent (**FIGURE 2.16**).

World map of tectonic plates

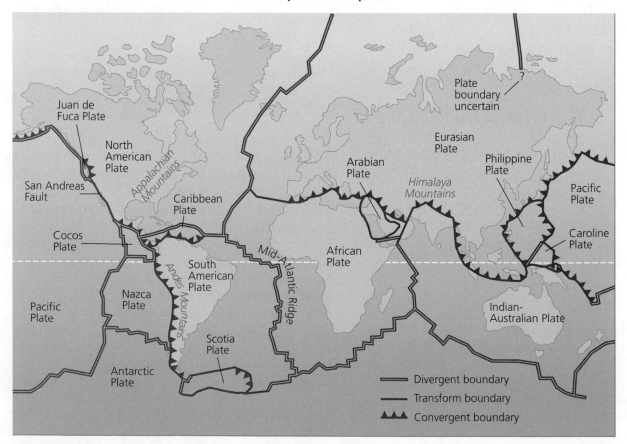

FIGURE 2.15 Earth's lithosphere has broken into approximately 15 major plates (shown here) and a number of minor plates that all move very slowly relative to one another, as part of the process of plate tectonics.

(a) Divergent plate boundary   **(b) Transform plate boundary**   **(c) Convergent plate boundary**

FIGURE 2.16   There are three basic types of plate boundaries: divergent, transform, and convergent. At a divergent boundary, such as a mid-ocean ridge **(a)**, magma extrudes from beneath the crust, and the two plates move gradually away from the boundary in the manner of a conveyor belt. At a transform plate boundary **(b)**, two plates slide alongside each other, creating friction that leads to earthquakes. Where plates collide at a convergent plate boundary **(c)**, one plate may be subducted beneath another (if oceanic plates are involved), leading to volcanism; or both plates may be uplifted (if continental plates are involved), causing mountain ranges to form.

At **divergent plate boundaries**, tectonic plates move apart from one another, or diverge. In these locations, **magma** (rock heated to a molten, liquid state) rises upward to the surface, forming new crust as it cools and solidifies (**FIGURE 2.16A**). An example is the Mid Atlantic Ridge, part of a 74 000-km-long system of divergent plate boundaries. Iceland is a volcanic island built when magma from underwater volcanoes along the Mid-Atlantic Ridge was extruded above the ocean surface and cooled. Iceland possesses numerous active volcanoes, including the Eyjafjallajökull and Grimsvötn volcanoes, both of which disrupted air travel extensively by erupting large clouds of ash in 2010 and 2011, respectively. In Iceland, geothermally heated water is piped throughout towns and cities, and nine out of ten people heat their homes with geothermal energy.

A **fault** is a fracture in Earth's crust, along which the blocks of rock on either side are displaced relative to one another. Where two plates meet along a strike-slip fault, they slip and grind alongside one another horizontally in opposite directions. Plate boundaries that are marked by strike-slip faults are called **transform plate boundaries** (**FIGURE 2.16B**). The horizontal movement of the plates creates friction that typically generates earthquakes. The Pacific Plate and the North American Plate are sliding past one another along the San Andreas Fault, which runs roughly north-south along the west coast of California. Southern California is slowly creeping toward the northwest relative to the rest of North America.

Convergent plate boundaries occur where two plates come together, or converge (**FIGURE 2.16C**). When oceanic crust is involved in a convergent plate boundary, a process called **subduction** occurs, in which the dense oceanic plate descends into the mantle. The subducted plate is heated and pressurized as it sinks. Water vapour escapes from the subducting plate, helping to melt the overlying rock by lowering its melting temperature. The molten rock rises, and this magma may erupt through the surface in the form of volcanoes.

When a plate of oceanic lithosphere is subducted beneath another plate of oceanic lithosphere, the resulting volcanism may form lines of volcanic islands, called a *volcanic arc*; examples include Japan and the Aleutian Islands. Subduction also creates deep trenches, such as the Mariana Trench in the western Pacific, our planet's deepest abyss—at 10 971 m deep, it is significantly deeper than Mount Everest is high. When oceanic lithosphere subducts beneath continental lithosphere, it leads to the formation of volcanic mountain ranges that parallel the coastline (**FIGURE 2.16C**, left). The Cascades, where Mount Saint Helens erupted violently in 1980 and renewed its activity in 2004, are fuelled by magma from the subduction of the Juan da Fuca Plate under the North American Plate along the coast of British Columbia, Washington, and Oregon. Another example is South America's Andes Mountains, where the Nazca Plate is subducting beneath the South American Plate.

When two plates of continental lithosphere converge, the continental crust on both sides resists subduction and instead crushes together, bending, buckling, and deforming layers of rock from both plates in a **continental collision** (**FIGURE 2.16C**, right). Portions of the accumulating masses of buckled crust are forced upward as they are pressed together, and mountain ranges result. The Himalayas, the world's highest mountains, result from the collision of the Indian-Australian Plate with the Eurasian Plate, which began 40 to 50 million years ago; these mountains are still rising today as the plates continue to converge. The Appalachian Mountains of eastern North America, once the world's highest mountains themselves, resulted from several ancient collisions with the edge of what is today Africa.

Tectonic processes produce Earth's landforms

The processes of plate tectonics create the landforms around us by building mountains; shaping the geography of oceans, islands, and continents; and giving rise to earthquakes and volcanoes. They also help determine the locations of geothermal energy resources and the formation of ore deposits of various types. The topography created by tectonic processes in turn shapes climate by altering patterns of rainfall, wind, ocean currents, heating, and cooling—all of which affect rates of weathering and erosion and the ability of plants and animals to inhabit different regions. Thus, the locations of plant and animal communities are fundamentally influenced by plate tectonics. Tectonics has even affected the history of life's evolution; for example, the convergence of landmasses into supercontinents is thought to have contributed to widespread extinctions by reducing the area of species-rich coastal regions and by creating arid continental interiors with extreme temperature swings.

Only in the last several decades have scientists learned about plate tectonics—this environmental system of such fundamental importance was unknown just half a century ago. Our civilization was sending people to the Moon by the time we were coming to understand the movement of land under our very feet. One of the early pioneers in developing the theory of plate tectonics in the 1960s was J. Tuzo Wilson, a Canadian geophysicist. The tectonic cycle of diverging oceanic lithosphere creation of new oceanic crust, horizontal plate motion, and eventual subduction of the lithosphere back into the mantle is called a *Wilson cycle* in his honour. Geologists and geophysicists continue to refine our understanding about how the complex processes of the tectonic cycle shape our environment.

Plate tectonics also leads to geological hazards

Plate tectonics gives rise to the creative forces that shape our planet, yet some of the consequences of tectonic movement can also pose hazards to us. Earthquakes and volcanic eruptions are examples of natural geological processes that are vital to the natural functioning of the environment, but risky when they occur in populated regions. We can see how such hazards relate to tectonic processes by examining a map of the circum-Pacific belt, or "ring of fire" (**FIGURE 2.17**). Compare the route of the circum-Pacific belt to some of the tectonic plate boundaries shown in **FIGURE 2.15**, and note how closely they match. Nine out of 10 earthquakes and over half the world's volcanoes occur along this 40 000-km arc of subduction zones and fault systems.

Let's look briefly at some common geological hazards. We will revisit these and consider their impacts on human populations when we address environmental health and hazards in a later chapter.

Earthquakes   Along tectonic plate boundaries, and in other places where faults occur, Earth may relieve

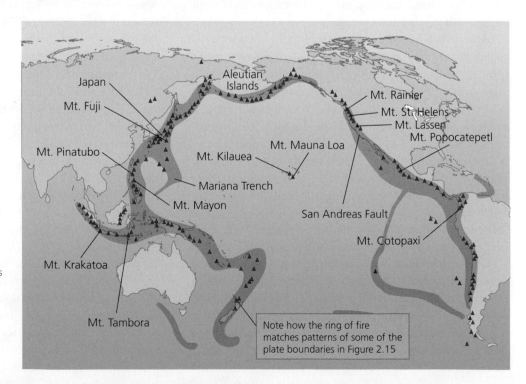

FIGURE 2.17
Many of our planet's earthquakes and volcanic eruptions occur along the circum-Pacific "ring of fire," the system of subduction zones and other plate boundaries that encircles the Pacific Ocean. The red symbols indicate major active volcanoes, and the grey shading indicates earthquake-prone areas. Compare the distribution of these hazards with the plate boundaries shown in **FIGURE 2.15**.

Japan
Mt. Fuji
Mt. Pinatubo
Mt. Krakatoa
Mt. Tambora
Aleutian Islands
Mt. Kilauea
Mariana Trench
Mt. Mayon
Mt. Mauna Loa
Mt. Rainier
Mt. St. Helens
Mt. Lassen
Mt. Popocatepetl
San Andreas Fault
Mt. Cotopaxi

Note how the ring of fire matches patterns of some of the plate boundaries in Figure 2.15

built-up pressure in fits and starts. Each release of energy causes what we know as an **earthquake**. Most earthquakes are barely perceptible, but occasionally they are powerful enough to do tremendous damage to human life and property (**FIGURE 2.18**). Earthquakes are a manifestation of the tremendous power of plate tectonic motion; they also provide a window into Earth's interior. By mapping the passage through Earth's interior of the energy released during earthquakes, geophysicists have built up a detailed picture of the planet's internal layering.

Volcanic eruptions   Where molten rock, hot gas, or ash erupts through Earth's surface, a **volcano** is formed, often creating a mountain over time as cooled lava accumulates. As we have seen, lava can extrude along mid-ocean ridges or over subduction zones as one tectonic plate dives beneath another. Lava may also be emitted at *hotspots*, localized areas where plugs of molten rock from the mantle erupt through the crust. As a tectonic plate moves across a hotspot, repeated eruptions from this source may create a linear series of volcanoes. The Hawaiian Islands provide an example of this process (**FIGURE 2.19**). At some volcanoes, lava flows slowly downhill, such as at Mount Kilauea in Hawaii, which has been erupting almost continuously since 1983. At other times, a volcano may let loose large amounts of ash and cinder in a sudden explosion, such as during the massive 1980 eruption of Mount Saint Helens in the Cascades Range.

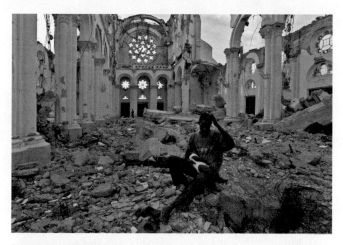

FIGURE 2.18
The 2010 earthquake in Haiti, which occurred along a strike-slip fault, devastated the capital city of Port-au-Prince and killed an estimated 230 000 people.

Landslides   **Landslides** occur when large amounts of rock or soil flow, fall, or slide downhill. Landslides are a severe and often sudden manifestation of the more general phenomenon of **mass wasting**, the downslope movement of soil and rock due to gravity. Mass wasting occurs naturally, and heavy rains may saturate soils and trigger mudslides of soil, rock, and water. However, mass wasting can also be brought about by human land use

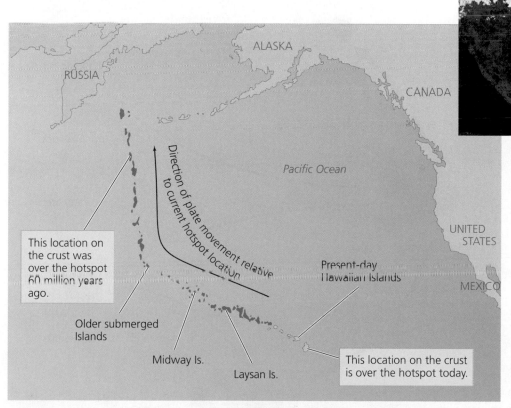

(b) Kilauea erupting

FIGURE 2.19
The Hawaiian Islands **(a)** have been formed by repeated eruptions from a hotspot of magma in the mantle, as the Pacific Plate passes over the hotspot. The Big Island of Hawaii is most recently formed, and it is still volcanically active. The other islands are older and have already begun to erode. To their northwest stretches a long series of former islands, now submerged. In the future, the newly forming volcano Loihi will one day rise above the sea to form a new island to the southeast of Hawaii. Active volcano Kilauea **(b)**, on the Big Island's southeast coast, is currently located above the edge of the hotspot.

This location on the crust was over the hotspot 60 million years ago.

Direction of plate movement relative to current hotspot location

RUSSIA

ALASKA

CANADA

Pacific Ocean

UNITED STATES

MEXICO

Present-day Hawaiian Islands

Older submerged Islands

Midway Is.

Laysan Is.

This location on the crust is over the hotspot today.

(a) Current and former Hawaiian islands, formed as crust moves over a volcanic hotspot

practices that expose or loosen soil, making slopes more prone to collapse.

Tsunamis   Earthquakes, volcanic eruptions, and large coastal landslides can all displace huge volumes of ocean water instantaneously and trigger a **tsunami**, an immense swell, or wave, of water that can travel across the ocean very quickly. The world's attention was drawn to this hazard on December 26, 2004, when a massive tsunami, triggered by an earthquake off Sumatra, devastated the coastlines of countries all around the Indian Ocean, including Indonesia, Thailand, Sri Lanka, India, and several African nations. Roughly 228 000 people were killed, 1–2 million were displaced, and whole communities were destroyed. Another tsunami in 2011 was triggered by a megathrust earthquake in a subduction zone off the coast of Japan; it destroyed coastal towns and damaged nuclear power plants, leading to one of the worst nuclear crises in history.

The rock cycle modifies Earth's physical environment

Just as plate tectonics shows geology's dynamism at a global scale, the rock cycle shows it at a more local scale. We tend to think of rock as pretty solid stuff. However,

rocks and the minerals that comprise them are heated, melted, cooled, broken down, and reassembled in a series of very slow steps, which, altogether, comprise the **rock cycle** (**FIGURE 2.20**).

Rock is a naturally occurring, solid aggregation of minerals. A **mineral**, in turn, is a naturally occurring solid element or inorganic compound that has a crystal structure, a specific chemical composition, and distinct physical properties. Minerals are thus the building blocks of rocks. The type of rock in a given region affects soil composition and characteristics and thereby influences the region's plant community. Understanding the rock cycle enables us to better appreciate the formation and conservation of soils, mineral resources, fossil fuels, groundwater sources, geothermal energy sources, and other natural resources—all of which we discuss in later chapters.

Igneous rock   All rock can melt. At high enough temperatures, rock will enter the molten, liquid state called *magma*. If magma is ejected to the surface during a volcanic eruption, it may flow or spatter across Earth's surface in the form of **lava**. Rock that forms when magma or lava cools is called **igneous rock** (from the Latin *ignis*, meaning "fire") (**FIGURE 2.20A**).

Igneous rock comes in two main classes, because magma can solidify in different ways. When magma cools

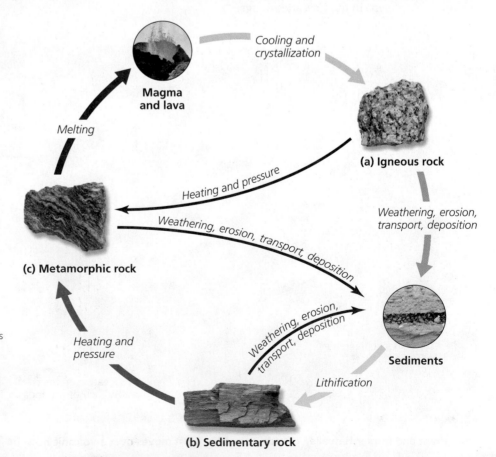

FIGURE 2.20   In the rock cycle, igneous rock **(a)** is formed when rock melts and the resulting magma or lava then cools. Sedimentary rock **(b)** is formed when rock is weathered and eroded, and the resulting sediment is compressed and cemented to form new rock. Metamorphic rock **(c)** is formed when rock is subjected to intense heat and pressure underground.

Cooling and crystallization

Melting

Magma and lava

(a) Igneous rock

Heating and pressure

Weathering, erosion, transport, deposition

Weathering, erosion, transport, deposition

(c) Metamorphic rock

Heating and pressure

Weathering, erosion, transport, deposition

Sediments

Lithification

(b) Sedimentary rock

slowly and solidifies while it is below Earth's surface, it forms *intrusive* or *plutonic* igneous rock. This process created the Coast Range Mountains of British Columbia (**FIGURE 2.21A**). Granite is the best-known type of intrusive rock. A slow cooling process allows minerals of different types to aggregate into large crystals, giving granite its multicoloured, coarse-grained appearance. In contrast, when molten rock is ejected from a volcano, it cools quickly, so minerals have little time to grow into coarse crystals. This class of igneous rock is called *extrusive* or *volcanic* igneous rock. Its most common representative is basalt, the principal rock type of the Hawaiian Islands (**FIGURE 2.21B**) and the main rock type of oceanic crust.

(a) Intrusive igneous rock—granite

(b) Extrusive igneous rock—basalt

(c) Sedimentary rock—limestone

(d) Sedimentary rock—sandstone

(e) Metamorphic rock—gneiss

FIGURE 2.21
The Coast Range Mountains of British Columbia **(a)** are made of granite, an intrusive igneous rock. The volcanic islands of Hawaii **(b)** are built of basalt, an extrusive igneous rock. These classic cliffs in Ha Long Bay, Vietnam **(c)**, are made of the sedimentary rock limestone. These "hoodoos" in Dinosaur Provincial Park, Alberta **(d)**, are made of layered sandstone, a sedimentary rock. The Canadian Shield, which makes up the core of the North American continent, is built of very ancient metamorphic rock **(e)**, mainly gneiss.

Sedimentary rock   All exposed rock is worn away with time. The relentless forces of wind, water, freezing, and thawing cause **weathering**, stripping off one tiny grain (or large chunk) after another. Through **erosion**, weathered particles of rock are blown by wind, washed away by water, or carried by slowly flowing glacial ice. The transported particles are called **sediment** (from the Latin *sedimentum*, "settling or sinking") when they come to rest downhill, downstream, or downwind from their source. Some sediment forms chemically from the precipitation of substances out of solution.

Sediment layers accumulate over time, causing the weight and pressure of overlying layers to increase. **Sedimentary rock (FIGURE 2.20B)** is formed when sediments are physically pressed together (*compaction*) and dissolved minerals seep through sediments and bind the sediment particles together (*cementation*). The formation of rock through these processes of compaction and cementation is termed *lithification*. Examples of sedimentary rock include limestone (**FIGURE 2.21C**), formed as dissolved calcite precipitates from water or as the remains of marine organisms settle to the bottom; sandstone (**FIGURE 2.21D**), made of cemented sand particles; and shale, comprised of still smaller mud particles. Related processes lead to the fossilization of organisms and, in just the right circumstances, the fossil fuels we use for energy. Because sedimentary layers pile up in chronological order, geologists and palaeontologists can assign relative dates to fossils they find in sedimentary rock, and thereby they make inferences about Earth's history.

Metamorphic rock   Geological forces may bend, uplift, compress, or stretch rock. When any type of rock is subjected to great heat or pressure, it may alter its form, becoming **metamorphic rock** (from the Greek for "changed form") (**FIGURE 2.20C**). The forces that metamorphose rock generally occur deep underground, at temperatures lower than the rock's melting point but high enough to change its appearance and physical properties. Metamorphic rock (**FIGURE 2.21E**) includes slate, formed when shale is subjected to heat and pressure, and marble, formed when limestone is heated and pressurized.

Early Earth and the Origin of Life

How Earth's physical environment came to be as it is today and how life originated are among the most centrally important questions in modern science. In searching for answers, scientists have learned a great deal about the history of this planet and what early Earth was like. That scientific interest has extended to other planets, such as Mars, which may prove to have once harboured life. We study the geological and chemical environments of both planets to learn more about what this part of the solar system was like billions of years ago, when life first took hold on this planet.

Early Earth was a very different place

Earth formed about 4.5 billion years ago in the same way as the other planets of our solar system; dispersed bits of material whirling through space around our Sun were drawn by gravity into one another, coalescing into a series of spheres. For several hundred million years after the planets formed, there remained enough stray material in the solar system that Earth and the other young planets were regularly bombarded by large chunks of debris in the form of asteroids, meteorites, and comets. The largest impacts were probably so explosive that they vaporized the newly formed oceans. This extraterrestrial rain of debris, combined with extreme volcanic activity, intense ultraviolet radiation, and a powerful greenhouse effect, made early Earth a pretty hostile place (**FIGURE 2.22**). Any life that got underway during this "bombardment stage" might easily have been killed off. Only after most debris was cleared from the solar system was life able to gain a foothold.

Earth's early atmosphere was very different from our atmosphere today. It was chemically reducing, and free oxygen (oxygen that was not part of a compound) was largely absent until photosynthesizing microbes started producing it. Whereas today's atmosphere is dominated by nitrogen and oxygen (see **TABLE 2.1**), Earth's early atmosphere is thought to have contained large amounts

FIGURE 2.22   The young Earth was a very different place from our planet today. Microbial life first evolved amid sulphur-spewing volcanoes, intense ultraviolet radiation, frequent extraterrestrial impacts, and an atmosphere containing ammonia.

CANADIAN ENVIRONMENTAL PERSPECTIVES

Praveen Saxena

Praveen Saxena researches endangered, spiritual and life sustain plants.

- **Researcher** at the Plant Cell Technology Laboratory, University of Guelph
- **Professor** of physiology and developmental biology
- **Horticulturalist** and herbal medicine expert
- **Conservationist** of rare and endangered plants

Praveen Saxena is interested in plants—mainly plants that have been used as herbal remedies for many generations. As he points out, plants naturally produce thousands of chemicals. Some of these are potentially useful in the treatment of human ailments, but others may be seriously harmful. When we use plants as herbal remedies, we ingest these chemicals; yet herbal remedies are poorly controlled in comparison to synthetic pharmaceuticals. There are wide variations in the chemical compositions of the plants used in various herbal mixtures, and there are gaps in the scientific understanding of how plants concentrate certain elements. One of the projects in Dr. Saxena's lab involves technologies for growing plants *in vitro* (that is, in test tubes), so their chemical characteristics can be more closely monitored and controlled, and their use as medicines rendered safer.

In addition to their natural chemical constituents, many plants absorb and bioconcentrate chemicals—some of them potentially harmful, such as heavy metals—from the surrounding environment. When soil is contaminated with heavy metals from mining, manufacturing, oil extraction, or military facilities, the standard solution is to dig up tons of soil and pile it into a hazardous waste dump. As an alternative, scientists are developing methods of *phytoremediation*, using plants (*phyto* means "plant") to remediate, or detoxify, contaminated soils.

Dr. Saxena's research team found that lemon-scented geraniums (*Pelargonium*) have a natural ability to absorb heavy metals such as copper, mercury, lead, and nickel from contaminated soil. They take up the metal ions through their roots and store them in their leaves and shoots. Chemicals called *chelating agents* can bind to the metals, making them more water soluble and thus more accessible to plant roots. Unlike many plants, the geranium can take up a wide variety of metals.

The lemon scented geranium grows quickly, and its large volume—it is dense, bushy, and grows as tall as one metre—allows it to accumulate lots of metal ions. Using a process called *embryogenesis*, Saxena's research team produces hundreds of geraniums from a small piece of plant tissue. The researchers are also testing different genes that may be inserted into the embryos to enhance the plant's ability to absorb metals.[2]

In addition to researching phytoremediation and herbal remedies, Dr. Saxena is also a plant conservationist. He is the director of a plant conservation program supported by the Gosling Research Institute for Plant Preservation (GRIPP) at the University of Guelph. The mission of this program is to advance the knowledge and application of *in vitro* culture technologies for the preservation, sustainable use, and replenishment of threatened plants. A special focus is on rare and endangered species critical to sustaining natural habitats, food security and medicinal and spiritual practices. The success of the innovative approaches in his Plant Cell Technology Lab is seen in the cloning of the few remaining century old American elms. The majority of these majestic trees have been devastated throughout North America due to fungal diseases. Many other important native Canadian species including trees such as Maple, Chestnut, Oak, and Cherry Birch are also susceptible and face extinction.

Plants support all forms of life through food, fiber, fuel, shelter and medicine. One third of all plant species on earth are under the threat of extinction due to overharvest, disease, pollution, and the escalating loss of natural habitats resulting from the activities of a rapidly growing human population. Rising global temperatures and climate changes also add more threats to the survival of plant species. Such rapid loss in plant diversity has serious consequences for the health and resilience of all ecosystems and for the quality of human life on the planet.[3]

"With each species becoming extinct, humanity loses irreplaceable resources, many of them not even explored. We must protect our important plant biodiversity before it is too late."[4]**—Praveen Saxena**

Thinking About Environmental Perspectives

We tend to think of herbal medicines as being "natural," or inherently safe. However, as Dr. Saxena points out, this is not always the case. Herbal remedies and their chemical constituents are much less actively studied, screened, regulated, and monitored than conventional pharmaceuticals. Do you think herbal remedies should be more tightly regulated? How might scientific research such as that of Saxena and his colleagues contribute to the safety of herbal medicines?

of hydrogen, ammonia (NH_3), methane, carbon dioxide, carbon monoxide (CO), and water vapour.

Figuring out how Earth's atmosphere evolved into its current state is an interesting and challenging area of research. We know where some of the constituents that were so abundant early in Earth history have gone; for example, much of the carbon dioxide from the early atmosphere is now bound up in thick sequences of carbonate rock—limestone. This is a good thing; if the carbon dioxide were released from carbonate rocks, we would have an atmosphere of 95% carbon dioxide, similar to that of Venus, and that would not be conducive to life as we know it.

Several hypotheses have been proposed to explain life's origin

Most scientists interested in life's origin think that life must have begun when inorganic chemicals linked themselves into small molecules and formed organic compounds. Some of these compounds gained the ability to replicate, or reproduce themselves, whereas others found ways to group together into proto-cells. There is much debate and ongoing research on the details of this process, especially concerning the location of the first chemical reactions and the energy source(s) that powered them.

The heterotrophic hypothesis   The hypothesis traditionally favoured is that life evolved from a "primordial soup" of simple inorganic chemicals—carbon dioxide, oxygen, and nitrogen—dissolved in the ocean's surface waters or tidal shallows. Scientists since the 1930s have suggested how simple amino acids might have formed under these conditions and how more complex organic compounds could have followed, including simple ribonucleic acids that could replicate themselves. This hypothesis is termed *heterotrophic* because it proposes that the first life forms used organic compounds from their environment as an energy source. In 1953, biochemists Stanley Miller and Harold Urey passed electricity through a mixture of water vapour, hydrogen, ammonia, and methane, which they thought to be representative of the early atmosphere. The experiments produced organic compounds, including amino acids. Subsequent experiments confirmed the basic validity of these experiments, but amino acids, on their own, are not life. Scientists since then also have modified their ideas about early atmospheric conditions.

The panspermia hypothesis   Another hypothesis proposes that microbes from elsewhere in the solar system travelled on meteorites that crashed to Earth, "seeding" our planet with life. Scientists had long rejected this idea, believing that even if amino acids or bacteria were to exist in space, the searing temperatures that comets and meteors attain as they enter our atmosphere should destroy them before they reach the surface. However, the Murchison meteorite, which fell in Australia in 1969, was found to contain many amino acids. Since then, experiments simulating impact conditions have shown that organic compounds and some bacteria can

withstand a surprising amount of abuse. Recent astrobiology research suggests that comets have brought large amounts of water, and possibly organic compounds, to Earth throughout its history. As a result of such findings, long-distance travel of microbes through space and into our atmosphere seems more plausible than previously thought.

The chemoautotrophic hypothesis   In the 1970s and 1980s, several scientists proposed that life originated at deep-sea hydrothermal vents, like those in **FIGURE 2.13**. In this scenario, the first organisms were chemoautotrophs, creating their own food from hydrogen sulphide, abundant in deep-sea vent environment. A related hypothesis suggests that life originated in the hot, moist environment of thermal pools and hot springs, like those in **FIGURE 2.12**—an environment that is currently favoured by specifically adapted types of bacteria. Current research on *extremophiles*—organisms that are adjusted to conditions of extreme heat, cold, pressure, acidity, or salinity—by scientists including Darlene Lim and her colleagues is helping to further our understanding of the earliest life forms on Earth and the environmental conditions in which they survived.

Genetic analysis of the relationships of present-day organisms suggests that some of the ancient ancestors of today's life forms did live in extremely hot, wet environments. The extreme heat of hydrothermal vents could act to speed up chemical reactions that link atoms together into long molecules, a necessary early step in life's formation. Scientists have shown experimentally that it is possible to form amino acids and begin a chain of steps that might potentially lead to the formation of life under high-temperature, high-pressure conditions similar to those of hydrothermal vents.

Conclusion

The chemical basis of matter, the nature of energy, and the geological processes that have shaped our planet (and continue to do so) provide the physical foundations for our present-day environment and support the existence of life. Matter, energy, and geology are in some way tied to nearly every significant process in environmental science.

An understanding of the characteristics and interactions of matter can provide tools for finding solutions to environmental problems, whether one wants to analyze agricultural practices, manage water resources, conduct toxicological studies, or find ways to mitigate global climate change. Likewise, an understanding of energy is of fundamental scientific importance, as well as considerable practical relevance. Physical processes of geology such as plate tectonics and the rock cycle are centrally important because they shape Earth's terrain and form the foundation for living systems.

Life has flourished on Earth for billions of years, stemming from an origin that scientists are eagerly attempting to understand. Deciphering how life originated requires an understanding of the geological processes that have shaped our physical environment over the course of this planet's history. Knowledge in all of these areas also enhances our understanding of how present-day organisms interact with one another, how they relate to their nonliving environment, and how environmental systems function.

REVIEWING OBJECTIVES

You should now be able to:

Outline some fundamental principles of matter and energy

- Matter may be transformed from one type of substance into others, but it cannot be created or destroyed.
- The total amount of energy in the universe is conserved; it cannot be created or destroyed.
- Systems tend to increase in entropy, or disorder, unless energy is added to build or maintain order and complexity.
- Understanding how matter and energy interact helps us understand the physical environment and provides tools for developing solutions to many environmental problems.

Summarize the basic types of matter that are the building blocks for all materials on Earth

- Atoms combine to form molecules.
- Changes at the atomic level can result in alternative forms of elements, such as ions and isotopes.
- The characteristics of the water molecule help facilitate life.
- Living things depend on organic compounds, which are carbon based, as well as inorganic compounds.
- Proteins, nucleic acids, carbohydrates, and lipids are key building blocks of life.

Differentiate among various types of energy and their roles in environmental systems

- Energy can be either potential (stored energy, or energy of position) or kinetic (energy of motion).
- Chemical energy is an example of potential energy stored in the bonds between atoms. Energy also resides in the nuclei of atoms and can be stored in the form of mechanical energy.
- Earth's systems are powered by mainly radiation from the Sun, as well as by geothermal heating from the planet's core and by tidal interactions among Earth, the Sun, and the Moon.

Describe how photosynthesis and cellular respiration turn energy into matter and back again

- In photosynthesis, autotrophs use carbon dioxide, water, and solar energy to produce the sugars they need, as well as oxygen.
- In respiration, organisms extract energy from sugars by converting them in the presence of oxygen into carbon dioxide and water.
- In chemosynthesis, specialized autotrophs use carbon dioxide, water, and chemical energy from minerals to produce the sugars they need.

Explain how plate tectonics and the rock cycle shape the landscape around us and Earth beneath our feet

- Geology is dynamic, and a human lifetime is a blink of an eye in the long course of Earth history.
- Earth consists of distinct layers that differ in composition, temperature, density, and other characteristics.
- Plate tectonics is a set of fundamental processes that shape Earth's physical environment.
- Tectonic plates meet at three types of boundaries: divergent, transform, and convergent.
- Matter is cycled and rocks are transformed from one type to another through the processes of the rock cycle.
- Geological hazards, including earthquakes, volcanic eruptions, landslides, and tsunamis, are closely related to the processes of plate tectonics.

Summarize the main hypotheses for the origin of life

- The heterotrophic hypothesis proposes that life arose from chemical reactions in surface or shallow waters of the ocean.
- The panspermia hypothesis proposes that substances needed for life's origin on Earth arrived from space.
- The chemoautotrophic hypothesis proposes that life arose from chemical reactions near deep-sea hydrothermal vents.

TESTING YOUR COMPREHENSION

1. How does an ion differ from an isotope? Differentiate among atoms, molecules, and compounds, and give an example of each.
2. Name four ways in which the chemical nature of the water molecule facilitates life.
3. What are three important types of biological polymer, and what are their functions?
4. Describe the two major forms of energy, and give examples of each.
5. State the first law of thermodynamics, and describe some of its implications.
6. What are the three major sources of energy that power Earth's environmental systems?
7. Name the primary layers that make up our planet. Which portions does the lithosphere include?
8. What are the three major types of plate boundaries? Compare and contrast the types of processes that typically happen at each of them.
9. Name the three main types of rocks, and describe how each type may be converted to the others via the rock cycle.
10. Compare and contrast three competing hypotheses for the origin of life.

THINKING IT THROUGH

1. Think about the ways we harness and use energy sources in our society—both renewable sources such as geothermal energy and nonrenewable sources such as coal, oil, and natural gas. What implications does the first law of thermodynamics have for our energy usage? How is the second law of thermodynamics relevant to our use of energy?
2. Can you think of an example of an environmental problem *not* mentioned in this chapter that a good knowledge of chemistry could help us solve?
3. Describe an example of energy transformation from one form to another that is *not* mentioned in this chapter.
4. Describe how plate tectonics accounts for the formation of (a) mountains, (b) volcanoes, and (c) earthquakes. Why do you think it took so long for scientists to discover an environmental system of such fundamental importance as plate tectonics?
5. Which lines of evidence in the debate over the origin of life strike you as the most convincing, and why? Which strike you as the least convincing, and why? Can you think of any further scientific research that could be done to address the question of how life originated?
6. Let's say that the Ministry of Environment has put you in charge of cleaning up an old industrial site so that it meets safety standards and does not contaminate drinking water supplies. Your staff's initial inspection of surface soil at the site shows that it is contaminated with oil and with lead, a toxic heavy metal. Your job allows you to engage experts in remediation at local universities, as well as environmental engineers in the private sector. You have a budget of several million dollars and five years to get the job done. What steps will you take to get the site cleaned up? Describe scientific research you would commission, economic questions you would ask, and engineering options you might consider.

INTERPRETING GRAPHS AND DATA

In phytoremediation, plants are used to clean up soil or water contaminated by heavy metals such as lead (Pb), arsenic (As), zinc (Zn), and cadmium (Cd). For plants to absorb these metals from soil, the metals must be dissolved in soil water. For any given instance, all metal can be accounted for as remaining bound to soil particles, being dissolved in soil water, or being stored in the plant.

In a study on the effectiveness of alpine penny-cress (*Thlaspi caerulescens*) for phytoremediation, Enzo Lombi and his colleagues grew crops of this small perennial plant for approximately one year in pots of soil from contaminated sites. They then measured the amount of zinc and cadmium in the soil and in the plants when they were harvested.

1. What were the zinc and cadmium concentrations in the soil prior to phytoremediation? What were the zinc and cadmium concentrations in the soil after one year of phytoremediation?

2. How much zinc and cadmium were removed from the soil? If the plants continued to remove zinc and cadmium from the soil at the rates shown above, approximately how long would it take to remove all the zinc and cadmium?

3. Alpine penny-cress is one of many plants that produce natural chelating agents (see "Canadian Environmental Perspectives: Praveen Saxena" in this chapter and "The Science Behind the Story: Letting Plants Do the Dirty Work," available on myenvironmentplace) that increase the solubility of metals in soil water. If these dissolved metals were *not* subsequently taken up by the plants, what might

Removal of zinc and cadmium from contaminated soil by alpine penny-cress, *Thlaspi caerulescens*.
Source: Data from Lombi, E., et al. (2001). Phytoremediation of heavy metal-contaminated soils: Natural hyperaccumulation versus chemically enhanced phytoextraction. Journal of Environmental Quality 30: 1919–1926.)

be an unintended consequence of having increased their solubility?

CHAPTER ENDNOTES

1. Pavilion Lake Research Project: Relevance to Astrobiology and Space Exploration, http://supercritical.civil.ubc.ca/~pavilion/information/relevance.htm

2. Based on www.carleton.ca/jmc/cnews/30031998/story1.html

3. www.plant.uoguelph.ca/faculty/psaxena/ and www.plant.uoguelph.ca/research/cellculture/index.html, among other sources.

4. From Ali, Amina, A geranium by any other name..., *Research*, University of Guelph, Spring 1997, vol. XII, no. 1, www.uoguelph.ca/research/publications/Assets/HTML_MAGS/newtech/saxena.html

MyEnvironmentPlace

Go to **www.myenvironmentplace.ca** where you will find quizzes, animations, your Pearson eText, and more.

Environmental Systems and Ecosystem Ecology

3

The estuary of the St. Lawrence River, seen here in a satellite image, is intimately connected to its broader surroundings. The swirling, lighter-coloured water is evidence of a large algal bloom.

Upon completing this chapter, you will be able to

- Describe the fundamental properties of environmental systems and the importance of linkages among environmental systems and processes

- Define *ecosystem* and discuss how living and nonliving entities interact in ecosystems

- Outline the fundamentals of landscape ecology, GIS, and the use of modelling in environmental science

- Assess ecosystem services and their benefits to us

- Summarize the main features of the global water, carbon, nitrogen, and phosphorus cycles

- Explain how human activity is affecting biogeochemical cycles

Beluga whales in the St. Lawrence estuary are suffering from pollution-related health problems.

Hudson Bay

CANADA   St. Lawrence Estuary

THE PLIGHT OF THE ST. LAWRENCE BELUGAS

"Nature does not show us any isolated 'building blocks,' but rather appears as a complicated web of relations between the various parts of the whole."

—FRITJOF CAPRA, THEORETICAL PHYSICIST

"The concept of a subtly interconnected world, of a whispering pond in and through which we are intimately linked to each other and to the universe ... is part of humanity's response to the challenges that we now face in common."

—ERVIN LASZLO, SYSTEMS THEORIST

This satellite image shows the St. Lawrence River and the estuary where it joins the Gulf of St. Lawrence and the Atlantic Ocean.

The St. Lawrence is one of the great river systems of Canada. From its origin in Lake Ontario (see map, above, and smaller satellite image) it flows approximately 1200 km to the Gulf of St. Lawrence, the world's largest estuary, where fresh water meets salt water. The cold Labrador Current brings an abundant food source of plankton and fish from the Atlantic Ocean into the estuary, supporting a small population of beluga whales. The playful, sociable beluga or white whale, *Delphinapterus leucas*, prefers cold salt-water estuaries as its habitat.

Health problems have plagued the St. Lawrence belugas for decades, causing their population to decrease to below 700—much less than the many thousands of belugas that occupied the estuary at the beginning of the twentieth century. The whales appear to be dying of cancer, at the rate of about 14 to 15 per year.

Daniel Martineau and a team of veterinarians from the Université de Montréal carried out autopsies on more than 100 dead whales from the St. Lawrence. They found that 27% of the adult and 17% of the young belugas had died of cancer, mainly gastrointestinal. "In dolphins and terrestrial animals, the figure is closer to 2%," says Dr. Martineau. In addition to cancers, the St. Lawrence belugas have very low reproductive rates and other health issues, including cysts and bacterial infections.

Toxicological studies show that the whales were exposed to organochloride pollutants, notably polycyclic aromatic hydrocarbons, or PAHs.[1] PAHs come primarily from the burning of fossil fuels and other combustion sources. They do not break down easily and have become one of the most widespread contaminants in aquatic and marine environments. Deposited from the air to the land surface, they are carried to waterways by runoff, accumulating in the bottom sediments of rivers and near shorelines. Belugas feed on organisms that live in these sediments. The concentration of contaminants increases in belugas and other animals that eat higher up the food chain. PAHs are also *lipophilic*, or "fat-loving" compounds, so they combine easily with fats and accumulate over time, or *bioaccumulate*, in the blubber of the belugas.

Where do the pollutants come from, and what does this have to do with the estuary and the health of the belugas? The answer may be found by looking at the Great Lakes and St. Lawrence River as a single, great, connected system, of which the beluga whales are a small but integral part. Any changes upstream in the system will be felt downstream. This includes the deposition of pollutants—some generated as far away as the Golden Horseshoe industrial zone in Ontario—that eventually make their way to the estuary and into the food chain of the beluga whales.

It is not clear to what extent the various health problems plaguing the belugas are directly attributable to exposure to PAH pollutants. Other organochloride compounds and toxic heavy metals from industrial, urban, and airborne sources are also concentrated in the waters of the estuary. Agricultural development along the St. Lawrence River has contributed pesticides into the system; some of these contaminants also find their way into the thousands of tonnes of fish harvested from St. Lawrence commercial fisheries each year.

Other factors may have additional indirect effects on the health of belugas and other organisms in the estuary. For example, excess organic matter and plant nutrients from fertilizer runoff and animal waste also have contributed to a sharp drop in oxygen concentration in the deepest waters of the estuary, where dissolved oxygen levels have declined by half since the 1930s. The lack of dissolved oxygen reflects a situation known as **hypoxia**, which is fairly common in estuarine and coastal waters around the world. It is caused by nutrient-rich runoff into the deep water of the estuary, where decomposition of the nutrients consumes the available oxygen. Nutrient over-enrichment can lead to algal overgrowths, called *blooms* (as seen in the satellite image of the St. Lawrence that opens this chapter), with subsequent decay of the organic matter and ecosystem degradation. The overall process of nutrient over-enrichment in a water body (either fresh or salt), leading to hypoxia, is called **eutrophication**; it can result from both natural and human (anthropogenic) influences. A probable natural contributor to hypoxia in the Gulf of the St. Lawrence is the influx of warm, oxygen-depleted water from the Gulf Stream, which displaces the cold, oxygen-rich water of the Labrador Current.

The most important thing to note is that all of these influences on the habitat and, ultimately, the health of the belugas come from sources that are external to the St. Lawrence Estuary but are intimately connected to it by a wide variety of environmental processes.

The St. Lawrence beluga population is classified as "threatened" by COSEWIC, the Committee on the Status of Endangered Wildlife in Canada. The health of the whales is an indicator of the overall health of the estuary, and a reminder of the interconnectedness of the Great Lakes–St. Lawrence ecosystem. Recognizing this interconnectedness, scientists are striving to understand the ecosystem as a whole and to develop strategies for protecting the estuary and the organisms that inhabit it.[2]

Earth's Environmental Systems

Our planet's environment consists of complex networks of interlinked systems. These systems include the webs of relationships among living species and the interactions of living species with the nonliving entities around them. Earth's systems also include **cycles** that shape the landscapes around us and guide the flow of key chemical elements and compounds that support life and regulate climate. We depend on these systems and cycles for our very survival.

Taking a "systems approach" to investigating problems such as the decline of the St. Lawrence belugas is helpful in environmental science, because so many issues are multifaceted and complex. Before we turn our attention to specific Earth systems and cycles, let's take a look at the general properties of systems.

Systems are networks of relationships

A **system** is a network of relationships among parts, elements, or components that interact with and influence one another through the exchange of energy, matter, or information. Systems receive inputs of energy, matter, or information, process these inputs, and produce outputs. Systems that receive inputs of both energy and matter and produce outputs of both are called **open systems**. Systems that receive inputs and produce outputs of energy, but not matter, are called **closed systems**. In a closed system, matter cycles among the various parts of the system but does not leave or enter the system. It is scientifically more straightforward to deal with closed systems, but in nature no system is truly, perfectly closed.

Energy inputs to Earth's environmental systems include solar radiation, as well as heat released by geothermal activity, organismal metabolism, and human activities such as fossil fuel combustion. Information inputs can come in the form of sensory cues from visual, olfactory (chemical), magnetic, or thermal signals. Inputs of matter occur when chemicals or physical material moves among systems, such as when seeds are dispersed long distances, migratory animals deposit waste far from where they consumed food, or plants convert carbon in the air to living tissue by photosynthesis.

As a system, for example, the Estuary of the St. Lawrence receives inputs of fresh water, sediments, nutrients, and pollutants from the St. Lawrence and other rivers, as well as salt water from the Atlantic Ocean. Large animals, such as the belugas, harvest some of the system's output, and so do human fishers: matter and potential energy in the form of fish and plankton. This output subsequently becomes input to the human economic system and to the digestive systems of the people and whales that consume seafood from the St. Lawrence.

Feedbacks are common in environmental systems

Sometimes a system's output can serve as input to that same system, a circular process described as a **feedback loop**. Feedback loops are of two types, negative and positive.

In a **negative feedback loop**, output that results from a system moving in one direction acts as input that moves the system in the other direction. Input and output essentially neutralize one another's effects, stabilizing the system. A thermostat, for instance, stabilizes a room's temperature by turning the furnace on when the room gets cold and shutting it off when the room gets hot. Similarly, negative feedback regulates our body temperature. If we get too hot, our sweat glands pump out moisture that evaporates to cool us down, or we may move from sun to shade. If we get too cold, we shiver, creating heat, or we move into the sunlight or put on more clothing. Another example of negative feedback would be a predator–prey system in which the populations of predator and prey rise and fall in response to one another (**FIGURE 3.1A**). Most systems in nature involve negative feedback loops. Negative feedback loops enhance stability, and in the long run, only those systems that are stable will persist.

Positive feedback loops have the opposite effect. Rather than stabilizing a system, they drive it further toward one extreme or another. Erosion, the removal of soil by water or wind, is one example of positive feedback. Once vegetation has been cleared to expose soil, erosion may become progressively more severe if the forces of water or wind surpass the rate of vegetative regrowth. Another example is climatic warming leading to the melting of ice, which exposes underlying darker surfaces. Darker surfaces absorb more sunlight, causing further warming and leading to additional melting (**FIGURE 3.1B**). Positive feedbacks can alter a system substantially. Positive feedback loops are rare in nature, but they are common in natural systems that have been altered by human impact.

The inputs and outputs of complex natural systems usually occur simultaneously, keeping the system constantly active. Earth's climate system, for instance, does not ever stop. When processes within a system move in opposing directions at equivalent rates so that their effects

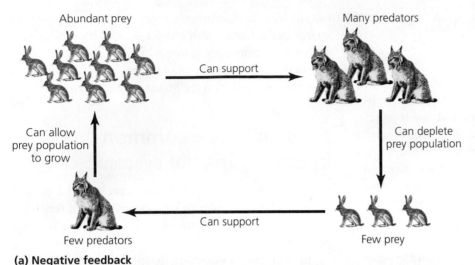

Abundant prey

Many predators

Can support

Can allow
prey population
to grow

Can deplete
prey population

Few predators

Can support

Few prey

(a) Negative feedback

FIGURE 3.1
Negative feedback loops **(a)** stabilize systems and are common in nature. In this example, abundant prey support many predators, which in turn deplete prey populations—but because fewer prey support fewer predators, the prey population rises again, and the cycle continues. Positive feedback **(b)** destabilizes systems, pushing them toward extremes. The melting of glaciers and sea ice due to global warming exposes darker surfaces, which absorb more sunlight, causing further warming and melting.

❶ In cool climate, sunlight reflects off white surfaces

Solid surface
of sea ice

Glacier completely
covers land

❷ As climate warms, sunlight is absorbed where dark surfaces are exposed

Sea ice
melting

Glacier
melting

❸ Light absorption speeds warming, exposing more dark surfaces

More water
exposed

More land
exposed

(b) Positive feedback

balance out, the process is said to be in a state of **dynamic equilibrium**. The term *dynamic* is used to indicate that even though the system is in balance or at equilibrium, it is an ever-changing, ever-adjusting balance, not static or unchanging.

Homeostasis is a state of balance

Processes in dynamic equilibrium can contribute to **homeostasis**, the tendency of a system to maintain constant or stable internal conditions. *Resistance* is a property of homeostatic systems; it refers to the strength of the system's tendency to remain constant—that is, to resist disturbance. *Resilience*, another characteristic of homeostatic systems, is a measure of how readily the system will return to its original state once it has been disturbed.

To illustrate the concepts of resistance and resilience, let's say that someone gives you a sharp push. If you are resistant, you might sway a little bit, but you won't stumble or fall over. On the other hand, if you did stumble or fall but got right back up to a standing position with no trouble, then you were demonstrating the characteristic of resilience—after the disturbance you had the capacity to recover, and to return to your original standing position. In nature, we can think of the example of a forest that is being subjected to a pest invasion. A forest with the property of resistance would be little-altered by the pest invasion. A forest with the property of resilience, on the other hand, would be affected by the pest invasion—tree health would likely suffer, and some trees might die—but the forest would quickly recover its former healthy state.

Homeostatic systems are often said to be in a stable or **steady state**; however, the state itself may change over time, even while the system maintains its ability to stabilize conditions internally. For instance, organisms grow, mature, and change, yet at each stage of life the organism can be said to be in a stable state. Similarly, Earth has experienced changes in the composition of the atmosphere over geologic time; yet life has adapted, and Earth remains, by most definitions, a homeostatic system.

A whole may be more than the sum of its parts

It is difficult to understand systems fully by focusing on their individual components because systems can show **emergent properties**, characteristics not evident in the components alone. Stating that systems possess emergent properties is a lot like saying, "The whole is more than the sum of its parts." For example, if you were to reduce a tree to its component parts (leaves, branches, trunk, bark, roots, fruit, and so on), you would not be able to predict the whole tree's emergent properties, which include the role the tree plays as habitat for birds, insects, parasitic vines, and other organisms (**FIGURE 3.2**). You could analyze the tree's chloroplasts (photosynthetic cell organelles), diagram its branch structure, and evaluate its fruit's nutritional content, but you would still be unable to understand the tree as habitat, as part of a forest landscape, or as a reservoir for carbon storage.

Complex systems have multiple subsystems

Systems seldom have well-defined boundaries, so deciding where one system ends and another begins can be difficult. No matter how we attempt to isolate or define a system, we soon see that it has many connections to systems larger and smaller than itself. Systems may exchange energy, matter, and information with other systems, and they may contain or be contained within other systems— so where we draw boundaries may depend on the spatial or temporal scale we wish to consider.

Consider a desktop computer system. It is certainly a network of parts that interact and exchange energy and information, but what are its boundaries? Is the system just what arrives in a packing crate and sits on top of your desk? Or does it include the network you connect it to? What about the energy grid you plug it into, with its distant power plants and transmission lines? What about the Internet? Browsing the web, you are drawing in digitized text, light, and sound from around the world. And what about the smaller systems that together comprise the computer, such as the motherboard, the keyboard, and the mouse? All of these systems, large and small, contribute and are linked to the complex system that is your desktop computer.

The Great Lakes, St. Lawrence River, and Atlantic Ocean are examples of environmental systems that interact with one another. On a map, the river appears as a branched network of water channels (**FIGURE 3.3**). But where are this system's boundaries? You might argue that the river consists primarily of water, originates in Ontario, and ends in the Atlantic Ocean. But what about the rivers that feed it, and the farms, cities, and forests that line its banks? Major rivers such as the Ottawa and

FIGURE 3.2
A system's emergent properties are not evident when we break the system down into its component parts. For example, a tree serves as wildlife habitat and plays roles in forest ecology and global climate regulation, but you would not know that from considering the tree only as a collection of leaves, branches, and chloroplasts. If we try to understand systems solely by breaking them into component parts, we will miss much of what makes them important.

FIGURE 3.3   The watershed of the Great Lakes and St. Lawrence is a complex system that covers much of Ontario and Québec and extends into the northern United States. Runoff from the land into the river carries water, sediment, and pollutants from a variety of sources downstream to the Gulf of the St. Lawrence, where pollution has given rise to a hypoxic zone and other environmental problems. Farms, cities, and industry are all contributors; so are natural sources, such as forests and soils.

Saguenay rivers flow into the St. Lawrence. Hundreds of smaller tributaries drain vast expanses of farmland, woodland, fields, cities, towns, and industrial areas before their water joins the St. Lawrence. These waterways carry with them millions of tonnes of sediment, hundreds of species of plants and animals, and numerous pollutants. The St. Lawrence River system is also intimately interconnected with the entire Great Lakes system—together they constitute an integrated hydrological system.

For an environmental scientist interested in runoff and the flow of water, sediment, or pollutants, it would make sense to view the Great Lakes–St. Lawrence River watershed as one great system. One must consider the entire area of land a river drains to comprehend and solve problems of river pollution. In contrast, for a scientist interested in the estuary's hypoxic zone, it might make the best sense to view the river + the Gulf + the coastal waters of the Atlantic as the system of interest, because their interaction is central to the problem. For a scientist interested in the question of beluga whale contamination, another useful system might be the whale + the fish and plankton eaten by the whale + the bottom sediments and local water in which the contaminants have accumulated. In environmental science, one's delineation of a system can and should depend on the questions one is addressing and on the temporal and spatial scale of interest.

Environmental systems may be perceived in various ways

There are many ways to delineate natural systems, and your choice will depend on the particular issues in which you are interested. Categorizing environmental systems can help make Earth's dazzling complexity comprehensible to the human brain and accessible to problem solving.

Scientists divide Earth's components into broad structural systems (**FIGURE 3.4**). The **geosphere** is the rock and sediment beneath our feet, in the planet's uppermost layers. (This is sometimes called the *lithosphere*, but as you may recall from the chapter on matter, energy, and the physical environment, geologists have a very specific definition for the term *lithosphere*, which refers to the topmost portion of the mantle and the crust.) The **atmosphere** is composed of the air surrounding our planet. The **hydrosphere** encompasses all water—salt or fresh, liquid, ice, or vapour—in surface water bodies and glaciers, the near underground. (Water in the atmosphere technically does not belong to the hydrosphere, but the two systems are linked through the water cycle.) The subsystem that consists of the perennially frozen parts of the hydrosphere has its own name: the **cryosphere**. The **biosphere** consists of all the planet's living (and recently deceased and decaying) organisms.

FIGURE 3.4
Scientists divide the complex Earth system into smaller subsystems that interact with each other.

roots

BIOTIC AND ABIOTIC

The word **biotic** refers to anything having to do with life or living organisms. It derives from the Greek word *biotikos*, "pertaining to life," and originally from the Greek *bios*, "life." (The same root is in the term *biosphere*.) The word **abiotic** refers to the nonliving parts of the environment. Any time you see the prefix *a-* you can assume that it means "not." It probably came originally from Latin and Greek words that meant "not" or "away from," and it is related in both meaning and word origin to the prefix *an-*. Other examples of similar word pairs in environmental science include *photic–aphotic* and *aerobic–anaerobic*.

Today many scientists also are arguing for the inclusion of another subsystem, variously called the **anthroposphere** (or *anthrosphere* or *technosphere*). This encompasses the parts of the environment that are built or modified by humans for human use, including the built environment in which we live, work, and study. In many ways, environmental science is the study of the interactions of the anthroposphere with the other subsystems of Earth.

Although these categories are useful, it is important to remember that their boundaries overlap and the subsystems interact. Picture a robin plucking an earthworm from the ground after a rain. You are witnessing an organism (the robin, part of the biosphere) consuming another organism (the earthworm) by removing it from part of the geosphere (the soil) that the earthworm had been modifying. This is possible because rain (from the hydrosphere) recently wet the ground. The robin might then fly through the air (the atmosphere) to a tree (an organism), in the process respiring (combining oxygen from the atmosphere with glucose from the organism, and adding water to the hydrosphere and carbon dioxide and heat to the atmosphere). Finally, the bird might defecate, returning nutrients to the geosphere.

The study of such cyclical interactions among the **biotic**, or living, and the **abiotic**, or nonliving, components of the environment is a key part of ecology at the ecosystem level, as scientists become more inclined to approach Earth systems holistically.

Ecosystems

An **ecosystem** consists of all organisms and nonliving entities that occur and interact in a particular area at the same time. The ecosystem concept is related to the idea of a biological community (a group of interacting organisms of various types, living together in a specific habitat), which we will address in subsequent chapters. It is important to note that ecosystems encompass abiotic as well as biotic components. In ecosystems, energy flows and matter cycles among these components.

Ecosystems are systems of interacting biotic and abiotic components

The idea of ecosystems originated in the early twentieth century, championed by British ecologist Arthur Tansley, who saw that biological entities are tightly intertwined with chemical and physical entities. Tansley and others felt that there was so much interaction and feedback between organisms and their abiotic environments that it made most sense to view living and nonliving elements together. Since then, **ecosystem ecology** has come to refer to the study of energy and nutrient flows among living and nonliving components of systems.

Ecosystem ecologists began analyzing ecosystems as an engineer might analyze the operation of a machine. In this view, ecosystems are systems that receive inputs of energy, process and transform that energy while cycling matter internally, and produce a variety of outputs (such as heat, water flow, and animal waste products) that can move into other ecosystems. Energy and matter are passed among organisms through feeding relationships. Energy flows *through* ecosystems, in one direction; most arrives as radiation from the Sun, powers the system, and exits in the form of heat (**FIGURE 3.5A**). Matter, in contrast, is generally recycled *within* ecosystems (**FIGURE 3.5B**).

roots

ECOSYSTEM

The term **ecosystem** was first used in 1930 by British botanist Arthur Roy Clapham and was later expanded upon by Arthur Tansley and others. It was based on the term **ecology**, referring to the branch of science dealing with the relationship between living things and their environment, which was coined by German zoologist Ernst Haeckel in 1866. The *eco-* in both terms is derived from the Greek word *oikos*, meaning "house or dwelling place." Interestingly, the Greek *systema*, or "system," originally had the connotation of "an organized whole."

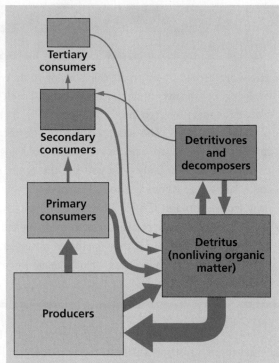

(a) Energy flowing through an ecosystem

(b) Matter (nutrients) cycling within an ecosystem

FIGURE 3.5   Energy enters, flows through, and exits an ecosystem. In **(a)**, light energy from the Sun (yellow arrow) drives photosynthesis in producers, which begins the transfer of chemical energy (green arrows) among organisms. Energy exits the system through respiration and other chemical conversions processes, in the form of heat (red arrows). In contrast, matter cycles within an ecosystem. In **(b)**, blue arrows show the movement of nutrients among organisms by way of their feeding relationships. In both diagrams, box sizes represent relative magnitudes of energy or matter content, and arrow widths represent relative magnitudes of energy or matter transfer. Such magnitudes may vary tremendously from one ecosystem to another. Some abiotic components (such as water, air, and inorganic soil content) of ecosystems are omitted from these schematic diagrams.

Matter is recycled because when organisms die and decay their nutrients remain in the system. In contrast, most energy that organisms take in is later lost through respiration, and the excess energy released as heat. The two flows are intimately related; the flow of energy through the ecosystem is what drives the constant recycling of matter.

Energy is converted to biomass

Energy flow in most ecosystems begins with radiation from the Sun. You have learned how autotrophs, such as green plants and phytoplankton, use photosynthesis to capture the Sun's energy and produce food. The result of this process is the production of **biomass**, organic material of which living organisms are formed.

The conversion of solar energy to the energy of chemical bonds in sugars by autotrophs is termed **gross primary production (GPP)**. Autotrophs use a portion of this production to power their own metabolism by respiration. The energy that remains after respiration, and that is used to generate biomass, is the **net primary production (NPP)**. Thus, net primary production equals gross primary production minus respiration (or NPP = GPP – respiration by autotrophs). Net primary production can

be measured by the organic matter stored by plants after they have metabolized enough for their own maintenance.

Another way to think of net primary production is that it represents the energy or biomass that is available for consumption by heterotrophs. Heterotrophs eat plants and use the energy they gain from plants for their own metabolism, growth, and reproduction (or they eat animals that have eaten plants and gain energy in that way). The total biomass that heterotrophs generate by consuming autotrophs is termed **secondary production**.

Ecosystems vary in the rate at which plants convert energy to biomass. The rate at which production occurs is termed **productivity**, and ecosystems whose plants convert solar energy to biomass rapidly are said to have high net primary productivity. (Note that because productivity is a *rate*, it is generally described in terms of an amount of production in a given area, *per unit of time*.)

Freshwater wetlands, tropical forests, coral reefs, and algal beds tend to have the highest net primary productivities, whereas deserts, tundra, and open ocean tend to have the lowest **(FIGURE 3.6A)**. Variation in net primary productivity among ecosystems and biomes results in geographic patterns of variation across the globe **(FIGURE 3.6B)**. In terrestrial ecosystems, net primary productiv-

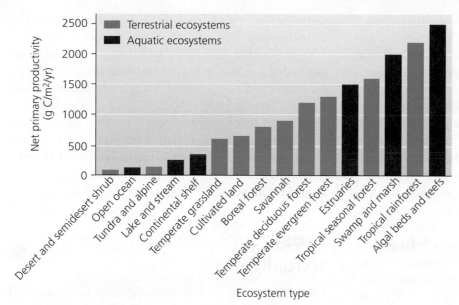

(a) Net primary productivity for major ecosystem types

FIGURE 3.6
(a) Freshwater wetlands, tropical forests, coral reefs, and algal beds show high net primary productivities on average. Deserts, tundra, and the open ocean are lower. **(b)** On land, net primary production varies geographically with temperature and precipitation. In the ocean, net primary production is highest around the margins of continents, where nutrients (of both natural and human origin) run off from land, and where deep, cold, nutrient-rich waters commonly well up to the surface. *Source: Data in (a) from Whittaker, R. H. (1975) Communities and Ecosystems, 2nd ed. New York, MacMillan. Map in (b) from satellite data presented by Field, C. B., et al. (1998) Primary production of the biosphere: Integrating terrestrial and oceanic components. Science 281: 237–240.*

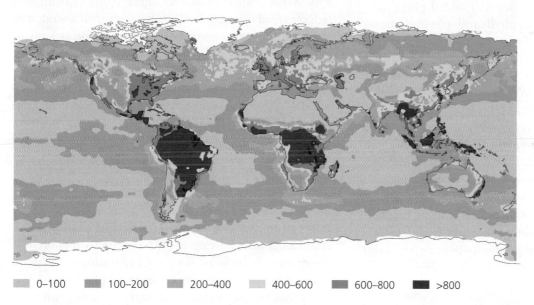

0–100   100–200   200–400   400–600   600–800   >800

(b) Global map of net primary production (g C/m²/yr)

ity tends to increase with temperature and precipitation. In aquatic ecosystems, net primary productivity tends to rise with light and the availability of nutrients.

Nutrient availability limits productivity

Nutrients are elements and compounds that organisms consume and require for survival. Organisms need several dozen naturally occurring chemical elements to survive. Elements and compounds required in relatively large amounts are called *macronutrients*; these include nitrogen, carbon, and phosphorus. Nutrients needed in small amounts are called *micronutrients*.

Nutrients stimulate production by autotrophs, and lack of nutrients can limit production. The availability of nitrogen or phosphorus frequently is a **limiting factor** for plant or algal growth. When these nutrients are added to a system, producers show the greatest response to whichever nutrient has been in shortest supply. Phosphorus tends to be limiting in freshwater systems, and nitrogen in marine systems. Thus marine hypoxic zones result primarily from excess nitrogen, whereas freshwater ponds and lakes tend to suffer eutrophication when they contain too much phosphorus.

Canadian ecologist David Schindler (profiled in "Canadian Environmental Perspectives" in the chapter on "Freshwater Systems and Water Resources") and colleagues demonstrated the effects of phosphorus on freshwater systems in the 1970s by experimentally manipulating entire lakes. In one experiment, the researchers divided a 16-ha lake in Ontario in half with a plastic barrier. To one half they added carbon, nitrate, and phosphate; to the other they added only carbon and nitrate. Soon after the experiment began, they saw a dramatic increase in algae in the half of the lake that received phosphate, whereas the other half hosted algal levels typical for lakes in the region (**FIGURE 3.7**). This difference held until shortly after they stopped fertilizing seven years later, when algae decreased to normal levels in the half that had previously received phosphate. Such experiments showed clearly that phosphorus addition can markedly increase primary productivity in lakes.

Similar experiments in coastal ocean waters show nitrogen to be the more important limiting factor for primary productivity. In experiments in the 1980s and 1990s, Swedish ecologist Edna Granéli took samples of ocean water from the Baltic Sea and added phosphate, nitrate, or nothing. Chlorophyll and phytoplankton increased greatly in the flasks with nitrate, whereas those with phosphate did not differ from the controls. Experiments in Long Island Sound by other researchers show similar results. For open ocean waters far from shore, research indicates that iron is a highly effective nutrient.

Because nutrients run off from land into the Baltic Sea, Long Island Sound, Gulf of the St. Lawrence, the Gulf of Mexico, and other coastal waters around the world, primary productivity in the oceans tends to be greatest in nearshore waters, and lowest in open ocean areas far from land (see **FIGURE 3.6B**). Satellite imaging technology that reveals phytoplankton densities has given scientists an improved view of productivity at regional and global scales, which has helped them track blooms of algae that contribute to coastal hypoxic zones.

The number of known hypoxic zones is increasing globally, with about 400 documented so far. Most are located off the coasts of Europe and eastern North America. Specific causes vary from place to place, but most result from rising nutrient pollution from farms, cities, and industry. In North America, the Gulf of Mexico and Chesapeake Bay may be the most severely affected. Decades of pollution and human impact have devastated fisheries and greatly altered the ecology of these water bodies.

Ecosystems are integrated spatially

Like all systems, we can conceptualize ecosystems at different scales. An ecosystem can be as small as an ephemeral puddle of water where brine shrimp and tadpoles feed on algae and detritus with mad abandon as the pool dries up. Or an ecosystem might be as large as a bay, lake, or forest. For some purposes, scientists even view the entire biosphere as a single all-encompassing ecosystem. The term is most often used, however, to refer to systems of moderate geographic extent that are somewhat self-contained. For example, the salt marshes that line the outer part of the St. Lawrence estuary where its waters mix with those of the Atlantic Ocean may be classified as ecosystems.

Adjacent ecosystems often share components and interact extensively. For instance, a pond ecosystem is very different from a forest ecosystem that surrounds it, but salamanders that develop in the pond live their adult lives under logs on the forest floor until returning to the pond to breed. Rainwater that nourishes forest plants may eventually make its way to the pond, carrying with it nutrients from the forest's leaf litter. Likewise, coastal dunes, the ocean, and a lagoon or salt marsh all may interact, as do forests and prairies where they converge. Areas where ecosystems meet often consist of transitional zones called **ecotones**, in which elements of each ecosystem mix.

FIGURE 3.7
A portion of this lake in Ontario was experimentally treated with the addition of phosphate. The treated portion experienced an immediate, dramatic, and prolonged algal bloom, visible in the opaque water in the topmost part of this photo.
Source: David W. Schindler.

weighing the issues
ECOSYSTEMS WHERE YOU LIVE

Think about the area where you live. How would you describe the ecosystems? How do these systems interact with one another? If one ecosystem were greatly disturbed (say, a wetland or forest replaced by a shopping mall), what impacts might that have on the system and others nearby?

Landscape ecologists study geographic patterns

Because components of different ecosystems may intermix, ecologists often find it useful to view these systems on a larger geographic scale that encompasses multiple ecosystems. For instance, if you are studying large mammals such as black bears, which move seasonally from mountains to valleys or between mountain ranges, you had better consider the overall landscape that includes all these areas. If you study fish such as salmon, which move between marine and freshwater ecosystems, you need to know how these systems interact.

In such a broad-scale approach, called **landscape ecology**, scientists study how landscape structure affects the abundance, distribution, and interaction of organisms. A landscape-level approach is also useful for scientists, citizens, planners, and policymakers in planning for sustainable regional development (see "The Science Behind the Story: Biodiversity Portrait of the St. Lawrence," available on myenvironmentplace).

For a landscape ecologist, a landscape is made up of a spatial array of *patches*, which may be ecosystems or areas of habitat for a particular organism. Patches are spread spatially over a landscape in a *mosaic*. This metaphor reflects how natural systems often are arrayed across landscapes in complex patterns, like an intricate work of art. Thus, a forest ecologist might refer to a mosaic of forested patches within an agricultural landscape, or a butterfly biologist might speak of a mosaic of grassland patches that acts as habitat for a particular species of butterfly.

One can view landscapes at different spatial scales. **FIGURE 3.8** illustrates a landscape consisting of four ecosystem types, with ecotones along their borders indicated by thick red lines. At this scale, we perceive a mosaic consisting of four patches plus a river. However, the inset shows a magnified view of an ecotone. At this finer resolution, we see that the ecotone consists of patches of forest and grassland in a complex arrangement. The scale at which an ecologist focuses will depend on the particular questions or organisms he or she is studying.

Every organism has specific habitat needs, so when its habitat is distributed in patches across a landscape, individuals may need to expend energy and risk predation travelling from one to another. If the patches are distant enough, the organism's population may become divided into subpopulations, each occupying a different patch in the mosaic. Such a network of subpopulations, most of whose members stay within their respective patches but some

FIGURE 3.8 Landscape ecology deals with spatial patterns above the ecosystem level. This generalized diagram of a landscape shows a mosaic of patches of five ecosystem types (three terrestrial types, a marsh, and a river). Thick red lines indicate ecotones. A stretch of lowland broadleaf forest running along the river serves as a corridor connecting the large region of forest on the left to the smaller patch of forest alongside the marsh. The inset shows a magnified view of the forest–grassland ecotone and how it consists of patches on a smaller scale.

of whom move among patches or mate with members of other patches, is called a *metapopulation*. When patches are still more isolated from one another, individuals may not be able to travel between them at all. In such a case, smaller subpopulations may be at risk of extinction.

Because of this extinction risk, metapopulations and landscape ecology are of great interest to *conservation biologists*, who study the loss, protection, and restoration of species and their habitats. Of particular concern is the fragmentation of habitat into small and isolated patches—something that often results from human impact. Establishing corridors to link patches is one approach that conservation biologists pursue as they attempt to maintain biodiversity in the face of human impact. We will return to these issues when we consider conservation biology and habitat fragmentation in subsequent chapters.

Remote sensing and GIS are important tools

Remote sensing technologies—that is, technologies that collect information about a target object from a distance—are improving our ability to take a landscape perspective on complex ecosystems. Satellites orbiting Earth are sending us more and better data than ever before on what the surface of our planet looks like (the chapter-opening photo is an example). By helping us monitor our planet from above, satellite imagery has become a vital tool in modern environmental science. (See also "The Science Behind the Story: Mission to Planet Earth," in the introductory chapter.)

A common tool that makes use of remotely sensed data is the **geographic information system (GIS)**. A GIS consists of computer software that takes multiple types of spatially referenced data (for instance, on geology, hydrology, vegetation, animal species, and human development) and combines them on a common set of geographic coordinates. The idea is to create a complete picture of a landscape and to analyze how elements of the different data sets are arrayed spatially and how they may be correlated.

FIGURE 3.9 illustrates in a simplified way how different datasets of a GIS are combined, layer upon layer, to form a composite map. GIS has become a valuable tool for geographers, landscape ecologists, resource managers, and conservation biologists. GIS technology also brings insights that affect planning and land-use decisions.

Principles of landscape ecology, and tools such as GIS, are increasingly used in local and regional planning processes. Some conservation groups, such as the Nature Conservancy of Canada, a land trust, apply a landscape ecology approach in their land acquisition and management strategies. (A *land trust* is an organization, usually nonprofit, that acquires land for the purpose of protec-

tion and conservation. The Bruce Trail Conservancy, mentioned in "Canadian Environmental Perspectives," is another example of a land trust.)

FIGURE 3.9

Geographic information systems (GIS) allow scientists to layer different types of data on natural landscape features and human land uses, from both remote sensing and ground-based observations, and to produce maps integrating this information. GIS can be used to explore correlations among these data sets.

Models help scientists understand complex systems

Another way in which ecologists and other environmental scientists seek to make sense of the complex systems they study is by working with models. In science, a **model** is a simplified representation of a complex natural process, designed to help us understand how the process occurs and to make predictions. Modelling is the practice of constructing and testing models that aim to explain and predict how natural systems function.

Models of complex natural systems such as ecosystems or the global climate system can be mathematically complicated. However, the general approach of modelling is easy to understand (**FIGURE 3.10**). Researchers gather data from nature on relationships that interest them and then form a hypothesis about what those relationships are. They construct a model that attempts to explain the relationships in a generalized way so that people can use the model to make predictions about how the system will behave. Modellers test their predictions by gathering new data from natural systems, and they use these new data to refine the model, making it increasingly accurate.

The process illustrated in **FIGURE 3.10** resembles the scientific method in general, in that it moves from observation through hypothesis, prediction, and refinement of the hypothesis. This is because models are essentially, themselves, hypotheses about how systems function. Accordingly, the use of models is a key part of environmental research today. For example, University of Michigan researcher Donald Scavia and colleagues have modelled nitrogen and phosphorus transport by the Mississippi River along with hypoxia in the Gulf of Mexico. Using models, they were able to reconstruct what past conditions were like before monitoring for the dead zone had begun. They concluded that hypoxic events in the Gulf started in the mid-1970s. They were also able to forecast future trends. As a result of these forecasts, they advised that the government's recommendation to reduce nutrient loads by 30% would not be enough to prevent hypoxia, but rather that reductions of 40–45% would be needed.

Ecosystems provide vital services

When scientists try to understand how ecosystems function, it is not simply out of curiosity about the world. They also know that human society depends on healthy, functioning ecosystems. When Earth's ecosystems function normally and undisturbed, they provide goods and services that we could not survive without. We rely not just on natural resources (which can be thought of as goods from nature), but also on the ecosystem services that our planet's systems provide (**TABLE 3.1**).

Ecological processes form the soil that nourishes our crops, purify the water we drink and the air that we breathe, store and stabilize supplies of water that we use, pollinate the food plants we eat, and receive and break down (some of) the waste we dump and the pollution we emit. The negative feedback cycles that are typical of ecosystems regulate and stabilize the climate and help

FIGURE 3.10
Modellers observe relationships among variables in nature and then construct models to explain those relationships and make predictions. They test and refine the models by gathering new data from nature and seeing how well the models predict those data.

Table 3.1 Ecosystem Services

Ecosystems provide many services that benefit us. They:

- Regulate oxygen, carbon dioxide, stratospheric ozone, and other atmospheric gases
- Regulate temperature and precipitation with ocean currents, cloud formation, and so on
- Protect against storms, floods, and droughts, mainly with vegetation
- Store and regulate water supplies in watersheds and aquifers
- Prevent soil erosion
- Form soil by weathering rock and accumulating organic material
- Cycle carbon, nitrogen, phosphorus, sulphur, and other nutrients
- Filter waste, remove toxins, recover nutrients, and control pollution
- Pollinate plant crops and wild plants so they reproduce
- Control crop pests with predators and parasites
- Provide habitat for organisms to breed, feed, rest, migrate, and winter
- Produce fish, game, crops, nuts, and fruits that people eat
- Supply lumber, fuel, metals, fodder, and fibre
- Furnish medicines, pets, ornamental plants, and genes for resistance to pathogens and crop pests
- Provide recreation such as ecotourism, fishing, hiking, birding, hunting, and kayaking
- Provide aesthetic, artistic, educational, spiritual, and scientific amenities

to dampen the impacts of the disturbances we create in natural systems. On top of all these services that are vital for our very existence, ecosystems also provide services that enhance the quality of our lives, ranging from recreational opportunities to scenery for aesthetic enjoyment to inspiration and spiritual renewal. Ecosystem goods and ecosystem services (**FIGURE 3.11**) support our lives and society in profound and innumerable ways.

Biogeochemical Cycles

Materials move through the environment in complex and fascinating ways. Energy enters an ecosystem from the Sun, flows from one organism to another, and is dissipated to the atmosphere as heat, but physical matter is circulated through natural systems over and over again. The cycling of nutrients is one of the most important and fundamental of the ecosystem services that support life on this planet. Through the processes that take place within and among ecosystems, the chemical elements and compounds that we need—carbon, nitrogen, phosphorus, water, and many more—move through the environment in complex, global biogeochemical cycles.

Nutrients and other materials move in biogeochemical cycles

Nutrients move through ecosystems in **nutrient cycles** or **biogeochemical cycles**. They are called *biogeochemi-*

cal because the processes involved are biological, geological, and chemical (as well as physical). In these cycles, materials travel through the atmosphere, hydrosphere, and geosphere, and from one organism to another, in dynamic equilibrium. A carbon atom in your fingernail today might have resided in the muscle of a cow a year ago, in a blade of grass a month before that, in soil organic matter a year before that, and in a dinosaur's tooth 100 million years before that. After we die, the nutrients in our bodies will spread widely through the physical environment, eventually being incorporated by an untold number of organisms far into the future.

Nutrients and other materials (including toxins, as you will see in subsequent chapters) move from one *pool*, or **reservoir**, to another, remaining for varying amounts of time—the **residence time**—in each reservoir. The dinosaur, the soil, the grass, the cow, and you are each reservoirs for carbon atoms. The average residence time for an atom of carbon in your body is longer than the average residence time for an atom of carbon in a blade of grass, which has a short lifespan and will soon die, releasing its carbon back to the surrounding environment.

The movement of materials among reservoirs is termed a **flux** (**FIGURE 3.12**). Fluxes are rates, so they are stated in terms of mass or volume of material moving among reservoirs *per unit of time*. The flux of a material between reservoirs can change over time. Human activity has influenced the fluxes of certain materials. For example, we have increased the flux of nitrogen from the atmosphere to terrestrial reservoirs, and we have shifted the flux of carbon in the opposite direction.

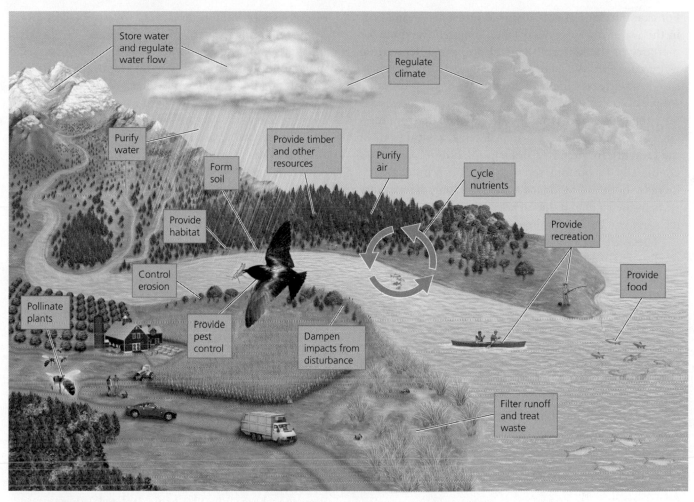

FIGURE 3.11 Ecosystems provide countless valuable services that support both natural and human systems; some of these services are illustrated here.

Reservoirs that release more nutrients (or any other material of interest) than they accept are called **sources**; reservoirs that accept more nutrients than they release are called **sinks**. Carbon sinks are of particular importance today, as we struggle to lower the rate at which carbon is released into the atmosphere, potentially affected our global climate system.

The time it would take for all of the atoms (or particles) of a particular material to be flushed through a particular reservoir is called the **turnover time**. Turnover time is a function of the balance between fluxes *into* the reservoir (from a source) and fluxes *out of* the reservoir (to a sink). If we stop all new sources of material incoming into the reservoir, then the turnover time is the amount of time it would take for the material to be completely flushed through and out of the system.

Turnover time also depends on processes that influence the residence time of the material, including any processes that might hold or bind the material within the reservoir or cause it to be flushed through more quickly.

FIGURE 3.12
The properties of reservoirs and how cyclical fluxes move materials into and out of reservoirs are fundamentally important concepts in environmental science today.

For example, let us say that we are interested in mercury in the water of a particular lake. The turnover time for mercury in the lake will depend on how quickly fresh water runs into the lake, and how quickly the mercury-laden water leaves the lake. It will also depend on other sources of mercury inputs, such as mercury deposited onto the lake surface from the air, or taken up from mercury-bearing rocks in the lake bed. Now, what if some of the mercury in the water sinks to the bottom and binds chemically to bottom sediments? This would greatly increase both the residence time (how long the mercury stays in the lake) and the turnover time (how quickly the mercury will be flushed through the lake).

These are extremely important concepts in environmental science today. For example, we are concerned about the presence in the atmosphere of substances that damage the stratospheric ozone layer. Many of these substances have very long residence times in the atmosphere. Even if we stop producing them altogether—which we have almost accomplished as a result of the Montreal Protocol—the turnover time for these materials to be cleared out of the atmosphere by natural processes will be measured in decades. As we discuss various biogeochemical cycles, think about how human actions can influence fluxes and generate feedback loops in these cycles.

Let's start with a look at the most fundamental of the biogeochemical cycles: the water cycle.

The hydrologic cycle influences all other cycles

Water is so integral to life that we take it for granted. The essential medium for all manner of biochemical reactions, water plays key roles in nearly every environmental system, including each of the nutrient cycles we have just discussed. Water carries nutrients and sediments from the continents to the oceans via rivers, streams, and surface runoff, and it distributes sediments onward in ocean currents. Increasingly, water also distributes artificial pollutants.

The *water cycle*, or **hydrologic cycle** (**FIGURE 3.13**), summarizes how water—in liquid, gaseous, and solid forms—flows through our environment. A brief introduction to the hydrologic cycle will set the stage for our more in-depth discussion of freshwater and marine systems in subsequent chapters.

The oceans are the main reservoir in the hydrologic cycle, holding 97% of all water on Earth. The fresh water we depend on for our survival accounts for less than 3% of the total, and two-thirds of this small amount is tied up in glaciers, snowfields, and ice caps. Thus, considerably less than 1% of the planet's water is in a form that we can

readily use—groundwater, surface fresh water, and rain from atmospheric water vapour.

Water moves from oceans, lakes, ponds, rivers, and moist soil into the atmosphere by **evaporation**, the conversion of a liquid to gaseous form. Warm temperatures and strong winds speed rates of evaporation. A greater degree of exposure has the same effect; an area logged of its forest or converted to agriculture or residential use will lose water more readily than a comparable area that remains vegetated. Water also enters the atmosphere by **transpiration**, the release of water vapour by plants through their leaves. Transpiration and evaporation act as natural processes of distillation, effectively creating pure water by filtering out minerals carried in solution.

Water returns from the atmosphere to Earth's surface as **precipitation** when water vapour condenses and falls as rain or snow. Precipitation may be taken up by plants and used by animals, but much of it flows as **runoff** into streams, rivers, lakes, ponds, and oceans. Amounts of precipitation vary greatly from region to region globally, helping give rise to the variety of biomes.

Some precipitation and surface water soaks down through soil and rock to recharge underground reservoirs called *aquifers*. Aquifers are porous bodies of rock and soil that hold **groundwater**, water found underground beneath layers of soil. Aquifers may hold groundwater for long periods of time, so the water may be quite ancient. In some cases groundwater can take hundreds or even thousands of years to recharge fully after being depleted. Where groundwater intersects the surface, the exposed water becomes surface runoff or evaporates into the atmosphere.

Our impacts on the hydrologic cycle are extensive

Human activity affects every aspect of the water cycle. By damming rivers to create reservoirs, we increase evaporation and, in some cases, infiltration of surface water into aquifers. By altering Earth's surface and its vegetation, we increase surface runoff and erosion. By spreading water on agricultural fields, we can deplete rivers, lakes, and streams and can increase evaporation. By removing forests and other vegetation, we reduce transpiration and may lower water tables. By emitting into the atmosphere pollutants that dissolve in water droplets, we change the chemical nature of precipitation, in effect sabotaging the natural distillation process that evaporation and transpiration provide.

Perhaps most threatening to our future, we are overdrawing groundwater to the surface for drinking, irrigation, and industrial use and have thereby begun to deplete groundwater resources. Water shortages have already given rise to numerous conflicts worldwide, and many

FIGURE 3.13   The hydrologic cycle summarizes the many routes that water molecules take as they move through the environment. Grey arrows represent fluxes. The hydrologic cycle is a system itself, but it also plays key roles in other biogeochemical cycles. Reservoir names are in black type, and the black numbers represent reservoir sizes expressed in units of cubic kilometres (km³). Transfer processes (red) give rise to fluxes, expressed in km³ per year.   *Source: Data from Schlesinger, W.H. (1997). Biogeochemistry: An Analysis of Global Change, 2nd ed. London, Academic Press.*

people think this situation will worsen (see the Central Case "Turning the Tap: The Prospect of Canadian Bulk Water Exports" in the chapter on "Freshwater Systems and Water Resources").

The carbon cycle circulates a vital organic nutrient

As the definitive component of organic molecules, **carbon (C)** is an ingredient in carbohydrates, fats, and proteins and in the bones, cartilage, and shells of all living things. From fossil fuels to DNA, from plastics to pharmaceuticals, carbon atoms are everywhere. The **carbon cycle** describes the routes that carbon atoms take through the environment (**FIGURE 3.14**).

Producers, including terrestrial and aquatic plants, algae, and cyanobacteria, pull carbon dioxide out of the atmosphere and out of surface water to use in photosynthesis. Photosynthesis breaks the bonds in carbon dioxide (CO_2) and water (H_2O) to produce oxygen (O_2) and carbohydrates (e.g., glucose, $C_6H_{12}O_6$). Autotrophs use some of the carbohydrates to fuel their own respiration, thereby releasing some of the carbon back into the atmo-

sphere and oceans as CO_2. When producers are eaten by primary consumers, which in turn are eaten by secondary consumers, more carbohydrates are broken down in respiration, producing carbon dioxide and water. The same process occurs when decomposers consume waste and dead organic matter. Respiration from all these organisms releases carbon back into the atmosphere and oceans.

All organisms use carbon for structural growth, so a portion of the carbon an organism takes in becomes incorporated into its tissues. The abundance of plants and the fact that they take in so much carbon dioxide for photosynthesis make plants a major reservoir for carbon. Because CO_2 is a greenhouse gas of primary concern, much research on global climate change is directed toward measuring the amount of CO_2 that plants tie up. Scientists are working toward understanding exactly how and to what extent this portion of the carbon cycle influences Earth's climate.

As organisms die, their remains may settle in sediments in ocean basins or in freshwater wetlands. As layers of sediment accumulate, older layers are buried more deeply, experiencing high pressure over long periods of time. These conditions can convert soft tissues into fossil fuels—coal, oil, and natural gas—and shells and skeletons into sedimentary rock, such as limestone.

FIGURE 3.14   The carbon cycle summarizes the many routes that carbon atoms take as they move through the environment. Grey arrows represent fluxes among carbon reservoirs. Reservoir names are in black, and the black numbers represent reservoir sizes expressed in petagrams (units of 10^{15} g) of C. Transfer processes give rise to fluxes, in red, expressed in petagrams (billion metric tons) of C per year. Fluxes of carbon to the atmosphere from human sources (fossil fuels and deforestation) have increased in recent decades.   *Source: Data from Schlesinger, W.H. (1997) Biogeochemistry: An Analysis of Global Change, 2nd ed. London, Academic Press.*

Sedimentary rock comprises the largest single reservoir in the carbon cycle. Although any given carbon atom spends a relatively short time in the atmosphere, carbon trapped in sedimentary rock may reside there for hundreds of millions of years.

Carbon trapped in sediments and fossil fuel deposits may eventually be released into the oceans or atmosphere by geological processes such as tectonic uplift and volcanic eruptions. It also re-enters the atmosphere when we extract and burn fossil fuels.

The ocean is the second-largest reservoir in the carbon cycle. Ocean waters absorbs carbon compounds from the atmosphere, from terrestrial runoff, from undersea volcanoes, and from the waste and detritus of marine organisms. Some carbon atoms absorbed by the ocean—in the form of carbon dioxide, carbonate ions (CO_3^{2-}), and

bicarbonate ions (HCO_3^-)—combine with calcium ions (Ca^{2+}) to form calcium carbonate ($CaCO_3$), an essential ingredient in the skeletons and shells of microscopic marine organisms. As these organisms die, their calcium carbonate shells sink to the ocean floor and begin to form sedimentary rock. The rates at which ocean water absorbs and release carbon depend on many factors, including temperature and the number of marine organisms converting CO_2 into carbohydrates and carbonates.

We are shifting carbon from the geosphere to the atmosphere

By mining fossil fuel deposits, we are removing carbon from an underground reservoir with a residence time of millions of years. When we combust fossil fuels in our automobiles, homes, and industries, we release carbon dioxide and greatly increase the flux of carbon from the geosphere to the atmosphere. Since the mid-eighteenth century, fossil fuel combustion has added over 250 billion metric tonnes of carbon to the atmosphere. Meanwhile, the movement of CO_2 *from* the atmosphere *back* to the hydrosphere, geosphere, and biosphere has not kept pace.

In addition, cutting down forests and burning fields removes carbon from the vegetation reservoir and releases it to the air. If less vegetation is left on the surface, there are fewer plants to draw CO_2 back out of the atmosphere.

As a result, scientists estimate that today's atmospheric carbon dioxide reservoir is the largest that Earth has experienced in at least the past 800 000 years, and perhaps in the past 20 million years. The anthropogenic flux of carbon out of the fossil fuel reservoir and into the atmosphere is a driving force behind global climate change. Some of the excess CO_2 in the atmosphere is now being absorbed by ocean water. This is causing ocean water to become more acidic, leading to problems that threaten many marine organisms.

Our understanding of the carbon cycle is not yet complete. Scientists have long been baffled by the so-called "missing carbon sink." Of the carbon dioxide we emit by fossil fuel combustion and deforestation, scientists have measured how much goes into the atmosphere and oceans, but there remain roughly 1 billion to 2 billion metric tonnes per year unaccounted for. Many researchers think this is taken up by plants or soils of the northern temperate and boreal forests. But they'd like to know for sure—because if forests are acting as a major sink for carbon, it would be a good idea to keep it that way. If forests that today are sinks were to turn into sources and begin releasing the "missing" carbon, climate change could accelerate drastically.

The nitrogen cycle involves specialized bacteria

Nitrogen (N) makes up 78% of our atmosphere by mass, and is the sixth most abundant element on Earth. It is an essential ingredient in the proteins that build our bodies, and an essential nutrient for plant growth. Thus the **nitrogen cycle** (**FIGURE 3.15**) is of vital importance to all organisms. Despite its abundance in air, nitrogen gas (N_2) is chemically inert and cannot cycle out of the atmosphere and into living organisms without assistance from lightning, highly specialized bacteria, or human intervention. For this reason, nitrogen in elemental form is scarce in the geosphere and hydrosphere and in organisms. However, once nitrogen undergoes the right

kind of chemical change, it becomes biologically active and available to the organisms that need it. Its scarcity makes biologically active nitrogen a limiting factor for plant growth.

To become biologically available, inert nitrogen gas (N_2) must be "fixed," or combined with hydrogen in nature to form ammonia (NH_3), whose water-soluble ions of ammonium (NH_4^+) can be taken up by plants. **Nitrogen fixation** in nature is accomplished in two ways: by the intense energy of lightning strikes, or by the action of specialized bacteria. One such group is aquatic cyanobacteria, either free-living or living inside corals; another group of specialized bacteria fixes nitrogen on land, in the top layer of soil. These bacteria live in a mutually beneficial relationship with many types of land plants, including clover, soybeans, and other legumes, providing them with nutrients by converting nitrogen to a usable form. Farmers have long nourished their soils by planting crops that host nitrogen-fixing bacteria among their roots (**FIGURE 3.16**).

Other types of specialized soil bacteria then perform a process known as **nitrification**, in which ammonium ions are first converted into nitrite ions (NO_2^-), and then into nitrate ions (NO_3^-). Plants can take up these ions, which can also become available after atmospheric deposition on soils or in water or after application of nitrate-based fertilizer.

Animals obtain the nitrogen they need by consuming plants or other animals, and decomposers obtain nitrogen from dead and decaying plant and animal matter and from animal urine and feces. Once the decomposers process the nitrogen-rich compounds they take in, they release ammonium ions, making these available to nitrifying bacteria to convert again to nitrates and nitrites. The final step in the nitrogen cycle occurs when denitrifying bacteria convert nitrates in soil or water back into gaseous nitrogen, via a multistep process. Denitrification thereby completes the cycle by releasing nitrogen back into the atmosphere as a gas.

Nitrogen fixation, nitrification, and denitrification are crucial processes in the nitrogen cycle, which are hosted by soils and facilitated by the resident soil bacteria. We will revisit these processes and the role of soil in the chapter on soil resources.

We have greatly influenced the nitrogen cycle

The impacts of excess nitrogen from agricultural fertilizers in the Great Lakes and St. Lawrence system have had a negative impact on both water quality and the health of marine organisms in downstream areas, as discussed in the

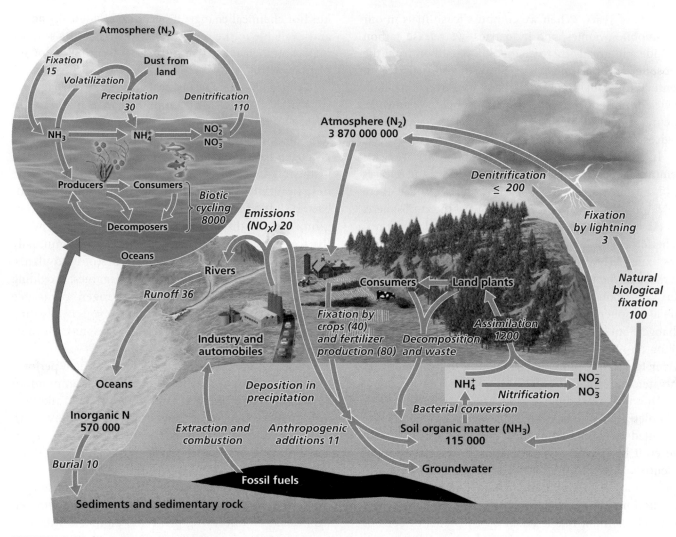

FIGURE 3.15 The nitrogen cycle summarizes the many routes that nitrogen atoms take as they move through the environment. Grey arrows represent fluxes among reservoirs for nitrogen. Reservoir names are in black, and the black numbers are reservoir sizes expressed in teragrams (units of 10^{12} g) of N. Transfer processes give rise to fluxes, in red, expressed in teragrams of N per year. *Source: Data from Schlesinger, W.H. (1997) Biogeochemistry: An Analysis of Global Change, 2nd ed. London, Academic Press.*

FIGURE 3.16

Specialized bacteria live in nodules on the roots of leguminous plants. Through nitrogen fixation, the bacteria convert nitrogen to a form that the plant can take up into its roots.

Root nodules

Nitrogen-fixing bacteria

Central Case. Similar impacts in Mississippi River watershed have become painfully evident to shrimpers and scientists with an interest in the Gulf of Mexico (see "The Science Behind the Story: The Gulf of Mexico's "Dead Zone").

Fertilizer-laden runoff increases the nitrogen available to aquatic plants and algae, boosting their growth (**FIGURE 3.17**). Algal populations soon outstrip the availability of other required nutrients and begin to die and decompose. As in the St. Lawrence estuary and Gulf of Mexico, this large-scale decomposition can lead to hypoxia, robbing aquatic organisms of oxygen and leading to shellfish die-offs and other significant impacts on ecosystems.

Hypoxia and eutrophication are not the only problems resulting from human manipulation of the nitrogen cycle. Historically, rates of nitrogen fixation limited the flux of nitrogen out of the atmosphere, but this changed when two German chemists discovered how to fix nitrogen industrially. Fritz Haber worked in the German army's chemical weapons program during World War I. He found a way to combine nitrogen and hydrogen gases to synthesize ammonia, a key ingredient in modern explosives and agricultural fertilizers. Several years later, Carl Bosch built on Haber's work and devised methods to produce ammonia on an industrial scale.

The work of these two scientists enabled people to overcome the limits on productivity long imposed by nitrogen scarcity in nature. The widespread application of their findings has made modern agriculture possible, but it has also led to dramatic alteration of the nitrogen cycle. Today, using the Haber-Bosch process, our species is fixing more nitrogen artificially than is fixed naturally. We have effectively doubled the natural rate of nitrogen fixation on Earth. By fixing atmospheric nitrogen, we increase its flux out of the atmosphere and into other reservoirs.

Human activity also affects fluxes in other parts of the cycle. When we burn forests and fields, we force nitrogen out of soils and vegetation and into the atmosphere. When we burn fossil fuels, we increase the rate at which nitric oxide (NO) enters the atmosphere and reacts to form nitrogen dioxide (NO_2). This compound is a precursor to nitric acid (HNO_3), a key component of acid precipitation. We introduce nitrous oxide (N_2O) by allowing anaerobic bacteria to break down the tremendous volume of animal waste produced in agricultural feedlots. We have also accelerated the introduction of nitrogen-rich compounds into terrestrial and aquatic systems by destroying wetlands and by cultivating crops that host nitrogen-fixing bacteria in their roots.

Researchers report that human activities have had the following impacts on the global nitrogen cycle:

■ Doubled the rate at which fixed nitrogen enters terrestrial ecosystems (and the rate is still increasing).

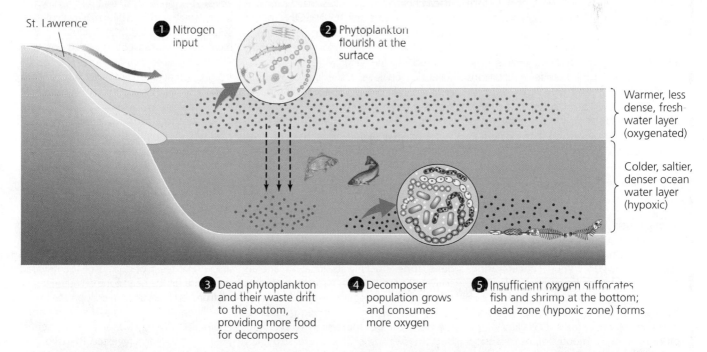

FIGURE 3.17 Excess nitrogen causes eutrophication in marine and freshwater systems such as the St. Lawrence Estuary. Coupled with stratification (layering) of the water, eutrophication can severely deplete dissolved oxygen. Surface water is warmer and fresher, and thus less dense; deeper water is colder and saltier, and thus denser. Nitrogen from river water **(1)** boosts the growth of phytoplankton in surface layers **(2)**, which eventually die and are decomposed at the bottom by bacteria **(3)**. Phytoplankton in surface water absorb light, preventing photosynthesis from occurring in deeper layers (thus inhibiting oxygen production in deeper waters). Stability of the surface layer also prevents deeper water from absorbing atmospheric oxygen to replace oxygen consumed by decomposers **(4)**. Oxygen depletion in lower layers suffocates or drives away bottom-dwelling marine life **(5)**, and gives rise to hypoxic zones.

THE SCIENCE BEHIND THE STORY

The Gulf of Mexico's "Dead Zone"

Fishers in the Gulf of Mexico have been dealt numerous challenging blows in recent years.

Fishers in Louisiana ply the rich waters of the Gulf of Mexico to send shrimp, fish, and shellfish to dinner tables around the world. But fishing in the Gulf has become difficult; catches of shrimp and other common species are half of what they were in the 1980s. The fisheries began declining years before oil gushed from the BP *Deepwater Horizon* drilling platform and fouled the region in 2010, and before Hurricanes Katrina and Rita pummelled the region in 2005 and left boats, docks, and marinas in ruins. Those disasters worsened a long decline that was already under way.

The reason for the decline? Billions of marine organisms have been suffocating in a hypoxic "dead zone," a region of water in the Gulf that is so depleted of oxygen that organisms are killed or driven away. Determining the causes of such dead zones involves understanding environmental systems and the complex behaviour they exhibit.

Aquatic animals obtain oxygen through their gills, and, like us, will asphyxiate if deprived of oxygen. Fully oxygenated water contains up to 10 parts per million (ppm) of oxygen. When concentrations drop below 2 ppm, creatures will leave, or die. The Gulf's hypoxic dead zone appears each spring and grows through the summer and fall, beginning in Louisiana waters offshore from the mouths of the Mississippi and Atchafalaya rivers. The zone reached its largest size in 2002 when it covered 22 000 km^2—almost half the size of Nova Scotia.

What is starving these waters of oxygen? Scientists studying the dead zone are pointing a finger at human activities hundreds of kilometres away.

Rain and runoff carry excess nitrogen and phosphorus from fertilized agricultural fields and into streams and rivers, eventually flushing these nutrients down the Mississippi and Atchafalaya rivers, which drain into the Gulf. Once the excess nutrients reach the Gulf, they trigger blooms of plankton in the surface waters. As the masses of plankton begin to die and drift toward the bottom, they nourish bacteria, which also become overabundant. Bacteria need oxygen, and as they decompose the masses of dead plankton, they deplete dissolved oxygen from the bottom waters. Urban runoff, industrial discharges, fossil fuel emissions, and municipal sewage outflow add additional nitrogen and phosphorus pollution to the rivers as they head toward the Gulf.

In 1985, Dr. Nancy Rabalais and other researchers from the Louisiana Universities Marine Consortium (LUMCON) began tracking oxygen levels at dozens of sites in the Gulf and nearshore locations. Sensors lowered into the water were used to measure oxygen levels, sending continuous readings back to a shipboard computer. Further data come from fixed, submerged oxygen meters that continuously measure dissolved oxygen and store the data. They collected hundreds of water samples and measured nitrogen, salt, bacteria, and phytoplankton. They monitored more than 70 sites in the Gulf, and donned scuba gear to observe the condition of shrimp, fish, and other sea life.

The long-term data collection allowed the researchers to build a "map" of the dead zone, tracking its location and its consequences. In 1991, Rabalais made that map public, earning immediate headlines. That year, her group mapped the size of the dead zone at more than 10 000 km^2. Bottom-dwelling shrimp were stretching out of their burrows, straining for oxygen.

Many fish had fled. The bottom waters, infused with sulphur from bacterial decomposition, smelled of rotten eggs.

The group's years of monitoring enabled them to predict the dead zone's emergence. As rivers rose each spring, and as fertilizers were applied on midwestern farms, oxygen would start to disappear in the northern Gulf. The hypoxia would last through the summer or fall, until seasonal storms mixed oxygen into hypoxic areas. The monitoring also linked the dead zone's size to the volume of river flow and its nutrient load. The 1993 flooding of the Mississippi created a zone much larger than the year before, whereas a drought in 2000 brought low river flows, low nutrient loads, and a small dead zone (see figure). In 2005, the dead zone was predicted to be large, but Hurricanes Katrina and Rita stirred oxygenated surface water into the depths, decreasing the dead zone that year.

In response to these findings, U.S. government regulators proposed that farmers in Midwestern states be required to cut down on fertilizer use. Farmers' advocates protested that farmers were being singled out while urban pollution sources are ignored. Meanwhile, scientists have documented coastal dead zones in 400 other areas throughout the world, from Chesapeake Bay to the St. Lawrence Estuary to the Black Sea.

Midwestern farming advocates and some scientists, such as Derek Winstanley, chief of the Illinois State Water Survey, challenged the link to farm practices. They argued that the Mississippi naturally carries high loads of nitrogen from the rich prairie soil, and that Rabalais' team had not ruled out upwelling in the Gulf as a source of nutrients. But sediment analyses showed that Mississippi River mud contained many fewer nitrates early in the twentieth century. In 2000, a federal assessment team of dozens of scientists laid the blame for the dead zone on nutrient runoff from fertilizers and other sources.

Then in 2004, U.S. Environmental Protection Agency water quality scientist Howard Marshall suggested that the best way to alleviate the dead zone would be

(a) Dissolved oxygen at bottom, July 2009

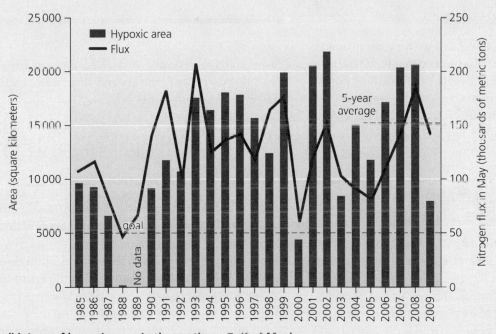

(b) Area of hypoxic zone in the northern Gulf of Mexico

The map in **(a)** shows dissolved oxygen concentrations in bottom waters of the Gulf of Mexico off the Louisiana coast from the July 2009 survey. Areas in red indicate the lowest oxygen levels. Regions considered hypoxic (< 2 mg/L) are encircled with a black line. The size of the Gulf's hypoxic zone varies **(b)** as a result of several factors. Floods increase its size by bringing additional runoff (as in 1993), whereas tropical storms decrease its size by mixing oxygen-rich water into the dead zone (as in 2003). Between 2005 and 2009, the hypoxic zone averaged 15 670 km^2 in size.   *Source: Data from Nancy Rabalais, LUMCON.*

to reduce phosphorus pollution from industry and sewage treatment. His reasoning: Phytoplankton need both nitrogen and phosphorus, but there is now so much nitrogen in the Gulf that phosphorus has become the principal limiting factor on phytoplankton growth.

Research has supported this contention, and most scientists now agree that nitrogen and phosphorus should be managed jointly. Large-scale restoration of wetlands along the river and at the river's delta would best effectively filtre pollutants before they reach the Gulf. The research is

guiding a plan to reduce farm runoff, clean up the Mississippi, restore wetlands, and ultimately, hopefully, shrink the Gulf's dead zone. It has also led to a better understanding of hypoxic zones around the world.

- Increased atmospheric concentrations of the greenhouse gas N_2O and of other oxides of nitrogen that produce smog.
- Depleted essential nutrients, such as calcium and potassium, from soils, because fertilizer helps flush them out.
- Acidified surface water and soils.
- Greatly increased transfer of nitrogen from rivers to oceans.
- Encouraged plant growth, causing more carbon to be stored within terrestrial ecosystems.
- Reduced biological diversity, especially plants adapted to low nitrogen concentrations.
- Changed the composition and function of estuaries and coastal ecosystems.
- Harmed many coastal marine fisheries.

Many of the impacts associated with excess nitrogen, including eutrophication, also occur when phosphorus—another plant nutrient that boosts the growth of phytoplankton—is present in excess in aquatic systems. Let's look briefly at the phosphorus cycle, the third major biogeochemical cycle.

The phosphorus cycle involves mainly geosphere and ocean

The element **phosphorus (P)** is a key component of cell membranes and of several molecules vital for life, including DNA, RNA, ATP, and ADP. Although phosphorus is indispensable for life, the amount of phosphorus in organisms is dwarfed by the vast amounts in rocks, soil, sediments, and the oceans. Unlike the carbon and nitrogen cycles, the **phosphorus cycle** (**FIGURE 3.18**) has no appreciable atmospheric component, aside from tiny amounts of windblown dust and sea spray.

The vast majority of Earth's phosphorus is contained in rocks and mobilized only by weathering, which releases phosphate ions (PO_4^{3-}) into water. Phosphates dissolved in lakes or in the oceans precipitate into solid form, settle to the bottom, and re-enter the geosphere's phosphorus reservoir in the form of sediment. Because most phosphorus is bound up in rock, environmental concentrations of phosphorus available to organisms tend to be very low. This relative rarity explains why phosphorus is frequently a limiting factor for plant growth, and why an artificial influx of phosphorus can produce immediate and dramatic effects.

Plants can take up phosphorus through their roots only when phosphate is dissolved in water. Primary consumers acquire phosphorus from water and plants, and pass it on to secondary consumers. Consumers release phosphorus

weighing the issues

NITROGEN POLLUTION AND ITS FINANCIAL IMPACTS

Most nitrate that enters the Great Lakes and the St. Lawrence River originates from farms and other sources in Ontario and Québec, yet many of its negative impacts are borne by downstream users, such as fishers and organisms in the estuary and the Gulf of the St. Lawrence. Who should be responsible for addressing this problem? How would you deal with the fact that the watershed straddles the international border between Canada and the United States?

through the excretion of waste. Decomposers break down phosphorus-rich organisms and their wastes and, in so doing, return phosphorus to the soil.

We affect the phosphorus cycle

Humans influence the phosphorus cycle in several ways. We mine rocks containing phosphorus to extract this nutrient for the inorganic fertilizers we use on crops and lawns. Our wastewater discharge also tends to be rich in phosphates. Phosphates that run off into waterways can boost algal growth and cause eutrophication, leading to murkier waters and altering the structure and function of aquatic ecosystems. Phosphates are also present in detergents, so one way each of us can reduce phosphorus input into the environment is to purchase phosphate-free detergents.

In the 1970s Lake Erie began to exhibit signs of hypoxia (see "Central Case: The Death and Rebirth of Lake Erie," in the chapter on freshwater systems and water resources). As in the Gulf of Mexico and St. Lawrence examples that we have touched on, the problem was traced to human inputs of phosphate from fertilizers, detergents, and municipal sewage. The sources were land based, but runoff carried the phosphate-bearing materials into the lake from surrounding farms and towns in Canada and the United States.

The International Joint Commission (IJC), set up under the International Boundary Waters Treaty of 1909, adopted the Great Lakes Water Quality Agreement (GLWQA) in 1972 to address the problems of eutrophication and phosphate runoff into Lake Erie. The broader goal of the agreement was to promote an integrated, cooperative, scientific, and ecosystem-based approach to the management of the international waters of the Great

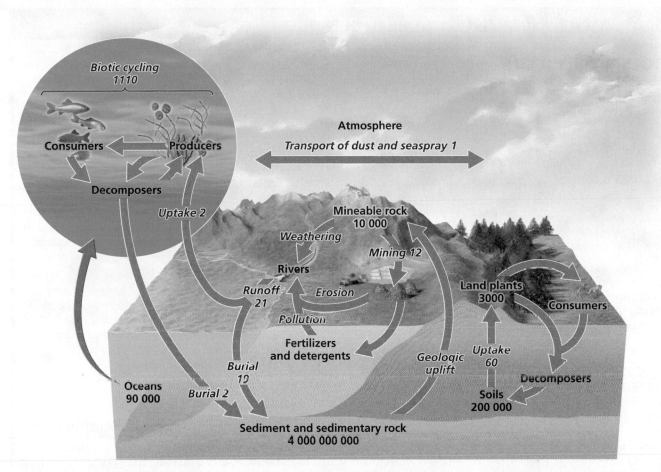

FIGURE 3.10 The phosphorus cycle summarizes the many routes that phosphorus atoms take as they move through the environment. Grey arrows represent fluxes among reservoirs for phosphorus. Reservoir names are in black, and the black numbers represent reservoir sizes expressed in teragrams (units of 10^{12} g) of P. Transfer processes give rise to fluxes, in red, expressed in teragrams of P per year. *Source: Data from Schlesinger, W.H. (1997). Biogeochemistry: An Analysis of Global Change, 2nd ed. London, Academic Press.*

Lakes. Initially, IJC activities under the GLWQA focused on reducing phosphate from detergents and municipal sewage, as these were the best understood pollutants from a scientific perspective.

Since then, the agreement has grown in both strength and scope, and now deals with all threats to water quality in the Great Lakes system from chemical, physical, and biological factors, as well as from other causes such as habitat destruction. Phosphate runoff into the lakes has been controlled to a degree, and Lake Erie has recovered from its most severely oxygen-depleted state. However, runoff of phosphates and many other pollutants into the Great Lakes continues to be problematic, and all of the lakes still face periodic episodes of oxygen depletion.

Conclusion

Thinking in terms of systems is important in understanding Earth's dynamics, so that we may learn how to avoid disrupting its processes. Addressing problems such as

those in the St. Lawrence Estuary and the Gulf of Mexico requires us to study the environment from a systems perspective and to integrate scientific findings with the policy and decision-making processes.

Earth hosts many interacting systems. The way we perceive them and define them depends on the questions we want to investigate. Life interacts with its nonliving environment in ecosystems, systems through which energy flows and matter is recycled. Understanding the biogeochemical cycles that describe the movement of nutrients within and among ecosystems is crucial, because human activities are causing significant changes in the ways those cycles function.

Unperturbed ecosystems use renewable solar energy, recycle nutrients, and are stabilized by negative feedback loops. The environmental systems we see on Earth today are those that have survived the test of time. Our industrialized civilization is young in comparison. Might we not take a few lessons about sustainability from a careful look at the natural systems of our planet?

CANADIAN ENVIRONMENTAL PERSPECTIVES

Robert Bateman

Robert Bateman is one of Canada's leading artists, and a lifelong naturalist.

■ Award-winning and internationally recognized **artist**
■ **Naturalist** and **environmentalist**
■ **Teacher**

It is hard to think of a painter with broader popular appeal than Robert Bateman. His works are so realistic, so close to the natural subjects he portrays, that we can almost smell the hot breath of the bear or the feel the dry, choking dust stirred by the buffalo's hooves.

Bateman started life as both an artist and a naturalist when, as a young boy in Toronto, he undertook a project to draw all of the birds in the neighbouring ravine. He describes his life since then as having been "immersed in nature."[3] Although he claims to have always been an artist at heart, there was a time when Bateman thought he could not make a living as an artist, so he chose to become a teacher. But he kept painting, travelling, and observing the natural world, and eventually his work began to receive wider notice.

Although he experimented with other painting styles, such as impressionism and even cubism, Bateman has settled into a meticulously realistic style that pays homage to each tiny detail of the ecological communities he portrays. He was inspired in this by American painter Andrew Wyeth, another great realist interpreter of the natural world.

Having spent his life devoted to the detailed interpretation and representation of the natural world, Bateman is a committed environmentalist. He actually destroyed one of his works—a painting of orca whales—to protest the possibility that oil tankers would be allowed into the pristine Douglas Channel of British Columbia. Bateman also was instrumental in the establishment of the 890-km Bruce Trail, the oldest and longest continuous public hiking path in Canada, which runs from Niagara to Tobermory along the Niagara Escarpment in Ontario.[4] He has expressed a wish that students could spend at least half of their time in the wilderness, stating that "In outdoor education you not only learn about nature, you learn about yourself, your limits and your relationship with others."[5]

In 2005 Bateman volunteered to be a test subject for Toxic Nation, an initiative of Environmental Defence, a Canadian environmental organization. For this study, children and adults—celebrities like Bateman, as well as ordinary citizens—were tested for 88 toxic chemicals. All subjects were found to contain at least some of the toxins. The tests on Bateman detected 32 carcinogens, 19 hormone disruptors, 16 respiratory toxicants, and 42 reproductive/developmental toxicants.[6] (You will learn more about these various categories of toxins in subsequent chapters.) Bateman viewed his participation in this study as a way to convince decision makers to take action on behalf of the natural environment and the health of humans.

"I can't conceive of anything being more varied and rich and handsome than the planet Earth. And its crowning beauty is the natural world. I want to soak it up, to understand it as well as I can, and to absorb it."
—Robert Bateman

Thinking About Environmental Perspectives

Robert Bateman spends a lot of time observing and studying the natural world. It is extremely important to him to portray the plant and animal communities in his paintings with as much scientific accuracy as possible. However, he has been known to say that "art wins" if he ever comes up against a conflict between science and art. Do you think this compromises the value of his works from a naturalist's perspective? Or does it add power to his environmental message?

REVIEWING OBJECTIVES

You should now be able to:

Describe the fundamental properties of environmental systems and the importance of linkages among environmental systems and processes

■ Systems are networks of interacting components that generally involve feedback loops, show dynamic equilibrium, and result in emergent properties.
■ Earth's natural systems are complex, so environmental scientists often take a holistic approach to studying environmental systems.

■ Because environmental systems interact and overlap, how we delineate and define systems depends on the questions we are interested in investigating.

Define *ecosystem* and evaluate how living and nonliving entities interact in ecosystem-level ecology

■ Ecosystems consist of all organisms and nonliving entities that occur and interact in a particular area at the same time.
■ Energy flows in one direction through ecosystems, whereas matter is recycled.

- Energy is converted to biomass, and ecosystems vary in their productivity.
- Input of nutrients can boost productivity, but an excess of nutrients can alter ecosystems in ways that cause severe ecological and economic consequences.

Outline the fundamentals of landscape ecology, GIS, and the use of modelling in environmental science

- Landscape ecology studies how landscape structure influences organisms.
- Landscapes consist of patches spatially arrayed in a mosaic. Organisms dependent on certain types of patches may occur in metapopulations.
- Remote sensing technology and GIS are assisting the use of landscape ecology in conservation and regional planning.
- Models help ecologists and other environmental scientists make sense of the complex systems they study.

Assess ecosystem services and their benefits to us

- Ecosystems provide "goods" we know as natural resources.
- Ecosystem processes naturally provide a wide variety of services that we depend on for everyday living.

Summarize the main features of the global water, carbon, nitrogen, and phosphorus cycles

- Water moves throughout the global environment as a result of processes in the hydrologic cycle.

- The carbon flux between organisms and the atmosphere occurs via photosynthesis and respiration. Most carbon is contained in sedimentary rock, but substantial amounts also occur in the oceans and in soil.
- Nitrogen is a vital nutrient for plant growth. Most nitrogen is in the atmosphere and must be "fixed" by specialized bacteria or lightning before plants can use it.
- Phosphorus is most abundant in sedimentary rock, with substantial amounts in soil and the oceans. Phosphorus, a key nutrient for plant growth, has no appreciable atmospheric pool.

Explain how human activity is affecting global biogeochemical cycles

- Humans are causing substantial impacts to Earth's biogeochemical cycles.
- These impacts include shifting carbon from long-term fossil fuel reservoirs into the atmosphere, shifting nitrogen from the atmosphere to the surface by industrial fixation, and depleting groundwater supplies, among many others.

TESTING YOUR COMPREHENSION

1. Which type of feedback loop is most common in nature, and which more commonly results from human action? How might the emergence of a positive feedback loop affect a system in homeostasis?
2. Describe how hypoxic conditions can develop in coastal marine ecosystems such as the Gulf of the St. Lawrence.
3. What is an ecosystem?
4. Describe the typical movement of energy through an ecosystem. Describe the typical movement of matter through an ecosystem.
5. What is the difference between net primary productivity and gross primary productivity?
6. Why are patches in a landscape mosaic important to scientists with an interest in conservation?
7. What role does each of the following play in the carbon cycle?
    - Cars
    - Photosynthesis
    - The oceans
    - Earth's crust
8. Contrast the function performed by nitrogen-fixing bacteria with that performed by denitrifying bacteria.
9. How has human activity altered the carbon cycle? The phosphorus cycle? The nitrogen cycle? To what environmental problems have these changes given rise?
10. What is the difference between evaporation and transpiration? Give examples of how the hydrologic cycle interacts with the carbon, phosphorus, and nitrogen cycles.

THINKING IT THROUGH

1. Once vegetation is cleared from a riverbank, water begins to erode the bank away. This erosion may dislodge more vegetation. Would you expect this to result in a feedback process? If so, which type— negative or positive? Explain your answer. How might we halt or reverse this process?

2. Consider the ecosystem(s) that surround(s) your campus. How do some of the principles from our discussion on ecosystems apply to the ecosystem(s) around your campus?

3. For an ecologist interested in sustaining populations of each organism below, why would it be helpful to take a landscape ecology perspective? Explain your answer in each case.
   - A forest-breeding warbler that suffers poor nesting success in small, fragmented forest patches
   - A bighorn sheep that must move seasonally between mountains and lowlands
   - A toad that lives in upland areas but travels cross-country to breed in localized pools each spring

4. A simple change in the flux rate between just two reservoirs in a single nutrient cycle can potentially have major consequences for ecosystems and, indeed, for the globe. Explain how this can be, using one example from the carbon cycle and one example from the nitrogen cycle.

5. One goal of this book is to encourage you to approach problems from a scientist's perspective; another goal, of this chapter in particular, is to introduce a systems perspective to the way we approach environmental problems. Please apply these perspectives to the following task:

You are a scientist with Environment Canada. You know that the beluga whale population in the St. Lawrence Estuary is stable but very low and that it is considered to be threatened. It has been proposed that a cause of the decline of the beluga population may be the influx of chemical pollutants into the river and estuary from adjacent farmlands, cities, suburbs, and industrial areas (see table, below). Your task is to design a scientific program of monitoring, observation, and/or experimentation that will help you determine whether contaminants are the main contributor to the poor status of the beluga population. Your answer should include a brief overview of how you see the problem and a description of your approach to solving the problem (that is, your proposed scientific program of monitoring, experimentation, and/or observation).

Theories explaining why the beluga population of the St. Lawrence Estuary shows no apparent signs of recovery

Anthropogenic
- Habitat degradation and changes
- Diseases (microorganisms from wastewater, agricultural and coastal runoff)
- Maritime traffic (noise disturbance, collisions with ships)
- Contaminants (carcinogenic, immunotoxic, neurotoxic, endocrine disruptors)

Ecosystemic
- Changes in prey abundance, diversity, and quality
- Competition with other marine mammals or with fisheries for prey
- New diseases or exotic diseases
- Decline in the area's carrying capacity

Genetic
- Inbreeding, low genetic diversity
- Immune incompetence
- Genetic predisposition to infectious and non-infectious diseases
- High frequency of deleterious genes caused by the absence of predators to eliminate weak, sick, or old individuals

Emigration
- Individuals emigrating outside the Estuary and Gulf of St. Lawrence and not contributing to growth of the population

Source: Table from Measures, Lena, Jean-François Gosselin, and Michel Lebeuf, Maurice Lamontagne Institute Fisheries and Oceans Canada, (2009) Beluga Whale Population of the Estuary, 2nd ed. www.planstlaurent.qc.ca/sl_obs/sesl/publications/fiches_indicateurs/Beluga2009_e_final.pdf

6. Imagine that you are a fisher in the St. Lawrence estuary and that your income is decreasing because nutrient pollution is causing algal blooms that affect your catch. One day your MP comes to town, and you have a one-minute audience with her. What steps would you urge her to take in Ottawa, to try to help alleviate the nutrient pollution in the St. Lawrence and help maintain the quality of the fishery?

Now imagine that you are a farmer in rural Québec who has learned that the government is insisting that you use 30% less fertilizer on your crops each year. In good growing years you could do without that fertilizer, and you'd be glad not to have to pay for it. But in bad growing years, you need the fertilizer to ensure a harvest so that you can continue making a living. You must apply the fertilizer each spring before you know whether it will be a good or bad year. What would you tell your MP when she comes to town?

INTERPRETING GRAPHS AND DATA

The use of PCBs has been closely regulated in Canada since 1970. In contrast, PBDEs have only recently been regulated in a few jurisdictions in North America. Environment Canada is still working with industry to regulate the production and release of PBDEs in Canada. The graph documents trends in the concentrations of two major pollutant groups (PCB, or polychlorinated biphenyls, and PBDE, or polybrominated diphenyl ethers) in the fatty tissues of beluga whales from the St. Lawrence. (The unit "ng/g lw" refers to "nanograms per gram of lipid weight," which is a unit of measure for the concentration of a material in fat.) The pie chart shows the causes of death of beluga whales in the St. Lawrence from 1983 to 2002, based on studies of 148 whale carcasses.

1. Are the data shown on the graph consistent with the regulatory histories of these two groups of pollut-

ants? Why (or why not)? Are there other factors that should be considered in interpreting the graph?

2. Are there any causes of death shown on the pie chart that you think might be directly attributable to the whales' exposure to toxic pollutants? Are there any that might be indirectly related to exposure to toxins? Are there any causes of death illustrated here that definitely do not seem to be related to exposure to toxins? (Note that the term *neoplasia* refers to the abnormal and uncontrolled growth of cells, resulting in the formation of tumours.)

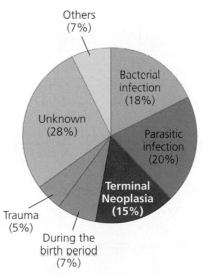

Principal causes of death of stranded belugas in the Estuary and Gulf of St. Lawrence from 1983 to 2002

Source: Pie chart based on studies of 148 whale carcasses; from Measures, Lena, Jean-François Gosselin, and Michel Lebeuf, Maurice Lamontagne Institute Fisheries and Oceans Canada (2009) Beluga Whale Population of the Estuary, 2nd ed. www.planstlaurent.qc.ca/sl_obs/sesl/publications/fiches_indicateurs/Beluga2009_e_final.pdf

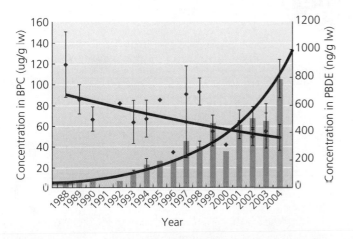

Trends over time of PCB (diamonds) and PBDE (bars) accumulations in the fatty tissue of male belugas between 1988 and 2004

Source: Graph from Measures, Lena, Jean-François Gosselin, and Michel Lebeuf, Maurice Lamontagne Institute Fisheries and Oceans Canada (2009) Beluga Whale Population of the Estuary, 2nd ed. www.planstlaurent.qc.ca/sl_obs/sesl/publications/fiches_indicateurs/Beluga2009_e_final.pdf

CHAPTER ENDNOTES

1. Environment Canada Enviro-Zine, *Great Lakes–St. Lawrence Basin: A Freshwater Giant*, www.ec.gc.ca/EnviroZine/english/issues/61/feature2_e.cfm

2. This piece is based on information from:

   IUCN Red List of Endangered Species (2007) www.iucnredlist.org/search/details.php/6335/summ;

   Université de Montréal Faculté de Médecine Vétérinaire, www.medvet.umontreal.ca/pathologie_microbiologie/beluga/anglais/default_ang.asp;

   Minister of the Environment, Canada (1999) *The Contribution of Agriculture to the Deterioration of the St. Lawrence River*, www.slv2000.qc.ec.gc.ca/communiques/phase3/enjeu_agricoles_a.pdf;

   Environment Canada Enviro-Zine, *Great Lakes–St. Lawrence Basin: A Freshwater Giant*, www.ec.gc.ca/EnviroZine/english/issues/61/feature2_e.cfm; and Environment Canada St. Lawrence Centre, www.qc.ec.gc.ca/csl/inf/inf069_e.html

3. Robert Bateman on Outdoor Education, www.batemanideas.com/outdooreducation.html

4. The Bruce Trail Conservancy, "What Is the Bruce Trail?" http://brucetrail.org/pages/what-is-the-bruce-trail, accessed May 20, 2011.

5. Robert Bateman on Education, www.batemanideas.com/education.html.

6. Environmental Defence, Toxic Nation Reports, Robert Bateman, www.toxicnation.ca/toxicnation-studies/pollution-in-adults/Robert

MyEnvironmentPlace

Go to **www.myenvironmentplace.ca** where you will find quizzes, animations, your Pearson eText, and more.

Evolution, Biodiversity, and Population Ecology

The Monteverde cloud forest in Costa Rica is a hotspot of biodiversity.

Upon successfully completing this chapter, you will be able to

- Explain the process of natural selection and cite evidence for this process
- Describe the ways in which evolution results in biodiversity and what the fossil record has taught us about evolution
- Discuss reasons for species extinction and mass extinction events

- Summarize the levels of ecological organization
- Outline the characteristics of populations that help predict population growth
- Define *logistic growth*, *carrying capacity*, *limiting factors*, and other fundamental concepts of population ecology

The golden toads of Monteverde have not been observed since 1989 and have been declared extinct.

Costa Rica

Pacific Ocean

CENTRAL CASE:
STRIKING GOLD IN A COSTA RICAN CLOUD FOREST

"What a terrible feeling to realize that within my own lifetime, a species of such unusual beauty, one that I had discovered, should disappear from our planet."
—DR. JAY M. SAVAGE, DESCRIBING THE GOLDEN TOAD IN 1998

"To keep every cog and wheel is the first precaution of intelligent tinkering."
—ALDO LEOPOLD

During a 1963 visit to Central America, biologist Jay Savage heard rumours of a previously undocumented toad living in Costa Rica's mountainous Monteverde region. The elusive amphibian, according to local residents, was best known for its colour: a brilliant golden yellow-orange. Savage was told the toad was hard to find because it appeared only during the early part of the region's rainy season.

Monteverde means "green mountain" in Spanish, and the name couldn't be more appropriate. The settlement of Monteverde sits beneath the verdant slopes of the Cordillera de Tilarán, mountains that receive over 400 cm of annual rainfall. Some of the lush forests above Monteverde, which begin at an altitude of around 1600 m, are known as *lower montane rainforests*. They are also known as *cloud forests* because much of the moisture they receive arrives in the form of low-moving clouds that blow inland from the Caribbean Sea.

Monteverde's cloud forest was not fully explored at the time of Savage's first visit, and researchers who had been there described the area as pristine, with a rich bounty of ferns, liverworts, mosses, clinging vines, orchids, and other organisms that thrive in cool, misty environments. Savage knew that such conditions create ideal habitat for many toads and other amphibians.

In May of 1964, Savage organized an expedition into the muddy mountains above Monteverde to try to document the existence of the previously unknown toad species in its natural habitat. Late in the afternoon of May 14, he and his colleagues found what they were looking for. Approaching the mountain's crest, they spotted bright orange patches on the forest's black floor. In one area that was only 5 m in diameter, they counted 200 golden toads. The discovery received international attention, making a celebrity of the tiny toad which Savage named *Bufo periglenes* (literally, "brilliant toad")— and making a travel destination of its mountain home.

At the time, no one knew that the Monteverde ecosystem was about to be transformed. No one foresaw that the oceans and atmosphere would begin warming due to global climate change and cause Monteverde's moisture-bearing clouds to rise, drying the forest. No one could guess that this newly discovered species of toad would become extinct in less than 25 years. By 1988 the annual count of golden toads had dropped to one individual; the count was the same in 1989, and not a single golden toad has been observed anywhere since then, in spite of extensive searches. Listed previously as "endangered," the toad's extinction was declared final in 2004 on the International Union for Conservation of Nature (IUCN) *Red List of Threatened Species* by Dr. Jay Savage, who first found the new species in 1964.[1]

Evolution as the Wellspring of Earth's Biodiversity

Although the golden toad was new to science, and countless species still await discovery, scientists understand in much detail how the world became populated with the remarkable diversity of organisms we see today. We know that the process of biological evolution has brought us from a stark planet inhabited solely by microbes to a lush world of perhaps 1.8 million (and likely millions more) species (**FIGURE 4.1**).

Evolution in the broad sense means change over time, but scientists most often use the term to refer specifically to biological evolution, which consists of genetic change in populations of organisms across generations. This genetic change often leads to modifications in the appearance, functioning, or behaviour of organisms through time. Biological evolution results from random genetic changes, and it may proceed randomly or may be directed by natural selection. **Natural selection** is the process by which traits that enhance survival and reproduction are passed on more frequently to future generations than those that do not, altering the genetic makeup of populations through time.

The theory of evolution by natural selection is one of the best-supported and most illuminating concepts in all of science. Recall that in order to be designated as a theory, a scientific hypothesis must be widely accepted and extensively validated, surviving repeated testing by numerous research teams, and successfully predicting experimental outcomes and observations accurately. Many, many scientists have contributed to our understanding of evolution and have helped to refine it and move it from the status of a hypothesis to an accepted theory.

From a scientific standpoint, evolutionary theory is indispensable; it is the foundation of modern biology. Perceiving how organisms adapt to their environments and change over time is crucial for understanding the history of life. Understanding evolution is also vital for a full appreciation of environmental science. Evolutionary processes are relevant to many aspects of environmental science, including pesticide resistance, agriculture, medicine, and environmental health.

roots

EVOLUTION

The term **evolution** was derived from the Latin *evolutionem* or *evolution*. In the 1600s, it referred to the action of "opening something that was rolled up." It was likely first used in its modern biological sense by Scottish geologist Charles Lyell in 1832. Although Charles Darwin is credited with developing the theory of evolution by natural selection, he first used the word *evolution* only in the sixth edition of *The Origin of Species** (1872), preferring the phrase "descent with modification" in earlier editions of the book.

*The title was shortened from *On the Origin of Species by Means of Natural Selection*, from the book's first publication in 1859.

(a) Resplendent quetzal

(b) Heliconia flower

(c) Harlequin frog

(d) Scutellerid bug

FIGURE 4.1   Much of our planet's rich biological diversity resides in tropical rainforests. For example, Monteverde's cloud-forest community includes organisms such as the **(a)** resplendent quetzal (*Pharomachrus mocinno*); **(b)** heliconia flower (*Heliconia wagneriana*); **(c)** harlequin frog (*Atelopus varius*); and **(d)** scutellerid bug (*Pachycoris torridus*).

Natural selection shapes organisms and diversity

In 1858, Charles Darwin and Alfred Russel Wallace each independently proposed the concept of natural selection as a mechanism for evolution, and as a way to explain the great variety of living things. Darwin and Wallace were English naturalists who had studied plants and animals in such exotic locales as the Galápagos Islands and the Malay Archipelago.

Both Darwin and Wallace recognized that organisms face a constant struggle to gain sufficient resources to survive and reproduce. They observed that organisms produce more offspring than can possibly survive, and they realized that some offspring may be more likely than others to survive and reproduce. Furthermore, they recognized that whichever characteristics give certain individuals an advantage in surviving and reproducing might be inherited by their offspring. These characteristics, they reasoned, would tend to become more prevalent in the population in future generations.

Natural selection is a simple concept that offers an astonishingly powerful explanation for patterns apparent in nature. The idea of natural selection follows logically from a few straightforward premises (**TABLE 4.1**). One is that individuals of the same species vary in their characteristics. Although not known in Darwin and Wallace's time, we now know that variation in characteristics is due to differences in genes, the environments within which genes are expressed, and the interactions between genes

and environment. (Recall that a *gene* is a sequence of nucleotides, part of the "twisted-ladder" or "double helix" structure of DNA. This structure stores or encodes, in its sequencing, all of the information that will be used by RNA to direct the building and maintenance of the proteins that comprise an organism's cells and to pass along characteristics from parents to offspring.)

Table 4.1 The Logic of Natural Selection

- Organisms produce lots of offspring, some of which do not survive.

- Individuals vary in their characteristics; some characteristics are accidental, but many characteristics are inherited by offspring from parents.

- The natural environment can be challenging; resources are limited, and environmental change is common.

- Some individuals will be better adapted to succeed in a challenging environment than others; as a result, they tend to survive longer and to have better reproductive success than poorly adapted individuals.

- By producing more offspring and/or offspring of higher quality, better-adapted individuals transmit more genes to future generations than poorly adapted individuals.

- Future generations will contain more genes (and thus more of the inherited characteristics) of the better-adapted individuals, and as a result the population as a whole will slowly shift its general characteristics.

- Over time, the genes (and thus the inherited characteristics) of the better-adapted individuals will come to dominate the population.

In other words, individuals vary, even when they belong to the same species. As a result of this variation, some individuals within a species will happen to be better suited to their particular environment than others and thus will be able to survive longer and/or have greater reproductive success. (Note, however, that the same genes that make an individual particularly well suited to one environment might be disadvantageous in a different environment.)

Many characteristics are passed from parent to offspring through the genes, and a parent that is long-lived, is robust, and produces many offspring will pass on genes to more offspring than a weaker, shorter-lived individual that produces only a few offspring. In the next generation, therefore, the genes of better-adapted individuals will be more prevalent than those of less well-adapted individuals. From one generation to another through time, species will evolve to possess characteristics that lead to better and better success in a given environment. A trait that promotes success is called an **adaptive trait**, or an **adaptation**. A trait that reduces success is said to be *maladaptive*.

Natural selection acts on genetic variation

For an organism to pass a trait along to future generations—that is, for the trait to be *heritable*—genes in the organism's DNA must code for the trait. Accidental alterations that arise during DNA replication give rise to genetic variations among individuals. In an organism's lifetime, its DNA will be copied millions of times by millions of cells. In all this copying and recopying, sometimes a mistake is made. Accidental changes in DNA, called **mutations**, can range in magnitude from the addition, deletion, or substitution of single nucleotides to the insertion or deletion of large sections of DNA. If a mutation occurs in a sperm or egg cell, it may be passed on to the next generation. Most mutations have little effect, but some can be deadly, whereas others can be beneficial. Those that are not lethal provide the genetic variation on which natural selection acts.

Sexual reproduction also generates variation. In sexual organisms, genetic material is mixed, or recombined, so that a portion of each parent's genome is included in the genome of the offspring. This process of *recombination* produces novel combinations of genes, generating variation among individuals.

Natural selection can act on genetic variation and alter the characteristics of organisms through time in three main ways (**FIGURE 4.2**). Selection that drives a feature in one direction rather than another—for example, toward larger or smaller, faster or slower—is called **directional selection**. In contrast, **stabilizing selection** produces intermediate traits, in essence preserving the status quo. Under **disruptive selection**, traits diverge from their starting condition in two or more directions.

FIGURE 4.2

Selection can act in three ways. Consider a population of snails with shells of different thicknesses (top graph). Shells protect snails against predators, so snails with thick shells may be favoured over those with thin shells, through *directional selection* **(a)**. Alternatively, suppose that a shell that is too thin breaks easily, whereas a shell that is too thick wastes resources that are better used for feeding or reproduction; in such a case, *stabilizing selection* **(b)** could act to favour snails with shells that are neither too thick nor too thin. In *disruptive selection* **(c)**, extreme traits are favoured. For example, perhaps thin-shelled snails are so resource-efficient that they can out-reproduce intermediate-shelled snails, whereas thick-shelled snails are so well protected from predators that they also out-reproduce intermediate-shelled snails. In such a case, each of the "extreme" strategies works more effectively than a compromise, and natural selection increases the relative numbers of thin- *and* thick-shelled snails, while reducing the number of intermediate-shelled snails.

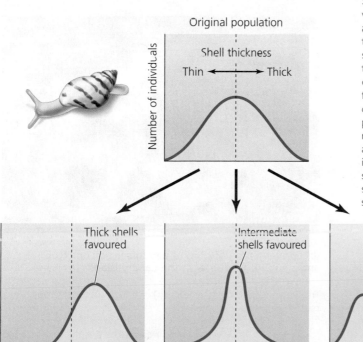

(a) **Directional selection**   (b) **Stabilizing selection**   (c) **Disruptive selection**

Selective pressures from the environment influence adaptation

Environmental conditions determine what pressures natural selection will exert, and these selective pressures affect which members of a population will survive and reproduce. Over many generations, this results in the evolution of traits that enable success within the environment in question. Closely related species that live in different environments and thus experience different selective pressures tend to diverge in their traits as the differing pressures drive the evolution of different adaptations (**FIGURE 4.3A**); this is called **divergent evolution**. Conversely, sometimes very unrelated species may have similar traits as a result of adapting to selective pressures from similar environments; this is called **convergent evolution** (**FIGURE 4.3B**).

However, environments change over time. Organisms also sometimes move to new places, where they can encounter new conditions. In either case, a trait that promotes success at one time or location may not do so at another. For example, the population of golden toads that had adapted to the moist conditions of Monteverde's cloud forest did not persist after Monteverde's climate started to become drier 25 years ago. Varying environmental conditions in time and space make adaptation a moving target.

In all these ways, variable genes and variable environments interact as species engage in a perpetual process

(a) Divergent evolution of Hawaiian honeycreepers.

(b) Convergent evolution of a cactus in Arizona (top) and a euphorb (spurge) in the Canary Islands (bottom).

FIGURE 4.3   Natural selection can cause closely related species to diverge in appearance and characteristics **(a)** as they adapt to selective pressures from different environments. In the Hawaiian honeycreepers, closely related species have adapted to different food resources and habitats, indicated by the diversity in their plumage colours and the shapes of their bills. Natural selection can also cause distantly related species to converge in appearance **(b)** if the selective pressures of their environments are similar. A classic case of convergent evolution involves cacti of the Americas and euphorbs of Africa. Plants in each family independently adapted to arid environments through the evolution of tough succulent stems to hold water, thorns to keep thirsty animals away, and photosynthetic stems without leaves to reduce surface area and water loss.

of adapting to the changing conditions around them. During this process, natural selection does not simply weed out unfit individuals. It also helps to elaborate and diversify traits that in the long term may help lead to the formation of new species and whole new types of organisms.

Evidence of natural selection is all around us

The results of natural selection are all around us, visible in every adaptation of every organism. In addition, countless lab experiments (mostly with fast-reproducing organisms, such as bacteria and fruit flies) have demonstrated rapid evolution of traits. The evidence for selection that may be most familiar to us is that which Darwin himself cited prominently in his work 150 years ago: our breeding of domestic animals. In our dogs, our cats, and our livestock, we have conducted our own version of selection. We have chosen animals with traits we like and bred them together, while not breeding those with variants we do not like. Through such *selective breeding*, we have been able to exaggerate particular traits we prefer.

Consider the great diversity of dog breeds, all of which comprise variations on a single subspecies, *Canis lupus familiaris*. From Great Dane to Chihuahua, they can interbreed freely and produce viable offspring, yet breeders maintain the striking differences between them by allowing only like individuals to breed with like (**FIGURE 4.4**). This process of selection conducted under human direction is termed **artificial selection**.

Artificial selection has also given us the many crop plants we depend on for food, all of which were domesticated from wild ancestors and carefully bred over years, centuries, or millennia. Through selective breeding, we have created corn with larger, sweeter kernels; wheat and rice with larger and more numerous grains; and apples, pears, and oranges with better taste. We have diversified single types into many—for instance, breeding variants of the plant *Brassica oleracea* to create broccoli, cauliflower, cabbage, and Brussels sprouts. Our entire agricultural system is based on artificial selection.

Evolution generates biological diversity

When Charles Darwin wrote about the wonders of a world full of diverse animals and plants, he conjured up the vision of a "tangled bank" of vegetation harbour-

(a) Ancestral wolf and derived dog breeds

(b) Ancestral *Brassica oleracea* and derived crops

FIGURE 4.4
Selection imposed by people (selective breeding, or artificial selection) has resulted in numerous breeds of dogs **(a)**. Starting with the grey wolf *(Canis lupus)* as the ancestral wild species, and by breeding and selecting for the traits we prefer, we have produced breeds as different as Great Danes and Chihuahuas. By this same process we have created the immense variety of crop plants **(b)** we depend on for food. Cabbage, Brussels sprouts, broccoli, and cauliflower were all generated from a single ancestral species, *Brassica oleracea*.

ing all kinds of creatures. Such a vision fits well with the arching vines, dripping leaves, and mossy slopes of the tropical cloud forest of Monteverde. Indeed, tropical forests worldwide teem with life and harbour immense biological diversity (see **FIGURE 4.1**).

Biological diversity, or **biodiversity**, refers to the total variety of all organisms in an area, taking into account the diversity of species, their genes, their populations, their habitats, and their communities. (In the chapter on conservation of species and habitats we will look more closely at the question of how scientists measure biodiversity.) We have already discussed genes, and we will introduce communities and habitats shortly. A **species** is

weighing the issues

ARTIFICIAL SELECTION

Consider the animals that humans have domesticated through artificial selection, such as horses, cows, dogs, and cats. In what ways do they differ from their wild relatives? For thousands of years, artificial selection has allowed plant and animal breeders to create new breeds by the careful selection of valued traits, expressed and reinforced through numerous generations of reproduction. If breeders could generate a new, prize-winning or useful breed of horse, or tomato, or chicken, or corn *without* waiting several generations for the desired traits to appear, should they? (This question will be important in the chapter on "Agriculture, Food, and Biotechnology," where we will look at new technologies for the genetic modification of crops.)

roots

SPECIES

From the 1550s, the word **species** originated from the Latin *species* meaning "kind, type, or sort" or, originally, "appearance." This, in turn, was derived from the Latin *specere*, meaning "to look at, to see." (The English words *inspect* and *spectacle* contain the same root.) The term was first used in its biological sense in about the year 1600.

a particular type of organism or, more precisely, a population or group of populations whose members share certain characteristics and can freely breed with one another and produce fertile offspring. A **population** is a group of individuals of a particular species that live in the same area.

Scientists have described about 1.8 million species, but many more remain undiscovered or unnamed. Estimates for the total number of species in the world range up to 100 million, with many of them thought to occur in tropical forests. In this light, the discovery of a new toad species in Costa Rica in 1964 seems far less surprising. Although Costa Rica covers a tiny fraction (0.01%) of Earth's surface area, it is home to 5–6% of all species known to scientists. And of the 500 000 species scientists estimate exist in the country, only 87 000 (17.4%) have been inventoried and described.

Tropical rainforests such as Costa Rica's are by no means the only places rich in biodiversity. Step outside anywhere on Earth, even in a major city, and you will find numerous species within easy reach. They may not always be large and conspicuous like polar bears or blue whales or elephants, but they will be there. Plants poke up from cracks in asphalt in every city in the world, and even Antarctic ice harbours microbes. In a handful of backyard soil there may exist an entire miniature world of life, including several insect species, several types of mites, a millipede or two, many nematode worms, a few plant seeds, countless fungi, and millions upon millions of bacteria.

Speciation produces new types of organisms

How did Earth come to have so many species? Whether there are 1.8 million or 100 million, such large numbers require scientific explanation. The process by which new species are generated is termed **speciation**. Speciation can occur in a number of ways, but most biologists consider the main mode of species formation to be *allopatric speciation,* the emergence of a new species as a result of the physical separation of populations over some geographic distance. To understand allopatric speciation, begin by picturing a population of organisms. Individuals within the population possess many similarities that unify them as a species because they are able to reproduce with one another and share genetic information. However, if the population is broken up into two or more populations that become isolated from one another, individuals from one population cannot reproduce with individuals from the others.

When a mutation or natural variation is present in the DNA of an organism in one of these isolated populations, it cannot spread to the other populations. Over time, each population will independently accumulate its own set of variations. Eventually, the populations may diverge, or grow different enough, that their members can no longer mate with one another. Individuals from the two differing populations may no longer recognize one another as being the same species because they have diverged so much in appearance or behaviour or they may simply become genetically incapable of producing viable offspring.

Once this has happened, there is no going back; the two populations cannot interbreed, and they have embarked on their own independent evolutionary trajectories as separate species (**FIGURE 4.5**). The populations will continue diverging in their characteristics as

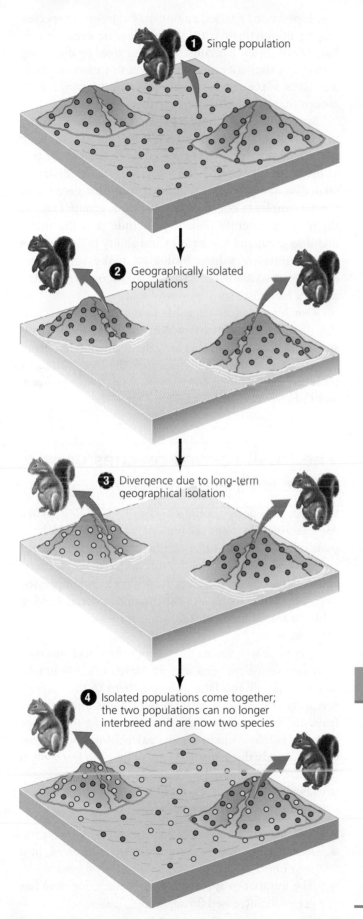

1 Single population

2 Geographically isolated populations

3 Divergence due to long-term geographical isolation

4 Isolated populations come together; the two populations can no longer interbreed and are now two species

FIGURE 4.5
In the long, slow process of allopatric speciation, some type of geographical barrier splits a population. In this diagram, two mountaintops **(1)** are turned into islands by rising sea level isolating populations of squirrels **(2)**. Each isolated population accumulates its own independent set of genetic changes over time, until individuals become genetically distinct and unable to breed with individuals from the other population **(3)**. The two populations now represent separate species and will remain so even if the geographical barrier is removed and the new species intermix **(4)**.

chance variations accumulate that confer traits causing the populations to become different in random ways. If environmental conditions happen to be different for the two populations, then natural selection may accelerate the divergence. Through the speciation process, single species can generate multiple species, each of which can in turn generate more.

Populations can be separated in many ways

The long-term geographic isolation of populations can occur in various ways (**TABLE 4.2**). Glacial ice sheets may move across continents during ice ages and split populations in two. Major rivers may change course and do the same. Mountain ranges may rise and divide regions and their organisms. Drying climate may partially evaporate lakes, subdividing them into multiple smaller bodies of water. Warming or cooling temperatures may cause whole plant communities to move northward or southward, or upslope or downslope, creating new patterns of plant and animal distribution. Oceanic currents may shift, or entire new islands may be created by seafloor volcanism.

Regardless of the mechanism of separation, in order for speciation to occur, populations must remain isolated for a long time, generally thousands of genera-

Table 4.2 Natural Mechanisms of Population Isolation That Can Give Rise to Allopatric Speciation

- Glacial ice sheets advance.
- Mountain chains are uplifted.
- Major rivers change course.
- Sea level rises, creating islands (see **FIGURE 4.5**).
- Climate warms, pushing vegetation up mountain slopes and fragmenting it.
- Climate dries, dividing large single lakes into multiple smaller lakes.
- Ocean current patterns shift.
- Islands are formed in the sea by volcanism.

tions. If the geological or climatic process that isolated the populations reverses itself—the glacier recedes, or the river returns to its old course, or warm temperatures turn cool again—then the populations can come back together. This is the moment of truth for speciation. If the populations have not diverged enough, their members will begin interbreeding and reestablish gene flow, mixing the variations that each population accrued while isolated. However, if the populations have diverged sufficiently, they will not interbreed, and two species will have been formed, each fated to continue on its own evolutionary path.

Although allopatric speciation has long been considered the main mode of species formation, speciation appears to occur in other ways as well. *Sympatric speciation* can occur when species form from populations that become reproductively isolated, occupying a new ecological role, or *niche*, within the same geographic area. For example, populations of some insects may become isolated by feeding and mating exclusively on different types of plants. Or they may mate during different seasons, isolating themselves in time rather than space. In some plants, speciation apparently has occurred as a result of hybridization between species. In others, it seems to have resulted from natural variations or from mutations that changed the numbers of chromosomes, creating plants that could not mate with plants with the original number of chromosomes. Biologists still actively debate the relative importance of each of these modes of speciation.

We can infer the history of life's diversification by comparing organisms

Innumerable speciation events have generated complex patterns of diversity at levels above the species level. Such patterns are studied by evolutionary biologists, who examine how groups of organisms arose and how they evolved the characteristics they show. For instance, how did we end up with plants as different as mosses, palm trees, daisies, and redwoods? Why do fish swim, snakes slither, and sparrows sing? How and why did the ability to fly evolve independently in birds, bats, and insects? To address such questions, one needs to know how the major groups diverged from one another, and this pattern ultimately results from the history of individual speciation events.

Scientists represent this history of divergence using treelike diagrams called *cladograms*, or **phylogenetic trees** (**FIGURE 4.6A**). Phylogenetic trees can show rela-

tionships among species, among major groups of species, among populations within a species, or even among individuals. Scientists construct these trees by analyzing patterns of similarity among the genes or external characteristics of present-day organisms and inferring which groups share similarities because they are related.

By mapping traits onto a phylogenetic tree according to which organisms possess them, one can trace how the traits themselves may have evolved. For instance, the tree of life shows that birds, bats, and insects are distantly related, with many other flightless groups between them. It is far simpler to conclude that the three groups evolved flight independently than to conclude that the many flightless groups all lost an ancestral ability to fly. Because phylogenetic trees help biologists make such inferences about so many traits, they have become one of the modern biologist's most powerful tools.

A major advance was made in recent years as scientists discovered an entire new domain of life, the archaea, single-celled organisms that are genetically different from bacteria. Today most biologists view the tree of life as a three-pronged edifice consisting of *Bacteria*, *Archaea*, and *Eukaryota* (**FIGURE 4.6B**).

The fossil record teaches us about life's long history

Scientists also decipher life's history by studying fossils. As organisms die, some are buried by sediment. The hard parts of their bodies, most commonly bones, shells, and teeth, and sometimes even the soft parts, such as feathers and skin, may be preserved as the sediment is compressed into rock. Minerals replace the organic material, leaving behind a **fossil**, an imprint in stone of the dead organism (**FIGURE 4.7**).

In countless locations throughout the world, geologic processes across millions of years have buried sedimentary rock layers and later brought them to the surface, revealing assemblages of fossilized plants and animals from different time periods. By determining the ages of rock layers that contain fossils, palaeontologists (scientists who study the history of Earth's life) can learn when particular organisms lived. The cumulative body of fossils worldwide is known as the **fossil record**.

The fossil record shows that:

■ Life has existed on Earth for at least 3.5 billion years.

■ Earlier types of organisms changed, or evolved, into later ones.

■ The number of species existing at any one time has generally increased through time.

■ The species living today are a tiny fraction of all

(a)

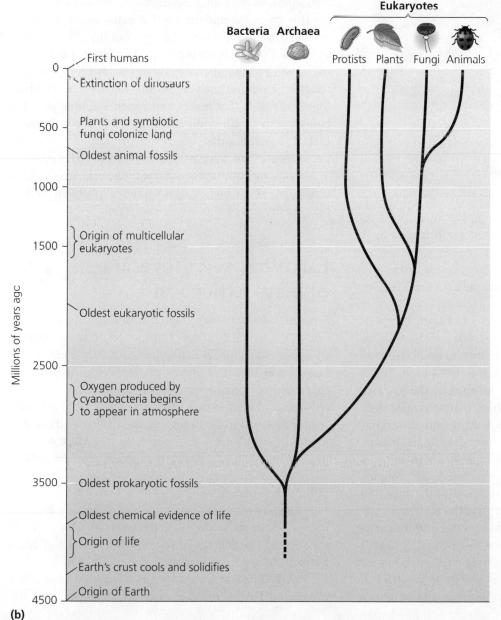

(b)

FIGURE 4.6

Phylogenetic trees show the history of life's divergence, and illustrate relationships among groups of organisms as inferred from the study of similarities and differences. Each branch results from a speciation event, and time proceeds upward from bottom to top. By mapping traits onto phylogenetic trees, biologists can study how traits have evolved over time. In **(a)**, several major traits are mapped, using triangular arrows indicating the point at which they originated. For instance, all vertebrates "above" the point at which jaws are indicated have jaws, whereas lampreys diverged before jaws originated and thus lack them. In **(b)**, each fork denotes the divergence of major groups of organisms, each group of which in this greatly simplified diagram includes many thousands of species. All are classified as Bacteria, Archaea, or Eukaryotes, the last of which includes all plants, fungi, and animals.

FIGURE 4.7
The fossil record has revealed the history of life on Earth. The numerous fossils of trilobites, like the one shown here, suggest that these animals, now extinct, were abundant in the oceans from roughly 540 million to 250 million years ago.

species that ever lived; the vast majority are long extinct.

■   There have been several episodes of mass extinction, or simultaneous loss of great numbers of species.

Across life's 3.5 billion years on Earth, complex structures have evolved from simple ones, and large sizes from small ones. However, simplicity and small size have also evolved when favoured by natural selection, and it is easy to argue that Earth still belongs to the bacteria and other microbes, some of them little changed over eons. Even fans of microbes, however, must marvel at some of the exquisite adaptations of animals, plants, and fungi: the heart that beats so reliably for an animal's entire lifetime that we take it for granted; the complex organ system to which the heart belongs; the stunning plumage of a peacock in full display; the ability of each and every plant on the planet to lift water and nutrients from the soil, gather light from the Sun, and turn it into food; the staggering diversity of beetles and other insects; the human brain and its ability to reason. All these and more have resulted as the process of evolution

has generated new species and whole new branches on the tree of life.

Speciation and extinction together determine Earth's biodiversity

Although speciation generates Earth's biodiversity, it is only one part of the equation, for the vast majority of species that once lived are now gone. The disappearance of a species from Earth is called **extinction**. From studying the fossil record, palaeontologists calculate that the average time a species spends on Earth is 1 to 10 million years. The number of species in existence at any one time is equal to the number added through speciation minus the number removed by extinction.

It is crucial to understand that extinction is a natural process, but human impact can profoundly affect the rate at which it occurs (**FIGURE 4.8**). The apparent extinction of the golden toad made headlines worldwide, but unfortunately it was not such an unusual occurrence. The biological diversity that makes Earth such a unique planet is being lost at an astounding rate. This loss affects humans directly because other organisms provide us with life's necessities—food, fibre, medicine, and ecosystem services. Species extinction brought about by human impact may well be the single biggest environmental problem we face because the loss of a species is irreversible.

Earth has seen several episodes of mass extinction

Most extinction occurs gradually, one species at a time. The rate at which this type of extinction occurs is referred to as the *background extinction rate*. However, Earth has seen at least five events of staggering proportions that killed off massive numbers of species at once. These episodes, called **mass extinctions**, have occurred at widely spaced intervals in Earth history and have wiped out half to 95% of our planet's species each time (**TABLE 4.3**).

The best-known mass extinction occurred 65 million years ago and brought an end to the age of dinosaurs (although birds are modern descendants of dinosaurs). Evidence suggests that the impact of a gigantic asteroid caused this event, called the Cretaceous-Tertiary (or K-T) event (see "The Science Behind the Story: The K-T Mass Extinction," available on myenvironmentplace).

The K-T event, as massive as it was, was moderate compared to the mass extinction at the end of the

CHAPTER FOUR EVOLUTION, BIODIVERSITY, AND POPULATION ECOLOGY   101

FIGURE 4.8   Until 10 000 years ago, the North American continent teemed with a variety of large mammals, including mammoths, camels, giant ground sloths, lions, sabre-toothed cats, and various types of horses, antelope, bears, and others. Nearly all of this megafauna went extinct suddenly about the time that humans first arrived on the continent. Similar extinctions occurred in other areas simultaneously with human arrival, suggesting to many scientists that overhunting or other human impacts were responsible.   *Source: National Museum of Natural History, Smithsonian Institution.*

Permian period 251 million years ago. Palaeontologists estimate that 95% of marine species and 70% of terrestrial species perished during this event. Precisely what caused the Permian extinction is unknown. The evidence for extraterrestrial impact is much weaker than it is for the K-T event, and other ideas abound. The hypothesis with the most support so far is that massive volcanism threw into the atmosphere a global blanket of volcanic ash and sulphur aerosols, smothering the planet, reducing sunlight, altering the chemistry of the ocean, and inducing severe climate changes.

Human activities have initiated another mass extinction

Many biologists have concluded that Earth is currently entering its sixth mass extinction event—and that we are the cause. Changes to Earth's natural systems set in motion by human population growth, development, and resource depletion have driven many species extinct and are threatening countless more. The alteration and outright destruction of natural habitats, the hunting and harvesting of species, and the introduction of invasive

Table 4.3 Mass Extinctions

Event	Date (millions of years ago)	Cause	Types of life most affected	Percentage of life depleted
Ordovician	440 mya	Unknown	Marine organisms; terrestrial record is unknown	>20% of families
Devonian	370 mya	Unknown	Marine organisms; terrestrial record is unknown	>20% of families
Permo-Triassic	250 mya	Possibly volcanism	Marine organisms; terrestrial record is unknown	>50% of families; 80–95% of species
End-Triassic	202 mya	Unknown	Marine organisms; terrestrial record is unknown	20% of families; 50% of genera
Cretaceous-Tertiary[2]	65 mya	Asteroid impact	Marine organisms; terrestrial record is unknown	15% of families; >50% of species
Current	Beginning 0.01 mya	Human impact, through habitat destruction and other means	Large animals, specialized organisms, island organisms, and organisms hunted or harvested by humans	Ongoing

species from one place to another where they can harm native species—these processes and many more have combined to threaten Earth's biodiversity.

When we look around us, it may not appear as though a human version of an asteroid impact is taking place, but we cannot judge such things on a human timescale. On the geologic timescale, extinction over 100 years or over 10 000 years appears every bit as instantaneous as extinction over a few days.

Many scientists say biodiversity loss is our biggest environmental problem today. But why should we be concerned about loss of biodiversity and extinction of species? The Vancouver Island marmot, a small mammal whose natural range is entirely within Canada, is on the brink of extinction as a result of habitat alteration. What would be lost if this animal were to become extinct? (Had you ever even heard of it?) Other endangered species in Canada include the northern abalone, the whooping crane, and the Atlantic halibut—each with its own appeal, certainly, but marmots are cute and furry; does that make them more compelling as examples of the value or importance of biodiversity?

Another of Canada's endangered species is the blue whale (*Balaenoptera musculus*), the largest animal that has *ever lived*. Is the blue whale more worthy of preservation than the Vancouver Island marmot, or the whooping crane, or the northern abalone? How should we define the criteria for what is "worthy" of preservation? Should we be concerned about the value of one species, or is the true importance that these species are part of a larger whole? We will return to questions like these in subsequent chapters.

Levels of Ecological Organization

The extinction of species, their generation through speciation, and other evolutionary mechanisms and patterns are of substantial importance in ecology. It's often said that ecology provides the stage on which the play of evolution unfolds; certainly they are tightly intertwined in many ways.

We study ecology at several levels

Life occurs in a hierarchy of levels. Atoms and molecules (for our purposes) represent the lowest levels in this hierarchy (**FIGURE 4.9A**). Organisms use natural poly-

mers and macromolecules to build *organelles*, which are grouped together in **cells**, basic functional units of life. All living things are composed of cells, and organisms range in their complexity from single-celled bacteria to plants and animals that contain millions of cells. Aggregations of cells of particular types form tissues, and tissues form organs, and organs function together as organ systems. All of these, together, comprise an individual living organism.

Ecologists study relationships on the higher levels of this hierarchy (**FIGURE 4.9B**), namely on the organismal, population, community, and ecosystem levels. At the organismal level, the science of ecology describes relationships between organisms and their physical environments. It helps us understand, for example, what aspects of the golden toad's environment were important to it, and why.

We have defined a *population* as a group of individuals of a particular species that live in the same area. *Population ecology* investigates the quantitative dynamics of how individuals within a species interact with one another. It helps us understand why populations of some species (such as the golden toad) decline, while populations of others (such as ourselves) increase.

Communities are different from populations, in that they include multiple interacting species that live in the same area. A population of golden toads, a population of resplendent quetzals, and populations of ferns and mosses, together with all of the other interacting plant, animal, fungal, and microbial populations in the Monteverde cloud forest, would comprise a community. *Community ecology* focuses on interactions among species, from one-to-one interactions to complex interrelationships involving entire communities of organisms. In the case of Monteverde, it allows us to study how the golden toad and many other species of its cloud-forest community interacted.

And *ecosystems*, as you have learned, encompass communities and the abiotic materials with which their members interact. Monteverde's cloud-forest ecosystem consists of the community plus the air, water, soil, nutrients, and energy that support the community's organisms. In *ecosystem ecology* we focus on patterns of energy and nutrient flow by studying living and nonliving components of systems in conjunction.

As improved technologies such as remote sensing allow scientists to learn more about the complex operations of natural systems on a global scale, ecologists are increasingly expanding their horizons beyond individual and regional ecosystems (or *biomes*), to the biosphere as a whole. We will consider these levels of study in subsequent chapters.

Hierarchy of Matter Within Organisms

	Organism	An individual living thing
	Organ system	An integrated system of organs whose action is coordinated for a particular function
	Organ	A structure in an organism composed of several types of tissues and specialized for some particular function
	Tissue	A group of cells with common structure and function
	Cell	The smallest unit of living matter able to function independently, enclosed in a semi-permeable membrane
	Organelle	A structure inside a eukaryotic cell that performs a particular function
	Macro-molecule	A large organic molecule (includes proteins, nucleic acids, carbohydrates, and lipids)
	Molecule	A combination of two or more atoms chemically bonded together
	Atom	The smallest component of an element that maintains the element's chemical properties

(a)

Each organism has habitat needs

Individual organisms relate to the surrounding environment in ways that tend to maximize survival and reproduction. One key relationship involves the specific environment in which an organism lives—its **habitat**. A species' habitat consists of both living and nonliving elements—rock, soil, leaf litter, and moisture, as well as the other organisms around it. The golden toad lived in a habitat of cloud forest—more specifically, on the moist forest floor, using seasonal pools for breeding and burrows for shelter.

Plants known as *epiphytes* use other plants as their habitat; they grow on trees for physical support, obtaining water from the air and nutrients from organic debris that collects among their leaves. Epiphytes thrive in cloud forests because they require a habitat with high humidity. Monteverde hosts more than 330 species of epiphytes, mostly ferns, orchids, and bromeliads (pineapple relatives). By collecting pools of rainwater and pockets

Levels of Ecological Organization

	Biosphere	The sum total of living things on Earth and the areas they inhabit
	Ecosystem	A functional system consisting of a community, its nonliving environment, and the interactions between them
	Community	A set of populations of different species living together in a particular area
	Population	A group of individuals of a species that live in a particular area
	Organism	An individual living thing

(b)

FIGURE 4.9 Life exists in a hierarchy of levels. Within an individual organism **(a)**, matter is organized in a hierarchy of levels, from atoms through cells through organ systems. Ecology **(b)** includes the study of the organismal, population, community, and ecosystem levels and, increasingly, the level of the biosphere.

of leaf litter, epiphytes create habitat for many other organisms, including many invertebrates and even frogs that lay their eggs in the rainwater pools (**FIGURE 4.10**).

Habitats vary with the body size and needs of the species. A tiny soil mite may use less than a square metre of soil in its lifetime. A vulture, elephant, or whale, in contrast, may traverse many kilometres of air, land, or water in just a day. Species may also have different habitat needs at different times of year; many migratory birds use distinct breeding habitats, wintering habitats, and migratory habitats.

The criteria by which organisms favour some habitats over others vary greatly. To a soil mite, the important characteristics of a habitat might be the chemistry, moisture, and compactness of the soil and the percentage and type of organic matter. A vulture may ignore not only soil but also topography and vegetation, focusing solely on the abundance of dead animals in the area that it scavenges for food. To a whale, water temperature and salinity, light level, and abundance of marine microorganisms might be the critical characteristics. Every species assesses habitats differently because every species has different needs.

Each organism thrives in certain habitats and not in others, leading to non-random patterns of habitat use. *Motile* organisms (those that are able to move about freely) actively select habitats from among the range of options they encounter, a process called *habitat selection*. In the case of plants and *sessile* animals (those that are not freely mobile and whose progeny disperse passively), patterns of habitat use result from success in some habitats and failure in others.

FIGURE 4.10
The strawberry poison dart frog (*Dendrobates pumilio*) places her tadpoles in pools of rainwater that collect in the leaves of epiphytic plants such as bromeliads. The pools also supply breeding habitat for mosquitoes, whose larvae are eaten by the frog's tadpoles. Some birds specialize on feeding on the insects and other animals that live in epiphytes. Just as epiphytes provide habitat for many small animals, trees provide habitat for epiphytes. The abundance of habitats and niches in just this one small system is an indicator of the rich complexity of tropical cloud forests.

Habitat use is an important consideration in environmental science because the availability and quality of habitat are crucial to an organism's well-being. Indeed, because habitats provide everything an organism needs, including nutrition, shelter, breeding sites, and mates, the organism's very survival depends on the availability of suitable habitats. Often this creates conflict with people who want to alter or develop a habitat for their own purposes.

Niche and specialization are key concepts in ecology

Another way in which an organism relates to its environment is through its niche. A species' **niche** reflects its use of resources and its functional role in a community. This includes its habitat use, its consumption of certain foods, its role in the flow of energy and matter, and its interactions with other organisms. Niche is a multidimensional concept, a kind of summary of everything an organism does. Eugene Odum, who pioneered the science of ecology, once wrote that "habitat is the organism's address, and the niche is its profession."[3] We will examine the niche concept further in the next chapter.

Organisms vary in the breadth of their niches. Species with narrow breadth, and thus very specific requirements, are said to be **specialists**. Those with broad tolerances, able to use a wide array of habitats or resources, are **generalists**. For example, in a study of eight Costa Rican bird species that feed from epiphytes, ornithologist T. Scott Sillett found that four were generalists. The other four were specialists feeding insects living on epiphytes provided and spent more than 75% of their foraging efforts feeding only from ephiphytes.

Specialist and generalist strategies each have advantages and disadvantages. Specialists can be successful over evolutionary time by being extremely good at the things they do, but they are vulnerable when conditions change and threaten the habitat or resource on which they have specialized. Generalists succeed by being able to live in many different places and weather variable conditions, but they may not thrive in any one situation to the degree that a specialist does. An organism's habitat, niche, and degree of specialization each reflect the adaptations of the species and are products of natural selection.

Population Ecology

Individuals of the same species inhabiting a particular area make up a population. Species may consist of multiple populations that are geographically isolated from one another. This is the case with one species that is characteristic of Monteverde—the resplendent quetzal

(Pharomachrus mocinno), considered one of the world's most spectacular birds (see **FIGURE 4.1A**). Although it ranges from southernmost Mexico to Panama, the resplendent quetzal lives only in high-elevation tropical forests, and is absent from low-elevation areas. Human development has destroyed much of its forest habitat; thus, the species today exists in many separate populations scattered across Central America.

In contrast, humans have become more mobile than any other species and have spread into nearly every corner of the planet. As a result, it is difficult to define a distinct human population on anything less than the global scale. Some would maintain that in the ecological sense of the word, all 7 billion of us comprise one population.

Populations show characteristics that help predict their dynamics

All populations—from humans to golden toads to quetzals—have characteristics that help population ecologists predict the future dynamics of that population. Attributes such as density, distribution, sex ratio, age structure, and birth and death rates all help the ecologist understand how a population may grow or decline. The ability to predict growth or decline is especially useful in monitoring and managing threatened and endangered species. It is also vital for understanding the dynamics of the human population, one of the prime challenges for our society today.

Population size Expressed as the number of individual organisms present at a given time, **population size** may increase, decrease, undergo cyclical change, or remain the same over time. Extinctions are generally preceded by dramatic population declines. As late as 1987, scientists documented a golden toad population at Monteverde in excess of 1500 individuals, but in 1988 and 1989 scientists sighted only a single toad. By 1990, the species had disappeared.

The passenger pigeon *(Ectopistes migratorius),* also now extinct, illustrates the extremes of population size (**FIGURE 4.11**). This was once the most abundant bird in North America; flocks of passenger pigeons literally darkened the skies, nesting in gigantic colonies in the forests of the U.S. Midwest and southern Canada. Once people began cutting the forests, the birds' great concentration made them easy targets for hunters, who shipped them to market by the wagonload. By the end of the nineteenth century, the passenger pigeon population had declined to such a low number that they could not form the large colonies they needed from protection from predators and to breed effectively. In 1914, the last passenger pigeon ("Martha") died in the Cincinnati Zoo, bringing the continent's most numerous bird species to extinction within just a few decades.

Population density The flocks and breeding colonies of passenger pigeons demonstrated high population density, another attribute that ecologists assess to better understand populations. **Population density** describes the number of individuals in a population per unit of area. For instance, the 1500 golden toads counted in 1987 within 4 km^2 indicated a density of 375 toads per km^2. In general, larger organisms tend to have lower population densities because they require more resources to survive.

(a) Passenger pigeon

(b) Nineteenth-century lithograph of pigeon hunting in Iowa

FIGURE 4.11 The passenger pigeon **(a)** was once North America's most numerous bird. Its flocks literally darkened the skies when millions of birds passed overhead **(b)**. However, hunting and clearing of forests drove the species to extinction within a few decades.

High population density can make it easier for organisms to group together and find mates, but it can also lead to conflict in the form of competition if space, food, or mates are in limited supply. Overcrowded organisms may also become more vulnerable to the predators that feed on them, and close contact among individuals can increase the transmission of infectious disease. For these reasons, organisms sometimes leave an area when densities become too high. In contrast, at low population densities, organisms benefit from more space and resources but may find it harder to locate mates and companions.

High population densities in small remnants of habitat may have doomed Monteverde's harlequin frog (*Atelopus varius*; see **FIGURE 4.1C**), an amphibian that disappeared from the cloud forest around the same time as the golden toad (see "The Science Behind the Story: Climate Change, Disease, and the Amphibians of Monteverde"). The harlequin frog is a specialist, favouring "splash zones," areas alongside rivers and streams that receive spray from waterfalls and rapids. As Monteverde's climate grew warmer and drier in the 1980s and 1990s, water flow decreased, and many streams dried up. Splash zones grew smaller and fewer, and harlequin frogs were forced to cluster together in what remained of the habitat. Researchers J. Alan Pounds and Martha Crump recorded frog population densities up to 4.4 times higher than normal, with more than two frogs per metre of stream. Such overcrowding likely made the frogs more vulnerable to disease transmission, predator attack, and assault from parasitic flies. The researchers concluded that these factors led to the harlequin frog's disappearance from Monteverde.

A new population of harlequin frogs was found in 2003 on a private reserve elsewhere in Costa Rica, so there is still hope that the species may survive. The frog was rediscovered by University of Delaware student Justin Yeager, who was doing field research during his study abroad trip in Costa Rica that summer.

Population distribution   It was not simply the harlequin frog's density, but also its distribution in space that led to its demise at Monteverde. **Population distribution** or **population dispersion** describes the spatial arrangement of organisms within an area. Ecologists define three distribution types: random, uniform, and clumped (**FIGURE 4.12**). In a *random distribution,* individuals are located haphazardly in space in no particular pattern. This type of distribution can occur when the resources an organism needs are found throughout an area, and other organisms do not strongly influence where members of a population settle. In nature, however, the distribution of organisms

is virtually never random; even the apparently randomly distributed trees in the forest shown here have grown in specific locations that are beneficial for access to the resources they need.

(a) "Random"

(b) Uniform

(c) Clumped

FIGURE 4.12
Individuals in a population can be spatially distributed over a landscape in three fundamental ways. In a random distribution **(a)**, organisms are dispersed at random through the environment. In nature, the distribution of organisms is virtually never random; even the trees in this forest have grown in specific locations that are beneficial for access to the resources they need. In a uniform distribution **(b)**, individuals are spaced evenly, at equal distances from one another. Territoriality can result in such a pattern. In a clumped distribution **(c)**, individuals occur in patches, concentrated more heavily in some areas than in others. Habitat selection or flocking to avoid predators can result in such a pattern.

A *uniform distribution* is one in which individuals are evenly spaced. This can occur when individuals hold territories or otherwise compete for space. For instance, in a desert where there is little water, each plant may need a certain amount of space for its roots to gather adequate moisture. As a result, each individual plant may be equidistant from others.

In a *clumped distribution,* the pattern most common in nature, organisms arrange themselves according to the availability of the resources they need to survive. Many desert plants grow in patches around isolated springs or along arroyos that flood with water after rainstorms. During their mating season, golden toads were found clumped at seasonal breeding pools. Humans, too, exhibit clumped distribution; people frequently aggregate together in urban centres. Clumped distributions often arise from habitat selection.

Distributions depend on the scale at which one measures them. At very large scales, all organisms show clumped or patchy distributions because some parts of the total area they inhabit are bound to be more hospitable than others.

Sex ratios For organisms that reproduce sexually and have distinct male and female individuals, the sex ratio of a population can help determine whether it will increase or decrease in size over time. A population's **sex ratio** is its proportion of males to females. In monogamous species (in which each sex takes a single mate), a 50/50 sex ratio maximizes population growth, whereas an unbalanced ratio leaves many individuals of one sex without mates. Most species are not monogamous, though, so sex ratios vary from species to species.

Age structure Populations consist of individuals of different ages. The **age distribution** or **age structure** describes the relative numbers of individuals of each age within a population. By combining this information with data on the reproductive potential of individuals in different age classes, a population ecologist can predict how the population may grow or shrink.

For many plants and animals that continue growing in size as they age, older individuals reproduce more; a tree that is large because it is old can produce more seeds, and a fish that is large because it is old may produce more eggs. In some animals, such as birds, the experience they gain with age often makes older individuals better breeders. Humans are unusual because we often survive past our reproductive years. As a result, a human population made up largely of older (post-reproductive) individuals will tend to decline over time, whereas one with many young people (of reproductive or pre-reproductive age) will tend to increase. We will use diagrams to explore

these ideas further when we turn our attention to human population growth.

Birth and death rates All the preceding factors can influence the rates at which individuals within a population are born and die. A convenient way to express birth and death rates is to measure the number of births and deaths per 1000 individuals for a given time period, termed the *crude birth rate* or *crude death rate.*

Just as individuals of different ages have different abilities to reproduce, individuals of different ages show different probabilities of dying. For instance, people are more likely to die at old ages than young ages; if you were to follow 1000 10-year-olds and 1000 80-year-olds for a year, you would find that at year's end more 80-year-olds had died than 10-year-olds. However, this pattern does not hold for all organisms. Amphibians such as the golden toad produce large numbers of young, which suffer high death rates. For a toad, death is less likely (and survival more likely) at an older age than at a very young age.

To show how the likelihood of death can vary with age, ecologists use graphs called **survivorship curves** (**FIGURE 4.13**). There are three fundamental types of survivorship curves. Humans, with higher death rates at older ages, show a *type I* survivorship curve. Toads, with higher death rates at younger ages, show a *type III* survivorship curve. A *type II* survivorship curve is intermediate and indicates equal rates of death at all ages. Many birds can be characterized with type II curves.

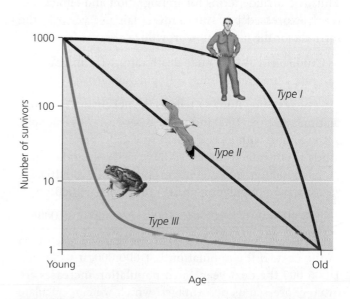

FIGURE 4.13

In a type I survivorship curve, survival rates are high when individuals are young and decrease sharply when individuals are old. In a type II survivorship curve, survival rates are equivalent regardless of an individual's age. In a type III survivorship curve, most mortality takes place at young ages, and survival rates are greater at older ages. Some examples include humans (type I), birds (type II), and amphibians (type III).

Populations may grow, shrink, or remain stable

Now that we have outlined some key attributes of populations, we are ready to take a quantitative view of population change by examining some simple mathematical concepts used by population ecologists and *demographers* (scientists who study human populations). Population growth, or decline, is determined by four factors:

1. Births within the population, or **natality**
2. Deaths within the population, or **mortality**
3. **Immigration**, the arrival of individuals from outside the population
4. **Emigration**, the departure of individuals from the population

Births and immigration add individuals to a population, whereas deaths and emigration remove individuals. If we are not interested in the effects of migration, we can measure the **natural rate of population growth** by subtracting the crude death rate from the crude birth rate:

Crude birth rate – Crude death rate = Natural rate of population growth

The natural rate of population growth reflects the degree to which a population is growing or shrinking as a result of its own internal factors.

To obtain an overall **population growth rate**, the total rate of change in a population's size per unit of time, we must also take into account the effects of migration. Thus, we include terms for immigration and emigration (each expressed per 1000 individuals per year) in the formula for the population growth:

(Crude birth rate – Crude death rate) + (Immigration rate – emigration rate) = Population growth rate

The resulting number tells us the net change in a population's size per 1000 individuals per year. For example, a population with a crude birth rate of 18 per 1000/yr, a crude death rate of 10 per 1000/yr, an immigration rate of 5 per 1000/yr, and an emigration rate of 7 per 1000/yr would have a population growth rate of 6 per 1000/yr:

$$(18/1000 - 10/1000) + (5/1000 - 7/1000) = 6/1000$$

Thus, a population of 1000 in one year will reach 1006 in the next. If the population is 1 000 000, it will reach 1 006 000 the next year. Such population increases are often expressed as percentages, which we can calculate using the following formula:

Population growth rate × 100%

Thus, a growth rate of 6/1000 would be expressed as:

$$6/1000 \times 100\% = 0.6\%$$

By measuring population growth in terms of percentages, scientists can compare increases and decreases in species that have far different population sizes. They can also project changes that will occur in the population over longer periods.

Unregulated populations increase by exponential growth

When a population, or anything else, increases by a fixed percentage each year, it is said to undergo *geometric growth*, or **exponential growth**. A savings account is a familiar frame of reference for describing exponential growth. If at the time of your birth your parents had invested $1000 in a savings account earning 5% interest compounded each year, with no additional investments you would have $1629 by age 10, and $2653 by age 20, but you would have over $30 000 when you turn 70. If you could wait just 10 years more, that figure would rise to nearly $50 000. Only $629 was added during your first decade, but approximately $19 000 was added during the decade between ages 70 and 80. The reason is that a fixed percentage of a small number produces a small increase, but that same percentage of a large number produces a large increase. Thus, as populations (or savings accounts) become larger, each incremental increase likewise gets larger. Such acceleration is a fundamental characteristic of exponential growth.

In contrast, if your parents added a fixed amount to your savings account every year, your savings would still grow, but by *arithmetic growth*, or **linear growth**. If both accounts (linear growth, with interest at a fixed *amount* per year, and exponential growth, with interest at a fixed *percentage* per year) were allowed to proceed unchecked, the account with the exponential growth would necessarily outstrip the linear-growth account. This will be the case even if the balance in the linear-growth account is higher for the first few years.

We can visualize changes in population size using population growth curves. The J-shaped curve in **FIGURE 4.14** shows an example of an exponential population increase. Populations of organisms can increase exponentially until they meet constraints. Each organism reproduces by a certain amount, and as populations get larger, more individuals reproduce by that amount. If there were no external limits on growth, ecologists theoretically would expect exponential growth to occur.

Exponential growth usually occurs in nature when a population is small, competition is minimal, and environmental conditions are ideal for the organism in question. Most often, these conditions occur when organisms are introduced to a new environment. Mould growing on a

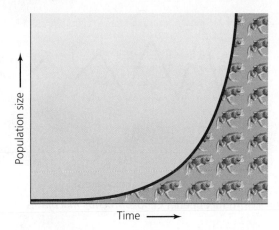

FIGURE 4.14
No species can maintain exponential growth indefinitely, but some may grow exponentially for a time when colonizing an unoccupied environment or exploiting an unused resource.

piece of bread or fruit, and bacteria colonizing a recently dead animal are cases in point. But species of any size may show exponential growth under the right conditions. We sometimes see this in urban areas where animals such as squirrels, raccoons, Canada geese, coyotes, and even moose can become nuisances when their populations expand quickly as a result of easy access to food supplies.

Limiting factors restrain population growth

Exponential growth rarely lasts long. If even a single species in Earth's history had increased exponentially for very many generations, it would have blanketed the planet's surface, and nothing else could have survived. Instead, every population eventually is constrained by **limiting factors**—physical, chemical, and biological characteristics of the environment that restrain population growth. The combination of these factors exerts environmental resistance on the population. Environmental resistance ultimately determines the **carrying capacity**, the maximum population size of a species that a given environment can sustain.

Ecologists use the S-shaped (or *sigmoidal*) curve in **FIGURE 4.15** to show how an initial exponential increase is slowed and finally brought to a standstill by limiting factors. Called a **logistic growth curve**, it rises sharply at first but then begins to level off as the effects of limiting factors become stronger. Eventually the force of these factors stabilizes the population size at its carrying capacity.

The logistic curve is a simplified model; real populations can behave quite differently. Some may cycle indefi-

nitely above and below the carrying capacity. Some may show cycles that become less extreme and approach the carrying capacity. Others may overshoot the carrying capacity and then crash, fated either for extinction or recovery (**FIGURE 4.16**).

Many factors contribute to environmental resistance and influence carrying capacity and population growth and decline. Space limits the number of individuals a given environment can support; if there is no physical room for additional individuals, they are unlikely to survive. Other limiting factors for animals in the terrestrial environment include the availability of food, water, mates, shelter, and suitable breeding sites; temperature extremes; prevalence of disease; and abundance of predators. Plants are often limited by amounts of sunlight and moisture, and the availability of nutrients from the soil, as well as disease and attack by plant-eating animals. In aquatic systems, limiting factors include salinity, sunlight, temperature, dissolved oxygen, and water chemistry. To determine limiting factors, ecologists often conduct experiments in which they increase or decrease a hypothesized limiting factor to observe its effects on population size.

The influence of limiting factors can vary with changing conditions. In particular, the density of a population can increase or decrease the impact of certain factors on that population. Recall that high population density can help organisms find mates, but also increases competition and the risk of predation and disease. Such

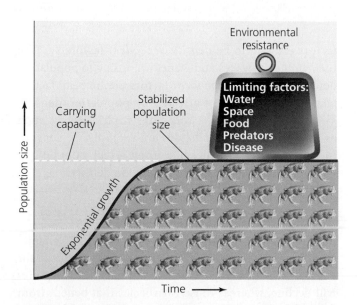

FIGURE 4.15
The logistic growth curve shows how population size may increase rapidly at first, then grow more slowly, and finally stabilize at a carrying capacity. Carrying capacity is determined both by the biotic potential of the organism and by various external limiting factors, collectively termed *environmental resistance*.

(a) Yeast cells, *Saccharomyces cerevisiae*

(c) Stored-product beetle, *Callosobruchus maculatus*

(b) Mite, *Eotetranychus sexmaculatus*

(d) St. Paul reindeer, *Rangifer tarandus*

FIGURE 4.16   Population growth in nature often departs from the stereotypical logistic growth curve, and it can do so in several fundamental ways. Yeast cells from a lab experiment show logistic growth **(a)** that closely matches the theoretical model. Some organisms, like the mite **(b)**, show cycles in which population fluctuates indefinitely above and below the carrying capacity. Population oscillations can also dampen, lessening in intensity and eventually stabilizing at carrying capacity **(c)**, as in a lab experiment with the stored-product beetle. Populations that rise too fast and deplete resources may crash just as suddenly **(d)**, like the population of reindeer introduced to the Bering Sea island of St. Paul.   *Source: Data from Pearl, R. (1927) The growth of populations.* Quarterly Review of Biology *2: 532–548, (a); Huffaker, C. B. (1958) Experimental studies on predation: Dispersion factors and predator-prey oscillations,* Hilgardia *27: 343–383, (b); Utida, S. (1967) Damped oscillation of population density at equilibrium,* Researches on Population Ecology *9: 1–9, (c); Scheffer, V.C. (1951) Rise and fall of a reindeer herd,* Scientific Monthly *73: 356–362, (d).*

factors are said to be *density-dependent* factors because their influence waxes and wanes according to population density. *Density-independent* factors are limiting factors whose influence is not affected by population density. Temperature extremes and catastrophic events such as floods, fires, and landslides are examples of density-independent factors because they affect populations without being influenced by population density.

Carrying capacities can change

Because environments are complex and ever-changing, carrying capacity can vary. If a fire destroys a forest, for example, the carrying capacities for most forest species will decline, whereas those for species that benefit from fire will increase. If limiting factors change as a result of environmental change, the carrying capacity for a species may increase (or decrease).

Our own species has proved capable of intentionally altering our environment so as to reduce environmen-

tal resistance and raise our carrying capacity. When our ancestors began to build shelters and use fire for heating and cooking, they reduced the environmental resistance of areas with cold climates and were able to expand into new territory. People have managed so far to increase the planet's carrying capacity for our species, but we have done so by appropriating immense proportions of the planet's resources. In the process, we have reduced the carrying capacities for countless other organisms and have called into question our own long-term survival.

Reproductive strategies vary from species to species

Limiting factors from an organism's environment provide only half the story of population regulation. The other half comes from the attributes of the organism itself. For example, organisms differ in their **biotic potential**, or maximum capacity to produce offspring under ideal

weighing the issues

CARRYING CAPACITY AND HUMAN POPULATION GROWTH

The global human population has risen from fewer than 1 billion 200 years ago to 7 billion today, and we have far exceeded our historic carrying capacity. In fact, some demographers argue that Earth's true carrying capacity for the human species is only about 10 million (the estimated human population at the time when the human species had expanded to cover most of the globe). What factors increased Earth's carrying capacity for people? Are there limiting factors for the human population? What might they be? Do you think we can keep raising Earth's carrying capacity in the future? Are there any factors that might cause Earth's carrying capacity for the human species to decrease?

environmental conditions. A fish with a short gestation period that lays thousands of eggs at a time has high biotic potential, whereas a whale with a long gestation period that gives birth to a single calf at a time has low biotic potential. The interaction between an organism's biotic potential and the environmental resistance to its population growth helps determine the fate of its population.

Giraffes, elephants, humans, and other large animals with low biotic potential produce a relatively small number of offspring and take a long time to gestate and raise each of their young. Species that take this approach to reproduction compensate by devoting large amounts of energy and resources to caring for and protecting the relatively few offspring they produce during their lifetimes. Such species are said to be **K-selected** (or are called *K-strategists*). K-selected species are so named because their populations tend to stabilize over time at or near their carrying capacity, and *K* is a commonly used abbreviation for carrying capacity. Because their populations stay close to carrying capacity, natural selection in these species favours individuals that invest in producing offspring of high quality that can be good competitors.

In contrast, species that are **r-selected** focus on quantity, not quality. Species considered to be r-selected (or are called *r-strategists*) have high biotic potential and devote their energy and resources to producing as many offspring as possible in a relatively short time. Their offspring do not require parental care after birth, and r-strategists commonly leave the survival of their offspring to chance. The abbreviation *r* denotes the rate at which a population increases in the absence of limiting factors. Population sizes of r-selected species fluctuate greatly, so they are often below carrying capacity. This is why natural selection in these species favours traits that lead to rapid population growth. Many fish, plants, frogs, insects, and others are r-selected. The golden toad is one example. Each adult female laid 200 to 400 eggs, and its tadpoles spent five weeks unsupervised in the breeding pools metamorphosing into adults.

TABLE 4.4 summarizes stereotypical traits of r-selected and K-selected species. However, it is important to note that these are two extremes on a continuum and that most species fall somewhere between these endpoints. Moreover, some organisms show combinations of traits that do not clearly correspond to a place on the continuum. A redwood tree (*Sequoia sempervirens*), for instance, is large and long-lived, yet it produces many small seeds and offers no parental care.

Changes in populations influence the composition of communities

In the late 1980s, the golden toad and the harlequin frog were the most diligently studied species that had been affected by changing environmental conditions in the Costa Rican cloud forest. However, once scientists began looking at populations of other species at Monteverde, they began to notice more troubling changes. By the early 1990s, not only had golden toads, harlequin frogs, and other organisms been pushed from their cloud-forest habitat into apparent extinction, but also many species from lower, drier habitats also had begun to appear at Monteverde. These immigrants included species tolerant of drier conditions, such as blue-crowned motmots (*Momotus momota*) and brown jays (*Cyanocorax morio*).

Table 4.4 Typical Characteristics of r-Selected and K-selected Species

r-selected species	K-selected species
Small size	Large size
Fast development	Slow development
Short-lived	Long-lived
Reproduction early in life	Reproduction later in life
Many, small offspring	Few, large offspring
Fast population growth rate	Slow population growth rate
No parental care	Parental care
Weak competitive ability	Strong competitive ability
Variable population size, often well below carrying capacity	Constant population size, close to carrying capacity
Variable and unpredictable mortality	More constant and predictable mortality

THE SCIENCE BEHIND THE STORY

Climate Change, Disease, and the Amphibians of Monteverde

Dr. J. Alan Pounds (left) with Dr. Luis Coloma, looking for harlequin frogs

Soon after the golden toad's disappearance, scientists began to investigate the potential role of global climate change in driving cloud-forest species toward extinction. The period from July 1986 to June 1987 was the driest on record at Monteverde, with unusually high temperatures and record-low stream flows. These conditions caused the golden toad's breeding pools to dry up in the spring of 1987, likely killing nearly all of the eggs and tadpoles in the pools.

By reviewing weather data, scientists found that the number of dry days and dry periods each winter in the Monteverde region had increased between 1973 and 1998. Because amphibians breathe and absorb moisture through their skin, they are susceptible to dry conditions. Based on these facts, herpetologists J. Alan Pounds and Martha Crump in 1994 hypothesized that hot, dry conditions were to blame for high adult mortality and breeding problems among golden toads and other amphibians.

Pounds and others reviewed the scientific literature on atmospheric and ocean science to analyze the impacts on Monteverde's local climate of warming patterns in the ocean regions around Costa Rica. Warmer oceans, the researchers

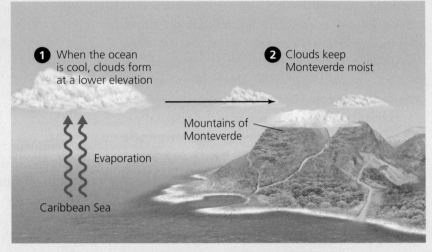

1. When the ocean is cool, clouds form at a lower elevation
2. Clouds keep Monteverde moist

Mountains of Monteverde

Evaporation

Caribbean Sea

(a) Cool ocean conditions

1. When the ocean is warm, clouds form at a higher elevation
2. Clouds pass by Monteverde at a higher elevation
3. Less moisture arrives in Monteverde; drought conditions prevail

Mountains of Monteverde

Evaporation

Caribbean Sea

(b) Warm ocean conditions

Monteverde's cloud forest gets its name and life-giving moisture from clouds that sweep inland from the oceans. When ocean temperatures are cool **(a)**, the clouds keep Monteverde moist. Warmer ocean conditions **(b)** resulting from global climate change cause clouds to form at higher elevations and pass over the mountains, drying the cloud forest.

By the year 2000, 15 dry-forest species had moved into the cloud forest and begun to breed. Meanwhile, population sizes of several cloud-forest bird species had declined. After 1987, 20 of 50 frog species vanished from one part of Monteverde, and ecologists later reported more disappearances, including those of two lizards native to the cloud forest. Scientists hypothesized that the warming, drying trends that researchers were documenting were causing population fluctuations and unleashing changes in the composition of the community (see "The Science Behind the Story: Climate Change, Disease, and the Amphibians of Monteverde").

found, caused clouds to pass over at higher elevations, where they were no longer in contact with the trees. Once the cloud forest's moisture supply was pushed upward, out of reach of the mountaintops, the forest began to dry out (see first figure).

In a 1999 paper in the journal *Nature*, Pounds and two colleagues reported that climate modification was causing local changes at the species, population, and community levels. They argued that higher clouds and decreasing moisture in the forest could explain the disappearance of the golden toad and harlequin frog and also the concurrent population crashes and subsequent disappearance of 20 other species of frogs and toads from the Monteverde region. As the forests dried out, drought-tolerant species of birds and reptiles shifted upslope, and moisture-dependent species were stranded at the mountaintops by a rising tide of aridity.

Pounds and his colleagues expanded the story further in *Nature* in 2006. Although clouds had risen higher in the sky, the extra moisture evaporating from warming oceans was increasing cloud cover overall, blocking sunlight during the day and trapping heat at night. As a result, at Monteverde and other tropical locations, daytime and nighttime temperatures were becoming more similar. Such conditions are optimal for chytrid fungi, pathogens that can lethally infect amphibians. In recent years the chytrid fungus *Batrachochytrium dendrobatidis* is thought to have contributed to the likely extinction of 67 of the world's 113 species of harlequin frogs. At Monteverde and elsewhere, Pounds' team argued, climate change is promoting disease epidemics that are driving extinct many of the world's amphibians.

Other researchers agree that chytrid fungus is a major threat but dispute

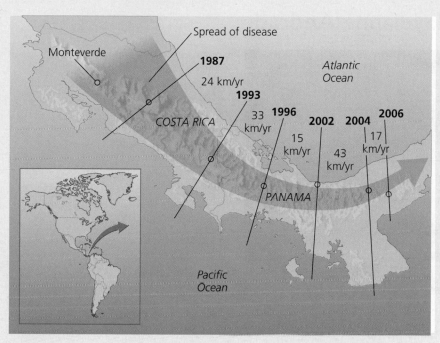

Dr. Karen Lips' research team used known dates of decline (years in figure) in harlequin frog populations at sites in Costa Rica and Panama to infer the spread of a wave of infection (arrow) by chytrid fungus across the region. By their analysis, chytrid reached Monteverde before 1987 and was well into Panama by 2000.
Source: Adapted from Lips, K.R., et al. (2008) Riding the wave: Reconciling the roles of disease and climate change in amphibian declines. PLoS Biology 6: 441–454.

a connection to climate change. In 2008, one team led by biologist Karen Lips of Southern Illinois University at Carbondale mapped amphibian declines and inferred the rapid spread of non-native and invasive chytrid fungus in waves across Central America and South America in recent years (see second figure). The analysis by Lips and her team suggested that the dramatic amphibian die-offs at Monteverde and elsewhere are directly due to the arrival of this devastating pathogen and do not necessarily involve climate change.

Additional research has since shown that harlequin frog extinctions were correlated with rising tropical air temperatures; however this does not confirm climate as a direct causal factor. Climate change is a fundamental influence on biological systems. It is likely a factor in amphibian declines, but as yet the evidence for a causal link is not solid. Clearly more research into the effects of both disease and climate change is needed. Biologists today are racing to find the answers, hoping to save many of the world's amphibian species from extinction.

Conclusion

Changes in populations and communities have been taking place naturally as long as life has existed. Studies of both living and long-extinct organisms have helped illuminate fundamental concepts of evolution and population ecology that are integral to environmental science. The evolutionary processes of natural selection, speciation, and extinction have been the driving forces behind the development of Earth's biodiversity.

Today human development, resource extraction, and population pressure are speeding the rate of

CANADIAN ENVIRONMENTAL PERSPECTIVES

Maydianne Andrade

Professor Maydianne Andrade studies how sex and cannibalism come together to ensure reproductive success for the redback spider.

- **Professor** of ecology and evolutionary biology at the University of Toronto at Scarborough
- **Entomologist, arachnologist,** and "Spider Woman"
- One of *Popular Science*'s **"Brilliant 10"** Scientists for 2005

Maydianne Andrade is interested in sex, but not just any kind of sex. She studies how sexual selection, social behaviour, and ecological conditions interact to affect the evolution of mating systems in the redback spider, *Latrodectus hasselti*.[4]

Andrade is an assistant professor in the Department of Ecology and Evolutionary Biology at the University of Toronto's Scarborough campus. She completed her B.Sc. at Simon Fraser University, her M.Sc. at the University of Toronto, and her Ph.D. at Cornell University. The animals she studies—the redback spider and its close relative, the black widow spider—are unusual because the males of the species make an extreme investment, actually, a "terminal investment," in seeking success in the mating process. This means pretty much what it sounds like: the male sacrifices himself to ensure his success in mating. He actually does this by offering himself to the female as "dinner." Yes, female redback spiders are cannibals.

This may seem counterintuitive; how can it be a beneficial adaptation for a male spider to sacrifice himself to achieve success in mating? Doesn't this mean that he gives up all possibility of any future mating opportunities?

Andrade has discovered some interesting features of the species. For one thing, the physiology of the male redback spider is such that he can transfer sperm to the female even as he is being consumed. Furthermore, the self-sacrifice gives such an enormous advantage to the male redback spider—which would likely mate only once anyway, even in the absence of cannibalism—that it is worth his while to give up future mating opportunities for success just this one time.

As Andrade points out,

This extreme form of male mating investment provides a unique opportunity to test sexual selection and life history theory because males are under strong selection to succeed in their single mating opportunity, but are constrained by ecology and physically dominant females. We have a good understanding of factors affecting the strength and natural selection on redback males, and can manipulate cues indicating the strength of selection in the field and laboratory.[5]

Andrade's current work, which has ramifications for the study not only of spiders but also of natural selection and evolutionary theory, is focused on furthering our understanding of the effects of factors such as diet on the ratio of males to females and how male competition and female choice affect the mating process.

"When we talk about 'thinking outside the box,' that's what thinking like a scientist is all about."—**Maydianne Andrade**

Thinking About Environmental Perspectives

How do researchers like Maydianne Andrade advance our *general* understanding of evolutionary theory through the study of *specific* unusual or extreme mating habits in individual organisms, such as those of the redback spiders? Visit Andrade's website and read some of her research papers to find out more about this (www.scar.utoronto.ca/~mandrade).

environmental change, altering the types of change, and threatening specific organisms and biodiversity as a whole. The ways we modify our environment cannot be understood in a scientific vacuum, however. Understanding how ecological processes work at the population level is crucial to protecting biodiversity threatened by the mass extinction event that many biologists maintain is already under way. The factors that threaten biodiversity have complex social, economic, and political roots, and environmental scientists appreciate that we must understand these aspects if we are to develop solutions.

Fortunately, there are things people can do to forestall population declines of species threatened with extinction. Millions of people around the world are already taking action to safeguard the biodiversity and ecological and evolutionary processes that make Earth such a unique place. We will look at many of these efforts in future chapters.

REVIEWING OBJECTIVES

You should now be able to:

Explain the process of natural selection and cite evidence for this process

- Because organisms produce excess young, individuals vary in their traits, and many traits are inherited, some individuals will prove better at surviving and reproducing. Their genes will be passed on and become more prominent in future generations.
- Mutations and recombination provide the genetic variation for natural selection.
- We have produced our pets, farm animals, and crop plants through artificial selection.

Describe the ways in which evolution results in biodiversity and what the fossil record has taught us about evolution

- Natural selection can act as a diversifying force as organisms adapt to their environments in myriad ways.
- Speciation (by geographic isolation and other means) produces new species.
- The branching patterns of phylogenetic trees reflect the historical pattern by which lineages of organisms have diverged.
- By preserving some of the long history of life on this planet, the fossil record has shown us that early organisms have evolved into later ones and that the number of species alive at any given time has generally increased through time.

Discuss reasons for species extinction and mass extinction events

- Extinction may occur when species that are highly specialized or that have small populations encounter rapid environmental change.
- Earth's life has experienced five known episodes of mass extinction, which were due to asteroid impact and possibly volcanism and other factors.

- Today, human impact may be initiating a sixth great extinction.

Summarize the levels of ecological organization

- Life is organized hierarchically, starting with the atoms, molecules, and cells that make up individual organisms.
- Ecologists study phenomena on the organismal, population, community, and ecosystem levels—and, increasingly, on the biosphere level.
- Habitat, niche, and specialization are important ecological concepts.

Outline the characteristics of populations that help predict population growth

- Populations are characterized by population size, population density, population distribution, sex ratio, age structure, and birth and death rates.
- Immigration and emigration, as well as birth and death rates, determine how a population will grow or decline.

Define *logistic growth, carrying capacity, limiting factors*, and other fundamental concepts of population ecology

- Populations unrestrained by limiting factors will undergo exponential growth until they meet environmental resistance.
- Logistic growth describes the effects of density dependence; exponential growth slows as population size increases, and population size levels off at a carrying capacity.
- K-selection and r-selection describe theoretical extremes in how organisms can allocate growth and reproduction.

TESTING YOUR COMPREHENSION

1. Explain the premises and logic that support the concept of natural selection.
2. How does allopatric speciation occur?
3. Name two examples of evidence for natural selection.
4. Name three organisms that have gone extinct, and give a probable reason for each extinction.
5. What is the difference between a species and a population? Between a population and a community?
6. Contrast the concepts of habitat and niche.
7. List and describe each of the five major population characteristics discussed in this chapter. Explain how each shapes population dynamics.
8. Could any species undergo exponential growth forever? Explain your answer.
9. Describe how limiting factors relate to carrying capacity.
10. Explain the difference between K-selected species and r-selected species. Can you think of examples of each that were not mentioned in the chapter?

THINKING IT THROUGH

1. In what ways has artificial selection changed people's quality of life? Give examples. Can you imagine a way in which artificial selection could be used to improve our quality of life further? Can you imagine a way it could be used to lessen our environmental impact?
2. What types of species are most vulnerable to extinction, and what kinds of factors threaten them? Can you think of any species in your region that are threatened with extinction today? What reasons lie behind their endangerment?
3. Do you think the human species can continue raising its global carrying capacity? How so, or why not? Do you think we *should* try to keep raising our carrying capacity? Why or why not?
4. Describe the evidence suggesting that changes in temperature and precipitation led to the extinction of the golden toad and to population crashes for other amphibians at Monteverde. Why do scientists think that disease also played a role? What do you think could be done to help make such declines less likely in the future?
5. If you were given the task of counting all of the species alive on Earth, how would you go about it? If you were asked to measure the biodiversity of one area and contrast it with that of another area, what indicators of biodiversity would you measure? (We will return to this question in the chapter on conservation of species and habitats.)
6. Let us say that you are a population ecologist studying animals in a national park. The government is asking for advice on how to focus its limited conservation funds. How would you rate the following three species, from most vulnerable (and thus most in need of attention) to least vulnerable? Give reasons for your choices.
   - A bird with an even sex ratio that is a habitat generalist
   - A salamander that is endemic to the park and lives only in high-elevation forest
   - A fish that specializes on a few types of invertebrate prey and has a large population size

INTERPRETING GRAPHS AND DATA

Amphibians are sensitive biological indicators of climate change because their reproduction and survival are so closely tied to water. One way in which drier conditions may affect amphibians is by reducing the depth of the pools of water in which their eggs develop. Shallower pools offer less protection from UV-B (ultraviolet) radiation, which some scientists maintain may kill embryos directly or make them more susceptible to disease.

Herpetologist Joseph Kiesecker and colleagues conducted a field study of the relationships among water depth, UV-B radiation, and survivorship of western toad (*Bufo boreas*) embryos in the Pacific Northwest. In manipulative experiments, the researchers placed toad embryos in mesh enclosures at three different depths of water. The researchers placed protective filters that blocked all UV-B radiation over some of these embryos, while leaving other embryos unprotected without the filters. Some of the study's results are presented in the accompanying graph.

1. If the UV-B radiation at the surface has an intensity of 0.27 watts/m^2, approximately what is its intensity at depths of 10 cm, 50 cm, and 100 cm?

2. Approximately how much did survival rates at the 10-cm depth differ between the protected and unprotected treatments? Why do you think survival rates differed significantly at the 10-cm depth but not at the other depths?

3. What do you think would be the effect of drier-than-average years on the western toad population if the average depth of pools available for toad spawning dropped? How do the data above address your hypothesis? Do they support cause-and-effect relationships among water depth, UV-B exposure, disease, and toad mortality?

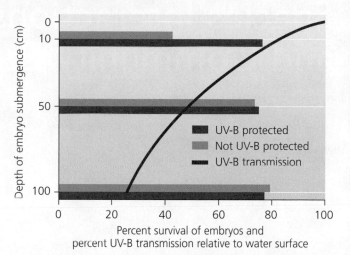

Embryo survivorship in western toads *(Bufo boreas)* at different water depths and UV-B light intensities. Red bars indicate embryos protected under a filter that blocked UV-B light; orange bars indicate unprotected embryos. The blue line indicates the amount of UV-B light reaching different depths in the water column, expressed as a percentage of the UV-B radiation at the water surface.
Source: Data from Kiesecker, J.M., et al. (2001) Complex causes of amphibian population declines. Nature 410: 681–684.

CHAPTER ENDNOTES

1. Pounds, A., & Savage, J. (2004) *Bufo periglenes*. In: IUCN 2007. *2007 IUCN Red List of Threatened Species.* www.iucnredlist.org. Accessed 24 September 2007.

2. Note that the term *Tertiary* is no longer in common use among geologists.

3. Odum, E. P. (1959) *Fundamentals of Ecology*, W. B. Saunders Co., Philadelphia and London.

4. Andrade Lab Research, Department of Ecology and Evolutionary Biology, University of Toronto Scarborough, www.scar.utoronto.ca/~mandrade

5. Andrade Lab Research, Department of Ecology and Evolutionary Biology, University of Toronto Scarborough, www.scar.utoronto.ca/~mandrade

MyEnvironmentPlace

Go to **www.myenvironmentplace.ca** where you will find quizzes, animations, your Pearson eText, and more.

Species Interactions and Community Ecology

5

This marsh–wetland community is one of the few remaining along the shores of Lake Ontario.

Upon successfully completing this chapter, you will be able to

- Compare and contrast the major types of species interactions
- Characterize feeding relationships and energy flow, using them to construct trophic pyramids and food webs
- Distinguish characteristics of a keystone species
- Describe how communities respond to disturbances

- Perceive and predict the potential impacts of invasive species on communities
- Explain the goals and methods of ecological restoration
- Describe and illustrate the terrestrial biomes of the world

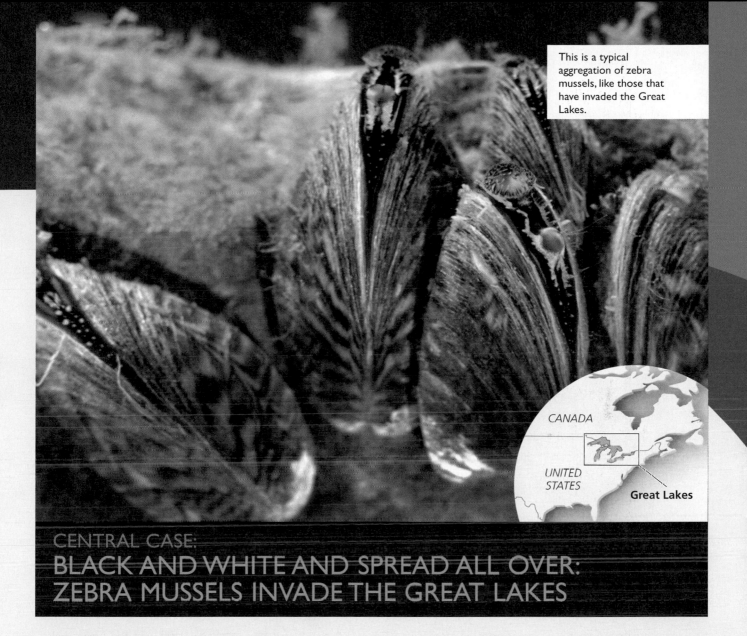

This is a typical aggregation of zebra mussels, like those that have invaded the Great Lakes.

CANADA

UNITED STATES

Great Lakes

BLACK AND WHITE AND SPREAD ALL OVER: ZEBRA MUSSELS INVADE THE GREAT LAKES

"The zebra mussel is helping us understand what makes a good invader."
—ANTHONY RICCIARDI, MCGILL UNIVERSITY

"The zebra mussel has altered aquatic ecosystems beyond recognition."
—MICHAEL BARDWAJ, *CANADIAN GEOGRAPHIC*[1]

As if the Great Lakes had not been through enough, the last thing they needed was the zebra mussel. The pollution-fouled waters of Lake Erie and the other Great Lakes had become gradually cleaner in the years following the establishment of the International Joint Commission and the signing of the Great Lakes Water Quality Agreement between Canada and the United States in 1972. As these international efforts brought

industrial discharges under control, people once again began to use the lakes for recreation, and populations of fish rebounded.

Then the zebra mussel arrived. Black-and-white-striped shellfish the size of a dime (see photo), zebra mussels (*Dreissena polymorpha*) attach to hard surfaces and feed on algae by filtering water through their gills. This mollusc is native to the Caspian Sea, Black Sea, and Azov Sea in western Asia and eastern Europe. It made its North American debut in 1988 when it was discovered in Canadian waters at Lake St. Clair, which connects Lake Erie with Lake Huron. Evidently ships arriving from Europe had discharged ballast water containing the mussels or their larvae into the Great Lakes.

Within two years of their discovery in Lake St. Clair, zebra mussels had reached all five of the Great Lakes. The next year, they entered New York's Hudson River to the east and the Illinois River at Chicago to the west.

From the Illinois River and its canals, they soon reached the Mississippi River, giving them access to a vast watershed covering 40% of the United States. By 2012, zebra mussel colonies and sightings had been confirmed in Ontario, Québec, and 40 U.S. states.

How could a mussel spread so quickly? The zebra mussel's larval stage is well adapted for long-distance dispersal. Its tiny larvae drift freely for several weeks, travelling as far as the currents take them. Adults that attach themselves to boats and ships may be transported from one place to another, even to isolated lakes and ponds well away from major rivers. They can survive out of the water for several days and are known to have been transported overland to many locations. In North America the mussels encountered none of the predators, competitors, and parasites that had evolved to limit their population growth in the Old World.

Why the fuss? Zebra mussels are best known for clogging up water intake pipes at factories, power plants, municipal water supplies, and wastewater treatment facilities. At one power plant, workers counted 700 000 mussels per square metre of pipe surface. Great densities of these organisms can damage boat engines, degrade docks, foul fishing gear, and sink buoys that ships use for navigation. Through such impacts, it is estimated that zebra mussels cost hundreds of millions of dollars each year. Over the first 10 years of the zebra mussel invasion, the total cost to Great Lakes economies is estimated to have reached $5 billion, with ongoing annual costs of $20 000 to $350 000 per industrial facility. These figures include only costs to industry, not to individuals or cottagers, who also suffer costs such as clogged water pipes, ruined motorboats, and fouled beaches.[2]

Zebra mussels also have severe impacts on the ecological systems they invade. They eat **phytoplankton**, microscopic algae that drift in open water. Because each mussel filters a litre or more of water every day, they consume so much phytoplankton that they can deplete populations. Phytoplankton is the foundation of the Great Lakes food web, so its depletion is bad news for **zooplankton**, the tiny aquatic animals that eat phytoplankton—and for the fish that eat both. Water bodies with zebra mussels have fewer zooplankton and open-water fish than water bodies without them, researchers are finding.

However, zebra mussels also provide benefits to some bottom-feeding invertebrates and fish. By filtering algae and organic matter from open water and depositing nutrients in their feces, they shift the community's nutrient balance to the bottom and benefit the species that feed there. Once they have cleared the water, sunlight penetrates deeper, spurring the growth of large-leafed underwater plants and algae. Such changes have ripple effects throughout the community that scientists are only beginning to understand.

In the past several years, scientists have noticed a surprising twist: One invader is being displaced by another. The quagga mussel (*Dreissena buensis*), a close relative of the zebra mussel, is spreading through the Great Lakes, replacing the zebra mussel in many locations. What consequences this may have for ecological communities, scientists are only beginning to understand.

Species Interactions

By interacting with many species in a variety of ways, zebra mussels have set in motion an array of changes in the ecological communities they have invaded. Interactions among species are the threads in the fabric of communities, holding them together and determining their nature. Ecologists have organized species interactions into several fundamental categories. Most prominent are competition, predation, parasitism, herbivory, and mutualism. **TABLE 5.1** summarizes the positive (+) and negative (−) impacts of each type of interaction for each participant. An interaction with no impact is shown by a "0" in the table.

Table 5.1   Effects of Species Interactions on Their Participants

Type of interaction	Effect on Species 1	Effect on Species 2
Mutualism	+	+
Commensalism	+	0
Predation, parasitism, herbivory	+	−
Amensalism	−	0
Competition	−	−

"+" denotes a positive effect; "−" denotes a negative effect; "0" denotes no effect.

Competition can occur when resources are limited

When multiple organisms seek the same limited resource, their relationship is said to be one of **competition**. Competing organisms do not usually fight with one another directly and physically. Competition is commonly more subtle and indirect, involving the consequences of one organism's ability to match or outdo others in procuring resources. The resources for which organisms compete can include just about anything an organism might need to survive, including food, water, space, shelter, mates, sunlight, and more. Competitive interactions can take place among members of the same species (*intraspecific competition*) or among members of two or more different species (*interspecific competition*).

We have already discussed intraspecific competition, without naming it as such. Recall that density dependence limits the growth of a population; individuals of the same species compete with one another for limited resources, such that competition is more acute when there are more individuals per unit area (denser populations). Thus, intraspecific competition is really a population-level phenomenon.

In contrast, interspecific competition can have substantial effects on the composition of communities. If one species is a very effective competitor, it may exclude another species from resource use entirely. This outcome, called **competitive exclusion**, occurred in Lake St. Clair and western Lake Erie as the zebra mussel outcompeted a native mussel species.

Alternatively, if neither competing species fully excludes the other, the species may live side by side at a certain ratio of population sizes. This result, called *species coexistence*, may produce a stable point of equilibrium, in which the population size of each remains fairly constant through time.

Coexisting species that use the same resources tend to adjust to their competitors to minimize competition with them. Individuals can do this by changing their behaviour so as to use only a portion of the total array of resources they are capable of using. In such cases, individuals are not fulfilling their entire *niche*, or ecological role. The full niche of a species is called its **fundamental niche** (**FIGURE 5.1A**). An individual that plays only part of its role because of competition or other species interactions is said to be displaying a **realized niche** (**FIGURE 5.1B**), the portion of its fundamental niche that is actually filled, or realized.

Species make similar adjustments over evolutionary time. They adapt to competition by evolving to use slightly different resources or to use their shared resources in different ways. If two bird species eat the same type of seeds, one might come to specialize on larger seeds and the other to specialize on smaller seeds. Or one bird might become more active in the morning and the other more active in the evening, thus avoiding direct interference. This process is called **resource partitioning**, because the species divide, or partition, the resource they use in common by specializing in different ways (**FIGURE 5.2**).

Resource partitioning can lead to *character displacement*, which occurs when competing species evolve physical characteristics that reflect their reliance on the portion of the resource they use. By becoming more different from one another, two species reduce their competition. Through natural selection, birds that specialize on larger seeds may evolve larger bills that enable them to make best use of the resource, whereas birds specializing on smaller seeds may evolve smaller bills. This is precisely

(a) Fundamental niche

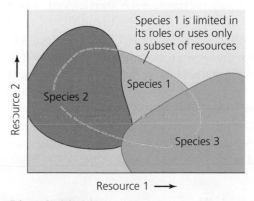

(b) Realized niche

FIGURE 5.1   An organism facing competition may be forced to play a lesser ecological role or use fewer resources than it would in the absence of its competitor. With no competitors, an organism can exploit its full fundamental niche **(a)**. But when competitors restrict what an organism can do or what resources it can use, the organism is limited to a realized niche **(b)**, which covers only a subset of its fundamental niche. In considering niches, ecologists have traditionally focused on competition, but they now recognize that other species interactions are also influential.

FIGURE 5.2
When species compete, they tend to partition resources, each specializing on a slightly different resource or way of attaining a shared resource. A number of types of birds—including the woodpeckers, creeper, and nuthatch shown here—feed on insects from tree trunks, but they use different portions of the trunk, seeking different foods in different ways.

what extensive research has revealed about the finches from the Galápagos Islands that were first described by Charles Darwin.

Several types of interactions are exploitative

In competitive interactions, each participant has a negative effect on other participants, because each takes resources the others could have used. This is reflected in the two minus signs shown for competition in **TABLE 5.1**. In other types of interactions, some participants benefit while others are harmed (the +/− interactions in the table). We can think of interactions in which one member exploits another for its own gain as exploitative interactions. Such interactions include predation, parasitism, herbivory, and related concepts, outlined below.

Predators kill and consume prey

Every living thing needs to procure food and, for most animals, that means eating other living organisms. **Predation** is the process by which individuals of one

FIGURE 5.3
Predator–prey interactions have ecological and evolutionary consequences for both prey and predator. Here, a fire-bellied snake (*Liophis epinephalus*) devours a frog in the Monteverde cloud forest.

species—the **predator**—hunt, capture, kill, and consume individuals of another species, the **prey** (**FIGURE 5.3**). Along with competition, predation has traditionally been viewed as one of the primary organizing forces in community ecology. Interactions between predators and prey structure the food webs that we will examine shortly, and they influence community composition by helping determine the relative abundance of predators and prey.

Zebra mussel predation on phytoplankton has reduced phytoplankton populations by up to 90%, according to many studies in the Great Lakes and Hudson River. Zebra mussels also consume the smaller types of zooplankton. This predation, combined with the competition mentioned above, has caused zooplankton population sizes and biomass to decline by up to 70% in Lake Erie and the Hudson River since zebra mussels arrived. Meanwhile, the mussels do not readily digest some cyanobacteria, so concentrations of these cyanobacteria rise in lakes with zebra mussels. Most predators are also prey, however, and zebra mussels have become a food source for a number of North American species since their introduction. These include diving ducks, muskrats, crayfish, flounder, sturgeon, eels, and several types of fish with grinding teeth, such as carp and freshwater drum.

Predation can sometimes drive population dynamics by causing cycles in population sizes. An increase in the population size of prey creates more food for predators, which may survive and reproduce more effectively as a result. As the predator population rises, additional predation drives down the population of prey. Fewer prey in turn causes some predators to starve, so that the predator population declines. This allows the prey population to begin rising again, starting the cycle anew. Most natural systems involve so many factors that such cycles

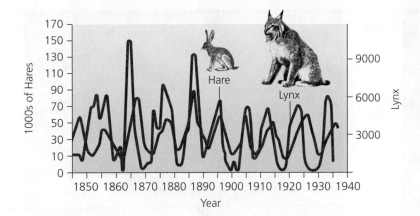

FIGURE 5.4
Predator–prey systems sometimes show paired cycles, in which increases and decreases in one organism apparently drive increases and decreases in the other. Although such cycles are predicted by theory and are seen in lab experiments, they are very difficult to document conclusively in natural systems.
Source: Data from Maclulich, D.A. (1937) Fluctuation in the numbers of varying hare (Lepus americanus). Univ. Toronto Stud. Biol. Ser. No. 43. Toronto, University of Toronto Press.

do not last long, but in some cases we see extended cycles (**FIGURE 5.4**).

Predation also has evolutionary ramifications. Individual predators that are more adept at capturing prey will likely live longer, healthier lives and be better able to provide for their offspring than will less adept individuals. Thus, natural selection on individuals within a predator species leads to the evolution of adaptations that make them better hunters. Prey are faced with an even stronger selective pressure—the risk of immediate death. For this reason, predation pressure has caused organisms to evolve an elaborate array of defences against being eaten (**FIGURE 5.5**).

Parasites exploit living hosts

Organisms can exploit other organisms without killing them. **Parasitism** is a relationship in which one organism, the **parasite**, depends on another, the **host**, for nourish-

ment or some other benefit while simultaneously doing the host harm. Unlike predation, parasitism usually does not result in an organism's immediate death, although it sometimes contributes to the host's eventual death.

Many parasites live in close contact with their hosts. These parasites include disease pathogens, such as the protists that cause malaria and dysentery, as well as animals, such as tapeworms, that live in the digestive tracts of their hosts. Other parasites live on the exterior of their hosts, such as the ticks that attach themselves to their hosts' skin, and the sea lamprey (*Petromyzon marinus*), another invader of the Great Lakes (**FIGURE 5.6A**). Sea lampreys are tube-shaped vertebrates that grasp the bodies of fish by using a suction-cup mouth and a rasping tongue, sucking blood from the fish for days or weeks. Sea lampreys invaded the Great Lakes from the Atlantic Ocean after people dug canals to connect the lakes for shipping, and the lampreys soon devastated economically important fisheries of chub, lake herring, whitefish, and lake trout. Since the 1950s, Great Lakes

(a) Cryptic coloration

(b) Warning coloration

(c) Mimicry

FIGURE 5.5 Natural selection to avoid predation has resulted in many fabulous adaptations. Some prey hide from predators by *crypsis*, or camouflage, such as this gecko on tree bark **(a)**. Other prey are brightly coloured to warn predators that they are toxic or distasteful, such as this monarch butterfly **(b)**. Still others fool predators with mimicry. Some, like walking sticks imitating twigs, mimic for crypsis. Others mimic toxic, distasteful, or dangerous organisms, like this caterpillar **(c)**; when it is disturbed, the caterpillar swells and curves its tail end and shows eyespots, to look like a snake's head.

(a) Sea lamprey

(b) *Fungus Cordyceps* infecting an insect

FIGURE 5.6   Parasites harm their host organism. With its suction-like mouth and rasping tongue, the sea lamprey (*Petromyzon marinus*) **(a)** attaches itself to fish and sucks the fish's blood for days or weeks, sometimes killing the fish. In **(b)**, an ant (*Pachycondlyla*) is infected by a fungus (*Cordyceps*) that will eventually kill it. In the meantime, fruiting bodies of the fungus are sprouting from the ant. The fungus will soon alter the ant's behaviour, causing it to climb to the highest branches of a nearby plant, so its spores will attain the broadest possible distribution.

fisheries managers have reduced lamprey populations by applying chemicals that selectively kill lamprey larvae.

Other types of parasites are free-living and come into contact with their hosts only infrequently. For example, the cuckoos of Eurasia and the cowbirds of the Americas parasitize other birds by laying eggs in their nests and letting the host bird raise the parasite's young.

Some parasites cause little harm, but others may kill their hosts. Many insects parasitize other insects, often killing them in the process, and are called *parasitoids*. Various species of parasitoid wasps lay eggs on caterpillars. When the eggs hatch, the wasp larvae burrow into the caterpillar's tissues and slowly consume them. The wasp larvae metamorphose into adults and fly from the body of the dying caterpillar.

Just as predators and prey evolve in response to one another, so do parasites and hosts, in a process termed *coevolution*. Hosts and parasites can become locked in a duel of escalating adaptations, a situation sometimes referred to as an "evolutionary arms race." Like rival nations racing to stay ahead of one another in military technology, host and parasite may repeatedly evolve new responses to the other's latest advance. In the long run, though, it may not be in a parasite's best interests to become too harmful to its host. Instead, a parasite might leave more offspring in the next generation—and thus be favoured by natural selection—if it allows its host to live a longer time, or even to thrive.

Herbivores exploit plants

One of the most common types of exploitation is **herbivory**, which occurs when animals feed on the tissues of plants. Insects that feed on plants are the most widespread type of herbivore; just about every plant in the world is attacked by some type of insect (**FIGURE 5.7**). In most cases, herbivory does not kill a plant outright, but may affect its growth and reproduction.

FIGURE 5.7

Herbivory is a common way to make a living. The world holds many thousands, perhaps millions, of species of plant-eating insects, such as this larva (caterpillar) of the death's head hawk moth (*Acherontia atropos*) from western Europe.

Like animal prey, plants have evolved a wide array of defences against the animals that feed on them. Many plants produce chemicals that are toxic or distasteful to herbivores. Others arm themselves with thorns, spines, or irritating hairs. In response, herbivores may evolve ways to overcome these defences, and the plant and the animal may embark on an evolutionary arms race.

Some plants go a step further and recruit certain animals as allies to assist in their defence. Many such plants encourage ants to take up residence by providing thorns or swelled stems for the ants to nest in or nectar-bearing structures for the ants to feed from. These ants protect the plant in return by attacking other insects that land or crawl on it. Other plants respond to herbivory by releasing volatile chemicals when they are bitten or pierced. The airborne chemicals attract predatory insects that may attack the herbivore. Such cooperative strategies as trading defence for food are examples of our next type of species interaction, mutualism.

Mutualists help one another

Mutualism is a relationship in which two or more species benefit from interaction with one another. Generally each partner provides some resource or service that the other needs.

Many mutualistic relationships—like many parasitic relationships—occur between organisms that live in close physical contact. (Indeed, biologists hypothesize that many mutualistic associations evolved from parasitic ones.) Such physically close association is called **symbiosis**. Thousands of terrestrial plant species depend on mutualisms with fungi; plant roots and some fungi together form symbiotic associations called mycorrhizae. In these symbioses, the plant provides energy and protection to the fungus, while the fungus assists the plant in absorbing nutrients from the soil,

detoxifies some harmful substances, and provides protection from some pathogens. In the ocean, coral polyps, the tiny animals that build coral reefs, share beneficial arrangements with algae known as zooxanthellae. The coral provide housing and nutrients for the algae in exchange for a steady supply of food—up to 90% of their nutritional requirements.

You, too, are part of a symbiotic association. Your digestive tract is filled with microbes that help you digest food—microbes for which you are providing a place to live. Indeed, we may owe our very existence to symbiotic mutualisms. It is now widely accepted that the eukaryotic cell originated after certain prokaryotic cells engulfed other prokaryotic cells and established mutualistic symbioses. Scientists have inferred that some of the engulfed cells eventually evolved into cell organelles.

Not all mutualists live in close proximity. One of the most important mutualisms in environmental science involves free-living organisms that may encounter each other only once in their lifetimes. This is *pollination* (**FIGURE 5.8**), an interaction of key significance to agriculture and our food supply. Bees, birds, bats, and other creatures transfer pollen (male sex cells) from one flower to the ova (female cells) of another, fertilizing the female egg, which subsequently grows into a fruit. The pollinating animals visit flowers for their nectar, a reward the plant uses to entice them. The pollinators receive food, and the plants are pollinated and reproduce. Various types of bees alone pollinate 73% of our crops, one expert has estimated—from soybeans to potatoes to tomatoes to beans to cabbage to oranges.

Some interactions have no effect on some participants

Two other types of species interaction get far less attention. **Amensalism** is a relationship in which one organism is harmed and the other is unaffected. In **commensalism**, one

FIGURE 5.8
In mutualism, organisms of different species benefit one another. An important mutualistic interaction for environmental science is pollination. This hummingbird visits flowers to gather nectar and in the process transfers pollen between flowers, helping the plant reproduce. Pollination is of key importance to agriculture, ensuring the reproduction of many crop plants.

species benefits and the other is unaffected. Amensalism has been difficult to pin down, because it is hard to prove that the organism doing the harm is not in fact besting a competitor for a resource. For instance, some plants release poisonous chemicals that harm nearby plants (a phenomenon called *allelopathy*), and some experts have suggested that this is an example of amensalism. However, allelopathy can also be viewed as one plant investing in chemicals to outcompete others for space.

One association commonly cited as an example of commensalism occurs when the conditions created by one plant happen to make it easier for another plant to establish and grow. For instance, palo verde trees in the Sonoran Desert create shade and leaf litter that allow the soil beneath them to hold moisture longer, creating an area that is cooler and moister than the surrounding sun-baked ground. Young plants find it easier to germinate and grow in these conditions, so seedling cacti and other desert plants generally grow up directly beneath "nurse" trees, such as palo verde. This phenomenon, called *facilitation*, influences the structure and composition of communities and how they change through time.

Ecological Communities

We have defined a *community* as a group of populations of organisms that live in the same place at the same time. The members of a community interact with one another in the ways described above, and the direct interactions among species often have indirect effects that ripple outward to affect other community members. The strength of interactions also varies, and together species' interactions determine the species composition, structure, and function of communities. *Community ecologists* are interested in which species coexist, how they relate to one another, how communities change through time, and why these patterns exist.

Energy passes among trophic levels

The interactions among members of a community are many and varied, but some of the most important involve who eats whom. The energy that drives such interactions in most systems comes ultimately from the sun via photosynthesis. As organisms feed on one another, this energy moves through the community, from one rank in the feeding hierarchy, or **trophic level**, to another (**FIGURE 5.9**).

Producers   **Producers**, or **autotrophs** ("self-feeders"), compose the first trophic level. Terrestrial green plants, cyanobacteria, and algae capture solar energy and use photosynthesis to produce sugars. The chemosynthetic bacteria of hot springs and deep-sea hydrothermal vents use geothermal energy in a similar way to produce food.

Consumers   Organisms that derive their food energy from other organisms, **heterotrophs**, are called **consumers**. Consumers that eat producers are known as *primary consumers*; they compose the second trophic level. Grazing animals, such as deer and grasshoppers, are primary consumers. The third trophic level consists of *secondary consumers*, which prey on primary consumers. Wolves that prey on deer are considered secondary consumers, as are rodents and birds that prey on grasshoppers. Predators that feed at even higher trophic levels are known as *tertiary consumers*. Examples of tertiary consumers include hawks and owls that eat rodents that have eaten grasshoppers. Note that most primary consumers are **herbivores** because they consume plants, whereas secondary and tertiary consumers are **carnivores** because they eat animals. Animals that eat both plant and animal food are referred to as **omnivores**.

Detritivores and decomposers   Some organisms consume nonliving organic matter. **Detritivores**, such as millipedes and soil insects, scavenge the waste products or the dead bodies of other community members. **Decomposers**, such as fungi and bacteria, break down leaf litter and other nonliving matter further into simpler constituents that can then be taken up and used by plants. These organisms play an essential role as the community's recyclers, making nutrients from organic matter available for reuse by living members of the community.

In Great Lakes communities, phytoplankton are the main producers, floating freely and photosynthesizing with sunlight that penetrates the upper layer of the water. Zooplankton are primary consumers, feeding on the phytoplankton. Phytoplankton-eating fish are primary consumers, and zooplankton-eating fish are secondary consumers. At higher trophic levels are tertiary consumers, such as larger fish and birds that feed on plankton-eating fish. Zebra mussels, by eating both phytoplankton and zooplankton, function on multiple trophic levels. When any of these organisms dies and sinks to the bottom, detritivores scavenge its tissues and microbial decomposers recycle its nutrients.

Energy, biomass, and numbers decrease at higher trophic levels

At each trophic level, most of the energy that organisms use is lost through respiration. Only a small amount of

Aquatic examples **Terrestrial examples**

FIGURE 5.9 Ecologists organize species hierarchically by their feeding rank, or trophic level. The diagram shows aquatic (left) and terrestrial (right) examples at each level. Arrows indicate the direction of energy flow. Producers produce food by photosynthesis, primary consumers (herbivores) feed on producers, secondary consumers eat primary consumers, and tertiary consumers eat secondary consumers. Communities can have more or fewer trophic levels than in this example. Detritivores and decomposers feed on nonliving organic matter and the remains of dead organisms from all trophic levels, and they "close the loop" by returning nutrients to the soil or the water column for use by producers.

the energy is transferred to the next trophic level through predation, herbivory, or parasitism. The first trophic level (producers) contains a large amount of energy, but the second (primary consumers) contains less energy—only that amount gained from consuming producers. The third trophic level (secondary consumers) contains still less energy, and higher trophic levels (tertiary consumers) contain the least. A general rule of thumb is that each trophic level contains just 10% of the energy of the trophic level below it, although the actual proportion can vary greatly.

This pattern, which can be visualized as a **trophic pyramid**, generally also holds for the numbers of

organisms at each trophic level (**FIGURE 5.10**). Typically, fewer organisms exist at higher trophic levels than at lower trophic levels. A grasshopper eats many plants in its lifetime, a rodent eats many grasshoppers, and a hawk eats many rodents. Thus, for every hawk in a community there must be many rodents, still more grasshoppers, and an immense number of plants. Because the difference in numbers of organisms among trophic levels tends to be large, the same pyramid-like relationship also often holds true for biomass. Even though rodents are larger than grasshoppers, and hawks larger than rodents, the sheer number of prey relative to the predators means that prey biomass will likely be greater overall. Unlike the pyramid

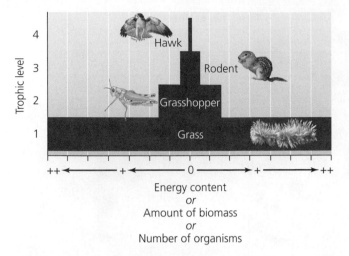

FIGURE 5.10
A trophic pyramid illustrates a rough rule of thumb for the way ecological communities are structured. Organisms at lower trophic levels generally exist in far greater numbers, with greater energy content and greater biomass, than organisms at higher trophic levels. When one organism consumes another, most energy gets used up in respiration rather than in building new tissue. The example shown here is generalized; the actual shape of any given pyramid may be different.

of energy, however, the pyramids of numbers and biomass can occasionally be inverted. For example, the number of trees is much smaller than the number of insects feeding on them, and in the ocean, a small biomass of producers often supports a higher biomass of zooplankton.

Food webs show feeding relationships and energy flow

As energy is transferred from species on one trophic level to species on other trophic levels, it is said to pass up a **food chain**. Plant, grasshopper, rodent, and hawk make up a food chain (as in **FIGURE 5.10**), a linear series of feeding relationships. Thinking in terms of food chains is conceptually useful, but in reality ecological systems are far more complex than simple linear chains. A more

roots

TROPHIC

Trophic means "pertaining to nutrition or food." In the context of ecosystems, it also carries a connotation of "energy" (because in ecosystems, food is energy and energy is food). It comes from the Greek root *trophe*, meaning "nourishment." If you consider terms like **autotroph** ("self-feeder"), **heterotroph** ("other-feeder"), and **trophic level** (a position in a food chain), you can easily find the root meaning of *trophe*.

accurate representation of the feeding relationships in a community is a **food web**, a visual map of feeding relationships and energy flow, showing the many paths by which energy passes among organisms as they consume one another.

FIGURE 5.11 shows a food web from a temperate deciduous forest of eastern North America. Like virtually all diagrams of ecological systems, it is greatly simplified, leaving out the vast majority of species and interactions that occur. Note, however, that even within this simplified diagram, we can pick out a number of different food chains involving different sets of species.

A Great Lakes food web would involve the phytoplankton and cyanobacteria that photosynthesize near the water's surface, the zooplankton that eat them, the fish that eat all these, the larger fish that eat the smaller fish, and the lampreys that parasitize the fish. It would include a number of native mussels and clams and, since 1988, the zebra and quagga mussels that are crowding them out. It would include diving ducks that used to feed on native bivalves and now are preying on mussels.

This food web would also show that an array of bottom-dwelling invertebrates feed from the refuse of the exotic mussels. These waste products promote bacterial growth and disease pathogens that harm native bivalves, but they also provide nutrients that nourish crayfish and many smaller *benthic* (bottom-dwelling) invertebrate animals. Finally, the food web would include underwater plants and macroscopic algae, whose growth is promoted by the non-native mussels. The mussels clarify the water by filtering out phytoplankton, and sunlight penetrates deeper into the water column, spurring photosynthesis and plant growth. Thus, zebra and quagga mussels alter this food web essentially by shifting productivity from the open-water regions to the benthic and *littoral* (nearshore) regions. In so doing, the mussels affect fish indirectly, helping benthic and littoral fishes and making life harder for open-water fishes (see "The Science Behind the Story: Assessing the Ecological Impacts of Zebra Mussels," available on myenvironmentplace).

Some organisms play especially important roles in communities

"Some animals are more equal than others," George Orwell wrote in his 1945 book *Animal Farm*. Although Orwell was making wry sociopolitical commentary, his remark hints at a truth in ecology. In communities, ecologists have found, some species exert greater influence than do others. A species that has a particularly strong or far-reaching impact is often called a **keystone species**. A keystone is the wedge-shaped stone at the top of an arch

FIGURE 5.11 Food webs are conceptual representations of feeding relationships in a community. This food web pertains to eastern North America's temperate deciduous forest and includes organisms on several trophic levels. In a food web diagram, arrows are drawn from one organism to another to indicate the direction of energy flow as a result of predation, parasitism, or herbivory. For example, an arrow leads from the grass to the cottontail rabbit to indicate that cottontails consume grasses. The arrow from the cottontail to the tick indicates that parasitic ticks derive nourishment from cottontails. Communities include so many species and are complex enough, however, that most food web diagrams are bound to be gross simplifications.

that is vital for holding the structure together; remove the keystone, and the arch will collapse. In an ecological community, removal of a keystone species will have substantial ripple effects and will alter a large portion of the food web.

Some keystone species have been removed from their natural communities with unintended consequences, in what are essentially uncontrolled large-scale experiments. A well-known example is the elimination of wolves (intentionally, for the most part) from many parts of North America. Wolves are voracious predators; when

they are eliminated from an area, the populations of large herbivores, such as elk and moose, can grow out of control. This can have far-reaching impacts on vegetation and, consequently, on all other animals in the area.

Ecologists also have verified the keystone species concept by careful observation and controlled experiments. For example, classic work by marine biologist Robert Paine established that the predatory starfish *Pisaster ochraceus* has great influence on the community composition of intertidal organisms on the Pacific coast of North America. When *Pisaster* is present in this community, species diversity is high, with several types of barnacles, mussels, and algae. When *Pisaster* is removed, the mussels it preys on become numerous and displace other species, suppressing species diversity. More recent work off the Atlantic coast published in 2007 suggests that the reduction of shark populations by commercial fishing has allowed populations of certain skates and rays to increase, which has depressed numbers of bay scallops and other bivalves they eat.

To understand the significance of one or two large species in an ecosystem, and the delicacy of the balance, we can consider the case of moose and wolves in the boreal forest of Cape Breton Highlands National Park. Moose were rare by 1900 and had completely disappeared from the area by 1924, because of excessive hunting and habitat destruction. Parks Canada reintroduced moose to the park during 1947 and 1948, by importing and releasing 18 animals from Elk Island National Park. The reintroduction was highly successful, and moose are currently plentiful in the park, possibly too plentiful.[3] In the absence of the moose's natural predator, the wolf, which disappeared from the area as early as the mid-1800s, there are few natural controls on the moose population within the park. Moose are selective eaters; their preferred winter food is the balsam fir. By browsing heavily on certain types of food but not others, they can alter the forest landscape, leading to significant changes in the ecosystem. The success of the reintroduced moose population in Cape Breton Highlands National Park may be leading to changes in the composition of the boreal forest there. In addition to dramatic impacts on vegetation, moose may have contributed to the decline of native caribou in some areas, by preventing regeneration of the mature forests, limiting the caribou's food, and opening the landscape to predators.

Animals at high trophic levels, such as wolves, starfish, and sea otters, are most often seen as keystone species. Other species attain keystone status as "ecosystem engineers" by physically modifying the environment shared by community members. Beavers build dams and turn streams into ponds, flooding vast expanses of dry land and turning it to swamp. Prairie dogs dig burrows that aerate the soil and serve as homes for other animals. Bees are absolutely crucial, for example, even for human food security, because they are pollinators, moving pollen from male to female plants to facilitate the plants' sexual reproduction, as well as ensuring plant genetic diversity.

Less conspicuous organisms and those toward the bottoms of food chains can potentially be viewed as keystone species, too. Remove the fungi that decompose dead matter or the insects that control plant growth or the phytoplankton that are the base of the marine food chain and a community may change very rapidly indeed. Because there are usually more species at lower trophic

levels, however, it is less likely that any one of them alone might have wide influence; if one species is removed, other species that remain may be able to perform many of its functions.

Identifying keystone species is no simple task, and there is no cut-and-dried definition of the term to help us. Community dynamics are complex, species interactions differ in their strength, and the strength of species interactions can vary through time and space. "The Science Behind the Story: Otters, Urchins, Kelp, and a Whale of a Chain Reaction" gives an idea of the surprises that are sometimes in store for ecologists studying these interactions.

Communities respond to disturbance in different ways

The removal of a keystone species is just one of many types of disturbance that can modify the composition, structure, or function of an ecological community. Over time, any given community may experience natural disturbances ranging from gradual phenomena, such as climate change, to sudden events, such as hurricanes, floods, or avalanches.

Communities are dynamic systems and may respond to disturbance in several ways. A community that resists change and remains stable despite disturbance is said to show **resistance** to the disturbance. Alternatively, a community may show **resilience**, meaning that it changes in response to disturbance but later returns to its original state. Or a community may be modified by disturbance permanently and may never return to its original state.

Succession follows severe disturbance

If a disturbance is severe enough to eliminate all or most of the species in a community, the affected site will undergo a somewhat predictable series of changes that ecologists call **succession**. In the traditional view of this process, ecologists described two types of succession.

Primary succession follows a disturbance so severe that no vegetation or soil life remains from the community that occupied the site. Primary succession starts with a clean slate; the biotic community is built essentially from scratch. In contrast, **secondary succession** begins when a disturbance dramatically alters an existing community but does not destroy all living things or all organic matter in the soil. In secondary succession, vestiges of the previous community remain; the surviving organisms have a head start over other organisms and these building blocks help shape the process of reconstruction.

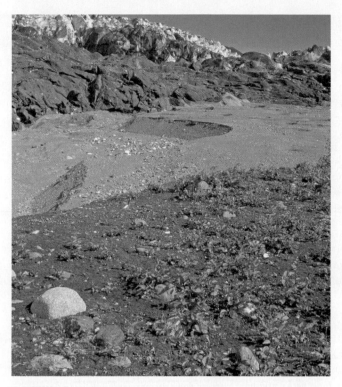

FIGURE 5.12
As this glacier retreats, small pioneer plants (foreground) begin the process of primary succession.

At terrestrial sites, primary succession takes place after a bare expanse of rock, sand, or sediment becomes newly exposed to the atmosphere. This can occur when glaciers retreat, lakes dry up, or volcanic lava flows spread across the landscape (**FIGURE 5.12**). Species that arrive first and colonize the new substrate are referred to as **pioneer species**. Pioneer species are well adapted for colonization, having such traits as spores or seeds that can travel long distances.

The pioneers best suited to colonizing bare rock are the mutualistic aggregates of fungi and algae known as **lichens**. Lichens succeed because their algal component provides food and energy via photosynthesis while the fungal component takes a firm hold on rock and captures the moisture that both organisms need to survive. As lichens grow, they secrete acids that break down the rock surface. The resulting waste material forms the beginnings of soil, and once soil begins to form, small plants, insects, and worms find the rocky outcrops more hospitable. As new organisms arrive, they provide more nutrients and habitat for future arrivals. As time passes, larger plants establish themselves, the amount of vegetation increases, and species diversity rises.

Secondary succession on land begins when a fire, a hurricane, logging, or farming removes much of the biotic community. Consider a farmed field in eastern North America that has been abandoned (**FIGURE 5.13**). In the first few years after farming ends, the site will be colonized by pioneer species of grasses, herbs, and forbs that were already in the vicinity and that disperse effectively. As time passes, shrubs and fast-growing trees, such as aspens, rise from the field. Pine trees subsequently rise above the aspens and shrubs, forming a pine-dominated forest. This pine forest develops an understory of hardwood trees, because pine seedlings do not grow well under mature pines, whereas some hardwood seedlings do. Eventually the hardwoods outgrow the pines, creating a hardwood forest (see **FIGURE 5.13**).

Processes of succession occur in many diverse ecological systems, from ponds to rocky intertidal areas to the carcasses of animals. A lake or pond that originates as nothing but water on a lifeless substrate begins to undergo succession as it is colonized by algae, microbes, plants, and zooplankton. As these organisms grow, reproduce, and die, the water body slowly fills with organic matter. The lake or pond acquires further organic matter and sediments from the water it receives from rivers, streams, and surface runoff. Eventually, the water body fills in, becoming a bog or even a terrestrial ecosystem.

Grasses, herbs, forbs

Shrubs, seedlings

Saplings, poplar trees

Pines

Hardwoods

Time ⟶

FIGURE 5.13
Secondary succession occurs after a disturbance, such as fire, landslides, or farming, removes most of the vegetation from an area. Shown here is a typical series of changes in a plant community of eastern North America following the abandonment of a farmed field.

THE SCIENCE BEHIND THE STORY

Otters, Urchins, Kelp, and a Whale of a Chain Reaction

Dr. James Estes, University of California at Santa Cruz, works at sea in Alaska.

Sea otters (*Enhydra lutris*) live in coastal waters of the Pacific Ocean. These mammals float on their backs amid the waves, feasting on sea urchins (*Strongylocentrotus spp.*) that they pry from the ocean bottom. Once abundant, sea otters were hunted nearly to extinction for their fur. Protection by international treaty in 1911 allowed their numbers to grow. Otters returned to high densities in some regions but failed to return in others.

Biologists noted that regions with abundant otters hosted dense "forests" of kelp, a brown alga (seaweed) that anchors to the seafloor, growing up to 60 m high toward the sunlit surface. Kelp forests provide complex physical structures in which diverse communities of fish and invertebrates find shelter and food. In regions without sea otters, scientists found kelp forests absent. In the absence of otters, urchins become so numerous that they eat every last bit of kelp, creating empty seafloors called "urchin barrens" that are relatively devoid of life.

Ecologists determined that otters were largely responsible for the presence of the kelp forests, simply by keeping urchin numbers in check through predation. This research—mostly by James Estes of the University of California at Santa Cruz and his colleagues—established sea otters as a prime example of a keystone species. Jane Watson investigated 60 randomly selected sites in the shallow rocky communities off the northwest coast of Vancouver Island. Sea otters were present in 40 sites and absent from 20. In the locations where sea otters were absent, urchins occupied 84% of the sea bottom. In contrast, areas with sea otters hosted large populations of kelp, and urchins occupied only 1.8% of the bottom.

But the story did not end there. In the 1990s, otter populations dropped precipitously near Alaska and the Aleutians. No one knew why. Estes and his co-workers placed radio tags on Aleutian otters and studied them at sea. Their first hypothesis was that fertility rates had dropped, but radio-tracking observations showed that females were raising pups without problem. Their second hypothesis was that the otters were simply moving to other locations. But the radio tracking showed no unusual dispersals.

They were left with only one viable hypothesis: increased mortality. Then one day in 1991, Estes's team witnessed something never seen before. They watched as a sea otter was killed and eaten by an orca, or killer whale (*Orcinus orca*). These striking black-and-white predators grow up to 10 m long, hunt in groups, and usually attack larger prey. A sea otter to them is a mere snack. Yet over the following years, Estes's team saw more cases of orca predation on otters. Could killer whales be killing off the otters?

The researchers compared a bay where otters were vulnerable to orcas with a lagoon where they were protected. Otter numbers in the lagoon remained stable over four years, whereas those in the bay dropped by 76%. Radio tracking showed no movement between these locations. Using data on otter birth rates, death rates, and population age structure, they estimated that to account for the otter decline, 6788 orca attacks per year would have had to occur in their study area. This *expected* rate of observed attacks matched their *actual* number of observed attacks. These lines of evidence led the researchers to propose that predation by orcas was eliminating otters.

As otters declined in the Aleutians, urchins increased, and kelp density fell dramatically (see figure). These changes supported the idea that otters were a keystone species, but now it seemed that one keystone species was being controlled by another.

Why had the orcas suddenly started eating otters? A possible answer came in 2003, after Alan Springer, James Estes, and others determined that sea otters were only the latest in a series of population crashes in the northern Pacific. Harbour seals had declined by more than 90%; fur seals had fallen by 60%; sea lions had crashed by 80%. Preceding these declines were collapses of the great grey, blue, and humpback whale populations.

Most orcas specialize in eating great whales, which they kill in groups, like a wolf pack taking down an elk. But industrial

---

In this traditional view of succession that we have described, the transitions between stages of succession eventually lead to a **climax community**, which remains in place, with little modification, until some disturbance restarts succession. Early ecologists felt that each region had its own characteristic climax community, determined by the region's climate.

Today, ecologists recognize that succession is far more variable and less predictable than originally thought. The trajectory of succession can vary greatly according to chance factors, such as which particular species happen to gain an early foothold. The stages of succession blur into one another and vary from place to place, and some stages may sometimes be skipped completely. In addition, climax communities are not predetermined solely by climate but may vary with other conditions from one time or place to another.

Once a climax community is disturbed and succession is set in motion, there is no guarantee that the community will ever return to that climax state. Many communities disturbed by human impact have not returned to their former conditions. This is the case with vast areas of the whaling by ships from Japan, Russia, and other nations caused populations of great whales to plummet by 99% between 1965 and 1973 in the northern Pacific. When hunting decimated the great whales, the orcas turned to smaller, less-favoured seals and sea lions. When their predation had depleted those populations, they turned to smaller prey still—sea otters.

Not all scientists are convinced by this bold hypothesis, and the debate has been vigorous. In the meantime, Estes and his colleagues continue to learn more. In 2005, Shauna Reisewitz, Estes, and Charles Simenstad reported that when kelp forests vanish, so do rock greenling, the community's most abundant fish species. The few greenling left also change their diet. Thus, the whale-orca-otter-urchin-kelp system also influences fish and their prey. The ongoing discoveries highlight the intriguing complexity of the species interactions that affect ecological communities.

Before the 1990s (left side of figure), otters kept urchin numbers in check, allowing kelp forests to grow. By the end of the 1990s (right side of figure), orcas (killer whales), deprived of their usual food sources, were eating otters. This set off a chain reaction across several trophic levels: Otters decreased, sea urchins increased, and kelp decreased. The lines in the top graph indicate trends in otter populations from four different Aleutian islands. The width of the arrows indicates the strength of interaction. Source: Estes, J., et al. (1998) Killer whale predation on sea otters linking oceanic and nearshore ecosystems. Science 282: 473–476.

Middle East that once were fertile enough to support productive farming but now are deserts.

Invasive species pose new threats to community stability

Traditional concepts of communities and successions involve sets of organisms understood to be native to an area. But what if a new organism arrives from elsewhere? And what if this non-native (also called *alien* or **exotic**)

organism spreads widely and becomes dominant? Such **invasive species** can alter a community substantially and are one of the central ecological forces in today's world.

Most often, invasive species are non-native species that people have introduced, intentionally or by accident, from elsewhere in the world. Any non-native organism introduced into an ecosystem will require adjustments, but species become invasive **pests** when the negative impacts outweigh the benefits, especially when the limiting factors that might regulate their population

FIGURE 5.14

The zebra mussel is a prime example of a biological invader that has modified an ecological community. By filtering phytoplankton and small zooplankton from open water, it generates a number of impacts on other species, both negative (red downward arrows) and positive (green upward arrows) **(a)**. This map **(b)** shows the range of zebra and quagga mussels in North America as of 2011. In less than three decades the zebra mussel has spread to Ontario, Québec, and 30 U.S. states, mainly by boats but in some cases by overland transport. The quagga mussel is rapidly following the zebra mussel's spread.
Source for (b): U.S. Geological Survey. Map showing 2011 distribution of zebra mussel sightings, Benson, A.J. 2011. Zebra mussel sightings distribution. Retrieved from http://nas.er.usgs.gov/tak/group/mollusks/zebramusseldistribution.aspx

(a) Impacts of zebra mussels on members of a Great Lakes nearshore community

(b) Distribution of zebra and quagga mussels on North America, 2011

growth are absent. Thus, the main characteristics of *problematic* invasive species include the ability to spread rapidly, and unimpeded, in the new environment, and the ability to have a negative impact on native species and ecosystems into which it has been introduced.

Plants and animals brought to one area from another may leave their predators, parasites, and competitors behind, freeing them from natural constraints on their population growth (**FIGURE 5.14**). If there happen to be few organisms in the new environment that can act as predators, parasites, or competitors, the introduced species may do very well. As it proliferates, it may exert diverse influences on its fellow community members. An example is the chestnut blight, an Asian fungus that killed nearly

every mature American chestnut (*Castanea dentata*), the dominant tree species of many forests of eastern North America, in the quarter-century preceding 1930. Asian trees had evolved defences against the fungus over long millennia of coevolution, but the American chestnut had not.

In other cases, a species may be considered a pest even in regions where it is native. An example is the Asian long-horned beetle (*Anoplophora glabripennis*), a voracious wood-eating insect that is native to China but is also a pest, with few natural predators. The Asian long-horned beetle feeds on many different species of temperate hardwood trees, including maple, birch, horse chestnut, poplar, willow, elm, ash, and black locust. The beetle, introduced to North America from China via packaging materials, has the potential to cause widespread destruction. To date, the only approach to controlling the spread of the beetle is to cut down and burn any infested trees.[4]

So far we have considered examples of the impacts of a non-native insect, a fungus, and a mollusc, but virtually any type of organism can become an invasive pest, given circumstances that facilitate its spread. Introduced grasses and shrubs, such as the Scotch broom (*Cytisus scoparius*), have had dramatic impacts on the Garry oak (*Quercus garryana*)–based ecosystem of southeastern Vancouver Island and the Gulf Islands, a disappearing ecosystem that supports many rare plant species.[5] Fish introduced into streams purposely for sport or accidentally via shipping compete with and exclude native fish.

A particularly troublesome example of a native invasive species is the sea lamprey (*Petromyzon marinus*), an eel-like fish that is native to the Atlantic Ocean and was probably introduced to the Great Lakes as early as the 1830s by oceangoing vessels. The sea lamprey is a pretty unpleasant creature to begin with, as it lives by attaching itself to the flanks of other fish and feeding parasitically on their blood. But lampreys have had tremendous success as they have spread—mainly via shipping channels and canals—into the Great Lakes, devastating some local fish populations.

Hundreds of native island-dwelling animals and plants worldwide have been driven extinct by the goats, pigs, and rats intentionally or accidentally introduced by human colonists. The cane toad (*Bufo marinus*), introduced to Australia to control insects in sugar cane fields (which it never did very successfully), is poisonous to just about anything that tries to eat it and has been extremely damaging to a wide variety of indigenous animal populations.

The impact of invasive species on native species and ecological communities is severe and it is growing year by year with the increasing mobility of humans and the globalization of our society. Global trade helped spread zebra mussels, which were unintentionally transported in the ballast water of cargo ships. To maintain stability at sea, ships take water into their hulls as they begin their voyage and discharge that water at their destination. Decades of unregulated exchange of ballast water have ferried hundreds of species across the oceans.

In North America, zebra mussels—and the media attention they generated—helped put invasive species on the map as a major environmental and economic problem. Scientific research into introduced species has proliferated, and many ecologists view invasive species as the second-greatest threat to species and natural systems, behind only habitat destruction.

Funding has now become more widely available for the control and eradication of invasive species, and control mechanisms are widely researched and shared across juris-

weighing the issues
ARE INVASIVE SPECIES ALL BAD?

Some ethicists have questioned the notion that all invasive species should automatically be considered bad. If we introduce a non-native species to a community and it greatly modifies the community, is it always a bad thing? What if it drives another species extinct? What if the invasive species arrived on its own, rather than through human intervention? What ethical standard would you apply to determine whether an invasive species should be battled or accepted?

dictional boundaries. Managers at all levels of government have been trying a variety of techniques to control the spread of zebra and quagga mussels—removing them manually, applying toxic chemicals, drying them out, depriving them of oxygen, introducing predators and diseases, and stressing them with heat, sound, electricity, carbon dioxide, and ultraviolet light. However, most of these are localized and short-term fixes that are not capable of making a dent in the huge populations at large in the environment. In case after case, managers are finding that controlling and eradicating invasive species is so difficult and expensive that preventive measures (such as ballast water regulations) represent a much better investment.

Some altered communities can be restored to their former condition

Invasive species are adding to the tremendous transformations that humans have already forced on natural landscapes through habitat alteration, deforestation, hunting of keystone species, pollution, and other impacts. With so much of Earth's landscape altered by human impact, it is impossible to find areas that are truly pristine. This realization has given rise to the conservation effort known as **ecological restoration**. The practice of ecological restoration is informed by the science of **restoration ecology**. Restoration ecologists research the historical conditions of ecological communities as they existed before our industrialized civilization altered them. They then try to devise ways to restore some of these areas to an earlier condition, often to a natural "presettlement" condition.

For example, activities underway at Chatterton Hill Park in Saanich, British Columbia, are aimed at the ecological restoration of Garry oak–associated ecosystems (**FIGURE 5.15**). As mentioned above, these delicate,

FIGURE 5.15
Garry oak ecosystems in south Vancouver Island and the Gulf Islands of British Columbia, like the one shown here, are being invaded by aggressive exotic species. Some have been targeted for ecological restoration.

complex ecosystems, which occur almost exclusively in south Vancouver Island and the Gulf Islands, are being invaded by aggressive exotic species that suppress the growth of native plants. Ecological restoration activities at Chatterton Hill, which began in 2002, include active restoration, removal of invasive plants, natural feature inventories (soil, vegetation, and animals), monitoring, and educational activities. In 2006, local restoration ecologists reevaluated the site, comparing it with a similar nearby site where no restoration activities had taken place; they concluded that biodiversity at the restoration site was increasing. At the comparison site, the tree layer was similar, but the understory vegetation was still dominated by grasses and the invasive exotic, Scotch broom.[6]

weighing the issues

RESTORING "NATURAL" COMMUNITIES

Practitioners of ecological restoration in North America aim to restore communities to their natural state. But what is meant by "natural"? Is it the state of the community before industrialization? Before Europeans came to the New World? Before any people laid eyes on the community? Let us say Aborigines altered a forest community 8000 years ago by burning the underbrush to improve hunting, and continued doing so until Europeans arrived 400 years ago and cut down the forest for farming. Should restorationists try to recreate the forest of Aboriginal time, or the forest that existed even before the Aboriginal peoples arrived? What are some advantages and disadvantages of each approach?

Perhaps the world's largest restoration project is the ongoing effort to restore parts of the Florida Everglades. The Everglades, a unique 7500 km^2 ecosystem of interconnected marshes and seasonally flooded grasslands, has been drying out for decades because the water that feeds it has been heavily managed for flood control and overdrawn for irrigation and development. The water management system inadvertently caused extensive degradation of the environment, resulting in the loss of more than half of the Everglades and the elimination of whole classes of ecosystems. Populations of wading birds have dropped by 90–95%, and economically important fisheries have suffered greatly. Extensive engineering of river channels also led to a loss of aesthetic appeal, problems with stagnancy and pollution of water in the channels, and a host of other problems. The 30-year, $7.8 billion restoration project intends to restore water by undoing damming and diversions of 1600 km of canals, 1150 km of levees, and 200 water control structures.

Ecosystem restoration is almost always expensive and only sometimes, or partially, successful. Regardless, the more our population grows and development spreads, the more ecological restoration will become a vital conservation strategy for the future.

Earth's Biomes

Across the world, each portion of each continent has different sets of species, leading to endless variety in community composition. However, communities in far-flung places often share strong similarities in their structure and function. This allows us to classify communities into broad types. A **biome** is a major regional complex of similar communities—a large ecological unit recognized primarily by its dominant plant type and vegetation structure. The world contains a number of biomes, each covering large geographic areas (**FIGURE 5.16**).

A term that is often used interchangeably with biome, but probably should not be, is ecoregion. An **ecoregion** is defined by the World Wildlife Fund as a large area of land or water that contains a geographically distinct assemblage of natural communities that share a large majority of their species and ecological dynamics, share similar environmental conditions, and interact ecologically in ways that are critical for their long-term persistence.[7] A particular ecoregion—such as the short grasslands of the Canadian Prairies of southern Alberta and Saskatchewan, for example—is thus a representative of a biome (the "temperate grasslands" biome) that is broader in scope and occurs in numerous localities around the world.

The difference between an ecoregion and a biome might be easiest to grasp for a highly distinctive envi-ronment, such as a desert. The desert biome has certain climatic and

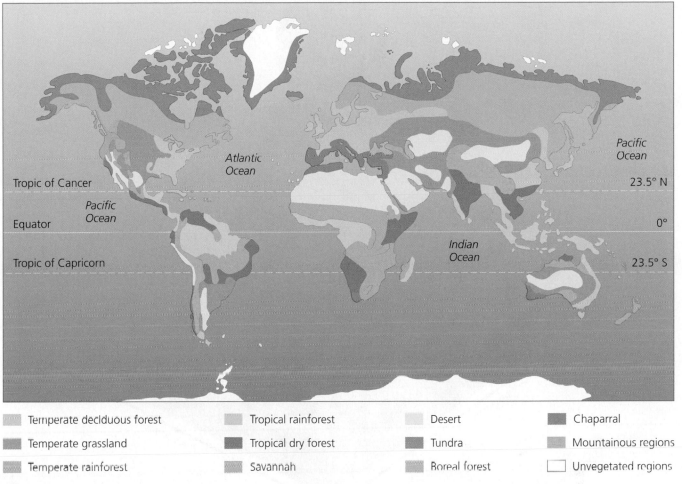

▨ Temperate deciduous forest	▨ Tropical rainforest	▨ Desert	▨ Chaparral
▨ Temperate grassland	▨ Tropical dry forest	▨ Tundra	▨ Mountainous regions
▨ Temperate rainforest	▨ Savannah	▨ Boreal forest	☐ Unvegetated regions

FIGURE 5.16 Biomes are distributed around the world according to temperature, precipitation, atmospheric and oceanic circulation patterns, and other factors.

ecological characteristics in common (see below), notably the lack of precipitation. There are many representatives of the desert biome around the world, including the Mojave Desert, the Gobi Desert, and the Sahara Desert, among many others. Each of these individual desert environments constitutes or is part of an eco-region, with its own particular characteristics and flora and fauna, but it is still consistent with the broad characteristics that define the desert biome.

roots

BIOME

The word **biome** comes from the Greek root *bios*, "life." The word is thought to have been first used in 1916 by American botanist and ecologist Frederic Clements, who defined it, at the time, as "the biotic community, regarded as an organic unit comprising all the species of plants and animals at home in a particular habitat." It is interesting that Clements considered a biome to consist solely of the *biotic community* and did not include abiotic components in his definition. Today, ecologists are still divided about whether biomes include abiotic factors or are simply influenced by them.

Climate influences the locations of biomes

Which biome covers any particular portion of the planet depends on a variety of abiotic factors, including temperature, precipitation, atmospheric circulation, and soil characteristics. Among these factors, temperature and precipitation exert the greatest influence (**FIGURE 5.17**), because, as you will recall from our discussion about productivity, these two factors have the dominant effect on net primary productivity of terrestrial ecosystems. Because biome type is largely a function of climate, and because average monthly temperature and precipitation are among the best indicators of an area's climate, scientists often use climate diagrams, or **climatographs**, to depict such information.

Global climate patterns cause biomes to occur in large patches in different parts of the world. For instance,

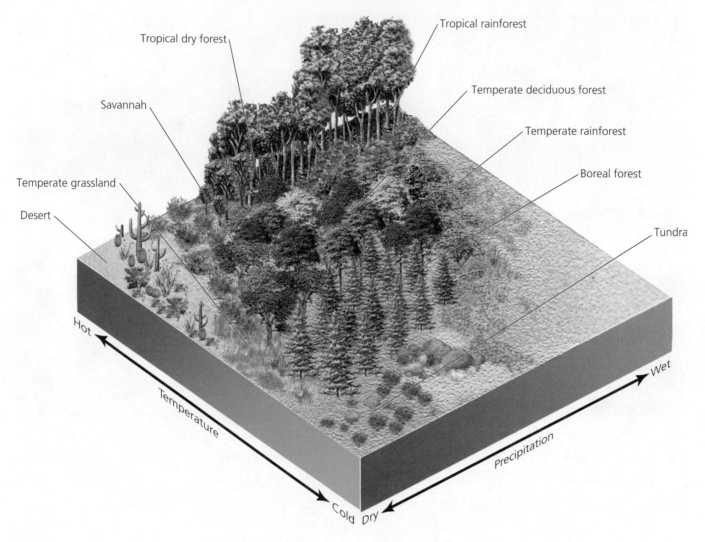

FIGURE 5.17   As precipitation increases, vegetation generally becomes taller and more luxuriant. As temperature increases, types of plant communities change. Together, temperature and precipitation are the main factors determining which biome occurs in a given area. For instance, deserts occur in dry regions, tropical rainforests occur in warm, wet regions, and tundra occurs in the cold, dry regions.

temperate deciduous forest occurs in eastern North America, north–central Europe, and eastern China. Note how patches representing the same biome tend to occur at similar latitudes. This is due to the north–south gradient in temperature and to atmospheric circulation patterns.

We can divide the world into roughly 10 terrestrial biomes

Each biome encompasses a variety of communities that share similarities. For example, the eastern United States and the southernmost part of eastern Canada support part of the temperate deciduous forest biome. From New Hampshire to the Great Lakes to eastern Texas, precipitation and temperature are similar enough that most of the region's natural plant cover consists of broad-leafed trees that lose their leaves in winter. Within this region, however, exist many different types of temperate

deciduous forest, such as oak–hickory, beech–maple, and pine–oak forests, each sufficiently different to be designated a separate community.

Let us look briefly at the characteristics that define the world's 10 major terrestrial biomes.

Tundra   The **tundra** (**FIGURE 5.18**) is a dry biome—nearly as dry as a desert—but located at very high latitudes along the northern edges of Russia, Canada, and Scandinavia. Extremely cold winters with little daylight and moderately cool summers with lengthy days characterize this landscape of lichens and low, scrubby vegetation without trees. The great seasonal variation in temperature and day length results from this biome's high-latitude location, angled toward the sun in the summer and away from the sun in the winter.

Because of the cold climate, underground soil remains more or less permanently frozen and is called *permafrost*. During the long, cold winters, the surface soils freeze

(a) Typical location: Cumberland Sound, Baffin Island, Nunavut

(b) Tundra

FIGURE 5.18
Tundra is a cold, dry biome found near the poles and atop high mountains at lower latitudes **(a)**. Scientists use climate diagrams **(b)** to illustrate an area's average monthly precipitation and temperature.[8] Typically in these diagrams, the x-axis marks months of the year (beginning in January for regions in the Northern Hemisphere and in July for regions in the Southern Hemisphere). Paired y-axes denote average monthly temperature and average monthly precipitation. The twin curves plotted on a climate diagram indicate trends in precipitation (blue) and in temperature (red) from month to month.

as well; then, when the weather warms, they melt and produce seasonal accumulations of surface water that make ideal habitat for mosquitoes and other biting insects. The swarms of insects benefit bird species that migrate long distances to breed during the brief but productive summer. Caribou also migrate to the tundra to breed, and then leave for the winter. Only a few large animals, such as polar bears (*Ursus maritimus*) and musk oxen (*Ovibos moschatus*), can survive year-round in this extreme climate. Tundra also occurs as **alpine tundra** at the tops of high mountains in temperate and tropical regions.

Because of the extreme climate in Canada's North, Alaska, Russia, and Scandinavia, much of the tundra biome remains intact and relatively unaltered by direct human occupation and interference. For example, the World Wildlife Fund reports the tundra ecoregions of North America to be 95–98% intact. However, much of

the tundra is unprotected by national or provincial or territorial legislation, rendering it potentially susceptible to alteration through human activities. Furthermore, the indirect effects of human modification of the global environment, especially the climate, are increasingly evident in the tundra. One problem that is of external origin is atmospheric fallout, which results in the deposition of heavy metals, and pesticide pollution.[9] In many areas of the tundra, seasonal ice connects the many islands with the mainland; with climatic warming and the associated melting of sea ice, these habitats and the animals that depend on them will be in increasing peril.

Boreal forest   The northern coniferous forest, or **boreal forest**, also called **taiga** (**FIGURE 5.19**), stretches in a broad band across much of Canada, Alaska, Russia, and Scandinavia. In Canada the boreal forest encompasses nearly 6 million km². A few species of **coniferous** or evergreen trees, which create seed cones, have needle-like leaves, and remain green year-round, dominate large stretches of the boreal forest, interspersed with bogs and

(a) Typical location: Jasper National Park, Alberta

(b) Boreal forest

FIGURE 5.19
Boreal forest is defined by long, cold winters, relatively cool summers, and moderate precipitation.

lakes. The black spruce (*Picea mariana*) is a common evergreen species.

The boreal forest's uniformity over huge areas reflects the climate common to this latitudinal band of the globe: These forests develop in cooler, drier regions than do temperate forests, and they experience long, cold winters and short, cool summers. Soils are typically nutrient poor and somewhat acidic. As a result of the strong seasonal variation in day length, temperature, and precipitation, many organisms compress a year's worth of feeding, breeding, and rearing of young into a few warm, wet months. Year-round residents of boreal forest include mammals, such as moose (*Alces alces*), wolves (*Canis lupus*), bears, lynx (*Felis lynx*), and many burrowing rodents. This biome also hosts many insect-eating birds that migrate from the tropics to breed during the brief, intensely productive summer season.

The boreal forest, one-third of which resides in Canada, is one of the largest continuous forest ecosystems. It hosts more wetland area than any other ecosystem on Earth, providing invaluable habitat for many species. The enormous global importance of the boreal forest highlights Canada's role as a steward for much of the world's forested area. We will revisit this role in the chapter on forests and forest management.

Temperate deciduous forest   The **temperate deciduous forest** (**FIGURE 5.20**) that dominates the landscape around the central and southern Great Lakes is characterized by broad-leafed trees that are **deciduous**, meaning that they lose their leaves each fall and remain dormant during winter, when hard freezes would endanger leaves. These mid-latitude forests occur in much of Europe and eastern China as well as in eastern North America—all areas in which precipitation is spread relatively evenly throughout the year. Although soils of the temperate deciduous forest are relatively fertile, the biome generally consists of far fewer tree species than are found in tropical rainforests. Oaks, beeches, and maples are a few of the most abundant types of trees in these forests. A sampling of typical animals of the temperate deciduous forest of eastern North America is shown in **FIGURE 5.11**.

Much of the temperate deciduous or broad-leafed forest in North America has been greatly altered since European settlement; for example, it has been estimated that only about 5% of New England–Acadian mixed broad-leafed forest in Canada remains intact, with about 50% of the habitat in this region described as "heavily altered" by human activity.[10] However, forest cover has been making a comeback in the New England–Acadia region in recent decades, thanks to changing land use and conservation efforts.

(a) Typical location: Kejimkujik National Park, Nova Scotia

(b) Temperate deciduous forest

FIGURE 5.20
Temperate deciduous forests experience relatively stable seasonal precipitation but more variation in seasonal temperatures. When the precipitation curve falls well above the temperature curve, as shown here, the region experiences relatively moist conditions, as indicated by the green shading.

Temperate grassland   Moving westward from the Great Lakes, we find **temperate grasslands** (**FIGURE 5.21**). This is because temperature differences between winter and summer become more extreme, and rainfall diminishes. The limited amount of precipitation in the Prairies and the Great Plains region can support grasses more easily than trees. Also known as *steppes* or *prairies*, temperate grasslands were once widespread throughout parts of North and South America and much of central Asia.

Today people have converted most of the world's grasslands for agriculture, greatly reducing the abundance of native plants and animals. Both the tallgrass prairies that characterize the midwestern United States and the shortgrass prairies of southern Alberta and Saskatchewan are described by the World Wildlife Fund as having been "virtually converted," mainly for wheat production and grazing, with only small undisturbed patches remaining (less than 2% remaining "intact" in Canada). However,

(a) Typical location: Moose Jaw, Saskatchewan

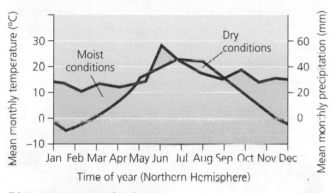

(b) Temperate grassland

FIGURE 5.21
Temperate grasslands experience temperature variations throughout the year and too little precipitation for many trees to grow. This climatograph indicates both "moist" (green) and "dry" (yellow) climate conditions. When the temperature curve is above the precipitation curve, as is the case in May and mid-June through September, the climate conditions are "dry."

restoration ecology efforts in this biome have seen some success, with efforts to reestablish populations of native species, such as the black-footed ferret (*Mustela nigripes*) and bison (*Bison bison*), well underway.[11] Other characteristic vertebrate animals of the North American grasslands include prairie dogs, pronghorn antelope (*Antilocapra americana*), and ground-nesting birds, such as meadowlarks.

Temperate rainforest Moving still further west in North America, the topography becomes more varied, and biome types are intermixed. The coastal Pacific region, with heavy coastal mountain rainfall, features **temperate rainforest (FIGURE 5.22)**, a forest type known for its potential to produce large volumes of commercially important forest products, such as lumber and paper. Coniferous trees such as cedars, spruces, hemlocks, and Douglas fir (*Pseudotsuga menziesii*) grow very tall in the temperate rainforest, so the forest interior is shaded

and damp. In the Queen Charlotte Islands, for example, moisture-loving animals, such as the bright yellow banana slug (*Ariolimax columbianus*) are common, and old-growth conifer stands host the endangered spotted owl (*Strix occidentalis*). The soils of temperate rainforests are usually quite fertile but are susceptible to landslides and erosion if forests are cleared.

Temperate rainforests have been the focus of controversy in Pacific coastal regions, where overharvesting has driven some species toward extinction. Clear-cut logging and road building into forested areas remain the greatest threats to temperate rainforest habitat in these areas (see "Central Case: Battling Over the Last Big Trees at Clayoquot Sound," in the chapter on forests and forest management).

Tropical rainforest In tropical regions we see the same pattern found in temperate regions: Areas of high rainfall grow rainforests, areas of intermediate rainfall host dry or deciduous forests, and areas of lower rainfall become dominated by grasses. However, tropical biomes differ from their temperate counterparts in other ways

(a) Typical location: Queen Charlotte Islands and Vancouver, BC.

(b) Temperate rainforest

FIGURE 5.22
Temperate rainforests receive a great deal of precipitation and feature moist, mossy interiors.

because they are closer to the equator and therefore warmer on average year-round. For one thing, they hold far greater biodiversity.

The **tropical rainforest** biome (**FIGURE 5.23**) is found in Central America, South America, Southeast Asia, West Africa, and other tropical regions, and is characterized by year-round rain and uniformly warm temperatures. Tropical rainforests have dark, damp interiors, lush vegetation, and highly diverse biotic communities, with greater numbers of species of insects, birds, amphibians, and various other animals than any other biome. These forests are not dominated by single species of trees, as are forests closer to the poles, but instead consist of very high numbers of tree species intermixed, each at a low density. Any given tree may be draped with vines, enveloped by strangler figs, and loaded with *epiphytes* (orchids and other plants that grow in trees), such that trees occasionally collapse under the weight of all the life they support. Despite this profusion of life, tropical rainforests have very poor, acidic soils that are low in organic matter. Nearly all nutrients present in this biome are contained in the trees, vines, and other

plants—not in the soil. An unfortunate consequence is that once tropical rainforests are cleared, the nutrient-poor soil can support agriculture for only a short time. As a result, farmed areas are abandoned quickly, and the soil and forest vegetation recover very slowly.

Tropical dry forest Tropical areas that are warm year-round but where rainfall is lower overall and highly seasonal give rise to **tropical dry forest**, or tropical deciduous forest (**FIGURE 5.24**), a biome widespread in India, Africa, South America, and northern Australia. Wet and dry seasons each span about half a year in tropical dry forest. Rains during the wet season can be extremely heavy and, coupled with erosion-prone soils, can lead to severe soil loss when forest clearing occurs over large areas. Across the globe, much tropical dry forest has been converted to agriculture. Clearing for farming or ranching is made easier by the fact that vegetation heights are much lower and canopies less dense than in tropical rainforest. Organisms that inhabit tropical dry

(a) Typical location: Bogor, Java, Indonesia

(a) Typical location: Darwin, Australia

(b) Tropical rainforest

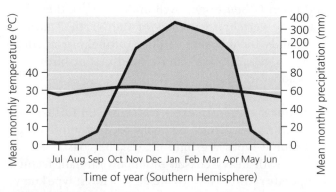

(b) Tropical dry forest

FIGURE 5.23
Tropical rainforests, famed for their biodiversity, grow under constant, warm temperatures and a great deal of rain.

FIGURE 5.24
Tropical dry forests experience significant seasonal variations in precipitation and relatively stable warm temperatures.

forests have adapted to seasonal fluctuations in precipitation and temperature. For instance, plants are deciduous and often leaf out and grow profusely with the rains, then drop their leaves during the driest times of year.

Savannah Drier tropical regions give rise to **savannah** (**FIGURE 5.25**), tropical grassland interspersed with clusters of acacias or other trees. The savannah biome is found today across stretches of Africa (the ancestral home of our species), South America, Australia, India, and other dry tropical regions. Precipitation in savannahs usually arrives during distinct rainy seasons and concentrates grazing animals near widely spaced water holes. Common herbivores on the African savannah include zebras, gazelles, and giraffes, and the predators of these grazers include lions, hyenas, and other highly mobile carnivores.

Desert Where rainfall is very sparse, **desert** (**FIGURE 5.26**) forms. This is the driest biome on Earth; most deserts receive well under 25 cm of precipitation per year, much of it during isolated storms months or years

apart. Depending on rainfall, deserts vary greatly in the amount of vegetation they support. Some, like the Sahara and Namib deserts of Africa, are mostly bare sand dunes; others, like the Sonoran Desert of Arizona and northwest Mexico, are quite heavily vegetated. Deserts are not always hot; the high desert of the western United States is one example. Because deserts have low humidity and relatively little vegetation to insulate them from temperature extremes, sunlight readily heats them in the daytime, but daytime heat is quickly lost at night. As a result, temperatures vary widely from day to night and across seasons of the year. Desert soils can often be quite saline and are sometimes known as lithosols, or stone soils, for their high mineral and low organic-matter content.

Desert animals and plants have evolved many adaptations to deal with the harsh climatic conditions. Most reptiles and mammals, such as rattlesnakes and kangaroo mice, are active in the cool of night, and many Australian desert birds are nomadic, wandering long distances to find areas of recent rainfall and plant growth. Many desert plants have thick leathery leaves to reduce water

(a) Typical location: Harare, Zimbabwe

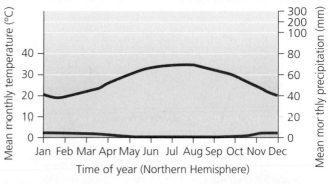
(a) Typical location: Cairo, Egypt

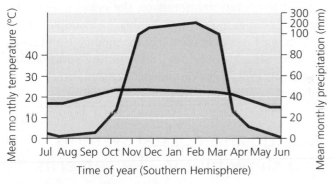
(b) Savannah

FIGURE 5.25
Savannahs are grasslands with clusters of trees. They experience slight seasonal variation in temperature but significant variation in rainfall.

(b) Desert

FIGURE 5.26
Deserts are dry year-round, but they are not always hot. Precipitation can arrive in intense, widely spaced storm events, and temperatures can vary dramatically within a 24-hour period.

loss, or green trunks so that the plant can photosynthesize without leaves, which would lose water. The spines of cacti and many other desert plants guard those plants from being eaten by herbivores desperate for the precious water they hold. These are examples of convergent evolution of plants and animals, adapting separately to the dry conditions that are characteristic of the desert biome.

Mediterranean   In contrast to the boreal forest's broad, continuous distribution, *chaparral* or **Mediterranean** woodland (**FIGURE 5.27**) is limited to fairly small patches widely flung around the globe. Scrub woodland consists mostly of evergreen shrubs and is densely thicketed. This biome is also highly seasonal, with mild, wet winters and warm, dry summers. This type of climate is induced by oceanic influences; in addition to ringing the Mediterranean Sea, chaparral occurs along the coasts of California, Chile, and southern Australia. In Europe it is called *maquis*; in Chile, *matorral*; and in Australia, *mallee*. Mediterranean-type communities experience frequent fires, and their plant species are adapted to resist fire or even to depend on it for germination of their seeds.

(a) Typical location: Baja Penisula, California, United States

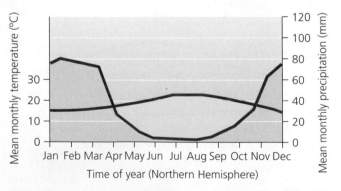

(b) Mediterranean or Chaparral

FIGURE 5.27
This is a highly seasonal biome dominated by shrubs, influenced by marine weather, and dependent on fire.

Altitude creates patterns analogous to latitude

As any hiker or skier knows, climbing in elevation causes a much more rapid change in climate than moving the same distance toward the poles. Vegetative communities change along mountain slopes in correspondence with this small-scale climate variation (**FIGURE 5.28**). These changes with altitude define the *alpine* biome. *Altitudinal zonation*, as it is referred to, is independent of latitude—the variation of temperature, precipitation, and ecological communities with altitude can occur anywhere from the equator to the Rockies. A hiker ascending one of southern Arizona's higher mountains, for example, would begin in the Sonoran Desert or desert grassland and proceed through oak woodland, pine forest, and finally spruce–fir forest—the equivalent of passing through several biomes, without any change in latitude. A hiker scaling one of the great peaks of the Andes in Ecuador, near the equator, could begin in tropical rainforest and end amid glaciers in alpine tundra.

Characteristics that are typical of the alpine biome on a high-mountain peak, compared with lowlands or foothills that surround it, include lower temperatures, lower atmospheric pressures (and less oxygen), higher exposure to ultraviolet radiation, and higher precipitation. The foothills of the Canadian Rockies, for example, are characterized by meadows, grasslands, and riparian (riverside) woodlands, which grade upward through boreal forests and into alpine tundra and glaciers on the mountain peaks; precipitation on the peaks can be as much as twice that of the foothill areas. The zonation of ecological communities on mountain slopes is also influenced by secondary climatic effects related to topographic relief, such as rainshadow effects and exposure to or shelter from the prevailing winds and sunlight.[12] For example, when moisture-laden air ascends a steep mountain, it releases precipitation as it cools; this explains the wet temperate rainforest on the ocean side of the mountain slopes in British Columbia, for example. By the time the air flows over the top of the mountain and down the other side, it can be very dry, creating a *rainshadow desert*; this explains environments like California's Death Valley, one of the driest locations on earth.

Aquatic and coastal systems also show biome-like patterns

In our discussion of biomes, we have focused exclusively on terrestrial systems, because the biome concept, as traditionally developed and applied, has been limited to terrestrial systems. Areas equivalent to biomes also exist in the oceans, but their geographic shapes would look very

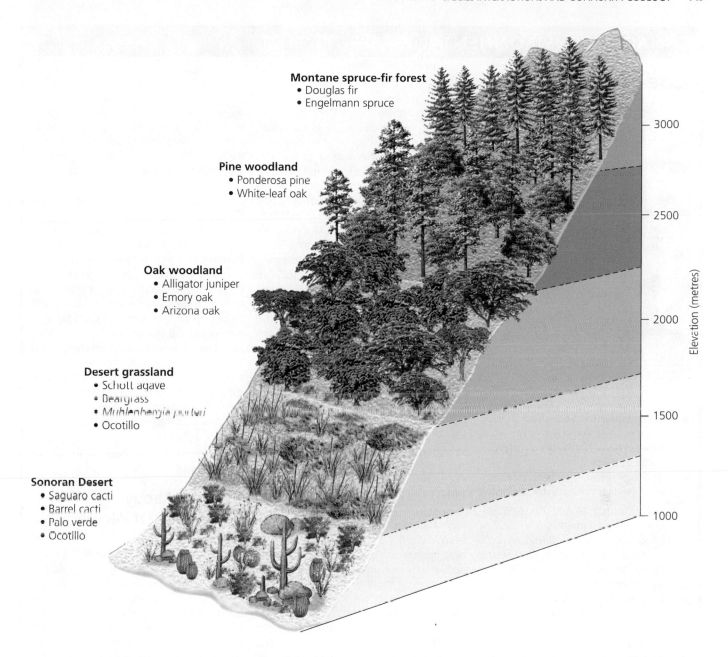

Montane spruce-fir forest
- Douglas fir
- Engelmann spruce

Pine woodland
- Ponderosa pine
- White-leaf oak

Oak woodland
- Alligator juniper
- Emory oak
- Arizona oak

Desert grassland
- Scholl agave
- Deargrass
- *Muhlenbergia porteri*
- Ocotillo

Sonoran Desert
- Saguaro cacti
- Barrel cacti
- Palo verde
- Ocotillo

Elevation (metres)

3000

2500

2000

1500

1000

FIGURE 5.28 As altitude increases, vegetation changes in ways similar to how it changes as one moves toward the poles, taking a hiker through the local equivalent of several biomes.

different from those of terrestrial biomes if plotted on a world map, because the forces that determine the productivity of aquatic systems have very different geographical patterns than those which dominate the productivity of terrestrial systems. We can consider the thin strips along the world's coastlines to represent one aquatic system, the continental shelves another, and the open ocean, deep sea, coral reefs, and kelp forests as still other distinct sets of communities. There are also many coastal systems that straddle the line between terrestrial and aquatic, such as salt marshes, rocky intertidal communities, mangrove forests, and estuaries. And, of course, there are freshwater systems, such as those of the Great Lakes.

Unlike terrestrial biomes, aquatic systems are shaped not by air temperature and precipitation but by such factors as water temperature, salinity, dissolved nutrients, wave action, currents, depth, and type of substrate (e.g., sandy, muddy, or rocky bottom). Light levels can play a role, too. Surface-water tends to be saltier (because of the evaporation of fresh water from the surface), with higher light levels and warmer temperatures, in comparison with deep-water environments. Coastal waters tend to be both warmer and fresher (because of the influx of fresh water from rivers), but may be more turbid (because of sediment load) compared to open-ocean environments. Marine communities are also more clearly delineated by

CANADIAN ENVIRONMENTAL PERSPECTIVES

Zoe Lucas

Zoe Lucas works with the wild horses of Sable Island.

- **Independent researcher** on the biology and ecology of wild horses
- **Advocate** for Sable Island and its unique ecology
- **Photographer** and **documenter** of life (and death) on Sable Island

As a student at the Nova Scotia School of Art and Design in Halifax, Zoe Lucas had not even considered environmental science as an option. Then Lucas had the opportunity to visit Sable Island, a 41 km patch of sand located about 300 km southeast of Halifax. Sable is known for its remote, windswept landscapes and bands of wild horses, as well as grey seals, harbour seals, and several types of rare and endangered migratory birds. It also boasts a long marine history involv-

ing frequent shipwrecks. After a couple of days on Sable Island, Lucas was captivated and became driven to find her way back there. Completing her master of fine arts degree, Lucas eventually started teaching and opened her own studio, but her desire to return to Sable remained strong. She describes it as a combination of esthetics ("Sable is an extremely beautiful place; it's like living in a watercolour painting") and being highly activated by being outdoors.

Lucas eventually made it back to Sable Island as a volunteer cook with a university research group. Still driven largely by the esthetics of the place, she found that the longer she spent on the island, the more curious she became about its nature (in both senses of the word). Eventually she began to participate in scientific research and environmental monitoring projects. She has now authored or contributed to numerous reports and scientific studies on the island's horses, vegetation, and seals, and collaborates with researchers at various universities.

Lucas carries out a complete search of the island's shoreline once every four to five weeks, looking for oiled birds, stranded cetaceans, and marine litter. Between beach surveys she records field data on the feral horses, including their range, reproductive activities, and band structure. She also works on short-term projects, such as collecting invertebrate or plant specimens requested by researchers.

Lucas says that, in addition to the benefits of working in such a unique and beautiful place, the work of environmental monitoring appeals to her because there

are endless questions. "Hardly a day passes without learning something new—sometimes just a snippet of a detail, sometimes a big aha! Being able to do this work in such a wonderful and occasionally challenging environment is very compelling."

The island is administered by the Canadian Coast Guard, and landing there without permission (except in the case of an emergency) is against the law. Scientific research on the island is carried out with logistical support provided by the Sable Island Station, originally set up by the Meteorological Service of Canada (a branch of Environment Canada) as a meteorological station but now also used as a base for year-round environmental stewardship. There has been some discussion about initiating ecotourism trips to the island, but this would require significant care and planning to ensure preservation of the island's fragile ecosystems.

"I can't imagine anyone not wanting to live and work here."—**Zoe Lucas, about Sable Island**

Thinking About Environmental Perspectives

Sable Island is a remote wilderness. Great care has been taken to preserve the fragile ecosystems and unique wild populations that live there. However, few people will ever visit Sable Island. What do you think about this? What is the value of wilderness? Do you think more people should be able to visit, even if their presence would be disruptive and potentially damaging to the natural environment?

---

their animal life than by their plant life. We will examine freshwater, marine, and coastal systems in greater detail in subsequent chapters.

Conclusion

The natural world is so complex that we can visualize it in many ways and at various scales. Dividing the world's communities into major types, or biomes, is informative at the broadest geographic scales. Understanding how communities function at more local scales requires understanding

how species interact with one another. Species interactions, such as predation, parasitism, competition, and mutualism, give rise to effects that are both weak and strong, direct and indirect. Feeding relationships can be represented by the concepts of trophic levels and food webs, and particularly influential species are sometimes called keystone species. Increasingly, humans are altering communities, in part by introducing non-native species that may turn invasive. But increasingly, through ecological restoration, we are also attempting to undo the changes we have caused.

REVIEWING OBJECTIVES

You should now be able to:

Compare and contrast the major types of species interactions

- Competition results when individuals or species vie for limited resources. It can occur within or among species and can result in coexistence or exclusion. It also can lead to realized niches, resource partitioning, and character displacement.

- In predation, one species kills and consumes another. It is the basis of food webs and can influence population dynamics and community composition.

- In parasitism, one species derives benefit by harming (but usually not killing) another.

- Herbivory is an exploitative interaction whereby an animal feeds on a plant.

- In mutualism, species benefit from one another. Some mutualists are symbiotic, whereas other mutualists are free-living.

Characterize feeding relationships and energy flow, using them to construct trophic pyramids and food webs

- Energy is transferred in food chains among trophic levels.

- Lower trophic levels generally contain more energy, biomass, and numbers of individuals than higher trophic levels.

- Food webs illustrate feeding relationships and energy flow among species in a community.

Distinguish characteristics of a keystone species

- Keystone species have impacts on communities that are far out of proportion to their abundance.

- Top predators are frequently considered keystone species, but other organisms may be thought of as keystones for other reasons.

Describe how communities respond to disturbances

- Succession is a stereotypical pattern of change within a community through time.

- Primary succession begins with an area devoid of life. Secondary succession begins with an area that has been severely disturbed.

Perceive and predict the potential impacts of invasive species on communities

- Invasive species, such as the zebra mussel, have altered the composition, structure, and function of communities.

- Humans are the cause of most modern species invasions, but we can also respond to invasions with prevention and control measures.

Explain the goals and methods of ecological restoration

- Ecological restoration aims to restore communities to a more "natural" state, variously defined as before human or industrial interference.

- Restoration efforts in the field are informed by the growing science of restoration ecology.

Describe and illustrate the terrestrial biomes of the world

- Biomes represent major classes of communities spanning large geographic areas.

- The distribution of biomes is determined by temperature, precipitation, and other factors.

- The biome concept by tradition refers to terrestrial systems. Aquatic systems can be classified in similar ways, determined by different factors.

TESTING YOUR COMPREHENSION

1. How does competition lead to a realized niche? How does it promote resource partitioning?
2. Contrast the several types of exploitation. How do predation, parasitism, and herbivory differ?
3. Give examples of symbiotic and nonsymbiotic mutualisms. Describe at least one way in which mutualisms affect your daily life.
4. Explain how trophic levels, food chains, and food webs are related.
5. Name several ways in which a species could be considered a keystone species.
6. Explain and contrast primary and secondary terrestrial succession.

7. Name five changes to Great Lakes communities that have occurred since the invasion of the zebra mussel.
8. What is restoration ecology?
9. What factors most strongly influence the type of biome that forms in a particular place on land? What factors determine the type of aquatic system that may form in a given location?
10. Draw climate diagrams for a boreal forest, a temperate rainforest, and a desert. Label all parts of the diagrams, and describe all the types of information an ecologist could glean from such diagrams.

THINKING IT THROUGH

1. Imagine that you spot two species of birds feeding side by side, eating seeds from the same plant, and that you begin to wonder whether competition is at work. Describe how you might design scientific research to address this question. What observations would you try to make at the outset? Would you try to manipulate the system to test your hypothesis that the two birds are competing? If so, how?
2. Spend some time outside on your campus or in your yard or in the nearest park or natural area. Find at least 10 species of organisms, and observe them long enough to watch them feed or to make an educated guess about what they feed on. Now, using FIGURE 5.11 as a model, draw a simple food web involving all the organisms you observed.
3. Can you think of one organism not mentioned in this chapter as a keystone species that you believe may be a keystone species? For what reasons do you suspect this? How could you experimentally test whether an organism is a keystone species?
4. Why do scientists consider invasive species to be a problem? What makes a species "invasive," and what ecological effects can invasive species have?
5. From year to year, biomes are stable entities, and our map of world biomes appears to be a permanent record of patterns across the planet. But are the locations and identities of biomes permanent, or could they change over time? Provide reasons for your answers.

6. Can you devise possible responses to the zebra mussel invasion? What strategies would you consider if you were put in charge of the effort to control this species' spread and reduce its impacts? Name some advantages of each of your ideas, and identify some obstacles it might face in being implemented.
7. Consider this real-life example of invasive-species management and restoration ecology, and then answer the questions that follow, in your new role as an environmental land manager: The Garry oak meadows on Trinity Western University's Crow's Nest Ecological Research Area are experiencing encroachment by the Douglas fir (*Pseudotsuga menziesii*), which threatens the health and survival of the meadow. Traditionally, Aborigines maintained the Garry oak meadows with frequent burnings. However, with European settlement and the resulting control and suppression of fires, Douglas firs have been increasingly successful at invading the meadows. Some Garry oak restoration projects have undertaken to remove Douglas firs physically and/or using controlled fires. However, when the Douglas firs are removed, the resulting disturbance of the soil apparently facilitates the establishment of other invasive species.[13]
   (a) How would you design a comprehensive scientific study to determine the best ways of removing Douglas firs without enhancing conditions for encroachment by other invasive species?

(b) Removing Douglas firs from the Garry oak meadows would not return the meadows to their "natural," pristine, or pre-human state; instead, it would represent a return to an earlier phase of human (Aboriginal) ecosystem management. Is this the best approach? Do you think the Douglas firs should be allowed to advance naturally, without interference by fire or other removal techniques? Or is it worthwhile to preserve the meadows—which are disappearing rapidly, and host a variety of unusual and threatened species—by returning to an earlier land management approach?

(c) Can you think of some general guidelines that might be used to make ecosystem management decisions in other cases of this type?

INTERPRETING GRAPHS AND DATA

The grey wolf (*Canis lupus*) is a keystone species in Yellowstone National Park's ecosystem. Wolf packs hunt elk, gorge themselves on the kill, and leave the carcass as carrion for scavenger species, such as ravens, magpies, eagles, coyotes, and bears. As the global climate has warmed, winters in Yellowstone have become shorter over the past 55 years. Fewer elk weaken and die in milder weather, and so less carrion is available to scavengers during warmer, shorter winters. Biologists Christopher Wilmers and Wayne Getz studied the links among climate change, wolves, elk, and scavenger populations in Yellowstone. They used empirical field data on wolf predation rates and elk carrion availability recorded over 55 years to develop a model that estimated carrion availability with and without wolves for each winter month. Some of their findings are presented in the graph.

1. How much less carrion is available in April than in November when wolves are present? When wolves are not present?

2. Wolves were hunted nearly to extinction in the 1930s and were reintroduced to Yellowstone only in 1995. How, would you suspect, has their reintroduction affected scavenger populations since then? Why?

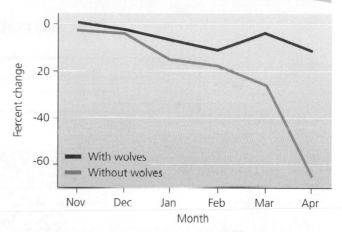

Changes in amount of winter carrion available to scavengers in Yellowstone National Park, with and without wolves, according to the model. Differences in March and April are statistically significant.
Source: Data from Wilmers, C.C. and W.M. Getz (2005) Gray wolves as climate-change buffers in Yellowstone. PLoS Biology 3(4): e92.

3. Predict what effect continued shorter, warmer winters would have on scavenger populations. Why? Are the predicted effects of wolf reintroduction and of climate change compounded, or do they tend to cancel one another out?

CHAPTER ENDNOTES

1. "'Musseling' in on an Ecosystem: Tracing the Natural History of the Zebra Mussel in Lake Erie," *Canadian Geographic*, September 2003.

2. Environment Canada Backgrounder: Lake Ontario Invasion Begins, (1999) www.on.ec.gc.ca/press/goby-invasion.html

3. Parks Canada Fact Sheet, (2007) "Moose a-plenty," Cape Breton Highlands National Park of Canada, www.pc.gc.ca/canada/pn-tfn/itm2/2007/2007-04-30_e.asp

4. Danoff-Burg, James, ed., *Introduced Species Summary Project*, Columbia University, Centre for Environmental Research and Conservation, and other sources.

5. Haber, Erich, *Guide to Monitoring Exotic and Invasive Plants*, Environment Canada Ecological Monitoring and Assessment Network (EMAN).

6. Carder, Judith E. W. *Restoration of Natural Systems Program*, Garry Oak Ecosystems Recovery Team, Research Colloquium 2006, University of Victoria, BC; and Garry Oak Restoration Project (GORP), www.gorpsaanich.com.

7. World Wildlife Fund, "Ecoregions," www.worldwildlife.org/science/ecoregions.

8. Climatographs adapted from Breckle, S. W. (1999) *Walter's vegetation of the Earth: The ecological systems of the geo-biosphere*, 4th ed., Berlin: Springer-Verlag.

9. World Wildlife Fund, "Ecoregions," www.worldwildlife.org/science/ecoregions/nearctic.cfm.

10. World Wildlife Fund, "Ecoregions," www.worldwildlife.org/science/ecoregions

11. World Wildlife Fund, "Ecoregions," www.worldwildlife.org/science/ecoregions/nearctic.cfm.

12. World Wildlife Fund, "Ecoregions," www.worldwildlife.org/science/ecoregions/nearctic.cfm

13. Roberts, Kimberly, Stephanie Koole, and David Clements, Garry Oak Ecosystems Recovery Team— Research Colloquium 2006, Trinity Western University, Langley, BC.

MyEnvironmentPlace

Go to **www.myenvironmentplace.ca** where you will find quizzes, animations, your Pearson eText, and more.

PART TWO

Twenty-year-old Meenakshi Diwan carries out maintenance in the solar village of Tinginapu, India.

ISSUES, IMPACTS, AND SOLUTIONS

Human Population

This crowded street is in Guangzhou, one of China's largest cities.

Upon successfully completing this chapter, you will be able to

- Assess the scope and historical patterns of human population growth
- Evaluate how human population, affluence, and technology affect the environment
- Explain and apply the fundamental concepts of demography
- Outline the concept of demographic transition
- Describe how wealth and poverty, the status of women, and family planning affect population growth
- Link population goals to sustainable development goals

A billboard in Chengdu promotes China's one-child policy.

计划生育 是我国的一项基本国
FAMILY PLANNING—A BASIS NATIONAL POLICY OF CHINA

ASIA

China

ASIA

China

CENTRAL CASE:
CHINA'S ONE-CHILD POLICY

"As you improve health in a society, population growth goes down. You know, I thought it was . . . before I learned about it, I thought it was paradoxical."
—BILL GATES, CHAIR, MICROSOFT CORP.

"Population growth is analogous to a plague of locusts. What we have on this earth today is a plague of people."
—TED TURNER, MEDIA MAGNATE AND SUPPORTER OF THE UNITED NATIONS POPULATION FUND

"There is no population problem."
—SHELDON RICHMAN, SENIOR EDITOR, CATO INSTITUTE

The People's Republic of China is the world's most populous nation, home to one-fifth of the 7 billion[1] people living on Earth as of 2011.

The first significant increases in China's population in the past 2000 years of the nation's history resulted from enhanced agricultural production and a powerful government during the Qing (Manchu) Dynasty in the 1800s. Population growth began to outstrip food supplies by the mid-1850s, and quality of life for the average Chinese peasant began to decline. From the mid-1800s (an era of increased European intervention in China) until 1949, China's population grew very slowly, at about 0.3% per year. This slow population growth was due, in part, to food shortages, war, and political instability, which caused high mortality and a decline in birth rates. Population growth rates rose again following the establishment of the People's Republic and have declined once again since the establishment of the one-child policy.

When Mao Zedong founded the country's current regime in 1949, roughly 540 million people lived in a mostly rural, war-torn, impoverished nation. Mao believed population growth was desirable, and under his leadership China grew and changed. By 1970, China's population had grown to approximately 790 million people. At that time, the average Chinese woman gave birth to 5.8 children in her lifetime.

Unfortunately, the country's burgeoning population and its industrial and agricultural development were eroding the nation's soils, depleting its water, levelling its forests, and polluting its air. Chinese leaders realized that the nation might not be able to feed its people if their numbers grew much larger. They saw that continued population growth could exhaust resources and threaten the stability and economic progress of Chinese society. The government decided to institute a population control program that prohibited most Chinese couples from having more than one child.

The program began with education and outreach efforts encouraging people to marry later and have fewer children. Along with these efforts, the Chinese government increased the accessibility of contraceptives and abortion. By 1975, China's annual population growth rate had dropped from 2.8% to 1.8%. To further decrease the birth rate, in 1979 the government took the more drastic step of instituting a system of rewards and punishments to enforce a one-child limit. One-child families received better access to schools, medical care, housing, and government jobs, and mothers with only one child were given longer maternity leaves. Families with more than one child, meanwhile, were subjected to social scorn and ridicule, employment discrimination, and monetary fines. In some cases, the fines exceeded half the offending couple's annual income.

Beginning in 1984, the one-child policy was loosened, strengthened, and then loosened again as government leaders sought to maximize population control while minimizing public opposition. Today the one-child program applies mostly to urban couples, whereas many rural farmers and ethnic minorities are exempt.

In enforcing these policies, China has, in effect, been conducting one of the largest and most controversial social experiments in history. In purely quantitative terms, the experiment has been a major success; the nation's growth rate is now down to 0.5%, making it easier for the country to deal with its many social, economic, and environmental challenges.

However, China's population control policies have also produced unintended consequences, such as widespread killing of female infants, an unbalanced sex ratio, and a black market trade in teenaged girls. It is expected to lead to further problems in the future, including an ageing population and shrinking workforce. Moreover, the policies have elicited intense criticism from those who oppose government intrusion into personal reproductive choices.

As other nations become more and more crowded, might their governments also feel forced to turn to drastic policies that restrict individual freedoms? In this chapter, we examine human population dynamics worldwide, consider their causes, and assess their consequences for the environment and our society.

The Human Population at 7 Billion

While China works to slow its population growth and speed its economic growth, populations continue to rise in most nations of the world. Most of this growth is occurring in poverty-stricken nations that are ill-equipped to handle it. India (**FIGURE 6.1**) is currently on course to surpass China as the world's most populous nation. Although the *rate* of global growth is slowing, we are still increasing in absolute numbers, and today more than 7 billion of us inhabit the planet.

Just how much is 7 billion? We often have trouble conceptualizing huge numbers like a billion; 1 billion is 1000 times greater than 1 million. If you were to count once each second without ever sleeping, it would take more than 30 years to reach 1 billion. To travel 1 billion kilometres, you would have to drive the entire length of the Trans-Canada Highway 128 000 times or fly to the Moon 2500 times.

The human population is growing nearly as fast as ever

The human population has been growing at a tremendous rate. The population has doubled since 1966 and is growing by roughly 80 million people annually (nearly 2.6 people are added—that is, births minus deaths—every *second*). This is the equivalent of adding two and a half times the population of Canada to the world each

FIGURE 6.1
Population growth in developing countries has led our global population toward 7 billion and beyond. India is on course to surpass China soon as the world's most populous nation. In this photo, Indian women wait in line for immunizations for their babies.

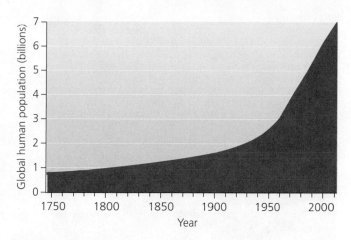

FIGURE 6.2
The global human population has grown exponentially, rising from less than 1 billion in 1800 to approximately 7 billion today. Nearly all growth has occurred in the last 200 years.
Source: Data from U.S Bureau of the Census.

year. It took until after 1800—most of human history—for our population to reach 1 billion. Yet we reached 2 billion by 1927, and 3 billion in just over 30 more years, in 1960. Our population added its next billion in just 14 years (1974), its next billion in a mere 13 years (1987), and the most recent billion in another 12 years (**FIGURE 6.2**). Think about when you were born and how many people have been added to the planet since that time. No previous generations have ever lived amid so many other people.

What accounts for such unprecedented growth? Exponential growth—the increase in a quantity by a fixed percentage per unit time—accelerates the absolute increase of population size over time, just as compound interest accrues in a savings account. The reason is that a given percentage of a large number is a greater quantity than the same percentage of a small number. Thus, even if the growth *rate* remains steady, population *size* will increase by greater increments with each successive generation.

In fact, the world's population growth rate has not remained steady. During much of the twentieth century the growth rate actually rose from year to year. It peaked at 2.1% per year during the 1960s and has declined to 1.2% per year since then. Although 1.2% may sound small, exponential growth endows small numbers with large consequences. For instance, a hypothetical population starting with one man and one woman, growing at 1.2% per year, gives rise to a population of 2939 after 40 generations and 112 695 after 60 generations. In today's world, rates of annual growth vary greatly from region to region. **FIGURE 6.3** maps this variation.

At a 2.1% annual growth rate, a population doubles in only 33 years. For low rates of increase, we can estimate doubling times with a handy rule of thumb. Just take the number 70, and divide it by the annual percentage growth rate: 70 ÷ 2.1 = 33.3. Had China not instituted its one-child policy—that is, had its growth rate remained unchecked at 2.8%—it would have taken only 25 years to double in size (70 ÷ 2.8 = 25). Had population growth continued at this rate, China's population would have exceeded 2 billion people by 2004; based on current projections, that milestone will not be reached, as China's population is expected to stabilize at around 1.4 billion by 2015.

Perspectives on human population have changed over time

At the outset of the Industrial Revolution in England of the 1700s, population growth was regarded as a good thing. For parents, a high birth rate meant more children to support them in old age. For society, it meant a greater pool of labour for factory work. British economist Thomas Malthus (1766–1834) had a different opinion. Malthus claimed that unless population growth was limited by laws or other social controls, the number of people would outgrow the available food supply until starvation, war, or disease arose and reduced the population (**FIGURE 6.4**). Malthus's most influential work, *An Essay on the Principle of Population*, published in 1798, argued that a growing population would eventually be checked by either limits on births or increases in deaths. If limits on births (such as abstinence and contraception)

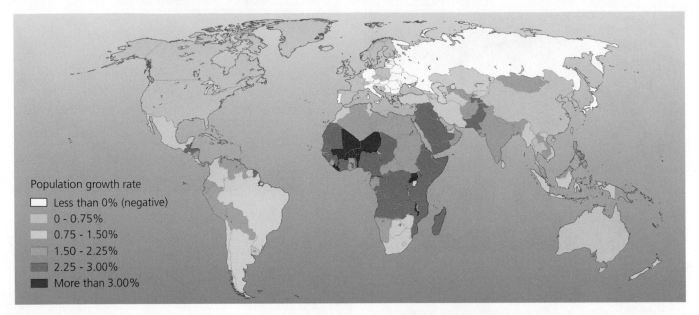

FIGURE 6.3 Population growth rates vary greatly from place to place. Population is growing fastest in poorer nations of the tropics and subtropics but is now beginning to decrease in some northern industrialized nations. Shown are natural rates of population change as of 2010.   Source: *Data from the Population Reference Bureau,* (2010) World Population Data Sheet.

Population growth rate
- Less than 0% (negative)
- 0 - 0.75%
- 0.75 - 1.50%
- 1.50 - 2.25%
- 2.25 - 3.00%
- More than 3.00%

were not implemented soon enough, Malthus wrote, deaths would increase.

Malthus's thinking was specifically shaped by the rapid urbanization and industrialization he witnessed during the early years of the Industrial Revolution. More recently, biologist Paul Ehrlich of Stanford University has been called a "neo-Malthusian" because—like

(a) Eighteenth-century London, England

(b) Thomas Malthus

FIGURE 6.4
The England of Thomas Malthus's era (1766–1834), shown in this engraving **(a)**, favoured population growth as society industrialized. Malthus **(b)** argued that the pressure of population growth on the availability of resources could lead to disaster.

Malthus—he warned that population growth would have disastrous effects on the environment and human welfare.

In his 1968 book, *The Population Bomb,* Ehrlich predicted that the rapidly increasing human population would unleash widespread famine and conflict that would consume civilization by the end of the twentieth century. Ehrlich and other neo-Malthusians have argued that population is growing much faster than our ability to produce and distribute food and that population control is the only way to prevent massive starvation, environmental degradation, and civil strife.

Is population growth really a "problem" today?

The world's ongoing population growth has been made possible by technological innovations, improved sanitation, better medical care, increased agricultural output, and other factors that have led to a decline in death rates, particularly a drop in rates of infant mortality. Birth rates have not declined as much, so births have outpaced deaths for many years now. Thus, the population "problem" actually arises from a very good thing—our ability to keep more people alive longer.

The mainstream view in Malthus's day held that population increase was a good thing, and today there are still many people who argue that population growth poses no problems. Even though human population has nearly quadrupled in the past 100 years—the fastest it has ever grown—Malthusian and neo-Malthusian predic-

roots

POPULATION

The word **population** comes from the Late Latin root word *population*, meaning "a multitude." It is related to the English word *popular*, meaning "beloved or approved by the people." The term *population explosion* in reference to very rapid rates of growth was first used in 1953.

tions have not materialized on a devastating scale. This is due, in part, to enormous increases in crop yields and advances in agricultural technology associated with the Green Revolution. Increasing material prosperity has also helped bring down birth rates—something Malthus and Ehrlich did not foresee.

Some cornucopian thinkers believe that resource depletion caused by population increase is not a problem if new resources can be found to replace depleted resources. Libertarian writer Sheldon Richman expressed this view as follows:

> *The idea of carrying capacity doesn't apply to the human world because humans aren't passive with respect to their environment. Human beings create resources. We find potential stuff and human intelligence turns it into resources. The computer revolution is based on sand; human intelligence turned that common stuff into the main component [silicon] of an amazing technology.*

The premise that the human population is not subject to the limitations of carrying capacity leads to some pretty ridiculous conclusions. For example, a simple calculation shows that if the human population continued to grow at the current rate of 1.2% per year, in 2500 years the people of Earth would weigh as much as Earth itself (assuming an average weight of 60 kg per person). This is clearly an impossible scenario; environmental limitations *do* exist.

In contrast to the idea that humankind will always be able to save itself with a "technological fix," environmental scientists recognize that few resources are actually "created" by humans and that not all resources can be replaced or reinvented once they have been depleted. For example, once species have gone extinct, we cannot replicate their exact function in ecosystems, or know what medicines or other practical applications we might have obtained from them, or regain the educational and esthetic value of observing them. Another irreplaceable resource is land; we cannot expand Earth like a balloon to increase its surface area.

Even if resource substitution could enable population growth to continue indefinitely, could we maintain the *quality* of life that we desire for our descendants and ourselves? Surely some of today's resources are easier or cheaper to use, and less environmentally destructive to harvest or mine, than the resources that might replace them. Unless resource availability keeps pace with population growth, the average person in the future will have less space in which to live, less food to eat, and less material wealth than the average person does today. Thus population increases are indeed a problem if they create stress on resources, social systems, or the natural environment, such that our quality of life declines.

In today's world, population growth is much more strongly correlated with poverty than with wealth. In spite of this, many governments have found it difficult to let go of the notion that population growth increases a nation's economic, political, or military strength. Many national governments still offer financial and social incentives to encourage their citizens to produce more children. Governments of countries currently experiencing population declines (such as many in Europe) feel especially uneasy. According to the Population Reference Bureau, more than three of every five European national governments now take the view that their birth rates are too low, and none states that its rate is too high. However, outside Europe, 49% of national governments feel their birth rates are too high, and only 12% feel they are too low.

Researchers in the Malthusian tradition are still making important contributions to our understanding of population and the environment today. Research has shown that environmental degradation and scarcity, particularly in situations of overcrowding in sensitive environments, can lead to migrantism, refugeeism, and even armed conflict. For example, political scientist Thomas Homer-Dixon of the University of Waterloo investigated the linkages between agricultural land scarcity and ethnic tensions in initiating the genocide in Rwanda in the mid-1990s, which cost the lives of 800 000 people. In other active conflicts we can see that global population growth and resulting environmental scarcity have played a central role in causing famine, disease, and social and political conflict around the world.

The dire predictions of Malthus, Ehrlich, and other neo-Malthusians were not accurate; however, the idea that a "technological fix" will always emerge in time to rescue humans from problems brought on by population growth is equally unsatisfactory. Our current understanding of the limitations of the resources of this planet suggests that the real answer lies somewhere between these extremes.

THE SCIENCE BEHIND THE STORY

Mapping Our Population's Environmental Impact

Dr. Helmut Haberl of Austria's Institute of Social Ecology attempts to quantify the human impact on the environment.

Burgeoning numbers of people are making heavy demands on Earth's natural resources and ecosystem services. How can we quantify and map the environmental impacts our expanding population is exerting? One way is to ask: Of all the biomass that Earth's plants can produce, what proportion do human beings use (for food, clothing, shelter, etc.) or otherwise prevent from growing?

This was the question asked by nine environmental scientists led by Helmut Haberl of the Institute of Social Ecology in Austria. They teamed up to measure our consumption of *net primary production* (NPP), the net amount of energy stored in plant matter as a result of photosynthesis. Human overuse of NPP diminishes

resources available for other species; alters habitats, communities, and ecosystems; and threatens our future ability to derive ecosystem services.

Haberl's team began with a well-established model that maps how vegetation varies with climate across the globe, and they used it to produce a detailed world map of "potential NPP"—vegetation that would exist if there were no human influence. The team then gathered data on crop harvests, timber harvests, grazing pressure, and other human uses of vegetation from global databases maintained by the United Nations Food and Agriculture Organization (FAO) and other sources. They also gathered data on how people affect vegetation indirectly, such as through fires, erosion and soil degradation, and other changes due to land use. To calculate the proportion of NPP that people appropriate, the researchers divided the amounts used up in these impacts by the total "potential" amount.

When the data analysis had been completed, Haberl's group concluded that people are harvesting 12.5% of global NPP. Land use reduces it 9.6% further, and fires another 1.7% (see first figure). This makes us responsible for using up fully 23.8% of the planet's NPP—a staggeringly large amount for just a single species! Half of this use occurred on cropland, where 83.5% of NPP was used. In urban areas, 73.0%

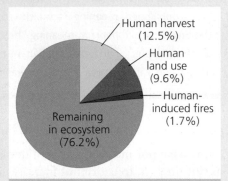

Humanity uses or causes Earth to lose 23.8% of the planet's net primary production. Direct harvesting (of crops, timber, etc.) accounts for most of this, and land use impacts and fire also contribute.
Source: Data from Haberl, H., et al., 2007. Quantifying and mapping the human appropriation of net primary production in Earth's terrestrial ecosystems. Proc. Natl. Acad. Sci. *104: 12942–12947.*

of NPP was consumed; on grazing land, 19.4%; and in forests, 6.6%.

To determine how human use of NPP varies across regions of the world, Haberl's group layered the data sets atop one another in a geographic information systems (GIS) approach. Again, they calculated the proportion of NPP that we appropriate and produced a global map (see second figure). The researchers

Population is one of several factors that affect the environment

The extent to which population increase can be considered a problem involves more than just numbers of people. One widely used formula gives us a handy way to think about factors that affect the environment. Nicknamed the **IPAT model**, it is a variation of a formula proposed in 1974 by Paul Ehrlich and John Holdren, a professor of environmental policy at Harvard University. The IPAT model represents how our total impact (I) on the environment results from the interaction among population (P), affluence (A), and technology (T):

$$I = P \times A \times T$$

Increased population intensifies impact on the environment as more individuals take up space, use natural resources, and generate waste. Increased affluence magnifies environmental impact through the greater per capita resource consumption that generally has accompanied enhanced wealth. Changes in technology may either decrease or increase human impact on the environment. Technology that enhances our abilities to exploit minerals, fossil fuels, old-growth forests, or ocean fisheries generally increases impact, but technology to reduce smokestack emissions, harness renewable energy, or improve manufacturing efficiency can decrease impact.

We might also add a sensitivity factor (S) to the equation to denote how sensitive a given environment is to human pressures:

$$I = P \times A \times T \times S$$

As this map shows, the proportion of Earth's net primary production that people appropriate varies from region to region. Regions that are densely populated or intensively farmed exert the heaviest impact. *Source: Haberl, H., et al., 2007. Quantifying and mapping the human appropriation of net primary production in Earth's terrestrial ecosystems. Proc. Natl. Acad. Sci. 104:12942–12947, Fig 1b. © 2007 National Academy of Sciences, U.S.A. By permission.*

published their results in 2007 in the *Proceedings of the National Academy of Sciences of the USA*.

In their global map of NPP consumption, densely populated and heavily farmed regions such as India, eastern China, and Europe show the greatest proportional use of NPP. The influence of population is clear. For instance, although people in southern Asia consume very little per capita, dense populations here result in a 63% use of NPP. In contrast, in sparsely inhabited regions of the world (such as the boreal forest, Arctic tundra, Himalayas, and Sahara Desert), humans consume almost no NPP. In North America, NPP use is heaviest in the East, Midwest, and Great Plains. In general, the map shows heavy appropriation of NPP in areas where population is dense relative to the area's vegetative production.

The map does not fully show the effects of resource consumption due to affluence. Wealthy societies commonly import food, fibre, energy, and products from other places, and this consumption can drive environmental degradation in poorer regions. For instance, North Americans and Europeans import timber logged from the Amazon basin, as well as soybeans and beef grown in areas where Amazonian forest was cleared. Through global trade, we redistribute the products we gain from the planet's NPP. As a result, the environmental impacts of our consumption are often felt far from where we consume products.

By showing areas of high and low impact, maps like the one produced in this project can help us understand the planet's biocapacity, and better decisions and minimize our impacts on ecosystems and ecosystem services.

For instance, the arid lands of western China are more sensitive to human disturbance than the moist regions of southeastern China. Plants grow more slowly in the arid west, making deforestation and soil degradation more likely. Thus, adding an additional person to western China should have more environmental impact than adding one to southeastern China (all other conditions being equal).

Various population researchers have refined the IPAT equation by adding terms for the effects of social institutions, such as education, laws, and their enforcement; stable and cohesive societies; and ethical standards that promote environmental well-being. Factors like these affect how population, affluence, and technology translate into environmental impact.

Impact can be thought of in various ways, but it generally boils down to either pollution or resource consumption. Pollution became a problem in the modern world once our population grew large enough that we produced great quantities of waste. The depletion of resources by larger and hungrier populations has been a focus of scientists and philosophers since before Malthus's time. Recall how the people of Rapa Nui brought down their civilization by depleting their most important limited resource, trees. History offers other cases in which resource depletion helped end civilizations, from the Mayans to the Mesopotamians. Some environmental scientists have predicted similar problems for our global society in the near future if we do not manage to embark on a path toward sustainability (**FIGURE 6.5**).

As discussed above, the neo-Malthusians have not seen their direst predictions come true. The reason is that we have developed technology—the T in the IPAT

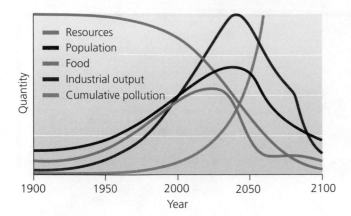

(a) Projection based on status quo policies

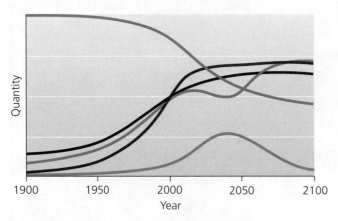

(b) Projection based on policies for sustainability

FIGURE 6.5
Environmental scientist Donella Meadows and colleagues used computer simulations to generate a series of projections of trends in human population, resource availability, food production, industrial output, and pollution. The projections are based on data from the past century and current scientific understanding of the environment's biophysical limits. Shown in **(a)** is their projection for a world in which "society proceeds in a traditional manner without any major deviation from the policies pursued during most of the twentieth century." In this projection, population and production increase until declining nonrenewable resources make further growth impossible, causing population and production to decline rather suddenly. The researchers ran their simulations with different parameters to examine possible alternative futures. Under a scenario with policies aimed at sustainability **(b)**, population levelled off at 8 billion, production and resource availability levelled off at medium-high levels, and pollution declined to low levels. *Source: Data from Meadows, D., et al. (2004)* Limits to Growth: The 30-Year Update. *White River Junction, VT: Chelsea Green Publishing.*

equation—time and again to alleviate our strain on resources and allow us to further expand our population. For instance, we have employed technological advances to increase global agricultural production faster than our population has risen.

Modern-day China shows how all elements of the IPAT formula can combine to cause tremendous environmental impact in very little time. While millions of Chinese are increasing their material wealth and con-

sumption of resources, the country is battling unprecedented environmental challenges brought about by its extremely rapid economic development. Intensive agriculture has expanded westward out of the country's historic moist rice-growing areas, causing farmland to erode and literally blow away, much like the Dust Bowl tragedy that befell the agricultural heartland of North America in the 1930s. China has overpumped many of its aquifers and has drawn so much water for irrigation from the Huang He (Yellow River) that the once-mighty waterway now dries up in many stretches.

Although China has been reducing its air pollution from industry and charcoal-burning homes, the country faces new urban pollution and congestion threats from rapidly increasing numbers of automobiles. As the world's developing countries try to attain the level of material prosperity that industrialized nations enjoy, China is a window on what much of the rest of the world could soon become.

Demography

It is a fallacy to think of people as being somehow outside nature. Humans exist within their environment as one species out of many. The principles of population ecology that apply to toads, frogs, and passenger pigeons apply to humans as well. The application of population ecology principles to the study of statistical change in human populations is the focus of the social science of **demography**.

The environment has a carrying capacity for humans

Environmental factors set limits on our population growth, and the environment has a carrying capacity for our species, as it does for every other. We happen to be a particularly successful organism, however—one that has repeatedly increased the carrying capacity of the environment by developing technology to overcome natural limits on population growth. Four significant periods of societal change appear to have fundamentally altered the human relationship with the environment and increased the carrying capacity, triggering remarkable increases in population size (**FIGURE 6.6**).

The first transition happened in the *paleolithic period* (or *Old Stone Age*), when early humans gained control of fire (as much as 1.5 million years ago) and began to shape and use stones (as much as 2.5 million years ago) as tools with which to modify their environment. We can speculate that this transition made life so much easier and the environment so much more manageable for our ancestors that their population grew substantially,

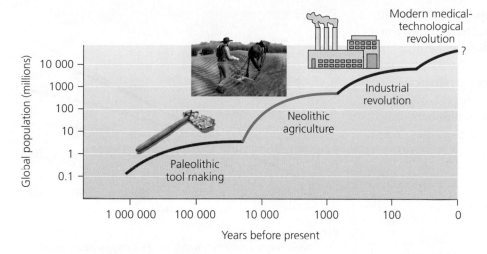

FIGURE 6.6

Tool making, agriculture, and industrialization each allowed our species to increase the global carrying capacity. The logarithmic scale of the axes makes it easier to visualize this pattern. We are currently in the midst of a fourth transition, involving the globalization of modern medical-technological advances; its impacts on population and the environment are as yet unknown.
Source: Data from Goudie, A. (2000) The Human Impact. *Cambridge, MA: MIT Press.*

although we have little direct evidence about world population dating from that period.

The second major change was the transition from a nomadic hunter-gatherer lifestyle to a settled agricultural way of life. This change began to occur around 10 000 to 12 000 years ago and is known as the Agricultural Revolution, in what is known as the *neolithic (or New Stone Age) period.* This agriculture-based lifestyle was much more intensive and manipulative in the production of resources from the land. As people began to grow their own crops, raise domestic animals, and live settled, sedentary lives in villages, they found it easier to meet their nutritional needs. As a result, they began to live longer and to produce more children who survived to adulthood. The Agricultural Revolution initiated a permanent change in the way humans relate to the natural environment. Agriculture also created surplus food that could be passed on to people not directly involved in food acquisition; in other words, agriculture made cities, trades, science, armies, and other aspects of modern culture possible.

The third major societal change, the Industrial Revolution, began in the mid-1700s. It entailed a shift from rural life, animal-powered agriculture, and manufacturing by craftsmen, to an urban society powered by fossil fuels. The Industrial Revolution introduced improvements in sanitation and medical technology. Another very important aspect was the impact on agriculture and animal husbandry. Agricultural production was greatly enhanced during the Industrial Revolution by the introduction of fossil-fuel-powered equipment, steam engines, and synthetic fertilizers, along with advances in plant and animal breeding.

We are currently in the midst of a fourth major transition, involving the globalization of modern medical and technological advancements. The Medical-Technological Revolution is marked by developments in medicine, sanitation, and pharmaceuticals; the explosion of communication technologies; and the shift to modern agricultural practices known as the *Green Revolution* that have collectively allowed more people to live longer, healthier lives. This transition is still in progress, and the long-term implications for the human population, individual health, and the environment are unknown. Perhaps this will also be a period during which human society makes the transition to more sustainable, renewable energy sources and away from dependence on fossil fuels.

Environmental scientists who have tried to quantify the human carrying capacity of this planet have come up with wildly differing estimates. Estimates range from

roots

CARRYING CAPACITY

The history of the term **carrying capacity** is interesting, complicated, and poorly known. Nathan Sayre[*] comments on four uses: (1) as a mechanical attribute of manufactured objects of systems, mainly used in the context of shipping, starting in the 1840s; (2) as an attribute of living organisms and natural systems, mainly used in range and game management, beginning in the 1870s; (3) as *K* (in the sense that we use it most commonly in environmental science), the intrinsic limit of population for organisms in a particular environment, used by ecologists since the mid-twentieth century; and (4) specifically, as the number of humans this planet can support, used by neo-Malthusians since the mid-twentieth century. Sayre cites well-known ecologists Aldo Leopold, Eugene Odum, Garrett Hardin, and Paul Ehrlich as the principal contributors to the two latter meanings of the term.

[*]For a detailed history of the concept, see Sayre, N. (2008) The genesis, history, and limits of carrying capacity. *Annals of the Association of American Geographers,* 98:1, 120–134, available online.

1 billion to 2 billion people living prosperously in a healthy environment to 33 billion living in extreme poverty in a degraded world of intensive cultivation without natural areas. As our population climbs beyond 7 billion, we may yet continue to find ways to increase carrying capacity. Given our knowledge of population ecology, however, we have no reason to presume that human numbers can go on growing indefinitely. Indeed, populations that exceed their carrying capacity can crash.

Demography is the study of human population

The field of demography developed along with and partly preceded population ecology, and the disciplines have influenced and borrowed from one another. Demographic data help us understand how differences in population characteristics and related phenomena (for instance, decisions about reproduction) affect human communities and their environments. Demographers study population size, density, distribution, age structure, sex ratio, and rates of birth, death, immigration, and emigration of humans, just as population ecologists study these characteristics in other organisms. Each of these characteristics is useful for predicting population dynamics and potential environmental impacts.

Population size   The global human population of over 7 billion comprises more than 200 nations, with populations ranging from China's 1.3 billion and India's 1.2 billion (**FIGURE 6.7**) to a number of island nations with populations below 100 000. The size that our global

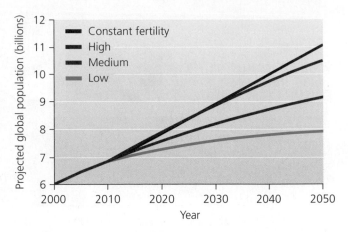

FIGURE 6.8
The United Nations predicts trajectories of world population growth, presenting its estimates in several scenarios based on different assumptions of fertility rates. In this 2008 projection, population was estimated to reach 11 billion in the year 2050 if fertility rates remained constant at 2008 levels (top line on graph). However, UN demographers expect fertility rates to continue falling, so they arrived at a best guess (*medium* scenario) of 9.15 billion for the human population in 2050. In the *high* scenario, if women on average have 0.5 children more than in the medium scenario, population will reach 10.5 billion in 2050. In the *low* scenario, if women have 0.5 children less than in the medium scenario, the world will contain 8 billion people in 2050.
Source: Data from United Nations Population Division, (2009), World Population Prospects: The 2008 Revision. *http://esa.un.org/unpp, Fig.1(c).*

population will eventually reach remains to be seen (**FIGURE 6.8**). However, **population size** alone—the absolute number of individuals—does not tell the whole story. Rather, a population's environmental impact depends on its density, distribution, and composition, as well as on affluence, technology, level of consumption, and other factors outlined earlier.

Population density and distribution   People are distributed very unevenly over the globe. In ecological terms, our distribution is clumped at all spatial scales. At the global scale (**FIGURE 6.9**), **population density**—the number of people per unit of land area—is particularly high in regions with temperate, subtropical, and tropical climates, such as China, Europe, Mexico, southern Africa, and India. Population density is low in regions with extreme-climate biomes, such as desert, deep rainforest, and tundra. Dense along seacoasts and rivers, human population is less dense at locations far from water. At intermediate scales, we cluster together in cities and suburbs and are spread more sparsely across rural areas. At small scales, we cluster in certain neighbourhoods and in individual households.

This uneven distribution means that certain areas bear far more environmental impact than others. Just as the Huang He has experienced intense pressure from millions of Chinese farmers, the world's other major rivers—from the Nile to the Danube, the Ganges, and the

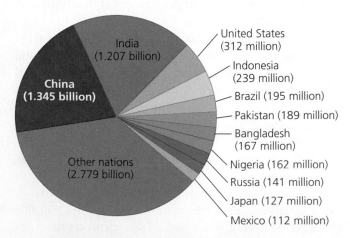

FIGURE 6.7
Almost one in five people in the world is Chinese, and more than one of every six people live in India. Three of every five people live in one of the 11 nations that have populations above 100 million.
Source: Data are projected for mid-2011, based on Population Reference Bureau (2010) 2010 World Population Data Sheet.

Persons/km²

0	25 - 249
1 - 4	250 - 999
5 - 24	1000+

FIGURE 6.9 Human population density varies tremendously from one region to another. Arctic and desert regions have the lowest population densities, whereas areas of India, Bangladesh, and eastern China have the densest populations. *Source: Data are for 2000, from the Center for International Earth Science Information Network (CIESIN), Columbia University; and Centro Internacional de Agricultura Tropical (CIAT), 2004.*

Mississippi—have all received more than their share of human impact. Urbanization entails the packaging and transport of goods, intensive fossil fuel consumption, and hotspots of pollution. However, the concentration of people in cities increases efficiency and economies of scale and relieves pressure on ecosystems in less-populated areas by releasing some of them from some human development.

At the same time, areas with low population density are often vulnerable to environmental impacts because the reason they have low populations in the first place is that they are sensitive and cannot support many people (a high S value in our revised IPAT model). Deserts, for instance, are easily affected by development that commandeers a substantial share of available water. Grasslands can be turned to deserts if they are farmed too intensively, as has happened across vast stretches of the Sahel region bordering Africa's Sahara Desert, in the Middle East, and in parts of China. The Arctic tundra, in the northern circumpolar region, is another environment that is highly sensitive to environmental change and human impacts. For example, a disturbance of vegetation—something as simple as a set of car tracks—can cause deep melting of permafrost and collapse of soil, the scars of which may last for years or even decades.

Age structure Data on the age structure or age distribution of human populations are especially valuable to demographers trying to predict future dynamics of populations. As you learned in the context of non-human populations, large proportions of individuals in young age groups portend a great deal of reproduction and,

thus, rapid population growth. Age structure diagrams, commonly called **population pyramids**, are visual tools scientists use to illustrate age structure (**FIGURE 6.10**). The width of each horizontal bar represents the number of people in each age class. A pyramid with a wide base denotes a large proportion of people who have not yet reached reproductive age—and this indicates a population soon capable of rapid growth. In this respect, a wide base of a population pyramid is like an oversized engine on a rocket—the bigger the booster, the faster the increase.

Examine the age structure diagrams, or age pyramids, for Canada and Madagascar (**FIGURE 6.11**). Not surprisingly, Madagascar has the greater population growth rate. In fact, its annual growth rate is nine times that of Canada.

By causing a dramatic reduction in the number of children born since 1970, China virtually guaranteed that its population age structure would change (**FIGURE 6.12**). In 1995 the median age in China was 27; by 2030 it will be 39. In 1997 there were 125 children under age five for

weighing the issues

CHINA'S REPRODUCTIVE POLICY

Consider the benefits as well as the problems associated with a reproductive policy, such as China's. Should a government be able to enforce strict penalties for citizens who fail to abide by such a policy? What alternatives can you suggest for dealing with the resource demands of a quickly growing population?

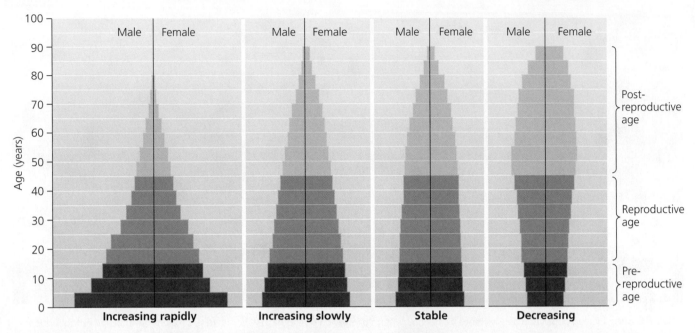

FIGURE 6.10   Age structure diagrams show numbers of individuals of different age classes in a population. A diagram like that on the left is weighted toward young age classes, indicating a population that will grow quickly. A diagram like that on the right is weighted toward old age classes, indicating a population that will decline. Populations with balanced age structures, like the one shown in the third diagram, will remain stable.

every 100 people aged 65 or older in China, but by 2030 there will be only 32. The number of people older than 65 will rise from 100 million in 2005 to 236 million in 2030.

This pattern of ageing in the population is occurring in many countries, including Canada (see **FIGURE 6.11A**). Older populations will present new challenges for many nations, as increasing numbers of older people require the care and financial assistance of relatively fewer working-age citizens.

This dramatic shift in age structure will challenge China's economy, health care systems, families, and military forces because fewer working-age people will be available to support social programs that assist the increasing number of older people. However, the shift in age structure also reduces the proportion of dependent children. The reduced number of young adults may mean a decrease in the crime rate. Moreover, older people are often productive members of society, contributing

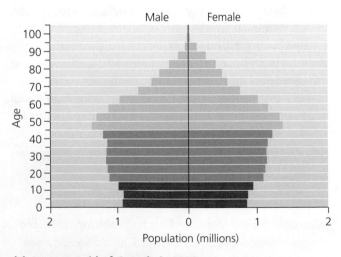

(a) Age pyramid of Canada in 2010

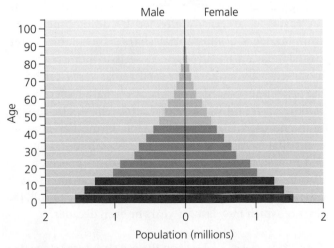

(b) Age pyramid of Madagascar in 2010

FIGURE 6.11   Canada **(a)** shows a balanced age structure, with relatively even numbers of individuals in various age classes. Madagascar **(b)** shows an age distribution heavily weighted toward young people. Madagascar's population growth rate is nine times that of Canada. The post–World War II "baby boom" is visible as a "bump" in the age pyramid for Canada, between the ages of 40 and 50. In future years the nation will experience an ageing population, as baby boomers grow older.   Source: *Data from Population Division of the Department of Economic and Social Affairs of the United Nations Secretariat, (2009). World Population Prospects: The 2008 Revision, http://esa.un.org/unpp. United Nations, 2009.*

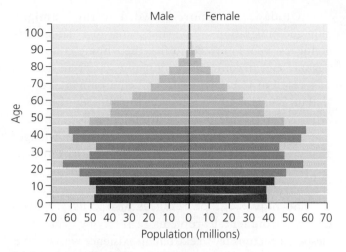

(a) Age pyramid of China in 2010

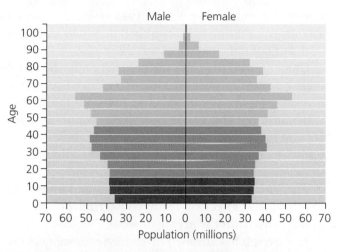

(b) Projected age pyramid of China in 2050

FIGURE 6.12
As China's population ages, older people will outnumber the young. Age pyramids show the predicted greying of the Chinese population between 2005 **(a)** and 2030 **(b)**. Today's children may, as working-age adults **(c)**, face pressures to support greater numbers of older citizens than has any previous generation. Can you point out on graph (a) the beginning of the one-child policy and on graph (b) the cohort that represents today's children?
Source: Data from United Nations Department of Economic and Social Affairs, Population Division: World Population Aging, 2009.

(c) Young female factory workers in China

volunteer activities and services to their children and grandchildren. Clearly, in terms of both benefits and drawbacks, life in China will continue to be profoundly affected by the particular approach its government has taken to population control.

Sex ratios   The ratio of males to females also can affect population dynamics. Imagine two islands, one populated by 99 men and 1 woman and the other by 50 men and 50 women. Where would we be likely to see the greatest population increase over time? Of course, the island with an equal number of men and women would have a greater number of potential mothers and thus a greater potential for population growth.

The naturally occurring sex ratio in human populations at birth features a slight preponderance of males; for every 100 female infants born, 105 to 106 male infants are born. This phenomenon may be an evolutionary adaptation to the fact that males are slightly more prone to death during any given year of life. It usually ensures that the ratio of men to women is approximately equal at the time people reach reproductive age; women then begin to predominate as the population ages, generally leading to a ratio of males to females that is slightly less than one-to-one in the population as a whole. Thus, a slightly uneven sex ratio at birth may be beneficial. However, a greatly distorted ratio can lead to problems.

In recent years, demographers have noted an unsettling trend in China, also observed in other nations where

there is a strong traditional preference for boys: The ratio of newborn boys to girls has become skewed. In the 2000 census, 120 boys were reported born for every 100 girls. Some provinces reported sex ratios as high as 138 boys for every 100 girls. The overall ratio of males per 100 females for the Chinese population as a whole is currently around 107, but that will change as the younger, male-dominated portion of the population ages, possibly ballooning to 135. The leading hypothesis for these unusual sex ratios is that many parents, having learned the sex of their fetuses by ultrasound, are selectively aborting female fetuses.

Traditionally, Chinese culture has valued sons because they can carry on the family name, assist with farm labour in rural areas, and care for ageing parents. Daughters, in contrast, will most likely marry and leave their parents, as the culture dictates. As a result, they will not provide the same benefits to their parents as will sons. Sociologists hold that this cultural gender preference, combined with the government's one-child policy, has led some couples to abort female fetuses or to abandon female infants. The Chinese government reinforced this gender discrimination when in 1984 it exempted rural peasants from the one-child policy if their first child was a girl, but not if the first child was a boy.

China is, of course, not the only nation in the world to experience the phenomenon of a skewed sex ratio. According to the UN Population Division, the United Arab Emirates and Qatar both have population sex ratios of more than 200, meaning that two boys survive to adulthood for every one girl, and Oman, Bahrain, and Kuwait are all more than 125.[2]

The unbalanced sex ratio in China and elsewhere may have the effect of further lowering population growth rates, with the ageing of today's children under 15. However, it has already proven tragic for some of the "missing girls." It is also beginning to have the undesirable social consequence of leaving many Chinese men single. This, in turn, has resulted in a grim new phenomenon: In parts of rural China, teenaged girls are being kidnapped and sold to families in other parts of the country as brides for single men.

Population change results from birth, death, immigration, and emigration

Rates of birth, death, immigration, and emigration help determine whether a human population grows, shrinks, or remains stable. The formula for measuring population growth that we used for non-human populations also pertains to humans: Birth and immigration add individuals to a population, whereas death and emigration remove individuals. It is convenient to express birth and death rates as the number of births and deaths per 1000 individuals for a given period—the **crude birth rate** (also called *nativity* or *natality*) and **crude death rate** (also, perhaps more commonly, called *mortality*). By subtracting crude death rate from crude birth rate, we obtain the rate of natural increase of the population—that is, the net increase from births alone, leaving aside migration. Other measures of birth rate and death rate are more specific than the "crude" rates; for example, *total fertility* is the average number of children born to each woman over the course of her life.

Technological advances have led to a dramatic decline in human death rates, widening the gap between crude birth rates and crude death rates and resulting in the global human population expansion. Just as individuals of different ages have different abilities to reproduce, individuals of different ages show different probabilities of dying. For instance, people are more likely to die at old ages than young ages; if you were to follow 1000 10-year-olds and 1000 80-year-olds for a year, you would find that at year's end more 80-year-olds had died than 10-year-olds.

In today's ever-more-crowded world, immigration and emigration are playing increasingly large roles. Refugees, people forced to flee their home country or region, have become more numerous in recent decades as a result of war, civil strife, and environmental degradation. The United Nations puts the number of refugees who flee to escape poor environmental conditions in the millions per year. It is also widely acknowledged that environmental degradation and resource shortages often contribute to other causes of refugeeism, including internal and international conflicts.

The movement of refugees also causes significant environmental problems in receiving regions, as desperate victims try to eke out an existence with no livelihood and no cultural or economic attachment to the land or incentive to conserve its resources. The millions who fled Rwanda following the genocide there in the mid-1990s, for example, inadvertently destroyed large areas of forest while trying to obtain fuelwood, food, and shelter to stay alive once they reached the Democratic Republic of Congo (**FIGURE 6.13**).

Since 1970, growth rates in many countries have been declining, even without population control policies, and the global growth rate has declined (**FIGURE 6.14**). This decline has come about, in part, from a steep drop in birth rates. Note, however, that this is the *rate of growth* that is slowing, while the *absolute size* of the population continues to increase.

Total fertility rate influences population growth

One key statistic demographers calculate to examine a population's potential for growth is the **total fertility**

FIGURE 6.13
The flight of refugees from Rwanda into the Democratic Republic of Congo in 1994 following the Rwandan genocide caused tremendous hardship for the refugees and tremendous stress on the environment into which they moved.

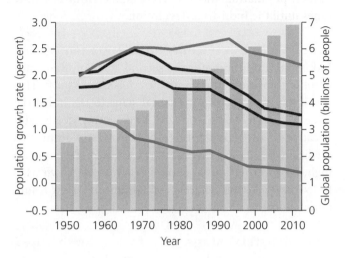

Legend:
- ■ World
- ■ More-developed regions
- ■ Less-developed regions
- ■ Least-developed countries
- ▨ Global population

FIGURE 6.14

The annual growth rate of the global human population (dark blue line) peaked in the 1960s and has declined since then. Growth rates of industrialized nations (green line) have fallen since 1950, while those of developing nations (red line) have fallen since the global peak in the late 1960s. For the world's least-developed nations (orange line), growth rates began to fall in the 1990s. Although growth *rates* are declining, global population *size* (grey bars) is still growing by about the same amount each year because smaller percentage increases of ever-larger numbers produce roughly equivalent additional amounts.
Source: Data from Population Division of the Department of Economic and Social Affairs of the United Nations Secretariat, 2009. World Population Prospects: The 2008 Revision. United Nations, 2009.

rate (**TFR**), or the average number of children born per female member of a population during her lifetime. **Replacement fertility** is the TFR that keeps the size of a population stable. For humans, replacement fertility is equal to a TFR of 2.1. When the TFR drops below 2.1, population size, in the absence of immigration, will shrink.

Various factors influence TFR and have acted to drive it downward in many countries in recent years. Historically, people tended to conceive many children, which helped ensure that at least some would survive. Lower infant

weighing the issues

CONSEQUENCES OF LOW FERTILITY?

In Canada, the United States, and every European nation, the total fertility rate has now dipped below the replacement fertility rate. What economic, social, or environmental consequences—positive or negative—do you think might result from below–replacement fertility rates?

Table 6.1 Total Fertility Rates (TFRs) for Major Continental Regions

Region	TFR 1970–1975	TFR 2005–2010
Africa	6.7	4.6
Latin America and Caribbean	5.0	2.4
Asia	5.0	2.3
Oceania	3.2	2.3
North America	2.0	2.0
Europe	2.2	1.5

Source: Data from United Nations Population Division, (2011), World Population Prospects: The 2010 Revision.

mortality rates have made this less necessary. Increasing urbanization has also driven TFR down; whereas rural families need children to contribute to farm labour, in urban areas children are usually excluded from the labour market, are required to go to school, and impose economic costs on their families. If a government provides some form of social security, as most do these days, parents need fewer children to support them in their old age when they can no longer work. Finally, with greater education and changing roles in society, women tend to shift into the labour force, putting less emphasis on child rearing.

All these factors have come together in Europe, where TFR has dropped from 2.6 to 1.5 in the past half-century. Every European nation now has a fertility rate below the replacement level, and populations are declining in 28 of 44 European nations. Worldwide by 2010, 72 countries had fallen below the replacement fertility rate of 2.1. These countries made up roughly 45% of the world's population and included China (with a TFR of 1.6). **TABLE 6.1** shows the TFRs of major continental regions.

Some nations have experienced the demographic transition

Many nations that have lowered their birth rates and TFRs have been going through a similar set of inter-related changes. In countries with good sanitation, good health care, and reliable food supplies, more people than ever before are living long lives. As a result, over the past 50 years the life expectancy for the average person has increased from 46 to 68 years as the global crude death rate has dropped from 20 deaths per 1000 people to 8 deaths per 1000 people. Strictly speaking, **life expectancy** is the average number of years that an individual in a particular age group is likely to continue to live, but often people use this term to refer to the average number of years a person can expect to live from birth. Much of the increase in life expectancy is due to reduced rates of infant mortality. Societies going through these changes are mostly the ones that have undergone urbanization and industrialization and have been able to generate personal wealth for their citizens.

To make sense of these trends, demographers developed a concept called the **demographic transition** (**FIGURE 6.15**). This is a model of economic and cultural change proposed in the 1940s and 1950s by demographer Frank Notestein and elaborated on by others to explain the declining death rates and birth rates that have occurred in Western nations as they became industrialized. Notestein observed that nations tend to move from a stable pre-industrial state of high birth and high death rates to a stable post-industrial state of low birth and low death rates. Industrialization, he proposed, caused these rates to fall naturally by first decreasing mortality and then lessening the need for large families. Parents would thereafter choose to invest in quality of life rather than quantity of children. Because death rates fall before birth rates fall, a period of net population growth results. Thus, under the demographic transition model, population growth is seen as a temporary phenomenon that occurs as societies move from one stage of development to another.

The pre-industrial stage   The first stage of the demographic transition model is the *pre-industrial stage*, characterized by conditions that have defined most of human history. In pre-industrial societies, both death rates and birth rates are high. Death rates are high because disease is widespread, medical care rudimentary, and food supplies unreliable and difficult to obtain. Birth rates are high because people must compensate for high mortality rates in infants and young children by having

several children. In this stage, children are valuable as additional workers who can help meet a family's basic needs. Populations within the pre-industrial stage are not likely to experience much growth, which is why the human population was relatively stable from neolithic times until the Industrial Revolution.

Industrialization and falling death rates
Industrialization initiates the second stage of the demographic transition, known as the *transitional stage*. This transition from the pre-industrial stage to the industrial stage is generally characterized by declining death rates because of increased food production and improved medical care. Birth rates in the transitional stage remain high, however, because people have not yet grown used to the new economic and social conditions. As a result, population growth surges.

The industrial stage and falling birth rates
The third stage in the demographic transition is the *industrial stage*. Industrialization increases opportunities for employment outside the home, particularly for women. Children become less valuable, in economic terms, because they do not help meet family food needs as they did in the pre-industrial stage. If couples are aware of this, and if they have access to birth control, they may choose to have fewer children. Birth rates fall, closing the gap with death rates and reducing the rate of population growth.

The post-industrial stage   In the final stage, the *post-industrial stage*, both birth and death rates have fallen to low levels. Population sizes stabilize or decline slightly. The society enjoys the fruits of industrialization without the threat of runaway population growth.

FIGURE 6.15

The demographic transition is an idealized process that has taken some populations from a pre-industrial state of high birth rates and high death rates to a post-industrial state of low birth rates and low death rates. In this diagram, the wide green area between the two curves illustrates the gap between birth and death rates that causes rapid population growth during the middle portion of this process. *Source: Data from Kent, M. M., and K. A. Crews. (1990). World Population: Fundamentals of Growth. Washington, DC: Population Reference Bureau.*

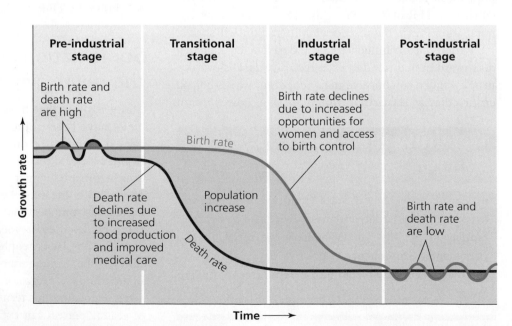

Is the demographic transition a universal process?

The demographic transition has occurred in many European countries, the United States, Canada, Japan, and several other developed nations over the past 200 to 300 years. Nonetheless, it is a model that may not apply to all developing nations as they industrialize now and in the future. Some social scientists doubt that it will apply; they point out that population dynamics may be different for developing nations that adopt the Western world's industrial model rather than devising their own. Some demographers assert that the transition will fail in cultures that place greater value on childbirth or grant women fewer freedoms.

Moreover, natural scientists warn that there are not enough resources in the world to enable all countries to attain the standard of living that developed countries now enjoy. It has been estimated that for people of all nations to have the quality of life that Canadians do, we would need the natural resources of at least two to three more Earths. Whether developing nations, which include the vast majority of the planet's people, will pass through the demographic transition as developed nations have is one of the most important and far reaching questions for the future of our civilization and Earth's environment.

Population and Society

Demographic transition theory links the statistical study of human populations with various societal factors that influence, and are influenced by, population dynamics. Let us now examine a few of these major societal factors more closely.

The status of women greatly affects population growth rates

Many demographers had long believed that fertility rates were influenced largely by degrees of wealth or poverty. However, affluence alone cannot determine the total fertility rate because a number of developing countries now have fertility rates lower than that of Canada. Instead, recent research is highlighting factors pertaining to the social empowerment of women. Drops in TFR have been most noticeable in countries where women have gained access to contraceptives and education, particularly family planning education (see **FIGURE 6.16**).

In 2010, 55% of married women worldwide (aged 15–49) reported using some modern method of contraception to plan or prevent pregnancy. China, at 86%, had the highest rate of contraceptive use of any nation.

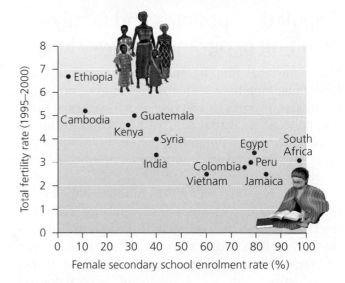

FIGURE 6.16

Increasing female literacy is strongly associated with reduced birth rates in many nations.
Source: Data from McDonald, M., and D. Nierenberg (2003) Linking population, women, and biodiversity. State of the World 2003. Washington, DC: Worldwatch Institute.

Five European nations showed rates of contraceptive use higher than 70%, as did Canada, Australia, the United States, and several others. At the other end of the spectrum, 26 African nations had rates of 10% or lower. These low rates of contraceptive use contribute to high fertility rates in sub-Saharan Africa, where the region's TFR is 5.2 children per woman. By comparison, in Asia, where the TFR in 1950 was 5.9, it is 2.2 today—in part a legacy of the population control policies of China and some other Asian countries.

These data clearly demonstrate that in societies where women have little power, substantial numbers of pregnancies are unintended. Studies show that when women are free to decide whether and when to have children, fertility rates have fallen and the resulting children are better cared for, healthier, and better educated. Unfortunately, in many societies, by tradition men restrict women's decision-making abilities, including decisions about how many children they will bear.

The gap between the power held by men and by women is just as obvious at the highest levels of government. Worldwide, only 19.2% of elected government officials in national legislatures are women. Canada (at about 22%) lags behind not only Europe (e.g., Sweden at 45%) but also many developing nations (e.g., Rwanda at 56% and Argentina at 39%) in the proportion of women in positions of power in government.[3] As more women win positions of power, it will have environmental consequences, for when women have economic and political power and access to education, they gain the option, and often the motivation, to limit the number of children they bear.

Population policies and family-planning programs are working

Data show that funding and policies that encourage family planning have been effective in lowering population growth rates in all types of nations, even those that are least industrialized. No nation has pursued a population control program as extreme as China's, but other rapidly growing nations have implemented less-restrictive programs.

When policy makers in India introduced the idea of forced sterilization as a means of population control in the 1970s, the resulting outcry brought down the government. Since then, India's efforts have been more modest and far less coercive, focusing on family planning and reproductive health care. A number of Indian states also run programs of incentives and disincentives promoting a "two-child norm," and current debate centres on whether this is a just and effective approach. Regardless, unless India strengthens its efforts to slow population growth, it seems set to overtake China and become the world's most populous nation by about the year 2030.

The government of Thailand relies on an education-based approach to family planning that has reduced birth rates and slowed population growth. In the 1960s,

Thailand's growth rate was 2.3%, but today it stands at 0.7%. This decline was achieved without a one-child policy. It has resulted, in large part, from government-sponsored programs devoted to family-planning education and increased availability of contraceptives. Brazil, Mexico, Iran, Cuba, and many other developing countries have instituted active programs to reduce their population growth. These programs entail setting targets and providing incentives, education, contraception, and reproductive health care.

Many of these programs are working. One study in 2000 examined four different pairs of nations located in the same parts of the world, with one country in each pair having a stronger program: Iran and Iraq, Pakistan and Bangladesh, Malawi and Kenya, and Haiti and Dominican Republic (**FIGURE 6.17**). The demographers concluded that in all four cases, the country with the stronger program (Iran, Bangladesh, Kenya, and Dominican Republic) initiated or accelerated a decline in fertility with its policies. The researchers also concluded that in some countries the strong presence of the Catholic church held back the success of family planning efforts.

In 1994, the United Nations hosted the milestone International Conference on Population and Development in Cairo, Egypt, at which 179 nations endorsed a platform calling on all governments to offer universal access to repro-

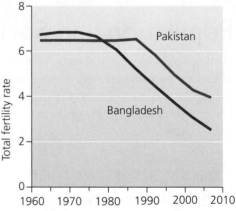

FIGURE 6.17

Data from four pairs of neighbouring countries demonstrate the effectiveness of family planning in reducing fertility rates. In each case, the nation that invested in family planning and (in some cases) made other reproductive rights, education, and health care more available to women (blue lines) reduced its total fertility rate (TFR) far more dramatically than its neighbour (red lines).
Source: Data from United Nation Population Division; and Harrison, P., and F. Pearce (2000) AAAS Atlas of Population and Environment. Berkeley, CA: University of California Press.

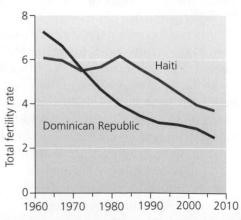

ductive health care within 20 years. The conference marked a turning away from older notions of command-and-control population policy geared toward pushing contraception and lowering population to preset targets. Instead, it urged governments to offer better education and health care and to address social needs that bear indirectly on population (such as alleviating poverty, disease, and sexism). Unfortunately, worldwide funding for family-planning programs fell by at least a third in the decade following the Cairo conference.

Poverty is strongly correlated with population growth

The alleviation of poverty was a prime target of the 1994 Cairo conference because poorer societies tend to show higher population growth rates than do wealthier societies. This pattern is consistent with demographic transition theory. **FIGURE 6.18** shows that poorer nations tend to have higher fertility rates. They also tend to have higher overall growth rates, higher birth and infant mortality rates, and lower rates of contraceptive use.

Such trends as these have affected the distribution of people on the planet. In 1960, 70% of all people lived in developing nations. By 2010, 82% of the world's population was living in these countries. Moreover, fully 99% of the next billion people to be added to the global population will be born in these poor, less-developed regions.

This is unfortunate from a social standpoint because these people will be added to the countries that are least

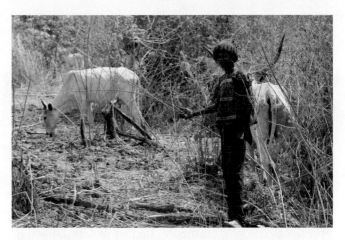

FIGURE 6.19
In the semi-arid Sahel region of Africa, where population is increasing beyond the land's ability to handle it, dependence on grazing agriculture has led to environmental degradation.

able to provide for them. It is also unfortunate from an environmental standpoint because poverty often results in environmental degradation. People dependent on agriculture in an area of poor farmland, for instance, may need to try to farm even if doing so degrades the soil and is not sustainable. This is largely why Africa's once-productive Sahel region, like many regions of western China, is turning to desert (**FIGURE 6.19**). Poverty also drives the hunting of many large mammals in Africa's forests, including the great apes that are now disappearing as local settlers and miners kill them for their "bush meat."

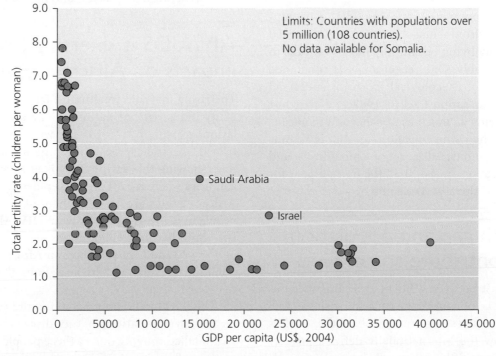

FIGURE 6.18 Total Fertility Rate is typically higher in poorer countries. *Source:* CIA World Fact Book *http://upload.wikimedia.org/wikipedia/commons/3/3d/Fertility_rate.jpg*

Consumption from affluence creates environmental impacts

Poverty can lead people into environmentally destructive behaviour, but wealth can produce even more severe and far-reaching environmental impacts. The affluence that characterizes such societies as Canada, the United States, Japan, or the Netherlands is built on massive and unprecedented levels of resource consumption. Much of this chapter has dealt with numbers of people rather than with the amount of resources each member of the population consumes or the amount of waste each member produces. The environmental impact of human activities, however, depends not only on the number of people involved but also on the way those people live. Recall the A for affluence in the IPAT equation. Affluence and consumption are spread unevenly across the world, and affluent societies generally consume resources from other localities as well as from their own.

Earlier in the book, we introduced the concept of the *ecological footprint*, the cumulative amount of Earth's surface area required to provide the raw materials a person or population consumes and to dispose of or recycle the waste that they produce. Individuals from affluent societies leave a considerably larger per capita ecological footprint. In this sense, the addition of 1 Canadian to the world has as much environmental impact as the addition of 6 Chinese, or 12 Indians or Ethiopians, or 40 Somalians. This fact should remind us that the "population problem" does not lie entirely with the developing world.

Indeed, just as population is rising, so is consumption, and some environmental scientists have calculated that we are already living beyond the planet's means to support us sustainably. One recent analysis concluded that humanity's global ecological footprint surpassed Earth's capacity to support us in 1987 and that our species is now living as much as 39% beyond its means (**FIGURE 6.20**). The rising consumption that is accompanying the rapid industrialization of China, India, and other populous nations makes it all the more urgent for us to find a path to global sustainability.

The wealth gap and population growth contribute to conflict

The stark contrast between affluent and poor societies in today's world is, of course, the cause of social as well as environmental stress. More than half the world's people live below the internationally defined poverty line. The richest one-fifth of the world's people controls more than 80 times the income of the poorest one-fifth

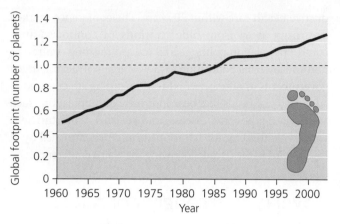

FIGURE 6.20

The global ecological footprint of the human population is now estimated by some analysts to be 40% greater than what Earth can bear in the long run. If population and consumption continue to rise (red line), we will increase our ecological deficit, or degree of overshoot, until systems give out and populations crash. If, instead, we pursue a path to sustainability (black dashed line), we can eventually repay our ecological debt and sustain our civilization.
Source: Adapted from WWF International. (2008) Living Planet Report 2008. *Published in October 2008 by WWF-World Wide Fund for Nature. © 2008 WWF. (panda.org). Zoological Society of London, and Global Footprint Network.*

(**FIGURE 6.21**). The richest one-fifth also uses 86% of the world's resources. That leaves only 14% of global resources—energy, food, water, and other essentials—for the remaining four-fifths of the world's population to share. As the gap between rich and poor grows wider and as the sheer numbers of those living in poverty continue to increase, it seems reasonable to predict increasing tensions between the "haves" and the "have-nots."

HIV/AIDS is exerting major impacts on African populations

The rising material wealth and falling fertility rates of many industrialized nations today are slowing population growth in accordance with the demographic transition model. Some other nations, however, are not following this script. This is especially the case in countries where the HIV/AIDS epidemic has taken hold. African nations are being hit hardest. Of the 33 million people in the world infected with HIV/AIDS as of 2008, two-thirds live in the nations of sub-Saharan Africa. One in every 20 adults in sub-Saharan Africa is infected with HIV, and for southern African nations, the figure is more than one in five.

The AIDS pandemic is having the greatest impact on human populations of any disease since the Black Death killed roughly one of three people in fourteenth-century Europe, and since smallpox brought by Europeans to the New World wiped out perhaps millions of native people. As AIDS takes roughly 3800 lives in Africa every day, the pandemic is unleashing a variety of demographic changes. Infant mortality in sub-Saharan Africa has risen to 9 deaths out of 100 live births—15 times the rate in the developed world. The high numbers of infant deaths and premature deaths of young adults have caused life expectancy in parts of southern Africa to fall from a high of close to 59 years in the early 1990s back down to less than 40 years, where it stood in the early 1950s.

Africa is not the only region with reason to worry (**FIGURE 6.22**). HIV is well established in the Caribbean and in Southeast Asia, and it is spreading quickly in eastern Europe and central Asia. As of 2006, an estimated 14 million children under the age of 15 worldwide had lost one or both parents to the disease.

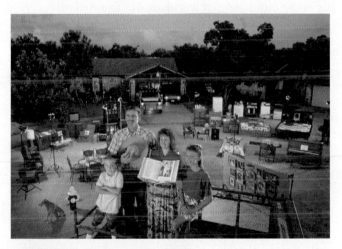

(a) A family living in North America

(b) A family living in Egypt

FIGURE 6.21

A typical North American family **(a)** may own a large house, keep numerous material possessions, and have enough money to afford luxuries, such as vacation travel. A typical family in a developing nation, such as Egypt **(b)**, may live in a small, sparsely furnished dwelling with few material possessions and little money or time for luxuries.

Demographic change has social, economic, and environmental repercussions

Everywhere in sub-Saharan Africa, AIDS is undermining the ability of developing countries to make the transition to modern technologies because it is removing many of the youngest and most productive members of society. In 1999 Zambia lost 1300 teachers to AIDS, and only 300 new teachers graduated to replace them. The loss of productive household members to AIDS causes families and communities to break down as income and food production decline. Valuable environmental and farming knowledge is being lost as an entire generation of Africans is decimated.

These problems are hitting many countries at a time when their governments are already experiencing what has been called *demographic fatigue*. Demographically fatigued governments face overwhelming challenges related to population growth, including educating and finding jobs for their swelling ranks of young people. With the added stress of HIV/AIDS, these governments face so many demands that they are stretched beyond their capabilities to address problems. As a result, the problems grow worse, and citizens lose faith in their governments' abilities to help them.

There is good news, however. Improved public health efforts (including sex education, contraceptives, and policies to address intravenous drug abuse) across the world have slowed HIV transmission rates, and improved medical treatments are lengthening the lives of people who are infected. Note in **FIGURE 6.22** that the number of AIDS deaths began to decrease in 2006, following a drop in new HIV infections since the late 1990s. We may finally be turning the corner on this challenge, thanks to government policy, international collaboration, medical research, nonprofit aid groups, and the grassroots efforts of patients and their advocates.

The U.N. has articulated sustainable development goals for humanity

In 2000, world leaders came together to adopt the *Millennium Declaration*, which set out a framework of basic goals for humanity over the next decade and a half. The *Millennium Development Goals* set an aggressive target date of 2015 to achieve many of the fundamental goals for sustainable development that aid organizations have worked so hard to achieve over the past few decades (**TABLE 6.2**). Each of the broad goals has several specific

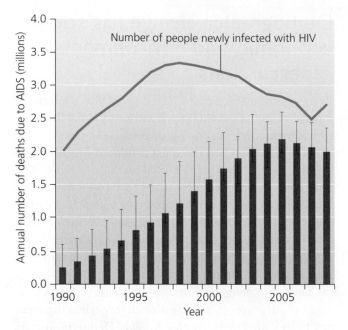

FIGURE 6.22

Two million people die from AIDS worldwide each year (red bars), and even more are newly infected with HIV each year (green line). However, extensive efforts to combat the disease are beginning to bear fruit; infections have been decreasing since 1998, and deaths began decreasing in 2006.

Source: Data from UNAIDS and WHO (2009) AIDS Epidemic Update 2009, Geneva, Switzerland.

underlying targets. You can find out more about these targets, and about our global progress toward them, at the United Nations Millennium Development Goals website, www.un.org/millenniumgoals/global.shtml.

Perhaps tellingly, population control is *not* one of the Millennium Development Goals. However, the interconnections we have discussed in this chapter should make it clear that in order to achieve the *other* goals, both population growth and resource consumption levels will need to be addressed.

If humanity's overarching goal is to generate a high standard of living and quality of life for all the world's people, then developing nations must find ways to reduce

Table 6.2　United Nations Millennium Development Goals for 2015

- Eradicate extreme poverty and hunger
- Achieve universal primary education
- Promote gender equality and empower women
- Reduce child mortality
- Improve maternal health
- Combat HIV/AIDS, malaria and other diseases
- Ensure environmental sustainability
- Develop a global partnership for development

Source: United Nations, End Poverty 2015, Millennium Development Goals, www.un.org/millenniumgoals/global.shtml.

their population growth. However, those of us living in the industrialized world must also be willing to reduce our consumption; otherwise, the goal of achieving environmental sustainability will elude us. Earth does not hold enough resources to sustain all 7 billion of us at the current North American standard of living, nor can we go out and find extra planets. We must make the best of the one place that supports us all.

Conclusion

Today's human population is larger than at any time in the past. Our growing population, as well as our growing consumption, affects the environment and our ability to meet the needs of all the world's people. Approximately 90% of children born today are likely to live their lives in conditions far less healthy and prosperous than most of us in the industrialized world are accustomed to.

However, there are at least two major reasons to be encouraged. First, although global population is still rising, the *rate* of growth has decreased nearly everywhere, and some countries are even seeing population declines. Most developed nations have passed through the demographic transition, showing that it is possible to lower death rates while stabilizing population and creating more-prosperous societies. Second, progress has been made in expanding rights for women worldwide. Although there is still a long way to go, women are slowly being treated more fairly, receiving better education, obtaining more economic independence, and gaining more ability to control their reproductive decisions. Aside from the clear ethical progress these developments entail, they are helping to slow population growth; where aggressive programs to control population growth have failed in many countries, educating girls and giving reproductive rights to women are succeeding.

Human population cannot continue to rise forever. The question, however, is how will it stop rising: through the gentle and benign process of the demographic transition; through restrictive governmental intervention, such as China's one-child policy; or through the miserable Malthusian checks of disease and social conflict caused by overcrowding and competition for scarce resources? Moreover, sustainability demands a further challenge—that we stabilize our population size in time to avoid destroying the natural systems that support our economies and societies. We are indeed a special species. We are the only one to come to such dominance as to fundamentally change so much of Earth's landscape and even its climate system. We are also the only species with the intelligence needed to turn around an increase in our own numbers before we destroy the very systems on which we depend.

CANADIAN ENVIRONMENTAL PERSPECTIVES

William Rees

With (then) graduate student Mathis Wackernagel, William Rees developed the concept of the ecological footprint.

■ **Professor** and **researcher**
■ **Bioecologist**
■ **Ecological economist**

As a young professor, William Rees spent his time calculating the carrying capacity of the land on which the University of British Columbia was located. One day, he turned the calculation upside down—literally—and ended up with one of the most useful tools we now have for understanding human impacts on the environment. Rees is a professor in the School of Community and Regional Planning at UBC, where he has taught since 1969. Rees teaches and carries out research on a variety of topics related to sustainability, but he is best known as the co-inventor (with Mathis Wackernagel, now executive director of the Global Footprint Network and at the time Rees's graduate student) of the ecological footprint concept.

Rees grew up on a farm in southern Ontario, and his connection to the land through farming led to his interest in sustainability. Rees describes a warm summer day at the farm when he was about 9 or 10: "We were in my grandmother's country porch, 13 of us or so, having lunch after a hard morning's work in the field. I happened to glance down at my plate full of young new carrots, little potatoes, fresh lettuce, and so on, and to make a long story short, I realized that there wasn't a single thing on the plate that I hadn't had a hand in growing. . . . I was so excited by that notion, I don't think I was able to eat my lunch."[4] He credits this early emotional connection to the land with his later decisions to study zoology and ecology.

The idea that humans—like all other species—rely on nature for sustenance and resources followed Rees throughout university and a Ph.D. in population ecology at the University of Toronto. As a young professor, Rees investigated the relationship between ecological economics and human ecology. Economic thought in the 1970s still relied on the idea that resource shortages could be resolved through technology, or by extensification or intensification of resource extraction. This did not sit well with Rees; surely this could not work indefinitely. While attempting to compute the carrying capacity of the Lower Fraser Valley (Lower Mainland) in BC, he had the idea of turning the calculation upside down—instead of computing the carrying capacity of the land, why not figure out how much land or ecosystem capacity would be needed to support a human population of a given size and consumption level? The ecological footprint concept was born.

Since the 1996 publication of *Our Ecological Footprint: Reducing Human Impact on the Earth*, both Rees and Wackernagel have continued their work on the ecological footprint as an indicator of human impact. Rees's current research is focused on environmental change and determining the necessary ecological conditions for biodiversity preservation and sustainable socioeconomic development. His current book asks the question, "Is humanity inherently unsustainable?"

"The whole thrust toward sustainability has been to treat it as an economic problem or a technological problem. . . . What we really ought to be thinking about is what makes for people's welfare.[5] —**William Rees**

Thinking About Environmental Perspectives

Bill Rees points to his childhood on a farm in southern Ontario as the origin of his interest in sustainability and human impacts on the environment. Did you have any childhood experiences that created in you a deep connection with the land or the natural environment? If so, did these influence your later decisions about what to study?

REVIEWING OBJECTIVES

You should now be able to:

Assess the scope and historical patterns of human population growth

■ The current global population of 7 billion people adds about 80 million people per year (2.6 people every second).

■ The world's population growth rate peaked at 2.1% in the 1960s and now stands at 1.2%. Growth rates vary among regions of the world.

■ Attitudes toward the "population problem" have changed over time. The Malthusian perspective holds that population is a problem to the extent that it depletes resources, intensifies pollution, stresses social systems, or degrades ecosystems, such that the natural environment or our quality of life declines.

Evaluate how human population, affluence, and technology affect the environment

- The IPAT model summarizes how environmental impact (I) results from interactions among population size (P), affluence (A), and technology (T).
- Rising population and rising affluence (leading to greater consumption) each increase environmental impact. Technological advances have frequently exacerbated environmental degradation, but they can also help mitigate our impact.
- Four major societal transitions (paleolithic tool-use; neolithic development of agriculture; Industrial Revolution switch to fossil fuels and mechanization; and the modern Medical-Technological and Green Revolutions) have fundamentally altered the way the human population interacts with the environment.

Explain and apply the fundamental concepts of demography

- Demography applies principles of population ecology to the statistical study of human populations.
- Demographers study size, density, distribution, age structure, and sex ratios of populations, as well as rates of birth, death, immigration, and emigration.
- Total fertility rate (TFR) contributes greatly to change in a population's size.

Outline the concept of demographic transition

- The demographic transition model explains why population growth has slowed in industrialized nations. Industrialization and urbanization have reduced the economic need for children, while education and the empowerment of women have decreased unwanted pregnancies. Parents in developed nations choose to invest in quality of life rather than quantity of children.
- The demographic transition may or may not proceed to completion in all of today's developing nations. Whether it does is of immense importance in the quest for population stabilization and sustainability.

Describe how wealth and poverty, the status of women, and family planning affect population growth

- When women are empowered and achieve equality with men, fertility rates fall, and children tend to be better cared for, healthier, and better educated.
- Family-planning programs and reproductive education have successfully reduced population growth in many nations.
- Poorer societies tend to have higher population growth rates than do wealthier societies.
- The high consumption rates of affluent societies may make their ecological impact greater than that of poorer nations with larger populations.
- Epidemics like HIV/AIDS claim large numbers of young and productive members of society. They can influence population dynamics and can have severe social and environmental ramifications, particularly for traditional food production.

Link population goals to sustainable development goals

- Achieving the UN Millennium Development Goals will require attention to both population growth and resource consumption.

TESTING YOUR COMPREHENSION

1. What is the approximate current human global population? How many people are being added to the population each day? How many have been added since you were born?
2. Why has the human population continued to grow in spite of environmental limitations?
3. Contrast the views of environmental scientists with those of libertarian writer Sheldon Richman and similar-thinking economists over whether population growth is a problem. Why does Richman think the concept of carrying capacity does not apply to human populations?
4. Explain the IPAT model. How can technology either increase or decrease environmental impact? Provide at least two examples.
5. What characteristics and measures do demographers use to study human populations? Which of these help determine the impact of human population on the environment?
6. What is the total fertility rate (TFR)? Can you explain why the replacement fertility for humans is approximately 2.1? Why would it not be exactly 2.0? How is Europe's TFR affecting its natural rate of population change?
7. Why have fertility rates fallen in many countries?
8. In the demographic transition model, why is the pre-industrial stage characterized by high birth and death rates, and the industrial stage by falling birth and death rates?

9. How does the demographic transition model explain the increase in population growth rates in recent centuries? How does it explain the decrease in population growth rates in recent decades?

10. Why do poorer societies have higher population growth rates than wealthier societies? How does poverty affect the environment? How does affluence affect the environment?

THINKING IT THROUGH

1. China's reduction in birth rates is leading to significant change in the nation's age structure. Review **FIGURE 6.12**, which portrays the projected change. You can see that the population is growing older, based on the top-heavy age pyramid for the year 2050. What sorts of effects might this situation ultimately have on Chinese society? Explain your answer.

2. The World Bank estimates that more than half the world's people survive on less than the equivalent of $2 per day. What effect would you expect this situation to have on the political stability of the world? Explain your answer.

3. Apply the IPAT model to the example of China provided in the chapter. How do population, affluence, technology, and ecological sensitivity affect China's environment? Now consider your own country, region, province, or territory. How do population, affluence, technology, and ecological sensitivity affect your environment? How can we regulate the relationship between population and its effects on the environment?

4. Do you think that all of today's developing nations will complete the demographic transition and come to enjoy a permanent state of low birth and death rates? Why or why not? What steps might we as a global society take to help ensure that they do? Now think about developed nations, including Canada. Do you think these nations will continue to lower their birth and death rates in a state of prosperity? What factors might affect whether they do so?

5. India's prime minister has put you in charge of that nation's population policy. India has a population growth rate of 1.7% per year, a TFR of 2.9, a 46% rate of contraceptive use, and a population that is 72% rural. What policy steps would you recommend, and why?

6. Now imagine that you have been tapped to design population policy for Germany. Germany is losing population at an annual rate of 0.2% and has a TFR of 1.3, a 72% rate of contraceptive use, and a population that is 88% urban. What policy steps would you recommend, and why?

INTERPRETING GRAPHS AND DATA

At right are graphed data representing the economic condition of the world's population. The *y* axis indicates the per capita income for each country or region expressed as standardized purchasing power (termed *gross national income in purchasing power parity*, or *GNI PPP*. The *x* axis indicates the cumulative percentage of the world population whose per capita GNI PPP is equal to or greater than that country's or region's per capita GNI PPP. The horizontal dotted line indicates the global average per capita GNI PPP.

1. What percentage of the world population lives at or below the global average per capita GNI PPP? What percentage lives at or below one-half of the global average per capita GNI PPP? What percentage lives at or above twice the global average per capita GNI PPP?

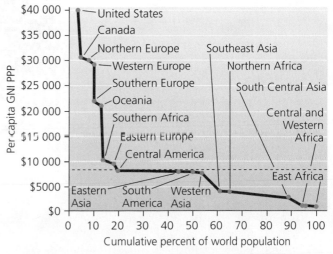

Percentage of world population at various income levels.
Source: Population Reference Bureau. 2006. World Population Data Sheet 2006.

2. Given a global average per capita GNI PPP of $9190 and a world population of 7 billion people, what is the total global GNI PPP? What would the global GNI PPP be if everyone lived at the level of affluence of Canada?

3. How do you personally resolve the ethical conflict between the desirable goal of raising the standard of living of the billions of desperately poor people in the world and the likelihood that increasing their affluence (*A* in the equation I = PAT) will have a negative impact on the environment?

CHAPTER ENDNOTES

1. Unless otherwise noted, population data in this chapter are from (or calculated from) the United Nations Department of Economic and Social Affairs, Population Division (2011) *World Population Prospects: The 2010 Revision.* http://esa.un.org/unpd/wpp/index.html

2. Data from United Nations Population Division (2007) *World Population Prospects: The 2006 Revision*, Table A.1.

3. Data from Inter-Parliamentary Union (March 2011) *Women in National Parliaments*, www.ipu.org/wmn-e/classif.htm

4. Quoted from Gismondi, M. (2000) Dr. William Rees Interviewed by Dr. Michael Gismondi. *Aurora Online,* http://aurora.icaap.org/index.php/aurora/article/view/18/29

5. Quoted from Gismondi, M. (2000) Dr. William Rees Interviewed by Dr. Michael Gismondi. *Aurora Online,* http://aurora.icaap.org/index.php/aurora/article/view/18/29

MyEnvironmentPlace

Go to **www.myenvironmentplace.ca** where you will find quizzes, animations, your Pearson eText, and more.

7 Soil Resources

This is the Mer Bleue provincial wetland, near Ottawa, Ontario.

Upon successfully completing this chapter, you will be able to

- Delineate the fundamentals of soil science, including soil-forming processes
- Describe some important properties of soil
- Characterize the role of soils in biogeochemical cycling
- State the importance of soils for agriculture and in supporting plant growth

- Identify the causes and predict the consequences of soil erosion and soil degradation
- Outline the history and explain the basic principles of soil conservation

This satellite image shows the ancient channel of the Ottawa River that is now occupied by the Mer Bleue wetland.

CANADA

Hudson Bay

Mer Bleue

UNITED STATES

MER BLEUE: A BOG OF INTERNATIONAL SIGNIFICANCE

"This soil of ours, this precious heritage, what an unobtrusive existence it leads! To the rich soil let us give the credit due. The soil is the reservoir of life."
—J.A. TOOGOOD, CANADIAN SOIL SCIENTIST

"The nation that destroys its soil destroys itself."
—FORMER U.S. PRESIDENT FRANKLIN D. ROOSEVELT

The Mer Bleue Conservation Area is a 35-km² provincially protected wetland situated just east of Ottawa, Ontario. It is located in an ancient, now-abandoned channel of the Ottawa River (see satellite photo) and hosts a number of plant species that are specially adapted to moist, boggy, acidic conditions, including *Sphagnum* moss, bog rosemary, blueberry, cottongrass, cattails, and tamarack. The area, classified as an open bog, has been recognized under the Ramsar Convention as a wetland of international importance.

The Mer Bleue wetland provides an example of a specific type of soil—peat—that has been accumulating in many northern areas since the end of the last ice age. Canada has some of the most extensive peatlands in the world, covering 14% of our land area, and the peat deposits in some parts of the Mer Bleue bog, which formed over the past 8000 years, are up to 6 m thick.

Northern peatlands are extremely important storage reservoirs for carbon and are thought to hold about one-third of all the carbon stored in soils. Through decomposition of organic matter, peat produces soil gases such as CO_2 and CH_4, which function as greenhouse gases in the atmosphere. Understanding the potential reaction of these very sensitive soils to climate change, particularly changes in water content and temperature, is of great interest to scientists. For example, if warming leads northern peat soils to decompose at faster rates and thus to release more soil gases, it could have a major impact on the concentration of these carbon-based gases in the atmosphere. This could set up a positive feedback loop and have a reinforcing influence on greenhouse warming.

The storage of carbon in peat depends on the balance between net primary production and decomposition. Plants store or sequester carbon as a result of photosynthesis, then contribute the stored carbon to the peat soil, where it accumulates in the form of plant litter. Temperature and light levels are of obvious importance to this balance, because the process of photosynthesis is involved. Moisture is another very important factor. When water levels are high, CH_4, the by-product of anaerobic (reduced) decomposition, is produced in large quantities; when conditions are drier, respiration tends to be aerobic (oxidized), producing less CH_4 but more CO_2.

The Peatland Carbon Study (PCARS) was initiated by a group of Canadian scientists in 1997. Researchers involved in the project, who are linked by an interest in ecosystem structure and function, include soil scientists, microclimatologists, hydrologists, a palynologist (a scientist who studies ancient pollen), plant ecologists, and graduate students from fields as varied as geochemistry, botany, physical geography, and microbial ecology.

The work continues today as part of the Canadian Carbon Project research network, measuring and modelling the influence of climatic and seasonal changes on the carbon balance of peatlands. Scientific activities at the Mer Bleue site include an instrument tower equipped for meteorological measurements, including energy balance, water vapour, and carbon dioxide and methane fluxes, combined with field investigations on plant growth and decomposition, hydrology, and plots for experimentation with factors such as drainage and excess nutrients (see photo).

On the basis of these ongoing measurements, now one of the longest-standing continuous sets of measurements of a northern peatland, scientists are developing a series of comprehensive ecosystem models for peatlands.[1] By studying this typical Canadian ecosystem, these scientists are contributing to our understanding of how soils may behave in a global context, in response to the phenomenon of climate change.

Graduate student Varun Gupta (left) and soil scientist Nate Basiliko use a raised boardwalk to sample sensitive peat soils from Mer Bleue. The experimental plots are being used to study the impacts of changes in nitrogen deposition on biogeochemical cycling.

Soil as a System

We generally overlook the complexity of soil. In everyday language we tend to equate *soil* with *dirt*. **Soil**, however, is not merely loose material derived from rock; it is a complex plant-supporting system that consists of disintegrated rock, organic matter, water, gases, nutrients, and microorganisms (**FIGURE 7.1**). Soil is also fundamental to the support of life on this planet and the provision of food for the growing human population. As a resource it is renewable if managed carefully, but it is easily degraded and is currently at risk in many locations around the world.

Soil is a complex, dynamic mixture

Soil consists very roughly of half solids, mostly mineral matter with varying proportions of organic matter, and the rest is pore space taken up by air, water, and other soil gases. The mineral particles in the soil are mostly

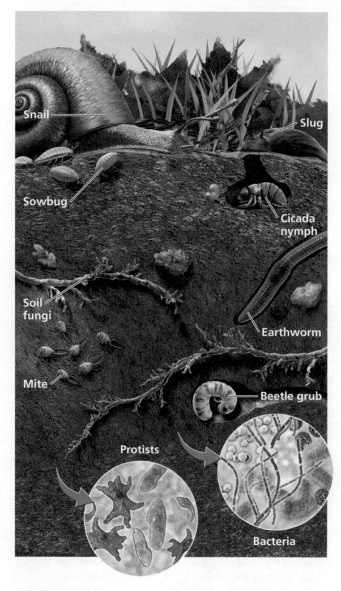

FIGURE 7.1
Soil is a complex mixture of organic and inorganic components and is full of living organisms whose actions help keep it fertile. Entire ecosystems exist in soil. Most soil organisms, from bacteria to fungi to insects to earthworms, decompose organic matter. Many, such as earthworms, also help to aerate the soil.

roots
SOIL

There are a lot of possible pathways that the word **soil** may have taken to arrive at it present-day usage, basically, "earth that plants can grow in." Most recently, it is derived from the Middle English (fifteenth-century) word *soile* (or *soyle*), meaning "ground" or "earth," which came, in turn, from the fourteenth-century Anglo-Norman (French) word *soyl*, "a piece of ground." These are thought to have come originally from the Latin word *solium*, meaning "seat." Another possible contributor is the Latin word *solum*, meaning "soil or ground."

Water partially fills the open spaces, or *pore spaces*, between the mineral grains and particles of organic matter in soils. This is never "pure" water; it contains a variety of dissolved constituents, both minerals and organics, and it is variously referred to as the *soil solution*, *soil water*, or *soil moisture*. These solutions are very important for the support of plant growth because they dissolve and mobilize soil constituents that plants require as nutrients.

Similarly, the "air" that partially fills soil pore spaces is not exactly the same as the air that we normally breathe. Like the atmosphere, *soil gas* contains oxygen and nitrogen, as well as carbon dioxide, methane, and other gases that reflect its chemical equilibrium with the liquid and solid constituents of the soil, including soil organisms. Soils also contain gases that are released from the underlying rock, such as radon, and gases that infiltrate from above, such as volatile constituents derived from spilled gas and oil.

Soil can have as much influence on a region's ecosystems as do the climate, latitude, and elevation. In fact, because soil is composed of living and nonliving components that interact with each other and with their surroundings in complex ways, soil itself meets the definition of an ecosystem. Together the mineral, organic, aqueous, and gaseous components of soil constitute a dynamic, ever-changing system that links the solid geosphere to the atmosphere, hydrosphere, and biosphere.

Soil formation is slow and complex

The formation of soil begins when the parent material is exposed to the effects of the atmosphere, hydrosphere, and biosphere. Parent material can be lava or volcanic

inherited from the **parent material**, the base geological material in a given location, from which the soil is formed. The parent material thus determines the starting composition of the soil.

The organic matter in soil includes living and dead microorganisms as well as decaying material derived from plants and animals. A single teaspoonful of soil can contain 100 million bacteria, 500 000 fungi, 100 000 algae, and 50 000 *protists* (simple eukaryotic microorganisms). Soil also provides habitat for earthworms, insects, mites, millipedes, centipedes, nematodes, sowbugs, and other invertebrates, as well as burrowing mammals, amphibians, and reptiles.

ash; rock or sediment deposited by glaciers; wind-blown dunes; sediments deposited by rivers, in lakes, or in the ocean; or, perhaps most commonly, any type of **bedrock**, the continuous mass of solid rock that makes up Earth's crust.

The processes most responsible for soil formation are weathering, erosion, and the deposition and decomposition of organic matter. **Weathering** describes the physical, chemical, and biological processes that break down rocks and minerals, turning large particles into smaller particles (**FIGURE 7.2**). These small, loose particles of mineral matter—collectively called *regolith*—are the precursors of soils.

Physical or **mechanical weathering** breaks rocks down without triggering a chemical change in the parent material. Temperature, wind, rain, and ice are the main agents of physical weathering. Daily and seasonal temperature variation aids their action by causing the thermal expansion and contraction of parent material; areas with extreme temperature fluctuations experience rapid rates of physical weathering. Flowing water, wind, and glacial ice move rock particles that scrape and abrade other rock surfaces, causing physical weathering. Water freezing and expanding in cracks in rock is another common cause of physical weathering.

Chemical weathering results when water or other substances chemically interact with parent material. If you have ever visited an old cemetery and noticed that some of the headstones seem worn and smooth, this is likely the influence of chemical weathering, slowly dissolving and carrying away the mineral constituents of the headstones. Notice that the headstones made of limestone are the ones that most clearly demonstrate chemical

weathering; limestone dissolves easily in normal, slightly acidic precipitation, whereas granite (the other common material used for headstones) is resistant to chemical weathering. Conditions where precipitation or groundwater are unusually acidic promote chemical weathering, as do warm, wet conditions.

Biological weathering occurs when living things break down parent material by physical or chemical means. For instance, lichens initiate primary terrestrial succession by producing acid, which chemically weathers rock. A tree may accelerate weathering through the physical action of its roots as they grow into fissures in rock. It may also accelerate weathering chemically through the decomposition of its leaves and branches or with chemicals it releases from its roots.

Biological activity further contributes to soil formation through the deposition, decomposition, and accumulation of organic matter. As plants, animals, and microbes die or deposit waste, this material is incorporated into the substrate, mixing with minerals. The deciduous trees of temperate forests, for example, drop their leaves each fall, making leaf litter available to the detritivores and decomposers that break it down and incorporate its nutrients into the soil. In decomposition, complex organic molecules are broken down into simpler ones, including those that plants can take up through their roots.

Partial decomposition of organic matter creates **humus**, a dark, spongy, crumbly mass of material made up of complex organic compounds. Soils with a high humus content hold moisture well and are productive for plant life. Soils that are dominated by partially decayed, compressed organic material—like the soil at Mer Bleue—are called **peat**. Peat is characteristic of (though not exclusive to) northern climates because cool temperatures and saturation by surface water slow the decay process, allowing great thicknesses of organic material to accumulate.

Physical weathering
(wind, rain, thermal expansion and contraction, water freezing)

Chemical weathering
(water and gases)

Biological weathering
(tree roots and lichens)

Parent material (rock)

Smaller particles of parent material

FIGURE 7.2
The weathering of parent material is the first step in soil formation. Rock is broken down into finer particles by physical, chemical, and biological processes.

roots

HUMUS

Humus comes from the Latin word *humus*, meaning "earth" or "soil." It is related to the English word *humility* and possibly even to the word *human*. The Latin probably came originally from the Proto-Indo-European root *dhghem-*, meaning "low" or "on the ground." The term *Proto-Indo-European* (abbreviated *PIE*) refers to the common ancestor of all Indo-European languages.

weighing the issues

EARTH'S SOIL RESOURCES

It can take anywhere from 500 to 10 000 years to produce 1 cm of natural topsoil, depending on local conditions. Much of Canada's land area was scraped free of soil during the last glaciation by the passage of huge ice masses, which retreated about 10 000 years ago. Today much of interior and northern Canada still lacks soil cover. Given this very long renewal time, is soil truly a renewable resource? How should the very long renewal time influence soil management?

Weathering produces fine particles and is the first step in soil formation. Another process often involved is **erosion**, the movement of particles from one location to another. When soil or regolith is transported by wind, water, or ice and then deposited somewhere else, it is generally referred to as **sediment**. The transport process itself can promote physical weathering as the transported particles collide and scrape against one another. Erosion is particularly prevalent when soil is denuded of vegetation, leaving the surface exposed to water and wind that may wash or blow it away.

Weathering, erosion, the accumulation and transformation of organic matter, and the other processes that contribute to soil formation are all influenced by environmental factors. Soil scientists cite five primary factors that influence the formation of soil (**TABLE 7.1**).

A soil profile consists of layers known as horizons

Once weathering has produced an abundance of small mineral particles, wind, water, and organisms begin to move and sort them, and water moves through, picking up and transporting soluble materials. Eventually, distinct layers develop. Each layer of soil is known as a **horizon**, and the cross-section as a whole, from surface to bedrock, is known as a **soil profile**.

Minerals are carried downward through the developing soil profile as a result of **leaching**, a process in which materials suspended or dissolved in liquid are transported through the subsurface. Soil that undergoes leaching is a bit like coffee in a drip filter. When it rains, water infiltrates the soil (just as it infiltrates coffee grounds), dissolves some of its components, and carries them downward into the deeper horizons. At depth in the soil profile, some of this material may be deposited

Table 7.1 The Five Factors That Influence Soil Formation	
Factor	**Effects**
Climate	Soil forms faster in warm, wet climates. Heat speeds chemical reactions and accelerates weathering, decomposition, and biological growth. Moisture is required for many biological processes and can speed weathering.
Organisms	Earthworms and other burrowing animals mix and aerate soil, add organic matter, and facilitate microbial decomposition. Plants add organic matter and affect a soil's composition and structure.
Topography	Hills and valleys affect exposure to sun, wind, and water, and they influence where and how soil and water move. Steeper slopes result in more runoff and erosion and in less leaching, slower accumulation of organic matter, and less differentiation of soil layers.
Parent material	Chemical and physical attributes of the parent material influence properties of the resulting soil.
Time	Soil formation takes decades, centuries, or millennia. The four factors above change over time, so the soil we see today may be the result of multiple sets of factors.

in zones of *accumulation*. Minerals that are commonly leached are those that are the most *soluble* (easily dissolvable), including various iron, aluminum, and silicate minerals. In some soils, minerals may be leached so rapidly that plants are deprived of nutrients. Minerals that leach rapidly from soils may be carried into groundwater, where they can affect water quality.

Soil scientists subdivide horizons according to their characteristics and the processes that take place within them. For our purposes we will discuss five major horizons, known as the O, A, B, C, and R horizons (**FIGURE 7.3**). Soils from different locations vary, and few soil profiles contain all of these horizons, but any given soil contains at least some of them. Generally, the degree of weathering and the concentration of organic matter decrease downward in the soil profile.

Peat deposits are classified as **O horizons**, whereas surface deposits of leaves, branches, mosses, animal waste, collectively termed **litter**, form another type of organic horizon in upland forests. These surface deposits (including *L*, *F*, and *H* horizons) are classified and subdivided on the basis of their degree of decomposition.

Just below the litter layer lies the **A horizon**, the uppermost mineral horizon, which consists of inorganic mineral components with organic matter and humus

FIGURE 7.3

Mature soil consists of layers, or horizons, that have different compositions and characteristics. The number and depth of horizons vary from place to place as a result of the mix of soil-forming factors at the location, producing different soil profiles. The O horizon consists mostly of organic matter deposited by organisms. The A horizon (or *topsoil*), is the uppermost mineral horizon and consists of some organic material mixed with mineral components. Materials tend to be leached from the A horizon and deposited in the B horizon. The C horizon consists largely of weathered material that is still identifiable as parent rock, and which may overlie an R horizon of pure parent material.

from above mixed in. The A horizon is often referred to as **topsoil**, that portion of the soil that is most nutritive for plants and therefore most vital to ecosystems and agriculture. Topsoil takes its loose texture and dark colour from its humus content. The A horizon is home to most of the countless organisms that give life to soil.

Minerals and organic matter that are leached from the topsoil move down into the **B horizon**, or *subsoil*, where they accumulate. If leached minerals are deposited in the B horizon, they can lead to the development of hard, mineral-rich layers that are variously called *hardpan*, *claypan*, *duripan*, or *caliche*, depending on their specific composition and structure. These hard layers can cause problems for plant growth because they interfere with drainage and prevent plant roots from penetrating to lower, nutrient-rich layers of the soil.

The **C horizon**, if present, is a transition zone located below the B horizon. It consists of broken-up parent

material only slightly altered by the processes of soil formation, and contains rock particles that are larger and less weathered than the layers above. The C horizon may sit directly above an **R horizon** of unaltered parent material (*R* for *rock*). Some soils also are characterized by the presence of a distinct layer of water, called a *W horizon*, and some arctic soils contain a perennially frozen layer called **permafrost**.

Soils vary in colour, texture, structure, and pH

The horizons presented above depict an idealized, "typical" soil, but soils display very great variety. Young soils tend to be thin, and not all horizons are present in all soils. Canadian soil scientists classify soils into 10 major groups, based largely on the processes through which the soils are formed (**TABLE 7.2**). Within these 10 *soil orders*, there are dozens of "great groups," hundreds of "subgroups," and thousands of soils belonging to lower categories, all arranged in a hierarchical or taxonomic system. Scientists classify soils into these various categories using properties such as colour, texture, structure, and pH.

Soil colour The colour of soil (**FIGURE 7.4**) can indicate its composition and sometimes its fertility. For example, the famously red colour of soils on Prince

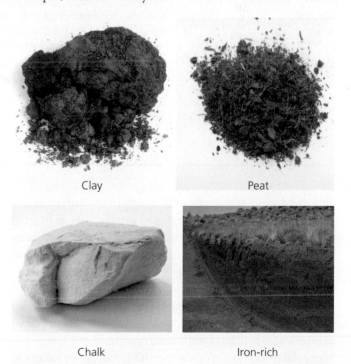

Clay

Peat

Chalk

Iron-rich

FIGURE 7.4

The colour of soil can vary drastically from one location to another. A soil's composition affects its colour; for instance, soils high in organic matter tend to be dark brown or black, light grey soils are often chalky in composition. Iron-rich soil, such as the one seen here in Central Australia, is often bright red in colour.

Table 7.2 The Canadian System of Soil Classification

Categories, or "Taxa," in the Canadian System of Soil Classification

Taxa	Principles used	No. of classes
Order	Dominant soil-forming process	10
Great group	Strength of soil-forming	31
Subgroup	Kind and arrangement of horizons	231
Family	Parent material characteristics	about 10 000
Series	Detailed features of the soil	about 100 000

Orders in the Canadian System of Soil Classification

Regosolic	Weakly developed soils, lacking a B horizon and typically forming in recent deposits.
Brunisolic	Poorly developed soils (i.e., lacking in horizon development, sometimes only lightly weathered, but slightly more developed than regosols, see below) that typically form under boreal forests.
Chernozemic	Well-drained to imperfectly drained soils with surface horizons darkened by the accumulation of organic matter from the decomposition of grasses; typical of the Interior Plains of Western Canada.
Luvisolic	Soils with light-coloured eluvial (E, or leached) horizons and B horizons in which clay has accumulated; characteristic of well-drained to imperfectly drained sites; in sandy loam to clay, base-saturated parent materials under forest vegetation in subhumid to humid and mild to very cold climates; from the southern extremity of Ontario to the zone of permafrost and from Newfoundland to British Columbia.
Vertisolic	Unstable soils with high clay contents, characterized by shrinking-swelling or wetting-drying cycles that either disrupt or inhibit the formation of soil horizons.
Solonetzic	Soils with a B horizon that is very hard when dry and swells to a sticky mass of very low permeability when wet; occur on saline parent materials in some areas of the Interior Plains in association with Chernozemic soils, mostly associated with a vegetative cover of grasses.
Podzolic	Soils with a B horizon in which the dominant accumulation product is amorphous material composed mainly of humified organic matter combined in varying degrees with Al and Fe; typically form in coarse soils under forest or heath vegetation in cool to very cold climates.
Gleysolic	Soils that are mottled (i.e., patchy) in colour, as a result of intermittent or continuous saturation with water and reducing (i.e., nonoxygenated) conditions; saturation may result from either a high groundwater table or temporary accumulation of water, or both.
Organic	Soils that are composed largely of organic materials, including soils commonly known as peat, muck, or bog and fen soils; commonly saturated with water for prolonged periods.
Cryosolic	Soils that form in either mineral or organic materials that have permafrost within 1 m of the surface; occupy much of the northern third of Canada.

Source: Based on Soil Classification Working Group (1998) The Canadian System of Soil Classification, 3rd ed. Agriculture and Agri-Food Canada Publication 1646, 187 pp. (available online through the National Land and Water Information Service, http://sis.agr.gc.ca/cansis/references/1998sc_a.html)

Edward Island is a result of the high iron content of the soil. Black or dark brown soils are usually rich in organic matter, whereas a pale grey to white colour often indicates a chalky composition, leaching, or low organic content. This colour variation occurs among soil horizons in any given location and also among soils from different geographic locations. Long before modern analytical tests of soil content were developed, the colour of topsoil provided farmers and ranchers with information about a region's potential to support crops and provide forage for livestock.

Soil texture Soil texture is determined by the size of particles and is the basis on which soils are assigned to one of three general categories (**FIGURE 7.5**). **Clay** consists of particles less than 0.002 mm in diameter, **silt** of particles 0.002 to 0.05 mm, and **sand** of particles 0.05 to 2 mm. Sand grains, as any beachgoer knows, are large enough to see individually and do not adhere to one another. Clay particles, in contrast, readily adhere to one another and give clay a sticky feeling when moist. Soil with a relatively even mixture of the three particle sizes is known as **loam**.

For a farmer, soil texture influences a soil's *workability*, its relative ease or difficulty of cultivation. Texture influences the soil's **porosity**, a measure of the relative volume of spaces within the soil, as well as its **permeability**, a measure of the interconnectedness of the spaces and the ease with which fluids can move around in the

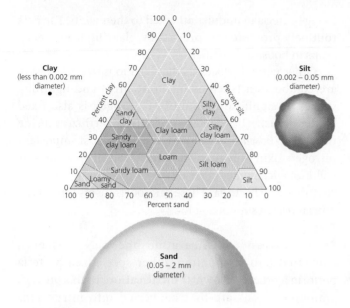

FIGURE 7.5
The texture of soil depends on its mix of particle sizes. Scientists classify soil texture according to the relative proportions of sand, silt, and clay. After measuring the percentage of each type of particle size in a soil sample, a scientist can trace the appropriate white lines extending inward from each side of the triangular graph to determine what type of soil texture that particular combination of values creates.

material. In general, the finer the texture of a sediment or soil, the smaller the pores. The smaller the pores, the harder it is for water and air to travel through the soil, slowing infiltration and reducing the amount of oxygen available to soil biota.

It is possible for a material to have a fairly high porosity but low permeability. This is typical of soils with high clay content. Conversely, soils with large particles tend to have larger spaces that are highly interconnected, allowing water to pass through (and beyond the reach of plant roots) too quickly. Thus, crops planted in sandy soils require frequent irrigation. For this reason, silty soils with medium-sized pores, or loamy soils with mixtures of pore sizes, are generally best for plant growth and crop agriculture.

Soil structure   **Soil structure** is a measure of the organization or "clumpiness" of soil. Some degree of structure encourages soil productivity, and organic matter, biological activity, and clay help promote this structure. However, soil clumps that are too large can discourage plant roots from establishing if soil particles are compacted too tightly together. Repeated tilling can compact soil and make it less able to absorb water. When farmers repeatedly till the same field at the same depth, they may end up forming a hardpan or *ploughpan* layer that resists the infiltration of water and the penetration of roots.

Soil pH   The degree of acidity or alkalinity of a soil influences the soil's ability to support plant growth. Plants can die in soils that are too acidic (low pH) or too alkaline (high pH), but even a moderate variation can influence the availability of nutrients for plants' roots. During leaching, for instance, acids from organic matter may remove some nutrients from the sites of exchange between plant roots and soil particles. Water leaches these nutrients, carrying them to deeper levels and making them less available for plants.

Biogeochemical Cycling in Soil

You have learned that soil is a complex mixture of organic and inorganic, living and nonliving, solid, liquid, and gaseous components. Soil and regolith physically blanket Earth's surface, and act as an important interface for exchanges of material through biological, geological, chemical, atmospheric, and hydrologic processes.

Soils support plant growth through ion exchange

Materials move through soils and plants gain many of their nutrients through a set of processes called **ion exchange** (**FIGURE 7.6**), in which positively charged particles (*cations*) and negatively charged particles (*anions*) are exchanged between the soil and the soil solution. Nutrients are held on *exchange sites*, along the positively or negatively charged edges of soil particles; in

Legend

Hydrogen ions (H^+; control acidity)
Contaminates such as heavy metals (e.g, Pb^{2+})
Plant nutrients (e.g, NH_4^+)

FIGURE 7.6
Negatively charged soil solids (mainly clay or humus, shown in brown here) in soils attract positively charged nutrients (cations), such as Ca^{2+}, NH_4^+, Mg^{2+} and K^+, making them available when needed for plant growth. Heavy metals such as lead (Pb^{2+}) can also be attracted to negatively charged soil particles, making it challenging to clean up contaminated soils.

clay and humus particles, negatively charged sites prevail. Soil particle surfaces that are negatively charged hold on to positively charged nutrients, such as calcium (Ca^{2+}), magnesium (Mg^{2+}), potassium (K^+), and ammonium (NH_4^+). Cations and anions move from the exchange sites into the soil solution; from there they are taken up by roots and other soil organisms. Nutrients are resupplied to the exchange sites and the soil solution by weathering of minerals and the decomposition of organic matter.

Cation exchange capacity is a measure of a soil's ability to hold cations, preventing them from leaching away, and thus making them available to plants. It is thus a useful indicator of *fertility*, the soil's ability to support plant growth. Soils with fine texture (lots of clay particles) and soils rich in organic matter have the greatest cation exchange capacity. As soil pH becomes lower (more acidic), cation exchange capacity diminishes, nutrients leach away, and soil instead may supply plants with harmful aluminum ions. This is one way in which acid precipitation can harm soils and plant communities.

Many pollutants are also positively charged, notably heavy metals such as cadmium, lead, arsenic, and mercury. These cations are attracted to the negatively charged clay and humus particles in soil, which can make it difficult to remediate soil that has been contaminated with heavy metals. It also can mean that heavy metal contaminants are held in soil instead of being released into aquatic ecosystems, which can be beneficial.

Soil is a crucial part of the nitrogen cycle

Soil is the locus for a crucial set of processes that are part of the global biogeochemical cycle of nitrogen. Nitrogen gas (N_2)—the most abundant component of the atmosphere—is chemically inert and must undergo a series of chemical changes in order to become biologically available to the organisms that need it. In its biologically active form, nitrogen is a powerful plant nutrient; its scarcity makes it a limiting factor for plant growth.

Nitrogen fixation   To become biologically available, inert nitrogen gas (N_2) from the atmosphere must be "fixed"—that is, combined with hydrogen to form ions of ammonium (NH_4^+). This transformation, called **nitrogen fixation**, can be accomplished when air in the top layer of soil comes in contact with various specialized nitrogen-fixing bacteria. Some of these bacteria are free-living in the soil. Others live in a symbiotic, mutualistic relationship with plants, particularly *leguminous* plants such as beans, peas, and clover, which host nitrogen-fixing bacteria in nodules attached to their roots. Farmers routinely promote this process by planting leguminous crops to boost soil fertility.

Other natural processes that lead to nitrogen fixation are combustion (such as in forest fires) and lightning strikes. A significant amount of nitrogen is also fixed by the industrial production of nitrate fertilizers, using the *Haber-Bosch process*. However, the most important nitrogen-fixing process—natural or anthropogenic—is still biologically mediated nitrogen fixation by soil- and root-dwelling bacteria. These microorganisms thus play a crucial role in supporting life.

Nitrification   Once atmospheric N_2 has been converted into ammonium, other specialized bacteria perform a process known as **nitrification**. In this process, ammonium ions are first converted into nitrite ions (NO_2^-), then (by yet another group of specialized microorganisms) into nitrate ions (NO_3^-). Plants can take up nitrate ions as nutrients, through their roots. The microorganisms that perform the task of nitrification are *chemoautotrophs*, because they are producing their own food energy (*autotroph*), not through photosynthesis but through chemical reactions.

Animals, in turn, obtain the nitrogen they need by consuming plants or other animals. Decomposers obtain nitrogen from dead and decaying plant and animal matter, and from animal urine and feces (as shown in **FIGURE 7.7**). Once decomposers process the nitrogen-rich compounds they take in, they release ammonium ions, again making these available to nitrifying bacteria to convert into nitrates and nitrites for plant use.

Denitrification   The next step in the nitrogen cycle is **denitrification**, which occurs when bacteria convert nitrates in soil or water into gaseous forms of nitrogen (either N_2, nitrous oxide, or nitric oxide). This, too, is a multistep process that is carried out by several varieties of microorganisms in anaerobic (nonoxygenated) conditions in soil. Denitrification thereby completes the cycle and balances the nitrogen-fixation process by releasing nitrogen back to the atmosphere.

Soil is an important terrestrial reservoir for carbon

The global carbon cycle is of considerable interest today, primarily because of its role in controlling climate. In studies of the carbon cycle, much attention is justifiably paid to the role of forests and the atmospheric and oceanic carbon reservoirs. However, it is also important to

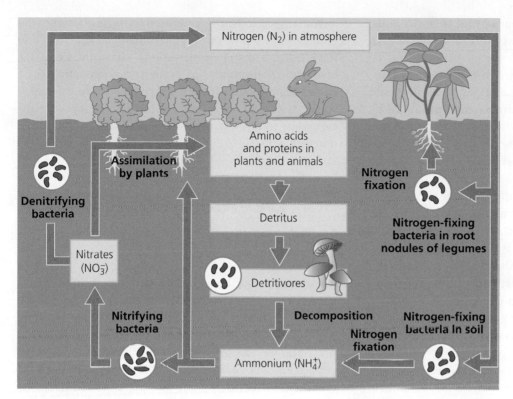

FIGURE 7.7
Specialized bacteria in soils convert atmospheric nitrogen into ammonium through the process of nitrogen fixation. Ammonium is transformed into nitrate, useable as a plant nutrient, by the process of nitrification. Finally, excess nitrate is converted back to the atmospheric gas N_2 through the process of denitrification. All of these processes are biologically mediated by microorganisms that live in soils and among the roots of certain plants.

recognize that soils play a crucial role in the global carbon cycle. Soil represents the largest terrestrial reservoir for carbon—about four times as large as the entire reservoir in terrestrial biota, including forests (**FIGURE 7.8**). The rock reservoir (below a depth of 1 metre or so) is considerably larger; however, carbon sequestered in rock is generally not active in the short-term carbon cycle unless it has been remobilized as a result of human activities, mainly through the burning of fossil fuels and manufacture of cement from carbonate rocks. (See The Science Behind the Story: "Dark Earth: A New (Old) Way to Sequester Carbon" for further discussion about carbon sequestration in soils.)

The main carbon fluxes in which soil is involved are driven by photosynthesis and the production of organic matter, followed by respiration and decay of organic matter. Carbon fluxes from the atmosphere to soils therefore generally pass through photosynthetic plants, which contribute litter and other organic matter to soils, either directly or via consumption by animals. The subsequent alteration of litter, animal waste, and soil organic matter results in the production of humus and the accumulation of carbon, especially in organic-rich soils such as peat.

In addition to producing humus, the decay of soil organic matter produces soil gas that contains carbon species. These decay processes are complex, and their specific chemistry depends on the decomposing micro-organisms that are involved and on the physical-

chemical conditions within the soil. For example, the decay of organic matter in aerobic (oxygenated) conditions typically produces soil gas with a higher concentration of carbon dioxide (CO_2), whereas decay in anaerobic conditions tends to be slower and produces soil gas with a higher concentration of methane (CH_4).

FIGURE 7.8
Soil is the largest active terrestrial reservoir for carbon. (The rock reservoir is considerably larger, but carbon in the rock reservoir is not active in the short-term global carbon cycle unless it is remobilized by human activity, mainly through the burning of fossil fuels and manufacture of cement from carbonate rocks.) Reservoir contents are shown in gigatonnes, and fluxes are shown in gigatonnes of carbon per year.

Wet soils are more likely to be anaerobic than dry soils, so the soil moisture conditions are also important to consider.

Carbon-bearing soil gases are released to the atmosphere (as shown in **FIGURE 7.8**) along with other soil gases, including the N_2 and nitrous oxides produced by denitrification, and radon produced by the radioactive decay of uranium in underlying bedrock. Both carbon dioxide and methane are greenhouse gases, so these fluxes are of significance in understanding the global climate system. In fact, methane is many times more effective than carbon dioxide as a greenhouse gas, so the specific conditions in which methane is produced in soils are of particular interest.

For example, soils in wetlands—which are (by definition) water-saturated for at least part of the year—vary both spatially and temporally in the relative proportions of carbon dioxide and methane gas they produce and in their ability to store and release carbon. Many perennially frozen soils (permafrost) are peat soils, which are significant reservoirs of carbon; scientists are beginning to investigate the potential consequences for the climate system if these carbon-rich soils were to thaw in a warming climate.

In short, most people recognize the importance of soils in supporting plant growth, particularly in the agricultural context (although this was not always the case—

as you will see, in North America it took the disaster of the Dust Bowl in the 1930s for governments to take seriously the challenge of soil conservation). Given the extensive environmental impacts of modern human activities, it is increasingly important that we also strive to understand the crucial role of soils in the global biogeochemical cycling of carbon, nitrogen, phosphorus, sulphur, and other elements.

Soil Degradation: A Global Concern

Healthy soil is vital for agriculture, for the growth of forests, and for the biogeochemical functioning of Earth's natural systems, including the climate system. Productive soil is a renewable resource, but not on a human time scale. If we abuse it through careless or uninformed practices, we can greatly reduce its productivity. Like other renewable resources, if soil is degraded or depleted at a rate that is faster than the rate at which it can be renewed, it effectively becomes nonrenewable.

Throughout the world, especially in drier regions, soils have become eroded and degraded (**FIGURE 7.9**). **Soil degradation**, that is, damage to or loss of soil, worldwide has resulted from erosion caused by roughly

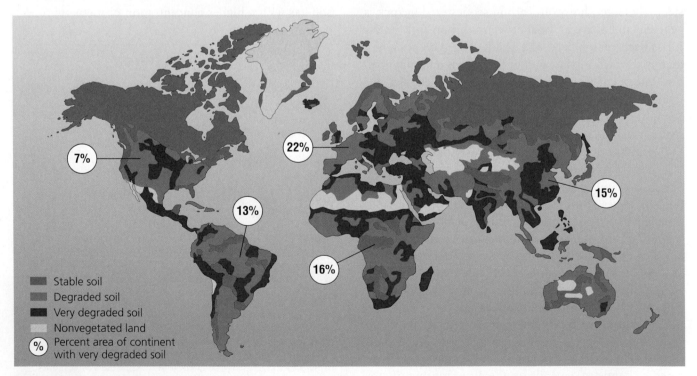

FIGURE 7.9 Soils are becoming degraded in many areas worldwide. Europe currently has a higher proportion of degraded land than other continents because of its long history of intensive agriculture, but degradation is rising quickly in developing countries in Africa and Asia. *Source: Data from United Nations Environment Programme (UNEP), 2002. Global Environmental Outlook 3. London: UNEP and Earthscan Publ.*

equal parts forest removal, poorly managed cropland agriculture, and over-grazing of livestock, with a much smaller (but still significant) contribution from industrial contamination (**FIGURE 7.10A**). Additional causes of soil degradation include mining, construction, acid rain, and other sources of chemical contamination; we will consider all of these in subsequent chapters.

Scientists' studies of soil and the practical experience of farmers have shown that the most desirable soil for agriculture is a loamy mixture with a pH close to neutral, which is workable and capable of holding nutrients. Many soils deviate from this ideal and prevent land from being arable or limit the productivity of arable land (**FIGURE 7.10B**). Increasingly, limits to productivity are being set by human impact that has degraded many once-excellent soils. Common problems affecting soil productivity include erosion, desertification, salinization, waterlogging, nutrient depletion, structural breakdown, and pollution.

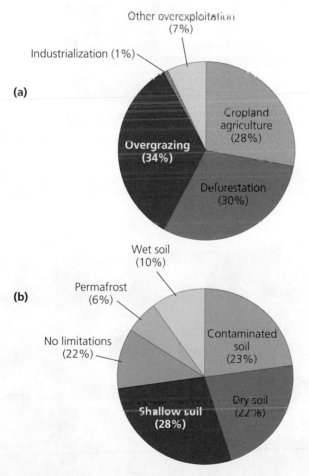

FIGURE 7.10
(a) Most of the world's soil degradation results from cropland agriculture, over-grazing by livestock, and deforestation. Data based on information from UNEP. **(b)** Various factors limit the agricultural productivity of soil, as shown in this diagram based on information from the United Nations Food and Agriculture Organization.

Regional differences affect soil productivity

The characteristics of soil and soil profiles vary from place to place. One striking example is the difference between soils of tropical rainforests and those of temperate grasslands. Although rainforest ecosystems have high primary productivity, most of their nutrients are tied up in plant tissues and are not in the soil (**FIGURE 7.11**). For example, the soil of Amazonian rainforest is much less productive than the soil of the grasslands in Saskatchewan.

To understand how this can be, consider the main differences between the two regions: temperature and rainfall. The enormous amount of rain that falls in the Amazon readily leaches minerals and nutrients out of the topsoil. Those not captured by plants are taken quickly down to the water table, out of reach of most plants' roots. High temperatures speed the decomposition of leaf litter and the uptake of nutrients by plants, so amounts of humus remain small, and the topsoil layer remains thin.

This means that most of the organic matter in the tropical rainforest environment is thus held in the aboveground plant biomass (as shown in **FIGURE 7.11**). Thus when forest is cleared for farming, cultivation quickly depletes the soil's fertility. This is why the traditional form of agriculture in tropical forested areas is *swidden* agriculture, in which the farmer cultivates a plot for one to a few years and then moves on to clear another plot, leaving the first to grow back to forest (**FIGURE 7.12**). This method may work well at low population densities, but with today's high human populations, soils may not be allowed enough time to regenerate. As a result, intensive agriculture has ruined the soils and forests of many tropical areas.

In temperate grassland areas such as the Saskatchewan prairies, in contrast, rainfall is low enough that leaching is reduced and nutrients remain high in the soil profile,

roots
SWIDDEN

Swidden agriculture is a practice where an area of forest is cleared and cultivated for a few years and then left to regrow while farmers move on to clear a new area for agriculture. The word **swidden**, first used around 1868, derives from the Old Norse word *svithinn* (from the verb *svitha*), meaning "to burn or singe," and therefore refers to land made available by burning.

Organic litter decomposes and is recycled quickly

Acidic, light–coloured

Mineral soil iron, aluminum, clay accumulations

Parent material

Tropical Rainforest

Organic acidic litter

Humus + mineral soil

Parent material

Coniferous (Boreal) Forest

Organic litter

Humus

Mineral soil

Parent material

Temperate Deciduous Forest

Dark, alkaline soil very rich in humus

Clay and calcium accumulations

Parent material

Grassland

Thin humus–mineral mixture

Dry mineral soil; accumulations of clay, carbonate, and soluble salts

Parent material

Desert

FIGURE 7.11   In tropical forests, most of the organic content tends to be held above the ground in plant biomass, rather than in soils; this is because decomposition proceeds rapidly in the warm, moist climate, and decomposed organic matter is readily carried away by runoff. In temperate and boreal forests, and especially in grasslands, a much greater percentage of the organic matter is stored in soils. In desert biomes there is little organic matter because of the relatively low biomass available.

FIGURE 7.12

In tropical forested areas, the traditional form of farming is swidden agriculture, as seen here in Surinam. In this practice, forest is cleared, often by burning; the plot is farmed for one to a few years; and the farmer then moves on to clear another plot, leaving the first to regrow into forest. Frequent movement is necessary because tropical soils are nutrient-poor, with nearly all nutrients held in the vegetation. Burning the cut vegetation adds nutrients to the soil, which is why this practice is often called "slash-and-burn" agriculture. At low population densities, this form of farming had little large-scale impact on forests, but at today's high population densities, it is a leading cause of deforestation.

within reach of plants' roots. Plants take up nutrients and then return them directly to the topsoil when they die; this cycle maintains the soil's fertility. In addition, cool temperatures slow the rate of decomposition of organic matter. Most of the organic matter in this system is stored below ground, in the soil (as shown in **FIGURE 7.11**), and the thick, rich topsoil of temperate grasslands can be farmed repeatedly with minimal loss of fertility if proper farming techniques are used.

However, even in the rich soils of temperate grasslands, growing and harvesting crops without returning adequate organic matter to the soil gradually depletes soil organic matter. Leaving soil exposed to the elements also increases the rate of erosion of topsoil. It is such consequences that farmers in many locations around the world have sought to forestall through the use of agricultural approaches to soil conservation.

Erosion can degrade ecosystems and agriculture

Erosion, as we have noted, is the removal of weathered material from one place and its transport to another by the action of wind, water, or (in some cases) glacial ice. **Deposition** of sediment is the other end of this process—the arrival of the eroded material at its new location. Erosion and deposition are natural processes that in the long run can help create soil. Flowing water can deposit eroded sediment in river valleys and deltas, producing rich and productive soils. This is why floodplains are excellent for farming and why flood control measures can decrease the productivity of agriculture in the long run.

However, accelerated erosion is associated with human activity and is a problem locally for ecosystems and agriculture because it takes place much more quickly than soil is formed. Furthermore, erosion tends to remove topsoil, the most valuable soil layer for living things. People have increased the vulnerability of fertile lands to erosion through three widespread practices:

1. Over-cultivating fields through poor planning or excessive ploughing, particularly when land is left bare of vegetative cover
2. Over-grazing rangelands with more livestock than the land can support, resulting in reduced vegetative cover
3. Clearing forested areas on steep slopes or with large clear-cuts

Erosion can be gradual and hard to detect, but still devastating in the long run. For example, an erosion rate of 12 tonnes/ha/yr removes only a penny's thickness of soil per year. That doesn't seem like much until you realize that it would have taken anywhere between 75 and 1500 years to produce a layer of soil the thickness of a penny. In many parts of the world, scientists, farmers, and extension agents are measuring erosion rates in hopes of identifying areas in danger of serious degradation before they become too badly damaged.

Soil erodes by several mechanisms

Several types of erosion can occur, including wind erosion and four principal kinds of water erosion (**FIGURE 7.13**).

Research indicates that rill erosion has the greatest potential to move topsoil, followed by sheet erosion and splash erosion, respectively. All types of water erosion—particularly gully erosion—are more likely to occur where slopes are steeper. In general, steeper slopes, greater precipitation intensities, and sparser vegetative cover all lead to greater water erosion.

The *Universal Soil Loss Equation (USLE)* was developed as a tool for estimating erosion losses by water from cultivated fields and to show how different soil and management factors influence soil erosion (**TABLE 7.3**). A revised version of the USLE is used in

Table 7.3 Universal Soil Loss Equation	
A = R K LS C P	
A Predicted soil loss due to water erosion	Results in t/ha/yr
R Erosivity factor	Quantifies the erosive energy of rainfall and runoff; takes into account both total amount of rainfall and its intensity.
K Soil erodibility factor	Represents the ease with which a soil is eroded; based on the cohesiveness of a soil and its resistance to detachment and transport.
LS Slope length and steepness factor	Steeper slopes lead to higher flow velocities; longer plots accumulate runoff from larger areas and result in higher flow velocities.
C Vegetative cover and management factor	Considers the type and density of vegetative cover as well as all related management practices such as tillage, fertilization, and irrigation.
P Erosion control practices factor	Influence of conservation practices such as contour planting, strip cropping, grassed waterways, and terracing relative to the erosion potential of simple up–down slope cultivation.

Source: Based on material from www.landfood.ubc.ca/soil200/soil_mgmt/soil_erosion.htm.

(a) Splash erosion

(b) Sheet erosion

(c) Rill erosion

(d) Gully erosion

FIGURE 7.13   *Splash erosion* **(a)** occurs as raindrops strike the ground with enough force to dislodge small amounts of soil. *Sheet erosion* **(b)** results when thin layers of water traverse broad expanses of sloping land. *Rill erosion* **(c)** leaves small pathways along the surface where water has carried topsoil away. *Gully erosion* **(d)** cuts deep into soil, leaving large gullies that can expand as erosion proceeds.

Canada to estimate losses from soil erosion, mainly for the purpose of soil conservation planning. It utilizes the same variables as the original format, but with refinements for quantifying their values in situations that are more common in Canada (for example, if frost is present, some of the factors will be applied differently).[2]

Wind, like water, is a moving fluid. Wind often flows very quickly over the surface, but it typically does not have the same ability to pick up and transport soil particles that water has. Nevertheless, wind can be a highly effective agent of erosion. Wind erosion, also called *aeolian erosion*, operates mainly by *deflation*, in which all loose, fine-grained material is picked up from the surface and carried away by wind. Another important mechanism of wind erosion is *abrasion*, whereby wind-transported particles become "projectiles," striking other rocks at the surface and causing them to break up.

Table 7.4 Wind Erosion Prediction Equation

$$E = f(I\,C\,K\,L\,V)$$

E	Predicted soil loss due to wind erosion	Results in t/ha/yr
I	Soil erodibility factor	Represents the ease with which a soil is eroded by the abrasive action of wind-carried particles; dependent upon a number of factors including soil texture and aggregation.
C	Local wind erosion climate factor	Quantified as the wind energy available to erode soil; takes into account moisture, wind speed, and wind direction. Wind erosion is most common in arid and semiarid regions.
K	Roughness factor	Describes the surface roughness of the soil; greater roughness indicates greater resistance to erosion.
L	Length of field factor	A measure of the unsheltered length of the field; a longer field will have higher wind velocities and thus greater erosion potential.
V	Vegetative cover factor	Accounts for cover type and density, including cover from crop residues; erosion risk is greatest when there is least cover.

The *Wind Erosion Prediction Equation* shows how wind erosion is a function of five factors and their interactions (**TABLE 7.4**).

Grasslands, forests, and any other healthy plant cover protect soil from both wind and water erosion. Vegetation breaks the wind and slows water flow, and plant roots hold soil in place and take up water. Removing plant cover will nearly always accelerate erosion.

Soil erosion is widespread

In today's world, humans are the primary cause of erosion, and we have accelerated it to unnaturally high rates. In a 2004 study, geologist Bruce Wilkinson analyzed prehistoric erosion rates from the geologic record and compared these with modern rates. He concluded that humans are over 10 times more influential at moving soil than are all other natural processes on the surface of the planet combined.

More than 19 billion ha of the world's croplands suffer from erosion and other forms of soil degradation resulting from human activities. In the last half of the twentieth century, China lost as much arable farmland as exists in Denmark, France, Germany, and the Netherlands combined. In Kazakhstan, industrial cropland agriculture has caused tens of millions of hectares to be degraded by wind erosion. For Africa, soil degradation over the next 40 years could reduce crop yields by half. Couple these declines in soil quality and crop yields with the rapid population growth occurring in many of these areas, and we begin to see why some observers describe the future of agriculture as a crisis situation.

Erosion of agricultural soil has been a significant concern in Canada for the past 25 years or more, but improvements are occurring. Soil researchers from Agriculture and Agri-Food Canada have determined the on-farm cost of agricultural land degradation in Canada to be almost $670 million per year.[3] However, the same report showed significant reductions in the area of cropland at risk of erosion in recent years. Approximately 85% of cropland area in Canada was deemed to be in the "tolerable" range of risk for water-related erosion as of 1996, a 22% improvement over the situation 15 years earlier. The wind erosion risk improved by 59% over the same period. A combination of reduced tillage, less intensive crop production, and removal of *marginal land* (that is, land ill-suited to agriculture) from production were cited as contributing to lower erosion rates.[4] Other sources[5] also point to changes in farming techniques since the recognition of a soil erosion crisis in the early 1980s; these changes have led to overall improvement in the health and stability of Canada's soils.

Desertification reduces productivity of arid lands

Much of the world's population lives and farms in arid environments, where **desertification** is a concern. This term describes a loss of more than 10% productivity due to erosion, soil compaction, forest removal, over-grazing, drought, salinization, climate change, depletion of water sources, and other factors. The terms *desertification* and *degradation* are often confused, and the United Nations is careful to distinguish them.[6] Land degradation is the reduction or loss of the biological or economic productivity of land. Desertification is a type of land degradation that occurs in arid and semiarid areas and can result from various factors, including climatic variations and human activities.

Severe desertification can result in the expansion of desert areas or creation of new ones in areas that once supported fertile land (**FIGURE 7.14A**). This process has occurred in many areas of the Middle East that have been inhabited, farmed, and grazed for long periods of time. To appreciate the cumulative impact of centuries of traditional agriculture, we need only look at the present desertified state of that portion of the Middle East where agriculture originated, nicknamed the "Fertile Crescent."

FIGURE 7.14
(a) Desertification occurs when formerly productive land turns into desert, as shown here in this photo from Mauritania, Africa. **(b)** Canada is not exempt from the impacts of wind erosion, as shown in this photo from the Dust Bowl of the 1930s.

(a)

(b)

These arid lands—in present-day Iraq, Syria, Turkey, Lebanon, and Israel—are not so fertile anymore.

Arid and semi-arid lands are prone to desertification because their precipitation is too meagre to meet the greater demands in productivity from a growing human population. According to the United Nations Environment Programme (UNEP), 40% of Earth's land surface can be classified as drylands, arid areas that are particularly subject to degradation. Declines of soil quality in these areas have endangered the food supply or well-being of more than 1 billion people around the world.

In the affected lands, most degradation results from wind and water erosion. In recent years, gigantic dust storms from denuded land in China have blown across the Pacific Ocean to North America, and dust storms from Africa's Sahara Desert have blown across the Atlantic Ocean to the Caribbean Sea. Such massive dust storms occurred in the Canadian Prairies and the Great Plains of the United States during the Dust Bowl days of the early twentieth century,

when desertification shook North American agriculture and society to their very roots (**FIGURE 7.14B**).

It has been estimated that desertification affects fully one-third of the planet's land area, impinging on the lives of 250 million people[7] and costing tens of billions of dollars in lost income per year. China alone loses $6.5 billion annually from desertification. In its western reaches, desert areas are expanding and joining one another because of over-grazing from over 400 million goats, sheep, and cattle. In the Sistan Basin, on the border of Iran and Afghanistan, an oasis that supported a million livestock recently turned barren in just five years, and windblown sand buried over 100 villages. In Kenya, over-grazing and deforestation fuelled by rapid population growth has left 80% of its land vulnerable to desertification. In a positive feedback cycle, the soil degradation forces ranchers to crowd onto more marginal land and farmers to reduce fallow periods, both of which further exacerbate soil degradation.

A 2007 United Nations report estimated that desertification, worsened by climate change, could result in the displacement of 50 million people in 10 years. The report suggested that industrialized nations fund reforestation projects in dryland areas of the developing world to slow desertification while gaining carbon credits in emissions trading programs.

The Dust Bowl was a monumental event in North America

Prior to large-scale cultivation of the Prairies and the Great Plains, native prairie grasses of this temperate grassland region held erosion-prone soils in place. The American bison played a significant role as a keystone species in this ecosystem. In the late nineteenth and early twentieth centuries, however, many homesteading settlers arrived with hopes of making a living there as farmers. Between 1879 and 1929, cultivated area in the region soared, driven primarily by rapid increases in the price of wheat. Bison were hunted almost to extinction. Farmers in the region grew abundant wheat, and ranchers grazed many thousands of cattle, sometimes expanding onto unsuitable land. Both types of agriculture contributed to erosion by removing native grasses and breaking down soil structure.

At the end of 1929 the stock market crashed, sending the price of wheat lower than the price of seed, the Great Depression began, and with it an inexorable cycle of poverty and land degradation that would last most of the decade. Starting in the early 1930s, a prolonged period of drought in the region exacerbated the ongoing human impacts on the soil from overly intensive agricultural practices. Strong winds began to carry away millions of tonnes of topsoil, and often newly planted seed, as well. Dust storms travelled up to 2000 km, blackening skies and coating the skins of farm workers. Some areas lost as much as 10 cm of topsoil in a few short years.

The affected region in the Prairies and Great Plains became known as the *Dust Bowl*, a term now also used for the historical event itself. The "black blizzards" of the Dust Bowl (see **FIGURE 7.14B**) destroyed livelihoods and caused many people to suffer a type of chronic lung irritation and degradation known as dust pneumonia, similar to the silicosis that afflicts coal miners exposed to high concentrations of coal dust. Large numbers of farmers were forced off their land; those who stayed faced infestations of grasshoppers so thick that they clogged car radiators and made the roads slippery. Chickens and turkeys ate the grasshoppers, which caused their meat and eggs to develop a bad taste. There were no pesticides (chemical pesticides had not yet been invented) and no way to control the grasshoppers.

By 1937, Dust Bowl conditions had reached their peak. Since the price of wheat was so low, farmers began to plant alternative crops, such as oats, rye, flax, peas, and alfalfa. They adapted to the dry weather with reduced tilling, crop rotations (to allow the soil a chance to replenish itself), and fertilizer applications. By the end of the decade, the slow recovery from the Dust Bowl had begun.[8]

The Soil Conservation Council emerged from the experience of drought

In 1935 the Prairie Farm Rehabilitation Administration (PFRA) was set up; interestingly, however, it was not until the early 1980s that the issue of soil erosion and the degradation of agricultural soils really took centre stage in Canada on a nationwide basis. This occurred partly as a result of another serious drought in the late 1970s, followed by the publication in 1984 of a book by the federal government titled *Soil at Risk: Canada's Eroding Future*.[9] In that publication, the Standing Committee on Agriculture, Fisheries, and Forestry (also known as the Sparrow Commission) concluded, "Canada risks permanently losing a large portion of its agricultural capability if a major commitment to conserving the soil is not made immediately by all levels of government and by all Canadians." The following year saw the first National Soil Conservation Week and the establishment of the National Soil Conservation Program.

The Soil Conservation Council of Canada was established in 1987, with the following goals:

- To develop a national spirit to foster a feeling of unity among those who are concerned for soil conservation
- To improve the level of understanding and awareness about the causes of soil degradation among all Canadians and to increase their support of soil conservation goals
- To facilitate communication among soil conservation groups, governments, and industry relating to soil conservation needs, programs, and policies
- To communicate to the general public policies, programs, or activities that affect the sustainable use of this country's soil resources
- To encourage the development of policies, production methods, and management systems for agriculture, forestry, and land use that enables sustainable use of our soil and related resources.[10]

Today a number of federal government agencies (as well as provincial and territorial agencies) provide services to assist farmers with all aspects of soil management and conservation in Canada. The PFRA still exists, but it is now one component of a broader organization, the Agri-Environment Services Branch (AESB) of Agriculture and Agri-Food Canada, which was set up specifically to address agricultural and soil-related environmental issues. The organization was an integration of three previously existing federal agencies: the PFRA, the National Land and Water Information Service (NLWIS), and the Agri-Environmental Policy Bureau. The AESB promotes "an integrated approach to sustainable agriculture in Canada which recognizes that environmentally responsible agriculture and competitive agriculture are part of an integrated system."[11]

Internationally, the United Nations promotes soil conservation and sustainable agriculture through a variety of programs of its Food and Agriculture Organization (FAO). The FAO's Farmer–Centred Agricultural Resource Management Program (FAR) is a project that supports innovative approaches to resource management and sustainable agriculture in China, Thailand, Vietnam, Indonesia, Sri Lanka, Nepal, the Philippines, and India. The program studies agricultural success stories and tries to help other farmers duplicate the successful efforts. Rather than following a top-down, government-controlled approach, the FAR program relies on the creativity of local communities to educate and encourage farmers throughout Asia to conserve soils and secure their food supply.

Protecting Soils

As environmental problems go, soil erosion has two good things going for it: most of the approaches that can be used to protect soils are neither technologically sophis-

ticated nor excessively costly. Most often, soil can be protected by modifying practices in farming and forestry.

Erosion-control practices protect and restore plant cover

Farming and forestry methods to control erosion make use of the general principle that maximizing vegetative cover will protect soils, and this principle has been applied widely. It is common to stabilize eroding banks along creeks and roadsides by planting plants to anchor the soil, or in rows to protect open fields from the wind (**FIGURE 7.15A**). In areas with severe and widespread erosion, some nations have planted vast plantations of fast-growing trees. For example, China has embarked on the world's largest tree-planting program to slow its soil loss (**FIGURE 7.15B**). Although such reforestation efforts do help slow erosion, they do not at the same time produce ecologically functioning forests, because tree species are selected only for their fast growth and are planted in monocultures.

Several farming techniques can reduce the impacts of conventional cultivation on soils. Such measures have been widely shared and applied in many places around the world, and some have been practised by traditional farmers for centuries.

Crop rotation   The practice of alternating the kind of crop grown in a particular field from one season or year to the next is called *crop rotation* (**FIGURE 7.16A**). Rotating crops can return nutrients to the soil, break cycles of disease associated with continuous cropping, and minimize erosion that can come from letting fields lie

(a)

(b)

FIGURE 7.15   Rows of trees designed to shelter farm fields against the wind are now common in Canada's Prairie agricultural lands **(a)**. Vast swaths of countryside in western China have been planted with fast-growing poplar trees **(b)**. These reforestation efforts can slow erosion but do not create ecologically functional forests because the plantations are too biologically simple.

exposed. Farmers in Alberta, Prince Edward Island, and elsewhere have returned to an earlier farming approach in which they plant alternating swaths of land each year, but leave the field stubble from the previous year to protect fields from exposure to wind and water erosion. Many farmers rotate between wheat or corn and soybeans from one year to the next. Soybeans are legumes, with nitrogen-fixing bacteria among their roots, so they can revitalize soil that the previous crop had partially depleted of nutrients. Crop rotation also reduces insect pests; if an insect is adapted to feed and lay eggs on one particular crop, planting a different crop will leave its offspring with nothing to eat.

Intercropping and agroforestry Farmers may also gain protection against erosion by *intercropping*, planting different types of crops in alternating bands or other spatially mixed arrangements (**FIGURE 7.16B**). Intercropping helps slow erosion by providing more complete ground cover than does a single crop. Like crop rotation, intercropping offers the additional benefits of reducing vulnerability to insect and disease incidence, and, when a nitrogen-fixing legume is one of the crops, of replenishing the soil. Cover crops can be physically mixed with primary food crops, which include maize, soybeans, wheat, onions, cassava, grapes, tomatoes, tobacco, and orchard fruit.

When crops are interplanted with trees, in a practice called **agroforestry**, even more benefits can be realized. Agroforestry systems are generally more biologically productive than farm systems in which food crops are grown alone. One reason is that trees draw nutrients and water from deep in the soil through their root systems, cycling them into the shallower layers of soil. They also contribute organic material to the topsoil, in the form of tree litter, such as fallen branches and leaves. Trees can also provide partial shade for crops, although light levels must be managed by appropriate pruning and spacing of the trees. In many agricultural regions, especially in the developing world where small-scale agriculture is still practised, agroforestry provides a low-cost way to close the nutrient cycle and rehabilitate soils while providing other sustainably harvested forest products such as fruits, nuts, and timber.

Contour farming and terracing Water running down a hillside can easily carry soil away, particularly if there is too little vegetative cover to hold the soil in place. Thus, sloped land is especially vulnerable to erosion. Several methods have been developed for farming on slopes. *Contour farming* (**FIGURE 7.16C**) consists of ploughing furrows sideways across a hillside, perpendicular to its slope, to help prevent formation of rills and gullies. The technique is so named because the furrows follow the natural contours of the land. In contour farming, the downhill side of each furrow acts as a small dam that slows runoff and catches soil before it is carried away. Contour farming is most effective on gradually sloping land with crops that grow well in rows.

On extremely steep terrain, *terracing* (**FIGURE 7.16D**) is the most effective method for preventing erosion. Terraces are level platforms, sometimes with raised edges, that are cut into steep hillsides to contain water from irrigation and precipitation. Terracing transforms slopes into series of steps like a staircase, enabling farmers to cultivate hilly land without losing huge amounts of soil to water erosion. Terracing is common in ruggedly mountainous regions, such as the foothills of the Himalayas and the Andes, and has been used for centuries by farming communities in such areas. Terracing is labour-intensive to establish but in the long term is likely the only sustainable way to farm in mountainous terrain.

Shelterbelts A widespread technique to reduce erosion from wind is to establish **shelterbelts** (**FIGURE 7.16E**). Shelterbelts are *windbreaks*—rows of trees or tall shrubs that are planted along the edges of fields to slow the wind. Shelterbelts have been widely planted across the Prairies and the Great Plains, where fast growing species such as poplars are often used. The Ontario Ministry of Agriculture, Food, and Rural Affairs documents more than 67 000 shelterbelts installations in Ontario alone.[12] They cite up to a 15% increase in crop yield associated with shelterbelt but decline to quantify the amount of soil conserved as a result of the approach. Shelterbelts are combined with intercropping in a practice known as *alley cropping*. In this approach, fields planted in rows of mixed crops are surrounded by or interspersed with rows of trees that provide fruit, wood, or protection from wind. Agroforestry and alley cropping methods are widely used in India, Africa, China, and Brazil, where coffee growers commonly combine farming and forestry.

Reduced tillage Repeated cycles of ploughing and planting over many decades diminishe the productivity of the soil and render it more susceptible to erosion. To plant using the *reduced tillage* or *no-till* method (**FIGURE 7.16F**), a tractor pulls a drill that cuts long, shallow furrows through the litter of dead weeds and crop residue and the upper levels of the A horizon. The device drops seeds into the furrow and closes the furrow over the seeds. Often a localized dose of fertilizer is added to the soil along with the seeds. By increasing organic matter and soil biota while reducing erosion, no-till and reduced tillage farming can build soil up, aerate it, restore it, and improve it. Proponents of no-till farming claim that the

(a) Crop rotation

(b) Intercropping

(c) Contour farming

(d) Terracing

(e) Shelterbelts

(f) No-till farming

FIGURE 7.16   The world's farmers have adopted various strategies to conserve soil. Rotating crops such as soybeans and corn **(a)** helps restore soil nutrients and reduce impacts of crop pests. Intercropping **(b)** can reduce soil loss while maintaining soil fertility. Contour farming **(c)** reduces erosion on hillsides, whereas terracing **(d)** is most useful in steep mountainous areas. Shelterbelts **(e)** protect against wind erosion. In **(f)**, corn grows up from amid the remnants of a "cover crop" used in reduced-tillage agriculture.

practice offers a number of benefits, including higher crop yields, reduced erosion, reduced costs of land preparation, and a reduced carbon footprint.

The no-till or reduced-tillage practice has been widely adopted in Canada, but not with unmitigated success.

The Soil Conservation Council of Canada estimates that as much as 50% of some crops in Ontario are now grown using a no-till approach, including wheat and soybeans. However, some crops—notably corn—are not amenable to reduced tillage, which tends to keep the soil colder and moister for longer than conventional tillage methods (because litter mulch is applied).[13] Critics of no-till and reduced-tillage farming also note that these techniques often require substantial use of chemical herbicides (because weeds are controlled chemically rather than physically removed from fields) and synthetic fertilizer (because other plants take up a significant portion of the soil's nutrients).

Irrigation can cause long-term soil problems

Erosion is not the only threat to the health and integrity of soils. Soil degradation can result from other factors as well, such as impacts caused by the application of water to support crop growth—that is, *irrigation*. If the climate is too dry or too much water evaporates or runs off before it can be absorbed into the soil, crops may require irrigation. The soil's ability to hold water and make it available to plant roots also influences the amount of irrigation required. Some crops, such as rice and cotton, require large amounts of water, whereas others, such as beans and wheat, require relatively little.

By irrigating croplands, people have managed to turn previously dry and unproductive regions into fertile farmland. Currently about 70% of all fresh water withdrawn by people is used for irrigation. Irrigated land area increased dramatically around the world starting in the 1950s, reaching almost 2.8 million ha by 2003. Since then, the rate of increase has declined as a result of limited availability of both fresh water and new arable land.

If some water is good for plants and soil, it might seem that more must be better. But this is not necessarily the case; there is indeed such a thing as too much water. Over-irrigation in poorly drained areas can cause or exacerbate certain soil problems. Soils too saturated with water may become waterlogged. When **waterlogging** occurs, the water table is raised to the point that water bathes plant roots, depriving them of access to gases and essentially suffocating them. If it lasts long enough, waterlogging can damage or kill plants.

An even more frequent problem is **salinization** (or *salination*), the buildup of salts in surface soil layers. In dryland areas where precipitation is minimal and evaporation rates are high, water evaporating from the A horizon may pull saline water up from lower horizons by capillary action. As this water rises through the soil, it carries dissolved salts; when the water evaporates at the surface, those salts precipitate and are left at the surface. Eventually, high salinity levels can make the soil inhospitable to plants. Irrigation in arid

FIGURE 7.17
Salinization can result from over-irrigation, especially in arid and semi-arid regions. It is a widespread problem affecting agricultural soils, as shown here in Alberta. The white crust on the surface is a toxic layer of salts.

areas generally hastens salinization, because it provides repeated doses of moderate amounts of water, which dissolve salts in the soil and gradually raise them to the surface. Moreover, because irrigation water often contains some dissolved salt in the first place, irrigation introduces new sources of salt to the soil. In many areas of farmland where over-irrigation has occurred, soils are turning white with encrusted salt (**FIGURE 7.17**).

Salinization now inhibits agricultural production on one-fifth of all irrigated cropland globally, costing more than $11 billion annually. As of 2000, the Food and Agriculture Organization of the United Nations estimated that the total area of salinized soil is 397 million ha. Of 230 million ha of irrigated land, 45 million ha (or 19.5%) of soil were affected by salt, and of 1500 million ha of dryland agriculture, 32 million ha (or 2.1%) of soil were affected by salinization due to human activities.[14]

The remedies for correcting salinization once it has occurred are more expensive and difficult to implement

weighing the issues
MEASURING AND REGULATING SOIL QUALITY

The Government of Canada has adopted comprehensive measures of air quality and water quality and has set legal standards for allowable levels of various pollutants in air and water. Could such standards be developed for soil quality? If so, what properties should be measured to inform the standards?

THE SCIENCE BEHIND THE STORY

Dark Earth: A New (Old) Way to Sequester Carbon

Prof. Johannes Lehmann holds a bowl of wood chips (right), biomass that can be turned into biochar (left).

About 15 years ago, while doing field work in the central Amazon of Brazil, Dr. Johannes Lehmann encountered patches of unusually dark, rich, fertile soil, locally called *terra preta*, or "black earth" in Portuguese. To Dr. Lehmann, a professor in the Department of Crop and Soil Sciences at Cornell University, these dark patches of soil stood out amongst the agriculturally degraded, nutrient-poor soils of the Amazon.

Further research on *terra preta* by Dr. Lehmann and other researchers has revealed that the black soil is a remnant of pre-Columbian indigenous residents of the area, from as long ago as 450 BCE. It is probable that the charcoal-like *terra preta* was not made intentionally, but rather accumulated over time as a black, carbon-rich residue of cooking fires and pottery

kilns. Indigenous farmers are thought to have used this residue as an addition to soils, to increase their fertility. Hundreds and even thousands of years later, the black earth is still in place, an indication of its surprising stability.

Dr. Lehmann, who is particularly interested in nutrient cycling and carbon storage in soils, recognized in *terra preta* the potential for a carbon reservoir that would be significantly longer lasting than trees or even natural soils. He began to research methods for producing black earth. The most promising technology for this has turned out to be *pyrolysis*, which is a relatively straightforward, low-temperature heating process, whereby biomass (either plant or animal matter) is reduced to a black, carbon-rich, charcoal-like residue. This residue has been named *biochar*.

A photomicrograph of biochar **(see photo)** reveals that it is riddled with tiny, micron-sized pore spaces. The complexity of the spaces and surfaces partly explain the efficiency of biochar at holding onto plant nutrients and thus enhancing the fertility of soils. Biochar also appears to be very effective at absorbing and holding some pollutants, notably heavy metals, potentially contributing to improvements in water quality.

But the most exciting prospect of all, according to Professor Lehmann and other biochar reasearchers, is the possibility of using biochar to enhance the ability of soils

to act as long-term reservoirs for carbon. Soils are already the most important terrestrial reservoir for carbon—even larger than forests and grasslands (see "Interpreting Graphs and Data"). If adding biochar could greatly increase the longevity and stability of the soil reservoir, thus sequestering carbon from the atmosphere, it could help in the fight against rising atmospheric carbon and global warming.

The success of biochar as a method of carbon sequestration depends on the

Biochar (seen here in a photomicrograph, magnified thousands of times) has many complex, micron-sized pore spaces and surfaces. This partly accounts for some of biochar's properties, such as the capacity to improve water and soil quality by absorbing pollutants and holding on to fertilizers and plant nutrients.

than the techniques for preventing it in the first place. The best way to prevent salinization is to avoid planting crops that require a great deal of water in areas that are prone to the problem. A second way is to irrigate with water that is as low as possible in salt content. A third way is to irrigate efficiently, supplying no more water than the crop requires, thus minimizing the amount of water that evaporates and hence the amount of salt that accumulates in the topsoil. This can be accomplished through the use of drip systems that target water directly to the plant roots.

If salinization has occurred, one possible way to mitigate it is to stop irrigating and wait for rain to infil-

trate and leach the salts from the soil. However, this solution is often unfeasible because salinization is mainly a problem in dryland areas, where precipitation is inadequate to flush salts from the soil. A better option may be to plant salt-tolerant plants, such as barley, that can be used as food or pasture. A third option is to bring in large quantities of less-saline water with which to flush the soil; however, using too much water may cause waterlogging. The most effective, but most expensive, option is to install artificial drainage to lower the level of the saline water table below a depth where it can be drawn up to the soil surface. Rain or irrigation can then flush the remaining salts away from the rooting zone.

technologies that are used. They require energy inputs, which contribute to carbon dioxide emissions. The key is to balance the carbon emitted to the atmosphere as a result of the pyrolysis process with the carbon sequestered through the production of biochar. Dr. Lehmann's calculations show that with low-temperature pyrolysis of biomass it should be possible to halve the amount of carbon being released to the atmosphere, as compared to natural decomposition of the biomass.

Using pyrolysis to produce biochar also has an economic cost, which represents a potential barrier to its adoption as an approach for mitigating carbon emissions. One way to improve its economic competitiveness is to promote the use of biochar as an agricultural amendment for the improvement of soil fertility (see diagram). Another is to capture the heat released during the pyrolysis process and use it as a form of bioenergy. One of the most intriguing aspects of biochar is that the technologies are simple and adaptable even in remote settings. It is possible that someday soon farmers all over the world will be enhancing their soils with biochar while capturing and sequestering carbon at the same time.

Other chemicals also contribute to soil contamination

Salinization is not the only source of chemical damage to soil. Over-application of fertilizers can also chemically damage soils. Even organic fertilizers such as manure, when applied in amounts needed to supply sufficient nitrogen for a crop, may introduce excess phosphorus that can run off into waterways. Inorganic (mineral-based, industrially produced) fertilizers are generally more susceptible than are organic fertilizers to leaching and runoff, and they are somewhat more likely to cause soil degradation and off-site impacts.

Nitrogen and phosphorus runoff from farms and other sources can lead to phytoplankton (algal) blooms, creating oxygen-depleted "dead zones" in river mouths, lakes, and marine coastal zones throughout the world. Moreover, nitrates readily leach through soil and contaminate groundwater, and components of some nitrogen fertilizers can even volatilize (evaporate) into the air. Nitrate and phosphate buildup in soil and water systems also pose human health risks, including cancer and methemoglobinemia, or "blue-baby" syndrome. Many negative side effects of fertilizer use can be reduced by proper timing and appropriate application methods, and by regular testing of the soil to determine whether, what type, and how much fertilizer is needed, thus matching the fertilizer delivery to the amount that can be utilized by crops.

Pesticides applied to agricultural fields are another important source of soil contamination. These chemicals, designed to attack specific weeds, insect pests, and crop fungi, unfortunately also affect nontarget species, including humans. Most insecticides, for example, are *neurotoxins*, which means that they affect the central nervous systems of organisms. Any excess pesticide that is not absorbed by plants or animals on the field can leave the system via runoff, infiltration into the soil, or volatilization. The amount, type, and timing of application are all crucially important in preventing pesticide-related contamination problems. For example, a pesticide that is water soluble and is applied just before a rainstorm will infiltrate quickly into the soil and be carried away by surface runoff, increasing the risk of contamination of adjacent groundwater and surface water bodies.

A growing problem worldwide is the contamination of soil as a result of industrial activity, particularly from inappropriate disposal or poorly designed storage of hazardous industrial wastes. An example occurred in Elmira, Ontario, in 1988 when a carcinogenic (cancer-causing) chemical, nitrosodimethylamine (NDMA) was found in the town's drinking water supply. The source of the chemical was traced to the Uniroyal Chemical Company, a producer of agrochemicals. The company had been disposing of hazardous chemical wastes in an above-ground storage pond (which met the legal requirements of Ontario's Ministry of Environment, it should be pointed out). The bottom of the pond was lined with clay, a common practice because of its capacity to seal ponds

and absorb contaminants. But when the bottom layers became saturated, the liquid waste began to seep through the soil. It percolated into the underlying groundwater, eventually contaminating several of the town's wells and nearby streams. Water for drinking and cooking had to be trucked in, and local residents were even advised not to bathe in water from the municipal wells.

The example of Elmira illustrates that soil and water contamination are so closely connected that they cannot be considered separately. We will return to these issues in greater detail when we look at freshwater contamination, waste management, and environmental health concerns.

Grazing practices can contribute to soil degradation

When sheep, goats, cattle, or other livestock graze on the open range, they feed primarily on grasses. As long as livestock populations do not exceed a range's carrying capacity and do not consume grasses faster than grasses can be replaced, grazing may be sustainable. However, when too many animals eat too much of the plant cover, impeding plant regrowth and preventing the replacement of biomass, the result is *over-grazing*.

Rangeland scientists have shown that over-grazing causes a number of impacts, some of which give rise to positive feedback cycles that exacerbate damage to soils, natural communities, and the land's productivity for grazing (**FIGURE 7.18**). When livestock remove too much of an area's plant cover, more soil surface is exposed and made vulnerable to erosion. Soil erosion makes it difficult for vegetation to regrow, perpetuating the lack of cover

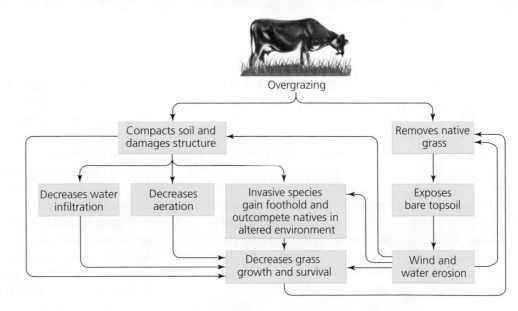

FIGURE 7.18
When grazing by livestock exceeds the carrying capacity of rangelands and their soil, over-grazing can set in motion a series of consequences and positive feedback loops that degrade soils and grassland ecosystems.

CANADIAN ENVIRONMENTAL PERSPECTIVES

Myrna Simpson

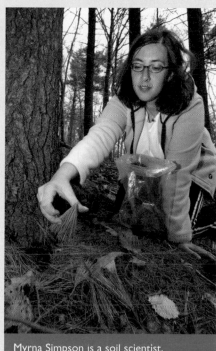

Myrna Simpson is a soil scientist, environmental chemist, and professor.

- **Professor** of environmental chemistry
- Soil resource **advocate**
- One of the *Toronto Star's* **"Top Ten to Watch"** for 2008

Soils are complex, changeable materials. They have many components—organic and inorganic; living and nonliving; microscopic and macroscopic; solid, liquid, and vapour. They also change continually in response to a wide variety of environmental conditions. Dr. Myrna Simpson has spent her research career at the University of Toronto investigating both the detailed characteristics of soil components, and their responses to environmental change.

Dr. Simpson is a professor of environmental chemistry, and co-director (with professor of chemistry André Simpson—and yes, they are married) of the Environmental Nuclear Magnetic Resonance (NMR) Centre at the University of Toronto's Scarborough campus. This is the only NMR facility in Canada that is dedicated specifically to environmental research. (Most are used for health-related applications or for research in chemistry and physics.)

NMR spectroscopy, or *nuclear magnetic resonance spectroscopy*, is a powerful chemistry technique that can be used to identify the properties of matter. In a general sense, *spectroscopy* refers to chemical analytical techniques used to measure the interactions of materials with various forms of energy. In NMR spectroscopy, certain atomic nuclei in the sample—nuclei that have a specific property called *spin*—are aligned in a strong magnetic field and then respond to radiofrequency irradiation in a way that is characteristic of that particular material. By measuring this reaction, which comes in the form of an output of energy in a characteristic frequency, scientists can determine the identity of the material.

NMR works only for analyzing materials whose nuclei possess the property of spin. Luckily, most elements do have naturally occurring isotopes with spin, including hydrogen, nitrogen, phosphorus, and carbon—all of which are important materials in soil. But the real strength of NMR spectroscopy is that it not only identifies the materials present, but also reveals the *form* in which the materials occur, including very detailed information about the molecular structure of the materials, how the atoms in the molecules are bonded, how far apart they are, the three-dimensional shape of the molecules, and the extent to which they are interacting with other materials in the sample.

Dr. Simpson and colleagues use NMR to study environmental and geochemical processes in soils and sediments from terrestrial, freshwater, and marine environments. Part of this work involves characterization of the forms in which organic matter occurs in soils and how soil organic matter interacts with water and minerals. This is fundamentally important because organic matter gives soil its fertility. Organic materials in soil also interact with contaminants, sometimes holding on to them in ways that can hinder efforts to clean up contaminated soil. To improve our capacity to manage contaminated soils, scientists need to develop a better understanding of how these interactions work. NMR can even reveal how metabolic processes in soil organisms, such as earthworms, change in response to environmental changes.

Another extremely important aspect of the work is to study the role of soils in carbon cycling. This involves the identification of environmental "fingerprints," called *biomarkers*, which allow the researchers to track the biogeochemical cycling of carbon as it moves through terrestrial ecosystems. Concerns about changes in our global climate have made it particularly urgent to understand the factors that control carbon cycling, particularly the reservoirs where carbon is sequestered in the global carbon cycle. Soil is one of the most important global carbon reservoirs, and the research of Dr. Simpson and her colleagues is contributing to our scientific understanding of how the soil carbon reservoir might respond to changes in temperature, moisture, and other environmental factors.

"Soil is the world's most underrated resource. Soil contains more than twice the amount of carbon as does the atmosphere; yet, until now, scientists haven't examined this significant carbon pool closely.... Through our research, we've sought to determine what soils are made up of at the molecular level and whether this composition will change in a warmer world."—**Myrna Simpson**

Thinking About Environmental Perspectives

In addition to being a soil scientist and environmental chemist, Professor Simpson is the mother of twins. She says, "As a mother, paving the way for environmental protection and solving environmental problems becomes more relevant and personal. I am constantly striving to ensure that our environment is healthy for my children as well as yours." In what ways do you think Professor Simpson's role as a parent affects her work as an environmental scientist and researcher?

and giving rise to more erosion. Moreover, non-native weedy plants may invade denuded soils. These invasive plants are usually less palatable to livestock and can out-compete native vegetation in the new, modified environment, further decreasing native plant cover.

Over-grazing can also compact soils and alter their structure. Soil **compaction**, in which pore space in the soil is reduced, makes it harder for water to infiltrate, for soils to be aerated, for plants' roots to expand, and for roots to conduct cellular respiration. All of these effects further decrease the growth and survival of native plants. Soil compaction also can be caused by over-tilling, use of heavy agricultural machinery, clear-cut logging, and rapid withdrawal of groundwater.

As a cause of soil degradation, over-grazing is equal to poorly managed cropland agriculture, and it is a greater cause of desertification. Humans keep a total of 3.4 billion cattle, sheep, and goats. Rangeland classified as degraded now adds up to 680 million ha, although some estimates put the number as high as 2.4 billion ha, fully 70% of the world's rangeland area. Rangeland degradation is estimated to cost $23.3 billion per year. Grazing exceeds the sustainable supply of grass in India by 30% and in parts of China by up to 50%. To relieve pressure on rangelands, both nations are now beginning to feed crop residues to livestock.

Range managers do their best to assess the carrying capacity of rangelands and inform livestock owners of these limits, so that herds are rotated from site to site as needed to conserve grass cover and soil integrity. Managers also can establish and enforce limits on grazing on publicly owned land when necessary. Today increasing numbers of ranchers are working cooperatively with government agencies, environmental scientists, and even environmental advocates to find ways to ranch more sustainably and safeguard the health of the soil.

Conclusion

Soil is a complex system, which functions as the interface between the geosphere, hydrosphere, and atmosphere. The importance of soil as a resource is often underestimated, but the preservation of arable soil is crucial for the maintenance of global food security.

Many of the policies enacted and the practices developed to combat soil degradation in Canada and worldwide have been quite successful, particularly in reducing the erosion of topsoil. However, soil is still being degraded at a rate that threatens the sustainability of the resource. Despite all we have learned about soil degradation and conservation, many challenges remain.

The role of soil as a reservoir in biogeochemical cycling is also of increasing interest to scientists. As long ago as 1945, Russian scientist Vladimir Vernadsky, considered to be one of the founders of biogeochemistry, declared that humans had become "a mighty and ever-growing geological force." This has never been truer than it is today, as we race to document, explain, and mitigate the global and potentially permanent environmental impacts of some human actions. Understanding the characteristics and behaviour of soils in this context will be a crucial part of this task.

REVIEWING OBJECTIVES

You should now be able to:

Delineate the fundamentals of soil science, including soil-forming processes

- Soil is a complex system that consists of mineral fragments with varying proportions of organic matter, with the rest of the pore space taken up by soil water and gases.
- The diverse biotic communities in soil include living and dead microorganisms, as well as larger organisms such as earthworms and other invertebrates, burrowing mammals, amphibians, and reptiles.

- Soil formation begins with the breakdown of parent rock by physical (mechanical), chemical, or biological weathering.
- Climate, organisms, relief, parent material, and time are factors that influence soil formation.

Describe some important properties of soil

- Soil profiles consist of distinct horizons that form as a result of weathering combined with leaching.
- Soil can be categorized according to properties such as colour (composition), texture, structure, and pH.

Characterize the role of soils in biogeochemical cycling

- Materials move from soil particles to soil solutions and back again by way of processes such as cation exchange.
- Soils play a crucial role in the nitrogen cycle by hosting free-living and symbiotic microorganisms that mediate nitrogen fixation, nitrification, and denitrification.
- Soils represent the largest terrestrial reservoir for carbon in the active carbon cycle—larger than all terrestrial vegetation and the atmosphere combined.

State the importance of soils for agriculture and in supporting plant growth

- Soil is crucial for providing nutrients for plant growth and, thus, for the support of life on Earth.
- Successful agriculture and a secure food supply require healthy soil.
- Soil properties affect (and may limit) the potential for plant growth and agriculture in any given location.

Identify the causes and predict the consequences of soil erosion and soil degradation

- As the human population grows, pressures from agriculture and other activities are degrading Earth's soil, and we are losing topsoil from productive cropland at an unsustainable rate.

- The main mechanisms of soil loss are splash, sheet, rill, and gully erosion by water, and deflation and abrasion by wind.
- Over-grazing, over-tilling, and careless forestry practices can cause soil degradation and negative impacts to native ecosystems.
- Desertification affects a large portion of the world's soils, especially in arid regions.
- Over-irrigation can cause salinization and water-logging, which lower crop yields and are difficult to mitigate.
- Over-application of fertilizers can cause pollution problems that affect ecosystems and human health.

Outline the history and explain the basic principles of soil conservation

- The Dust Bowl in North America and similar events elsewhere have encouraged scientists and farmers to develop ways of better protecting and conserving topsoil.
- Techniques such as crop rotation, contour farming, intercropping, terracing, shelterbelts, and reduced tillage can help protect soils from erosion.
- In Canada and across the world, governments are devising innovative policies and programs to deal with the problems of soil degradation.

TESTING YOUR COMPREHENSION

1. What is soil?
2. Describe the three types of weathering that may contribute to the process of soil formation.
3. What processes most influence the formation of soil? What is leaching, and what is its role in soil formation?
4. Name the five primary factors thought to influence soil formation, and describe one effect of each.
5. How are soil horizons created? What is the general pattern of distribution of organic matter in a typical soil profile?
6. Why is erosion generally considered a destructive process? Name three human activities that can promote soil erosion.
7. Describe the principal types of soil erosion by water and by wind.
8. How does terracing effectively turn very steep and mountainous areas into arable land?
9. How can fertilizers and irrigation contribute to soil degradation?
10. Describe the effects of over-grazing on soil.

THINKING IT THROUGH

1. How and why might actual soils differ from the idealized five-horizon soil profile presented in the chapter? How might departures from the idealized profile indicate the impact of human activities? Provide at least three examples.

2. Some pollutants, such as heavy metals, are positively charged and adhere to negatively charged soil particles. This can make it difficult to clean up contaminated soils and can reduce nutrient availability for plants. Explain why this is so, making reference to the process of cation exchange in soils.

3. How do you think a farmer can best help to conserve soil? How do you think a scientist can best help to conserve soil? How do you think a national government can best help to conserve soil?

4. Wetlands, with their highly organic-rich soils, are important reservoirs for carbon in the terrestrial ecosystem. Global warming may cause some wetlands to dry up or cause seasonally fluctuating water levels. What might be the impacts of these changes on the capacity of wetlands to store carbon and on the rate of flux of greenhouse gases to the atmosphere from wetlands? (If you cannot find a simple answer to this question, do not worry; scientists also do not yet know what the final answer is.)

5. You are a land manager with your provincial government and you have just been put in charge of 200 000 ha of public lands that have been severely degraded by over-grazing. Soil is eroding, creating large gullies. Shrubs have encroached on grassland areas because fire was suppressed. Environmentalists want an end to ranching on the land, and they want to bring back wolves and other endemic species. Ranchers want continued grazing and are strongly opposed to the reintroduction of native species, especially wolves. However, the ranchers are concerned about the land's condition and are willing to entertain new ideas. What steps would you take to assess the land's condition and begin restoring its soil and vegetation? Would you allow grazing, and if so, would you set limits on it? Would you try to reintroduce wolves to the area?

6. You are the head of an international granting agency that assists farmers with soil conservation and sustainable agriculture. You have $10 million to disburse. Your agency's staff has decided that the funding should go to (1) farmers in an arid area of Africa prone to salinization, (2) farmers in a fast-growing area of Indonesia where swidden agriculture is practised, (3) farmers in southern Brazil practising no-till agriculture, and (4) farmers in a dryland area of Mongolia undergoing desertification. What types of projects would you recommend funding in each of these areas, how would you apportion your funding among them, and why?

INTERPRETING GRAPHS AND DATA

Dr. Henry Janzen is a soil scientist at the Lethbridge Research Centre in Alberta and an adjunct professor at the University of Manitoba. He is an expert on carbon cycling and the emission of greenhouse gases from soils, and he carries out research on the effects of different management approaches on carbon storage in agricultural soils. In a 2004 paper in the journal *Agriculture, Ecosystems and Environment*, Dr. Janzen summarized many of the main scientific questions concerning carbon storage in terrestrial reservoirs.

One concern outlined in Dr. Janzen's study was the impact of land-use changes on carbon storage in terrestrial reservoirs. The following figure from the paper summarizes major land-use changes since 1700:

1. On the basis of this graph, which of the biomes or managed ecosystems (forest/woodland, steppe/savannah/grassland/shrubland, tundra/desert, or pasture/cropland) *increased* the most, in terms of percentage increase, from 1700 to 1990? Which one of them *decreased* the most, in terms of percentage

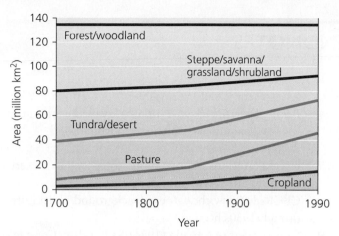

This graph shows the change in terrestrial area for three groups of major biome types and the increase in area of pasture and croplands since 1700.

Source: Figure 2 from Janzen, H.H. (2004) Carbon cycling in earth systems—a soil science perspective. Agriculture, Ecosystems and Environment *104, 399–417, plotted from values in Goldewijk, K.K. (2001) Estimating global land use change over the past 300 years: the HYDE database.* Global Biogeochem. Cycles *15(2), 417–433.*

decrease? What happened to the area covered by tundra/desert over the time period represented on the graph?

2. The table below presents some information about carbon storage in various terrestrial reservoirs, based on data from Janzen's study. It also provides the current total area occupied by each of the biome types. For each biome type and pasture/cropland, calculate and fill in the last column of the table, which shows the amount of carbon stored per hectare (in units of t/ha, or tonnes per hectare). One calculation (for the steppe/savannah grouping) has been completed as an example.

3. From the calculations you made and the information that is now in the final column of your table, which biome type stores the *most* carbon per hectare? Which stores the *least* carbon per hectare? How does the pasture/cropland carbon storage per hectare compare to that in the natural ecosystems?

4. Based on the data provided in the table, which of the natural ecosystems stores the highest proportion of its carbon in *plants*? Which of the natural ecosystems stores the highest proportion of its carbon in the *soil*? How does the proportion of carbon stored in plants vs. soils in pasture/cropland compare to the natural systems? Do these results surprise you? (Why or why not?)

5. In terms of carbon storage in terrestrial reservoirs, what do you think would be the overall result of the shift, shown in the graph (above), to increasing pasture/cropland at the expense of forests and grasslands?

Biome type	Global Carbon Reservoir (in Gt, or tonnes × 10⁹)			Current total area (ha × 10⁹)	C stored per hectare (t/ha)
	In Plants	In Soils	Total		
Forest/woodland	359	787	1146	4.17	
Steppe/savannah/grassland/shrubland	75	559	634	3.50	181.1
Tundra/desert (incl. ice-covered)	14	312	326	5.50	
Pasture/cropland	3	128	131	1.60	

This table shows the approximate area of three sets of biome types and pasture/cropland, in billions of hectares (ha × 10⁹), and the size of the carbon stock in each of them, in gigatonnes (Gt, or tonnes × 10⁹).
Source: Based on information in Table 1 from Janzen, H.H. (2004) Carbon cycling in earth systems—a soil science perspective. Agriculture, Ecosystems and Environment *104, 399–417.*

CHAPTER ENDNOTES

1. Based on information from www.trentu.ca/academic/bluelab/research_merbleue.html and personal communications with Nigel Roulet, Tim Moore, and Nathan Basiliko, August, 2008.

2. Wall, G.J., D.R. Coote, E.A. Pringle, and I.J. Shelton (eds.) (2002) *RUSLEFAC—Revised Universal Soil Loss Equation for Application in Canada: A Handbook for Estimating Soil Loss from Water Erosion in Canada.* Research Branch, Agriculture and Agri-Food Canada, Ottawa, Contribution No. AAFC/AAC2244E. 117 pp.

3. Agriculture and Agri-Food Canada (1997) *Profile of Production Trends and Environmental Issues in Canada's Agriculture and Agri-food Sector* http://www4.agr.gc.ca/resources/prod/doc/policy/environment/pdfs/sds/profil_e.pdf

4. van Vlietl, L.J.P, G.A. Padbury, and D.A. Lobb (2003) Soil erosion risk indicators used in Canada. Paper presented at the OECD Expert Meeting on Soil Erosion and Biodiversity.

5. Agriculture and Agri-Food Canada (1997) *Profile of Production Trends and Environmental Issues in Canada's Agriculture and Agri-food Sector, 1997.*

6. From the U.N. Convention to Combat Desertification, as cited in the Millennium Ecosystem Assessment (2005) *Ecosystems and Human Well-Being: Desertification Synthesis* available online at www.millenniumassessment.org/documents/document.355.aspx.pdf

7. United Nations Convention to Combat Desertification, http://www.unccd.int/

8. CBCRadiowww.cbc.ca/news/background/agriculture/drought1930s.html

9. Government of Canada (1984) *Soil at Risk: Canada's Eroding Future.*

10. Soil Conservation Council of Canada, www.soilcc.ca.

11. Agriculture and Agri-Food Canada, Agri-Environmental Services Branch, www4.agr.gc.ca/AAFC-AAC/display-afficher.do?id=1187362338955&lang=eng

12. Ontario Ministry of Agriculture, Food, and Rural Affairs, Agroforestry Statistics, www.omafra.gov.on.ca/english/crops/facts/info_statistics.htm.

13. Soil Conservation Council of Canada, www.soilcc.ca

14. FAO Land and Plant Nutrition Management Service, Global Network on Integrated Soil Management for Sustainable Use of Salt-Affected Soils, http://193.43.36.103/ag/AGL/agll/spush/intro.htm

MyEnvironmentPlace

Go to **www.myenvironmentplace.ca** where you will find quizzes, animations, your Pearson eText, and more.

8

Agriculture, Food, and Biotechnology

For a farm to be certified as organic, the farmer must adhere to strict regulations.

Upon successfully completing this chapter, you will be able to

- Outline the historical development of agriculture and the transition to industrialized agriculture
- Explain the challenge of feeding a growing human population
- Identify the main approaches and summarize the environmental impacts of the Green Revolution
- Summarize the strategies and impacts of pest management and the importance of pollination
- Describe the science and evaluate the controversies associated with genetically modified food

- State the importance of crop diversity and some approaches to preservation
- Assess the positive and negative aspects of feedlots and aquaculture for raising animals for food
- Summarize the main goals of sustainable agriculture

Farmer in maize field in Oaxaca, Mexico.

MEXICO

Oaxaca

GM MAIZE AND ROUNDUP-READY CANOLA

"If you desire peace, cultivate justice, but at the same time cultivate the fields to produce more bread; otherwise there will be no peace."

—NORMAN BORLAUG, CONSIDERED TO BE THE FATHER OF THE GREEN REVOLUTION

"Worrying about starving future generations won't feed them. Food biotechnology will . . . . At Monsanto, we now believe food biotechnology is a better way forward."

—MONSANTO COMPANY ADVERTISEMENT

"I never put those plants on my land. The question is, where do Monsanto's rights end and mine begin?"

—PERCY SCHMEISER

Corn is a staple grain of the world's food supply. We can trace its ancestry back roughly 5500 years, when people in the highland valleys of what is now the state of Oaxaca in southern Mexico first domesticated that region's wild maize plants. The corn we eat today arose from some of the many varieties that evolved from the early selective crop breeding conducted by the people of this region.

Today Oaxaca remains a world centre of biodiversity for maize, with many native varieties growing in the rich soil (see photo). Preserving such varieties of crops in their ancestral homelands is important for securing the future of our food supply, scientists maintain, because these varieties serve as reservoirs of genetic diversity—reservoirs we may need to draw on to sustain or advance our agriculture.

In 2001, Mexican government scientists conducting routine genetic tests of Oaxacan farmers' maize announced that they had turned up DNA that matched *transgenes*, that is, genes transferred from genetically modified (GM) corn, even though Mexico had banned its cultivation since 1998. Corn is one of many crops that scientists have genetically engineered to express desirable traits such as large size, fast growth, and resistance to insect pests.

Activists opposed to GM food trumpeted the disturbing news and urged a ban on imports of transgenic crops from producer countries such as the United States into developing nations. The agrobiotech industry defended the safety of its crops and questioned the validity of the research. Further research by Mexican government scientists confirmed the presence of transgenes in Mexican maize. Those studies were controversial and still have not been definitively verified, although the findings were accepted by a special commission of experts convened under the North American Free Trade Agreement (NAFTA). The commission concluded that corn imported from the United States was the source for the transgenes, which spread by wind pollination and interbreeding with native cultivars once in Mexico.

Meanwhile, back in Canada, Monsanto, a producer of GM foods, was engaged in a high-publicity battle with 74-year-old Saskatchewan farmer Percy Schmeiser (see photo) over Schmeiser's canola crop. Canola is an edible oil derived from rapeseed. It is widely grown throughout the Canadian prairies, and 80% of the rapeseed grown in Canada is genetically modified.

Schmeiser maintained that pollen from Monsanto's Roundup-Ready canola had blown from a neighbouring farm onto his land and pollinated his non-GM canola. Schmeiser had not purchased the patented seed and did not want the crossbreeding. Monsanto investigators took seed samples from his plants and charged him with violating a Canadian law that makes it illegal for farmers to reuse or grow patented seed without a contract. The courts sided with Monsanto, ordering the farmer to pay the corporation $238,000. Schmeiser appealed to the Supreme Court of Canada, which ruled that Monsanto's patent had indeed been violated but acknowledged that the farmer had not benefited from the GM seeds and had not intended their use. The Court exempted him from paying any fines or fees to the company.

Saskatchewan farmer Percy Schmeiser was accused by the Monsanto Company of planting its patented canola without a contract with the company. Schmeiser said his non-GM plants were contaminated with Monsanto's transgenes from neighbouring farms, and he became a hero to small farmers and anti–GM food activists worldwide.

In spite of the Supreme Court loss, Schmeiser received wide public support. He and his wife, Louise, were given the 2007 Right Livelihood Award in recognition of their struggle. A government committee sought a revision in the patent law, and the National Farmers Union of Canada called for a moratorium on GM food. Schmeiser says that the most difficult part of the entire saga was the loss, through contamination by transgenes, of the local variety of rapeseed that he had planted throughout his 60-year farming career.[1]

The larger question of the legality of holding patents on living organisms remains unresolved. In 2002, Canada became the first nation in the industrialized world to prohibit the holding of patents on higher organisms (a genetically modified mouse was the organism in question). Monsanto continues to demand that farmers heed patent laws and is continuing with several similar lawsuits. In a fascinating turn of events, Percy Schmeiser reached an out-of-court settlement with Monsanto in March of 2008, in which the company admitted that contamination had occurred and agreed to pay all costs of remediating it.

The Race to Feed the World

Although human population growth has slowed, we can still expect our numbers to swell to 9 billion by the middle of this century. For every two people living in the year 2000, there will likely be three in 2050. Feeding 50% more mouths will require significant advances in agricultural technology and food distribution processes; doing all of this while protecting the integrity of soil, water, and ecosystems will require that sustainability be a guiding principle of these advances.

As the human population has increased, so have the amounts of land and resources we devote to agriculture, which currently covers 38% of Earth's land surface. We can define **agriculture** as the practice of raising crops and livestock for human use and consumption. We obtain most of our food, fibre, and (increasingly) biofuels from **cropland**, land used to raise plants for human use, and **rangeland**, land used for grazing livestock.

Agriculture is not something that people have "always done." The development of agriculture was a major achievement—perhaps the most important technological leap forward by humans in our history as a species. In the past 60 years or so, agricultural technology has undergone massive, rapid changes. These changes have allowed food production to keep pace with population growth, more or less, but they have led to some unanticipated environmental impacts. In this chapter we look at the development of agricultural technologies over time and in recent decades, the challenge of offering food security to the world's population, and the environmental implications of both.

Agriculture first appeared around 10 000 years ago

During most of our species' 200 000-year existence[2] we were hunter-gatherers, dependent on wild plants and animals. Then about 10 000 years ago, as the climate

roots

AGRICULTURE

The word **agriculture** comes from the Latin *agricultura*, a combination of *ager*, "field," and *cultura*, "to cultivate." *Cultivar*—a cultivated plant that has been selected for specific desirable traits—is a term that was coined in 1923 by an American horticulturalist by combining the terms *cultivated* and *variety*.

warmed following a period of glaciation, people in some cultures began to **cultivate**, or raise plants (*cultivars*) from seeds, and to **domesticate** animals as a source of both food and labour.

Agriculture most likely began as hunter-gatherers brought back to their encampments wild fruits, grains, and nuts. Some of these foods fell to the ground, were thrown away, or were eaten and survived passage through the digestive system. The plants that grew from these seeds near human encampments likely produced fruits that were on average larger and tastier than those in the wild because they sprang from seeds of fruits people selected for their size and flavour. As these plants bred with others nearby that shared their characteristics, they gave rise to subsequent generations of plants with large and flavourful fruits.

Eventually, people realized that they could guide this process and began intentionally planting seeds from the plants whose produce was most desirable. This is *artificial selection*, or *selective breeding*, at work. The practice of selective breeding continues to the present day and has produced the many hundreds of crops we enjoy, all of which are artificially selected versions of wild plants. People followed the same process of selective breeding with animals, creating domesticated livestock from wild species—by accident at first, then by intention.

Evidence from archaeology and paleoecology suggests that agriculture was invented independently by different cultures in at least 5 and possibly 10 or more areas of the world at around the same time (**FIGURE 8.1**). The earliest widely accepted archaeological evidence for plant domestication is from the "Fertile Crescent" region of the Middle East about 10 500 years ago, and the earliest evidence for animal domestication, also from that region, just 500 years later. Crop remains have been dated using radiocarbon dating and similar methods. Wheat and barley originated in the Fertile Crescent, as did rye, peas, lentils, onions, garlic, carrots, grapes, and other food plants familiar to us today. The people of this region also domesticated goats and sheep. Meanwhile, in China, domestication began as early as 9500 years ago, leading eventually to the rice, millet, and pigs we know today. Agriculture in Africa (coffee, yams, sorghum, and more) and the Americas (corn, beans, squash, potatoes, llamas, and more) developed later in several areas, 4500 to 7000 years ago.

Once our ancestors learned to cultivate crops and domesticate animals, they began to settle in more permanent camps and villages near water sources. Agriculture and a *sedentary* (that is, settled) lifestyle likely reinforced one another. The need to harvest crops kept people sedentary, and once they were sedentary it was necessary to plant more crops to support the population.

FIGURE 8.1   Agriculture appears to have originated independently in multiple locations throughout the world, as different cultures domesticated certain plants and animals from wild species living in their environments. This map summarizes conclusions from diverse sources of research on evidence for early agriculture. Areas where people are thought to have independently invented agriculture are coloured green. (China may represent two independent origins.) Areas coloured blue represent regions where people either invented agriculture independently or obtained the idea from cultures of other regions. A few of the many crop plants domesticated in each region are shown.   *Source: Data from syntheses in Diamond, J. (1997)* Guns, Germs, and Steel. *New York: W.W. Norton; and Goudie, A. (2000)* The Human Impact, *5th ed. Cambridge, MA: MIT Press.*

Population increase resulted from these developments and further promoted them, in a positive feedback cycle.

Agriculture is a form of **intensification**—a way to increase the productivity and carrying capacity of a given unit of land. A hunter-gatherer lifestyle requires a very large land area to support a given population; switching to a sedentary lifestyle based on agriculture increased the carrying capacity and allowed for larger groups to be supported on much smaller areas of land. The development of agriculture thus permitted—or possibly caused—a sudden dramatic increase in population. The ability to grow excess farm produce enabled some people to leave farming and to live off the food that others produced. This led to the development of professional specializations, commerce, technology, densely populated urban centres, social stratification, and politically powerful elites. For better or worse, the advent of agriculture eventually brought us the civilization we have today.

For thousands of years, crops were cultivated, harvested, stored, and distributed by human and animal muscle power, using hand tools and simple machines (**FIGURE 8.2**). This biologically powered agriculture is known as **traditional agriculture**. In the oldest form of traditional agriculture, known as **subsistence agriculture**, farming families produce only enough food for themselves and do not make use of large-scale irrigation, fertilizer, farm machinery, or teams of labouring animals. Intensive traditional agriculture sometimes uses draft animals and employs significant quantities of irrigation water and fertilizer, but stops short of using fossil fuels. This type of agriculture aims to produce food for the farming family, as well as extra food to sell in the market. Today there are still many subsistence farmers, especially in the developing world.

Industrialized agriculture is more recent

The Industrial Revolution introduced large-scale mechanization and fossil fuels to agricultural fields, enabling farmers to replace horses and oxen with faster and more powerful means of cultivating, harvesting, transporting, and processing crops. Other advances facilitated irrigation and fertilization, while the invention of chemical pesticides reduced competition from weeds and herbivory by insects and other crop pests.

FIGURE 8.2
Hunting and gathering was the predominant human lifestyle until the onset of agriculture and sedentary lliving, which centred on farms, villages, and cities, beginning around 10 000 years ago. Over the millennia, societies practicing traditional agriculture gradually replaced hunter-gatherer cultures. Within the past century and a half, industrialized agriculture has spread, replacing much traditional agriculture.

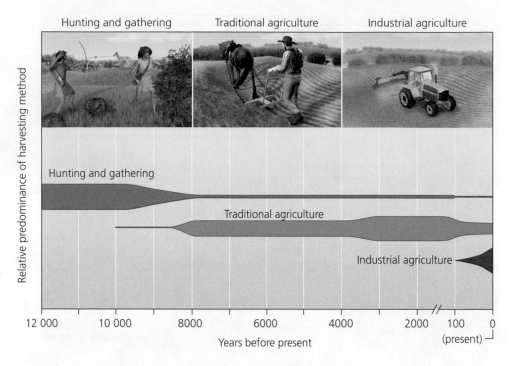

To be efficient, modern **industrialized agriculture** requires that vast fields be planted with single types of crops. The uniform planting of a single crop type over a large expanse of land, termed **monoculture**, is distinct from the *polyculture* approach of much traditional agriculture, such as Native American farming systems that mixed maize, beans, squash, and peppers in the same fields. Today, industrialized agriculture, characterized by monoculture, occupies about 25% of the world's cropland.

We are producing more food per person

Over the past half century, our ability to produce food has grown even faster than population (**FIGURE 8.3**). However, largely because of political obstacles and inefficiencies in distribution, today over 900 million people in the world still do not have enough to eat. Every five seconds, somewhere in the world, a child starves to death.

Agricultural scientists and policy makers pursue the goal of **food security**—the guarantee of an adequate and acceptable food supply to all people at all times. Making a food supply sustainable depends on maintaining healthy soil, water, and biodiversity, but careless agricultural practices can have devastating effects on the environment and the long-term ability of the world's soils to support crops and livestock.

In the 1960s there were predictions of widespread starvation and catastrophic failure of agricultural systems,

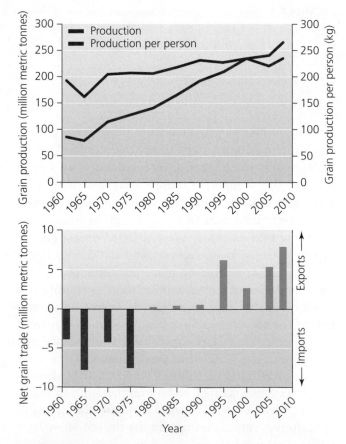

FIGURE 8.3
India increased its grain production even faster than its population grew during the years of the Green Revolution, so grain per person also increased (upper graph). As production rose, India began exporting grain to other nations (lower graph). The same trends can be seen in global grain production over this period.
Source: Data from U.N. Food and Agriculture Organization (FAO).

amidst concerns that the human population could not continue to grow without outstripping its food supply. However, the population has continued to increase well past the predictions. It is tragic that more than 900 million people are still chronically hungry today, but in percentage terms hunger has been reduced by half—from 26% of the population in 1970 to 13% today.

Although agricultural production has so far outpaced population growth, there is no guarantee that it will continue to do so. Already with grain crops, the world's staple foods, we are producing less food per person each year. Since 1985, world grain production per person has fallen by 9%. Moreover, the world's soils are in decline, and a significant portion of the planet's **arable** land (land that is suitable for the annual planting of crops) has already been brought into production.

We face undernourishment, overnutrition, and malnutrition

Although many people lack access to adequate food, others are affluent enough to consume more than is healthy. People who are *undernourished*, receiving less than 90% of their daily caloric needs, mostly live in the developing world. Meanwhile, in the developed world, many people suffer from *overnutrition*, taking in too many calories each day. In Canada, where food is available in abundance and people tend to lead sedentary lives with little exercise, 48% of adults exceed healthy weight standards, and 14% are obese (according to World Health Organization standards).[3]

For most people who are undernourished, the reasons are economic. One-fifth of the world's people live on less than $1 per day, and over half live on less than $2 per day, the World Bank estimates. Hunger is a problem even in Canada, where over 850 000 people used the services of a food bank during a typical month in 2010, according to Food Banks Canada;[4] almost 40% of them were children. This measure underrepresents the true situation, particularly for rural areas that lack access to food banks. The National Population Health Survey has estimated that *food insecurity*—the inability to procure sufficient food when needed—is a factor in 10.2% of Canadian households, affecting well over 3 million people.[5]

In a wealthy, food-producing nation such as Canada, the cause of hunger is more than just a lack of available food. Many factors coalesce to cause hunger insecurity around the world, and these factors have as much to do with poverty and the weaknesses of our food delivery systems as with the abundance and availability of food.

Just as the *quantity* of food a person eats is important for health, so is the *quality* of food. **Malnutrition**,

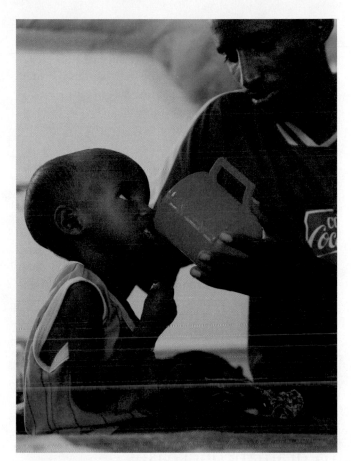

FIGURE 8.4
Millions of children, including this child in Somalia, suffer from forms of malnutrition such as marasmus.

a shortage of nutrients the body needs, including a complete complement of vitamins and minerals, can occur in both undernourished and overnourished individuals. Malnutrition can lead to disease (**FIGURE 8.4**). A diet without enough protein or essential amino acids

roots

KWASHIORKOR AND MARASMUS

The disease **kwashiorkor** is common in children who eat a diet high in starch but low in protein or essential amino acids. The word *kwashiorkor* derives from one of the languages of coastal Ghana. It literally means "first-second," but is commonly translated as "rejected one." It refers to the first child, who is weaned off breast milk when the second child is born and therefore loses that important source of nutrition. The word **marasmus**, which refers to a disease caused by protein deficiency and low caloric intake, originates from the Greek *marasmus*, meaning "wasting away, withering, decay."

can result in *kwashiorkor*, which causes bloating of the abdomen, deterioration and discolouration of hair, mental disability, anaemia, immune suppression, developmental delays, and reduced growth in children. Protein deficiency together with a lack of calories can lead to *marasmus*, which causes wasting or shrivelling among millions of children in the developing world.

Impacts of the Green Revolution

Beginning around 1950, agricultural advancement allowed new technologies, crop varieties, and farming practices to be exported to the developing world. Although many people saw growth in production and increased agricultural efficiency as the key to ending starvation, hunger still exists in the world. We now realize that boosting agricultural production is only part of the solution to hunger. Nevertheless, technological advances allowed farmers to dramatically increase yields per hectare of cropland and helped millions of people avoid starvation.

The Green Revolution led to dramatic increases in agricultural productivity

The desire for greater quantity and quality of food for the growing human population led directly to a so-called **Green Revolution**, with enormous increases in agricultural productivity during the mid- to late twentieth century. We have increased food production and per capita food consumption worldwide by devoting more energy (especially fossil fuel energy) to agriculture; by planting and harvesting more frequently; by greatly increasing the use of irrigation, fertilizers, and pesticides; by planting monocultures; by increasing the amount of cultivated land; and by developing (through crossbreeding and genetic engineering) more productive crop and livestock varieties.

Prior to the Green Revolution, the best way to increase agricultural productivity was to plant more land with crops or to increase the size of a herd. This is a form of **extensification**—increasing resource productivity by bringing more land into production (as opposed to *intensification*, in which new technologies permit greater resource productivity from each unit of land). Realizing that farmers could not go on indefinitely cultivating more and more land to increase crop output, agricultural scientists consciously worked to develop technologies to increase crop output per unit area of cultivated land. In the end, the Green Revolution was characterized by both extensification *and* intensification of agricultural production.

FIGURE 8.5
Norman Borlaug holds examples of the wheat variety he bred that helped launch the Green Revolution. The high-yielding disease-resistant wheat helped increase agricultural productivity in many developing countries. Borlaug, quoted at the beginning of this chapter, won the Nobel Peace Prize for his work.

The transfer of agricultural technology to the developing world that marked the Green Revolution began in the 1940s, when U.S. agronomist Norman Borlaug introduced Mexico's farmers to a specially bred type of wheat (**FIGURE 8.5**). This strain of wheat produced large seed heads, was short in stature to resist wind, was resistant to diseases, and produced high yields. Within two decades of planting and harvesting this specially bred crop, Mexico tripled its wheat production and began exporting wheat.

The stunning success of this program inspired others. Next were India and Pakistan, and soon many developing countries were increasing their crop yields using selectively bred strains of wheat, rice, corn, and other crops from developed nations. Some varieties yielded three or four times as much per hectare as did their predecessors.

The Green Revolution has had both positive and negative impacts

Along with the new grains, developing nations adopted the methods of modern, industrialized agriculture. They began applying large amounts of synthetic fertilizers and chemical pesticides to their fields, irrigating crops with generous amounts of water, and using heavy equipment powered by fossil fuels. This high-input agriculture allowed farmers to harvest dramatically more corn, wheat, rice, and soybeans from each hectare of land. From 1900 to 2000, humans expanded the world's total cultivated area by 33% but increased energy inputs into agriculture by 800%. Intensive agriculture saved millions in India from starvation in the 1970s and eventually turned that nation into a net exporter of grain.

These developments had mixed impacts on the environment. On the positive side, the intensified use of already-cultivated land reduced pressures to convert additional natural lands for new cultivation. Between 1961 and 2002, food production rose 150% and population rose 100%, while land area converted for agriculture increased only 10%. For this reason, the Green Revolution can be said to have prevented some degree of deforestation and habitat conversion in many countries while those countries were experiencing their fastest population growth rates. In this sense, the Green Revolution was beneficial for natural ecosystems.

However, despite its successes, the Green Revolution has exacted a high price. The intensive cultivation of farmland has created new environmental problems and exacerbated some old ones. Many of these problems pertain to the integrity of soil and water supplies, which are the very foundation of our food supply. The intensive use of water, fossil fuels, and chemical fertilizers and pesticides had negative environmental impacts in the form of pollution, salinization, and desertification. The social and economic impacts of the Green Revolution on small-scale farmers in the developing world—many of whom are disadvantaged by lack of income, lack of education, or both, preventing them from accessing or benefiting from these technologies—are particularly controversial.

Fertilizer impacts. One hallmark of the Green Revolution was greatly increased use of industrial fertilizers. Plants remove nutrients from soil as they grow, and water also carries away nutrients. If agricultural soils come to contain too few nutrients, crop yields decline. Therefore, a great deal of effort has aimed to enhance productivity in nutrient-limited soils by adding **fertilizer**, any of various substances that contain essential nutrients.

There are two main types of fertilizers. **Inorganic (or industrial) fertilizers** are mined or synthetically manufactured mineral supplements, mainly various combinations of nitrogen, phosphorus, and potassium. **Organic fertilizers** consist of natural materials (largely the remains or wastes of organisms) and include animal manure; crop residues; fresh vegetation (or "green manure"); and *compost*, a mixture produced when decomposers break down organic matter, including food and crop waste, in a controlled environment. Organic fertilizers offer some benefits that inorganic fertilizers cannot, but they are not a panacea.

Applying substantial amounts of fertilizer to croplands can have impacts far beyond the boundaries of the fields (**FIGURE 8.6**). Nitrogen and phosphorus runoff

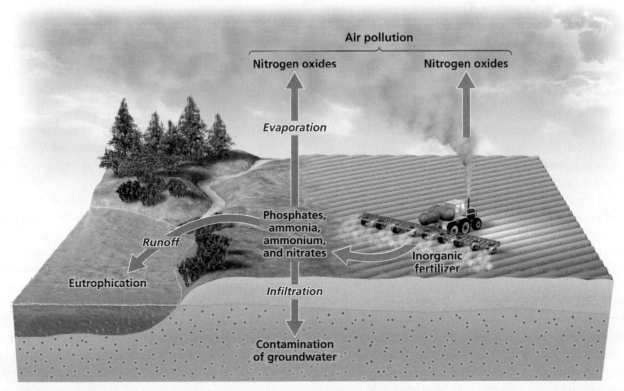

FIGURE 8.6 The overapplication of inorganic (or organic) fertilizers can have effects beyond the farm field because nutrients that are not taken up by plants may end up in other reservoirs. Anthropogenic inputs of nitrogen have greatly modified the nitrogen cycle and now account for one-half the total nitrogen flux on Earth.

from farms and other sources can lead to phytoplankton blooms, creating an oxygen-depleted "dead zone." Such eutrophication occurs at many river mouths, lakes, and ponds throughout the world. Moreover, nitrates readily leach through soil and contaminate groundwater, and components of some nitrogen fertilizers can even volatilize (evaporate) into the air.

Through these processes, unnatural amounts of nitrates and phosphates spread through ecosystems and pose human health risks, including cancer and methemoglobinaemia, or "blue-baby" syndrome. Health Canada and the U.S. Environmental Protection Agency both have determined that nitrate concentrations in excess of 10 mg/L for adults and 5 mg/L for infants in drinking water are unsafe, yet many sources around the world exceed even the looser standard of 50 mg/L set by the World Health Organization. Careful timing and regular soil testing can help to minimize applications of fertilizers that exceed what the plants need and can absorb.

Irrigation impacts.

Another key feature of the Green Revolution was an enormous increase in the amount of irrigated cropland, with the result that agriculture is the main reason for extraction and use of fresh water worldwide. Unfortunately, irrigation efficiency worldwide is quite low; only 43% of the water applied actually gets used by plants. *Drip irrigation* systems (**FIGURE 8.7**) that target water directly to plants are one solution to the problem. These systems allow more control over where water is aimed and waste far less water. Once considered expensive to install, they are becoming less costly, such that more farmers in developing countries will be able to afford them.

Poorly designed irrigation can also lead to the problems of waterlogging and salinization of soils, especially in hot, dry regions. When croplands are overwatered, soils can become soggy and saturated. As this water evaporates, it moves up through the soil profile, carrying dissolved mineral salts toward the surface. At the surface, only the fresh water evaporates, leaving a concentrated layer of salts encrusting the surface. Salinized agricultural soils are problematic in many parts of the world, and once soil has been degraded in this way it is almost impossible to restore it.

Monoculture impacts.

One key aspect of Green Revolution techniques has had particularly negative consequences for biodiversity and mixed consequences for crop yields. Monoculture, the planting of large expanses of single crop types (**FIGURE 8.8**), has made planting and harvesting more efficient and has thereby increased output. However, when all plants in a field are genetically similar, all will be equally susceptible to viral diseases,

(a) Conventional irrigation

(b) Drip irrigation

FIGURE 8.7
Currently, plants take up less than half the water we apply in irrigation. Conventional methods lose a great deal of water to evaporation **(a)**. In more-efficient drip irrigation approaches, such as this one watering grape vines **(b)**, hoses are arranged so that water drips from holes in the hoses directly onto the plants that need the water.

fungal pathogens, or insect pests that can spread quickly from plant to plant. For this reason, monocultures require large amounts of pesticides and bring significant risks of catastrophic failure.

Monocultures have also contributed to a narrowing of the human diet. Globally, 90% of the food we consume now comes from only 15 crop species and 8 livestock species—a drastic reduction in diversity from earlier times. The nutritional dangers of such dietary restriction have been alleviated by the fact that expanded global trade has provided many people access to a wider diversity of foods from different locations around the world. However, this effect has benefited wealthy people far more than poor people. One reason that farmers and scientists were so concerned about transgenic contamination of Oaxaca's native maize is that Oaxacan maize varieties serve as a valuable source of genetic variation in a world where so much variation is being lost to monocultural practices.

FIGURE 8.8
Most agricultural production in industrialized countries comes from monocultures—large stands of single types of crop plant, such as this wheat field. Clustering crop types in uniform fields on large scales greatly improves the efficiency of planting and harvesting, but it also decreases biodiversity and makes crops more susceptible to outbreaks of pests that specialize on particular crops.

Pests and Pollinators

Throughout the history of agriculture, the insects, fungi, viruses, rodents, and weeds that eat or compete with our crops have taken advantage of the ways we cluster food plants into agricultural fields. These organisms, in making a living for themselves, cut crop yields and make it harder for farmers to make a living. As just one example of thousands, various species of moth caterpillars known as armyworms decrease yields of everything from beets to sorghum to millet to canola to pasture grasses. Pests and weeds have always caused problems in traditional agriculture; they pose an even greater threat in a monoculture situation, where a pest adapted to specialize on that particular crop can easily move from one individual plant to many others of the same type.

What humans term a **pest** is any organism that damages crops that are valuable to us, and a **weed** is any plant that competes with crops. These are subjective categories that

weighing the issues

WHAT A PEST!

Compare the concept of a pest or weed species with that of alien and invasive species. At what point should a species be considered a pest? Does it have to cause damage to human interests? What if it causes harm only to natural ecosystems? How should pest species be managed?

we define entirely by our own economic interests. There is nothing inherently malevolent in the behaviour of a pest or a weed; the organisms are simply trying to survive and reproduce. From the viewpoint of an insect that happens to be adapted to feed on corn, grapes, or apples, a grain field, vineyard, or orchard represents an endless buffet.

Thousands of chemical pesticides have been developed

To prevent pest outbreaks and to limit competition with weeds, people have developed thousands of artificial chemicals to kill insects (*insecticides*), plants (*herbicides*), and fungi (*fungicides*). Poisons that target pest organisms are collectively termed **pesticides**. Enormous increases in the use of a wide variety of pesticides were another key feature of the Green Revolution.

In Canada today more than 7000 pesticides are registered for use. Many of the over 500 active ingredients in these pesticides have not been evaluated for health or environmental impacts for many years—over 150 were approved for use in Canada prior to 1960. The *Pest Control Products Act*, which came into effect as federal legislation in Canada in 2006, requires products to be reevaluated 15 years after they are initially approved for use, among other provisions designed to improve the safety and minimize the environmental impacts of pesticide use.[6] **TABLE 8.1** shows the main categories of chemical pesticides used in Canada.

Today more than $32 billion is expended annually on pesticides, $1.5 billion of that in Canada. Most pesticides used in Canada are for agricultural purposes (91% of sales), while the remaining nonagricultural pest management products—primarily for domestic use, but also used in the forestry and industrial sectors and for the management of golf courses and other landscapes—represent 9% of total sales. Eighty-five percent of the total pesticides sold in Canada are herbicides, followed by fungicides, insecticides, and other specialty pest-management chemicals such as rodenticides.[7]

Pesticides are, by definition, designed to be toxic to organisms, and the toxic effects may not be limited to the target organisms. Consequently, the application of synthetic pesticides can have health consequences for both humans and other nontarget organisms (see the "Effects" column of **TABLE 8.1**).

Pests evolve resistance to pesticides

Despite the toxicity of these chemicals, their usefulness tends to decline with time as pests evolve resistance to

Table 8.1 Categories of Pesticides Used in Canada

Class of Chemical Pesticide	First Used	Examples	Types	Current Status	Effects
Organochlorines	1942	Aldrin; chlordane; dieldrin; endrin; heptachlor; lindane; methoxychlor; toxaphene; HCB; PCP; DDT	Mostly insecticides	Some registered in Canada; others (such as DDT) discontinued in Canada but still used in developing nations	Persistent; bioaccumulative; affect ability to reproduce, develop, and withstand environmental stress
Organophosphates	Very early 1940s	Schradan; parathion; malathion	Insecticides	Schradan discontinued in 1964, resulting in a move toward less toxic groups (malathion, parathion)	Nonpersistent; systemic; not very selective; toxic to humans
Carbamates	First appeared in 1930; large-scale use in 1950s	Carbaryl; methomyl; propoxur; aldicarb	Fungicides, insecticides	Aldicarb discontinued in 1964; the others are registered in Canada	Nonpersistent; not very selective; toxic to birds and fish
Phenoxy	1946	2,4-D 2,4,5-T	Herbicides	2,4-D is widely used 2,4,5-T banned in Canada	Selective effects on humans and mammals are not well known; some potential to cause cancer in laboratory animals
Pyrethroids	1980	Fenpropanthrin; deltamethrin; cypermethrin	Insecticides	Fenpropanthrin is not registered in Canada, unlike the two other pesticides	Target-specific: more selective than organophosphates or carbamates; not acutely toxic to birds or mammals, but particularly toxic to aquatic species

Source: Government of Canada, Pesticides: Making the Right Choice for Health and the Environment. (2000) Report of the Standing Committee on Environment and Sustainable Development. http://cmte.parl.gc.ca/cmte/CommitteePublication.aspx?COM=173&Lang=1&SourceId=36396

them. Recall from our discussion of natural selection that organisms within populations vary in their traits. Because most insects and microbes occur in huge numbers, it is likely that a small fraction of individuals may by chance have genes that confer some degree of immunity to a given pesticide. Even if a pesticide application kills 99.99% of the insects in a field, 1 in 10 000 survives. If an insect survives by being genetically resistant to a pesticide, and if it mates with other resistant individuals of the same species, the insect population may grow. This new population will consist of individuals that are genetically resistant to the pesticide. As a result, pesticide applications will cease to be effective (**FIGURE 8.9**).

In many cases, industrial chemists are caught up in an "evolutionary arms race" with the pests they battle, racing to increase or retarget the toxicity of their chemicals while the armies of pests evolve ever-stronger resistance to their efforts. The number of species known to have evolved resistance to pesticides has grown over the decades. As of 2007, there were more than 2700 known cases of resistance by 550 species to over 300 pesticides,

and some species have evolved resistance to multiple pesticides. Resistant pests can take a significant economic toll on crops. In Canada, resistance to herbicides is of great concern; both the number of herbicide-resistant weeds and the area of land covered by such weeds are increasing.[8]

Biological control pits one organism against another

Because of pesticide resistance and the health risks of some synthetic chemicals, agricultural scientists increasingly battle pests and weeds with organisms that eat or infect them. This strategy is called **biological control**, or *biocontrol* for short. For example, parasitoid wasps are natural enemies of many caterpillars. These wasps lay eggs on a caterpillar, and the larvae that hatch from the eggs feed on the caterpillar, eventually killing it. Parasitoid wasps have been used as biocontrol agents in many situations. Some such efforts have succeeded at pest control and have led to steep reductions in chemical pesticide use.

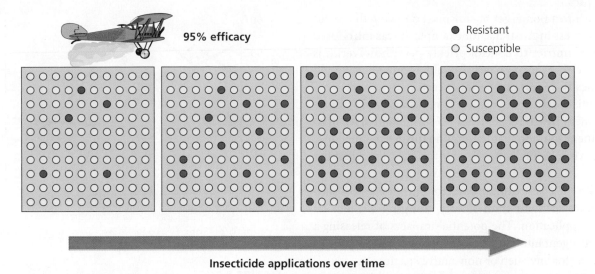

95% efficacy

● Resistant
○ Susceptible

Insecticide applications over time

FIGURE 8.9   Through natural selection, pests can evolve resistance to the poisons we apply to kill them. This simplified diagram shows that when a pesticide is applied to an outbreak of insect pests, it may kill virtually all individuals except those few with an innate immunity to the poison. Those surviving individuals may found a population with genes for resistance to the poison. Future applications of the pesticide may then be ineffective, forcing us to develop a more potent poison or an alternative means of pest control.

One classic case of successful biological control is the introduction of the cactus moth, *Cactoblastis cactorum*, from Argentina to Australia in the 1920s to control invasive prickly pear cactus that was overrunning rangeland (**FIGURE 8.10**). Within just a few years, the moth managed to free millions of hectares of rangeland from the cactus.

A widespread modern biocontrol tool has been the use of *Bacillus thuringiensis* (Bt), a naturally occurring soil bacterium that produces a protein that kills many caterpillars and the larvae of some flies and beetles. Farmers have used the natural pesticidal activity of this bacterium to their advantage by spraying spores of this bacterium on their crops. If used correctly, Bt can protect crops from pest-related losses.

Biocontrol agents themselves may become pests

In most cases, biological control involves introducing an animal or microbe into a foreign ecosystem. Such relocation helps ensure that the target pest has not already evolved ways to deal with the biocontrol agent, but it also introduces risks. In some cases, biocontrol can produce unintended consequences if the biocontrol agent becomes invasive and

(a) Before cactus moth introduction

(b) After cactus moth introduction

FIGURE 8.10   In one of the classic cases of biocontrol, larvae of the cactus moth, *Cactoblastis cactorum*, were used to clear non-native prickly pear cactus from millions of hectares of rangeland in Queensland, Australia. These photos from the 1920s show an Australian ranch before **(a)** and after **(b)** introduction of the moth.

begins to affect nontarget organisms. Following the cactus moth's success in Australia, for example, it was introduced in other countries to control prickly pear; however, it is now feared that the moth larvae could decimate native and economically important species of cacti.

Scientists debate the relative benefits and risks of biocontrol measures. If biocontrol works as planned, it can be a permanent solution that requires no further maintenance and is environmentally benign. However, if the agent has nontarget effects, the harm done may become permanent. Removing the agent from the system once it is established is far more difficult than simply stopping a chemical pesticide application. The potential impacts of releasing a biocontrol agent into the natural environment are basically the same as for any alien or non-native species.

Because of concerns about unintended impacts, researchers now study biocontrol proposals carefully before putting them into action, and government regulators must approve these efforts. Canada has been a world leader in this regard. However, there will never be a sure-fire way of knowing in advance whether a given biocontrol program will work as planned.

IPM combines biocontrol and chemical methods

Since chemical and biocontrol approaches have drawbacks, agricultural scientists and farmers developed a more sophisticated strategy, combining the best attributes of each approach. In **integrated pest management (IPM)**, numerous techniques are integrated to achieve long-term suppression of pests, including biocontrol, use of chemicals, close monitoring of populations, habitat alteration, crop rotation, transgenic crops, alternative tillage methods, and mechanical pest removal. IPM is broadly enough defined that it encompasses a wide variety of strategies.

IPM has now become popular in many parts of the world. Indonesia (**FIGURE 8.11**) subsidized pesticide use heavily for years, but its scientists came to understand that pesticides were actually making pest problems worse. They were killing the natural enemies of the brown planthopper, which began to devastate rice fields as its populations exploded. Concluding that pesticide subsidies were costing money, causing pollution, and decreasing yields, the Indonesian government in 1986 banned the importation of 57 pesticides, slashed pesticide subsidies, and encouraged IPM. Within 4 years, pesticide production fell to below half its 1986 level, imports fell to one-third, and subsidies were phased out (saving $179 million annually), but rice yields rose by 13%.

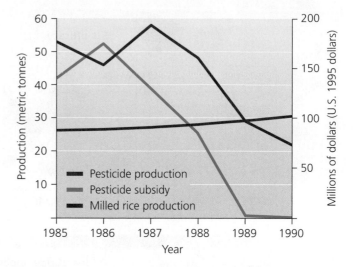

FIGURE 8.11
The Indonesian government threw its weight behind integrated pest management starting in 1986. Within just a few years, pesticide production and pesticide imports were down drastically, pesticide subsidies were phased out, and yields of rice increased slightly.

We depend on insects to pollinate crops

Managing insect pests is such a major issue in agriculture that many people fall into a habit of thinking of all insects as somehow bad or threatening. But in fact, most insects are harmless to agriculture, and some are absolutely essential. The insects that pollinate agricultural crops are one of the most vital, yet least understood and least appreciated, factors in cropland agriculture.

Pollination is the process by which male sex cells of a plant (pollen) fertilize female sex cells of a plant. Without pollination, no plants could reproduce. Many plants achieve pollination by wind distribution. Millions of minuscule pollen grains are blown long distances, and by chance a small number land on the female parts of other plants of their species. The many kinds of plants that sport showy flowers, however, typically are pollinated by animals, such as hummingbirds, bats, and insects (**FIGURE 8.12**). Flowers are, in fact, evolutionary adaptations that function to attract pollinators. The sugary nectar and protein-rich pollen in flowers serve as rewards to lure these sexual intermediaries, and the sweet smells and bright colours of flowers are signals that advertise these rewards.

Although our staple grain crops are derived from grasses and are wind-pollinated, many other crops depend on insects for pollination. This environmental service has economic, not just ecological, value; the estimated value of pollination services rendered by insects in Canada each year is $1.2 billion.[9] A comprehensive survey by tropical bee biologist Dave Roubik documented 800 species of

FIGURE 8.12
Many agricultural crops depend on insects or other animals to pollinate them. Our food supply, therefore, depends partly on conservation of these vital organisms. These apple blossoms are being visited by a European bee. Plants use flowers with colours and sweet smells to advertise nectar and pollen, enticements that attract pollinators.

cultivated plants that rely on bees and other insects for pollination. An estimated 73% of cultivars are pollinated, at least in part, by bees; 19% by flies; 5% by wasps; 5% by beetles; and 4% by moths and butterflies. In addition, bats pollinate 6.5% and birds 4%. According to Seeds of Diversity and Environment Canada,

> *Animals pollinate three-quarters of the world's staple crops, 80% of all flowering plants in temperate climates, and 90% globally. One mouthful in three requires insect pollination. Since 25% of all birds eat seeds or fruit, they are also dependent on pollinators. Quite simply, without pollinators, the entire terrestrial globe would look entirely different and would not be able support the number of people that it currently does.[10]*

Many pollinating insects are at risk from the same pressures that threaten other species, including habitat loss, land degradation, habitat fragmentation, pesticide use, invasive species, and climate change. These are not new phenomena; for example, habitat destruction in the 1930s caused the failure of native leafcutter bee populations in Manitoba; this, in turn, led to the collapse of alfalfa seed production in the Canadian Prairies (see "The Science Behind the Story: The Alfalfa and the Leafcutter"). Increases in the rate and extent of environmental change now put these ecological relationships at even greater risk. The relationship between flowering plants and insect pollinators is so specific (the precise shape of an insect's appendages can determine its suitability for pollinating a particular plant species) that even minor changes can have devastating impacts.

Conservation of pollinators is vital

Preserving the biodiversity of native pollinators is especially important today. The domesticated workhorse of pollination, the European honeybee *(Apis apis)*, is being devastated by parasites and, more recently, by *Colony Collapse Disorder*, the causes of which are poorly understood but may include pathogens, pesticides, environmental stress, or insect-resistant GM crops. North American farmers regularly hire beekeepers to bring colonies of this introduced honeybee to their fields when it is time to pollinate crops (**FIGURE 8.13**). In recent years, parasitic mites have swept through honeybee populations, decimating hives. Moreover, research indicates that honeybees are sometimes less effective pollinators than many native species but often outcompete them, keeping the native species away from the plants.

Farmers and homeowners can help maintain populations of pollinating insects by reducing or eliminating pesticide use. All insect pollinators, including honeybees, are vulnerable to insecticides that are applied to crops, lawns, and gardens. Some insecticides are designed to specifically target certain types of insects, but many are not. Without full and detailed information on the effects of pesticides, farmers and homeowners trying to control the "bad" bugs that threaten the plants they value all too often kill the "good" insects as well.

Homeowners, even in the middle of a city, can encourage populations of pollinating insects by planting gardens of flowering plants and by providing nesting sites for bees. By allowing noncrop flowering plants (such as clover) to grow around the edges of their fields, farmers

FIGURE 8.13
European honeybees are widely used to pollinate crop plants, and beekeepers transport hives of bees to crops when it is time for flowers to be pollinated. However, honeybees have recently suffered devastating epidemics of parasitism, making it increasingly important for us to conserve native species of pollinators.

THE SCIENCE BEHIND THE STORY

The Alfalfa and the Leafcutter

Leafcutter bee pollinating an alfalfa flower.

In the first half of the twentieth century, land clearing for agriculture destroyed many nesting sites of native leafcutter bees in the Canadian Prairies. As a result, Canadian alfalfa seed production decreased dramatically, virtually collapsing by mid-century. Alfalfa is an important forage crop for livestock, and it is used to control moisture and nutrient levels in agricultural fields. Honeybees are ineffective alfalfa pollinators because they can steal nectar without "tripping" the alfalfa flower, a process that uncovers the plant's stigma and is required for the pollination to be successful. With the loss of the most effective native pollinators, by 1950 Canada was importing alfalfa seed to meet 95% of its domestic needs.

In response to this crisis, the European alfalfa leafcutter bee (*Megachile rotundata*) was introduced to Canada in 1961 (see photo). Scientists, beekeepers, and seed growers worked together to develop a management system for the new bees, which eventually resulted in a six-fold increase in alfalfa yields. By the end of the twentieth century, Canada was meeting or exceeding its demand for alfalfa seed, thanks to the alfalfa leafcutter bee. The bees are now being used by blueberry producers in eastern Canada and to pollinate buckwheat and hybrid canola in the Prairies.

The importation of leafcutter bees also led to a new kind of beekeeper who sells bee larvae to other growers for pollination. The leafcutter bee is gentler than the honeybee and typically will sting only if it is squeezed. Leafcutters are solitary (rather than gregarious, like other kinds of bees) and less likely to wander than honeybees. These characteristics make leafcutters easier to manage and handle than other bees. Management of leafcutters, which do not build colonies or store honey, involves building large nesting arrays of layered, grooved materials. These arrays mimic the sites in which the bees would naturally build their individual nests, in cracks and grooves in soft, decaying wood.

By controlling temperature, the emergence of the adult bees can be synchronized with the alfalfa bloom. The bees are kept dormant at 4°C until about three weeks before the expected crop bloom, when the temperature is turned up to 29°C to trigger the development of adult leafcutter bees. This management system has made Canada the leading producer of alfalfa leafcutters, currently producing 4 billion bees for pollination of domestic and international crops each year.

Interestingly (but not surprisingly, given their name) leafcutters can also become a pest species. To line their nests, the bees carefully incise small, round pieces of leaves and carry them back to the nesting site, which can potentially damage the leaf. The damage is usually minor, unless there is an unusually large population of feral (escaped domesticated) or native leafcutter bees in a small area.[11]

can maintain a diverse community of insects—some of which will pollinate their crops.

Genetically Modified Food

The Green Revolution enabled us to feed a greater number and proportion of the world's people, but relentless population growth demands still more. A new set of potential solutions began to arise in the 1980s and 1990s, as advances in genetics enabled scientists to directly alter the genes of organisms, including crop plants and livestock. The genetic modification of organisms that provide us food holds promise for increasing nutrition and the efficiency of agriculture while lessening the impacts of agriculture on the planet's environmental systems.

However, genetic modification of food organisms raises concerns and may pose risks that are not yet thoroughly understood. This has given rise to protest around the globe from consumer advocates, small farmers, opponents of big business, and environmental activists. Because genetic modification of food organisms has generated so much emotion and controversy, it is vital at the outset to clear up the terminology and clarify exactly what is involved in the process.

Genetic modification of organisms depends on recombinant DNA

The genetic modification of crops and livestock is one type of **genetic engineering**, any process whereby scientists directly manipulate an organism's genetic material in the lab by adding, deleting, or changing segments of its DNA. To genetically engineer organisms, scientists extract genes from the DNA of one organism and transfer them into the DNA of another to create a **genetically modified (GM) organism**. The technique uses *recombinant DNA* technology, referring to DNA that has been patched together from the DNA of multiple organisms. In this process, scientists break up DNA from multiple organisms and then splice segments together, trying to place genes that produce certain proteins and code for certain desirable traits (such as rapid growth, disease or pest resistance, or higher nutritional content) into the genetic information, or *genome*, of organisms lacking those traits.

Recombinant DNA technology was developed in the 1970s by scientists studying the bacterium *Escherichia coli*. As shown in **FIGURE 8.14**, scientists first isolate *plasmids*, small, circular DNA molecules, from a bacterial culture. DNA containing a gene of interest is removed from the cells of another organism. Scientists insert the gene of interest into the plasmid to form recombinant

DNA. This recombinant DNA enters new bacteria, which then reproduce, generating many copies of the desired gene. These copies are then introduced into the cells of the organism that is to be genetically modified.

An organism that contains DNA from another species is called a **transgenic** organism, and the genes that have moved between them are called *transgenes*. The creation of transgenic organisms is one type of **biotechnology**, the application of biological science to create products derived from organisms.

Recombinant DNA and other types of biotechnology have helped us develop medicines; clean up pollution; understand the causes of cancer and other diseases; dissolve blood clots after heart attacks; and make better beer and cheese. **FIGURE 8.15** details several notable developments in GM foods. These examples and the stories behind them illustrate both the promises and the pitfalls of food biotechnology.

Genetic engineering is like, and unlike, traditional breeding

The genetic alteration of plants and animals by humans is nothing new; we have been influencing the genetic makeup of our livestock and crop plants for thousands of years. Our ancestors altered the gene pools of domesticated plants and animals through selective breeding by preferentially mating individuals with favoured traits, so that offspring would inherit those traits. Early farmers selected plants and animals that grew faster, were more resistant to disease and drought, and produced large amounts of fruit, grain, or meat.

FIGURE 8.14

To create recombinant DNA, a gene of interest is excised from the DNA of an organism and inserted into a stretch of bacterial DNA called a plasmid. The plasmid is then introduced into cells of the organism to be modified. If all goes as planned, the new gene will be expressed in the GM organism as a desirable trait, such as rapid growth or high nutritional content in a food crop.

weighing the issues

GM FOODS AND YOU

Have you ever eaten a food product that contains genetically modified organisms? If you live in North America, the answer is almost certainly "yes." As many as 70% of the food products on shelves in North American grocery stores contain at least some GM ingredients. Check your kitchen for any foods that contain products or ingredients made from corn, soy, or canola. The probability that some of those ingredients came from genetically modified plants is very high. The European Union requires labelling of foods that contain GM ingredients. Do you want your food to be labelled? Would you choose foods based on whether they are organic or genetically modified?

Several Notable Examples of Genetically Modified Food Technology

Food	Development	Food	Development
Bt crops	By equipping plants with the ability to produce their own pesticides, scientists hoped to reduce crop losses from insects. Scientists working with *Bacillus thuringiensis* (Bt) pinpointed the genes responsible for producing that bacterium's toxic effects on insects and inserted the genes into the DNA of crops. The USDA and EPA approved Bt versions of 18 crops for field testing, from apples to broccoli to cranberries. Corn and cotton are the most widely planted Bt crops today. Proponents say Bt crops reduce the need for chemical pesticides. Critics worry that they induce insects to evolve resistance to the toxins, cause allergic reactions in people, and harm nontarget species.	Roundup Ready crops	The Monsanto Company's widely used herbicide, Roundup, kills weeds, but it kills crops, too. So Monsanto engineered soybeans, corn, cotton, and canola to withstand the effects of its herbicide. With these "Roundup Ready crops," farmers can spray Roundup without killing their crops. Of course, this also creates an incentive for farmers to use Roundup rather than a competing brand. Unfortunately, Roundup's active ingredient, glyphosate, is a leading cause of illness for California farm workers, and weeds are starting to evolve resistance to glyphosate.
Golden rice	Millions of people in the developing world get too little vitamin A in their diets, causing diarrhea, blindness, immune suppression, and even death. The problem is worst with children in east Asia, where the staple grain, white rice, contains no vitamin A. Researchers took genes from plants that produce vitamin A and spliced the genes into rice DNA to create more-nutritious "golden rice" (the vitamin precursor gives it a golden colour). Critics charged that biotech companies over-hyped their product.	Sunflowers and superweeds	Research on Bt sunflowers suggests that transgenes might spread to other plants and turn them into vigorous weeds that compete with the crop. This is most likely to happen with crops like squash, canola, and sunflowers that can breed with their wild relatives. Researchers bred wild sunflowers with Bt sunflowers and found that hybrids with the Bt gene produced more seeds and suffered less herbivory than hybrids without it. They concluded that if Bt sunflowers were planted commercially, the Bt gene might spread and turn wild sunflowers into superweeds.
Ice-minus strawberries	Researchers removed a gene that facilitated the formation of ice crystals from the DNA of a bacterium, *Pseudomonas syringae*. The modified, frost-resistant bacteria could then serve as a kind of antifreeze when sprayed on the surface of crops such as strawberries, protecting them from frost damage. However, news coverage of scientists spraying plants while wearing face masks and protective clothing caused public alarm.	StarLink corn	StarLink corn, a variety of Bt corn, had been approved and used in the United States for animal feed but not for human consumption. In 2000, StarLink corn DNA was discovered in taco shells and other corn products. These products were recalled amid fears of allergic reactions. No such health effects were confirmed, but the corn's manufacturer chose to withdraw the product from the market.

FIGURE 8.15   As genetically modified foods were developed, a number of products ran into public opposition or trouble in the marketplace. A selection of such cases serves to illustrate some of the issues that proponents and opponents of genetically modified foods have been debating.

Proponents of GM crops often stress this continuity with our past and say there is little reason to expect that today's GM food will be any less safe than traditionally bred food. However, as biotech's critics are quick to point out, the techniques used to create GM organisms differ from traditional selective breeding in several important ways.

For one, selective breeding generally mixes genes of individuals of the same species, whereas with recombinant DNA technology, scientists mix genes of different species, as different as spiders and goats. For another, selective breeding deals with whole organisms living in the field, whereas genetic engineering involves lab experiments dealing with genetic material apart from the organism. And whereas traditional breeding selects from among combinations of genes that come together on their own, genetic engineering creates novel combinations directly. Thus, traditional breeding changes organisms through the process of selection, whereas genetic engineering is more akin to the process of mutation.

Biotechnology is transforming the products around us

In just three decades, GM foods have gone from science fiction to big business. As recombinant DNA technology was first developed in the 1970s, scientists debated among themselves whether the new methods were safe. They collectively regulated and monitored their own research until most scientists were satisfied that reassembling genes in bacteria did not create dangerous superbacteria. Once the scientific community declared itself confident that the technique was safe in the 1980s, industry leaped at the chance to develop hundreds of applications, from improved medicines to designer plants and animals.

Most GM crops today are engineered to resist herbicides, so that farmers can apply herbicides to kill weeds without having to worry about killing their crops. Other crops are engineered to resist insect attacks. Some are modified for both types of resistance. Crop resistance to herbicides and pests enables large-scale commercial farmers to grow crops more efficiently and economically. As a result, sales of GM seeds to farmers have risen quickly.

Today three-fourths of the world's soybean plants are transgenic, as is one of every four corn plants, one of every five canola plants, and half of all cotton plants. Globally in 2009, 14 million farmers grew GM crops on 134 million ha of farmland—nearly 9% of all cropland in the world. Of the 29 nations growing GM crops in 2009, 6 (Canada, USA, Argentina, Brazil, China, and India), 4 crops (soybean, cotton, maize, and canola), and 2 controlled traits (herbicide tolerance and insect resistance) account for about 99% of the area devoted to the production of transgenic crops worldwide (**FIGURE 8.16**). Because these nations are major food exporters, much of the produce on the world market is now transgenic, and the market value of GM crops in 2009 was $10.5 billion.

What are the impacts of GM crops?

As GM crops were adopted, as research proceeded, and as biotech business expanded, many citizens, scientists, and policy makers became concerned. Some feared the new foods might be dangerous for people to eat—what if there were unexpected health consequences, such as unanticipated allergic reactions to transgenes in GM foods? Others were concerned that transgenes might escape, pollute ecosystems, and damage nontarget organisms. Still others worried that pests would evolve resistance to the supercrops and become "superpests" or that transgenes would be transferred from crops to other plants

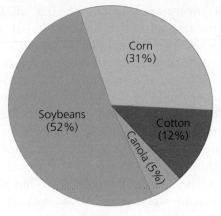

(a) GM crops by type

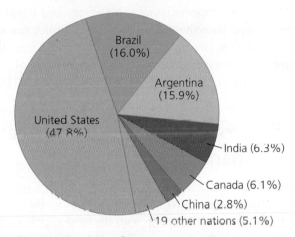

(b) GM crops by nation

FIGURE 8.16
Of the world's genetically modified crops **(a)**, soybeans now constitute the majority. Of the world's agricultural nations **(b)**, the United States devotes the most land area to GM crops.
Source: Data are for 2009, from the International Service for the Acquisition of Agri-Biotech Applications.

and turn them into "superweeds." Some worried that transgenes might ruin the integrity of native ancestral races of crops.

Because the technology is new and its large-scale introduction into the environment is newer still, there remains a lot scientists don't know about how transgenic crops behave in the field. Millions of North Americans eat GM foods every day without any obvious signs of harm, and evidence for negative ecological effects is limited so far. However, it is still too early to dismiss all concerns without further scientific research. There are numerous mechanisms whereby transgenes can "escape" from the confines of the organism into which they have been implanted and move out into native populations, as well as locations where it is has happened. Therefore, critics argue that we should adopt the **precautionary principle**, the idea that one should not proceed until the ramifications of an action are well understood.

The British government, in considering whether to allow the planting of GM crops, commissioned three large-scale studies between 2003 and 2005. The first study, on economics, found that GM crops could produce long-term financial benefits for Britain, although short-term benefits would be minor. The second study addressed health risks and found little to no evidence of harm to human health, but it noted that effects on wildlife and ecosystems should be tested before crops are approved. The third study looked at effects on bird and invertebrate populations from four GM crops modified for herbicide resistance. Results showed that fields of GM beets and GM spring oilseed rape supported less biodiversity than fields of their non-GM counterparts. Fields of GM maize supported more, however, and fields of winter oilseed rape showed mixed results. Policy makers had hoped that the biodiversity study would end the debate, but the science showed that the impacts of GM crops are complex.

Debate over GM foods involves more than science

Far more than science is involved in the debate over GM foods. Ethical issues have played a large role. For many people, the idea of "tinkering" with the food supply seems dangerous or morally wrong. Even though our agricultural produce is the highly artificial product of thousands of years of selective breeding, people tend to think of food as natural. Furthermore, because every person relies on food for survival and cannot choose *not* to eat, the genetic modification of dietary staples such as corn, wheat, and rice essentially forces people to consume GM products or to go to special effort to avoid them.

The perceived lack of control over one's own food has driven widespread concern about domination of the global food supply by a few large businesses. Gigantic agrobiotech companies, among them Monsanto, Syngenta, Bayer CropScience, Dow, DuPont, and BASF, develop GM technologies. Many activists say these multinational corporations threaten the independence and well-being of the small farmer and raise concerns about the global food supply being dominated by a few large corporations. This perceived loss of democratic control is a driving force in the opposition to GM foods, especially in Europe and the developing world. Critics of biotechnology also voice concern that much of the research into the safety of GM organisms is funded, overseen, or conducted by the corporations that stand to profit if their transgenic crops are approved for human consumption, animal feed, or ingredients in other products.

So far, GM crops have not lived up to their promise of feeding the world's hungry—perhaps because they haven't been allowed to. Nearly all commercially available GM crops have been engineered to express either pesticidal properties (e.g., Bt crops) or herbicide tolerance. Often, these GM crops are tolerant to herbicides that the same company manufactures and profits from (e.g., Monsanto's Roundup Ready crops). Crops with traits that might benefit poor small-scale farmers of developing countries (such as increased nutrition, drought tolerance, and salinity tolerance) have not been widely commercialized, perhaps because corporations have less economic incentive to do so. Similarly, crops such as the infamous "golden rice"—engineered with a higher than usual content of vitamin A and proposed as the solution to vitamin A deficiencies throughout the developing world—have met with limited success.

The development of GM crops has been largely driven by market considerations of companies selling proprietary products. When the U.S.-based Monsanto Company began developing GM products in the mid-1980s, it foresaw public anxiety and worked hard to inform, reassure, and work with environmental and consumer advocates, whom the company feared would otherwise oppose the technology. Monsanto even lobbied the U.S. government to regulate the industry so the public would feel safer about it. These efforts were undermined, however, when the company's first GM product, a growth hormone to spur milk production in cows, alarmed consumers concerned about children's health. Then, when the company went through a leadership change, its new head changed tactics and pushed new products aggressively without first reaching out to opponents. Opposition built, and the company lost the public's trust, especially in Europe and in the developing world.

David-and-Goliath battles that pitted giant Monsanto against lone farmers such as Canadian Percy Schmeiser have not helped to repair the company's public image. As of late 2007, Monsanto had launched 112 such lawsuits against 372 farmers and 49 farm companies in 27 U.S. states, winning judgements averaging $385 000, according to the Center for Food Safety (CFS), a watchdog organization. In addition, Monsanto has forced thousands of other farmers into out-of-court settlements. Monsanto says it is merely demanding that farmers heed the patent laws. North Dakota farmer Tom Wiley, who spoke on behalf of farmers at the World Trade Organization meeting in 2005, sees it differently. Wiley has said, "Farmers are being sued for having GMOs on their property that they did not buy, do not want, will not use, and cannot sell."[12]

Given such developments, the future of GM foods seems likely to hinge on social, economic, legal, and political factors as well as scientific ones. European consumers have been particularly vocal in expressing their unease about the possible risks of GM technologies. Opposition in nations of the European Union resulted in a *de facto* moratorium on GM foods from 1998 to 2003, blocking the importation of hundreds of millions of dollars in agricultural products. This prompted the United States to bring a case before the World Trade Organization in 2003, complaining that Europe's resistance was hindering free trade.

Europeans now widely demand that GM foods be labelled as such and criticize the United States for not joining 100 other nations in signing the Cartagena Protocol on Biosafety (part of the United Nations Convention on Biodiversity), a treaty that lays out guidelines for open information about exported crops. Canada has been a party to the Convention on Biodiversity since 1992 but has never ratified the Cartagena Protocol.[13]

Transnational spats will surely affect the future direction of agriculture, but consumers and the governments of the world's developing nations could exert the most influence in the end. Decisions by the governments of India and Brazil to approve GM crops (following long and divisive debates) are already adding greatly to the world's transgenic agriculture, and China is aggressively expanding its use of transgenic crops.

A counterexample is Zambia, one of several African nations that refused U.S. food aid meant to relieve starvation during a drought in late 2002. The governments of these nations worried that their farmers would plant some of the GM corn seed that was meant to be eaten and that GM corn would thereby establish itself in their countries. They viewed this as undesirable because African economies depend on exporting food to Europe, which has put severe restrictions on GM food. In the end, Zambia's neighbours accepted the grain after it had been milled (so none could be planted), but Zambia held out. Citing health and environmental risks, uncertain science, and the precautionary principle, the Zambian government declined the aid, despite the fact that 2 to 3 million of its people were at risk of starvation (**FIGURE 8.17**). Intense debate followed within the country and around the world. Eventually the United Nations delivered non-GM grain, and in April 2003 the Zambian government announced a plan to coordinate a comprehensive long-term policy on GM foods.

The Zambian experience demonstrates some of the ethical, economic, and political dilemmas modern nations face. The corporate manufacturers of GM crops naturally aim to maximize their profits, but they also aim to develop products that can boost yields, increase food security, and reduce hunger. Although industry, activists,

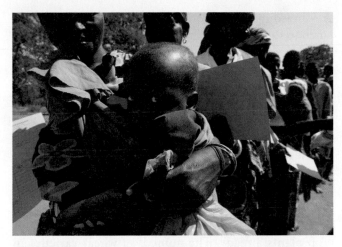

FIGURE 8.17
Debate over GM foods reached a dramatic climax in Zambia in 2002, when the government refused U.S. shipments of GM corn that were intended to relieve starvation due to drought. Here a Zambian mother and child wait in a line for food assistance.

policy makers, and scientists all agree that hunger and malnutrition are problems and that agriculture should be made environmentally safer, they often disagree about the solutions to these dilemmas and the risks that each proposed solution presents.

Preserving Crop Diversity

One concern many people harbour about GM crops is that transgenes might move, by pollination, into local native races of crop plants. There is certainly now abundant evidence that this has already happened in some localities. The monocultures of modern industrial agriculture essentially place all our eggs in one basket, such that any single catastrophic cause could potentially wipe out entire crops. Preserving crop diversity—domesticated varieties and the wild relatives of crop plants—gives us the genetic diversity that may include ready-made solutions to unforeseen problems.

Crop diversity provides insurance against failure

Preserving the integrity of native variants provides insurance against widespread commercial crop failure. The regions where crops first were domesticated generally remain important repositories of crop biodiversity. Although modern industrial agriculture relies on a small number of plant types, its foundation lies in the diverse varieties that still exist in places like Oaxaca. These varieties contain genes that, through conventional crossbreeding or genetic engineering, might confer resistance to disease, pests, inbreeding, and other pressures that challenge modern agriculture.

Because accidental interbreeding can decrease the diversity of local variants, many scientists argue that we need to protect areas like Oaxaca. For this reason, the Mexican government helped create the Sierra de Manantlán Biosphere Reserve around an area harbouring the localized plant thought to be the direct ancestor of maize. For this reason, too, it imposed a national moratorium in 1998 on the planting of transgenic corn (although that ban was lifted in 2005).

We have lost a great deal of genetic diversity in our crop plants already. The number of wheat varieties in China is estimated to have dropped from 10 000 in 1949 to 1000 by the 1970s, and Mexico's famed maize varieties now number only 30% of what was grown in the 1930s. In the United States, many fruits and vegetables have decreased in diversity by 90% in less than a century. Note, however, that the number of varieties that exist is not, on its own, indicative of the robustness of biodiversity. For example, in recent years the number of wheat varieties in China has actually increased, but the genetic diversity among those varieties has narrowed.[14]

A primary cause of the loss of crop diversity is that market forces discourage diversity in the appearance of fruits and vegetables. Commercial food transporters and processors prefer items to be similar in size and shape, for convenience. Consumers, for their part, have shown preferences for uniform, standardized food products over the years. Now that local organic agriculture is growing in affluent societies, however, consumer preferences for diversity are increasing.

Seed banks are living museums for seeds

Protecting areas with high crop diversity is one way to preserve genetic assets for our agricultural systems. Another is to collect and store seeds from crop varieties and periodically plant and harvest them to maintain a diversity of cultivars. This is the work of **seed banks** and **gene banks**, institutions that preserve seed types as a kind of living museum of genetic diversity (**FIGURE 8.18**). In total, these facilities hold roughly 6 million seed samples, keeping them in cold, dry conditions to encourage long-term viability. The $300 million in global funding for these facilities is not adequate for proper storage and for the labour of growing out the seed periodically to renew the stocks. Therefore, it is questionable how many of these 6 million seeds are actually preserved.

(a) Traditional food plants of the Desert Southwest

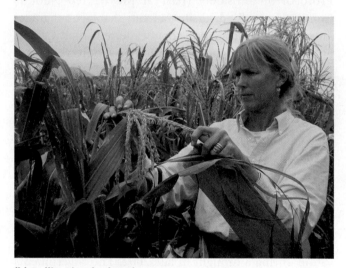

(b) Pollination by hand

FIGURE 8.18
Seed banks preserve genetic diversity of traditional crop plants. Native Seeds/SEARCH of Arizona preserves seeds of food plants important to traditional diets of Native Americans of Arizona, New Mexico, and northwestern Mexico. Beans, chiles, squashes, gourds, maize, cotton, and lentils are all in its collections, as well as less-known plants such as amaranth, lemon basil, and devil's claw **(a)**. Traditional foods such as mesquite flour, prickly pear pads, chia seeds, tepary beans, and cholla cactus buds help fight diabetes, which has become more common in Native Americans since they adopted a Western diet. At the farm where seeds are grown, care is taken to pollinate varieties by hand **(b)** to protect their genetic distinctiveness.

The Royal Botanic Garden's Millennium Seed Bank in Britain holds over 1 billion seeds and aims to bank seed from 20% of the world's plants by 2020. In Arctic Norway, construction has begun on a "doomsday vault" seed bank, intended to hold seeds from around the world as a safeguard against global agricultural calamity. Other major efforts include large seed banks such as the U.S. National Seed Storage Laboratory at Colorado State University, Seed Savers Exchange in Iowa, Plant

Gene Resources of Canada, and the Wheat and Maize Improvement Centre (CIMMYT) in Mexico.

Raising Animals for Food

Food from cropland agriculture makes up a large portion of the human diet, but most people also eat animal products. People don't *need* to eat meat or other animal products to live full, active, healthy lives, but for most people it is difficult to obtain a balanced diet without incorporating animal products. Many of us do eat animal products, and this choice has environmental, social, agricultural, and economic impacts.

Consumption of animal products is growing

As wealth and global commerce have increased, so has our consumption of meat, milk, eggs, fish, and other animal products (**FIGURE 8.19**). The world population of domesticated animals and animals raised in captivity for food rose from 7.2 billion animals to 24.9 billion animals between 1961 and 2008. Most of these animals are chickens, although the most-eaten meat per unit of weight is pork. Global meat production has increased fivefold since 1950, to approximately 282 000 tonnes as of 2009,[15] and per capita meat consumption has more than doubled over the same period.

Like other domesticated species, livestock and other farm animals can be at risk of biodiversity loss and even extinction. The FAO's Global Databank for Animal Genetic Resources for Food and Agriculture contains information on almost 8000 livestock breeds, of which about 20% are classified as "at risk." During the first six years of the twenty-first century, for example, 62 livestock breeds became extinct, which amounts to a loss of almost one breed per month.[16]

High consumption has led to feedlot agriculture

In traditional agriculture, livestock were kept by farming families near their homes or were grazed on open grasslands by nomadic herders or sedentary ranchers. These traditions have survived, but the advent of industrial agriculture, responding to the pressure of global population growth, has added a new method. **Feedlots**, also known as "factory farms" or *concentrated animal feeding operations (CAFOs)*, are essentially huge warehouses or pens designed to deliver energy-rich food to animals living at extremely high densities (**FIGURE 8.20**). Today over half of the world's pork and most of the poultry come from feedlots.

Feedlot operations allow for greater production of food and are probably necessary to keep up with levels of meat consumption in Canada and the United States. Feedlots have one overarching benefit for environmental quality: Taking cattle, sheep, goats, and other livestock

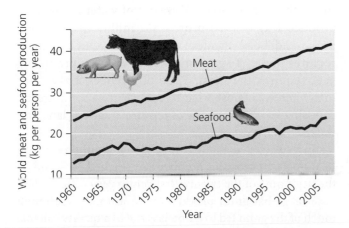

FIGURE 8.19

Per capita consumption of meat from farm animals has increased steadily worldwide over the past few decades, as has per capita consumption of seafood (marine and freshwater, harvested and farmed).

Source: Data from Food and Agriculture Organization of the United Nations (FAO).

FIGURE 8.20

These chickens at a factory farm are housed in crowded conditions and have been "debeaked," the tips of their beaks cut off, to prevent them from pecking one another. The hens cannot leave the cages and spend their lives eating, defecating, and laying eggs, which roll down slanted floors to collection trays. The largest chicken farms house hundreds of thousands of individuals.

off the land and concentrating them in feedlots reduces the impact they would otherwise exert on large portions of the landscape; as you have learned, overgrazing can degrade soils and vegetation, and hundreds of millions of hectares of land are considered overgrazed. Animals that are densely concentrated in feedlots will not contribute to overgrazing and soil degradation.

However, feedlots can have significant environmental impacts. Waste from feedlots emit strong odours and can pollute surface water and groundwater. Livestock produce prodigious amounts of feces and urine; one dairy cow can produce about 20 400 kg of waste in a single year. Greeley, Colorado, is home to North America's largest meatpacking plant and two adjacent feedlots, owned by the agribusiness firm ConAgra. Each feedlot can house 100 000 cattle that are fed surplus grain and injected with anabolic steroids to stimulate growth. During its stay at the feedlot, a typical steer will eat 1360 kg of grain, gain 180 kg in body weight, and generate 23 kg of manure each day.

Poor waste containment practices at some feedlots have been linked to outbreaks of disease, including virulent strains of *Pfiesteria*, a microbe that poisons fish. In 2000 in Walkerton, Ontario, a deadly strain of *E. coli* bacteria, thought to have originated from the contamination of municipal water wells by runoff from factory farms, caused the deaths of seven people and serious illness in hundreds of others.

The crowded and dirty conditions under which animals are often kept at factory farms necessitate the use of antibiotics to control disease. These chemicals can be transferred up the food chain, and their overuse can cause microbes to evolve resistance to them. Crowded conditions also can exacerbate outbreaks of diseases such as *avian influenza* ("bird flu") and *bovine spongiform encephalitis* (*BSE*, or "mad cow" disease), which are now known to be transferable to humans in serious and even deadly forms.

weighing the issues

FEEDLOTS AND ANIMAL RIGHTS

Animal rights activists decry factory farming because they say it mistreats animals. Chickens, pigs, and cattle are kept in crowded pens, fattened up, and slaughtered. Do you think animal rights concerns should be given weight as we determine how best to raise our food? Should we concern ourselves with the quality of life—and death—of the animals that constitute part of our diet?

Feedlot impacts can be minimized when properly managed, and both the federal and provincial governments regulate feedlots in Canada. Feedlot manure can be applied to farm fields, reducing the need for chemical fertilizers. Manure in liquid form can be injected into the ground where plants need it, and farmers can conduct tests to determine amounts that are appropriate to apply.

Our food choices are also energy choices

What we choose to eat has significant ramifications for how we use energy, water, and the land that supports agriculture. Whenever energy moves from one level to the next in a trophic pyramid, as much as 90% of the energy is lost. For example, if we feed grain to a cow and then eat beef from the cow, we lose a great deal of the grain's energy to the cow's digestion and metabolism. Energy is used up when the cow converts the grain to tissue as it grows and as the cow uses its muscle mass on a daily basis to maintain itself. For this reason, eating meat is far less energy-efficient than relying on a vegetarian diet. The lower in the food chain we take our food sources, the greater the proportion of the Sun's energy we put to use as food.

Some animals convert grain feed into milk, eggs, or meat more efficiently than others (**FIGURE 8.21**). Scientists have calculated relative energy conversion efficiencies for different types of animals. Such energy efficiencies have ramifications for land use—land and water are required to raise food for the animals, and some animals require more than others. **FIGURE 8.22** shows the area of land and weight of water required to produce 1 kg of food protein for milk, eggs, chicken, pork, and beef. Producing eggs and chicken meat requires the least space and water, whereas producing beef requires the most. Such differences make clear that when we choose what to eat, we are also indirectly choosing how to make use of resources such as land and water.

In 1900 we fed about 10% of global grain production to animals. In 1950 this number had reached 20%, and by the beginning of the twenty-first century we were feeding 45% of global grain production to animals. Although much of the grain fed to animals is not of a quality suitable for human consumption, the resources required to grow it could have instead been applied toward growing food for people. One partial solution is to feed livestock crop residues, plant matter such as stems and stalks that we would not consume anyway, and this is increasingly being done.

Feed input

Produce output (edible weight)

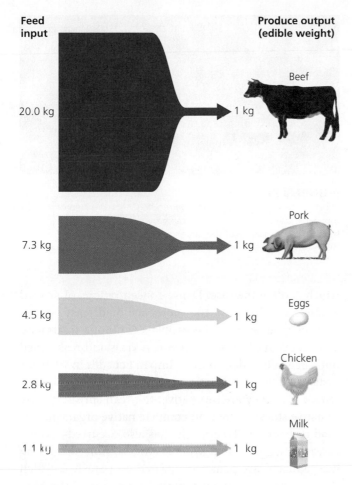

Beef
20.0 kg — 1 kg

Pork
7.3 kg — 1 kg

Eggs
4.5 kg — 1 kg

Chicken
2.8 kg — 1 kg

Milk
1.1 kg — 1 kg

FIGURE 8.21
Different animal food products require different amounts of input of animal feed. Chickens must be fed 2.8 kg of feed for each 1 kg of resulting chicken meat, for instance, whereas 20 kg of feed must be provided to cattle to produce 1 kg of beef.
Source: Data from Smil, V. 2001. Feeding the World: A Challenge for the Twenty-First Century. *Cambridge, MA: MIT Press.*

Beef (245.0 m^2)

Pork (90.0 m^2) Eggs (22.0 m^2) Chicken (14.0 m^2) Milk (23.5 m^2)

(a) Land required to produce 1 kg of protein

Beef (750 kg)

Pork (175 kg) Eggs (15 kg) Chicken (50 kg) Milk (250 kg)

(b) Water required to produce 1 kg of protein

FIGURE 8.22
Producing different types of animal products requires different amounts of land and water. Raising cattle for beef requires by far the most land and water of all animal products.
Source: Feeding the World: A Challenge for the Twenty-First Century. *Cambridge, MA: MIT Press.*

An additional environmental problem associated with meat production is that the plants required to feed the livestock must be grown on large ranches, which are basically domesticated grasslands. The growth in meat consumption thus requires that forested land worldwide be converted to rangelands in support of livestock production. In the 1970s, this was first dubbed "the hamburger connection"—by purchasing a hamburger made from South American beef, one was unwittingly contributing to the deforestation of tropical rainforests and their conversion into rangelands.

We also raise fish on "farms"

In addition to plants grown on croplands and animals raised on rangelands and in feedlots, we rely on aquatic organisms for food. Wild fish populations are plummeting throughout the world's oceans as increased demand and new technologies have led us to overharvest most marine fisheries. This means that raising fish and shellfish on "fish farms" may be the only way to meet the growing demand for these foods.

Raising aquatic organisms in controlled environments is called **aquaculture**. Many aquatic species are grown in open water in large, floating net-pens. Others are raised in land-based ponds or holding tanks. People pursue both freshwater and marine aquaculture, and both plants and animals are grown. Aquaculture is the fastest-growing type of food production; in the past 20 years, global output has increased sevenfold. Aquaculture today provides a third of the world's fish for human consumption, is most common in Asia, and involves over 220 species (**FIGURE 8.23**). Some, such as carp, are grown for local consumption, whereas others, such as salmon and shrimp, are exported to affluent countries.

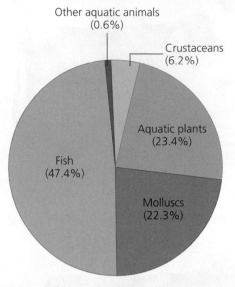

FIGURE 8.23
Aquaculture involves a wide diversity of marine and freshwater organisms, and global production has risen steeply in the past two decades.
Source: Data from FAO 2004. The State of World Fisheries and Aquaculture, 2004.

FIGURE 8.24
Efforts to genetically modify fish have resulted in the creation of transgenic salmon (behind), which can grow considerably faster and larger than wild salmon of the same age and species (front).

Aquaculture has benefits and drawbacks

When conducted on a small scale by families or villages, aquaculture helps ensure people a reliable protein source. Small-scale aquaculture can be sustainable, and it is compatible with other activities. For instance, uneaten fish scraps make excellent fertilizers for crops. Aquaculture on larger scales can help improve a region's or nation's food security by increasing overall amounts of fish available.

Aquaculture on any scale has the benefit of reducing fishing pressure on overharvested and declining wild stocks, as well as providing employment for fishers who can no longer fish from depleted natural stocks. Reducing fishing pressure also reduces *bycatch*, the unintended catch of nontarget organisms that results from commercial fishing. Furthermore, aquaculture relies far less on fossil fuels than do fishing vessels and provides a safer work environment. Fish farming can also be remarkably energy-efficient, producing as much as 10 times more fish per unit area than is harvested from oceanic waters on the continental shelf and up to 1000 times as much as is harvested from the open ocean.

Along with its benefits, however, aquaculture has some serious disadvantages. Counterintuitively, aquaculture can increase the pressure on wild stocks if the feed for the cultured fish is meal made from fish caught in the wild,

which is often the case. Dense concentrations of farmed animals can increase the incidence of disease, which reduces food security, necessitates antibiotic treatment, and results in additional expense. A virus outbreak wiped out half a billion dollars in shrimp in Ecuador in 1999, for instance. If farmed aquatic organisms escape into ecosystems where they are not native, they can spread disease to native stocks or may outcompete native organisms for food or habitat. The opposite has also occurred—recent research suggests that wild Pacific salmon swimming near aquaculture pens have passed on parasites, which then are able to spread rapidly as a result of the high densities of organisms in the pens.

The possibility of competition also arises when farmed animals have been genetically modified. For example, genetic engineering of Pacific salmon has produced transgenic fish that weigh up to 11 times more than nontransgenic ones. Transgenic Atlantic salmon raised in Scotland have been engineered to grow to 5 to 50 times the normal size for their species (**FIGURE 8.24**). GM fish such as these could outcompete their non-GM wild cousins. They may also interbreed with native and hatchery-raised fish and weaken already troubled stocks. Researchers have concluded that under certain circumstances, escaped transgenic salmon may increase the extinction risk that native populations of their species face, in part because the larger male fish have better odds of mating successfully.

Sustainable Agriculture

Post–Green Revolution industrialized agriculture has allowed food production to keep pace with the growing population, but it also has caused negative environmental impacts. These range from the degradation of soils to reliance on fossil fuels to problems arising from pesticide use, genetic modification, and intensive feedlot and aquaculture operations. Although developments in intensive commercial agriculture have alleviated some environmental pressures, they have exacerbated others. Industrial agriculture in some form seems necessary to feed our planet's 7 billion people, but many feel we might be better off in the long run by practicing less-intensive methods of raising animals and crops.

Farmers and researchers have made great advances toward sustainable agriculture in recent years. **Sustainable agriculture** is agriculture that does not deplete soils faster than they form. It is farming and ranching that does not reduce the amount of healthy soil, clean water, and genetic diversity essential to long-term crop and livestock production. It is, simply, agriculture that can be practiced in the same way far into the future. For example, *no-till agriculture*, in which the depth and frequency of ploughing and tilling are kept to a minimum to protect soil moisture and prevent compaction, appears to fit the notion of sustainable agriculture and it can be implemented on the scale of modern agriculture (**TABLE 8.2**).

Table 8.2   No-Till Farming

Direct benefits of no-till farming

- Conserves biodiversity in soil and in terrestrial and aquatic ecosystems
- Produces sustainable, high crop yields
- Heightens environmental awareness among farmers
- Provides shelter and winter food for animals
- Reduces irrigation demands by 10–20%
- Crop residues act as a sink for carbon (1 metric tonne/ha)
- Reduces fossil fuel use by 40–70%
- Enhances food security by increasing drought resistance
- Reduces erosion by 90%

Indirect benefits arising from the reduction in erosion

- Reduces silt deposition in reservoirs
- Reduces water pollution from chemicals
- Increases groundwater recharge and lessens flooding
- Increases sustained crop yields and lowers food prices
- Lowers costs of treating drinking water
- Reduces costs of maintaining dirt roads
- Eliminates dust storms in towns and cities
- Increases efficiency in use of fertilizer and machinery

Source: Modified from Shaxson, T. F. (1999) The roots of sustainability: Concepts and practice: Zero tillage in Brazil, ABLH Newsletter ENABLE; World Association for Soil and Water Conservation (WASWC) Newsletter.

Sustainable agriculture is closely related to *low-input agriculture*, agriculture that uses smaller amounts of pesticides, fertilizers, growth hormones, water, and fossil fuel energy than are currently used in industrial agriculture. Food-growing practices that use no synthetic fertilizers, insecticides, fungicides, or herbicides—but instead rely on biological approaches such as composting and biocontrol—are termed **organic agriculture**.

As population and consumption increase, soils are being degraded

If we are to feed the world's rising human population, we will need to change our diet patterns or increase agricultural production—and do so sustainably, without degrading the environment and reducing its ability to support agriculture. We cannot simply keep expanding agriculture into new areas because land suitable and available for farming is running out. Instead, we must find ways to improve the efficiency of food production in areas that are already in agricultural use.

Today many lands unsuitable for farming are being farmed, causing considerable environmental damage. Mismanaged agriculture has turned grasslands into deserts and has removed ecologically precious forests. It has extracted nutrients from soils and added them to water bodies, harming both systems. It has diminished biodiversity; encouraged invasive species; and polluted soil, air, and water with toxic chemicals. Poor agricultural practices have allowed countless tonnes of fertile soil to be blown and washed away.

As our planet gains over 80 million people each year, we lose 5 to 7 million ha of productive cropland annually. Throughout the world, especially in drier regions, it has gotten more difficult to raise crops and graze livestock as soils have become eroded and degraded. **Soil degradation**, damage to or loss of soil, around the globe has resulted from roughly equal parts forest removal, cropland agriculture, and overgrazing of livestock, with a much smaller (though still significant) contribution from industrial contamination.

Soil degradation has direct impacts on agricultural production. Scientists estimate that over the past 50 years soil degradation has reduced potential rates of global grain production by 13% on cropland and 4% on rangeland. By the middle of the twenty-first century, there will likely be 3 billion more mouths to feed. For these reasons, it is imperative that we learn to farm in sustainable ways that are gentler on the land and that maintain the integrity of soil.

Organic agriculture is on the increase

Citizens, government officials, farmers, and agricultural industry representatives have debated the meaning of the word *organic* for many years. Experimental organic gardens began to appear in North America in the 1940s, but in Canada the federal Organic Products Regulations only came into effect in December 2006, as a new part of the Canadian Agricultural Products Act. This law establishes national standards for organic products and facilitates the labelling, quality, and sale of organic food. The organic certification logo (**FIGURE 8.25**) is permitted only on food products that meet specific Canadian standards for organic production, such as using natural fertilizers and raising animals in conditions that mimic nature as much as possible. Multi-ingredient products must also contain at least 95% organic ingredients.

Long viewed as a small niche market, the market for organic foods is on the increase. Although it still accounts for only a small percentage of food expenditures in Canada, sales of organic products are increasing by about 20% annually. Worldwide, sales of organic food tripled between 2001 and 2008, when sales surpassed $50 billion.

Production is increasing along with demand. Although organic agriculture takes up less than 1% of cultivated land worldwide (35 million ha in 2008), this area is rapidly expanding. In North America, the amount of land used in organic agriculture has recently increased 15–20% each year. Today more than 500 000 ha are used to grow organic products in Canada, by almost 4000 producers,[17] and farmers in more than 130 nations practice organic farming commercially to some extent. In addition, 430 000 ha of aquaculture worldwide are now certified as organic.

Several motivating forces have fuelled these trends. Many consumers favour organic products because of better taste, the desire to buy locally, and concern that consuming produce grown with pesticides may pose risks to their health. Consumers also buy organic produce out of a desire to improve environmental quality by reducing chemical pollution and soil degradation (see "The Science Behind the Story: Organic Farming Put to the Test"). Other consumers do not buy organic produce because it usually is more expensive and often looks less uniform and esthetically appealing in the supermarket aisle compared to the standard produce of high-input agriculture.

Overall, though, enough consumers are willing to pay more for organic meat, fruit, and vegetables that businesses are making such foods more widely available. In early 2000, one of Britain's largest supermarket brands announced that it would sell only organic food—and that the new organic products would cost their customers no more than had nonorganic products. In addition to food products, many textile makers (among them The Gap, Levi's, and Patagonia) are increasing their use of organic cotton. (We tend to think of cotton as a "natural" fibre, but it is actually a highly *erosive* crop, meaning that it has an intensive impact on agricultural land. It takes about a half-kilogram of pesticides and fertilizers to grow, by conventional agricultural means, the cotton required to manufacture one T-shirt.[18]) Roots, a company founded in Canada, was one of the first major clothing manufacturers to begin experimenting with large-scale use of organic cotton, in 1989.[19]

Organic agriculture succeeds in part because it alleviates many problems introduced by high-input agriculture, even while passing up many of the benefits. For instance, although in many cases more insect pests attack organic crops because of the lack of chemical pesticides, biocontrol methods can often keep these pests in check. Moreover, the lack of synthetic chemicals maintains soil quality and encourages helpful pollinating insects. In the end, consumer choice will determine the future of organic agriculture. Falling prices and wider availability suggest that organic agriculture will continue to increase. In addition, sustainable agriculture, whether organic or not, will sooner or later need to become the rule rather than the exception.

Government initiatives have also spurred the growth of organic farming. For example, several million hectares of land have undergone conversion from conventional to organic farming in Europe since the European Union

FIGURE 8.25
The new organic certification logo will be used to designate food products that meet the Canadian standards for organic production.

THE SCIENCE BEHIND THE STORY

Organic Farming Put to the Test

Dr. Paul Voroney of the University of Guelph researches the impacts of organic farming methods.

Fields of wheat and potatoes, some grown organically and some cultivated with the synthetic chemicals favoured by industrialized agriculture, stand side by side on an experimental farm in Switzerland. Although conventionally farmed fields receive up to 50% more fertilizer, they produce only 20% more food than organically farmed fields. How are organic fields able to produce decent yields without synthetic agricultural chemicals? The answer, scientists have found, lies in the soil.

Swiss researchers at the Research Institute of Organic Agriculture have been comparing organic and conventional fields since 1978, using a series of growing areas that feature four different farming systems. One group of plots mirrors conventional farms, in which large amounts of chemical pesticides, herbicides, and fertilizers are applied to soil and plants. Another set is treated with a mixed approach of conventional and organic practices, including chemical additives, synthetic sprays, and livestock manure as fertilizer. Organic plots use only manure, mechanical weed-

ing machines, and plant extracts to control pests. A fourth group of plots follows organic practices but also uses extra natural boosts, such as adding herbal extracts to compost. The two organic plots receive about 35–50% less fertilizer than the conventional fields and 97% fewer pesticides.

Over more than 20 years of monitoring, the organic fields yielded 80% of what the conventional fields produced, researchers reported in the journal *Science* in 2002. Organic crops of winter wheat yielded about 90% of the conventional wheat crop yield. Organic potato crops averaged about 68% of the conventional potato yields. The comparatively low potato yield was due to nutrient deficiency and a fungus-caused potato blight.

Scientists have hypothesized that organic farms keep their yields high because organic agricultural practices better conserve soil quality, keeping soil fertile over the long term. Soil scientist Paul Voroney (see photo) from the University of Guelph in Ontario has been looking at the impact of organic methods. Using adjacent fields in nine different locations, he compared the impact of conventional practices with organic practices. On average, organic matter levels were 15% higher in the organically managed fields. There were also better soil structure and a 20% increase in the number of living soil microbes in the top 10 centimetres of the soil profile.[20]

Other researchers have shown that organic farming produces soils that contained more naturally occurring nutrients, held greater quantities of water, and had higher concentrations of microbial life than conventionally farmed soil (see graphs). Organic farms also have deeper nutrient-rich topsoil and greater earthworm activity—all signs of soils healthy enough to

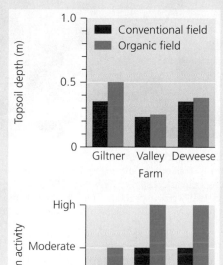

Researchers demonstrated that organic farming at three sites increased topsoil depth moderately and activity of earthworms dramatically.
Source: Data from Liebig, M. A., and J. W. Doran, 1999. Impact of organic production practices on soil quality indicators, Journal of Environmental Quality 28: 1601–1609.

produce crops without help from synthetic chemicals. Increasingly, researchers are concluding that organically managed soil supports a more diverse range of microbial and plant life, which translates into increased biodiversity, self-sustaining fields, and strong crop yields. Such findings may be pivotal as large growers increasingly debate whether to turn to organic farming.

adopted a policy in 1993 to support farmers financially during the first years of conversion. Such support is important because conversion often means a temporary loss in income for farmers. More and more studies, however, suggest that reduced inputs and higher market prices can, in the long run, make organic farming more profitable for the farmer than conventional methods.

Locally supported agriculture is growing

Increasing numbers of farmers and consumers are also supporting local small-scale agriculture. Farmers' markets (**FIGURE 8.26**) are becoming more numerous as consumers rediscover the joys of fresh, locally grown

FIGURE 8.26
Farmers' markets, like this one in Toronto, have become more widespread as consumers have rediscovered the benefits of buying fresh, locally grown produce. There has been farmers' market activity at this particular site, the St. Lawrence Market, since 1803.

produce. The average food product sold in North American supermarkets travels at least 2300 km between the farm and the shelf, and supermarket produce is often chemically treated to preserve freshness and colour. At farmers' markets, consumers can buy fresh produce in season from local farmers and often have a wide choice of organic items and unique local varieties.

Some consumers are partnering with local farmers in a phenomenon called **community-supported agriculture (CSA)**. In this practice, consumers pay farmers in advance for a share of their yield, usually in the form of weekly deliveries of produce. Consumers get fresh seasonal produce, while farmers get a guaranteed income stream up front to invest in their crops—an alternative to taking out loans and being at the mercy of the weather. As of 2005, the CSA network in Québec, alone, counted almost 100 farm members, supplying 20 000 people with local organic meats and produce.[21]

Organic agriculture can even succeed in cities

One surprising place that organic agriculture is making inroads is within cities. Many urban areas now offer community gardens in which residents can grow small plots of fruits and vegetables.

For example, organic agriculture is deeply entrenched in both the cities and the rural areas of Cuba. Long a close ally of the former Soviet Union, Cuba suffered economic and agricultural upheaval following the Soviet Union's dissolution. In 1989, as the USSR was breaking up, Cuba lost 75% of its total imports, 53% of its oil imports, and 80% of its fertilizer and pesticide imports. Faced with such losses, Cuba's farmers had little choice but to "go organic."

Because far less oil was available to fuel Cuba's transportation system, farmers began growing food closer to cities and even within them. By 1998 the Cuban government's Urban Agriculture Department had encouraged the development of more than 8000 gardens in the capital city of Havana (**FIGURE 8.27**). Over 30 000 people, including farmers, government workers, and private citizens, worked in these gardens, which covered 30% of the city's available land. Cuba has also taken steps to compensate for the loss of fossil fuels, fertilizers, and pesticides by, for example, using oxen instead of tractors, using integrated pest management, encouraging people to live outside urban areas and to remain involved in agriculture, and establishing centres to breed organisms for biological pest control.

Cuba's agriculture likely requires more human labour per unit output than do intensive commercial farms of developed nations, and Cuba's economic and agricultural policies are guided by tight top-down control in a rigid state socialist system. Nevertheless, Cuba's low-input farming has produced some positive achievements. The practices have led to the complete control of the sweet-potato borer, a significant pest insect, and in the 1996–1997 growing season the Cuban people produced record yields for 10 crops. Although Cuba's move toward organic agriculture was involuntary, its response to its economic and agricultural crisis illustrates how other nations might, by choice, begin to farm in ways that rely less on enormous inputs of fossil fuels and synthetic chemicals.

FIGURE 8.27
Organic gardening takes place within the city limits of Havana, Cuba, out of necessity. With little money to pay for the large amounts of fertilizers and pesticides required for industrialized agriculture, Cubans get much of their food from local agriculture without these inputs.

CANADIAN ENVIRONMENTAL PERSPECTIVES

Alisa Smith and James MacKinnon

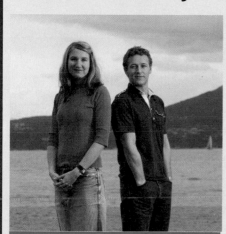

Alisa Smith and J.B. MacKinnon invented the "100-mile diet" concept.

■ **Environmentalists**
■ **Writers** and **bloggers**
■ **Locavores** and inventors of the 100-Mile Diet

One night Alisa Smith and James MacKinnon were expecting company but found that they were out of food. They scrounged outside around their cabin in northern British Columbia and came up with a trout, wild mushrooms, potatoes, garlic, dandelion leaves, apples, sour cherries, and rose hips. Everything tasted so good that the two embarked upon a venture to learn more about the food they ate—specifically, where it comes from and how far it has to travel to get to the dinner table. After learning that food travels almost 2000 km to reach the average North American dinner table, Smith

and MacKinnon pledged to spend one year eating only foods that were grown and produced within 100 miles of their Vancouver apartment. They blogged their way through the entire experience, and the result was a book, *The 100-Mile Diet: A Year of Local Eating*, and a new concept in eating.

They were surprised both by the benefits of the 100-mile diet ("It rolls off the tongue easier than 160-km diet") and by the enthusiastic response they received from people around the world. Some of the benefits—on top of the environmental benefits of cutting back on the long-distance transportation of food products—included fresher taste, more fruits and vegetables in a generally healthier diet, seasonal awareness of food, and support of the local economy.[22]

However, there were many challenges. It took a while to figure out how to find some local products and how to tell the provenance of ingredients (which usually don't specify their origin, even if they are listed on food labels). Among the items they could not find in local production were sugar, rice, lemons, ketchup, olive oil, peanut butter, and orange juice.[23] One of the only exceptions, or "cheats," they allowed themselves during that first year was the occasional beer (it may be brewed locally, but the ingredients come from elsewhere).

The 100-mile diet is just one entry—though perhaps the best-known—in the growing movement of local and "slow" food enthusiasts; some are now calling

themselves "locavores." MacKinnon and Smith, for their part, are still eating locally—about 85%, by their reckoning—and don't believe they will ever abandon this way of life. They firmly believe that local eating will continue to grow in popularity, especially with rising prices for grains and other basic food products and the rising cost of transporting them. In fact, they believe that local eating will fundamentally transform our approach to food in the coming decades.

"Alisa and I are increasingly convinced that much larger numbers of people could be fed from smaller landscapes than we think; we'd just have to put food closer to the centre of daily life (where it belongs!)." [24]
—*J.B. MacKinnon and Alisa Smith*

Thinking About Environmental Perspectives

What foods would you have to do without if you decided to try to eat locally? Remember to think about where the individual ingredients come from, as well as where the item is produced. Next time you are in the supermarket read the labels on items that you normally buy, and try to determine their place of origin. (You might have to do some additional research; does this suggest anything to you about how food is labelled?) What are some local substitutions you could make for the "missing" items on your dinner table? What are some of the local specialities that you would be able to enjoy, and how would they vary from season to season?

Conclusion

Many of the intensive commercial agricultural practices we have discussed have substantial negative environmental impacts. At the same time, it is important to realize that many aspects of industrialized agriculture have had positive environmental effects by relieving certain pressures on land and resources.

Whether Earth's natural systems would be under more pressure from 7 billion people practicing traditional agriculture or from 7 billion people living under the industrialized agriculture model is a very complicated question. Additional unanswered questions remain, such as whether genetic modification of food organisms will ultimately prove to be beneficial and whether the environmental and nutritional benefits of locally grown foods will outweigh the efficiencies of modern agriculture.

What is certain is that if our planet is to support 9 billion people by mid-century without further degradation of the soil, water, pollinators, and other ecosystem services that support our food production, we must find ways to shift to more sustainable agricultural practices. Approaches such as biological pest control, organic agriculture, pollinator conservation, preservation of native crop diversity, sustainable aquaculture, and likely some degree of careful and responsible genetic modification of food may all be parts of the game plan we will need to set in motion. What remains to be seen is the extent to which individuals, governments, and corporations will be able to put their own interests and agendas in perspective to work together toward a sustainable future.

REVIEWING OBJECTIVES

You should now be able to:

Outline the historical development of agriculture and the transition to industrialized agriculture

- Agriculture emerged as a human technology about 10 000 years ago.
- The transition to a sedentary lifestyle based on agriculture increased the carrying capacity of land and led to a significant increase in population.
- The Industrial Revolution brought mechanization to farming, along with advances in farm equipment and artificial selection.
- Although there are still many traditional and subsistence farmers, much of the world's cropland is now devoted to modern, industrialized farming.

Explain the challenge of feeding a growing human population

- Food production has outpaced the growth of our population, yet there are still over 900 million hungry people in the world.
- Ensuring food security for all people requires a combination of increased agricultural productivity, a decrease in poverty, and better food distribution methods.

Identify the main approaches and summarize the environmental impacts of the Green Revolution

- The goal of the Green Revolution was to increase agricultural productivity per unit area of land to feed the world's people.
- Agricultural scientists used selective breeding to develop strains of crops that grew quickly, were more nutritious, or were resistant to disease or drought.
- The greatly expanded use of fossil fuels, chemical fertilizers, and irrigation led to enormous increases in productivity, but also caused unintended environmental consequences, including pollution and soil degradation.
- Monoculture—the planting of large tracts of a single crop type—is a hallmark of the Green Revolution that greatly increased agricultural efficiency but reduced crop diversity.

Summarize the strategies and impacts of pest management and the importance of pollination

- Most "pests" and "weeds" are killed with synthetic chemicals that also can pollute the environment and pose health hazards.
- Pests tend to evolve resistance to chemical pesticides, forcing chemists to design ever more toxic poisons.
- Natural enemies of pests can be employed against them in the practice of biological control.
- Integrated pest management includes a combination of techniques, and attempts to minimize use of synthetic chemicals.
- Insects and other organisms are essential for ensuring the reproduction of many of our crop plants.
- Conservation of native pollinating insects is vitally important to our food supply.

Describe the science and evaluate the controversies associated with genetically modified food

- Genetic modification depends on the technology of recombinant DNA. Genes containing desirable traits are moved from one type of organism into another.
- Modification through genetic engineering is both like and unlike traditional selective breeding.
- GM crops may have ecological impacts, including the spread of transgenes and indirect impacts on biodiversity. More research is needed to determine how widespread or severe these impacts may be.
- Little evidence exists so far for human health impacts from GM foods, but anxiety over health impacts inspires wide opposition to GM foods.
- Many people have ethical qualms about altering the food we eat through genetic engineering, and opponents view multinational biotechnology corporations as a threat to the independence of small farmers.

State the importance of crop diversity and some approaches to preservation

- Protecting regions of diversity of native crop varieties, such as Oaxaca, can provide insurance against failure of major commercial crops.

- Seed banks preserve rare and local varieties of seed, acting as storehouses for genetic diversity.

Assess the positive and negative aspects of feedlots and aquaculture for raising animals for food

- Increased consumption of animal products has driven the development of high-density feedlots.
- Feedlots create tremendous amounts of waste and other environmental impacts, but they also relieve pressure on lands that could otherwise be overgrazed.
- Aquaculture provides economic benefits and food security, can relieve pressures on wild fish stocks, and can be sustainable.

- Aquaculture also creates pollution, habitat loss, and other environmental impacts.

Summarize the main goals of sustainable agriculture

- Organic agriculture has fewer environmental impacts than industrial agriculture. It is a small part of the market but is growing rapidly.
- Locally supported agriculture, as shown by farmers' markets and community-supported agriculture, is also growing.

TESTING YOUR COMPREHENSION

1. What kinds of techniques have people employed to increase agricultural food production? How did agricultural scientist Norman Borlaug help inaugurate the Green Revolution?
2. Explain how pesticide resistance occurs.
3. Explain the concept of biocontrol. List several components of a system of Integrated Pest Management (IPM).
4. About how many and what types of cultivated plants are known to rely on insects for pollination? Why is it important to preserve the biodiversity of native pollinators?
5. What is recombinant DNA? How is a transgenic organism created? How is genetic engineering different from traditional agricultural breeding? How is it similar?
6. Describe several reasons why many people support the development of genetically modified organisms, and name several uses of such organisms that have been developed so far.
7. Describe the scientific concerns of those opposed to genetically modified crops. Describe some of the other concerns.
8. Name several positive and negative environmental effects of feedlot operations. Why is beef an inefficient food from the perspective of energy consumption?
9. What are some economic benefits of aquaculture? What are some negative environmental impacts?
10. What are the objectives of sustainable agriculture? What factors are causing organic agriculture to expand?

THINKING IT THROUGH

1. Assess several ways in which high-input agriculture can be beneficial for the environment and several ways in which it can be detrimental to the environment. Now suggest several ways in which we might modify industrial agriculture to lessen its environmental impact.
2. What factors make for an effective biological control strategy of pest management? What risks are involved in biocontrol? If you had to decide whether to use biocontrol against a particular pest, what questions would you want to have answered before you decide?
3. Those who view GM foods as solutions to world hunger and pesticide overuse often want to speed

their development and approval. Others adhere to the precautionary principle and want extensive testing for health and environmental safety. How much caution do you think is warranted before a new GM crop is introduced?
4. Can we call the Green Revolution a success? Has it solved problems, or delayed our resolution of problems, or just created new ones? How sustainable are Green Revolution approaches? Norman Borlaug hoped that the Green Revolution would give us "breathing room" in which to deal with what he called "the Population Monster." Have we dealt effectively with population during the breathing

room that the Green Revolution has given us?

5. Imagine that it is your job to make the regulatory decision as to whether to allow the planting of a new genetically modified strain of cabbage that produces its own pesticide and has twice the vitamin content of regular cabbage. What questions would you ask of scientists before deciding whether to approve the new crop? What scientific data would you want to see, and how much would be enough? Would you also consult nonscientists or take ethical, economic, and social factors into consideration?

6. Cuba adopted low-input organic agriculture out of necessity. If the country were to become economically prosperous once more, do you think Cubans would maintain this form of agriculture, or do you think they would turn to intensive, high-input farming instead? What path do you think they should pursue, and why?

INTERPRETING GRAPHS AND DATA

In the year 2000, over 80 million metric tonnes of nitrogen fertilizer was used in producing food for the world's 6 billion people. Food production, use of nitrogen fertilizers, and world population all had grown over the preceding 40 years, but at somewhat different rates. Food production grew slightly faster than population while relatively little additional land was converted to agricultural use during this time. Fertilizer use grew most rapidly.

1. Express the year 2002 values of the four graphed indices as percentages of the value of each index in 1961.

2. Calculate the ratio of the food production index to the nitrogen fertilizer use index in 1961 and in 2002. What does comparing these two ratios tell you about how the efficiency of nitrogen use in agriculture has changed? Is this an example of the law of diminishing returns?

3. As world population has grown, so has the demand for food, yet little additional land has been devoted to food production. Calculate the ratio of the agricultural land index to the population index for 1961

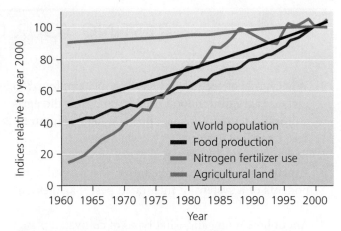

Global food production, nitrogen fertilizer use, human population, and land converted to agriculture, 1961–2002, relative to 2000 levels (2000 = 100). Data from Food and Agriculture Organization of the United Nations.

and 2002. What does comparing these two ratios tell you about how the per capita demand on agricultural land has changed over the years? To what factors can you attribute this change?

CHAPTER ENDNOTES

1. www.percyschmeiser.com

2. The species *Homo sapiens* is thought to have originated in Africa approximately 200 000 years BP (before present). The modern human subspecies, *H. sapiens sapiens*, which is the only subspecies of *H. sapiens* that survives today, probably originated about 130 000 BP. Smithsonian Institution Human Origins Project, www.mnh.si.edu/anthro/humanorigins/

3. Canadian Institute for Health Information (2004) *Overweight and Obesity in Canada: A Population Health Perspective, 2004*, http://secure.cihi.ca/cihi-

web/dispPage.jsp?cw_page=GR_1130_E

4. Food Banks Canada (2011) *Hunger Count 2010: A Comprehensive Report on Hunger and Food Bank Use in Canada, and Recommendations for Change*, www.foodbankscanada.ca/documents/HungerCount2010_web.pdf

5. Rainville, B., and S. Brink (2001) Food Insecurity in Canada, 1998–1999. Research paper R-01-2E. Ottawa: Applied Research Branch, Human Resources Development Canada.

6. Health Canada, Pest Management Regulatory Agency, www.pmra-arla.gc.ca/english/legis/pcpa-e.html

7. Government of Canada (2000) *Pesticides: Making the Right Choice for Health and the Environment.* Report of the Standing Committee on Environment and Sustainable Development. http://cmte.parl.gc.ca/cmte/CommitteePublication.aspx?COM=173&Lang=1&SourceId=36396

8. McEwan, K. and W. Deen (1997) *A Review of Agricultural Pesticide Pricing and Availability in Canada*, prepared for Saskatchewan Agriculture and Food; the Ontario Ministry of Agriculture, Food and Rural Affairs; and Agriculture and Agri-Food Canada.

9. Kevan, P. G., E. A. Clark, and V. G. Thomas (1990) Pollinators and sustainable agriculture. *American Journal of Alternative Agriculture.* 5(1): 13–22.

10. Dyer, J. S. (2006) Raising awareness among Canadians about plant pollinators and the importance of monitoring and conserving them. Published electronically by Seeds of Diversity Canada (SoDC) for the Ecological Monitoring and Assessment Network Coordinating Office (EMAN CO) of Environment Canada, www.pollinationcanada.ca/lit/Pollinator%20Awareness%20Paper.pdf

11. Based on information from Kevan, P. G., E. A. Clark, and V. G. Thomas (1990) Pollinators and sustainable agriculture. *American Journal of Alternative Agriculture.* 5(1): 13–22.

12. Leah, S. (2004) Monsanto "Seed Police" Scrutinize Farmers *Inter Press Service*, http://www.commondreams.org/headlines05/0115-04.htm

13. Convention on Biological Diversity, www.cbd.int/default.shtml

14. Eaton, D., J. Windig, S. J. Hiemstra, and M. van Veller (2006) *Indicators for Livestock and Crop Diversity, North-South Policy Brief 2006-1.* Programme International Cooperation, Wageningen International, www.wi.wur.nl/NR/rdonlyres/FADBC382-F7C9-4D2E-B39D-E209AF3C32D2/42280/Policybrief20061.pdf

15. Food and Agriculture Organization of the United Nations (2011) *FAOSTAT: Livestock Primary Production—World Total.* http://faostat.fao.org/site/569/DesktopDefault.aspx?PageID=569#ancor, accessed January 13, 2011.

16. Commission on Genetic Resources for Food and Agriculture, Food and Agriculture Organization of the United Nations (2007) *The State of the World's Animal Genetic Resources for Food and Agriculture.*

17. Canadian Organic Growers. *Quick Facts About Canada's Organic Sector*, www.cog.ca/orgquickfacts.htm

18. Sustainable Cotton Project. www.sustainablecotton.org/

19. Roots, Organic Cotton. www.roots.com

20. Carter, J. (2006) Researchers show soil microbes increase in organic fields—Timing of cover crop planting is important to good performance, depending on variety, *Ontario Farmer*, February 7, 2006, as reported by Ontario Agriculture Centre of Canada, www.organicagcentre.ca/ResearchDatabase/res_microbes_covercrop_of.asp

21. Equiterre. www.equiterre.org/en/agriculture/paniersBios/index.php

22. Smith, A., and J. MacKinnon (2007) *100-Mile Diet: Local Eating for Global Change,* http://100milediet.org/home/

23. Smith, A., and J. MacKinnon (2007) *The 100-Mile Diet: A Year of Local Eating.* Random House Canada.

24. MacKinnon, J. *The 100-Mile Diet: Blog.* http://100milediet.org/category/the-latest

MyEnvironmentPlace

Go to **www.myenvironmentplace.ca** where you will find quizzes, animations, your Pearson eText, and more.

Conservation of Species and Habitats

9

The polar bear (*Ursus maritimus*) is native to the Arctic Circle and depends on sea ice for hunting its main prey, seals.

Upon successfully completing this chapter, you will be able to

- Characterize the scope and value of biodiversity on Earth
- Describe ways to measure biodiversity
- Evaluate the primary causes of biodiversity loss
- Specify the benefits and challenges of conserving habitat and the role of habitat fragmentation

- Contrast *in situ* and *ex situ* conservation approaches
- Compare and contrast traditional and innovative conservation efforts
- Outline reasons for setting aside parks, reserves, and other protected areas

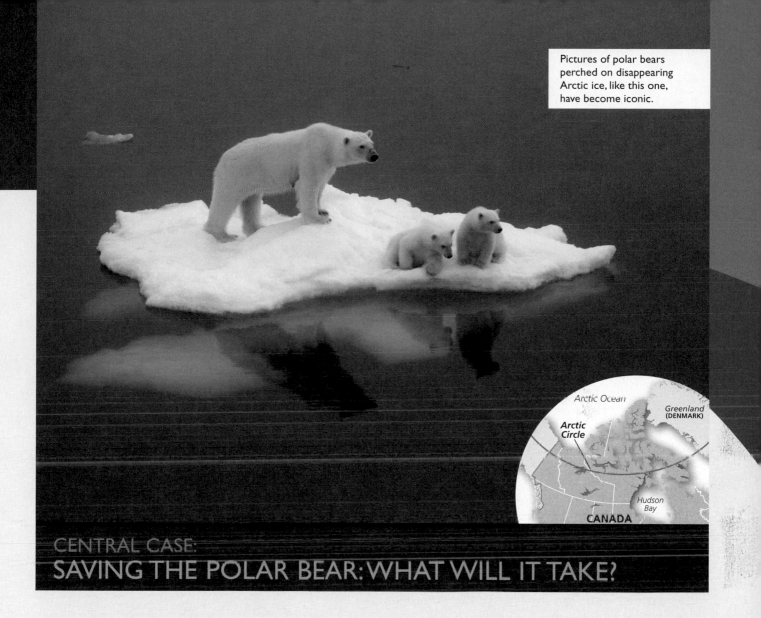

Pictures of polar bears perched on disappearing Arctic ice, like this one, have become iconic.

Arctic Ocean
Greenland (DENMARK)
Arctic Circle
Hudson Bay
CANADA

SAVING THE POLAR BEAR: WHAT WILL IT TAKE?

"There will be no polar ice by 2060. Somewhere along that path, the polar bear drops out."

—LARRY SCHWEIGER, PRESIDENT AND CHIEF EXECUTIVE OFFICER OF THE NATIONAL WILDLIFE FEDERATION

"Polar bears are constrained in that the very existence of their habitat is changing and there is limited scope for a northward shift in distribution. Due to the long generation time of polar bears and the current pace of climate warming, we believe it unlikely that polar bears will be able to respond in an evolutionary sense…We conclude that the future persistence of polar bears is tenuous."

—ANDREW DEROCHER, PROFESSOR OF BIOLOGICAL SCIENCE, UNIVERSITY OF ALBERTA (WITH CO-AUTHORS)[1]

"Scientists saying that the polar bear population is decreasing are just taking advantage of the Inuit.

Scientists come here for just a few days and don't know everything…There are more bears now. [We] hear about global warming, but [we] see more polar bears. There are more bears on land as well as on sea ice. You can see polar bear tracks in any direction from Arctic Bay."

—COMMENTS MADE AT A PUBLIC CONSULTATION IN ARCTIC BAY, NUNAVUT (CONSULTATIONS ON THE PROPOSED LISTING OF THE POLAR BEAR AS SPECIAL CONCERN UNDER THE *SPECIES AT RISK ACT*, CONDUCTED FEBRUARY–APRIL 2009 BY THE CANADIAN WILDLIFE SERVICE)

"There aren't just a few more bears. There are a hell of a lot more bears. Scientific knowledge has demonstrated that Inuit knowledge was right… Right now, the bears are so abundant there's a public safety issue."

—MITCHELL TAYLOR, POLAR BEAR BIOLOGIST WITH THE GOVERNMENT OF NUNAVUT, CLYDE BAY

The year 2008 was an interesting one for polar bears. That year, partly in response to a lawsuit by environmental groups, the U.S. Fish and Wildlife Service asked the Secretary of the Interior to add the polar bear to the Endangered Species List as a "threatened" species. The official reason was the recognition that the survival of polar bears depends on sea ice for hunting. Arctic sea ice has receded dramatically over the past decade (see graph). Climate models predict that this trend will continue, ending with a largely ice-free Arctic Ocean well before the end of this century. The FWS also recognized the ingestion of or exposure to toxic contaminants, mostly transported from lower latitudes, as a threat to the polar bear's survival.[2] The IUCN Red List of Threatened Species recognizes the polar bear as "vulnerable" (one category below "endangered") on the basis of a global assessment carried out in 2008.[3]

In that same year, 2008, the government of Nunavut announced that it would proceed to allow a cull of 105 polar bears by hunters. The Committee on the Status of Endangered Species in Canada (COSEWIC) also reconfirmed that the polar bear would not be listed as a "threatened" species, but would retain its previous status as a species of "special concern."

The polar bear (*Ursus maritimus*), native to sea ice and land masses within the Arctic Circle, is uniquely adapted to life on the ice. The individual hairs of its outer fur layer are hollow, providing both waterproofing and insulation against the cold. They have a thick layer of blubber that contributes to their ability to retain heat. The fur, which is actually transparent, appears white against their underlying black skin, providing camouflage. On the pads of their paws are small bumps which, along with their thick, strong claws, provide traction on the ice. Polar bears are born on land but spend most of their lives hunting bearded seals and other marine prey from sea ice platforms. What will happen to this animal if its habitat of sea ice disappears?

Also native to the Arctic in Canada, Greenland, Russia, and Alaska are the Inuit, a group of culturally similar indigenous peoples and one of the three Aboriginal groups officially recognized by Canadian law. The Inuit traditionally hunt polar bears, as well as seals, walrus, narwhals, and whales (see painting). They also eat various seabirds, fish, and land mammals such as caribou and Arctic hares. Arctic plants such sorrel, willow, blueberry, soapberry, wintergreen, and lichens complete the traditional diet, which varies seasonally. Inuit hunters seek to maintain an ecological balance between hunting on the sea and on the land. They believe that if this balance is not maintained, and if they do not respect the animals they are hunting, the resource may disappear.[4] They also carefully use all parts of the organisms they harvest.

The right of the Inuit to carry out subsistence hunting in support of their traditional way of life is protected by federal law in Canada, as well as in Alaska. However, other laws, both federal and provincial, are in place to protect wildlife and other aspects of the environment, and this is where the complications begin. There are about 20 polar bear populations in the world, 14 of which have been identified for management purposes in Canada; most of these populations lack long-term monitoring data.[5] The total population of polar bears globally is around 20 000 to 25 000, as of 2011.[6]

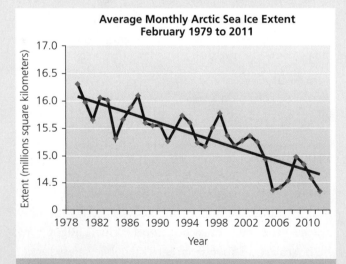

Average Monthly Arctic Sea Ice Extent February 1979 to 2011

Extent (millions square kilometers)

Year

Sea ice, which is monitored by satellite, has been declining rapidly for the past couple of decades. February 2011 tied with February 2005 for the lowest extent of sea ice ever recorded.
Source: Data from U.S. National Sea Ice Data Center http://nsidc.org/ arcticseaicenews/20111/030211.html.

Polar bear is a traditional staple in the winter diet of Inuit people in Canada's North.

Canada cooperates with other national governments, state and provincial governments, international organizations, and Aboriginal groups in setting harvest quotas for the polar bear by mutual agreement. Some of these agreements are internal, some are international, and some are bilateral. In Canada, traditional hunters must deal with a confusing bureaucratic landscape to find out what their annual hunting quota will be. For example, early in 2011 the Amarok Hunters and Trappers Association in Iqaluit announced that its members would be allowed a significant increase, from the usual quota of 23 bears to 41, on the basis of accumulated hunting credits. The Qikiqtaaluk Wildlife Board subsequently announced that the hunters would not be allowed to use all of the credits, and it approved an increase of only 10 polar bears to the annual hunt. This came in the context of a decision in 2010 by the Government of Nunavut Environment Minister to reduce the total allowable harvest by 10 bears per year. Final approval for the annual quota comes from the Nunavut Wildlife Management Board.[7] The management system in Nunavut was established in 1970, when quotas were first introduced.

The complexity of this situation is hard to grasp. Fundamentally, the prospect of an ice-free Arctic Ocean calls into question the ability of the polar bear to survive as a species. If sea ice continues to deteriorate, polar bear populations will be forced to migrate and possibly even merge. With warming, sea ice is also changing in its physical character, making hunting more precarious. As the bears migrate they are encountering other types of bears, such as brown bears and grizzlies, with which they are interbreeding; this, too, may affect the survival chances of the species.

Meanwhile, polar bears are appearing more frequently in human settlements, necessitating the killing of nuisance bears for public safety. Most scientists interpret the appearance of the bears in settlements as a sign of their increasing stress and desperation for food; many Inuit interpret it as a sign that the number of bears is increasing. This is indicative of a fundamental mistrust that many Inuit hold for scientists, whom they feel do not spend sufficient time on the land to understand the real status of polar bears.

At the same time, traditional Inuit hunting practices are being affected by the loss of sea ice; some hunters have changed their patterns, or the timing of the hunt, in response to these changes. This will eventually affect bear populations but also impacts the survival of traditional Inuit cultures. Many Inuit feel that global warming is not a problem of their making and that finding a solution to the problem should not come at the risk of their cultural survival.

What will it take to save the polar bear? This case illustrates some of the complexity inherent in challenges related to the conservation of species, which almost never present simple solutions. Conservation entails not only ecological concerns, but political, legal, economic, social, and ethical concerns that cross jurisdictional boundaries. As of 2011 the legal status of the polar bear remains unchanged: "threatened" in the United States, but not in Canada.

Our Planet of Life

Changes in biological populations and communities have been taking place naturally as long as life has existed. But today, as never before in the history of this planet, population pressure, human development, and resource extraction are speeding the rate of change and altering the types of changes being imposed on Earth's flora and fauna. Some of our actions are diminishing Earth's diversity of life, the very quality that makes our planet so special. Fortunately, there are steps that we can take to safeguard the diversity of species and habitats, and the ecological and evolutionary processes that make Earth such a unique place.

The ways in which we modify our environment, the impacts of these modifications on species, and the steps we take to mitigate our impacts cannot be understood in a scientific vacuum. Actions that threaten species and habitats have complex social, economic, and political roots, as you have seen in the case of the polar bear. Environmental scientists appreciate that we must understand all of these aspects if we are to develop viable solutions that will contribute to the conservation of species and habitats.

Previously we introduced the concept of **biological diversity**, or **biodiversity**, and defined it as the sum total of all organisms in an area, taking into account the diversity of species, their genes, their populations, and their communities. In this chapter we will refine this definition and examine current biodiversity trends and their relevance to our lives. We will then explore some solutions to biodiversity loss and consider some modern approaches to the conservation and preservation of species and habitats.

Biodiversity encompasses several levels

Biodiversity is a concept as multifaceted as life itself, and definitions of the term are plentiful. Different biologists use different working definitions according to their own aims, interests, and values. Nonetheless, there is broad agreement that the concept applies across several major levels in the organization of life (**FIGURE 9.1**). We will look, in turn, at the concepts of species diversity, genetic diversity, and ecosystem and habitat diversity.

Species diversity   As you will recall from previous discussions, a *species* is a distinct type of organism, a set of individuals that uniquely share certain characteristics and can breed with one another to produce fertile offspring. Biologists use differing criteria to delineate species boundaries; some emphasize characteristics shared because of common ancestry, whereas others emphasize ability to interbreed. In practice, however, scientists broadly agree on species identities.

We can express **species diversity** in terms of the number and the variety of species in the world, or in a particular region (**FIGURE 9.2**). One component of species diversity is **species richness**, the number of species in a particular area. Another is **evenness** or **relative abundance**, the extent to which the population numbers of individuals of each different species are equal or skewed.

Speciation generates new species, adding to global species richness. *Extinction*, the disappearance of a species, decreases species richness. *Immigration* (the in-

Ecosystem diversity

Species diversity

Genetic diversity

FIGURE 9.1

The concept of biodiversity encompasses several levels in the hierarchy of life. *Species diversity* refers to the number or variety of species. *Genetic diversity* refers to variety of genes among individuals within a given population or species. *Ecosystem diversity* and related concepts refer to variety at levels above the species level, such as ecosystems, communities, habitats, and landscapes.

roots
BIODIVERSITY

The word *biodiversity* was first used in the 1960s by wildlife conservationist Raymond Dasmann. It was not widely adopted by the scientific community until the 1980s, when it was introduced by conservation biologist Thomas Lovejoy, now the Chief Biodiversity Advisor to the World Bank, who is often credited with having coined the term. The word is a combination of the Greek *bios*, "life," and the Old French *diversité*, "difference, uniqueness," originally from the Latin *diversitas*.

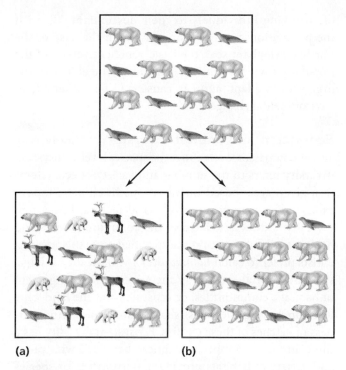

FIGURE 9.2
Compared with the boxed area at the top, which has an even number of individuals of each of the two species, **(a)** has greater species richness because it contains four species instead of just two. In contrast, **(b)** has the same species richness as the top box but reduced evenness, because one species shows a greater relative abundance than the other

migration of a species to an area), *emigration* (the out-migration of a species from an area), and *extirpation* (the local extinction of a species) may increase or decrease species richness locally; however, only speciation and extinction change it in an overall sense.

Taxonomists, scientists who classify species, use an organism's physical appearance and genetic makeup to determine its species. Taxonomists also group species by their similarities, into a hierarchy of categories meant to reflect evolutionary relationships. Related species are grouped together into *genera* (singular: *genus*). Related genera are grouped into *families*, which are grouped into *orders*, and so on (**FIGURE 9.3**).

Every species is given a two-part Latin-based scientific name denoting its genus and species. The polar bear, *Ursus maritimus*, differs from other species of bear, such as the brown bear (*Ursus arctos*, of which the grizzly is a subspecies), the American black bear (*Ursus americanus*), and the Asian black bear (*Ursus thibetanus*). These four species are closely related in evolutionary terms, as indicated by the genus name they share, *Ursus*. They are more distantly related to species such as the giant panda (*Ailuropoda melanoleuca*) and the spectacled bear (*Tremarctos ornatus*), even though they are all classified together in the family Ursidae.

Biodiversity exists below the species level in the form of *subspecies*, populations of a species that occur in

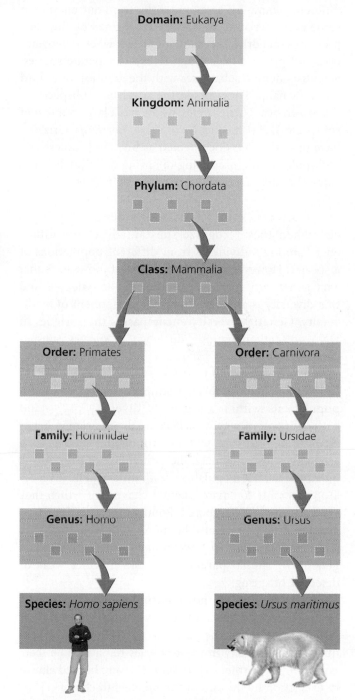

FIGURE 9.3
Taxonomists classify organisms using a hierarchical system meant to reflect evolutionary relationships. Species that are similar in appearance, behaviour, and genetics are placed in the same genus. Organisms of similar genera are placed within the same family. Families are placed within orders, orders within classes, classes within phyla, phyla within kingdoms, and kingdoms within domains. For instance, humans (*Homo sapiens*, a species in the genus *Homo*) and polar bears (*Ursus maritimus*, a species in the genus *Ursus*) are both in the class Mammalia. However, the differences between our two species, which have evolved over millions of years, are great enough that we belong to different orders and families.

different geographic areas and differ from one another in some characteristics. Subspecies are formed by the same processes that drive speciation but result when divergence does not proceed far enough to create separate species. Scientists denote subspecies with the addition of a third scientific name. For example, the grizzly is a subspecies of the brown bear (*Ursus arctos*, which has a large number of subspecies), classified as *Ursus arctos horribilis*. Grizzlies have recently been documented as breeding successfully with polar bears, producing offspring colloquially (and somewhat unattractively) referred to as "pizzlies."

Genetic diversity   Scientists designate subspecies when they recognize substantial genetic differences among individuals from different populations of a species. However, all species consist of individuals that vary genetically from one another to some degree, and this diversity is another important component of biodiversity. **Genetic diversity** encompasses the varieties in DNA present among individuals within species, subspecies, and populations.

Genetic diversity provides the raw material for adaptation to changes in local conditions. In the long term, populations with more genetic diversity may stand better chances of persisting because their variation better enables them to cope with environmental change, such as changes in the climate, the availability of prey, or the quality of habitat. Populations with little genetic diversity are vulnerable to environmental change for which they are not genetically prepared. Populations with depressed genetic diversity may also be more vulnerable to disease and may suffer *inbreeding depression*, which occurs when genetically similar parents mate and produce weak or defective offspring.

Scientists have sounded warnings over low genetic diversity in many species that have dropped to very low population sizes in the past, but the full consequences of reduced diversity in these species remain to be seen. For example, northern elephant seals were hunted almost to extinction by the end of the nineteenth century. They were decreased to one breeding population, and the global number may have fallen to as low as 20 individuals. Since the early twentieth century they have been protected by law, and through various conservation efforts their numbers have recovered to over 100 000. Nevertheless, the existing population is extremely limited in genetic diversity, because all individuals are descended from the 20 individuals that survived the dramatic population decline.

A dramatic decrease in population can cause a **genetic bottleneck**, in which a limited variety of genetic material is available to be passed along by the small number of surviving individuals to their descendants. Even if the population number rebounds, as in the case of the northern elephant seal, the basic genetic diversity of the population will be limited. This limits the ability of the organism to adapt, and can cause it to be vulnerable to environmental changes.

Ecosystem and habitat diversity   Biodiversity also encompasses levels above the species level. **Ecosystem diversity** refers to the number and variety of ecosystems in a given area, based on variations in climate, topography, soil type, and other physical factors. Ecosystem diversity is directly related to the community types and habitat availability within the specified area, so some scientists prefer to call it *habitat diversity*. If the area is large, scientists may also consider the geographic arrangement of habitats, communities, or ecosystems at the landscape level, including the sizes, shapes, and interconnectedness of patches of these entities. Ecosystem diversity has a direct influence on species richness, because a wide range and variety of habitats provide opportunities for species to specialize.

Generally, habitats that are structurally diverse allow for more ecological niches and support greater species richness and evenness. In any given geographic area, species diversity tends to increase with diversity of habitats, because each habitat supports a somewhat different community of organisms. Thus, *ecotones*, where different types of habitat intermix, often have high biodiversity. Because human disturbance (such as clearing plots of forest) can sometimes increase habitat diversity (which ecologists call *habitat heterogeneity*), species diversity may be higher in disturbed areas. However, this is true only at local scales. At larger scales, human disturbance decreases diversity because species that rely on large unbroken expanses of single habitat will disappear.

Some groups hold more species than others

Species are not evenly distributed among taxonomic groups. In terms of number of species, insects show a staggering predominance over all other forms of life (**FIGURE 9.4** and **FIGURE 9.5**). Within insects, about 40% are beetles. Beetles outnumber all non-insect animals and all plants. No wonder the twentieth-century British biologist J. B. S. Haldane famously quipped that God must have had "an inordinate fondness for beetles."

Some groups have given rise to many species in a relatively short period of time (geologically speaking), through the process of *adaptive radiation*. Others have

FIGURE 9.4
This illustration shows organisms scaled in size to the number of species known from each major taxonomic group. This gives a visual sense of the disparity in species richness among groups. Because most species are not yet discovered or described, some groups (such as bacteria, archaea, insects, nematodes, protists, and fungi) may contain far more species than we now know of.
Source: Data from Groombridge, B., and M. D. Jenkins (2002) Global Biodiversity: Earth's Living Resources in the 21st Century. *UNEP-World Conservation Monitoring Centre. Cambridge, U.K.: Hoechst Foundation.*

diversified as a result of having been separated by barriers that promote *allopatric speciation*. Still other groups have accumulated species through time simply because of low rates of extinction.

Measuring biodiversity is not easy

Coming up with precise quantitative measurements to express a region's biodiversity is difficult. This is partly why scientists often express biodiversity in terms of its most easily measured component, species diversity, especially species richness. Species richness is a good gauge for overall biodiversity, but we still are profoundly ignorant of the number of species that exist worldwide. So far, scientists have identified and described about 1.8 million species of plants, animals, and microorganisms. Estimates for the actual total number of species range from 3 million to 100 million, with the most widely accepted estimates in the region of 14 million.

Our knowledge of species numbers is incomplete for several reasons. First, some areas of Earth remain little explored. We have barely sampled the ocean depths, hydrothermal vents, or the tree canopies and soils of tropical forests. Second, many species are tiny and easily overlooked. These inconspicuous organisms include bacteria, nematodes (roundworms), fungi, protists, and soil-dwelling arthropods. Third, many organisms are so difficult to identify that ones thought to be identical sometimes turn out, once biologists look more closely, to be multiple species. This is frequently the case with microbes, fungi, and small insects, but also sometimes with organisms as large as birds, trees, and whales.

Smithsonian Institution entomologist Terry Erwin pioneered one method of estimating species numbers. In 1982, Erwin's crews fogged rainforest trees in Central America with clouds of insecticide and then collected insects, spiders, and other arthropods as they died and fell from the treetops. Using this method, Erwin concluded that 163 beetle species specialized on the tree species *Luehea seemannii*. If this were typical, he calculated,

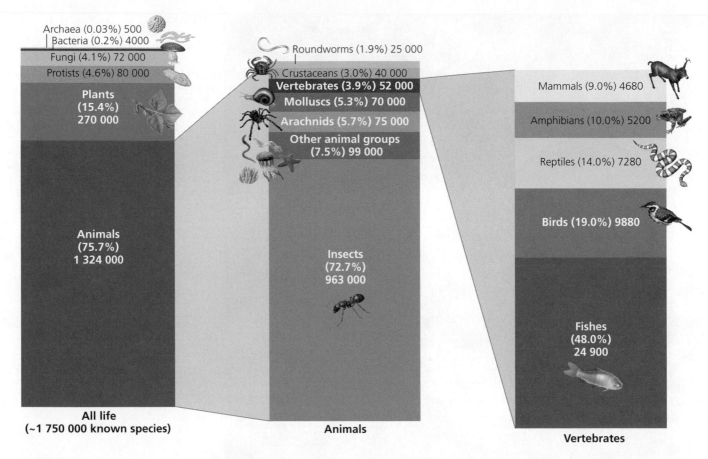

FIGURE 9.5   In the left portion of the figure, we see that three-quarters of known species are animals. The central portion subdivides animals, revealing that nearly three-quarters of animals are insects and that vertebrates comprise only 3.9% of animals. Among vertebrates (right), nearly half are fishes, and mammals comprise only 9%. Most species are not yet discovered or described, so some groups may contain far more species than we now know of.   *Source: Data from Groombridge, B., and M. D. Jenkins (2002) Global Biodiversity: Earth's Living Resources in the 21st Century. UNEP-World Conservation Monitoring Centre. Cambridge, U.K.: Hoechst Foundation.*

then the world's 50 000 tropical tree species would hold 8 150 000 beetle species and—since beetles represent 40% of all arthropods—20 million arthropod species. If canopies hold two-thirds of all arthropods, then arthropod species in tropical forests alone would number 30 million. Many assumptions were involved in this calculation, and several follow-up studies have revised Erwin's estimate downward, but it remains one of the most robust methods for estimating numbers of species.

Measuring and quantifying biodiversity also requires weighting the relative importance of different types of diversity. For example, which would you consider to be more biologically diverse: (1) a region that has high species diversity (lots of different species), in which one species is overwhelmingly dominant and the others are present in vanishingly small numbers; or (2) a region with lower species diversity (a smaller number of species), but in which each species is well represented with numerous individuals? Scientists have devised a number of indices in their attempts to quantify these differences in meaningful ways, but none of them conveys a complete picture of biodiversity.

Biodiversity is unevenly distributed on the planet

Living things are distributed across our planet unevenly, and scientists have long sought to explain the distributional patterns they see. For example, species richness generally increases as one approaches the equator (**FIGURE 9.6**). This pattern of variation with latitude, called the *latitudinal gradient*, is one of the most obvious patterns in ecology, but it also has been one of the most difficult ones for scientists to explain.

Hypotheses abound for the cause of the latitudinal gradient in species richness. It seems likely that plant productivity and climate stability play key roles (**FIGURE 9.7**). Greater amounts of solar energy, heat, and humidity at tropical latitudes lead to more plant growth, making areas nearer the equator more biologically productive and able to support larger numbers of animals. In addition, the relatively stable climates and *aseasonality* of equatorial regions help ensure that single species won't dominate ecosystems, but instead that numerous species can coexist. Variable environmental conditions favour *generalists*—species that can deal with a wide range of circumstances but that do no single thing extremely well. In contrast, stable conditions favour *specialists*—organisms with very specialized niches that do particular things very well.

Another reason that polar and temperate regions may be relatively lacking in species is that glaciation events repeatedly forced organisms out of these regions and toward more tropical latitudes. In other words, species in the tropics have simply had a longer period of geological and climatic stability in which to evolve.

The latitudinal gradient influences the species diversity of Earth's biomes overall. Tropical dry forests and rainforests tend to support far more species than tundra and boreal forests, for instance. Tropical biomes typically show more evenness, as well, whereas in high-latitude biomes with low species richness, particular species may greatly outnumber others. For example, the Canadian boreal forest is characterized by immense expanses dominated by black spruce, whereas Panamanian tropical forest contains hundreds of tree species, no one of which greatly outnumbers the others. Understanding such patterns of biodiversity is vital for landscape ecology, regional planning, and forest management, as well as for the conservation of species and habitats.

FIGURE 9.6

For many types of organisms, the number of species per unit area tends to increase toward the equator. This trend, the latitudinal gradient in species richness, is one of the most readily apparent—yet least understood—patterns in ecology. One example is bird species in North and Central America: In any one spot in arctic Canada and Alaska, 30 to 100 species can be counted; in areas of Costa Rica and Panama, the number rises to over 600.

Source: Adapted from Cook, R. E. (1969) Variation in species density in North American birds. Systematic Zoology 18: 63–84.

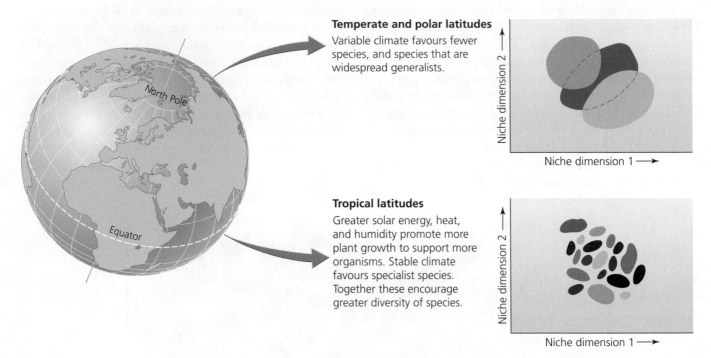

Temperate and polar latitudes
Variable climate favours fewer species, and species that are widespread generalists.

Niche dimension 2 ↑

Niche dimension 1 ⟶

Tropical latitudes
Greater solar energy, heat, and humidity promote more plant growth to support more organisms. Stable climate favours specialist species. Together these encourage greater diversity of species.

Niche dimension 2 ↑

Niche dimension 1 ⟶

FIGURE 9.7   There are many hypotheses for the latitudinal gradient in species richness; one set of ideas is summarized here. The variable climates (days, seasons, and years) of polar and temperate latitudes favour organisms that can survive a wide range of conditions. Such generalist species have expansive niches; they can do many things well enough to survive, and they spread over large areas. In tropical latitudes, the abundant solar energy, heat, and humidity induce greater plant growth, which supports more organisms. The stable climates of equatorial regions favour specialist species, which have restricted niches but do certain things very well. Together these factors promote greater species richness in the tropics.

Biodiversity Loss and Species Extinction

Extinction occurs when the last member of a species dies and the species ceases to exist. Once lost to extinction, a species can never return. As mentioned above, the disappearance of a particular population from a given area, but not the entire species globally, is termed **extirpation**. For example, the Siberian tiger, once native across much of Asia, has been extirpated from most of its historic range, but it is not yet extinct—it still exists in one small mountainous location in the far east of Russia.

Although a species that is extirpated from one place may still exist in others, extirpation is an erosive process that can, over time, lead to extinction. A species that is in imminent danger of extirpation or extinction is referred to as **endangered**. One that is likely to become endangered in the near future, if limiting factors are not reversed, is called **threatened**. These categories—threatened, endangered, extirpated, and extinct—are the main classifications used by the Canadian *Species-At-Risk Act* (also known as **SARA**), and, with some variations in definition, by most organizations that keep track of that status

of species. Any species that is agreed to have fallen within one of these categories is considered to be *at risk*, and is listed on the SARA Public Registry, by a process that is described in greater detail later in this chapter.

Extinction and extirpation occur naturally

If organisms did not naturally go extinct, we would be up to our ears in dinosaurs, trilobites, ammonites, and the millions of other types of creatures that vanished from Earth long before humans appeared. Palaeontologists estimate that roughly 99% of all species that have ever lived are now extinct, leaving only about 1% as the wealth of species on our planet today.

Most extinctions prior to the appearance of humans occurred one by one for independent reasons, at a rate that palaeontologists refer to as the *background rate of extinction*. The fossil record indicates that for mammals and marine animals, one species out of 1000 would typically become extinct every 1000 to 10 000 years. This translates to a background rate of about one extinction per 1 to 10 million species per year.

In the past 440 million years, our planet has experienced five distinct episodes of *mass extinction* (**FIGURE 9.8**), each of which has eliminated at least half of existing species. There is evidence for further mass extinctions in the Cambrian period and earlier, more than half a billion years ago. The best-known episode of mass extinction occurred at the end of the Cretaceous period, 65 million years ago, when the global side-effects of a large asteroid impact drove the dinosaurs and many other groups to extinction. The most severe episode occurred at the end of the Permian period, 248 million years ago, when close to 54% of all families, 90% of all species, and 95% of marine species went extinct. The cause of this extinction is still being researched.

Some species are more vulnerable to extinction than others

In general, extinction occurs when environmental conditions change rapidly or severely enough that a species cannot adapt genetically to the change; natural selection simply does not have enough time to work. All manner of environmental events can lead to extinction, from climate change to the rise and fall of sea level, to the arrival of new harmful species, to severe weather events such as extended droughts. In general, small populations and species narrowly specialized on a particular resource or way of life are most vulnerable to extinction from environmental change. Thus, **vulnerable** is yet another SARA category, referring to species that are of particular concern because of characteristics that make them particularly sensitive to human activities or natural events.

The golden toad was a prime example of a vulnerable species that did, eventually, become extinct (see "Central Case: Striking Gold in a Costa Rican Cloud Forest"). The golden toad was **endemic** to the Monteverde cloud forest in Costa Rica, meaning that it occurred nowhere else on the planet. Endemic species face relatively high risks of extinction because all of their members belong to a single, sometimes small, population. At the time of its discovery in 1964, the golden toad was known in an area of only 4 km². It required very specific conditions to breed successfully. The golden toads gathered to breed in springtime in small, root-bound pools. Monteverde provided an ideal living environment for the golden toad, but the minuscule extent of that environment meant that any stresses that deprived the toad of the resources it needed might doom the entire world population of the species. Less than 25 years after its discovery by biologist Jay Savage and colleagues, the golden toad was extinct, probably because of several factors including climate change, habitat alteration, and disease.

Today many amphibian species around the globe are at a high level of risk of vulnerability and risk of extinction, in some cases because of specialized habitat and breeding requirements, in others because of exposure to contaminants or disease. The Global Amphibian Assessment ranked nearly one-third (32%) of the world's amphibians as "threatened," compared with 23% of mammal species and 12% of bird species. Of Canada's 45 amphibian species, 16 (35%) are designated as "at risk" or "sensitive."[8]

Vulnerability resulting from restricted or specialized habitat, lifestyle, or resource requirements is certainly not limited to amphibians. Consider the Vancouver Island marmot (*Marmota vancouverensis*),

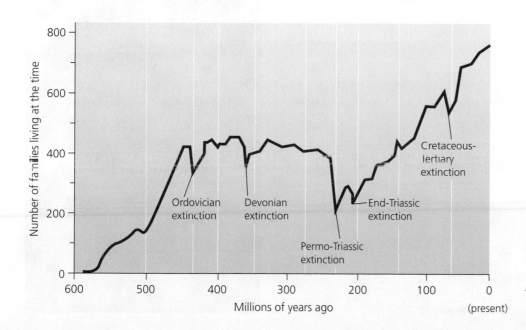

FIGURE 9.8
The fossil record shows evidence of five mass extinctions during the past half-billion years of Earth history. At the end of the Ordovician, Devonian, Permian, Triassic, and Cretaceous periods, 50–95% of the world's species became extinct. Each time, biodiversity later rebounded to equal or higher levels, but the rebound required millions of years in each case.
Source: Data from Raup, D. M., and J. J. Sepkoski (1982) Mass extinctions in the marine fossil record. Science 215: 1501–1503.

one of the rarest mammals in North America, and one of only five species of mammals whose natural range is entirely within Canada. Marmots require small patches of south- to southwest-facing, steeply sloping, boulder-filled meadow, between 800 and 1500 m in altitude—pretty specific! The marmot's range has been drastically reduced over the past few decades, primarily by habitat alteration resulting from logging. As of 2010 only about 300 individuals of this species were alive in the wild, with only a handful of colonies in a few locations in southern Vancouver Island (**FIGURE 9.9**). This number has increased over the past few years from near-extinction (as few as 21 individuals in 2003). The increase was the result of conservation efforts, including captive breeding programs at the Toronto Zoo, Calgary Zoo, and Mountainview Conservation and Breeding Centre in Langley, B.C. The Vancouver Island marmot is listed as endangered on the SARA Registry.

Humans may have started a sixth mass extinction

Biodiversity at all levels is currently being lost as a result of human impacts, most irretrievably in the extinction of species. If the current trend continues, the modern era may see the extinction of more than half of all species. Although similar in scale to previous mass extinctions, today's ongoing mass extinction is different in three primary respects. First, humans are causing it. Second, humans will suffer as a result of it. And third, it may be happening even more rapidly than the previous "Big Five" mass extinctions.

There have been many instances of human-induced species extinction over the past few hundred years. Sailors documented the extinction of the dodo on the Indian Ocean island of Mauritius in the seventeenth century, and we still have a few of the dodo's body parts in museums. Among North American birds in the past two centuries, we have driven into extinction the Carolina parakeet, great auk, Labrador duck, and passenger pigeon, and probably the Bachman's warbler, Eskimo curlew, and ivory-billed woodpecker. Several more species, including the whooping crane, California condor, and Kirtland's warbler are teetering on the brink of extinction.

However, species extinctions caused by humans precede written history. Indeed, people may have been hunting and out-competing species into extinction for thousands of years. Archaeological evidence shows that in case after case, a wave of extinctions followed close on the heels of human arrival on islands and continents (**FIGURE 9.10**). After Polynesians reached Hawaii, half of its birds went extinct. Birds, mammals, and reptiles vanished following human arrival on many other oceanic islands, including large islands such as New Zealand and Madagascar. Dozens of species of large vertebrates died off in Australia after Aborigines arrived roughly 50 000

FIGURE 9.9
An extremely restricted natural range with very specific habitat requirements can leave some species highly vulnerable, especially if local environmental changes occur. The Vancouver Island marmot, seen here, is one of the rarest mammals in North America, and one of only five species of mammals that are found only in Canada. This marmot's range (shown in purple on the map) has been drastically reduced to only a few locations with a handful of colonies, primarily as a result of logging.

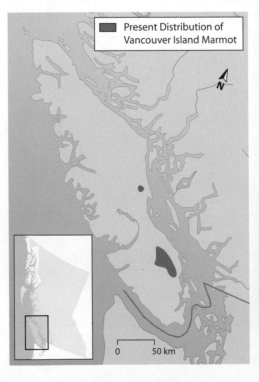

Present Distribution of Vancouver Island Marmot

0   50 km

years ago, and North America lost 33 genera of large mammals after people arrived on the continent about 10 000 years ago.

Today, species loss is accelerating as our population growth and resource consumption put increasing strain on habitats and wildlife. In 2005, scientists with the Millennium Ecosystem Assessment calculated that the current global extinction rate is 100 to 1000 times greater than the background rate. They noted a decrease in genetic diversity as well as declining population sizes and numbers of species, accompanied by greater demands on ecosystem services in the past few decades. Moreover, they projected that the rate of species extinctions would increase tenfold or more in future decades.[9]

To keep track of the current status of endangered species, the *World Conservation Union* (or *IUCN*), a non-governmental organization, maintains the **Red List**, a regularly updated list of species facing high risks of extinction. The 2011 Red List reports that at least 21% (1134) of mammal species and 12.5% (1240) of bird species are threatened. (On the Red List, Threatened species include species that are Critically Endangered, Endangered, or Vulnerable.) Among other major groups (for which

assessments are not fully complete), estimates of the percentage of threatened species range from 17% to 75%.[10] For all of these figures, the *actual* numbers of threatened species extinct, like the actual number of total species in the world, are doubtless greater than the *known* numbers.

In 2011, Anthony Barnosky of the University of California at Berkeley and colleagues carried out a detailed statistical comparison of the current rate of species extinction with the rates of extinction during the "Big Five" mass extinctions. They published their findings in the journal *Nature*. It was an extremely complex undertaking; data limitations and complexities make the analysis very difficult. For example, as the authors pointed out, some 49% of bivalves went extinct at the end of the Cretaceous, but only 1% of the bivalve species alive today have even been assessed, making meaningful comparison difficult. Furthermore, some assessments of threatened and extinct species are inflated because endangered species tend to be assessed first, whereas others are probably grossly underestimated because so few living species have been assessed. The authors concluded from their study that extinctions in the past 500 years do not yet constitute a mass extinction, but they also concluded that rates of

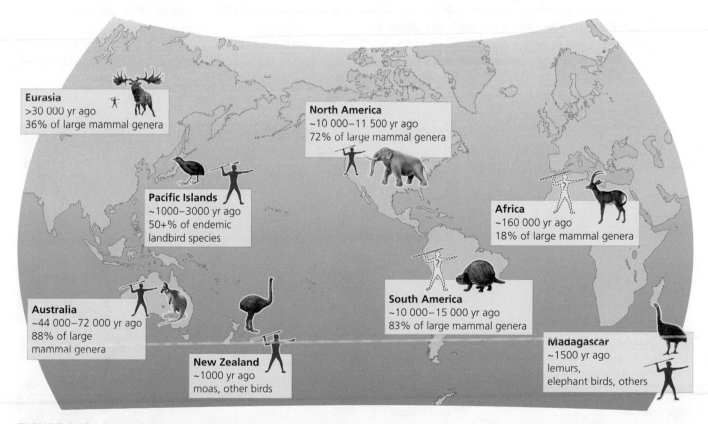

FIGURE 9.10 This map shows for each region the time of human arrival and the extent of the recent extinction wave. Illustrated are representative extinct megafauna from each region. The human hunter icons are sized according to the degree of evidence that human hunting was a cause of extinctions; larger icons indicate more certainty that humans (as opposed to climate change or other forces) were the cause. Data for South America and Africa are too sparse to be conclusive; future archaeological and palaeontological research could alter these interpretations. Source: *Adapted from Barnosky, A. D., et al. (2004) Assessing the causes of late Pleistocene extinctions on the continents. Science 306: 70–75; and Wilson, E. O. (1992) The Diversity of Life. Cambridge, MA: Belknap Press.*

extinction today are much higher than in similar periods during the "Big Five" (**FIGURE 9.11**) and that conservation efforts are urgently needed.[11]

Extinction is only part of the story of biodiversity loss. The larger part of the story is the decline in population sizes of many organisms. Declines in numbers are accompanied by shrinkage of species' geographical ranges. Thus, many species today are less numerous and occupy less area than they once did. Tigers numbered well over 100 000 worldwide in the nineteenth century but number only about 5000 today. The Vancouver marmot population dipped to 21 in a greatly reduced geographical range, making a comeback only as a result of captive breeding. The northern elephant seal population may have been as low as 20 at the end of the nineteenth century, in just one breeding population.

To measure and quantify this degradation, scientists at the World Wildlife Fund and the United Nations Environment Programme (UNEP) developed a metric called the *Living Planet Index*. This index summarizes trends in 7953 different populations of 2544 species of mammals, birds, amphibians, fish, and reptiles that are well enough monitored to provide reliable data. Between 1970 and 2007, the Living Planet Index fell by roughly 30%. This means that the monitored populations are roughly 30% smaller than they were in 1970 (**FIGURE 9.12**), although the decline varies from region to region, species to species, and differing level of human activity. The index for fresh-water species fell by 35%, the index for tropical species fell by 60%, and the index for low-income regions fell by 58% (as compared to 5% in high-income regions).[12]

There are several major causes of biodiversity loss

Reasons for the decline of any given species are often multifaceted and complex, so they can be difficult to determine. The current precipitous decline in populations of amphibians throughout the world provides an example. Frogs, toads, and salamanders worldwide are decreasing drastically in abundance. Many have already gone extinct, and scientists are struggling to explain why. Recent studies have implicated a wide array of factors, and most scientists now suspect that such factors may be interacting synergistically (see "The Science Behind the Story: Amphibian Diversity and Decline").

Overall, scientists have identified four primary causes of population decline and species extinction: habitat alteration, invasive species, pollution, and overharvesting. Global climate change is becoming the fifth. Each of these factors is intensified by human population growth and by our increase in per capita consumption of resources.

Habitat alteration   Nearly every human activity alters the habitat of organisms. Farming replaces

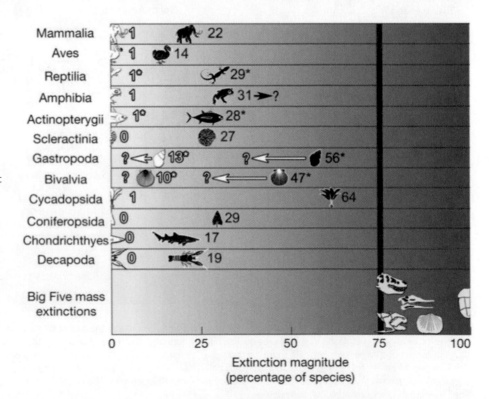

FIGURE 9.11
This diagram shows extinctions for taxonomic groups assessed by the IUCN Red List, compared to the 75% species-loss mark that defines the "Big Five" mass extinctions (red line, and bottom right). The white icons show species that are Extinct or Extinct in the Wild. The black icons add groups that are Threatened (Critically Endangered or Endangered). The numbers are percentages of each group that have become extinct or endangered during the past 500 years. The arrows indicate cases where the assessments may be either inflated or underestimated. *Source: From Barnosky, et al. (2001) Has the Earth's sixth mass extinction already arrived? Nature, 471: 51.*

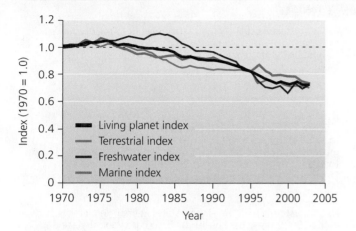

FIGURE 9.12
The Living Planet Index is calculated from trends in populations of individual species. As shown here, some species have increased over the time they have been monitored, but more have decreased; thus, the Living Planet Index overall declined globally. From World Wildlife Fund (2010) *2010 Living Planet Report.*

diverse natural communities with simplified ones of only one or a few plant species. Grazing modifies the structure and species composition of grasslands. Either type of agriculture can lead to desertification. Clearing forests removes the food, shelter, and other resources that forest-dwelling organisms need to survive. Hydroelectric dams turn rivers into reservoirs upstream and affect water conditions and flood plain communities both upstream and downstream. Urbanization and suburban sprawl supplant diverse natural communities with simplified human-made ones, driving many species from their homes.

Because organisms are adapted to the habitats in which they live, any major change is likely to render it less suitable for them. Of course, human-induced habitat change benefits some species. Animals such as starlings, house sparrows, pigeons, raccoons, and grey squirrels do very well in urban and suburban environments and benefit from our modification of natural habitats. However, the species that benefit are relatively few; for every species that gains, more lose. Furthermore, the species that do well in our midst tend to be weedy, cosmopolitan generalists that are in little danger of disappearing any time soon.

Habitat alteration is by far the greatest cause of biodiversity loss today. It is the primary source of population declines for 83% of threatened mammals and 85% of threatened birds, according to UNEP data. As just one example of thousands, the prairies native to central North America have been almost entirely converted to agriculture, especially south of the border in the United States, where the area of prairie habitat has been reduced by more than 99%. As a result, grassland bird populations have declined by an estimated 82–99%. Many grassland species have been extirpated from large areas, and the two species of prairie chickens still persisting in pockets of the Great Plains could soon go extinct.

Habitat destruction has occurred widely in every biome. Over half of temperate forests, grasslands, and shrublands had been converted by the year 1950 (mostly for agriculture). Today habitat is being lost most rapidly in tropical rainforests, tropical dry forests, and savannas. And the Arctic sea ice habitat required by polar bears is disappearing faster than ever in the history of scientific monitoring of its extent.

Invasive species Our introduction of non-native species to new environments, where some may become invasive (**FIGURE 9.13**), has also pushed native species toward extinction. Some introductions have been accidental. Examples include aquatic organisms such as the zebra mussel, transported among continents in the ballast water of ships; animals that have escaped from the pet or food trade; and weed seeds that cling to us as we travel from place to place. Many other introductions have been intentional. People have brought with them food crops, domesticated animals, and other organisms as they colonized new places, generally unaware of the ecological consequences that could result.

Species native to islands are especially vulnerable to disruption from introduced species because native species have been in isolation for so long with relatively few parasites, predators, and competitors. As a result, they have not evolved the defences necessary to resist invaders that are better adapted to these pressures.

Most organisms introduced to new areas perish, but the few types that survive may do very well, especially if they find themselves without the predators and parasites that attacked them back home or without the competitors that had limited their access to resources. Once released from the limiting factors of predation, parasitism, and competition, an introduced species may increase rapidly, spread, and displace native species. Invasive species cause billions of dollars in economic damage each year.

Pollution Pollution can harm organisms in many ways. Air pollution can degrade forest ecosystems; water pollution can adversely affect fish and amphibians; agricultural runoff (including fertilizers, pesticides, and sediments) can harm many terrestrial and aquatic species. Heavy metals, PCBs, endocrine-disrupting compounds, and various other toxic chemicals can poison both people and wildlife, and the effects of oil and chemical spills on wildlife are dramatic and well known.

Invasive Species

Species	Native to...	Invasive in...	Effects
Zebra mussels (*Dreissenna polymorpha*)	Caspian Sea	Freshwater ecosystems including the Great Lakes of Canada and the United States	Zebra mussels most likely made their way from their home by travelling in ballast water taken on by cargo ships. They compete with native species and clog water treatment facilities and power plant cooling systems.
Kudzu (*Pueraria montana*)	Japan	Southeastern United States	Kudzu is a vine that can grow 30 m in a single season. The U.S. Soil Conservation Service introduced kudzu in the 1930s to help control erosion. Adaptable and extraordinarily fast-growing, kudzu has taken over thousands of hectares of forests, fields, and roadsides in the southeastern United States.
Asian long-horned beetles (*Anoplophora glabripennis*)	Asia	United States	Having first arrived in the United States in imported lumber in the 1990s, these beetles burrow into hardwood trees and interfere with the trees' ability to absorb and process water and nutrients. They may wipe out the majority of hardwood trees in an area. Several U.S. cities, including Chicago in 1999 and Seattle in 2002, have cleared thousands of trees after detecting these invaders.
Cane toad (*Bufo marinus*)	Southern United States to tropical South America	Northern Australia and other locations	Since being introduced 70 years ago to control insects in sugarcane fields, the cane toad has wreaked havoc across northern Australia (and other locations). The skin of this tropical American toad can kill its predators, and the cane toad outcompetes native amphibians.
Gypsy moth (*Lymantria dispar*)	Eurasia	Northeastern United States	In the 1860s, a scientist introduced the gypsy moth to Massachusetts in the mistaken belief that it might be bred with others to produce a commercial-quality silk. The gypsy moth failed to start a silk industry, and instead spread through the northeastern United States and beyond, where its outbreaks defoliate trees over large regions every few years.
European starling (*Sturnus vulgaris*)	Europe	North America	The bird was first introduced to New York City in the late nineteenth century by Shakespeare devotees intent on bringing every bird mentioned in Shakespeare's plays to the new continent. It took only 75 years for the birds to spread to the Pacific coast, Alaska, and Mexico, becoming one of the most abundant birds on the continent. Starlings are thought to outcompete native birds for nest sites.
Indian mongoose (*Herpestes auropunctatus*)	Southeast Asia	Hawaii	Rats that had invaded the Hawaiian islands from ships in the seventeenth century were damaging sugarcane fields, so in 1883 the Indian mongoose was introduced to control rat populations. Unfortunately, the rats were active at night and the mongooses fed during the day, so the plan didn't work. Instead mongooses began preying on native species like ground-nesting seabirds and the now-endangered Nene or Hawaiian goose (*Branta sandvicensis*).
A green alga (*Caulerpa taxifolia*)	Tropical oceans and seas	Mediterranean Sea	Dubbed the "killer algae," *Caulerpa taxifolia* has spread along the coasts of several Mediterranean countries since it apparently escaped from Monaco's aquarium in 1984. Creeping underwater over the sand and mud like a green shag carpet, it crowds out other plants, is inedible to most animals, and tangles boat propellers. It has been the focus of intense eradication efforts since arriving recently in Australia and California.
Cheatgrass (*Bromus tectorum*)	Eurasia	Western United States	In just 30 years after its introduction to Washington state in the 1890s, cheatgrass has spread across much of the western United States. Its secret: fire. Its thick patches, which choke out other plants and use up the soil's nitrogen, burn readily. Fire kills many of the native plants, but not cheatgrass, which grows back even stronger amid the lack of competition.

FIGURE 9.13 Invasive species are species that thrive in areas where they are introduced, outcompeting, preying on, or otherwise harming native species. Of the many thousands of invasive species, this chart shows just a few.

Exposure to contaminants, almost exclusively transported by atmospheric and oceanic processes from low latitudes, was cited by the U.S. Fish and Wildlife Service as one of the potential threats to the survival of the polar bear. The damage to wildlife and ecosystems caused by pollution can be severe, but it tends to be less than the damage caused by habitat alteration or invasive species.

Overharvesting   For most species, a high intensity of hunting or harvesting by humans will not *in itself* pose a threat of extinction, but for some species it can. The polar bear is one such species. Large in size, few in number, long-lived, and raising few young in its lifetime—a classic *K-strategist* species—the polar bear is just the type of animal to be vulnerable to population reduction by hunting. Inuit traditional hunters have always carefully balanced and monitored their harvest, informed by their deep ecological knowledge of the environment. The traditional and sport hunt for polar bears is now closely monitored and limited by governments in Canada, the United States, Russia, and other Arctic nations, in conjunction with Aboriginal groups. Whether the balance of sustainable harvesting will be tipped by the impacts of climate change on the polar bear's habitat remains to be seen.

Over the past century, hunting has led to steep declines in the populations of many other K-selected animals. The Atlantic grey whale has gone extinct, and several other whales remain threatened or endangered. Illegal harvesting, poaching, and the sale of contraband wildlife products on the black market contribute to the problem. For example, three of eight tiger species are now extinct; remaining species (such as the Siberian tiger) have been extirpated from much of their natural range. Tiger body parts fetch a high price on the black market (**FIGURE 9.14**). Gorillas and other primates that are killed

for their meat may be facing extinction soon. Thousands of sharks are killed each year for their fins, which are used in soup. Today the ocean contains only 10% of the large animals it once did.

Climate change   The preceding four types of human impacts affect biodiversity in discrete places and times. In contrast, our manipulation of Earth's climate system is beginning to have global impacts on both habitat and biodiversity. As we will explore in subsequent chapters, our emissions of carbon dioxide and other "greenhouse gases" that trap heat in the atmosphere are causing average temperatures to warm worldwide, modifying global weather patterns and increasing the frequency of extreme weather events. Scientists foresee that these effects, together termed *global climate change*, will accelerate and become more severe in the years ahead until we find ways to reduce our emissions from fossil fuels.

Climate change is beginning to exert effects on plants and animals. Extreme weather events such as droughts put increased stress on populations, and warming temperatures are forcing species to move toward the poles and higher in altitude. Some species will be able to adapt, but others will not. Mountaintop organisms cannot move further upslope to escape warming temperatures, so they will likely perish. Trees may not be able to move poleward fast enough. Polar bears may find their sea ice habitat disappearing altogether, with no available replacement. Animals and plants may find themselves among different communities of prey, predators, and parasites to which they are not adapted. All in all, scientists now predict that a 1.5–2.5° global temperature increase could put 20–30% of the world's plants and animals at increased risk of extinction.

FIGURE 9.14
Body parts from tigers have long been used as medicines or aphrodisiacs in some traditional Asian cultures. Hunters and poachers have illegally killed countless tigers through the years to satisfy market demand for these items. Here a street vendor in northern China displays tiger body parts for sale.

THE SCIENCE BEHIND THE STORY

Amphibian Diversity and Decline

Dr. Madhava Meegaskumbura searches for frogs at night in Sri Lanka.

New species of most vertebrate classes are discovered at a rate of only a few per year, but the number of known amphibian species—6300 as of 2010—has jumped by 38% since 1985. At the same time, over 2500 amphibian species worldwide are in decline. Researchers feel they may be naming some species just before they go extinct, and losing others before they are even discovered. The *Global Amphibian Assessment* ranked nearly one-third of the world's amphibians as threatened, compared with 23% of mammals and 12% of bird species. About 170 species of frogs, toads, and salamanders studied just years or decades ago, including the golden toad, are now gone.

These losses are especially worrying because amphibians are regarded as "biological indicators" of the condition of an ecosystem. Amphibians rely on both aquatic and terrestrial environments, and may breathe and absorb water through their skin, so they are sensitive to environmental stresses. Studying the reasons for their decline can tell us much about the state of our environment. The major threats to amphibians worldwide include habitat loss and degradation, exotic species, overharvesting, increases in UV radiation, pollution, disease, and road mortality. Fungal and viral diseases have been implicated in some amphibian declines. Some of these causes of mortality are exacerbated by climate change.[13]

The status of amphibians in Canada is documented in *Wild Species 2005 Report*, the most recent report from the *National General Status Working Group (NGSWG)*.[14] The Wild Species 2005 Report concluded that habitat loss, especially draining of wetlands, is a leading threat to amphibians in Canada.[15] Wetlands that remain within agricultural or urban landscapes may be polluted. Habitat fragmentation also reduces or prevents the movement of individuals among populations, leading to reduced

Raorchestes manohari is one of many new frog species recently discovered in India and Sri Lanka. Its name means "beautiful" in Malayalam.

population stability and reduced exchange of genes.[16]

In some parts of the world, scientific scrutiny has revealed amphibian "hot spots." In the 1990s, an international team of scientists set out to determine whether Sri Lanka, a large tropical island off the coast of India, held more than the 40 frog species that were already known. Researcher Madhava Meegaskumbura and his team combed through trees, rivers, ponds, and leaf litter for 8 years, collecting

All five of these primary causes of population decline are intensified by human population growth and rising per capita consumption. More people and more consumption mean more habitat alteration, more invasive species, more pollution, more overharvesting, and more climate change. Growth in population and growth in consumption are the ultimate or root causes behind the proximate threats to biodiversity.

Benefits of Biodiversity

Just as we now have a solid scientific understanding of the causes of biodiversity loss, we are also coming to appreciate its consequences as we begin to erode the many benefits that biodiversity brings us. The loss of one species may or may not affect us as individuals in any discernible way, but it is important to consider biodiversity from a holistic perspective. A comparison has been made (probably first by population biologist Paul Ehrlich) to the rivets in an airplane wing. The loss of one rivet, or two, or three, will not cause the plane to crash. But at some point the structure will be compromised, and the loss of just one more rivet will cause it to fail. If individual species are like the rivets in the airplane wing, then we might well ask how many more we can afford to lose before the structure is compromised.

This suggests the question, "Why does biodiversity matter?" There are many ways to answer this question, but we can begin by considering the ways that biodiversity benefits people. Scientists have offered a number of tangible, pragmatic reasons for preserving biodiversity, showing how biodiversity directly or indirectly supports human society. In addition, many people feel that organisms have an intrinsic right to exist and that ethical and aesthetic dimensions to biodiversity preservation cannot be ignored. (We will consider these questions in greater detail in subsequent chapters.)

more than 1400 frogs at 300 study sites. They analyzed the frogs' physical appearance, habitat use, and vocalizations, as well as their genes.

The studies led to the discovery, on this one island, of more than 100 previously unknown species of frogs. Some of these unusual animals live on rocks and have leg fringes and markings that help disguise them as clumps of moss. Others are tree frogs that lay their eggs in baskets they construct. These discoveries, however, come against the backdrop of distressing amphibian declines worldwide. Most worrisome is that populations are vanishing even when no direct damage to habitat is apparent. Researchers surmised that a combination of factors might be at work.

In one study, researchers presented young frogs with two common dangers—pesticides and predators—to see how the mix affected their survival. Groups of tadpoles were put in different tubs of water. Some tubs contained pure water, others contained varying levels of the pesticide carbaryl (a popular lawn care pesticide in Canada), and others contained a harmless solvent as a control. To some of the tubs, the researchers added a hungry predator—a young salamander. The salamander was caged and couldn't reach the tadpoles, but they were aware of its presence. Researchers watched to see how many tadpoles survived the different combinations of stress factors.

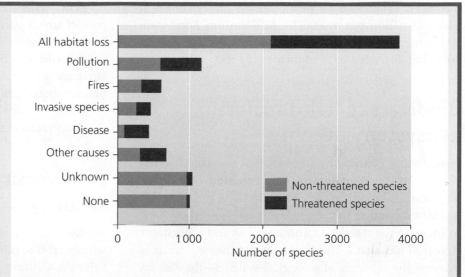

Habitat loss is the main cause of population decline for the world's amphibian species. Pollution is second in importance, but many declines are not yet attributable to cause. *Source: Data from IUCN (2008)* Global Amphibian Assessment.

Their results revealed that tadpoles that withstood one type of stress might not survive two. All tadpoles in clean water with no predators survived, and all tadpoles exposed to high concentrations of carbaryl died within several days, regardless of predator presence. But when carbaryl levels were lower, the presence of the salamander made a noticeable difference. In one trial, 75% of tadpoles survived the pesticide if no predator was present, but in the presence of the salamander, survival rates dropped to 25%. Thus when both stresses were present, death rates increased by two to four times.

As scientists learn more about how factors combine to threaten amphibians, they are gaining a clearer picture of how the fate of these creatures may foreshadow the future for other organisms.

Biodiversity provides ecosystem services

Contrary to popular opinion, some things in life can indeed be free, as long as we choose to protect the living systems that provide them. Intact forests provide clean air and buffer hydrologic systems against flooding and drought. Native crop varieties provide insurance against disease and drought. Abundant wildlife can attract tourists and boost the economies of developing nations. Intact ecosystems provide these and other valuable processes, known as *ecosystem services*, for all of us, free of charge.

Maintaining these ecosystem services is one clear benefit of protecting biodiversity. According to the United Nations Environment Programme (UNEP), biodiversity:

- Provides food, fuel, and fibre
- Provides shelter and building materials

- Purifies air and water
- Detoxifies and decomposes wastes
- Stabilizes and moderates Earth's climate
- Moderates floods, droughts, wind, and temperature extremes
- Generates and renews soil fertility and cycles nutrients
- Pollinates plants, including many crops
- Controls pests and diseases
- Maintains genetic resources as inputs to crop varieties, livestock breeds, and medicines
- Provides cultural and aesthetic benefits
- Gives us the means to adapt to change

Organisms and ecosystems support a vast number of vital processes that humans could not replicate or would need to pay for if nature did not provide them. The annual value of just 17 of these ecosystem services has been calculated to be in the neighbourhood of $16–54 trillion per year. The Millennium Ecosystem Assessment estimated that 60% of ecosystem services are being degraded or used unsustainably.[17]

Biodiversity helps maintain ecosystem integrity

Functioning ecosystems are vital, but does biodiversity really help them maintain their function? Ecologists have found that the answer appears to be yes. Research has demonstrated that high levels of biodiversity tend to increase the *stability* of communities and ecosystems. Research has also found that high biodiversity tends to increase the *resilience* of ecological systems—their ability to weather disturbance, bounce back from stresses, and adapt to change. Most of this research has dealt with species diversity, but new work is finding similar effects for genetic diversity. Thus, a decrease in biodiversity could diminish a natural system's ability to function and to provide services to our society.

What about the extinction of individual species, however? Sceptics have asked whether the loss of a few endangered species will really make much difference in an ecosystem's ability to function. Ecological research suggests that the answer to this question depends on which species are removed. Removing a species that can be functionally replaced by others may make little difference.

Recall, however, our previous discussion of *keystone species*. Like the keystone that holds together an arch, a keystone species is one whose removal results in significant changes in an ecological system. If a keystone species is extirpated or driven extinct, other species may disappear or experience significant population changes as a result.

Top predators such as polar bears and tigers are often considered keystone species. A single top predator may prey on many other carnivores, each of which may prey on many herbivores, each of which may consume many plants. Thus the removal of a single individual at the top of a food chain can have impacts that multiply as they cascade down the food chain. Moreover, top predators such as tigers, wolves, and grizzly bears are among the species most vulnerable to human impact. Large animals are frequently hunted, and also need large areas of habitat, making them susceptible to habitat loss and fragmentation. Top predators are also vulnerable to the buildup of toxic pollutants in their tissues through the process of biomagnification, as seen in the example of beluga whales in the St. Lawrence estuary and polar bears in the Arctic.

Ecosystems are complex, though, and it is difficult to predict which particular species may be important. The influence of tiny "ecosystem engineers," such as ants and earthworms, can be every bit as far-reaching as those of keystone species. Thus, many people prefer to apply the precautionary principle in the spirit of ecologist Aldo Leopold, who advised, "To keep every cog and wheel is the first precaution of intelligent tinkering."[18]

Biodiversity enhances food security

Biodiversity benefits agriculture, as well. Genetic diversity within crop species and their ancestors is enormously valuable. California's barley crops annually receive $160 million in disease resistance benefits from Ethiopian strains of barley. During the 1970s a researcher discovered a maize species in Mexico known as *Zea diploperennis*. This maize is highly resistant to disease, and it is a perennial, meaning it will grow back year after year without being replanted. Yet this valuable plant had almost been lost; at the time of its discovery, its entire range was limited to a 10-ha plot of land in the mountains of the Mexican state of Jalisco.

Other potentially important food crops await utilization (**FIGURE 9.15**). The babassu palm (*Orbignya phalerata*) of the Amazon produces more vegetable oil than any other plant. The serendipity berry (*Dioscoreophyllum cumminsii*) produces a sweetener that is 3000 times sweeter than table sugar. Several species of salt-tolerant grasses and trees are so hardy that farmers can irrigate them with saltwater. These same plants also produce animal feed, a substitute for conventional vegetable oil, and other economically important products. Such species could be immeasurably beneficial to areas undergoing soil salinization due to poorly managed irrigation.

Biodiversity provides drugs and medicines

People have made medicines from plants for centuries, and many of today's widely used drugs were discovered by studying chemical compounds present in wild plants, animals, and microbes (**FIGURE 9.16**). Each year pharmaceutical products owing their origin to wild species generate up to $150 billion in sales and save thousands of lives.

It can truly be argued that every species that goes extinct represents one lost opportunity to find a cure

Food Security and Biodiversity: Potential new food sources		
Species	Native to...	Potential uses and benefits
Amaranths (three species of *Amaranthus*)	Tropical and Andean America	Grain and leafy vegetable; livestock feed; rapid growth, drought resistant
Buriti palm (*Mauritia flexuosa*)	Amazon lowlands	"Tree of life" to Amerindians; vitamin-rich fruit; pith as source for bread; palm heart from shoots
Maca (*Lepidium meyenii*)	Andes Mountains	Cold-resistant root vegetable resembling radish, with distinctive flavour; near extinction
Tree tomato (*Cyphomandra betacea*)	South America	Elongated fruit with sweet taste
Babirusa (*Babyrousa babyrussa*)	Indonesia: Moluccas and Sulawesi	A deep-forest pig; thrives on vegetation high in cellulose and hence less dependent on grain
Capybara (*Hydrochoeris hydrochoeris*)	South America	World's largest rodent; meat esteemed; easily ranched in open habitats near water
Vicuna (*Lama vicugna*)	Central Andes	Threatened species related to llama; valuable source of meat, fur, and hides; can be profitably ranched
Chachalacas (*Ortalis*, many species)	South and Central America	Birds, potentially tropical chickens; thrive in dense populations; adaptable to human habitations; fast-growing
Sand grouse (*Pterocles*, many species)	Deserts of Africa and Asia	Pigeon-like birds adapted to harshest deserts; domestication a possibility

FIGURE 9.15
By protecting biodiversity, we can enhance food security. The wild species shown here are a tiny fraction of the many plants and animals that could someday supplement our food supply.
Source: Adapted from Wilson, E. O. (1992) The Diversity of Life. *Cambridge, MA: Belknap Press.*

Medicines and Biodiversity: Natural sources of pharmaceuticals		
Plant	Drug	Medical application
Pineapple (*Ananas comosus*)	Bromelain	Controls tissue inflammation
Autumn crocus (*Colchicum autumnale*)	Colchicine	Anticancer agent
Yellow cinchona (*Cinchona ledgeriana*)	Quinine	Antimalarial
Common thyme (*Thymus vulgaris*)	Thymol	Cures fungal infection
Pacific yew (*Taxus brevifolia*)	Taxol	Anticancer (especially ovarian cancer)
Velvet bean (*Mucuna deeringiana*)	L-Dopa	Parkinson's disease suppressant
Common foxglove (*Digitalis purpurea*)	Digitoxin	Cardiac stimulant

FIGURE 9.16
By protecting biodiversity, we can enhance our ability to treat illness. Shown here are just a few of the plants that have so far been found to provide chemical compounds of medical benefit.
Source: Adapted from Wilson, E. O. (1992) The Diversity of Life. *Cambridge, MA: Belknap Press.*

for cancer or AIDS. The rosy periwinkle (*Catharanthus roseus*) produces compounds that treat Hodgkin's disease and a particularly deadly form of leukemia. Had this native plant of Madagascar become extinct prior to its discovery by medical researchers, two deadly diseases would have claimed far more victims than they have to date. In Australia, where the govern-

ment has placed high priority on research into products from rare and endangered species, a rare species of cork, *Duboisia leichhardtii*, now provides hyoscine, a compound that physicians use to treat cancer, stomach disorders, and motion sickness. Another Australian plant, *Tylophora*, provides a drug that treats lymphoid leukemia. Researchers are now exploring the potential of the compound prostaglandin E2 in treating gastric ulcers. This compound was first discovered in two frog species unique to the rainforest of Queensland, Australia. Scientists believe that both species are now extinct.

A compound that forms the basis for the anticancer drug Taxol is derived from the bark of the Pacific yew (genus *taxus*), native to British Columbia. At first, over-harvesting threatened not only the very slow-growing yew but also another endangered species, the spotted owl, which relies on the yew as part of its natural habitat. Today the basic ingredient for Taxol is still extracted from the bark of the Pacific yew, but the tree is cultivated specifically for this purpose.

Biodiversity provides additional economic benefits

Besides providing products and contributing to our food security and health, biodiversity can represent a direct source of income through tourism, particularly for developing countries in the tropics that have impressive species diversity. Many people like to travel to experience protected natural areas, and in so doing they create economic opportunity for residents living near those natural areas. Visitors spend money at local businesses, hire local people as guides, and support the parks that employ local residents.

Costa Rica is an example of a country that has benefited in this way. Between 1945 and 1995, the population of Costa Rica grew from 860 000 to 3.34 million, and the percentage of land devoted to pasture increased from 12% to 33%. With much of the formerly forested land converted to agriculture, the proportion of the country covered by forest decreased from 80% to 25%. In 1991, Costa Rica was losing its forests faster than any other country in the world—nearly 140 ha per day. As a result, populations of innumerable species were declining, and some were becoming endangered (**FIGURE 9.17**). Few people foresaw the need to conserve biological resources until it became clear that they were being rapidly lost.

weighing the issues

BIOPROSPECTING IN COSTA RICA

Bioprospectors for pharmaceutical companies scour biodiversity-rich countries, searching for organisms that might provide new drugs, foods, or other valuable products. Many have been criticized for harvesting indigenous species to create commercial products that do not benefit the country of origin. To make sure it would not lose the benefits of its own biodiversity, Costa Rica reached an agreement with the Merck pharmaceutical company in 1991. The nonprofit National Biodiversity Institute of Costa Rica (INBio) allowed Merck to evaluate a limited number of Costa Rica's species for their commercial potential in return for $1.1 million, a small royalty rate on any products developed, and training for Costa Rican scientists.

Do you think both sides won in this agreement? What if Merck discovers a compound that could be turned into a billion-dollar drug? Does this provide a good model for other countries, and for other companies?

In 1970, the Costa Rican government and international representatives came together to create the country's first national parks and protected areas. In 1972 the efforts of local residents, along with contributions from interna-

(a) Green sea turtle

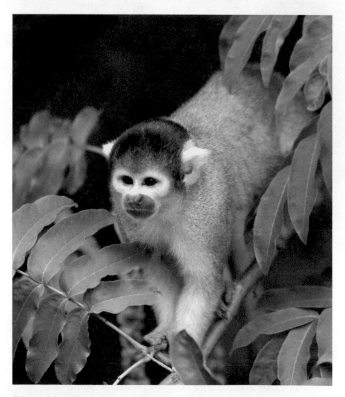

(b) Red-backed squirrel monkey

FIGURE 9.17
Costa Rica is home to a number of species classified as globally threatened or endangered. The green sea turtle (*Chelonia mydas*) **(a)**, which lays its eggs on beaches in Costa Rica, has undergone steep population declines. The red-backed squirrel monkey (*Saimiri oerstedii*) **(b)** is endemic to a tiny area in Costa Rica and is vulnerable to forest loss because of its small geographic range.

tional conservation organizations, provided the beginnings of what is today the Monteverde Cloud Forest Biological Reserve. This privately managed reserve, which occupies 10 500 ha, was established to protect the forest and its populations of 2500 plant species, 400 bird species, 500 butterfly species, 100 mammal species, and 120 reptile and amphibian species, including the golden toad.

Costa Rica and its citizens are now reaping the benefits of their conservation efforts—not only ecological benefits, but also economic ones. Because of its parks and its reputation for conservation, tourists from around the world now visit Costa Rica for **ecotourism** (**FIGURE 9.18**). The ecotourism industry draws more than 1 million visitors to Costa Rica each year, provides thousands of jobs, and is a major contributor to the country's economy. Today the Costa Rican economy is fuelled in large part by commerce and ecotourism, whose contributions outweigh those of industry and agriculture combined.

It remains to be seen how effectively ecotourism can help preserve natural systems in Costa Rica in the long term. As forests outside the parks disappear, the parks are beginning to suffer from illegal hunting and timber extraction. Conservationists say the parks are poorly protected and underfunded. Ecotourism will likely need to generate still more money to preserve habitat, protect endangered species, and restore altered communities to their former condition. In the meantime, ecotourism has become a vital source of income for Costa Rica, with its rainforests; Australia, with its Great Barrier Reef; Belize, with its reefs, caves, and rainforests; and Kenya and Tanzania, with their savannah wildlife. Canada, too, benefits from ecotourism; our national and provincial parks draw millions of visitors annually. Ecotourism provides a financial incentive to preserve natural areas and reduce impacts on the landscape and on native species.

FIGURE 9.18
Costa Rica has protected a wide array of its diverse natural areas. This protection has stimulated the nation's economy through ecotourism. Here, visitors experience a walkway through the forest canopy in one of the nation's parks.

weighing the issues
HOW BEST TO CONSERVE BIODIVERSITY?

Most people view national parks and ecotourism as excellent ways to help keep ecological systems intact. Yet the golden toad went extinct despite living within a reserve established to protect it, and climate change does not pay attention to park boundaries. What lessons can we learn from this about the conservation of biodiversity?

As ecotourism increases in popularity, however, critics warn that too many visitors to natural areas can degrade the outdoor experience and disturb wildlife. Anyone who has been to Yellowstone Park on a crowded summer weekend can attest to this. As ecotourism continues to increase, so will the debate over its costs and benefits for local communities and for biodiversity.

People value and seek out connections with nature

Not all of the benefits of biodiversity to humans can be expressed in the hard numbers of economics or the day-to-day practicalities of food and medicine. Some scientists and philosophers argue that there is a deeper importance to biodiversity. E. O. Wilson (**FIGURE 9.19**)

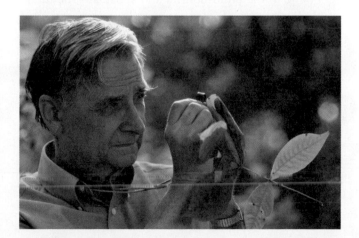

FIGURE 9.19
Edward O. Wilson is the world's most recognized authority on biodiversity and its conservation and has inspired many people who study our planet's life. A Harvard professor and world-renowned expert on ants, Wilson has written over 20 books and has won two Pulitzer prizes. His books *The Diversity of Life* and *The Future of Life* address the value of biodiversity and its outlook for the future.

has described a phenomenon he calls **biophilia**, "the connections that human beings subconsciously seek with the rest of life."[19] Wilson and others have cited as evidence of biophilia our affinity for parks and wildlife, our keeping of pets, the high value of real estate with a view of natural landscapes, and our interest—despite being far removed from a hunter-gatherer lifestyle—in hiking, bird-watching, fishing, hunting, backpacking, and similar outdoor pursuits.

In a 2005 book, writer Richard Louv adds that as today's children are increasingly deprived of outdoor experiences and direct contact with wild organisms, they suffer what he calls "nature-deficit disorder."[20] Although it is not a medical condition, this alienation from biodiversity and the natural environment, Louv argues, may damage childhood development and lie behind many of the emotional and physical problems young people in developed nations face today.

If Wilson, Louv, and others are right, then biophilia may not only affect ecotourism and real estate prices, but also may influence our ethics. We humans are part of nature, and like any other animal we need to use resources and consume other organisms to survive. In that sense, there is nothing immoral about our doing so. However, we have reasoning ability and are able to control our actions and make conscious decisions. Our ethical sense has developed from this intelligence and ability to choose. As our society's sphere of ethical consideration has widened over time, more people have come to believe that other organisms have intrinsic value and an inherent right to exist.

Despite our ethical convictions, however, and despite biodiversity's many benefits—from the pragmatic and economic to the philosophical and spiritual—the future of biodiversity is far from secure. Even our protected areas and parks are not big enough or protected well enough to ensure that biodiversity is fully safeguarded within their borders. The search for solutions to today's biodiversity crisis is an exciting and active one, and scientists are playing a leading role in developing innovative approaches to maintaining the diversity of life on Earth.

Approaches to Conservation

In his 1994 autobiography, *Naturalist*, E. O. Wilson wrote, "In one lifetime exploding human populations have reduced wildernesses to threatened nature reserves. Ecosystems and species are vanishing at the fastest rate in 65 million years. Troubled by what we have wrought, we have begun to turn in our role from local conqueror to global steward."[21] Today, more and more scientists and

roots

CONSERVATION AND PRESERVATION

The word **conservation**, used in reference to the environment since 1922, comes from the Latin *conservationem*, "keeping, conserving." The word **preservation** comes from the Latin *preservationem*, "keeping safe, preserving."

citizens perceive a need to do something to stem the loss of biodiversity.

In theory, there is a distinction between the concepts of conservation and preservation. *Preservation* implies the maintenance of a natural area or species in a pristine or unaltered state, or as close to it as possible. *Conservation* implies that natural habitat and species should be cared for and maintained for multiple purposes, and that they have not only their own intrinsic value, but also multiple values (potential or actual) for people. You will learn more about these distinctions, and the modern history of these concepts in environmental and resource management, in the chapter on environmental ethics and economics. For now, let's look at some of the approaches that environmental scientists and managers have developed to help us conserve both habitats and species.

Conservation biology addresses habitat degradation and species loss

The loss of biodiversity, the urge to act as responsible stewards of natural systems, and the desire to use science as a tool in that endeavour helped spark the rise of conservation biology. **Conservation biology** is a scientific discipline devoted to understanding the factors, forces, and processes that influence the loss, protection, and restoration of biological diversity. It arose as scientists became increasingly alarmed at the degradation of the natural systems they had spent their lives studying.

Conservation biologists choose questions and pursue research with the aim of developing solutions to the problems of habitat degradation and species loss (**FIGURE 9.20**). Conservation biology is thus an applied and goal-oriented science, with implicit values and ethical standards. This perceived element of advocacy sparked some criticism of conservation biology in its early years. However, as scientists have come to recognize the scope of human impact on the planet, more of them have directed their work to address environmental problems. Today conservation biology is a thriving pursuit that is

FIGURE 9.20
Conservation biologists integrate lab and field research to develop solutions to biodiversity loss. Here, a conservation biologist checks on a jabiru stork nest in the Pantanal region of Brazil.

central to environmental science and to achieving a sustainable society.

Conservation biologists integrate an understanding of evolution and extinction with ecology and the dynamic nature of environmental systems. They use field data, lab data, theory, and experiments to study the impacts of humans on other organisms. They also attempt to design, test, and implement ways to mitigate human impact.

These researchers address the challenges facing biological diversity at all levels, from genetic diversity to species diversity to ecosystem diversity. At the genetic level, *conservation geneticists* study genetic attributes of organisms, to infer the status of their populations. If two populations of a species are found to be genetically distinct enough to be considered subspecies, they may have different ecological needs and may require different types of management. Conservation geneticists also ask how small a population can become and how much genetic variation it can lose before running into problems such as inbreeding depression. By determining a minimum viable population size for a given population, conservation geneticists and population biologists provide wildlife managers with an indication of how important it may be to increase the population.

Many conservation research efforts also revolve around habitats, communities, ecosystems, and landscapes. Organisms are sometimes distributed across a landscape as a network of subpopulations. Because small and isolated subpopulations are most vulnerable to extirpation, conservation biologists pay special attention to them. By examining how organisms disperse from one habitat patch to another, and how their genes flow among subpopulations, conservation biologists try to learn how likely a population is to persist or succumb in the face of habitat change or other threats.

Island biogeography can help address habitat fragmentation

Safeguarding habitat for species and conserving communities and ecosystems require thinking and working at the landscape level. One key conceptual tool for doing so is the *equilibrium model of island biogeography*. This model, introduced by conservation biologist E. O. Wilson and ecologist Robert MacArthur in 1963, originally explained how species came to be distributed among oceanic islands. Since then, researchers have also applied it to "habitat islands"—patches of one habitat type isolated within "seas" of others.

The island biogeography model explains how the number of species on an island results from an equilibrium balance between the number added by immigration and the number lost through extirpation. It predicts an island's species richness based on its size and distance from the mainland:

- The farther an island is located from a continent, the fewer species tend to find and colonize it; this is called the *distance effect*. Thus, remote islands host fewer species because of lower immigration rates (**FIGURE 9.21A**).
- Large islands have higher immigration rates because they present fatter targets for wandering or dispersing organisms to encounter (**FIGURE 9.21B**).
- Large islands have lower extinction rates because more space allows for larger populations, which are less vulnerable to dropping to zero by chance (**FIGURE 9.21C**).

Together, these latter two trends give large islands more species at equilibrium than small islands—a phenomenon called the *area effect*. Large islands also tend to contain more species because they generally possess more habitats than smaller islands, providing suitable environments for a wider variety of arriving species. Very roughly, the number of species on an island is expected to double as island size increases tenfold. This effect can be illustrated through *species-area curves*, which quantify the number of species per area in a particular habitat (**FIGURE 9.22**).

The patterns established by island biogeography and the species-area relationship hold up for terrestrial habitat "islands," as well, such as forests cut into smaller areas by logging and road building (**FIGURE 9.23**), a process known as **habitat fragmentation**. Expanding agriculture, spreading cities, highways, logging, and many other impacts have chopped up large contiguous expanses of habitat into small, disconnected ones. Fragmentation of

(a) Distance effect   **(b) Target size**   **(c) Differential extinction**

FIGURE 9.21   Islands located close to a continent receive more immigrants than islands that are distant **(a)**, so that near islands end up with more species. Large islands present fatter targets for dispersing organisms to encounter **(b)**, so that more species immigrate to large islands than to small islands. Large islands also experience lower extinction rates **(c)**, because their larger area can support larger populations.

forests and other habitats constitutes one of the prime threats to biodiversity. In response, conservation biologists have designed landscape-level strategies to try to optimize the arrangement of areas to be preserved.

Habitat fragmentation has the greatest impact on large species and, especially, migratory species. Bears, mountain lions, elephants, caribou, and other animals that need large ranges in which to roam may disappear. Bird species that thrive in the interior of forests may fail to reproduce when forced near the edge of a fragment of habitat. Their nests often are attacked by predators

FIGURE 9.22
The larger the island, the greater the number of species—a prediction borne out by data from around the world. By plotting the number of amphibians and reptile species on Caribbean islands as a function of the areas of these islands, the species-area curve shows that species richness increases with area. The increase is not linear, but logarithmic; note the scales of the axes.
Source: Data from MacArthur, R. H., and E. O. Wilson (1967) The Theory of Island Biogeography. Princeton University Press.

and parasites that favour open habitats surrounding the fragment or that travel along habitat edges. Avian ecologists judge forest fragmentation to be a main reason why populations of many songbirds of eastern North America are declining; an additional significant impact is predation by feral (escaped) house cats.

Because habitat fragmentation is such a central issue in biodiversity conservation, and because there are limits on how much land can be set aside, conservation biologists have argued heatedly about whether it is better to make wildlife reserves large in size and few in number, or many in number but small in size. Nicknamed the **SLOSS dilemma**, for "**S**ingle **L**arge **o**r **S**everal **S**mall," this debate is ongoing and complex, but it seems clear that large species that roam great distances, such as the caribou, would benefit more from the "single large" approach to reserve design. In contrast, creatures such as insects that live as larvae in small areas may do just fine in a number of small isolated reserves, especially if they can disperse as adults by flying from one reserve to another.

A related issue is whether **corridors** of protected land are important for allowing animals to travel between islands of protected habitat. In theory, connections between fragments provide animals with access to more habitats, and help enable gene flow to maintain populations in the long term. Many land management agencies and environmental groups try, when possible, to join new reserves to existing reserves for these reasons. The establishment and maintenance of greenbelts and natural corridors is one of the guiding principles in environmental and natural resource management in Canada today.

FIGURE 9.23
Forest clearing, farming, road building, and other types of human land use and development can fragment natural areas, leaving small "islands" of habitat. Habitat fragmentation usually begins when gaps are created within a natural habitat. As development proceeds, these gaps expand, join together, and eventually dominate the landscape, stranding islands of habitat in their midst. As habitat becomes fragmented, fewer populations can persist, and numbers of species in the fragments decrease with time.

Captive breeding and cloning are single-species approaches

Conservation efforts that aim to save species by maintaining their habitat are examples of *in situ* conservation; *in situ* is a Latin phrase that means "in its natural or original place." In conjunction with this, many conservation biologists are going to impressive lengths to save individual threatened and endangered species. Traditional *ex situ* (out-of-place) conservation efforts involve the preservation of species in zoos, aquaria, seed banks, arboretums, and the like. In the past few decades, many zoos and

weighing the issues
FRAGMENTATION AND BIODIVERSITY

Suppose a critic of conservation tells you that human development increases biodiversity, pointing out that when a forest is fragmented, new habitats, such as grassy lots and gardens, may be introduced to an area and allow additional species to live there. How would you respond?

botanical gardens have become centres for the **captive breeding** of endangered species, raising individuals for the purpose of reintroducing them into the wild.

One example of a captive breeding program is aimed at saving the California condor, North America's largest bird (**FIGURE 9.24**). Condors were persecuted in the early twentieth century, collided with electrical wires, and succumbed to lead poisoning from scavenging carcasses of animals killed with lead shot. By 1982, only 22 condors remained, and biologists decided to take all the birds into captivity, in hopes of boosting their numbers and then releasing them. The ongoing program is succeeding. So far, over 100 of the 250 birds raised in captivity have been released into the wild at sites in California and Arizona, where a few pairs have begun nesting.

Other reintroduction programs have been more controversial. Reintroducing wolves to Yellowstone National Park—an effort that involved imported wolves from across the border in Canada—has proven popular with the public. However, reintroducing wolves to sites in Arizona and New Mexico met stiff resistance from ranchers who fear the wolves will attack their livestock. The program is making slow headway, and several of the wolves have been shot. China is considering a reintroduction program for the Siberian tiger, which has been extirpated from China, part of its natural range. The Chinese government is preparing 600 captive Siberian tigers for release into the forests in the far northeastern part of the country. However, critics note that the forests are so fragmented that efforts would be better focused on improving habitat first.

Some reintroduction programs require international cooperation. For example, the only naturally occurring wild population of whooping cranes nests and breeds each spring in Wood Buffalo Park, straddling the border between Alberta and the Northwest Territories. The flock then migrates and winters over in the Aransas National Wildlife Refuge on the Gulf coast of Texas. The population of almost 2000 cranes in the late 1800s dipped to an all-time low of just 15 in 1941, after being decimated by hunting. In the past few years the population has slowly increased to

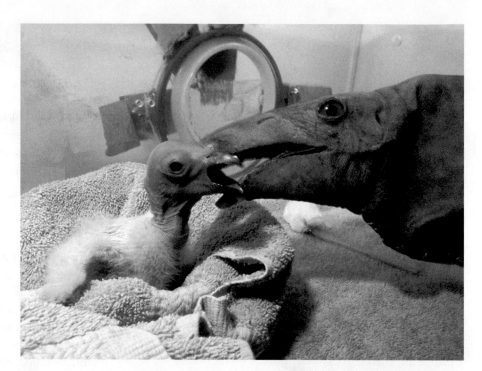

FIGURE 9.24
In efforts to save the California condor (*Gymnogyps californianus*) from extinction, biologists have raised hundreds of chicks in captivity with the help of hand puppets designed to look and feel like the heads of adult condors. Using these puppets, biologists feed the growing chicks in an enclosure and shield them from all contact with humans, so that when the chick is grown it does not feel an attachment to people.

about 180 birds as a result of careful reintroductions, led by the International Crane Recovery Team consisting of scientists from both Canada and the United States.[22]

Another example of (tentatively) successful captive breeding and reintroduction is that of the swift fox (*Vulpes velox*), a small, slender, tan-coloured fox whose natural habitat is the prairies of Manitoba, Saskatchewan, and Alberta, as well as the western grasslands of the United States (**FIGURE 9.25**). It is mainly nocturnal and is named for its speed (*velox*); it races through the prairie grasslands at up to 60 km per hour. In the first part of the twentieth century, the swift fox disappeared entirely from the wild in Canada, mostly as a result of the loss of habitat. The last swift fox was captured in Canada in 1928; it was considered extirpated by 1938 and officially declared as such by COSEWIC in 1978.[23]

In 1971 Miles and Beryl Smeeton of the Wildlife Reserve of Western Canada imported two pairs of swift foxes from the U.S., with the intention of starting a captive breeding and release program. Over the next decade or so the organization (later renamed the Cochrane Ecological Institute) developed partnerships, first with the University of Calgary, then with the Canadian Wildlife Service, and finally with the government of Saskatchewan and Fish and Wildlife Service of Alberta. In 1983 a reintroduction program was started to replace swift foxes back into parts of their native territory in Canada.[24] Many of the foxes that were reintroduced came from wild populations in the United States; some were bred in captivity in Canada.

In the mid- to late 1980s, 155 reintroduced foxes were radio-collared and tracked by program-related research-

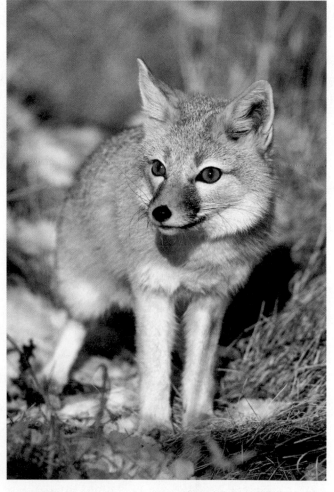

FIGURE 9.25
The swift fox has been successfully reintroduced into parts of its natural range in Canada, where it had been declared extirpated.

ers, who determined that relocation was considerably more successful than captive breeding and relocation; the survival rate after the first year for the relocated foxes was 85%, as compared with 25% for the captive-bred foxes.[25] But with fewer and fewer foxes available for relocation, program scientists began to experiment with different release approaches for the captive-bred foxes. In a "soft" release, young foxes are kept in an outdoor pen over the winter to acclimatize, then released in the spring or winter. In a "hard" release, the young foxes are released straight into the wild. Researchers determined that the hard release is as successful as the soft release, in terms of the survival rates for the animals, and more cost-effective.[26]

According to Joel Nicholson, a biologist with Alberta Fish and Wildlife, "the swift fox reintroduction program has been one of the most successful *canid* reintroductions in the world."[27] A 2005–2006 count of the swift fox population in Alberta, Saskatchewan, and Montana counted 1162 foxes, mostly born in the wild. The swift fox is no longer considered extirpated, but it is still designated as an endangered species under SARA in Canada.

The newest idea for saving species from extinction is to create more individuals by cloning them. In this technique, DNA from an endangered species is inserted into a cultured egg without a nucleus, and the egg is implanted into a closely related species that can act as a surrogate mother. So far two Eurasian mammals have been cloned in this way. With future genetic technology, some scientists even talk of recreating extinct species from DNA recovered from preserved body parts. However, even if cloning can succeed from a technical standpoint, most biologists agree that such efforts are not an adequate response to biodiversity loss. Without ample habitat and protection in the wild, having cloned animals in a zoo does little good.

Some species act as "umbrellas" to protect communities

Sometimes individual species can be used as tools for the broader conservation of communities and ecosystems. Species-specific legislation can provide legal justification and resources for species conservation, but no such laws exist for communities, habitats, or ecosystems. Large species that roam great distances, such as tigers, bears, and elephants, require large areas of habitat. Meeting the habitat needs of these so-called *umbrella species* automatically helps meet those of thousands of less charismatic animals, plants, and fungi that would never elicit as much public interest.

Environmental advocacy organizations have found that using large, charismatic vertebrates as spearheads for biodiversity conservation has been an effective strategy.

This approach of promoting particularly visible *flagship species* is evident in the long-time symbol of the World Wide Fund for Nature (World Wildlife Fund in North America, or WWF), the giant panda. The panda is a large endangered animal requiring sizeable stands of undisturbed bamboo forest. Its lovable appearance has made it a favourite with the public—and an effective tool for soliciting funding for conservation efforts that protect far more than just the panda.

At the same time, many conservation organizations today are moving beyond the single-species approach. The Nature Conservancy, for instance, is a *land trust* that focuses on whole communities and landscapes by acquiring large tracts of land for conservation. The most ambitious effort may be the Wildlands Network, a group proposing to restore huge amounts of North America's land to its pre-settlement state in an interconnected network of habitats.

Conservation efforts are both international and national

Canada enacted its long-awaited endangered species law, the *Species at Risk Act (SARA)*, in 2002. The federal government was careful to stress cooperation with landowners and provincial governments, rather than presenting the law as a decree from the national government. Canada's environment minister at the time, David Anderson, wanted to avoid the hostility unleashed by the "command-and-control" approach of the U.S. *Endangered Species Act (ESA)* some 30 years before. That hostility against ESA continues to this day in the United States, although the legislation can point to some significant successes in protecting endangered species.

Environmentalists and many scientists in Canada have protested that SARA is too weak and fails to protect species and habitat adequately. One of the main objections is that the process of listing a species is not based strictly on scientific information but is heavily influenced by both politics and economics. The process for listing a species in the SARA Registry, which qualifies it for legal protection under the Act, begins with monitoring and an assessment of the status of the species by the *National General Status Working Group (NGSWG)*. The *Committee on the Status of Endangered Wildlife in Canada (COSEWIC)* may then propose designation (or a change in designation) for a particular species. The Minister of the Environment then responds to the assessment and the proposed designation. Between 2003 and 2006, for example, COSEWIC recommended 186 plants and animals for SARA listing, of which 30 were turned down.

Arne Mooers and colleagues from Simon Fraser University have studied the final decisions made by the federal government on SARA listings recommended by COSEWIC, and they have found that science often takes a back seat to economics and politics. A 2006 study by the researchers showed that animals that are of economic value (including fish) and animals from Canada's North have the least chance of being approved for legal protection under SARA. For example, none of the 10 species from Nunavut that were recommended for listing by COSEWIC was approved. The only marine fish that was approved for listing (of the 11 recommended) was the green sturgeon, which is considered inedible and is thus avoided by the commercial fishing industry.[28] At the beginning of this chapter, you learned about some of the complexities involved in designating the polar bear as a threatened species; to date, the polar bear has retained its SARA designation of "special concern."

Today many nations have laws protecting species, although they are not always well enforced. At the international level, the United Nations has facilitated several treaties to protect biodiversity. The 1973 *Convention on International Trade in Endangered Species of Wild Fauna and Flora (CITES)* protects endangered species by banning the international transport of their body parts. When nations enforce it, CITES can protect the tiger and other rare species whose body parts are traded internationally.

In 1992, leaders of many nations agreed to the *Convention on Biological Diversity*. This treaty embodies three goals: to conserve biodiversity, to use biodiversity in a sustainable manner, and to ensure the fair distribution of biodiversity's benefits. The Convention aims to help:

- Provide incentives for biodiversity conservation
- Manage access to and use of genetic resources
- Transfer technology, including biotechnology
- Promote scientific cooperation
- Assess the effects of human actions on biodiversity
- Promote biodiversity education and awareness
- Provide funding for critical activities
- Encourage every nation to report regularly on their biodiversity conservation efforts

The treaty's many accomplishments so far include ensuring that Ugandan people share in the economic benefits of wildlife preserves, increasing global markets for "shade-grown" coffee and other crops grown without removing forests, and replacing pesticide-intensive farming practices with sustainable ones in some rice-producing Asian nations. As of 2007, 188 nations had become parties to the Convention on Biological Diversity. Those choosing *not* to do so include Iraq, Somalia, the Vatican, and the United States. This decision is one example of why the U.S. government is no longer widely regarded as a leader in biodiversity conservation efforts.

Hot spots highlight areas of high biodiversity

One international approach oriented around geographic regions, rather than single species, has been the effort to map **biodiversity hot spots**. The concept of biodiversity hot spots was introduced in 1988 by British ecologist Norman Myers as a way to prioritize regions that are most important globally for biodiversity conservation. A hot spot is an area that supports an especially great number of species that are endemic, that is, found nowhere else in the world (**FIGURE 9.26**). To qualify as a hotspot, a location must harbour at least 1500 endemic plant species, or 0.5% of the world total. In addition, a hot spot must have already lost 70% of its habitat as a result of human impact and be in danger of losing more.

The nonprofit group Conservation International maintains a list of 34 biodiversity hot spots (**FIGURE 9.27**). The ecosystems of these areas together once covered 15.7% of the planet's land surface, but today, because of habitat loss, cover only 2.3%. This small amount of land is the exclusive home for 50% of the world's plant species and 42% of all terrestrial vertebrate species. The hot spot concept gives incentive to focus on these areas of endemism, where the greatest number of unique species can be protected with the least amount of effort.

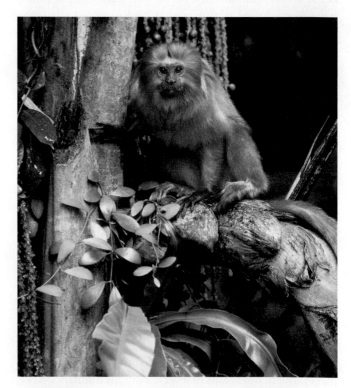

FIGURE 9.26
The golden lion tamarin *(Leontopithecus rosalia)*, a species endemic to Brazil's Atlantic rainforest, is one of the world's most endangered primates. Captive breeding programs have produced roughly 500 individuals in zoos, but the tamarin's habitat is fast disappearing.

FIGURE 9.27 Some areas of the world possess exceptionally high numbers of species found nowhere else. Some conservation biologists have suggested prioritizing habitat preservation in these areas, dubbed *biodiversity hot spots*. Shown in red are the 34 biodiversity hot spots mapped by Conservation International. *Source: Data from Conservation International, 2008.*

The World Wide Fund for Nature (WWF) has organized its conservation efforts around the concept of the **ecoregion**, a large area of land or water with a geographically distinct assemblage of natural communities that share similar environmental conditions and ecological dynamics, and interact ecologically in ways that are critical for their long-term persistence.[29] The organization has identified a "Global 200" list of ecoregions that are priorities for conservation, including ecoregions (there are actually 238 of them on the list) from both terrestrial and marine settings.

Community-based conservation is increasingly popular

Taking a global perspective and prioritizing optimal locations to set aside as parks and reserves makes good sense. However, setting aside land for preservation affects the people that live in and near these areas. In past decades, many conservationists from developed nations, in their zeal to preserve ecosystems in other nations, too often neglected the needs of people in the areas they wanted to protect. Many developing nations came to view this international environmentalism as a kind of neocolonialism.

Today this has largely changed, and many conservation biologists actively engage local people in efforts to protect land and wildlife in their own backyards, in an approach sometimes called *community-based conservation*. Setting aside land for preservation deprives local people of access to natural resources, but it can also guarantee that these resources will not be used up or sold to foreign corporations and can instead be sustainably managed. Moreover, parks and reserves draw ecotourism, which can support local economies.

In the small Central American country of Belize, conservation biologist Robert Horwich and his group Community Conservation have helped start a number of community-based conservation projects. The Community Baboon Sanctuary consists of tracts of riparian forest that farmers have agreed to leave intact, to serve as homes and traveling corridors for the black howler monkey, a centrepiece of ecotourism. The fact that the reserve uses the local nickname for the monkey signals respect for residents, and today a local women's cooperative is running the project. A museum was built, and residents receive income for guiding and housing visiting researchers and tourists. Community-based conservation has not always been so successful, but in a world of increasing human population, locally based management that meets people's needs sustainably will likely be essential.

Innovative economic strategies are being employed

As conservation moves from single-species approaches to the hotspot approach to community-based conservation, innovative economic strategies are also being attempted. One strategy that has increased over the past couple of decades is the *debt-for-nature swap*, conceived in the early 1980s by Thomas Lovejoy and pioneered by Conservation International more than 25 years ago with partners in Costa Rica. In debt-for-nature swaps, an environmental group or a corporation takes on a portion of the debt of a developing country, usually in exchange for some form of environmental protection or conservation. Because national debt is one of the principal driving forces of habitat destruction in developing nations (because of the need to extract natural resources and generate foreign capital), debt-for-nature swaps hold the promise of protecting the environment while addressing one of its fundamental threats. So far, in spite of millions of dollars devoted to debt-for-nature swaps worldwide, results have been mixed.

A newer strategy that Conservation International has pioneered is the *conservation concession*. Nations often sell concessions to foreign multinational corporations, allowing them to extract resources from the nation's land. A nation can, for instance, earn money by selling to an international logging company the right to log its forests. Conservation International has stepped in and paid nations for concessions for conservation rather than resource extraction. The nation gets the money *and* keeps its natural resources intact. The South American country of Surinam, which still has extensive areas of pristine rainforest, entered into such an agreement and has virtually halted logging while pulling in $15 million. It remains to be seen how large a role such strategies will play in the future protection of biodiversity.

Parks and Reserves

As resources dwindle, as forests, grasslands, and soils are degraded, as species disappear, and as the landscape fills with more people, the arguments for conservation of resources—for their conservation, as well as their sustainable use—have grown stronger. Also growing stronger is the argument for the preservation of land—setting aside tracts of relatively undisturbed land and habitat intended to remain forever undeveloped.

Why do we create parks and reserves?

Historian Alfred Runte cited four traditional reasons that parks and protected areas have been established:

1. Enormous, beautiful, or unusual features such as the Rocky Mountains and Clayoquot Sound inspire people to protect them—an impulse termed *monumentalism* (**FIGURE 9.28**).

FIGURE 9.28
The awe-inspiring beauty of some regions of Canada was one reason for the establishment of national parks. Scenic vistas such as this one in Banff National Park have inspired millions of people to visit them.

2. Protected areas offer recreational value to tourists, hikers, fishers, hunters, and others.
3. Protected areas offer *utilitarian* benefits and ecosystem services. For example, undeveloped watersheds provide cities with clean drinking water and a buffer against floods.
4. Parks make use of sites lacking economically valuable material resources or that are hard to develop; land that holds little monetary value is easy to set aside.

In Canada, the protection of exploitable resources and the benefits to human health have also been historical reasons for the establishment of parks. To these traditional reasons, another has been added in recent years: the preservation of biodiversity and ecosystems. A park or reserve is widely viewed as an island of habitat that can, scientists hope, maintain species that might otherwise disappear.

Today there are 43 national parks in the Parks Canada system, covering a total of 27 million ha, or 2.7% of the total land area of Canada.[30] Approximately 16 million people visit Canada's national parks each year. Yellowstone National Park in the United States was the very first national park, established in 1872, followed soon after by Yosemite National Park. Canada's first national park was established in Banff, Alberta, in 1885. Provincial parks in Canada number in the hundreds, and cover more area than national parks. Canada's parks system includes other types of protected areas as well, such as marine conservation areas and cultural, historic, and natural heritage sites.

The Canadian Wildlife Service, part of Environment Canada, contributes to the management and scientific understanding of wildlife and habitat management in Canada. Many sites in the parks system also serve as wildlife refuges, which are havens for the conservation of wildlife and habitat, as well as, in some cases, being available for hunting, fishing, wildlife observation, photography, environmental education, and other public uses.

Some wildlife advocates find it objectionable that hunting is allowed in many parks and refuges. However, hunters have long been in the forefront of the conservation movement and have traditionally supplied the bulk of funding for land acquisition and habitat management for the refuges. Ducks Unlimited Canada is an example of a nonprofit, nongovernmental organization founded by hunters, but with the specific goal of conserving wetlands. Canada's Aboriginal peoples also retain some of their traditional hunting rights in federal and provincial parklands.

Not everyone supports land set-asides. The restriction of activities in some wilderness areas has generated opposition among those who seek to encourage resource extraction and development, as well as hunting and increased motor vehicle access, on protected Crown lands. The drive to extract more resources, secure local control of lands, and expand recreational access to public lands is epitomized by the *wise-use movement*, a loose confederation of individuals and groups that coalesced in the 1980s and 1990s in response to the increasing success of environmental advocacy. Wise-use advocates are dedicated to protecting private property rights; opposing government regulation; transferring federal lands to state, local, or private hands; and promoting motorized recreation on public lands. The wise-use movement, which has been described as "anti-conservation," includes many farmers, ranchers, trappers, and mineral prospectors, as well as groups representing the industries that extract timber, mineral, and fossil fuel resources.

Debate between mainstream environmental groups and wise-use spokespeople has been vitriolic. Each side claims to represent the will of the people and paints the other as the oppressive establishment. Wise-use advocates have played key roles in ongoing debates over policy issues such as whether recreational activities that disturb wildlife should be allowed.

Nongovernmental entities, including private nonprofit groups, also preserve land. **Land trusts** are local or regional organizations that purchase land with the aim of preserving it in its natural condition. The Nature Conservancy can be considered the world's largest land trust, but smaller ones are springing up throughout North America. Probably the earliest private land trust in Canada was the Hamilton Naturalists Club in Ontario, which began to acquire land for conservation purposes in 1919.[31] **FIGURE 9.29** shows the dramatic increase in land trusts operating in Canada, particularly since the 1970s.

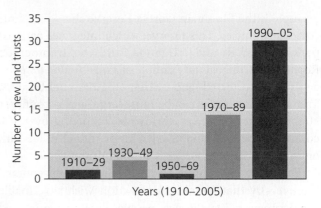

FIGURE 9.29
Land trusts that acquire land for the purpose of conservation and promote private land stewardship have increased dramatically in Canada since the first, the Hamilton Naturalists Club, in 1919.

Parks and reserves are increasing internationally

Many nations have established national park systems and are benefiting from ecotourism as a result—from Costa Rica to Ecuador to Thailand to Tanzania. The total worldwide area in protected parks and reserves increased more than fourfold from 1970 to 2000, and in 2003 the world's 38 536 protected areas covered 1.3 billion ha, or 9.6% of the planet's land area. However, parks in developing countries do not always receive the funding, legal support, or enforcement support they need to manage resources, provide for recreation, and protect wildlife from poaching and timber from logging. Thus many of the world's protected areas are merely *paper parks*—protected on paper but not in reality.

For example, the parks system in Costa Rica—now a significant source of national income and pride—initially received little real support from the government. According to Costa Rican conservationist Mario Boza, in their early years the parks were granted only five guards, one vehicle, and no funding. Today government support for protected areas in Costa Rica is much stronger. Fully 12% of the nation's area is contained in national parks, and a further 16% is devoted to other types of wildlife and conservation reserves. (In comparison, 6.3% of Canada's land area is protected as a nature reserve or wilderness area, with a total of all protected areas of any type only 10.4%.[32])

Some types of protected areas fall under national sovereignty but are designated or partly managed internationally by the United Nations. *World Heritage Sites* are an example; currently over 830 sites across 184 countries are listed for their natural or cultural value. Gros Morne National Park and Nahanni National Park are two Canadian examples of World Heritage Sites. Another example is the Mountain Gorilla Reserve shared by three African countries. This reserve, which integrates national parklands of Rwanda, Uganda, and the Democratic Republic of Congo, is an example of a *transboundary park*, an area of protected land overlapping national borders. Transboundary parks can be quite large, and account for 10% of protected areas worldwide, involving over 100 countries; the Waterton Glacier International Peace Park on the Canada–U.S. border is another example.

Biosphere reserves are tracts of land with exceptional biodiversity that couple preservation with sustainable development to benefit local people. They are designated by UNESCO (the United Nations Educational, Scientific, and Cultural Organization), following application by local stakeholders. Each biosphere reserve consists of (1) a *core* area that is isolated from the surroundings, and serves to preserve habitat and biodiversity, (2) a *buffer zone* that allows local activities and limited development that do not hinder the core area's function, and (3) an outer *transitional zone* in which agriculture, human settlement, and other land uses can be pursued in a sustainable way (**FIGURE 9.30**). Edge habitat can be quite different in character from habitat in the forest core, particularly in terms of properties such as light levels, density of vegetation, and moisture. The design of biosphere reserves seeks to address this concern and to reconcile human needs with the interests of wildlife and the goal of habitat preservation.

Clayoquot Sound was designated as Canada's 12th biosphere reserve in 2000 (**FIGURE 9.31**), in an attempt to build cooperation among environmentalists, timber companies, native people, and local residents and busi-

FIGURE 9.31
Clayoquot Sound was declared a UNESCO Biosphere Reserve in 2000.

nesses (see "Central Case: Battling Over the Last Big Trees at Clayoquot Sound"). The core area consists of provincial parks and Pacific Rim National Park Reserve. Environmentalists hoped the designation would help promote stronger land preservation efforts. Local residents supported it because outside money was being offered for local development efforts. The timber industry did not stand in the way once it was clear that harvesting operations would not be affected. The designation has brought Clayoquot Sound international attention, but it has not created new protected areas and has not altered land use policies.

Conclusion

The erosion of biological diversity on our planet is threatening to result in a modern mass extinction event equivalent to the mass extinctions of the geological past. Human-induced habitat alteration, invasive species, pollution, and overharvesting of biotic resources, now amplified by global climatic change, are the primary causes of biodiversity loss.

The loss of biodiversity matters. Human society could not function without biodiversity's pragmatic benefits. As a result, conservation biologists and environmental scientists are rising to the challenge of conducting science aimed at saving endangered species, preserving their habitats, restoring their populations, and keeping natural ecosystems intact. The innovative strategies of these scientists and of environmental and natural resource managers around the world hold promise to slow the degradation of habitat and loss of biodiversity that threatens life on Earth.

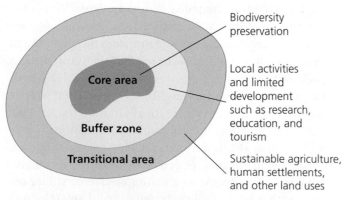

FIGURE 9.30
Biosphere reserves are international efforts that couple preservation with sustainable development to benefit local residents. Each reserve includes a core area that preserves biodiversity, a buffer zone that allows limited development, and a transition zone that permits various uses.

CANADIAN ENVIRONMENTAL PERSPECTIVES

Biruté Mary Galdikas

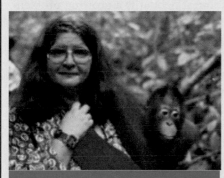

Canadian Biruté Mary Galdikas is an advocate for endangered orangutans in the rainforests of Indonesia.

- Biological **anthropologist**
- Field **primatologist**
- **Conservationist** and orangutan **advocate**

They are sometimes called the "tri-mates"—three women who made such groundbreaking expansions upon our understanding of primate behaviour that they practically carved out their own private niche in the world of science. All three—Jane Goodall, who studies chimpanzees and works to conserve their habitat; Dian Fossey, who worked with mountain gorillas; and Biruté Mary Galdikas, whose research provided the baseline for what we know today about orangutans—were hand-picked and funded originally by Louis Leakey, the famous palaeontologist whose work helped uncover the prehistory of our own species. Leakey was convinced that the women would make great strides in "field primatology," the observation of our closest genetic relatives in their own natural habitat, because of their comparative lack of scientific training (an "uncluttered mind") and what he felt was the greater patience and empathy of female researchers. For whatever reason, Leakey was right.

Galdikas was born in Germany but grew up as a naturalized Canadian in Toronto. She met Leakey in California in 1969, several years after Goodall and Fossey had begun to establish their names and unconventional research techniques. She convinced him upon their first meeting that she deserved a place among them, and he set about gathering the funds needed to sponsor her first research outing to the rainforests of Indonesia. Once there, Galdikas had an even tougher time than her predecessors. The approach of all three was to allow the primates to gradually become accustomed to their presence, so that they could observe the animals' natural behaviour. It was a tall order for Goodall and Fossey, but even more so for Galdikas. Orangutans are more solitary than chimps or gorillas; not only did they not welcome Galdikas, but they actively tried to dissuade her from approaching by throwing things at her and even defecating on her. It took 12 long years for Galdikas to habituate one of the orangutans to her presence.

Her patience paid off in scientific results. In her doctoral thesis for UCLA in 1978, Galdikas documented a number of behaviours that had never before been witnessed in wild orangutans, including the observation that male and female orangutans form relationships that last for extended periods. She later made observations on tool use among orangutans that would come to be considered as classic research. For example, in the journal *Science* she documented her observation that wild orangutans spontaneously use tools for a number of different purposes. It had previously been thought that only captive orangutans—influenced by constant exposure to humans—were tool users.

This provided a basis for later research suggesting that some orangutan groups in the wild have developed basic "cultural" differences, such as having specific sounds for communicating with members of the group.

Today Galdikas has part-time affiliations with Simon Fraser University in British Columbia and Universitas Nasional in Jakarta, Indonesia. Like Goodall and Fossey (until the latter's death in 1985), she devotes most of her time to advocacy for the critically endangered orangutans and conservation of their rapidly disappearing habitat—the rainforests of Borneo and Sumatra. Her group, Orangutan Foundation International, runs a rescue and rehabilitation centre that saves young orangutans orphaned by fire, deforestation, or hunting; nurses them back to health; and returns them to the wild.

"To follow them, you would have had to just jump in the swamp, which was neck-deep there, and that's when I thought, 'Gee, this is going to be really hard.'"—**Biruté Mary Galdikas, on her first encounter with orangutans in the rainforest of Indonesia.**

Thinking About Environmental Perspectives

In June of 2008, Spain's parliament voted in favour of new legislation that would extend, for the first time ever, certain limited rights to great apes. The proposed laws make it illegal to kill, torture, or arbitrarily imprison apes, including their use in medical experimentation, circuses, and films. What do you think of this? Is it "about time" for a law of this type, to provide protection to our closest genetic relatives? Or is it an ill-conceived attempt to extend "human" rights to nonhumans?

REVIEWING OBJECTIVES

You should now be able to:

Characterize the scope and value of biodiversity on Earth

- Roughly 1.8 million species have been described so far, but scientists agree that the world holds millions more. Some taxonomic groups (such as insects) hold far more diversity than others.
- Diversity is unevenly spread across different habitats and areas of the world.
- Biodiversity is vital for functioning ecosystems and the services they provide us.
- Wild species are sources of food, medicine, and economic development. Many people also feel that humans have a psychological need to connect with the natural world.

Describe ways to measure biodiversity

- Biodiversity is important not only at the species level, but also at the genetic level and at the levels of ecosystems, communities, and habitats.
- Global estimates of biodiversity are based on extrapolations from scientific assessments in local areas and certain taxonomic groups.

Evaluate the primary causes of biodiversity loss

- Extinction occurs naturally. Species have gone extinct at a background rate of roughly one species per 1 to 10 million species each year. Earth's life has experienced five mass extinction events in the past 440 million years.
- Human impact is now causing the beginnings of a sixth mass extinction.
- Habitat alteration is the main cause of current biodiversity loss. Invasive species, pollution, and overharvesting are also important causes. Climate change threatens to become a major cause of environmental change and biodiversity loss.

Specify the benefits and challenges of conserving habitat and the role of habitat fragmentation

- Conservation biology is an applied science that studies biodiversity loss and seeks ways to protect and restore biodiversity at all its levels.

- The fragmentation of habitat is a growing problem. It affects organisms because edge habitat differs from core habitat, and because many species need to be able to migrate over large areas. The establishment of natural corridors can help to address the problem.
- The equilibrium model of island biogeography and the area-size relationship explain how size and distance influence the number of species occurring on islands. This model can be applied to "islands" of habitat in fragmented terrestrial landscapes.

Contrast *in situ* and *ex situ* conservation approaches

- *In situ* conservation efforts involve the preservation of habitat so that species can continue to exist in their natural state. Increasingly, landscape-level conservation is being pursued in its own right.
- *Ex situ* conservation efforts, in addition to the preservation of species in zoos, seed banks, and aquaria, include captive breeding and reintroduction programs.

Compare and contrast traditional and innovative conservation efforts

- Most conservation efforts and laws so far have focused on threatened and endangered species. Species that are charismatic and well known are often used as tools to conserve habitats and ecosystems.
- International conservation approaches include treaties, identification of biodiversity hotspots, community-based conservation, debt-for-nature swaps, and conservation concessions.

Outline reasons for setting aside parks, reserves, and other protected areas

- Public demand for preservation and recreation has led to the creation of parks, reserves, and wilderness areas in North America and across the world.
- Biosphere Reserves and World Heritage Sites are two types of internationally-designated protected lands.
- Because habitat fragmentation affects wildlife, conservation biologists are working on how best to design parks and reserves.

TESTING YOUR COMPREHENSION

1. What is biodiversity? List and describe three levels of biodiversity.
2. What are the five primary causes of biodiversity loss? Can you give a specific example of each?
3. List and describe five invasive species and the adverse effects they have had.
4. Define the term *ecosystem services*. Give five examples of ecosystem services that humans would have a hard time replacing if their natural sources were eliminated.
5. What is the relationship between biodiversity and food security? Between biodiversity and pharmaceuticals? Give three examples of potential benefits of biodiversity conservation for food security and medicine.
6. Describe four reasons why people suggest biodiversity conservation is important.
7. What is the difference between an umbrella species and a keystone species? Could one species be both an umbrella species and a keystone species?
8. Explain the island biogeography model. In what way is this model relevant to the management of habitat fragmentation?
9. What is a biodiversity hot spot?
10. Describe community-based conservation.

THINKING IT THROUGH

1. Biologist E. O. Wilson has said that, "Except in pockets of ignorance and malice, there is no longer an ideological war between conservationists and developers. Both share the perception that health and prosperity decline in a deteriorating environment." Do you agree or disagree? How do people in your community view biodiversity?
2. Many arguments have been advanced for the importance of preserving biodiversity. Which argument do you think is most compelling, and why? Which argument do you think is least compelling, and why?
3. Some people argue that we shouldn't worry about endangered species because extinction has always occurred. How would you respond to this view?
4. According to most scientists, the polar bear population in Canada's North is declining, but some Inuit hunters believe that the population is stable or even increasing. Please offer two reasons why it might be extremely difficult to settle this scientific question.
5. What would you say are some advantages of focusing on conserving single species, versus trying to conserve broader communities, ecosystems, or landscapes? What might be some of the disadvantages? Which do you think is the better approach, or should we use both?
6. You are attending a town meeting, called to discuss the proposed development of a shopping mall and condominium complex. The development would eliminate a 40 hectare stand of forest, the last sizeable forest stand in the town. The developers say the forest loss will not matter because plenty of small forest stands still exist scattered throughout town. One of the town's decision makers asks you to comment about the development's possible impacts on the community's biodiversity. What will you choose to tell your fellow citizens and the town's decision makers at this meeting?
7. You are an influential legislator in a country that has no endangered species act, and you want to introduce legislation to protect your country's vanishing biodiversity. Consider the Canadian Species at Risk Act, as well as international efforts such as CITES and the Convention on Biological Diversity. What strategies would you write into your legislation? How would your law be similar to and different from the existing Canadian and international efforts?

INTERPRETING GRAPHS AND DATA

Habitat alteration is the primary cause of present-day biodiversity loss. Of all human activities, the one that has resulted in the most habitat alteration is agriculture. Between 1850 and 2000, 95% of the native grasslands of the midwestern United States were converted to agricultural use. As a result, conventional farming practices replaced diverse natural communities with greatly simplified ones. The vast monocultures of industrialized agriculture produce bountiful harvests, but at substantial costs in lost ecosystem services.

Data from a recent study reviewing the scientific literature on the effects of organic farming practices on biodiversity are shown in the graph.

1. Overall, how many studies showed a positive effect of organic farming on biodiversity, relative to conventional farming? How many studies reported a negative effect? How many studies reported no effect?

2. For which group or groups of organisms is evidence of positive effects the strongest? Reference the numbers to support your choice(s).

3. Recall the ecosystem services provided by biodiversity. What services do the groups you chose in question 2 provide?

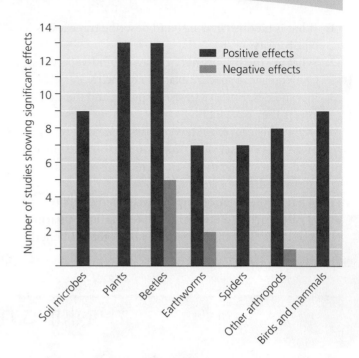

Numbers of scientific studies reporting negative or positive effects on biodiversity of organic agriculture versus conventional farming practices..
Source: Data from Hole, D., et al. (2005) Does organic farming benefit biodiversity? Biological Conservation *122: 113–130.*

CHAPTER ENDNOTES

1. Derocher, A. E., N. J. Lunn, and I. Stirling (2004) Polar bears in a warming climate, *Integr. Comp. Biol,* 44: 163–176.

2. U.S. Fish and Wildlife Service (2009) *Spotlight Species Action Plan: Polar Bear.* http://ecos.fws.gov/speciesProfile/profile/speciesProfile.action?spcode=A0IJ#recovery

3. IUCN (2011) *IUCN Red List of Threatened Species.* Version 2011.1 *Ursus maritimus: Summary.* www.iucnredlist.org/apps/redlist/details/22823/0

4. *Encyclopedia of Food and Culture.* Arctic: Inuit food lists and categories. www.enotes.com/food-encyclopedia/arctic. Accessed 18 June 2011.

5. Derocher, A. E., N. J. Lunn, and I. Stirling (2004) Polar bears in a warming climate, *Integr. Comp. Biol,* 44:163–176.

6. IUCN (2011) *IUCN Red List of Threatened Species.* Version 2011.1 *Ursus maritimus: Summary.* www.iucnredlist.org/apps/redlist/details/22823/0

7. CBC News (January 5, 2011) Iqaluit polar bear hunting quota unclear. www.cbc.ca/news/canada/north/story/2011/01/05/iqaluit-polar-bear-quota.html Accessed 18 June 2011.

8. Environment Canada Environmental Monitoring and Assessment Network (EMAN). *Status of Amphibian and Reptile Species in Canada.* www.eman-rese.ca/eman/reports/publications/2004/amph_rept_status/.

9. Millennium Ecosystem Assessment (2005) *Ecosystems and Human Well-Being: Synthesis,* Island Press, Washington, DC.

10. IUCN (2011) *IUCN Red List of Threatened Species.* Version 2011.1. www.iucnredlist.org. Accessed 18 June 2011.

11. Bamosky, A. D., N. Matzke, et al. (2011) Has the Earth's sixth mass extinction already arrived? *Nature* 471: 51.

12. World Wide Fund for Nature and U.N. Environment Programme (2010) *The 2010 Living Planet Report,* Gland, Switzerland: WWF.

13. Wild Species 2005, National General Status Working Group (2005) www.wildspecies.ca/wildspecies2005/index.cfm?lang=e

14. The National General Status Working Group is composed of representatives from the provinces and territories and the three federal agencies whose mandate includes wildlife: Canadian Wildlife Service, Department of Fisheries and Oceans, and Parks Canada, with additional ex officio input from Natural Resources Canada and Agriculture and Agri-Food Canada. NGSWG advises COSEWIC, the Committee on the Status of Endangered Wildlife in Canada, which in turn recommends the listing of species on the SARA Registry.

15. Wild Species 2005, National General Status Working Group (2005) www.wildspecies.ca/wildspecies2005/index.cfm?lang=e. This report is updated every five years; the 2010 report has been completed but is not yet available as of June 2011.

16. Wild Species 2005, National General Status Working Group (2005) www.wildspecies.ca/wildspecies2005/index.cfm?lang=e

17. Millennium Ecosystem Assessment (2005) *Ecosystems and Human Well-Being: Synthesis*, Island Press, Washington, DC.

18. Leopold, A. (1953) *Round River*, Oxford University Press, New York, pp. 145–146.

19. Wilson, E. O. (1984) *Biophilia*, Havard University Press, Cambridge, MA.

20. Louv, R. *Last Child in the Woods: Saving Our Children from Nature-Deficit Disorder*, Algonquin Books of Chapel Hill, Chapel Hill, NC.

21. Wilson, E. O. (1994) *Naturalist*, Shearwater Books, Washington, DC.

22. Whooping Crane Eastern Partnership. www.bringbackthecranes.org/back/proj-facts.htm

23. Species at Risk Public Registry, Government of Canada. www.sararegistry.gc.ca/species/speciesDetails_e.cfm?sid=140

24. Weagle, K., and C. Smeeton. Captive breeding of swift fox for reintroduction: Final report to funding bodies 1994 to 1997. Cochrane Ecological Institute. www.ceinst.org/Final%20Report%20to%20Funders%2097.pdf

25. Cotterill, S. E. (1997) Status of the swift fox (*Vulpes velox*) in Alberta. Alberta Environmental Protection, Wildlife Management Division, Wildlife Status Report No. 7, Edmonton, AB. www.srd.gov.ab.ca/fishwildlife/status/swfox/cons.html

26. Cotterill, S. E. (1997) Status of the swift fox (*Vulpes velox*) in Alberta. Alberta Environmental Protection, Wildlife Management Division, Wildlife Status Report No. 7, Edmonton, AB. www.srd.gov.ab.ca/fishwildlife/status/swfox/cons.html

27. Nature Conservancy of Canada. The endangered swift fox. www.natureconservancy.ca/site/News2?abbr=ncc_work_&page=NewsArticle&id=5047.

28. Mooers, A. Ø., L. R. Prugh, M. Festa-Bianchet, and J. A. Hutchings (2006) Biases in legal listing under Canadian endangered species legislation. *Conservation Biology*, 21(3): 572–575.

29. Worldwide Fund for Nature. Ecoregions, www.worldwildlife.org/science/ecoregions/item1847.html

30. Parks Canada, Canada's National Parks and National Reserves. http://www.pc.gc.ca/docs/v-g/nation/nation103_e.asp

31. Campbell, L., and C. D. A. Rubec (2006) *Land Trusts in Canada: Building Momentum for the Future*. Ottawa: Wildlife Habitat Canada and the Stewardship Section, Canadian Wildlife Service, Environment Canada.

32. Environment Canada. *State of the Environment Infobase*. www.ec.gc.ca/soer-ree/English/Indicator_series/techs.cfm?tech_id=1&issue_id=2

MyEnvironmentPlace

Go to **www.myenvironmentplace.ca** where you will find quizzes, animations, your Pearson eText, and more.

Forests and Forest Management

Old-growth trees like this one at Clayoquot Sound, BC, have long been the focus of conflicts between logging companies and environmentalists.

Upon completing this chapter, you will be able to

- Describe the basic functional processes of trees and their role in biogeochemical cycling
- Summarize the principal types of forest biomes, especially those indigenous to Canada
- Describe the ecological roles and economic contributions of forests
- Trace the history and scale of forest loss and identify the current drivers of deforestation

- Outline the major methods of harvesting timber
- Explain the fundamentals of forest management, including approaches to fire management, and identify forest management agencies in Canada and internationally

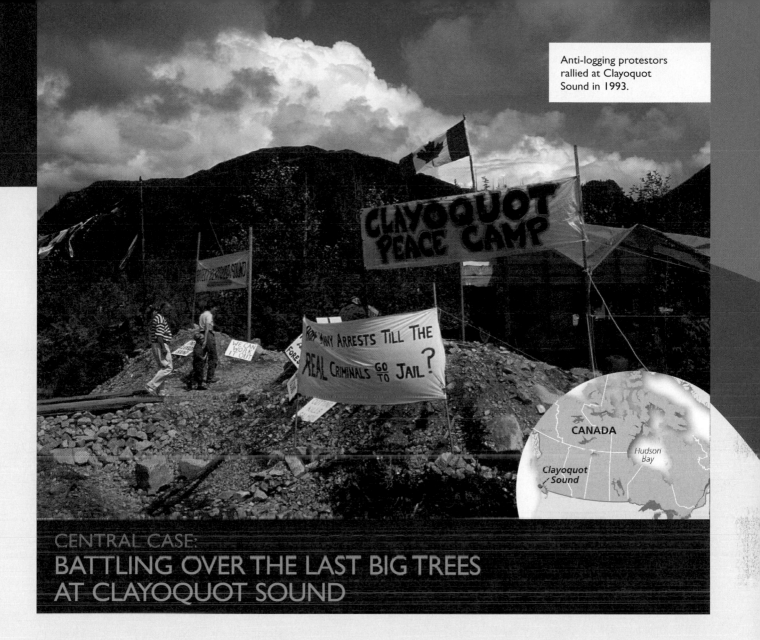

Anti-logging protestors rallied at Clayoquot Sound in 1993.

CANADA

Clayoquot Sound

Hudson Bay

CENTRAL CASE:
BATTLING OVER THE LAST BIG TREES AT CLAYOQUOT SOUND

"Clear-cutting . . . may be either desirable or undesirable, acceptable or unacceptable, according to the type of forest and the management objectives."
—DR. HAMISH KIMMINS, UNIVERSITY OF BRITISH COLUMBIA, 1992

"What we have is nothing less than an ecological Holocaust occurring right now in British Columbia."
—MARK WAREING, WESTERN CANADA WILDERNESS COMMITTEE, 1990

It was the largest act of civil disobedience in Canadian history, and it played out along a seacoast of majestic beauty, at the foot of some of the world's biggest trees. At Clayoquot Sound on the western coast of Vancouver Island, British Columbia, protestors blocked logging trucks, preventing them from entering stands of ancient temperate rainforest. The activists chanted slogans, sang songs, and chained themselves to trees.

Loggers complained that the protestors were keeping them from doing their jobs and making a living. In the end, 850 of the 12 000 protestors were arrested, and this remote, mist-enshrouded land of cedars and hemlocks became ground zero in the debate over how we manage forests.

That was in 1993, and the activists were opposing **clear-cutting**, the logging practice that removes all trees from an area. Most of Canada's old-growth temperate rainforest had already been cut, and the forests of Clayoquot Sound were among the largest undisturbed stands of temperate rainforest left on the planet.

Timber from **old-growth forests**—complex, primary forests in which the trees are at least 150 years old—had long powered British Columbia's economy. Historically, one in five jobs in BC depended on its $13 billion timber industry, and many small towns would have gone under without it. By 1993, however, the timber industry was cutting thousands of jobs a year because of mechanization, and the looming depletion of old growth threatened to slow the industry. Meanwhile, Greenpeace was convincing overseas customers to boycott products made from trees clear-cut by multinational timber company MacMillan-Bloedel. Soon British Columbia's premier found himself trying to persuade European nations not to boycott his province's main export.

In 1995, the provincial government called for an end to clear-cutting at Clayoquot Sound, after its appointed scientific panel of experts submitted a new forestry plan for the region. The plan recommended reducing harvests, retaining 15–70% of old-growth trees in each stand, decreasing the logging road network, designating forest reserve areas, and managing *riparian* (water's-edge) zones. Two years later, the provincial government reversed many of these regulations, and a new premier pronounced forest activists "enemies of British Columbia."

The antagonists struck a deal; wilderness advocates and MacMillan-Bloedel agreed to log old growth in limited areas, using environmentally friendly practices. In 1998, First Nations people of the region formed a timber company, Iisaak Forest Resources, in agreement with MacMillan-Bloedel's successor, Weyerhaeuser, and began logging at Clayoquot Sound in a more environmentally sensitive manner (see photo).

In the Nuu-chah-nulth language of First Nations people from the Clayoquot Sound area, *iisaak* (pronounced *E-sock*) means "respect," which became a guiding principle for forestry in Clayoquot Sound. The *variable retention harvesting* they applied—logging selectively with the goal of retaining a certain percentage and particular characteristics of the forest ecosystem—is more expensive than normal clear-cutting. Iisaak Forest Resources hoped to recoup some of the extra cost by achieving a premium price for the cut timber and through ecotourism and the sustainable exploitation of other forest resources.

Logging continues at some parts of Clayoquot Sound.

Leaving most of the trees standing accomplished what forest advocates had predicted: People from all over the world—1 million each year—are now visiting Clayoquot Sound for its natural beauty and are kayaking and whale-watching in its waters. Ecotourism (along with fishing and aquaculture) has surpassed logging as a driver of local economies. The United Nations designated the site as a biosphere reserve in 2000, encouraging land protection and sustainable development. From the perspective of ecotourism, the trees appear to be worth more standing than cut down.

Tensions continue today, and logging has never completely stopped at Clayoquot Sound—even in areas near park and biosphere reserve boundaries—to the dismay of environmental activists.[1] Local forest advocates worry that the provincial government's new Working Forest Policy will increase logging, and the town of Tofino petitioned the province to exempt Clayoquot Sound's forests from the policy.

Ultimately, Iisaak Forest Resources found it difficult to make money doing sustainable forestry and entered into an agreement with the environmental organization Ecotrust Canada in 2006. Today logging is being done more sustainably, and at a profit, under this arrangement. The provincial government is considering new forestry plans that would shift logging out of old-growth forests and into younger forests that were already logged in the past. As long as our demand for lumber, paper, and forest products keeps increasing, pressures will keep building on the remaining forests on Vancouver Island and around the world.

The Forest and the Trees

Forest covers roughly 31% of Earth's land surface (**FIGURE 10.1**), about 4 billion hectares.[2] Forests provide habitat for countless organisms and help maintain soil, air, and water quality. They play key roles in our planet's biogeochemical cycles, serving as one of the most important reservoirs in the carbon cycle. Forests have also long provided humanity with wood for fuel, construction, paper production, and more.

Trees have several basic requirements

Trees are the fundamental biological component of forests, although, as you will learn, forests have many other crucial components, both biotic and abiotic, and not all forests are completely dominated by trees.

Trees, like all other plants, are autotrophs. They create their own food energy by photosynthesis, through which they extract carbon from atmospheric carbon dioxide and recombine it with water to make carbohydrates (sugars, such as glucose; **FIGURE 10.2**). For photosynthesis to occur and the tree to survive, there are several fundamental requirements:

- An amenable temperature (the specific temperature range varies by species)

- Air (with which the tree exchanges carbon, hydrogen, oxygen, and nitrogen)
- Light (the energy source for photosynthesis)
- Soil (the source for mineral nutrients)
- Water (needed for a variety of reasons)

The nutrients required for plant growth are supplied through the tree's roots from the soil, using soil water as the transfer medium. As we have discussed previously (in the context of soil and agriculture), nutrients that are required in relatively large amounts are called **macronutrients**; for trees, these include nitrogen (N), phosphorus

roots
FOREST

Forest is a late-thirteenth-century word from the Old French *forest* (modern *forêt*). It originally referred to an extensive tree-covered district set aside under the protection of the king for royal hunting. It probably came from the Latin term *forestem silvam*, "the outside woods," used during the time of Charlemagne to refer to a royal forest. It may also be related to the Latin root of the word *forum*, referring to a court or a judgment—in other words, "legally protected land."

Forest
Other wooded land

FIGURE 10.1 About 31% of Earth's land surface is covered by forest. Most of this consists of the boreal forests of the north and the tropical forests of South America and Africa. Other lands (including tundra, shrubland, and savannah) can be classified as "wooded land," implying a more open forest type that supports trees, but at sparser densities. *Source: Data from U.N. Food and Agriculture Organization (FAO) (2005)* Global Forest Resources Assessment 2005 *(with updated information from* Global Forest Resources Assessment 2010).

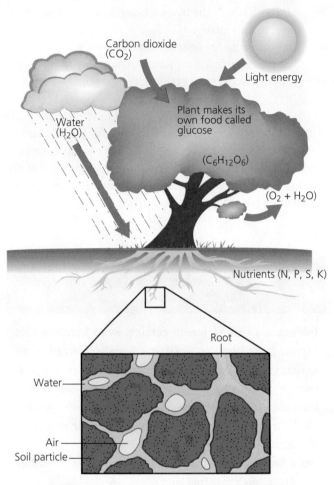

FIGURE 10.2

Trees acquire carbon from the air, via photosynthesis. They utilize light energy to carry out photosynthesis for the production of carbohydrates, such as glucose, from atmospheric carbon dioxide. Macronutrients such as phosphorus, sulphur, and potassium are provided by the mineral components of the soil, through the tree's roots by way of soil water. Nitrogen comes from a variety of sources, but primarily from the atmosphere via nitrogen fixation.

(P), potassium (K), magnesium (Mg), calcium (Ca), and sulphur (S), in addition to the carbon (C) that the tree acquires from the atmosphere. Recall that the process of *nitrogen fixation* by soil-dwelling bacteria converts atmospheric nitrogen into a form that is usable by plants, including trees. Lightning is another natural process that leads to the fixation of atmospheric nitrogen in the soil. Thus trees acquire much of their nitrogen from the atmosphere, by way of the soil. Nitrogen also can come from the decomposition of organisms, fecal matter from animals, and artificial fertilizers. The rest of the macronutrients come mainly from the dissolution of mineral grains in soil water.

Nutrients that are required by living organisms only in small amounts are called **micronutrients**; for trees, these include iron (Fe), manganese (Mn), zinc (Zn),

copper (Cu), boron (B), chlorine (Cl), and molybdenum (Mo).

Trees, like all plants, need water for several reasons. First, water is used in photosynthesis, for which the general simplified reaction is:

$$6CO_2 + 6H_2O = C_6H_{12}O_6 + 6O_2$$

Second, water acts as a solvent, dissolving mineral constituents from particles in the soil. As shown in **FIGURE 10.2**, these are taken up by the tree's roots, to be used as nutrients. Third, in addition to transporting nutrients, water transports chemicals from one part of the tree to wherever they are needed to carry out the metabolic processes that keep the tree alive. Fourth, water provides support for cells. All plant cells require internal water pressure (called *turgidity*) in their cells, or they will wilt and eventually die. (Turgidity is the main way that nonwoody plants stay upright. Trees have additional structural support in the form of woody trunks that help them to remain upright.)

Trees (and other plants) require water to pass from their roots through their trunks and branches and evaporate from their leaf surfaces (**FIGURE 10.3**); this is called **transpiration**. Transpiration cools the plant, as well as assisting in the movement of nutrients. It also helps small openings in the leaves, called *stomata*, to open, allowing for the intake of carbon dioxide during photosynthesis. Transpiration occurs when solar energy causes water to evaporate from leaf surfaces, resulting in negative internal water pressure. Water is drawn up through the roots and trunk through narrow, strawlike tubes called *xylem*. Soil water moves into the roots by *osmosis* and is drawn up through the xylem by *adhesion*, upward movement that results from the surface tension between water (a polar molecule, you will recall from an earlier chapter) and the capillary-like walls of the xylem. *Cohesion*, the attraction between water molecules, then serves to draw additional water into the xylem.

This helps to explain why it is useful to plant trees in close proximity to crops, a practice known as **agroforestry**, as we discussed in the chapter on "Soils and Soil Resources." Crop plants have much shallower root systems than trees, in general; a tree can draw water and minerals from depth, making them available to nearby crops. At the same time, some trees can be harvested for wood, fruits, nuts, honey, and other products, and domesticated animals can graze on fallen leaf litter.

Trees also function as an important link between the biogeochemical cycles of the atmosphere, hydrosphere, biosphere, and geosphere. Transpiration is an important step in the hydrologic cycle, moderating the movement of water from the atmosphere to the ground and from the ground back to the atmosphere.

How water moves through a tree

Transpiration

Evaporation

H_2O

Air

Cohesion

Water uptake

Air

H_2O

FIGURE 10.3 The driving force for transpiration is evaporation from leaf surfaces. Water is drawn into root hairs and upward through the xylem by adhesion and cohesion.

When trees draw mineral nutrients and water from depth through their root systems, they deliver them to near-surface soil layers, where they become available for other plants (**FIGURE 10.4**). This is sometimes referred to as *water and nutrient pumping*. Trees also deliver organic material back to the topsoil, in the form of **litter**, which consists of fallen branches and leaves.

There are three major groups of forest biomes

A **forest**, strictly speaking, is a land area with significant tree cover, in which the **canopy** (the upper level of leaves and branches defined by the treetops) is largely **closed**. A **woodland** is a wooded (treed) area in which the canopy is more **open**; that is, there are some openings between the trees that allow light to penetrate to the ground, or **floor**, of the forest (**FIGURE 10.5**).

There are three major types of forest biomes, corresponding roughly to the high, middle, and equatorial latitudes. However, there are *many* local variations, as well as altitudinal variations; we will look more closely at the forests of Canada later in this chapter.

Boreal forest. The **boreal forest** is a high-latitude forest type (mainly in the Northern Hemisphere) that is characterized by cold, relatively dry climates with short growing seasons. The boreal forest biome stretches across much of Canada, Russia, and Scandinavia. Further to the north, the boreal forest grades through the **taiga** into the more open northern **tundra** biome. Boreal forests are characterized by evergreen, **coniferous** trees—trees whose "leaves" take the form of needles and that produce seed pods in the form of cones. Evergreen, waxy-coated needles and cones are energy- and water-saving adapta-

Organic Matter (Litter)

Water

Nutrients absorbed by deep roots

FIGURE 10.4
Trees act like pumps, drawing nutrients and water from depth through their root systems. In this way, they can provide nutrients and water to plants with shallower root systems. They also act as a link in biogeochemical cycles and the hydrologic cycle.

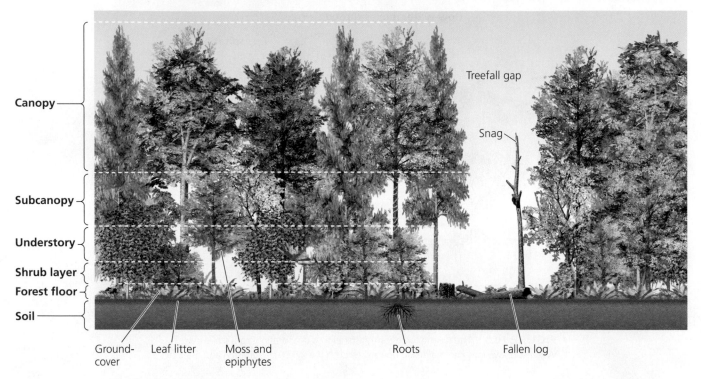

Canopy

Subcanopy

Understory

Shrub layer

Forest floor

Soil

Treefall gap

Snag

Ground-cover   Leaf litter   Moss and epiphytes   Roots   Fallen log

FIGURE 10.5   In this generalized cross-section of a mature forest, the crowns of the largest trees form the canopy, and smaller trees beneath them form the shaded subcanopy and understory. Shrubs and groundcover grow just above the forest floor, which may be covered in leaf litter rich with invertebrate animals. Vines, mosses, lichens, and epiphytes cover portions of trees and the forest floor. Snags (standing dead trees), whose wood can be easily hollowed out, provide food and nesting and roosting sites for woodpeckers and other animals. Fallen logs nourish the soil and young plants and provide habitat for countless invertebrates as the logs decompose. Gaps caused by fallen trees let light through the canopy and create small openings in the forest, allowing early successional plants to grow in patches within the mature forest.

tions that help trees cope with short growing seasons and low precipitation.

Temperate forest   The **temperate forest**, the second major forest biome type, occurs in midlatitude areas of seasonal climate, which typically experience a distinct winter season and summer growing season. Temperate forests occur throughout eastern North America, northeastern Asia, and western and central Europe. Temperate forests cover much less area globally than boreal forests, in part because people have already cleared so many of them. Trees in temperate forests must be adapted to a seasonal climate and wide ranges in temperature and precipitation. Temperate forests are often characterized by **deciduous** trees—trees whose leaves turn colour (*senesce*) and drop off in the fall, in preparation for a period of winter dormancy.

Tropical forest   The third major forest biome type is the **tropical forest**. Tropical rainforests, which host extremely diverse flora and fauna, occur in the wet, tropical climates of equatorial South and Central America, equatorial Africa, and Indonesia and Southeast Asia. Trees in rainforests are often evergreen, but not for the energy-saving reasons that boreal trees are evergreen;

in tropical forests, trees remain green because they have year-round growing conditions.

For **rainforests** we tend to think first of the tropical environment, but in fact their central characteristic is not high temperature, but high rainfall. Thus, rainforest variations include the evergreen rainforests of the cool, wet Pacific Northwest. Similarly, there are tropical forests in which the climate is warm but not wet year-round, alternating instead between a rainy season and a dry season. As the dry season gets longer, the character of the forest changes and other wooded biome types

roots

BOREAL AND TAIGA

Boreal is a late fifteenth-century word deriving from the Latin *boreas*, meaning "north wind." It originated from the Greek *Boreas*, "god of the north wind." **Taiga** is a Russian word of Mongolian origin, used in the late nineteenth century in reference to the coniferous forest of Siberia.

emerge, such as the more open tropical dry forest and savannah biomes.

An additional unique type of forest biome comprises coastal forests, such as *mangroves*. Trees in mangrove forests are adapted to conditions of constant standing water and fluctuating water salinity. They provide valuable habitat for shallow-water marine organisms and they protect shorelines from the battering of storm waves. Mangroves and other coastal forests are discussed in the chapter on marine and coastal systems and fisheries.

Forests grade into open wooded lands

These broad descriptions of the major types of forest biomes should make it obvious that not all "forests" are completely dominated by trees. At the drier end of the climatic spectrum (in cold, high-latitude regions as well as hot, low-latitude regions), the canopies of wooded areas tend to be even more open. **Shrublands** are wooded areas that are covered by smaller, bushier trees, or *shrubs*, often interspersed with occasional taller trees. Tundra is a high-latitude (and high-altitude), cold version of shrubland. **Savannah** is an open area dominated by grasses, with widely scattered trees. Finally, **grasslands** are lands that are dominated by grasses and other nonwoody vegetation. Again, all of these basic biome types have many local variations (**FIGURE 10.6**).

Grasslands, savannahs, and even shrublands are not forests, strictly speaking, although any of them can be partially "wooded." It is common to group these biome types together under the category of **drylands**, emphasizing their central defining characteristic of low precipitation. This is a broad category that includes some areas with a relatively long dry season alternating with a rainy season; some semi-arid regions that experience low precipitation year-round; and—at the extreme end of the dryland spectrum—the arid *desert* biome.

Because drylands are characterized by low overall precipitation, they tend to be extremely sensitive to environmental change and are easily damaged if land use practices become overly intensive. Therefore, *desertification* and *land degradation* are major environmental issues in dryland management. Much of the world's dry woodland and grassland has been converted for the purpose of agriculture or rangeland. We will discuss this in greater detail below.

Canada is a steward for much of the world's forest

Canada's current 402 million ha of forested and other wooded land (310 million ha of which is "true" forest)[3] represent over 10% of the world's forest cover, 40% of Canada's total land area, 25% of the world's natural (rather than planted) forest, 30% of the world's boreal forest, and 20% of the world's temperate rainforest. Canada's wooded lands include some of the world's largest intact forest ecosystems. Canada has the highest amount of forested land per capita in the world.[4] About one-third of the nation's forested land is in British Columbia, and 38% is in Québec and Ontario.[5]

According to the Food and Agriculture Organization of the United Nations, which monitors the status of the world's forests, more than 50% of Canada's primary forest remains more or less intact.[6] In comparison, of the original 4 million km² (400 million ha) of forested land in the United States, the vast majority was deforested by the late nineteenth century. (In the early 1900s, forest cover in the United States began to stabilize, however, and in the past few decades, the United States has seen an increase in forested land.)

Canada clearly has an obligation to the rest of the world to manage our forests as effectively and sustainably as possible. The Boreal Forest Conservation Framework puts Canada's stewardship responsibilities with regard to the boreal forest in perspective, stating, in part, that

Canada's boreal region contains one-quarter of the world's remaining original forests. The largest intact forest ecosystem left on Earth, Canada's boreal is home to a rich array of wildlife including migratory songbirds, waterfowl, bears, wolves and some of the world's largest woodland caribou herds. The boreal region's natural wealth sustains many of Canada's Aboriginal communities, who have lived in harmony with the boreal for thousands of years. It also sup-

FIGURE 10.6
Savannah and grassland are characterized by a relatively dry climate and dispersed trees.

ports thousands of jobs and contributes billions to the Canadian economy.

The Boreal Forest Conservation Framework is based on a shared vision to sustain the ecological and cultural integrity of the Canadian boreal forest region, in perpetuity. The Framework's goal is to conserve the cultural, sustainable economic and natural values of the entire Canadian boreal region by employing the principles of conservation biology to protect at least 50% of the region in a network of large interconnected

protected areas, and to support sustainable communities, world-leading ecosystem-based resource management practices, and state-of-the-art stewardship practices in the remaining landscape.[7]

The members of the Boreal Leadership Council are described as "historically unlikely partners" and include representatives from industry and finance; nongovernmental organizations, nonprofits, and environmental groups; and Aboriginal organizations and governing bodies. This type of collaborative, cross-disciplinary, cross-sectoral management process is typical of Canada's historical approach to the management of complex and sometimes thorny environmental issues, and it is one of the reasons that Canada has been considered a leader in environmental management.

Canada's forests are varied

Canada's forest biomes include many regional variations, some of which are described next.

Forests of the north   The boreal forest, the largest forested region of Canada, stretches through all of the provinces and territories except Nova Scotia and Prince Edward Island (**FIGURE 10.7A**). White spruces,

(a) Northern boreal forest

FIGURE 10.7
Canada's forest biomes include many regional variations, some of which are seen here.

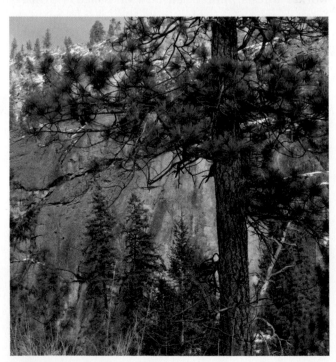

(b) Western ponderosa pine forest

(c) Eastern deciduous forest

tamarack, and jack and lodgepole pines are the main coniferous species in the boreal forest, and white birch, aspen, and balsam poplars are the main deciduous trees. In the north the boreal forest merges with the tundra, an open woodland biome. The term *taiga* is sometimes used casually as a synonym for boreal forest, but technically the taiga is the transitional zone between the boreal forest and the northern tundra.

Forests of the west In the west is the *subalpine forest region* of the mountains of British Columbia and western Alberta, with characteristic Engelmann spruce, alpine fir, and lodgepole pines, and the *montane forest region* in British Columbia's central plateau, with Rocky Mountain Douglas fir, lodgepole pine, trembling aspen, and ponderosa pine (**FIGURE 10.7B**). The *coast forest region*, found at Clayoquot Sound and elsewhere on Vancouver Island, is the temperate rainforest, characterized by western red cedar, western hemlock, Sitka spruce, yellow cypress, and deciduous big-leaf maple, red alder, cottonwoods, Garry oak and arbutus. The *Columbia forest region* of the Kootenay, Thompson, and Fraser river valleys includes species like western white pine, Engelmann spruce, western larch, and grand fir.

Forests of the east In the east, the *deciduous forest region* north of Lake Erie and Lake Ontario is the smallest forest region in Canada, characterized by deciduous species such as sugar maple, beech, elms, and oaks and by conifers such as the eastern white pine and eastern hemlock (**FIGURE 10.7C**). In this region there are also pockets of "Carolinian" species such as the tulip tree and black gum, which are more common further to the south in the eastern United States. The *Great Lakes–St. Lawrence forest region* extends from northwestern New Brunswick, through the St. Lawrence, Lac St. Jean, and Saguenay river valleys, over southern and central Ontario, and into Manitoba. Typical conifers include the eastern white and red pine and eastern hemlock. The characteristic deciduous species is yellow birch. Finally, the *Acadian forest region* of Nova Scotia, New Brunswick, and Prince Edward Island is typified by spruce and balsam fir, with common deciduous sugar maple, yellow birch, and beech.[8]

Forests are ecologically valuable

Because of their structural complexity and their ability to provide many niches for organisms, forests comprise some of the richest ecosystems for biodiversity (**FIGURE 10.8**). Trees furnish food and shelter for an immense diversity of vertebrate and invertebrate animals. Countless

FIGURE 10.8
Forests are ecologically valuable. They are especially important as habitat because of their structural complexity, as shown here in the old-growth forest of Cathedral Grove on Vancouver Island.

insects, birds, mammals, and other organisms subsist on the leaves, fruits, and seeds that trees produce.

Some animals are adapted for living in the dense treetop canopy, where beetles, caterpillars, and other leaf-eating insects abound, providing food for birds such as tanagers and warblers, while arboreal mammals from squirrels to sloths to monkeys consume fruit and leaves. Other animals specialize on the *subcanopies* of trees, and still others utilize the bark, branches, and trunks. Cavities in trunks provide nest and shelter sites for a wide variety of vertebrates. Dead and dying trees are valuable for many species; these *snags* are decayed by insects that, in turn, are eaten by woodpeckers and other animals.

Meanwhile, the shrubs and groundcover plants of the **understory**, the forest floor and the lowest levels of growth, give a forest structural complexity and provide habitat for still more organisms. Moreover, the leaves, stems, and roots of forest plants are colonized by an extensive array of fungi and microbes, in both parasitic and mutualistic relationships. Much of a forest's diversity resides on the forest floor, where the soil is generally nourished by fallen leaves and branches, called *litter*. There, myriad soil organisms help decompose plant material and cycle nutrients.

An additional habitat consideration in forests is the difference between the forest **core**, in the middle of a large forested area, and the forest **edge**. Edge habitat—even if it is still forested—can be quite different in character from habitat in the forest core, particularly in light levels, density of vegetation, and moisture. Research has demonstrated that wildlife adapted to forest core habitats declines when forced to occupy edge habitats, in parts of the forest that are immediately adjacent to surrounding areas. Fragmentation of wooded areas greatly increases the ratio of edge to core habitat, even if the total wooded area is not greatly reduced.

In general, forests with a greater diversity of plants, such as tropical rainforests, host a greater diversity of organisms overall. And in general, fully mature forests, such as the undisturbed old-growth forests remaining at Clayoquot Sound, contain more biodiversity than younger forests. Older forests offer more structural diversity and thus more microhabitats and resources to support more species.

Trees provide ecosystem services of value to people

In addition to hosting a significant proportion of the world's biodiversity, forests provide all manner of vital ecosystem services that are of value to people. Forest vegetation stabilizes soil and prevents erosion. The principal direct cause of soil erosion and degradation is the removal of vegetation. This is especially true in tropical rainforests where, counterintuitively, soils are not particularly fertile because most of the biomass of the system resides in the trees and other forest plants. Once the trees have been removed, the soil is exposed to wind and water and can quickly erode.

As mentioned above, trees and other forest plants help regulate the hydrologic cycle, slowing runoff, lessening flooding, and purifying water as they take it in from the soil and release it to the atmosphere. Tree branches and leaves physically block and soften the fall of rain, which further protects the soil from degradation. Forests also store carbon, release oxygen, and act as a moderating influence on climate. By performing these and other ecological functions, forests are indispensable for human survival and well-being.

Harvesting Forest Products

In addition to the immense value of their ecological services, forests provide people with economically valuable harvestable products. It has been estimated that over 1.6 billion people worldwide depend on forests directly for their livelihood, but all of us use forest products in our daily lives.

Forest products are economically valued

For millennia, wood from forests has fuelled our fires, keeping people warm and well fed. It has housed people, keeping us sheltered. It built the ships that carried people and cultures from one continent to another. It allowed us to produce paper, the medium of the first information revolution.

In recent decades, industrial harvesting has allowed the extraction of more timber than ever before, supplying all these needs of a rapidly growing human population and its expanding economy. The exploitation of forest resources has been instrumental in helping our society achieve the standard of living we enjoy today. Indeed, without industrial timber harvesting, you would not be reading this book.

Most commercial logging today takes place in Canada, Russia, and other nations that hold large expanses of boreal forest and in tropical countries with large amounts of rainforest, such as Brazil and Indonesia. Timber harvested from coniferous trees (such as those that dominate the boreal forest) is called **softwood**, whereas timber that comes from deciduous trees is called **hardwood**. (The terms are not related to the actual hardness of the wood.) The softwood lumber industry is extremely important to Canada's economy.

Forests also supply non-wood products in abundance. Some of these *NTFPs* (for *non-timber forest products*) include medicinal and herbal products, such as ginseng, echinacea, and St. John's wort; decorative products, such as Christmas trees, wreaths, and other greenery; and many edible products, including fruits, honey, edible mushrooms including truffles, and a large variety of nuts. Many Aboriginal and indigenous peoples make their livelihoods by harvesting non-timber forest products. The *seringeiro* rubbertappers of the Brazilian Amazon come to mind as one example of a group of people whose lifestyle is adapted to the sustainable extraction of forest resources.

Nations maintain and use forests for all these economic and ecological reasons. An international survey in 2010 found that globally, about 30% of forests were designated primarily for timber production and harvesting of other forest products.[9] Others are designated for a variety of functions, including conservation of biodiversity, protection of soil and water quality, and social services such as recreation, tourism, education, and conservation of culturally important sites (**FIGURE 10.9**).

Timber is harvested by several methods

When they harvest trees, timber companies use any of several methods. From the 1950s through the 1970s, many timber harvests were conducted using the **clear-**

Designated functions of the world's forests 2010

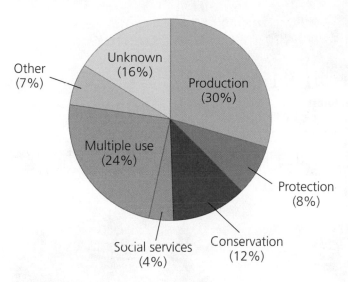

FIGURE 10.9
Worldwide, nations designate over one-third of forests primarily for production of timber and other forest products. Smaller areas are designated for conservation of biodiversity, protection of soil and water quality, and "social services" such as recreation, tourism, education, and conservation of culturally important sites. About one-third of forests are designated for combinations of these functions.
Source: Data from U.N. Food and Agriculture Organization (FAO) (2010) Global Forest Resources Assessment 2010, Key Findings, p. 10.

FIGURE 10.10
Clear-cutting is the most cost-efficient method for timber companies, but it can have severe ecological consequences, including soil erosion and species turnover. Although certain species do use clear-cut areas as they regrow, most people find these areas esthetically unappealing, and public reaction to clear-cutting has driven changes in forestry methods.

cutting method, in which all trees in an area are cut, leaving only stumps. Clear-cutting is generally the most cost-efficient method in the short term, but it has the greatest impacts on forest ecosystems (**FIGURE 10.10**). In the best-case scenario, clear-cutting may mimic natural disturbance events such as fires, tornadoes, or windstorms that knock down trees across large areas. In the worst-case scenario, entire communities of organisms are destroyed or displaced, soil erodes, and the penetration of sunlight to ground level changes microclimatic conditions such that new types of plants replace those that had comprised the native forest. Essentially, clear-cutting sets in motion an artificially driven process of succession in which the resulting climax community may turn out to be quite different from the original climax community.

Clear-cutting occurred widely across North America at a time when public awareness of environmental problems was blossoming. The combination produced public outrage toward the timber industry and public forest managers. Eventually the industry integrated other harvesting methods (**FIGURE 10.11**). A set of approaches dubbed **new forestry** called for timber cuts that came closer to mimicking natural disturbances. For instance, "sloppy clear-cuts" that leave a variety of trees standing were intended to mimic the changes a forest might experience if hit by a severe windstorm.

Clear-cutting (**FIGURE 10.11A**) is still widely practised, but other methods involve cutting some trees and leaving some standing. In the *seed-tree* approach (**FIGURE 10.11B**), small numbers of mature and vigorous seed-producing trees are left standing so that they can reseed the logged area. In the *shelterwood* approach (also **FIGURE 10.11B**), small numbers of mature trees are left in place to provide shelter for seedlings as they grow. These three methods all lead to even-aged stands of trees.

Selection systems, in contrast, allow uneven-aged stand management. In selection systems (**FIGURE 10.11C**), such as the variable retention harvest system practised on Clayoquot Sound, only some trees in a forest are cut at any one time. The stand's overall rotation time may be the same as in an even-aged approach because multiple harvests are made, but the stand remains mostly intact between harvests. Selection systems include single-tree selection, in which widely spaced trees are cut one at a time, and group selection, in which small patches of trees are cut.

It was a form of selection harvesting that Iisaak Forest Services and other logging organizations pursued at Clayoquot Sound after old-growth advocates applied pressure and the scientific panel published its guidelines. Not wanting to bring a complete end to logging when so many local people depended on the industry for work, these activists and scientists instead promoted what they considered a more environmentally friendly method of timber removal.

However, selection systems are by no means ecologically harmless. Moving trucks and machinery over an extensive network of roads and trails to access individual trees

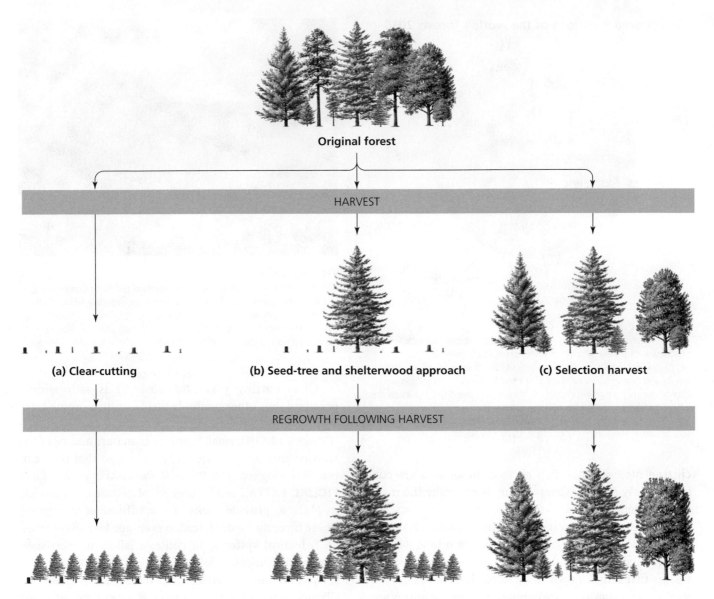

FIGURE 10.11   Foresters and timber companies have devised various methods to harvest timber from forests. In clear-cutting **(a)**, all trees in an area are cut, extracting a great deal of timber inexpensively but leaving a vastly altered landscape. In seed-tree systems and shelterwood systems **(b)**, small numbers of large trees are left in clear-cuts to help reseed the area or provide shelter for growing seedlings. In selection systems **(c)**, a minority of trees is removed at any one time, while most are left standing. These last two methods involve less environmental impact than clear-cutting, but all methods can cause significant changes to the structure and function of natural forest communities.

compacts the soil and disturbs the forest floor. Selection methods are also unpopular with timber companies because they are expensive.

The bottom line, from an ecological perspective, is that all methods of logging result in habitat disturbance, which invariably affects the plants and animals inhabiting an area. All methods change forest structure and composition. Most methods increase soil erosion, leading to siltation of waterways, which can degrade habitat and affect drinking water quality. Most methods also speed runoff, sometimes causing flooding. In extreme cases, as when steep hillsides are clear-cut, landslides can result.

Plantation forestry has grown in North America

The North American timber industry is largely centred on production from plantations of fast-growing tree species that are single-species monocultures. Forest plantations now make up about 7% of forested land globally (**FIGURE 10.12A**).[10] Logging in Canada is largely offset by **reforestation**, the planting of trees after logging, and **afforestation**, the planting of trees where forested cover has not existed for some time (over 50 years). Because all trees in a given stand are planted at the same time, the stands are **even-aged**, with all trees the same age (**FIGURE**

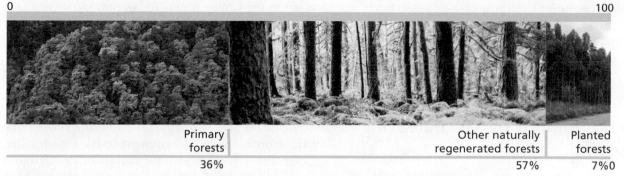

0   100

Primary forests	Other naturally regenerated forests	Planted forests
36%	57%	7%0

(a) Primary and planted forests, % 2010

(b) Tree plantation

FIGURE 10.12
(a) Approximately 7% of global forested land today is forest plantation and this is increasing. **(b)** Even-aged tree stand management is practised on tree plantations where all trees are of equal age, as seen in the stand in the foreground that is regrowing after clear-cutting. In uneven-aged tree stand management, harvests are designed to maintain a mix of tree ages, as seen in the more mature forest in the background. The increased structural diversity of uneven-aged stands provides superior habitat for most wild species and makes these stands more akin to ecologically functional forests.

10.12B). Stands are cut after a certain number of years (called the *rotation time*), and the land is replanted with seedlings.

It is important to acknowledge that planting new trees will not replace complex old-growth forests that may have taken hundreds of years to develop. Even when regrowth outpaces removal, the character of forests may still change. In North America and worldwide, primary forest continues to be lost and to be replaced by younger second-growth forest. Most ecologists and foresters view these plantations more as crop agriculture than as ecologically functional forests. Because there are few tree species and little variation in tree age, plantations do not offer many forest organisms the habitat they need.

The principle of **maximum sustainable yield**, a basic principle of renewable resource management, argues for cutting trees shortly after they have gone through their fastest stage of growth, and trees often grow most quickly at intermediate ages. Thus, trees may be cut long before they have grown as large as they would in the absence of harvesting. Although this practice may maximize timber production over time, it can cause drastic changes in the ecology of a forest by eliminating habitat for species that depend on mature trees. However, some harvesting methods aim to maintain **uneven-aged** stands, where a mix of ages (and often a mix of tree species) makes the stand more similar to a natural forest.

Land Conversion and Deforestation

The harvesting of timber and other forest products is not new; it has occurred throughout human history. We all depend in some way on wood, and people have cleared forests for millennia to exploit forest resources. Historically, as agriculture emerged and some cultures began to adopt a sedentary or settled lifestyle, the clearing of forested land for settlement and farming would have been one of the very first significant human-generated environmental impacts. Forest clearing has even been used as an approach in warfare (both modern and ancient) and to flush out game for hunting purposes. Land conversion, combined with some bad practices in agriculture, ranching, and forestry, has led to **deforestation**, the loss of forested area worldwide.

The growth of Canada and the U.S. were fuelled by land clearing and logging

Historically, logging for timber and the clearing of land for settlement and farming propelled the growth of both Canada and the United States throughout the phenomenal expansion westward across the North American continent over the past 400 years. The vast deciduous forests of the eastern United States were virtually stripped of their trees by the mid-nineteenth century, making way for countless small farms. Timber from these forests built the cities of eastern North America.

As the farming economy shifted to an industrial one, wood was used to stoke the furnaces of industry. Once most of the mature trees were removed from the eastern hardwood forests, timber companies moved to the south and west, eventually harvesting some of the continent's biggest trees in the Rocky Mountains, the Sierra Nevada, and the Pacific Coast ranges (**FIGURE 10.13**).

By the early twentieth century, very little **primary forest**—long-standing natural forest, uncut by people—

was left in the United States. Today, the largest oaks and maples found in eastern North America, and even most redwoods of the California coast, are **second-growth** trees: trees that have sprouted and grown to partial maturity after old-growth timber has been cut. The size of the gargantuan trees they replaced can be seen in the enormous stumps that remain in the more recently logged areas of the Pacific Coast. The scarcity of old-growth trees on the North American continent today explains the concern that scientists have for old-growth ecosystems and the passion with which environmental advocates have fought to preserve ancient forests in areas such as Clayoquot Sound.

In spite of vigorous historical logging, much of Canada remains forested (**FIGURE 10.14A**). The principal cause of deforestation in Canada today is not logging but land clearing for agriculture. Deforestation continues in Canada, but in 2008 it affected less than 0.02% (approximately 46 000 ha in net loss) of Canada's forests (**FIGURE 10.14B,C**). Fire, urban development, hydroelectric dams, and, increasingly, outbreaks of parasites and other invasive pest species such as the Asian longhorned beetle, mountain pine beetle, and spruce budworm are also significant causes of deforestation (see "The Science Behind the Story: Changing Climate and the Spruce Budworm on Vancouver Island"). Many scientists expect that climate change will be an important driver of deforestation in the near future.

FIGURE 10.13

Huge trees were harvested in many locations in Canada in the first part of the nineteenth century, including the pines shown here in Madawaska River Valley near Ottawa. Early timber harvesting practices in North America caused significant environmental impacts and removed virtually all the virgin timber from one region after another.

% of area % de la superficie	Area Superficie M ha
0 - < 5	1.2
5 - < 20	7.9
20 - < 40	21.6
40 - < 60	40.9
60 - < 80	86.2
80 - 100	243.7
Total	401.5

Canada's Forest Inventory 2001
Natural Resources Canada
Canadian Forest Service

Inventaire des forêts du Canada 2001
Ressources naturelles Canada
Service canadien des forêts

map printed July 12, 2004

(a) Forested land in Canada

(b) Causes of deforestation in Canada today

Urban development, transportation, and recreation — 19%
Agriculture — 53%
Industry and resource extraction — 8%
Hydroelectricity — 10%
Forest roads — 10%

(c) Land-clearing for agriculture

FIGURE 10.14 In spite of vigorous logging and deforestation during the westward expansion from the 1600s to the early 1900s, much of Canada remains forested today **(a)**. This is in contrast to the United States, where the majority of primary forest had been removed by the late 1800s. Today in Canada the principal causes of deforestation **(b)** are urban development and land clearing for agriculture **(c)**, as seen here in a photo of Quyon, Québec.

THE SCIENCE BEHIND THE STORY

Changing Climate and the Spruce Budworm on Vancouver Island

Spruce budworm larva on a Douglas fir.

As climate changes, ecosystems change too. On southern Vancouver Island, the invasive parasitic western spruce budworm (see photo) is no longer the problem that it once was, as a result of a local increase in sea temperature over the past century that has limited the availability of the pest's food.[11]

Ross Benton and Dr. Alan Thomson, research scientists at Natural Resources Canada's Pacific Forestry Centre in Victoria, have investigated the effects of changing climate at a local level. Their research shows that a 90-year increase in overall winter temperature on southern Vancouver Island has nearly eliminated western spruce budworm outbreaks in the area. "This pest will always be there at a very low level, but its population can't expand," says Benton. "The opportunity for the bug to infest its host, the Douglas fir, is less and less."

Although spruce budworm outbreaks have been known in this area since 1909, it is unlikely to happen again, says Benton. During outbreaks in the first part of the twentieth century, the budworm defoliated a total area of 35 732 ha on southern Vancouver Island. However, the changing climate now means that food isn't available when the budworm larvae hatch. Budworm development is triggered by temperature, whereas development of Douglas firs is triggered more by light and day length. As a result, the budworm larvae are emerging from their shelters earlier than a century ago, whereas development of Douglas fir buds has remained constant. "The pest is starting to develop earlier and can't bore into the outer sheathing that protects new buds," says Benton. "The food is there, but not accessible," adds Thomson.

Although this may sound like good news, it may not be, according to Dr. Thomson. "Previous problems with budworm outbreaks are gone, but new species that weren't a problem before may become one." He points out that although spruce budworm outbreaks are no longer a problem in this part of the Island, British Columbia's interior forests are experiencing large-scale outbreaks.

Meanwhile, another invasive insect, the mountain pine beetle (see photo), has been one of the highest-profile forestry problems in British Columbia in the past two decades. "Without the mountain pine beetle, the budworm would be big news," says Dr. Thomson. According to the government of British Columbia, by 2011 the pine beetle had affected more than 17.5 million ha of lodgepole pine forest in the province (see photo), killing more than 700 million cubic metres of timber, and the province has invested more than $756 million to fight the infestation.[12] However, the British Columbia Ministry of Forests, Land, and Natural Resources Operations concludes that the infestation of mountain pine beetles, which are killed by cold winters, peaked in 2005 and has declined considerably since then.[13]

Mountain pine beetles have killed millions of cubic metres of timber in British Columbia. Warmer summers and milder winters promote the activity of these invasive beetles.

Agriculture is the major cause of conversion of forests and grasslands

Agriculture now covers more of the planet's surface than does forest. Thirty-eight percent of Earth's terrestrial surface is devoted to agriculture—more than the area of North America and Africa combined. Of this land, 26% supports pasture, and 12% consists of crops and arable land. Agriculture is the most widespread type of human land use and the principal driver of land conversion today, causing tremendous impacts on land and ecosystems (see **FIGURE 10.14B** and **C**). Although agricultural methods such as organic farming and no-till farming can be sustainable, the majority of the world's cropland hosts either intensive traditional agriculture or monocultural industrial agriculture, involving heavy use of fertilizers, pesticides, and irrigation.

In many parts of the developing world, forests are cleared for traditional *swidden* agriculture, in which a small area of forest is cleared (often by *slash-and-burn*), and crops are planted. After one or two seasons of planting, when the soil has been depleted of nutrients, the farmer moves on to clear another patch of forest, leaving the first clearing in a *fallow* or resting state, giving it time to replenish itself. This can be a sustainable practice if the initial clearings are given sufficient time—often as much as 7 years is needed—in which to replenish the nutrient content of the soil. However, social and economic pressures in the developing world, including population pressure, have led to shorter and shorter fallow times, with the result that the cleared forest soils erode away, rather than regenerating. After that, the soil will no longer support either crops or forests.

In theory, the marketplace should discourage people from farming with intensive methods that degrade land they own if such practices are not profitable. But agriculture in many countries (including Canada) is supported by government subsidies, which amount to billions of dollars in some cases. For example, the Brazilian government provides financial incentives to farmers to clear areas of the Amazon rainforest for agriculture. Proponents of agricultural subsidies stress that the vagaries of weather make profits and losses from farming unpredictable from year to year. To persist, these proponents say, an agricultural system needs some way to compensate farmers for bad years. Opponents of subsidies argue that subsidization of environmentally destructive agricultural practices is unsustainable.

Livestock graze one-fourth of Earth's land surface

Most cattle in North America today are raised in feedlots, but they have traditionally been raised by grazing on open **rangelands**, grasslands or wooded areas converted for the purpose of supporting livestock (**FIGURE 10.15**). Grazing can be sustainable, but overgrazing damages soils, waterways, and vegetative communities. Range managers are responsible for regulating ranching on public lands, and they advise ranchers on sustainable grazing practices.

Cropland agriculture uses less than half the land taken up by livestock grazing, which covers a quarter of the world's land surface. Human use of rangeland, however, does not necessarily exclude its use by wildlife or its continued functioning as a grassland ecosystem. Grazing can be sustainable if done carefully and at low intensity. In the West, some ranching proponents claim that cattle are merely taking the place of the vast herds of bison that once roamed the plains. Indeed, most of the world's grasslands have historically been home to large herds of grass-eating mammals, and grasses have adapted to herbivory.

Poorly managed grazing can have adverse impacts on soil and grassland ecosystems. In Central and South America, the conversion of forested land and grass lands to rangelands occurred with phenomenal rapidity during the decades from the 1940s to the 1970s. The dramatic loss of forested land has led a few countries, notably Costa Rica, to institute some tough new environmental restrictions.

Ranchers and environmentalists have traditionally been at loggerheads. In the past several years, however, they have been finding some common ground, teaming up to preserve ranchland against what each of them views

FIGURE 10.15
Livestock grazing, shown here in Alberta, covers a quarter of Earth's land surface.

in common as a threat—the encroaching housing developments of suburban sprawl. Although developers often pay high prices for ranchland, many ranchers do not want to see the loss of the wide-open spaces and the ranching lifestyle that they cherish.

Bad practices and other pressures have led to deforestation

Deforestation has altered the landscapes and ecosystems of much of our planet. Forest resources can, in principle, be harvested sustainably, but unfortunately this hasn't always happened. Impacts are greatest in tropical areas because of the potentially massive loss of biodiversity, and in dryland regions because of the vulnerability of these lands to desertification. In addition, deforestation adds carbon dioxide (CO_2) to the atmosphere: CO_2 is released when plant matter is burned or decomposed, and thereafter less vegetation remains to soak up CO_2. Deforestation is thereby one contributor to global climate change. Deforestation can cause soil degradation and species extinctions, and, as we saw in the case of Easter Island, it has in some cases helped bring whole civilizations to ruin.

Globally, about 13 million ha of forest are deforested each year—equivalent to the area of Nova Scotia and New Brunswick combined. This has been the average yearly rate of deforestation from 2000 to 2011, down from an average of about 16 million ha per year in the 1990s.[14] In Canada, as in some other economically developed nations, reforestation and afforestation have more than offset losses to forested area in the past decade or so, leading to a (small) net increase in forested land.

Today forests are being felled at the fastest rates in the tropical rainforests of Latin America and Africa (**FIGURE 10.16**). Developing countries in these regions are striving to expand areas of settlement for their burgeoning populations and to boost their economies by extracting natural resources and selling them abroad. Moreover, many people in these societies cut trees for fuelwood for their daily cooking and heating needs. In contrast, areas of Europe and eastern North America are slowly gaining forest cover as they recover from severe deforestation of past decades and centuries. Overall, the world is losing its forests (see "The Science Behind the Story: Surveying Earth's Forests").

Land uses such as grazing, farming, and timber harvesting need not have strongly adverse impacts. It is not these activities themselves that inherently cause environmental problems, but rather the overexploitation of resources beyond what ecosystems can handle. Unfortunately, economic and social pressures, particularly in the developing world, often drive overexploitation and unsustainable practices.

Deforestation is proceeding rapidly in many developing nations

Uncut primary tropical forests still remain in many developing countries. These nations are in the position Canada faced a century or two ago: having a vast frontier that they can develop for human use. Today's advanced technology, however, has allowed these countries to exploit their resources and push back their frontiers even faster than occurred in North America. As a result, deforestation is

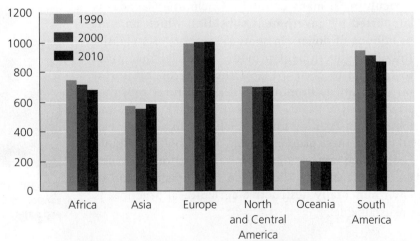

FIGURE 10.16

South America and Africa are experiencing rapid deforestation as they develop, extract resources, and clear new agricultural land for growing populations. In Europe, forested area is slowly increasing as some formerly farmed areas are allowed to grow back into forest. The data for North and Central America reflect a balance of forest regrowth in North America and forest loss in Central America. In Asia, natural forests are being lost, but the extensive planting of tree plantations (here counted as forests) in China has increased forest cover for Asia since 2000.

Source: Data from U.N. Food and Agriculture Organization, Global Forest Resources Assessment, 2010.

(a) Logging in Borneo

(b) *Rafflesia arnoldii* in bloom

FIGURE 10.17
Logging, both illegal and legal **(a)**, and associated deforestation are rampant in Borneo, Malaysia. The central habitat of *Rafflesia arnoldii*, the world's largest flower **(b)**, and that of many other important and threatened species, is in Borneo.

extremely rapid in places such as Brazil, Indonesia, and parts of West Africa.

Developing nations are often desperate enough for economic development, and for foreign capital with which to maintain the interest payments on enormous national debt loads, that they impose few or no restrictions on logging. Often their timber is extracted by foreign multinational corporations, which have paid fees to the developing nation's government for a *concession*, or right to extract the resource. In such cases, the foreign corporation has little or no incentive to manage forest resources sustainably. Many of the short-term economic benefits are reaped not by local residents but by the corporations that log the timber and export it elsewhere. Local people may or may not receive temporary employment from the corporation, but once the timber is harvested they no longer have the forest and the ecosystem services it once provided.

weighing the issues

LOGGING HERE OR THERE

Imagine you are an environmental activist protesting a logging operation that is cutting old-growth trees near your hometown. If the protest is successful, the company will move to a developing country and cut its primary forest instead. Would you still protest the logging in your hometown? Would you pursue any other approaches?

In Sarawak, the Malaysian portion of the island of Borneo, foreign corporations that were granted logging concessions have deforested several million hectares of tropical rainforest since 1963 (**FIGURE 10.17A**). The clearing of this forest—one of the world's richest, hosting such organisms as orangutans and the world's largest flower, *Rafflesia arnoldii* (**FIGURE 10.17B**)—has had direct impacts on the 22 tribes of people who live as hunter-gatherers in Sarawak's rainforest. The Malaysian government did not consult the tribes about the logging, which decreased the wild game on which these people depended. Oil palm agriculture was established afterward, leading to pesticide and fertilizer runoff that killed fish in local streams. The tribes protested peacefully and finally began blockading logging roads. The government, which at first jailed them, now is negotiating, but it insists on converting the tribes to a farming way of life.

Forest Management Principles

Professionals who manage forests through the practice of **forestry** (or **silviculture**) must balance the central importance of forests as ecosystems with civilization's demand for wood products. Sustainable forest management, like the management of other renewable natural resources, is based on maintaining equilibrium between *stocks* and *flows*. In principle, the removal or **harvesting** of material from the resource by logging should not occur at a rate that exceeds the capability of the resource to replenish or regenerate itself.

Public forests in Canada are managed for many purposes

Nearly 94% of Canada's forest is publicly owned; the majority of this is under provincial jurisdiction. Only about 6–8% of forested land in Canada is privately owned,

THE SCIENCE BEHIND THE STORY

Surveying Earth's Forests

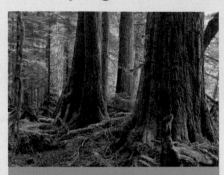

This old-growth forest is in British Columbia.

In the time it takes you to read this sentence, 2 hectares of tropical forest will have been cleared.

Where do such numbers come from? How do we know how much forest our planet is losing—or how much forest there was to begin with?

Every 5 to 10 years since 1948, the United Nations Food and Agriculture Organization (FAO) has conducted a global inventory of forest resources. FAO researchers ask the world's national governments to respond to provide data on forest area, types of forest, deforestation, regrowth, and other parameters. However, nations may not keep accurate data or may not care to share it.

In recent years, satellite technology has provided a way to confirm information from national surveys. With remote sensing data from satellites, we can measure and map forest cover from space.

Satellites that observe Earth's surface measure wavelengths of energy being emitted. This information is processed and used to infer what materials are on the surface. Plants absorb most wavelengths of light but reflect infrared radiation and green light (which is why plants appear green). When satellite data show green and infrared wavelengths reflected from the surface but an absence of other wavelengths such as red and blue, the presence of vegetation can be inferred.

Researchers use data from a number of satellites (for instance, the Land Remote Sensing Satellite [Landsat], the Advanced Very High Resolution Radiometer [AVHRR], and the Moderate Resolution Imaging Spectroradiometer [MODIS]) to infer vegetative cover. By quantifying plant cover, researchers can compare one site to another and can measure how sites change across seasons or years.

The 2001 study of global forest cover by the United Nations Environment Programme (UNEP) used AVHRR data and loaded this into a geographic information system, or GIS. Researchers then added data on human population distribution, political boundaries, and land protected against development. The study found that forests in densely populated nations such as India and Indonesia were under pressure from expanding human settlement and require urgent conservation efforts.

The global forest inventory is updated on a continuing basis. In 2011, the FAO released its latest global accounting of forests. In the *Global Forest Resources Assessment 2010*, researchers combined remote sensing data, questionnaire responses, analysis from forestry experts, and statistical modeling to form a comprehensive picture of the state of the world's forests, globally, by region, and by individual country.

Major findings of the most recent FAO assessment included the following:

- Forests cover 31% of the world's land area.
- Just 10 nations account for two-thirds of all forests.
- 30% of forests are designated primarily for wood production.
- Forests store 289 billion metric tonnes of carbon in living tissue, and more overall than the atmosphere.
- Some rare tree species valued for wood (such as teak and mahogany) are in danger of vanishing.
- 80% of forests are publicly owned, but private ownership is increasing.
- Forestry directly employs 10 million people.

By comparing the results with those of previous assessments, the FAO could

---

about 1.5% by logging companies, with the remainder under federal or territorial control.[15] An increasing amount of land in Canada, including forested land, is under Aboriginal jurisdiction as land claims are settled.[16]

In Canada, timber is extracted from both privately owned and publicly held forests by private timber companies. In fact, much of the resource extraction industry in Canada—both logging and mining—is carried out on Crown lands (mainly provincial). The provinces and territories and the federal government have different requirements governing the acquisition of rights to carry out resource extraction on Crown lands. Under the Constitution, provinces and territories own and regulate the natural resources within their boundaries.

The federal role in forestry is based on its responsibility for the national economy, trade, science and technology, the environment, and federal Crown lands and parks, as well as Aboriginal and treaty rights, which are constitutionally protected by the federal Constitution Act of 1982.

The Canadian Forest Service, part of Natural Resources Canada, was established in 1899, and given the responsibility to preserve timber on Crown lands and to develop policies to encourage tree culture.[17] Since then, the Canadian Forest Service has been involved in the scientific study and monitoring of Canada's forests and in managing the extraction of timber and non-timber forest products from national forests. The National Forest Strategies began to be offialso reveal trends through time. Major findings included the following:

- Globally, we deforest 13 million hectares per year (the annual average from 2000 to 2010). This is down from about 16 million hectares per year in the 1990s.
- Regions vary in rates of forest loss or gain.
- Primary forests are being lost more quickly than second-growth forests.
- Forest plantations make up only 7% of forested land, but are increasing in area.

- Carbon storage by the world's forests decreased by approximately 0.5 Gt per year from 2000 to 2010, primarily because of a decrease in world forested area.

The study examined how our society was progressing toward sustainable management of forests. Researchers examined a number of indicators (see the figure). Among other trends, they found that more forests are being managed for multiple uses and that the use of forests for recreation and education is increasing rapidly. About 12% of forests are designated for biodiversity conservation, and only 8% for soil and water conservation.[18]

These trends are occurring against a backdrop of continued net loss of forests, especially primary forests. Overall, the report concludes that the outlook is mixed: "There are many good signs and positive trends, but many negative trends remain. While intensive forest plantation and conservation efforts are on the rise, primary forests continue to become degraded or converted to agriculture at alarming rates in some regions."

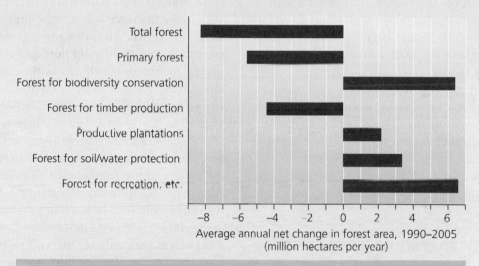

Average annual net change in forest area, 1990–2005 (million hectares per year)

Progress toward sustainable forestry is mixed, as shown by 7 of 21 indicators assessed by the Food and Agriculture Organization (FAO). Forest uses are shifting toward conservation and away from production, but forest area is still shrinking. (The numbers represented on the graph don't balance because some of the categories are overlapping.)
Source: Data from U.N. Food and Agriculture Organization (2005) Global Forest Resources Assessment.

cially developed in 1980. The current National Forest Strategy makes reference to Canada's obligation to the world to maintain and preserve the vast forests of which we are the stewards. The vision statement of this document reads, in part:

The health of the forest is directly linked to environmental processes on local, regional and international scales as well as to the social, cultural, spiritual and economic well-being of us all. As a result, we want to improve our understanding of how we are a part of and how we affect the forest—in short, to act on our increasingly informed understanding to become even better stewards of our forest resource.[19]

For the past half century, forest management throughout North America has nominally been guided by the policy of **multiple use**, meaning that forests were to be managed for recreation, wildlife habitat, mineral extraction, and various other uses. In reality, however, timber production was most often the primary use. In recent decades, increased awareness of the problems associated with logging has prompted many citizens to protest the way public forests are managed in Canada. These citizens have urged that provincial forests be managed for recreation, wildlife, and ecosystem integrity, rather than for timber. They want forests managed as ecologically functional entities, not as cropland for trees.

The National Forest Strategy for 2003–2008 includes the following objectives:

- Implementing ecosystem-based management (as described above)
- Improving the environmental, social, and economic sustainability of forest communities, through legislation and policies
- Recognizing the historical and legal rights of Aboriginal peoples and their fundamental connection to the forest ecosystem
- Stimulating the diversification of markets for forest products, benefits, and services
- Enhancing the skills and knowledge of forest practitioners, to promote innovation for competitiveness and sustainability
- Actively engaging Canadians in sustainability through the planning, maintenance, and management of urban forests
- Strengthening policies and services that support the contribution of private woodlots to forest sustainability
- Creating a comprehensive national forest reporting system that consolidates data, information, and knowledge for all valued features of the forest, both urban and rural.[20]

Today many managers practise ecosystem-based management

Increasing numbers of renewable resource managers today espouse ecosystem-based management. **Ecosystem-based management** attempts to manage the harvesting of resources in ways that minimize impact on the ecosystems and ecological processes of the forest. In Canada, ecosystem-based management aims to preserve forest health, structure, functions, composition, and biodiversity. This has been partly achieved by the establishment, over time, of a system of provincially, federally, and internationally protected areas (discussed below). An additional goal of ecosystem-based forest management is to maintain Canada's forests as viable reservoirs, or *sinks*, for atmospheric carbon.[21] This is crucial for managing carbon emissions in the global effort to control climate change.

As an example, the plan proposed in 1995 by the Scientific Panel for Sustainable Forest Practices on Clayoquot Sound and approved by British Columbia's government was essentially a plan for ecosystem-based management. By carefully managing ecologically important areas such as riparian corridors, by considering patterns at the landscape level, and by affording protection to some forested areas, the plan aimed to allow continued timber harvesting at reduced levels while preserving the functional integrity of the ecosystem.

Although ecosystem-based management has gained a great deal of support in recent years, it is challenging for managers to determine how best to implement this type of management. Ecosystems are complex, and our understanding of how they operate is limited. Thus, ecosystem-based management has often come to mean different things to different people.

Adaptive management evolves and improves

Some management actions will succeed, and some will fail. A wise manager will try new approaches if old ones are not effective. **Adaptive management** involves systematically testing different management approaches and aiming to improve methods as time goes on. It entails monitoring the results of one's practices and continually adjusting them as needed, based on what is learned. This approach is intended as a fusion and partnership of science and management because hypotheses about how best to manage resources are explicitly tested and the results of the testing used to modify management approaches. Adaptive management can be time-consuming and complicated, however. It has posed a challenge for many managers because those who adopt new approaches must often overcome inertia and resistance to change from proponents of established practices.

Adaptive management has become a guiding principle for forest management in Canada. In British Columbia the Ministry of Forests and Range has embraced adaptive management, promoting the approach through collaborative projects that range from testing alternative forestry practices, to monitoring whole watersheds, to evaluating the effectiveness of various land and resource management strategies.[22] The following are some examples of adaptive management projects that have been undertaken in British Columbia forests:

- The West Arm Demonstration Forest Experiments, which were designed to study a broad range of forest values and to evaluate the effectiveness and impacts of several new forest management approaches
- The Donna Creek Biodiversity Project, which tested whether maintenance of tall stumps and small residual tree islands benefits cavity-using animals within clear-cuts
- The Grizzly Bear Habitat Project, which was designed to assist in the development of forestry management systems to maintain grizzly habitat, while at the same time producing timber[23]

Fire is a natural phenomenon in forests

Ecological research shows that many ecosystems depend on fire, particularly in the boreal forest. Certain plants such as jack pines have seeds that germinate only in response to fire. This makes evolutionary sense; when a seedling grows after a fire, there are no big trees to take the light from it, and it can benefit from nutrients contained in the ash of the burnt forest. Researchers studying tree rings have documented that many ecosystems historically experienced frequent fires. Burn marks in tree rings reveal past fires, giving scientists an accurate history of fire events extending back hundreds or even thousands of years. Many wooded dryland ecosystems also depend on fire. For example, researchers have found that North America's grasslands and open pine woodlands burn regularly in the natural system.

Ecosystems dependent on fire are adversely affected by its suppression; pine woodlands become cluttered with hardwood understory that ordinarily would be cleared away by fire, for instance, and animal diversity and abundance decline.

Fires depend on the triad of oxygen, heat, and fuel to progress. In the forest context, branches, fallen logs, sticks, and leaf litter accumulate on the forest floor, producing kindling and fuel for future fires. Climate and weather are crucial components. An overall dry climate or unusually dry weather can contribute to dry litter and upper soil layers in which organic matter can be easily ignited. This leads to *ground fires* (**FIGURE 10.18A**), in which the litter layer itself burns, as opposed to *crown fires*, in which the upper tree canopy is ignited (**FIGURE 10.18B**). Storms also bring winds that can fan fires. Topography is another important component of forest fires. A fire burning up the slope of a canyon (**FIGURE 10.18C**) can be particularly challenging to contain. Winds blowing up the hillslope can fan the fire, whereas the heat from below ignites dry fuel on upslope areas. Lightning is responsible for igniting the majority of naturally induced forest fires. (Other causes of forest fires are volcanic eruptions and, of course, human carelessness.)

Fire policy has stirred controversy

The management of fires is one of the most controversial aspects of forest management today. For over a century, land management agencies throughout North America have suppressed fire whenever and wherever it breaks out (as per the warnings of "Smokey the Bear": "Only *you* can prevent forest fires!").

In the long term, fire suppression can lead to a buildup of dead wood; this can fuel catastrophic fires that truly damage forests, destroy human property, and threaten human lives. Fuel buildup helped cause the 1988 fires

(a) Ground fire

(b) Crown fire

(c) Slope fire

FIGURE 10.18
Fires need fuel, oxygen, and a heat source. The buildup of dry litter and organic matter in soil layers can lead to ground fires **(a)**, in which the litter layer itself burns. Fires that move into the top part of the canopy **(b)** are called crown fires. Fires can move very quickly up slopes **(c)**, fanned by wind and fuelled by heat from below.

FIGURE 10.19
Forest fires are natural phenomena to which many plants are adapted and which maintain many ecosystems. However, climate change combined with the suppression of fire over the past century has led to a buildup of dry litter and woody debris, which serve as fuel to increase the severity and frequency of fires. As a result, catastrophic wildfires have become more common in recent years. Shown here, a devastating forest fire ripped through Slave Lake, Alberta, in May 2011, destroying much of the town.

in Yellowstone National Park, the 2003 fires in southern California, the 2003 fires in British Columbia, and thousands of other wildfires across the continent each year (**FIGURE 10.19**). Fire suppression and fuel buildup have made catastrophic fires significantly greater problems than they were in the past. Now, global climate change is bringing drier weather to much of the Canadian Prairies, further worsening the wildfire risk. At the same time, increasing residential development on the edges of forested land is placing more homes in fire-prone situations.

To reduce fuel load and improve the health and safety of forests, forest management agencies have in recent years been burning areas of forest under carefully controlled conditions. These **prescribed burns**, or **controlled burns**, have worked effectively, but they have been implemented on only a relatively small amount of land.

weighing the issues

HOW TO HANDLE FIRE?

A century of fire suppression has left vast swaths of forested lands in North America in danger of catastrophic wildfires. Yet we will probably never have adequate resources to conduct careful prescribed burning over all these lands. Can you suggest any solutions to help protect people's homes near forests while improving the ecological condition of some forested lands? Do you think people should be allowed to develop homes in fire-prone areas?

Another significant and controversial aspect of fire management concerns what happens after a fire, which may include the physical removal of small trees, underbrush, and dead trees by timber companies. The removal of dead trees, or snags, following a natural disturbance is called **salvage logging**. From an economic standpoint, salvage logging may seem to make good sense. Proponents of salvage logging argue that forests regenerate best after a fire if they are logged and replanted with seedlings. Moreover, they maintain, salvage logging reduces future fire risk by removing woody debris that could serve as fuel for the next fire. However, snags have immense ecological value; the insects that decay them provide food for wildlife, and many birds, mammals, and reptiles depend on holes in snags for nesting and roosting sites. Removing timber from recently burned land can also cause severe erosion, collapse of streambanks, and soil damage.

Sustainable forestry is gaining ground

Any company can claim that its timber harvesting practices are sustainable, but how is the purchaser of wood products to know whether they really are? In the last several years, a consumer movement has grown that is making informed consumer choice possible. Several organizations now examine the practices of timber companies and offer **sustainable forestry certification** to products produced using methods they consider sustainable (**FIGURE 10.20**).

FIGURE 10.20
A Brazilian woodcutter taking inventory marks timber harvested from a forest certified for sustainable management in Amazonian Brazil. A consumer movement centred on independent certification of sustainable wood products is allowing consumer choice to promote sustainable forestry practices.

CANADIAN ENVIRONMENTAL PERSPECTIVES

Tzeporah Berman

Thinking About Environmental Perspectives

- **Co-founder** of the environmental nonprofit organization **ForestEthics**
- **Anti-logging activist**
- **Market campaigner** and **"corporate re-educator"**

In the spring of 1992, 22-year-old Tzeporah Berman returned to Vancouver Island to continue her university fieldwork studying marbled murrelet nests. But she could not find the nesting area. The approach to the site had been logged, and with the landmarks obliterated, she could not get her bearings. Gradually, the reality dawned: this *was* the nesting site. She found a ring of stumps that had been the 70-metre-high Sitka spruce trees under which she had camped. She found a trickle of water that had been a waterfall and pool where she had swum. Eagles wheeled overhead, surveying their fallen nests.

Sitting on a stump, in tears, Berman reconsidered her summer and her future.

She had planned to finish environmental studies and then go into law. But by the time she did that, she decided, there would be no marbled murrelets left. The next day, a van stopped on its way to a blockade in Clayoquot Sound. Berman climbed in.[24]

The rest, as they say, is history. Berman was right in the midst of the historic protests at Clayoquot Sound, described in the Central Case. Eventually she was arrested and dragged into court for "aiding and abetting" the commission of hundreds of criminal acts by the thousands of other Clayoquot protestors (the charges were dropped). She became a figurehead for the cause—sometimes hugged and sometimes attacked in public, she experienced death threats and even had her apartment burned by an unknown arsonist. The reference to "enemies of the state" made by the premier of British Columbia was aimed at Berman and her associates.

Working for Greenpeace, Berman began her transformation into "corporate re-educator" while helping to organize a huge (and very successful) public boycott against logging company MacMillan-Bloedel. The boycott, or "market campaign," focused specifically on MacMillan-Bloedel's customers. Did Pacific Bell know, they would ask, that their phone books were made from the ancient rainforest of Clayoquot Sound? Surely the company would be alarmed at this, and if they weren't, certainly Pacific Bell's customers would be. Alarmed, Pacific Bell called MacMillan-Bloedel; so did Scott Paper and the *New York Times*.[25] As the tide began to turn, Berman realized that money and the wishes of customers could be leveraged to convince large corpora-

tions that having environmentally responsible policies is not only the *right* thing to do, but also the most *financially sound* thing to do.

Today ForestEthics, the nonprofit group that Berman and others founded in 1994, collaborates with some of the same corporations they previously boycotted. Through its Corporate Action Program, ForestEthics has turned "corporate adversaries into allies."[26] It works with companies such as The Home Depot, Dell, Victoria's Secret, Estée Lauder, and Staples (the largest paper retailer in the world) to develop strong, financially sound, cutting-edge corporate environmental policies. By some accounts, Berman's actions and her work through ForestEthics have saved as many as 5 million hectares of forest from destruction in Canada and elsewhere in the world.

"The influence of the marketplace is integral to protecting the key areas of the natural forest that are left. Economic prosperity in the long term is tied to ecological prosperity now."[27]**—Tzeporah Berman**

Thinking About Environmental Perspectives

Tzeporah Berman and her colleagues used the threat of public dissatisfaction and boycotts to convince large corporations to adopt responsible policies regarding logging and product sources. Can you think of other cases where large, multinational corporations have been convinced to change their policies because of environmental or social justice concerns and campaigns on the part of their customers?

Organizations such as the International Organization for Standardization (ISO), the Sustainable Forestry Initiative (SFI) program, and the Forest Stewardship Council (FSC) have varying standards for certification. Consumers can look for the logos of these organizations on forest products they purchase. The FSC is widely perceived to have the strictest certification standards. In 2001, Iisaak, the Native-run timber company at Clayoquot

Sound, became the first tree farm license holder in British Columbia to receive FSC certification.

Consumer demand for sustainable wood has been great enough that The Home Depot and other major retail businesses have begun selling sustainable wood. The decisions of such retailers are influencing the logging practices of many timber companies. In British Columbia, 70% of the province's annual harvest now is certified or meets ISO requirements. Sustainable forestry is more costly for the timber industry, but if certification standards can be kept adequately strong, then consumer choice in the marketplace can be a powerful driver for good forestry practices for the future.

Conclusion

Forests and other terrestrial biomes provide crucial ecosystem services, supporting a vast diversity of species and providing goods that have economic value to humans as well. Managing natural resources sustainably is particularly important for resources such as timber and soil, which otherwise can be carelessly exploited, degraded, or overharvested. Canada and many other nations have established various federal and regional agencies to oversee and manage publicly held land and the natural resources that are extracted from public land. Historically, forest management in North America has reflected general trends in land and resource management. Early emphasis on resource extraction evolved into policies on sustained yield and multiple use, a shift that occurred as land and resource availability declined and as the public became more aware of environmental degradation.

Public forests today are managed not only for timber production, but also for recreation, wildlife habitat, and ecosystem integrity. Meanwhile, support for the preservation of natural lands has resulted in parks, wilderness areas, and other reserves, both in North America and abroad. These trends are positive ones because the preservation and conservation of land and resources are essential if we wish our society to be sustainable and to thrive in the future.

REVIEWING OBJECTIVES

You should now be able to:

Describe the basic functional processes of trees and their role in biogeochemical cycling

- Trees have the same basic requirements as other plants: sunlight, water, nutrients, air, and an amenable temperature.
- Trees function as a link between the biogeochemical cycles of the atmosphere, hydrosphere, biosphere, and geosphere.

Summarize the principal types of forest biomes, especially those indigenous to Canada

- About 30% of Earth's land surface is covered by forest—land with significant tree cover. Canada is a steward for much of this.
- There are three main sets of forest biomes: northern or boreal forests; temperate forests; and tropical forests.
- Canada's north is dominated by coniferous boreal forest. The west is characterized by subalpine, montane, and coastal forest types, and the east by temperate deciduous forests. The central Prairies are characterized by more-open woodland and grassland ecosystems.

Describe the ecological roles and economic contributions of forests

- Forests provide habitat and support biodiversity.
- Forests contribute ecosystem services that are of great value to people, including protection of soils, moderation of the climate system and the hydrologic cycle, carbon storage, and oxygen cycling.

- Forests provide us economically important timber, as well as a wide variety of nontimber forest products such as fruit, nuts, honey, rubber, and many others.

Trace the history and scale of forest loss and identify the current drivers of deforestation

- Forests have been cleared since the beginnings of human civilization, for a wide variety of reasons.
- Developed nations deforested much of their land during the process of settlement, farming, and industrialization.
- Agriculture has contributed greatly to deforestation and has had enormous impacts on landscapes and ecosystems worldwide.
- Today deforestation is taking place most rapidly in developing nations, driven by proximate factors such as logging and pest infestations and by root factors that are largely economic or political.

Outline the major methods of harvesting timber

- Harvesting methods for timber include clear-cutting and other even-aged techniques, as well as selection strategies that maintain uneven-aged stands that more closely resemble natural forest.
- Harvesting timber and other forest products can be sustainable as long as the principle of maximum sustainable harvest is maintained, so the stock does not become depleted.
- Certification of sustainable forest products allows consumer choice in the marketplace to influence forestry techniques.

Explain the fundamentals of forest management, including approaches to fire management, and identify forest management agencies in Canada and internationally

■ Forest managers increasingly focus not only on extraction of forest products, but also on sustaining the ecological systems that make resources available.

■ Forest managers are beginning to implement ecosystem-based management and adaptive management.

■ Fire policy has been politically controversial, but scientists agree that we need to address the impacts of a century of fire suppression.

■ The Canadian Forest Service, Parks Canada, Canadian Wildlife Service, and Environment Canada each play a role in managing Canada's forests at the federal level. Agriculture and Agri-Foods Canada oversees the management of rangelands. The United Nations Food and Agriculture Organization monitors the status of the world's forests.

TESTING YOUR COMPREHENSION

1. Where do trees acquire the nitrogen that they need? What about the carbon?

2. How does water move through trees, and why is water important for tree survival?

3. What is a forest, and how does a forest differ from a woodland or savannah?

4. How do minerals differ from timber when it comes to resource management?

5. Compare and contrast maximum sustainable yield, adaptive management, and ecosystem-based management. Why would pursuing maximum sustainable yield sometimes conflict with what is ecologically desirable?

6. Name several major causes of deforestation. Where is deforestation most severe today?

7. Compare and contrast the major methods of timber harvesting.

8. Describe several ecological effects of logging. How has the Canadian Forest Service responded to public concern over the ecological effects of logging?

9. Are forest fires a bad thing? Explain your answer.

10. What are some of the organizations—both governmental and non-governmental—that are important in forest management today, both in Canada and internationally? Name three and briefly describe their roles.

THINKING IT THROUGH

1. Do you think maximum sustainable yield represents an appropriate policy for resource managers to follow? Why or why not?

2. People in developed countries are fond of warning people in developing countries to stop destroying the rainforest. People in developing countries often respond that this is hypocritical because the developed nations became wealthy by deforesting their land and exploiting its resources in the past. What would you say to the president of a developing nation, such as Brazil, that is seeking to clear much of its forest?

3. Can you think of a land use conflict, similar to what occurred at Clayoquot Sound, but closer to your home? How was it resolved? If it is unresolved, then how could it be resolved?

4. Your town is proposing a development that would cut through a large forested area. The size of the forested area would not be substantially reduced, but it would be cut into several smaller pieces by road. Explain to the town council the difference between core and edge habitat and why they should reconsider the development.

5. You have just become the supervisor of a national forest. Timber companies are requesting to cut as many trees as you will let them, and environmentalists want no logging at all. Ten percent of your forest is old-growth primary forest, and the remaining 90% is secondary forest. Your forest managers are split among preferring maximum sustainable yield, ecosystem-based management, and adaptive management. What management approach(es) will you take? Will you allow logging of all, none, or some old-growth trees? Will you allow logging of secondary forest? If so, what harvesting strategies will you encourage? What would you ask your scientists

before deciding on policies on fire management and salvage logging?

6. You have just been elected mayor of a town on Clayoquot Sound. A timber company that employs 20% of your town's residents wants to log a hillside above the town, and the provincial government is supportive of the harvest. But owners of ecotourism businesses that run whale-watching excursions and rent kayaks to out-of-town visitors are complaining that the logging would destroy the area's esthetic appeal and devastate their businesses—and these businesses provide 40% of the tax base for your town. Greenpeace is organizing a demonstration in your town soon, and news reporters are beginning to call your office, asking what you will do. How will you proceed?

INTERPRETING GRAPHS AND DATA

The invention of the movable-type printing press by Johannes Gutenberg in 1450 stimulated a demand for paper that has only increased as the world population has grown.

The twentieth-century invention of the xerographic printing process used in photocopiers and laser printers has accelerated our demand for paper, with most raw fibre for paper production coming from wood pulp from forest trees.

1. How many millions of tonnes of paper and paperboard were consumed worldwide in 1970? 1980? 1990? 2000?

2. By what percentage did worldwide consumption of paper and paperboard increase from 1970 to 1980? From 1980 to 1990? From 1990 to 2000?

3. Name three steps that your campus could take to reduce its paper consumption.

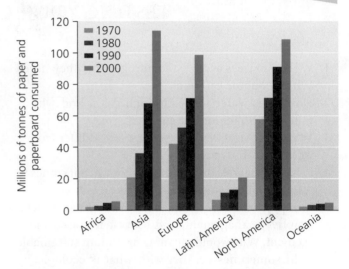

Global consumption of paper and paperboard, 1970–2000.
Source: Data from the Food and Agriculture Organization of the United Nations.

CHAPTER ENDNOTES

1. *Friends of Clayoquot Sound Newsletter* (Fall 2007–Winter 2008).

2. Food and Agriculture Organization of the United Nations (2011) *Global Forest Resources Assessment 2010*. www.fao.org/docrep/013/i1757e/i1757e.pdf

3. Food and Agriculture Organization of the United Nations (2011) *Global Forest Resources Assessment 2010: Canada Country Report (2009)*. www.fao.org/docrep/013/al472E/al472e.pdf

4. Canadian Council of Forest Ministers (2008) *A Vision for Canada's Forests: 2008 and Beyond*. www.ccfm.org/pdf/Vision_EN.pdf

5. National Forest Strategy 2003–2008: *A Sustainable Forest: The Canadian Commitment*. National Forest Strategy Steering Committee. http://nfsc.forest.ca/strategies/strategy5.html

6. Food and Agriculture Organization of the United Nations. (2010). *Global Forest Resources Assessment 2010: Canada Country Report (2009)*. www.fao.org/docrep/013/al472E/al472e.pdf (Primary forests are defined by the FAO as forests of native species in which there are no clearly visible indications of human activity and ecological processes are not significantly disturbed.)

7. Canadian Boreal Institute, Boreal Leadership Council, www.borealcanada.ca

8. Armson, K., Knowledge of the Environment for Youth (KEY) Environmental Literacy Series, The KEY Foundation (1999) *Canadian Forests: A Primer*.

9. Food and Agriculture Organization of the United Nations (2010) *Global Forest Resources Assessment 2010*. www.fao.org/docrep/013/i1757e/i1757e.pdf

10. Food and Agriculture Organization of the United Nations (2010) *Global Forest Resources Assessment 2010*. www.fao.org/docrep/013/i1757e/i1757e.pdf

11. Turner, J. (2008) Changing climate stops pest outbreaks on Vancouver Island. Forest NewsTips. http://cfs.nrcan.gc.ca/news/585

12. Government of British Columbia (April 15, 2011) News release. www2.news.gov.bc.ca/news_releases_2009-2013/2011JTI0056-000378.htm

13. Government of British Columbia (2011) Mountain pine beetle facts. www.for.gov.bc.ca/hfp/mountain_pine_beetle/facts.htm

14. Food and Agriculture Organization of the United Nations (2010) *Global Forest Resources Assessment 2010*. www.fao.org/docrep/013/i1757e/i1757e.pdf

15. Canada's National Forest Inventory, 2001; Canadian Forest Service, http://nfi.cfs.nrcan.gc.ca/canfi/facts_e.html

16. National Forest Strategy 2003–2008: *A Sustainable Forest: The Canadian Commitment*. National Forest Strategy Steering Committee. http://nfsc.forest.ca/strategies/strategy5.html

17. NRCAN, Canadian Forest Service. *About the Canadian Forest Service: Our History*. http://cfs.nrcan.gc.ca/aboutus/organization/3

18. Food and Agriculture Organization of the United Nations (2010) *Global Forest Resources Assessment 2010*. www.fao.org/docrep/013/i1757e/i1757e.pdf

19. National Forest Strategy 2003–2008: *A Sustainable Forest: The Canadian Commitment*. National Forest Strategy Steering Committee. http://nfsc.forest.ca/strategies/strategy5.html

20. National Forest Strategy 2003–2008: *A Sustainable Forest: The Canadian Commitment*. National Forest Strategy Steering Committee. http://nfsc.forest.ca/strategies/strategy5.html

21. National Forest Strategy 2003–2008: *A Sustainable Forest: The Canadian Commitment*. National Forest Strategy Steering Committee. http://nfsc.forest.ca/strategies/strategy5.html

22. British Columbia, Ministry of Forestry and Range, Forest Practices Branch. Adaptive Management Initiatives in the BC Forest Service. www.for.gov.bc.ca/hfp/amhome/amhome.htm

23. British Columbia, Forest Services Branch, Ministry of Forestry and Range. www.for.gov.bc.ca/hfp/amhome/canadaprojects.htm

24. These two paragraphs are directly quoted from *The Clayoquot Women* by Bob Bossin. www3.telus.net/oldfolk/women.htm

25. The preceding three sentences are quoted directly from *The Clayoquot Women* by Bob Bossin. www3.telus.net/oldfolk/women.htm

26. ForestEthics. *About ForestEthics*. http://forestethics.org/article.php?list=type&type=9

27. As quoted by Julia Dault, *Enviro Heroes: Tzeporah Berman*. Green Living Online. www.greenlivingonline.com/EnviroHeroes/enviro-heroes-tzeporah-berman

MyEnvironmentPlace

Go to **www.myenvironmentplace.ca** where you will find quizzes, animations, your Pearson eText, and more.

Mineral Resources and Mining

Processing coltan ore mined in Central Africa.

Upon successfully completing this chapter, you will be able to

- Outline the main types of mineral resources
- Summarize the ways in which mineral resources contribute to our economy and society
- Describe the major methods of mining
- Characterize the environmental and social impacts of mining

- Assess reclamation efforts and mining policy in Canada
- Evaluate ways to encourage sustainable use of mineral resources

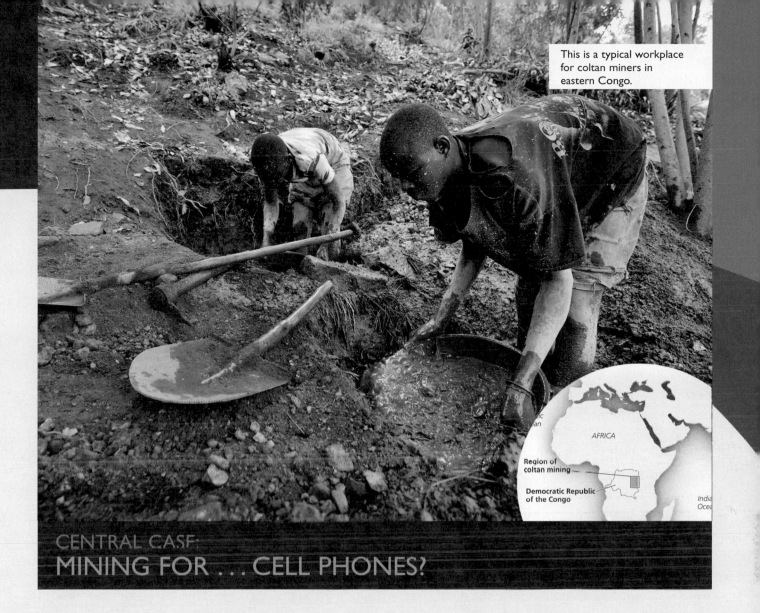

This is a typical workplace for coltan miners in eastern Congo.

AFRICA

Region of coltan mining

Democratic Republic of the Congo

Indian Ocean

CENTRAL CASE:
MINING FOR ... CELL PHONES?

"The conflict in the Democratic Republic of the Congo has become mainly about access, control, and trade of five key mineral resources: coltan, diamonds, copper, cobalt, and gold."
—REPORT TO THE UNITED NATIONS SECURITY COUNCIL, APRIL 2001

"Coltan ... is not helping the local people. In fact, it is the curse of the Congo."
—AFRICAN JOURNALIST KOFI AKOSAH-SARPONG

Pulling a cell phone from her pocket, a student on a university campus in Canada dials a friend. Inside her phone is a little-known metal called tantalum—just a tiny amount, but no cell phone could operate without it.

Half a world away, a dirt-poor miner in the heart of Africa toils all day in a jungle streambed (see photo), sifting sediment for nuggets of coltan ore, which contain tantalum. At nightfall, rebel soldiers take most of his ore, leaving him to sell what little remains to buy food for his family at the squalid mining camp where they live.

In bedeviling ways, tantalum links our glossy global high-tech economy with one of the most badly wrecked regions on Earth. The Democratic Republic of the Congo has been embroiled in a sprawling conflict that has involved six nations and various rebel militias. Over 5 million people have lost their lives in this war since 1998—a devastating loss for a country with a population just twice the size of Canada's. It is the latest chapter in the sad history of a nation rich in natural resources—copper, cobalt, gold, diamonds, uranium, and timber—whose impoverished people keep losing control of those resources to others.

At the centre of the recent conflict is tantalum (Ta), element number 73 on the periodic table of the elements. We rely on this metal for our cell phones, computer chips, DVD players, game consoles, and digital cameras. Tantalum powder is ideal for capacitors (the components that store energy and regulate current in miniature circuit boards) because it is highly heat resistant and readily conducts electricity.

Tantalum comes from a dull, blackish mineral called tantalite. Tantalite often occurs with a mineral called columbite, so the ore is referred to as columbite-tantalite, or *coltan* for short. In eastern Congo, men dig craters in rainforest streambeds, panning for coltan much as early miners in the Yukon panned for gold.

As information technology boomed in the late 1990s, global demand for tantalum rose, and market prices for the metal shot up to $500/kg in 2001. High prices led some Congolese men to mine coltan by choice, but many more were forced into it. As the war began in 1998, local militias, supported by forces from neighbouring Rwanda and Uganda, overran eastern Congo. Farmers were chased off their land, villages were burned, and civilians were raped, tortured, and killed. Soldiers from each army seized control of mining operations. They forced farmers, refugees, prisoners, and children to work, and the soldiers skimmed profits from the coltan the people mined. Children and teachers abandoned school and worked in the mines, while prostitution and sexual assault spread AIDS and other sexually transmitted diseases through the mining camps. The turmoil also caused ecological havoc as miners and soldiers streamed into national parks, clearing rainforests and killing wildlife for food, including forest elephants, hippopotamuses, endangered gorillas, and the okapi, a rare relative of the giraffe.

Most miners ended up with little, while rebels, soldiers, and bandits enriched themselves selling coltan to traders, who sold it to processing companies in Europe and the United States. These companies refine and sell tantalum powder to capacitor manufacturers, which in turn sell capacitors to Nokia, Motorola, Sony, Intel, Compaq, Dell, and other high-tech corporations.

In 2001, an expert panel commissioned by the United Nations Security Council concluded that coltan riches were fuelling, financing, and prolonging the war. The panel urged a U.N. embargo on coltan and other minerals smuggled from Congo and exported by neighbouring nations. A grass-roots activist movement advanced the slogan, "No blood on my cell phone!"

Sony, Nokia, Ericsson, and other corporations rushed to assure consumers that they were not using tantalum from eastern Congo—and the region was in fact producing less than 10% of the world's supply. Meanwhile, some observers felt an embargo could hurt the long-suffering Congolese people, rather than help them. The mining life may be miserable, but it pays better than most alternatives in a land where the average income is 20 cents a day.

Soon, however, the high-tech boom went bust, and global demand for tantalum diminished. This occurred just as Australia and other countries were ramping up industrial-scale tantalite mining. As supply outpaced demand, the market price of tantalum plummeted, and several major producers quit mining tantalum. But nations began to work through their stockpiles, and by 2010 demand had grown, driving prices up once again; it is currently around $230/kg.

Today, the war is declared over and foreign troops are out of Congo, but internal factions continue to fight, and thousands of people continue to die or to flee their homes. Western electronics companies avoid knowingly purchasing tantalum from Congo, but as a result, much of it ends up being sold to China. The trade has so many middlemen and so little transparency that many companies find it difficult to determine where their tantalum actually comes from. Some Congolese men are returning to the coltan mines, while others mine for tin, copper, or cobalt. Similar stories are playing out with these and other "conflict minerals," such as diamonds, that we in wealthy nations use in our products every day.

Earth's Mineral Resources

Coltan provides just one example of how we extract raw materials from beneath our planet's surface and turn them into products we use in our everyday lives. In previous chapters we examined some of the physical processes that take place in the lithosphere, the region that includes the uppermost layers of rock near Earth's surface. We saw how the rock cycle creates new rock and alters existing rock. We saw how plate tectonics builds mountains; shapes the geography of oceans, islands, and continents; and gives rise to earthquakes and volcanoes. The coltan mining areas of eastern Congo are situated along the western edge of Africa's Great Rift Valley system, a region where the African tectonic plate is slowly pulling itself apart. Some of the world's largest lakes have formed in the immense valley floors, far below towering volcanoes such as Mount Kilimanjaro.

In Congo and throughout the world, geological processes are fundamental to shaping the world around us; they also control the distribution of rocks and minerals in the lithosphere, and their availability to us. In this chapter we take a closer look at how resources from the lithosphere contribute directly to our economies and our lives. We will first examine mineral resources and the products they provide us, and the various ways we extract them. We will then examine the many social and environmental impacts that our mining efforts exert, and see what we can do to mitigate these impacts. Finally, because mineral resources are nonrenewable on human time scales, we need to be attentive to finite and decreasing supplies of economically important minerals. Thus we will examine solutions we can pursue to make our mineral use more sustainable.

Rocks provide the minerals we use

A **rock** is a solid aggregation of minerals, and a **mineral** is a naturally occurring solid chemical element or inorganic compound with a crystal structure, a specific chemical composition, and distinct physical properties. For instance, the mineral tantalite consists of the elements tantalum, oxygen, iron, and manganese. Tantalite occurs most commonly in *pegmatite*, a type of coarse-grained igneous rock that is similar to granite. In addition to tantalite, pegmatite generally contains the minerals feldspar, quartz, and mica, and occasionally even includes gemstones and other rare minerals.

We depend on a wide array of mineral resources as raw materials for our products, so we mine and process these resources. Consider a typical scene from a student lounge at a college or university (**FIGURE 11.1**), and note how many items are made with elements from the minerals we take from Earth. Without the resources from beneath the ground that we use to make building materials, wiring, clothing, appliances, fertilizers for crops, and so much more, civilization as we know it could not exist.

We obtain minerals and metals by mining

We obtain the minerals we use in all these ways through the process of mining, and Canada is one of the world's leading mining nations. The term *mining* in the broad sense describes the extraction of any resource that is nonrenewable on the timescale of our society. In this sense, we mine fossil fuels and groundwater, as well as minerals. It can even be said that we mine fish, soils, and trees, if we withdraw from the stocks of those renewable resources at rates that are faster than the rate of recharge. When used specifically in relation to minerals, **mining** refers to the systematic removal of rock, soil, or other material for the purpose of extracting minerals of economic interest. Because most minerals of interest are widely spread but in low concentrations, miners and mining geologists first try to locate concentrated sources of minerals before mining begins.

Some minerals can be mined for metals. A **metal** is a type of chemical element that typically is shiny, opaque, and malleable, and can conduct heat and electricity.

roots

TANTALUM

The element **tantalum** was discovered in 1802 (one year after the discovery of its companion element *columbium*, now called *niobium*). The discoverer, Swedish chemist Anders Ekeberg, named the element so because it had been "tantalisingly" difficult to isolate. The word *tantalise* comes from the ancient Greek ruler *Tantalus*. In Greek mythology, Tantalus is said to have killed and boiled his own son, Pelops, and offered him as a sacrifice to the gods. The gods were so offended that they brought Pelops back to life and punished Tantalus by making him stand in a pool of water under a fruit tree with low-hanging branches. When he tried to drink, the water in the pool receded before he could get any, and when he tried to grasp the low-hanging fruit, the branches raised the fruit out of his reach. Thus, Tantalus became symbolic of a desired object that is always just out of reach.

FIGURE 11.1   Elements from minerals that we mine are everywhere in the products we use in our everyday lives. This scene from a typical student lounge points out just a few of the many elements from minerals that surround us.

Most metals are not found in a pure state in Earth's crust, but instead are present in **ore**, a rock in which valuable minerals have been concentrated by geologic processes, and from which we can extract metals and other useful mineral resources. The waste rock and nonvaluable minerals associated with ores are referred to as **gangue**

roots

MINE

The word *mine* comes from an Old French word *mine*, which probably in turn comes from the Old Celtic word *meini*. Similar words occur in Welsh (*mwyn*) and Irish (*mein*), meaning "ore" or "mine." Interestingly, Italy and Greece did not have much mining in ancient times, so Latin and Greek—the sources for so many scientific terms—did not contribute to the development of this word in English. However, mining was common in some Celtic lands (now France, England, Wales, and Ireland), going back as far as the Late Bronze Age (ca. 1300 BCE).

(pronounced "gang"). The higher the proportion of gangue to ore, the more waste rock is generated by the mining process.

Copper, iron, lead, gold, and nickel are among the many economically valuable metals we extract from mined ores; Canada has been a leading producer of all these metallic resources, and many others, including tantalum. These metals and others serve so many purposes that our modern lives would be impossible without them. For example, tantalum used in the electronic components of computers, cell phones, DVD players, and other devices is a metal that comes from the mineral tantalite (**FIGURE 11.2**), which occurs, along with the mineral columbite, in the form of coltan ore. Columbite contains the metal niobium, formerly known as columbium, which is utilized in ways similar to tantalum.

We process metals after mining

Extracting minerals from the ground is the first step in putting them to use, and some 60 different minerals are mined in Canada. Most of these minerals then

(a) Tantalum ore   **(b) Purified tantalum**   **(c) Capacitor containing tantalum**

FIGURE 11.2   Tantalum ore **(a)** is mined from the ground and then processed to extract the pure metal tantalum **(b)**. This metal is used in capacitors **(c)** and other electronic components in computer chips, cell phones, and many other devices.

need to be processed in some way to become useful for our products. Typically, after ores are mined, the rock is crushed and pulverized, and the desired metals are isolated by chemical or physical means. The material is then processed to purify the metals we desire, through a set of processes called **refining**. With coltan, processing facilities use acid solvents to separate tantalite from columbite. Other chemicals are then used to produce metallic tantalum powder. This powder can be consolidated by various melting techniques and then shaped into wire, sheets, or other forms.

Sometimes metals are melted and mixed with another metal or a nonmetal substance to form an *alloy*. For example, steel is an alloy of the metal iron that has been fused with a small quantity of carbon. The strength and malleability of this particular alloy make steel ideal for its many applications in buildings, vehicles, appliances, and more. To make steel, we first mine iron ore, which consists of iron-containing compounds such as iron oxide. Steelmakers then heat the ore and chemically extract the iron with carbon in a process known as **smelting** (heating ore beyond its melting point and combining it with other metals or chemicals). They then melt and reprocess the mixture, removing precise amounts of carbon and shaping the product into rods, sheets, or wires. During this melting process, certain other metals may be added to modify the strength, malleability, or other characteristics of the steel, as desired.

Processing minerals exerts environmental impacts. Most methods are water-intensive and energy-intensive. Moreover, many chemical reactions and heating processes used for extracting metals from ore emit air pollution, and smelting plants in particular have long been hotspots of toxic air pollution. In addition, soil and water may become polluted by **tailings**, the remnants that are left

over after metals have been extracted from ores. Tailings may contain heavy metals present in the ore waste, as well as chemicals used in the extraction process. For instance, miners use cyanide and (in a different process) mercury to extract gold from ore, and sulphuric acid to extract copper. Mining operations often pump a toxic slurry of tailings into a tailings pond, from which water is allowed to evaporate. It is difficult to isolate such ponds well enough to prevent leakage into the environment.

We also mine nonmetallic minerals and fuels

We also mine and use many minerals that do not contain metals. Nonmetallic resources such as limestone, salt, and many others are mined for a number of diverse purposes. **FIGURE 11.3** illustrates a selection of economically useful

weighing the issues
MINING IN NATIONAL PARKS?

Mining and other forms of commercial resource extraction are prohibited by Canada's *National Parks Act*. Even so, mining has occurred in or near the boundaries of about half of our national parks, and many administrators still identify mining (and principally acid mine drainage) as a major source of adverse environmental impacts in the parks. Some countries do allow mining in their parks. Do you think it would ever be acceptable or advisable to allow mining in our national parks? Why (or why not), and under what conditions?

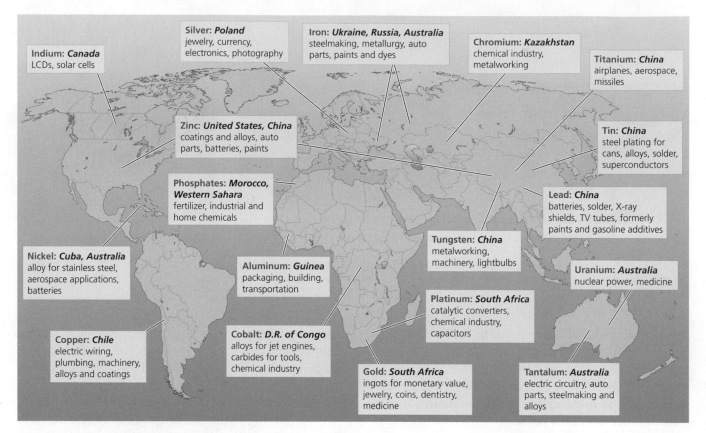

Indium: *Canada*
LCDs, solar cells

Silver: *Poland*
jewelry, currency, electronics, photography

Iron: *Ukraine, Russia, Australia*
steelmaking, metallurgy, auto parts, paints and dyes

Chromium: *Kazakhstan*
chemical industry, metalworking

Titanium: *China*
airplanes, aerospace, missiles

Zinc: *United States, China*
coatings and alloys, auto parts, batteries, paints

Tin: *China*
steel plating for cans, alloys, solder, superconductors

Phosphates: *Morocco, Western Sahara*
fertilizer, industrial and home chemicals

Lead: *China*
batteries, solder, X-ray shields, TV tubes, formerly paints and gasoline additives

Nickel: *Cuba, Australia*
alloy for stainless steel, aerospace applications, batteries

Aluminum: *Guinea*
packaging, building, transportation

Tungsten: *China*
metalworking, machinery, lightbulbs

Uranium: *Australia*
nuclear power, medicine

Platinum: *South Africa*
catalytic converters, chemical industry, capacitors

Copper: *Chile*
electric wiring, plumbing, machinery, alloys and coatings

Cobalt: *D.R. of Congo*
alloys for jet engines, carbides for tools, chemical industry

Gold: *South Africa*
ingots for monetary value, jewelry, coins, dentistry, medicine

Tantalum: *Australia*
electric circuitry, auto parts, steelmaking and alloys

FIGURE 11.3   The minerals we use come from all over the world. Shown is a very small selection of economically important minerals (mostly metals), together with their major uses and main nation of origin.

mineral resources, both metallic and nonmetallic. For each one, its major nation of origin and several main uses are shown.

Sand and gravel (the most commonly mined mineral resources) are used as **aggregate** for road-building fill and construction materials and for the manufacture of concrete. Each year over $1.5 billion of sand and gravel are mined in Canada, in almost every province and territory. Canada is the world's leading producer of potash, an industry that is worth almost $3.5 billion; potash is used to make fertilizers for crops. Asbestos is another non-metallic mineral resource that has been economically important in Canada, especially in Québec. Asbestos is problematic because its use is strictly limited in Canada because of concerns that some forms of the mineral are carcinogenic; yet Canada exports a significant quantity of asbestos every year, to the United States and to many countries in the developing world.

Gemstones are nonmetallic mineral resources, treasured for their rarity and beauty. For instance, diamonds have long been prized—and, like coltan, they have fuelled resource wars. The diamond trade has acted to fund, prolong, and intensify wars in Congo, Angola, Sierra Leone, Liberia, and elsewhere, as armies exploit local people for mine labour, and sell the diamonds for profit. This is why you may hear the phrase "blood diamonds,"

just as coltan has been called a "conflict mineral." Canada is a party to the *Kimberley Process Certification Scheme*, an international agreement set up in 2003 to certify the country of origin of rough diamonds in an effort to stop blood diamonds. Canada is a diamond-mining nation, the third-largest producer in the world (after Botswana and Russia). The first diamond mine in Canada was the Ekati Mine in Northwest Territories, which started production in 1998. All diamonds mined and processed in NWT are laser-inscribed and have their information entered into a database to verify their origin as Canadian diamonds.

We also mine nonmetallic substances that we use for fuel. Uranium ore is a mineral from which we extract the metal uranium, used in nuclear power generation. Canada has traditionally been the world's largest producer of uranium, although the top spot was taken over by Kazakhstan in 2009. One of the most common fuels we mine is coal. Coal is technically a rock, not a mineral, because it is an aggregate that consists mainly of organic matter. However, we consider coal mining in this chapter because it has been economically important in Canada and has relevance for many issues related to mining and the environment. Other fossil fuels—petroleum, natural gas, and alternative fossil fuels such as oil sands, oil shale, and methane hydrates—are also extracted from the ground, as you will learn in future chapters.

Mining Methods and Their Impacts

Mining for minerals is an important industry that provides jobs for people and revenue for communities in many regions. Mining supplies raw materials for countless products we use daily, so it is necessary for the lives we lead. In 2009, mineral production contributed $32 billion to the Canadian economy.[1] About 58 000 Canadians were employed directly in mining and quarrying in 2008; the non-fuel mining industry, together with processors and manufacturers of products from mined materials, employed more than 351 000 people.[2]

At the same time, mining also exacts a price in environmental and social impacts. Because minerals of interest often make up only a small portion of the rock in a given area, typically very large amounts of material must be removed in order to obtain the desired minerals. This frequently means that mining disturbs large areas of land, thereby exerting severe impacts on the environment and on people living nearby.

Depending on the nature of the mineral deposit, any of several mining methods may be employed to extract the resource from the ground. Mining companies select which method to use based largely on economic efficiency. We will examine seven major mining approaches commonly used throughout the world, and will also take note of the impacts of each approach as we proceed.

Strip mining removes surface layers of soil and rock

When a resource occurs in shallow horizontal deposits near the surface, the most effective mining method is often **strip mining**, whereby layers of surface soil and rock are removed from large areas to expose the resource. Heavy machinery removes the overlying soil and rock (termed *overburden*) from a strip of land, and the resource is extracted. This strip is then refilled with the overburden that had been removed, and miners proceed to an adjacent strip of land and repeat the process. Strip mining is commonly used for coal (**FIGURE 11.4A**) and oil sands and sometimes for sand and gravel.

Strip mining can be economically efficient, but it causes severe environmental impacts. By completely removing vegetative cover and nutrient-rich topsoil, strip mining obliterates natural communities over large areas, and soil from refilled areas easily erodes away. It also can pollute waterways through **acid mine drainage** (or **AMD**), which occurs when sulphide minerals in newly exposed rock surfaces react with oxygen and rainwater to

(a) Strip mining

(b) Subsurface mining

FIGURE 11.4
In strip mining **(a)**, often used in coal mining, soil is removed from the surface in strips, exposing seams from which the coal is mined. In subsurface mining **(b)**, miners work below ground in shafts and tunnels blasted through the rock. These passageways provide access to underground seams of coal or minerals.

produce sulphuric acid. As the sulphuric acid runs off, it leaches metals from the rocks, many of which are toxic to organisms (**FIGURE 11.5**). This toxic liquid is called *leachate*, a term that is also used to describe the toxic liquids that form in landfills. Whereas leachates from landfills are caused by anaerobic reactions in organic substances, leachates from mining sites result from aerobic reactions in inorganic substances. Acid drainage is a natural phenomenon, but mining greatly accelerates this process by exposing many new rock surfaces at once.

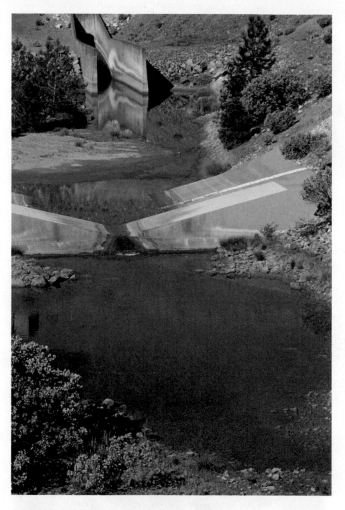

FIGURE 11.5
The discoloured water in this stream, downstream from a mine site, is a sign of acid drainage. Acid drainage can make stream water toxic and reduce aquatic biodiversity. The site shown here is near the Iron Mountain Mine in northern California. A century of mining for iron, gold, silver, zinc, and copper has made the area a hazardous waste site.

Subsurface mining takes place in underground tunnels

When a resource occurs in concentrated pockets or seams deep underground, and the rock allows for safe tunnelling, mining companies can pursue **subsurface mining**. In this approach, shafts are excavated deep into the ground, and networks of tunnels are dug or blasted out to follow deposits of the mineral (**FIGURE 11.4B**). Miners remove the resource systematically and ship it to the surface.

We use subsurface mining for metals such as zinc, lead, nickel, tin, gold, copper, and uranium, as well as for diamonds, phosphate, salt, and potash. In addition, a great deal of coal is mined using the subsurface technique. The scale of subsurface mining can be mind-boggling; the world's deepest mines (certain gold mines in South Africa) extend nearly 4 km underground. The incident

of August, 2010, when 33 miners were trapped in a mine in Copiapó, Chile, occurred in a subsurface copper-gold mine. The miners were trapped 700 m under the surface by a cave-in until they were finally rescued more than two months later.

Subsurface mining is the most dangerous form of mining and indeed one of society's most dangerous occupations. Fatal accidents are not unusual, even today; for instance, 29 coal miners died underground after an explosion in the Upper Big Branch mine in Montcoal, West Virginia, in 2010. In China, coal-mining conditions are so dangerous that in 2009 over 2600 miners lost their lives. Besides risking injury or death from dynamite blasts, natural gas explosions, and collapsing shafts and tunnels, miners inhale toxic fumes and coal dust, which can lead to respiratory diseases, including fatal black lung disease.

In Canada, some of the most famous historical mine disasters have occurred in subsurface coal mines. An example is the Springhill Mine Disaster, memorialized in popular culture, which actually refers to three different incidents in the Springhill coalfield in Nova Scotia. First was an underground coal-dust fire in 1891, which killed 125 miners. Next was an explosion in 1956, set off when a spark ignited coal dust in an underground mine shaft; the explosion killed 39 in total. The third Springhill disaster (in 1958) was a mining-induced earthquake, called a *mine tremor*, a *rock burst*, or, colloquially, a "bump." The mine tremor was caused by the buildup of stresses in the rock, related to the opening of underground tunnels and shafts more than 4 km in length. Seventy-four miners died in the resulting mine collapse.

Subsurface mines can affect people years after they are closed. Mine tunnels at the Retsof Salt Mine in Genessee Valley, New York, collapsed after a minor earthquake in 1994. The collapse of the tunnels created sinkholes at the surface that damaged roads, bridges, and homes and sucked groundwater from neighbourhood wells. In Centralia, Pennsylvania, a fire that started on the surface in 1962 continues to burn in underground coal mine workings, even today. Toxic gas and smoke from the fire rise through cracks in the surface, and all efforts to extinguish the fire have been unsuccessful. The town has been abandoned and the few remaining buildings are scheduled for demolition.

Subsurface mines, both active and abandoned, can pollute surface and groundwater by generating acid mine drainage through the chemical interaction of water with sulphur-bearing tailings and waste rock piles. AMD is widely considered to be the most significant environmental liability facing the mining industry in North America. In Canada, a collaborative program called *Mine Environment Neutral Drainage (MEND)* was established in 1988. It was funded by the Mining Association of Canada and Natural Resources Canada to facilitate the development of new technologies and approaches to prevent, control, and remediate the effects of acid mine drainage.

Regulations in developed nations now require that waste heaps be capped with clay, then covered with soil, and then planted with vegetation once mines are closed. Canada's *Metal Mining Effluent Regulation,* or *MMER* (2002), governs the composition of any contaminated liquid, or **effluent**, issuing from a mine site. The MMER established limits for cyanide, arsenic, and other hazardous constituents of mine runoff, as well as limiting pH and suspended solids. These regulations help protect both natural ecosystems and human health.

In spite of tighter regulations, however, many abandoned sites will likely continue to leach acid for many decades. One site in Canada that has suffered from acid mine drainage is Britannia Beach, British Columbia. The Britannia Copper Mine was opened in the early 1900s, and there followed a long history of pollution and mine-related accidents. Mining ceased in 1974, but acid mine drainage continued to be a severe problem until remediation efforts were undertaken in the early 2000s by scientists from the University of British Columbia, in conjunction with the provincial government. These efforts finally appear to be having an impact on water quality in the Britannia Beach area.

Open-pit mining creates immense holes at the surface

When a mineral is spread widely and evenly throughout a rock formation, or when the rock is unsuitable for tunnelling, the method of choice is **open-pit mining**. This essentially involves digging a large hole and removing the desired ore, along with waste rock that surrounds the ore. Some open-pit mines are enormous. The world's largest, the Bingham Canyon Mine near Salt Lake City, Utah, is about 4 km across and 1.2 km deep (**FIGURE 11.6**). Conveyor systems and immense trucks with tires taller than a person carry out nearly half a million tonnes of ore and waste rock each day.

Open-pit mines are terraced so that men and machinery can move about, and waste rock is left in massive heaps outside the pit. The pit is expanded until the resource runs out or becomes unprofitable to mine. Open-pit mining is used for copper, iron, gold, diamonds, and coal, among other resources. We also use this technique to extract clay, gravel, sand, and stone such as limestone, granite, marble, and slate; a pit used for this purpose is called a **quarry**.

Open-pit mines are so large because huge volumes of waste rock need to be removed in order to extract relatively small amounts of ore, which in turn contain still smaller traces of valuable minerals. The sheer size of most open pit mines means that the degree of land disruption, habitat loss, and aesthetic degradation is considerable.

Another impact of both open-pit and subsurface mining can be chemical contamination from acid mine drainage. Once mining has been completed, abandoned pits generally fill up with groundwater, which becomes toxic as water and oxygen react with sulphides from the ore to produce sulphuric acid. Acidic water from the pit can harm wildlife, and can percolate into aquifers and spread through the region. In the United States, the Berkeley Pit, a former open-pit copper mine near Butte, Montana, is one of the largest of the Environmental Protection Agency's "Superfund" toxic waste cleanup

FIGURE 11.6
The Bingham Canyon open-pit mine outside Salt Lake City, Utah, is one of the world's largest human-made holes. This immense mine produces mostly copper. For scale, each of the terraces visible in the photo is a full-scale road. The trucks that are just barely discernible in the foreground portion of the pit are enormous mining haulers, with tires almost twice the height of an average person.

sites. After its closure in 1982, it filled with groundwater and became so acidic (pH = 2.2) and concentrated with toxic metals that microbiologists discovered new species of microbes in the water—the harsh conditions were so rare in nature that scientists had never before encountered microbes adapted to them! (See "The Science Behind the Story: Using Bacteria to Clean Mine Water.")

Placer mining uses running water to isolate minerals

Some relatively heavy metals and gems accumulate in riverbed deposits, having been displaced from elsewhere and carried along by flowing water. To search for these metals and gems, miners sift through material in modern or ancient riverbed deposits, generally using running water to separate lightweight mud and gravel from heavier minerals of value (**FIGURE 11.7**). This technique is called **placer mining** (pronounced "plasser").

Placer mining is the method used by Congo's coltan miners, who wade through streambeds, sifting through large amounts of debris by hand with a pan or simple tools, searching for high-density tantalite that settles to the bottom while low-density material washes away. Today's African miners practise small-scale placer mining similar to the method used long ago by miners who ventured to California in the Gold Rush of 1849, Fraser Canyon in British Columbia in 1858, and the Yukon in the Klondike Gold Rush of 1896–1899. Placer mining for gold is still practised in areas of Alaska and Canada, although today it uses large dredges and heavy machinery.

FIGURE 11.7

Miners in eastern Congo find coltan by placer mining. Sediment is placed in plastic tubs and water is run through them. A mixing motion allows the sediment to be poured off while the heavy coltan settles to the bottom.

roots

GOLD

"They wonder much to hear that gold, which in itself is so useless a thing, should be everywhere so much esteemed."– Sir Thomas More, *Utopia* (1516)

We can trace two pathways to arrive at our modern word **gold** and its original elemental name, *aurum* (from which its elemental symbol, *Au*, is derived). The Latin word *aurum* comes from the ancient Etruscan word *ausom* and the Sanskrit word *hari*, both meaning "yellow." The word *gold* itself is a Germanic word, the root of which is *gelwa*, from the Sanskrit *jval*, to "shine."

Besides the many social impacts of placer mining in places like Congo, placer mining is environmentally destructive because most methods wash large amounts of debris into streams, making them uninhabitable for fish and other life for many miles downstream. Gold mining in northern California's rivers in the decades following the Gold Rush washed so much debris all the way to San Francisco Bay that a U.S. district court ruling in 1884 finally halted the practice. Placer mining also disturbs stream banks, causing erosion and harming ecologically important riparian plant communities.

Unfortunately, placer mining is still the method of choice among many small-scale, or *artisanal*, miners in developing countries, because it can be carried out with relatively accessible technologies. One easy way to remove gold from ore in placer operations is to use a solution of caustic soda and cyanide, or mercury. Accidental releases of these extremely toxic combinations into waterways have occurred at small mining operations in Central Europe, South America, and Africa.

Mountaintop mining reshapes ridges and can fill valleys

When a resource occurs in underground seams near the tops of ridges or mountains, companies may practise **mountaintop removal** mining, in which a hundred or more vertical metres of mountaintop may be removed to allow recovery of entire seams of the resource (**FIGURE 11.8A**). This method of mining is used primarily for coal in the Appalachian Mountains of the eastern United States; probably the closest equivalent in Canada is the removal of forests, wetlands, and overburden for tar-sand mining in the Athabasca region of Alberta.

(a) Mountaintop removal mining in eastern Kentucky

(b) Train hauls coal past homes in West Virginia

FIGURE 11.8   In the Appalachians, mountaintop mining for coal **(a)** takes place on massive scales. Communities near these sites **(b)** experience negative environmental and social impacts.

In mountaintop removal mining, a mountain's forests are clear-cut and the timber is sold, topsoil is removed, and then rock is repeatedly blasted away to expose the coal for extraction. Overburden is placed back onto the mountaintop, but this waste rock is unstable and typically takes up more volume than the original rock, so generally a great deal of waste rock is dumped into adjacent valleys (a practice called "valley filling").

Mountaintop removal mining is an economically efficient way for companies to extract coal. However, scientists are finding that dumping tons of debris into valleys degrades or destroys immense areas of habitat, clogs streams and rivers, and pollutes waterways with acid drainage. With slopes deforested and valleys filled with debris, erosion intensifies, mudslides become frequent, and flash floods ravage the lower valleys.

People living in communities near the sites experience social and health impacts (**FIGURE 11.8B**). Blasts from mines crack house foundations and wells, loose rock tumbles down into yards and homes, overloaded coal trucks speed down once-peaceful rural roads, and floods tear through properties. Health impacts come from inhaling air pollution and dust, drinking contaminated groundwater, and eating fish contaminated with toxic substances. A 2009 study documented that people who live in mountaintop mining areas show elevated levels of lung cancer, heart disease, kidney disease, pulmonary disorders, hypertension, and mortality.

Solution mining dissolves and extracts resources in place

When a deposit is especially deep and the resource can be dissolved in a liquid, miners may use a technique called *solution mining* or *in situ recovery*. In this technique, a narrow borehole is drilled deep into the ground to reach the deposit, and water, acid, or another liquid is injected down the borehole to leach the resource from the surrounding rock and dissolve it in the liquid. The resulting solution is sucked out, and the desired resource is then isolated from the solution. Salt can be mined in this way; water is pumped into deep salt caverns, the salt dissolves in the water, and the salty solution is extracted. Besides sodium chloride (table salt), salts mined in this manner include lithium, boron, bromine, magnesium, and potash. *In situ* recovery also is sometimes used for copper (dissolved with acids) and uranium (dissolved with acids or carbonates).

Solution mining generally exerts less environmental impact than other mining techniques, because less area at the surface is disturbed. The main potential impacts involve accidental leakage of acids into groundwater surrounding the borehole; the contamination of aquifers with acids, heavy metals, or uranium leached from the rock; and surface collapse into large cavities opened up by solution underground, as happened at the Retsof Mine in New York.

Some mining occurs in the ocean

The ocean holds many minerals useful to our society. We extract some minerals from seawater, such as magnesium from salts held in solution. We extract other minerals from the ocean floor. Using large vacuum-cleaner-like hydraulic dredges, miners collect sand and gravel from beneath the sea. Other valuable minerals found on or beneath the seafloor include calcium carbonate (used in making cement) and silica (used as fire-resistant insulation and in manufacturing glass), as well as copper, sulphur, zinc, silver, and gold. Many minerals are concentrated in manganese nodules, small ball-shaped accretions that are scattered across parts of the ocean floor. Over 1.5 trillion tonnes of manganese nodules may exist in the Pacific Ocean alone, and their reserves of metal may exceed all terrestrial reserves. The logistical difficulty of mining them, however, has kept their extraction uneconomical so far.

As land resources become scarcer and as undersea mining technology develops, mining companies may turn increasingly to the seas. Some companies already are exploring hydrothermal vents as potentially concentrated sources of metals such as gold, silver, and zinc, because these vents emit dissolved metals resulting from underground volcanic activity. A partly Canadian-owned company initiated the first seafloor copper-gold mining project in 2010.

Impacts of undersea mining are largely unknown, but such mining would undoubtedly destroy marine habitats and organisms that have not yet been studied. It would also likely cause some metals to diffuse into the water column at toxic concentrations and enter the food chain.

Restoring mined sites can be very challenging

Because of the environmental impacts of mining, governments of Canada and other developed nations now require that mining companies restore surface-mined sites following mining. The aim of such restoration, or **reclamation**, is to restore the site to a condition similar to its condition before mining. To restore a site, companies

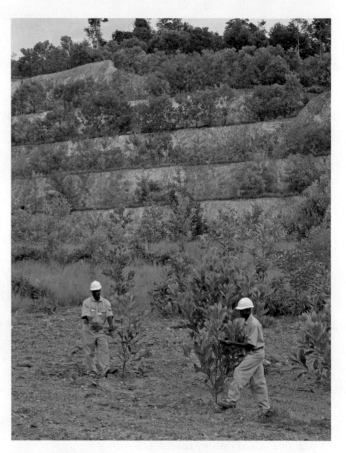

FIGURE 11.9
More mine sites are being restored today, but restoration rarely is able to recreate the natural community present before mining. Here, reclamation workers in Ghana, West Africa, plant trees on the benches and floor of an abandoned gold-mining pit.

are required to remove buildings and other structures used for mining, replace overburden, fill in shafts, and replant the area with vegetation (**FIGURE 11.9**). In Canada, mining companies are required to post bonds to cover reclamation costs before the development of a mine can even be approved. This ensures that if the company fails to restore the land for any reason, the government will have the money to do so. Most other nations exercise less oversight, and in nations such as Congo, there is no regulation at all.

The mining industry has made great strides in reclaiming mined land and employs many ecologists and engineers to conduct these efforts. However, even on sites that are restored, impacts from mining (such as soil and water damage from acid drainage) can be severe and long-lasting. Moreover, reclaimed sites do not generally regain the same biotic communities that were naturally present before mining. One reason is that fast-growing grasses are generally used to initiate and anchor restoration efforts. This helps control erosion quickly from the outset, but it can hinder the longer-term establishment of forests, wetlands, or other complex natural commu-

weighing the issues

RESTORING MINED AREAS

Mining has severe environmental impacts, but restoring mined sites to their pre-mining condition is costly and difficult. How much do you think we should require mining companies to restore after a mine is shut down, and what criteria should we use to guide restoration? Should we require complete restoration? No restoration? What should our priorities be—to minimize water pollution, health impacts, biodiversity loss, soil damage, or other factors? Should the amount of restoration we require depend on how much money the company made from the mine? Explain your recommendations.

nities. Instead, grasses may outcompete slower-growing native plants in the acidic, compacted, nutrient-poor soils that usually result from mining. Inconspicuous but vital symbiotic relationships that maintain ecosystems—such as specialized relationships between plants and fungi and plants and insects—can be eliminated by mining, and they are difficult or impossible to restore.

Water polluted by mining and acid drainage can also be reclaimed, if pH can be moderated and if toxic heavy metals can be removed. Like the reclamation of land, this is a challenging and imperfect process, but researchers and the mining industry are making progress in improving techniques. "The Science Behind the Story: Using Bacteria to Clean Mine Water" profiles an example of one such method to clean up acid drainage and recover excess metals at the same time.

Toward Sustainable Mineral Use

Mining exerts plenty of environmental impacts, but we also have another concern to keep in mind: Minerals are nonrenewable resources in finite supply. Like fossil fuels, they form far more slowly than we use them, and if we continue to mine them, they will eventually be depleted. As a result, it will benefit us to find ways to conserve the supplies we have left and to make them last. Reducing waste and developing means of recovering and recycling used mineral resources are ways we can pursue the use of mineral resources more sustainably. We will never achieve 100% recovery, but we can do much better than we are doing today.

Minerals are nonrenewable resources in limited supply

Unlike sunlight or water or forests, minerals do not regenerate fast enough to provide us a new supply once we have mined all known reserves. They are therefore considered nonrenewable resources. Some minerals we use are abundant in their supply and will likely never run out, but others are rare enough that they could soon become unavailable.

For instance, geologists in 2008 calculated that the world's known reserves of tantalum will last about 129 more years at today's rate of consumption. If demand for tantalum increases, it could run out faster. And if everyone in the world began consuming tantalum at the rate of North Americans, it would last for only 18 years! The supply of indium, an obscure metal used for LCD screens, might last only another 32 years. A lack of

indium would threaten the production of high-efficiency cells for solar power. Because of these supply concerns and price volatility, industries now are working hard to develop ways of substituting other materials for indium. Platinum is dwindling too, and if it became unavailable this would make it harder to manufacture fuel cells for vehicles. However, platinum's high market price encourages recycling, which may keep it available longer.

FIGURE 11.10 shows estimated years remaining for several selected minerals at today's consumption rates. Note that each bar in the figure consists of two parts. The left (dark red) portion of the bar shows the number of years researchers calculate that we will have the mineral available under today's economic conditions, that is, the portion of the resource that is *economically recoverable* at today's prices, using current extraction and processing technologies. As minerals become scarcer, demand for them increases and prices rise. Higher market prices make it more profitable for companies to mine the resource, so they become willing to spend more to reach further deposits that were not economically worthwhile originally. The entire length of each bar (red + orange) shows the number of years researchers calculate that we will have the mineral available in total. The orange bars thus represent the *technically recoverable* portion of the resource, which but would come into play if prices rise or when new, more efficient extraction and processing technologies are developed.

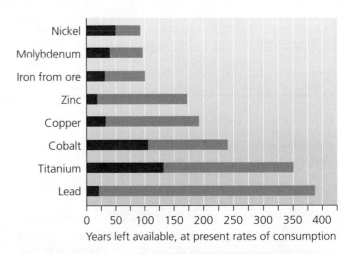

Years left available, at present rates of consumption

FIGURE 11.10

Minerals are nonrenewable resources, so supplies are limited. Shown in dark red are the numbers of remaining years that certain metals are estimated to be economically recoverable at current prices, given known global reserves and assuming current rates of consumption. The entire lengths of the bars (dark red plus orange) show the numbers of remaining years that certain metals are estimated to be available using current technology on all known deposits, whether economically recoverable or not. All these time periods could increase if more reserves are found, or decrease if consumption rates rise.
Source: Data are for 2009, from U.S. Geological Survey, 2010. Mineral Commodity Summaries 2010. USGS, Washington, D.C.

THE SCIENCE BEHIND THE STORY

Using Bacteria to Clean Mine Water

The toxic waters of the Berkeley Pit near Butte, Montana, have registered pH values as low as 2.2.

Mining poses two dilemmas: It exerts environmental impacts, and it can deplete non-renewable minerals. Now, some scientists are seeking to address both these drawbacks in one fell swoop. They're aiming to clean up polluted mine sites and amass valuable minerals at the same time. Their secret weapon? Bacteria.

In 1982 the Atlantic Richfield Company ceased mining at the Berkeley Pit, a massive open-pit copper mine in western Montana, covering almost 3 km². Once the mine was shut down and pumps were turned off, groundwater started to fill the 540-m-deep crater. As water bathed the rock walls, it mixed with oxygen from the air and reacted with sulphide miner-

als in the freshly exposed rock, producing acid drainage. Sulphuric acid formed, and the accumulating water became as acidic as lemon juice, reaching pH values as low as 2.2.

Metals began to leach from the rock walls into the acidic water, including iron, zinc, aluminum, manganese, nickel, cadmium, cobalt, arsenic, and copper. The metals reacted with sulphuric acid to form metal sulphates; for instance, zinc formed zinc sulphate ($ZnSO_4$) and iron formed iron sulphate ($FeSO_4$). High concentrations of these dissolved metals made the water toxic to wildlife, and waterfowl landing at the site were later found dead. The water was so unusually acidic and metal-rich that biologists discovered species of microbes that had never before been encountered, living in the harsh conditions of the pit.

As groundwater continued to fill the pit at a rate of almost 4 vertical metres per year, experts estimated that by the year 2015 water would overflow into the Clark Fork River, polluting ecosystems and poisoning people's drinking water. The race was on to find a solution.

Traditionally, mining engineers have treated acid mine drainage by adding a strongly alkaline substance, such as lime or sodium hydroxide, to raise the water's pH and precipitate the dissolved heavy metals. In recent years, researchers have

begun to put sulphate-reducing bacteria to work in converting metal sulphates in acid mine drainage to metal sulphides, harmless compounds that allow the metals to be removed and processed.

Sulphate-reducing bacteria are microbes that thrive in the absence of oxygen by chemically reducing sulphates to support their metabolism and creating sulphides that they expel as waste. In nature, some such bacteria degrade organic materials in the mud of swamps and produce hydrogen sulphide, the gas that gives swamps and mudflats their distinctive rotten-egg odour. Hydrogen sulphide in turn reacts with metal sulphates to create metal sulphides, which give swamp mud its blackish colour.

At the Berkeley Pit, U.S. Environmental Protection Agency scientist Henry Tabak, University of Cincinnati chemical engineer Rakesh Govind, and three colleagues examined whether they could use sulphate-reducing bacteria to clean up the water and recover valuable metals.

Highly acidic water harms most bacteria, so Tabak and Govind's team designed a two-step process. They grew their bacteria in water kept at a neutral pH in a tank called a bioreactor and fed them sulphates from the mine water, along with carbon-containing nutrients, letting them produce hydrogen sulphide. They then

Several factors affect how long mineral deposits may last

Mineral resources are widespread, but the entirety of a mineral resource is not necessarily mineable. In the context of mineral resources, we define a **reserve** as that portion of the resource that is economically (and legally) mineable using current technologies. Calculating how long a given mineral resource will be available to us (as in **FIGURE 11.10**) involves estimating the sizes of known reserves, and comparing these to current (and estimated future) levels of consumption. There are causes of uncertainty in such calculations, and several major reasons why estimates may increase or decrease over time.

Discovery of new reserves   As we discover new deposits of a mineral, the known reserves—and thus how long the mineral should remain available to us—increase. For this reason, some previously predicted shortages have not come to pass, and we may have access to these minerals for longer than currently estimated. As one recent example, in 2010 geologists associated with the U.S. military in Afghanistan discovered that Afghanistan holds immense mineral riches that were previously unknown. The newly discovered reserves of iron, copper, niobium, lithium, and many other metals are estimated to be worth over $900 billion—enough to realign the entire Afghan economy around mining. (Note, however, that this find is not guaranteed to make Afghanistan a wealthy

Acidic mine water rich in sulphates is fed into two tanks. Bacteria in the bioreactor produce hydrogen sulphide (H_2S), which circulates to the metal precipitation tanks. In the presence of hydrogen sulphide, metal ions bond to sulphur to form metal sulphides. The sulphides precipitate out of the water and are collected and processed to harvest minerals of economic value. The treated water is discharged from the system, clean enough to use for agriculture.

Percent Recovery of Metals from Mine Water Using Sulphate-Reducing Bacteria

Metal	Percent recovery of metal
Aluminum	99.8
Cadmium	99.7
Cobalt	99.1
Copper	99.8
Iron	97.1
Manganese	87.4
Nickel	47.8
Zinc	100.0

Source: Adapted with kind permission from Springer Science and Business Media from Tabak, H. H., et al. (2003) Advances in biotreatment of acid mine drainage and biorecovery of metals: I. Metal precipitation for recovery and recycle. Biodegradation 14: 423–436.

funnelled this hydrogen sulphide into a series of tanks, where it reacted with the acid mine drainage from the Berkeley Pit. The reactions in these tanks caused the metals to precipitate out as insoluble metal sulphides.

A simple schematic diagram (see figure) shows this process. In the bioreactor, the bacteria take sulphate ions (SO_4^{2-}) from the mine water and use carbon based compounds (CH_2O) to create hydrogen sulphide (H_2S) and bicarbonate (HCO_3^-):

$$SO_4^{2-} + 2CH_2O \rightarrow H_2S + 2HCO_3^-$$

The hydrogen sulphide is fed back to the metal precipitation tanks, where it drives reactions in which metal ions bond to sulphur atoms to form metal sulphides, which are insoluble in water and thus precipitate into a solid and settle to the bottom. For example, with the metal zinc (Zn), the equation would be as follows:

$$H_2S + Zn^{2+} \rightarrow ZnS + 2H^+$$

Thus, overall, soluble metal sulphates, such as zinc sulphate ($ZnSO_4$), are converted to insoluble metal sulphides, such as zinc sulphide (ZnS). The metal sulphides are then removed from the precipitation tanks. The research team measured its success recovering metals by this process by calculating the average percent recovery for each of several metals (see table). Precipitates of the various metals ranged in purity from 75% to 98%.

Besides recovering high percentages of metals that can be processed and recycled, the process cleaned heavy metals from the mine water and made it less acidic, with help from the bicarbonate. After full treatment, the water was pure enough to meet safety standards for use to irrigate agricultural crops.

This research, published in 2003, was done at the lab-bench scale, and more work remains to scale it up to treat large amounts of water from the mine. Today, a wide variety of similar efforts are ongoing around the world as scientists develop better ways of removing metals from acid mine drainage and as engineers work to scale these systems up. These approaches are showing promise to reclaim mine water and recycle metals at the same time.

nation; history teaches us that regions rich in nonrenewable resources, such as Congo, have often been unable to prosper from them.)

New extraction technologies

Just as rising prices of scarce minerals encourage companies to expend more effort to reach difficult deposits, rising prices also may favour the development of enhanced mining technologies that can reach more minerals at less expense. If more powerful technologies are developed, making it easier (and also, therefore, less expensive) to extract or process the ore, it may increase the amounts of minerals that are technically feasible for us to mine.

Changing social and technological dynamics

New societal developments and new technologies in the marketplace can modify demand for minerals in unpredictable ways. Just as cell phones and computer chips boosted demand for tantalum, fibre-optic cables decreased demand for copper as they replaced copper wiring in communications applications. The advent of legal requirements for catalytic converters, which limit polluting automobile emissions and contain platinum as a crucial component, greatly increased demand for platinum. Lithium-ion batteries are replacing nickel-cadmium batteries in many devices; this will have an impact on demand for lithium (and nickel-cadmium). Synthetically made diamonds are driving down prices of natural diamonds and extending their availability. Additionally, health concerns sometimes motivate change. For example, we have replaced toxic substances such as lead and mercury with safer materials in many applications.

Changing consumption patterns   Changes in the rates and patterns of consumption also alter the speed with which we exploit mineral resources. For instance, economic recession depressed demand and caused the production and consumption of most minerals to decrease in 2008 and 2009. However, over the long term, demand has been rising. This is especially true today as China, India, and other major industrializing nations rapidly increase their consumption.

Recycling   Advances in recycling technologies and increased prices for the recovered substances have helped to make recycling more technically and economically feasible. Recycling rates will continue to increase and, in turn, will allow us to extend the lifetimes of many mineral resources.

Even so, we would be wise to be concerned about Earth's finite supplies of mineral resources, and to try to use them more sustainably. Sustainable use will benefit future generations by conserving resources for them to use. It will also benefit us today, because conserving mineral resources through reuse and recycling can prevent price hikes that result from reduced supply. Also, domestic conservation of resources helps make our national economy less vulnerable in instances when other nations decide to withhold resources.

We can make our mineral use more sustainable

We can begin to address both major challenges facing us regarding mineral resources—finite supply and environmental damage—by encouraging recycling of these resources. Metal-processing industries regularly save resources and money by reusing some of the waste products produced during their refining processes. In addition, municipal recycling programs help provide metals by handling used items that we as consumers place in recycling bins and divert from the waste stream (**FIGURE 11.11**).

As of 2007, 84% of households in Canada had access to curbside recycling programs, and 98% of those households reported that they do recycle, although only about half of them report that they recycle all of the recyclable materials in their household waste each week.[3] Even among households without access to curbside pickup, 92% reported that they do recycle. Programs have been

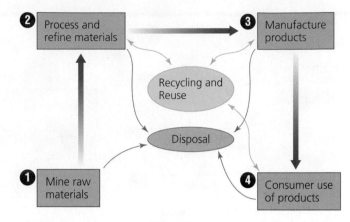

FIGURE 11.11
After we **(1)** mine ore or other raw materials, we **(2)** process and refine the minerals of interest and then **(3)** manufacture products from them, which are then sold to and used by consumers **(4)**. At each of these stages, some waste is disposed of, but at each stage there are also opportunities for reusing and recycling of materials.

established to recycle steel, iron, platinum, and other metals from auto parts. Recycling of car batteries has resulted in enough recovery of lead that fully 80% of the lead we consume today comes from recycled materials. Similarly, 35% of our copper comes from recycled copper sources such as pipes and wires. We have also found ways to recycle much of our gold, lead, iron and steel scrap, chromium, zinc, aluminum, and nickel.

In many cases, recycling can decrease energy use substantially. For instance, making steel by remelting recycled iron and steel scrap requires much less energy than producing steel from virgin iron ore. Because this practice saves money, the steel industry today is designed to make efficient use of iron and steel scrap. Over half its scrap comes from discarded consumer items like cars, cans, and appliances; scrap produced within their plants and scrap produced by other types of plants in the industry each account for nearly one-fourth of the total. Similarly, recycling of aluminum is a good thing because it takes over 20 times more energy to extract virgin aluminum from ore (called *bauxite*) than it does to obtain it from recycled sources. Every tonne of aluminum cans your community recycles saves the energy equivalent of more than 6000 litres of gasoline (**FIGURE 11.12**).

Tantalum is recycled from scrap by-products generated during the manufacture of electronic components and also from scrap from tantalum-containing alloys and manufactured materials. Currently the industry estimates that recycling accounts for 20–25% of the tantalum available for use in products. This percentage has been growing quickly, but its future growth will depend on how quickly we expand recycling efforts for used cell phones and other electronic waste and on how well we enable recycling facilities to recover metals from

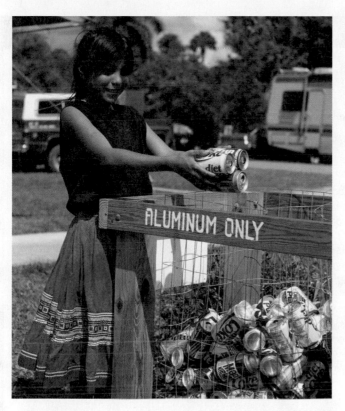

FIGURE 11.12
When you recycle aluminum cans, you contribute to valuable efforts to save mineral resources, money, and energy.

Table 11.1 Metal Content of 500 Million Unused Cell Phones and Its Market Value (as of 2005)

Metal	Amount (tonnes)	Value
Copper	7900	$17 million
Silver	178	$31 million
Gold	17	$199 million
Palladium	7.4	$63 million
Platinum	0.18	$3.9 million
Total	**8102**	**$314 million**

Source: Data are for 2005, from U.S. Geological Survey, 2006. Recycled Cell Phones—A Treasure Trove of Valuable Metals. USGS Fact Sheet 2006-3097. Prices of all these commodities have increased since 2005.

these products. One way to achieve this would be to make changes at the design stage, so that our electronic accessories are designed to make the disassembly and recycling process more straightforward.

We can recycle metals from e-waste

Electronic waste, or **e-waste**, from discarded computers, printers, cell phones, handheld devices, and other electronic products is rising fast—and that e-waste contains hazardous substances. Recycling old electronic devices helps keep them out of landfills and also helps us conserve valuable minerals such as tantalum. About 96% of the material in old cell phones is recyclable by one process or another.

In fact, each of the 1.2 billion cell phones sold each year contains about 200 chemical compounds and close to a dollar's worth of precious metals. In 2005, researchers estimated that about 500 million old cell phones were left inactive in people's homes and offices. **TABLE 11.1** shows estimates of the value of mineral resources they contain.

When you turn in your old phone to a recycling and reuse centre rather than discarding it, the phone may be refurbished and resold in a developing country. People in African nations in particular readily buy used cell phones, because they are inexpensive and because land-line phone service does not always exist in poor and rural areas. Alternatively, the phone may be dismantled in a developing country and the various parts refurbished and reused, or recycled for their metals. Either way, you are helping to extend the availability of resources through reuse and recycling and to decrease waste of valuable minerals.

Today in Canada more than 70% of the population owns a cell phone, but only about 12% percent of old cell phones are recycled. That leaves a long way to go! As more of us recycle our phones, computers, and other electronic items, more tantalum and other metals may be recovered and reused. By recycling more, we can reduce demand for virgin ore and decrease pressure on the health of people and ecosystems in places where coltan is mined. Throughout the world, using recycling to make better use of the mineral resources we have already mined will help minimize the impacts of mining and assure us access to resources farther into the future.

Conclusion

We depend on a diversity of minerals and metals to help manufacture products widely used in our society. We mine these nonrenewable resources by various methods, according to how the minerals are distributed. Economically efficient mining methods have greatly contributed to our material wealth, but they have also resulted in extensive environmental impacts, ranging from habitat loss to acid drainage. Restoration efforts and enhanced regulation help to minimize the environmental and social impacts of mining, although to some extent these impacts will always exist. We can lengthen our access to mineral resources and make our mineral use more sustainable by maximizing the recovery and recycling of key minerals.

CANADIAN ENVIRONMENTAL PERSPECTIVES

Eira Thomas

Eira Thomas has been dubbed Canada's "Queen of Diamonds."

- **Exploration geologist**
- Former **CEO** and **President** of Stornoway Diamond Corp.
- One of **Canada's Top 40 Under 40**, 2004

Eira Thomas began her career as a geologist earlier than most. At eight years old, she and her sister began to accompany their geologist father on summer expeditions to mineral exploration camps outside Yellowknife, Northwest Territories. Later, as an undergraduate at the University of Toronto, Thomas was attracted to the cross-disciplinary nature of geology. "I wasn't one of those individuals who went to university knowing exactly what I wanted to do. I was interested in science. I chose geology because it was more of a generalist science, encompassing physics and chemistry and biology."[4]

After graduation, Thomas returned to the Northwest Territories to work with Aber Resources, the exploration company started by her father. In 1994 and 1995 (aged 26), she led the team of exploration geologists that discovered the site that would eventually become Diavik Diamond Mine. (A photo of the Diavik Mine opens the chapter on environmental ethics and economics.) Only the second producing diamond mine in Canada, Diavik went into production in 2003 and is one of the highest-grade diamond deposits in the world.

Thomas served as vice president of exploration for Aber for two years. Until August, 2011 she was president and CEO of Stornoway Diamond Corp. and remains actively involved with many other business-related aspects of mining. In 2004, she was the recipient of Canada's "Top 40 Under 40" award.

However, field geology remains her passion. "I spent a lot of time travelling around with my father, prospecting in the North.... It's a pretty infectious type of business, especially when you're a child and you're out prospecting along and looking for things. It's the ultimate treasure-hunting career."[5] Thomas is also devoted to Canada's North. She believes strongly that diamond development is important for long-term economic growth and social development in the North, where unemployment is often extremely high. She was instrumental in establishing a partnership with Nunavut Tunngavik, an Aboriginal organization set up to ensure that promises made under the Nunavut Land Claims Agreement are carried out. Mining in Canada's North takes place in environmentally sensitive locations. Says Thomas, "Diamond mining requires no chemicals and has a limited impact on the landscape. We leave a very small footprint and don't need any infrastructure. You can fly out a week's worth of production in a suitcase."[6]

"There is something magical about the North, and we are very involved with the local communities with regard to training initiatives. I spoke with an elder and he explained how he wanted his grandson to go to university. But he also needs to find a reason for his grandson to come back home."[7]
—Eira Thomas

Thinking About Environmental Perspectives

Eira Thomas feels strongly that mining is important for the economic and social prosperity of Canada's North. Many Aboriginal leaders agree. But mining can be highly disruptive to the environment. What kinds of steps should mining companies be required to take to ensure a proper balance between environmental costs and economic or social benefits? What role should Aboriginal leaders and organizations play in making decisions regarding exploration and mining on traditional lands?

REVIEWING OBJECTIVES

You should now be able to:

Outline the main types of mineral resources

- Rocks are composed of minerals. The valuable parts of a rock are called ore; the nonvaluable parts are waste rock, or gangue.
- We mine ore to extract metals; we also mine for non-metallic minerals and fuels.

- Processing and refining metals through methods such as smelting is an important step between mining ore and manufacturing products.

Summarize the ways in which mineral resources contribute to our economy and society

- The minerals we mine provide raw materials for most of the products we use and depend on every day.

- Canada has traditionally been a mineral producing and exporting nation.

Describe the major methods of mining

- Strip mining removes surface layers of soil and rock to expose resources.
- Subsurface mining involves tunnelling underground.
- Open-pit and mountaintop removal mining requires large surface excavations.
- Placer mining uses running water to isolate minerals.
- Solution mining uses water to dissolve minerals in place and extract them.
- A great deal of mineral wealth exists in the oceans, but it is mostly uneconomical (so far) to extract.

Characterize the environmental and social impacts of mining

- Many methods of mining completely remove vegetation, soil, and habitat.
- Acid mine drainage, probably the most significant environmental liability facing the mining industry in North America, occurs when water leaches compounds from freshly exposed waste rock. It is often toxic to aquatic organisms.
- Erosion, sediment disturbance, and other impacts add to water pollution.

- Mining may have health impacts on miners, and diverse health, economic, and social impacts on people living near mines.

Assess reclamation efforts and mining policy in Canada

- Although mining companies have made great advances environmentally, reclamation efforts still generally fall short of effective ecological restoration.
- In Canada, mining companies are required to post a bond, before mining is even approved, to ensure that the funds will be available for reclamation purposes.
- Mining is not allowed in national parks in Canada.
- Contaminated mine drainage in Canada is regulated by the Metal Mining Effluent Regulation.

Evaluate ways to encourage sustainable use of mineral resources

- Minerals are nonrenewable resources, and some are limited in supply.
- Several factors affect how long a given mineral resource will last.
- Reuse and recycling by industry and consumers are the keys to more sustainable practices of mineral use.
- E-waste can be a source of recovered metals.

TESTING YOUR COMPREHENSION

1. Define each of the following, and contrast them with one another: (1) mineral, (2) metal, (3) ore, (4) alloy, (5) gangue.
2. A mining geologist locates a horizontal seam of coal very near the surface of the land. What type of mining method will the mining company use to extract it? What is one common environmental impact of this type of mining?
3. How does strip mining differ from subsurface mining? How does each of these approaches differ from open-pit mining?
4. What type of mining is used for both coltan and gold? What does a miner do to conduct this type of mining?
5. Describe and contrast how water is used in placer mining and solution mining.

6. What is acid drainage, and why can it be toxic to fish?
7. Describe three major environmental or social impacts of mountaintop removal mining.
8. Explain why reclamation efforts after mining frequently fail to effectively restore natural communities. Include reference to both soil and vegetation in your answer.
9. List five factors that can influence how long global supplies of a given mineral will last, and explain how each might increase or decrease the time span the mineral will be available to us.
10. Name three types of metal that we currently recycle, and identify the products or materials that are recycled to recover these metals.

THINKING IT THROUGH

1. List three impacts of mining on the natural environment, and describe how particular mining practices can lead to each of these impacts. How are these impacts being addressed? Can you think of additional solutions to prevent, reduce, or mitigate these impacts?

2. List three impacts of mining on people's health, lifestyles, or well-being, and describe how particular mining practices can lead to each of these impacts. How are these impacts being addressed? Can you think of additional solutions to prevent, reduce, or mitigate these impacts?

3. You have been hired for a summer job by Environment Canada to work with a mining company to develop a more effective way of restoring a mine site that is about to be abandoned. Describe a few preliminary ideas for carrying out restoration more effectively than it is typically being done. Now describe a field experiment you would like to run to test one of your ideas.

4. If you wanted to recycle your old cell phone, where would you take it? Do you know what would happen to the materials in the phone? You can get more information about cell phone recycling from www.recyclemycell.ca.

5. The story of coltan in the Congo is just one example of how an abundance of exploitable resources can often worsen or prolong military conflicts in nations that are too poor or ineffectively governed to protect these resources. In such "resource wars," civilians often suffer the most as civil society breaks down. Suppose you are the head of an international aid agency that has earmarked $10 million to help address conflicts related to mining in the Democratic Republic of the Congo. You have access to government and rebel leaders in the Congo and neighbouring countries, to ambassadors of the world's nations in the United Nations, and to representatives of international mining corporations. Based on what you know from this chapter, what steps would you consider taking to help improve the situation in the Congo?

6. Let's say that you have learned that the mountains behind your childhood home are slated to be mined or quarried. Your parents, who still live there, are worried for their health and safety and do not want to lose the beautiful forested creek and ravine behind their property. However, your brother is out of work and could use a mining job. What would you attempt to do in this situation?

INTERPRETING GRAPHS AND DATA

"Coltan" is the industrial name for two minerals—columbite (also known as niobium) and tantalite, which usually occur together in a coarse-grained igneous rock type called *pegmatite*. Tantalum from coltan is an important component in a variety of electronic devices, including cell phones, DVD players, and video game systems.

The Democratic Republic of the Congo is a relatively small producer of coltan (see table). However, as discussed in the Central Case, coltan mining in DRC (and other African nations) has been cited as a factor that contributes to civil conflicts, because it provides funds for military groups and encourages smuggling and other illegal activities. Because coltan mining in Africa is largely an unregulated, artisanal (small-scale) activity, it also contributes to environmental degradation and unsafe working conditions.

Canada is a significant producer of both tantalum (mainly from Manitoba) and columbium/niobium (mainly from Québec). Canadian production has been promoted as a source of "conflict-free coltan" to electronics manufacturers concerned about the ethics of coltan mining in Africa.

Based on the data provided in the table, answer the following questions:

1. How many metric tonnes of tantalum were produced in Canada in 2009, and what proportion of production did that represent?

Metric tonnes of tantalum mined

	1990	1991	1992	1993	1994	1995	1996	1997	1998	1999
Australia	165	218	224	170	238	274	276	302	330	350
Brazil	90	84	60	50	50	50	55	55	310	165
Canada	86	93	48	25	36	33	55	49	57	54
DRCongo	10	16	8	6	1	1	0	0	NA	NA
Africa*	45	66	59	59	8	3	3	3	82	76
World	396	477	399	310	333	361	389	409	779	645

	2000	2001	2002	2003	2004	2005	2006	2007	2008	2009
Australia	485	660	940	765	807	854	478	441	557	81
Brazil	190	210	200	200	213	216	176	180	180	180
Canada	57	77	58	55	57	63	56	45	40	25
DRCongo	130	60	30	15	20	33	14	71	100	87
Africa*	208	173	242	245	333	324	146	135	313	297
World	1070	1180	1470	1280	1430	1380	870	872	1190	670

Source. Data for 1990–1993 from U.S. Geological Survey, Minerals Yearbook (MYB) 1994, Columbium (Niobium) and Tantalum, by L. D. Cunningham, Table 10; 1994–1997 from USGS MYB 1998, Table 10; 1998–2001 from USGS MYB 2002, p. 21.13; 2002–2003 from USGS MYB 2004, p. 20.13; 2004 from USGS MYB 2008, p. 52.12; 2005–2009 from USGS MYB 2009, p. 52.13. USGS did not report data for other countries owing to data uncertainties.

*Other than Democratic Republic of the Congo

NA = Data not available

2. For the years represented on this chart, in which year was Canada's contribution to world production highest? In which year was it lowest?

3. What about the Democratic Republic of the Congo— what was its proportion of world production in 1990, compared to the proportion in 2009?

4. Australia has traditionally been the world's largest producer of tantalum, reaching 75.9% of world production in 1995. How many metric tonnes of tantalum did Australia produce in that year? In what year did Australia produce the highest number of metric tonnes? What was Australia's production in 2008 and 2009, in terms of metric tonnes and proportion of world production? Do you think the decline in Australian production (which resulted from the bankruptcy of the major Australian producer) had a major impact on world production? Refer to the graph to check your answer, and describe what seems to have happened to world production in 2009.

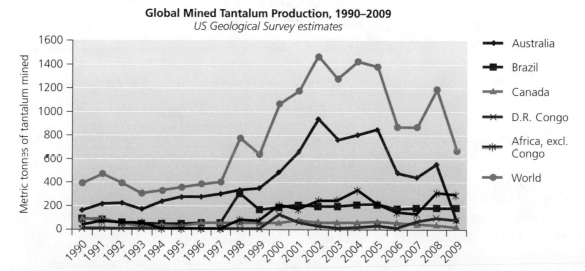

Global Mined Tantalum Production, 1990–2009
US Geological Survey estimates

Graph of mined tantalum output from 1990 to 2009 for Australia, Brazil, Canada, Democratic Republic of the Congo, Africa (excluding DRC), and World, based on estimates from the U.S. Geological Survey's *Mineral Yearbooks*.
Source: Wikimedia http://en.wikipedia.org/wiki/File:Global-mined-tantalum-production-1990-2009.png. Accessed 22 July 2011.

CHAPTER ENDNOTES

1. Natural Resources Canada. *Statistics: Mineral Production: Annual Production.* http://mmsd.mms. nrcan.gc.ca/stat-stat/prod-prod/2009p-eng.aspx. Accessed 01/15/11.

2. Natural Resources Canada. *Canadian Minerals Yearbook: Statistical Report*, Section 6: Employment, Salaries, and Wages. www.nrcan-rncan.gc.ca/mms-smm/busi-indu/cmy-amc/2008revu/stat-stat/tab22-30-eng.htm#t22. Accessed 15 January 2011.

3. Statistics Canada. *Recycling by Canadian Households, 2007.* www.statcan.gc.ca/pub/16-001-m/2010013/aftertoc-aprestdm1-eng.htm. Accessed 23 January 2011.

4. Quoted in the *Toronto Star* (28 October 2007) Queen of diamonds gets personal. www.thestar.com/Business/article/271199

5. Quoted in the *Toronto Star* (28 October 2007) Queen of diamonds gets personal. www.thestar.com/Business/article/271199

6. Quoted in the *Toronto Star* (28 October 2007) Queen of diamonds gets personal. www.thestar.com/Business/article/271199

7. Quoted in Wohlberg, T. (May 2005) Top 40 under 40: Eira Thomas. *Women in Mining.*

MyEnvironmentPlace

Go to **www.myenvironmentplace.ca** where you will find quizzes, animations, your Pearson eText, and more.

12 Freshwater Systems and Water Resources

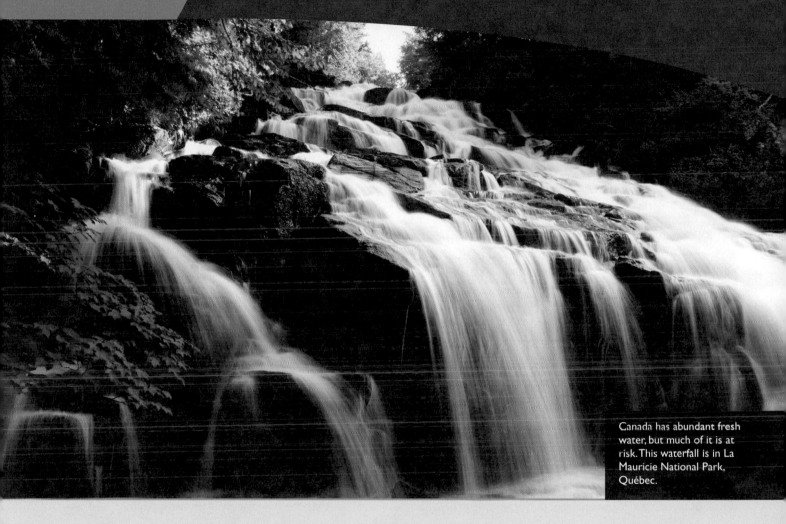

Canada has abundant fresh water, but much of it is at risk. This waterfall is in La Mauricie National Park, Québec.

Upon successfully completing this chapter, you will be able to

- Explain the importance of water and the hydrologic cycle to ecosystems, human health, and economic pursuits
- Delineate the distribution of fresh water on Earth
- Describe major types of freshwater ecosystems
- Discuss how we use water and alter freshwater systems

- Assess problems of water supply and propose solutions to address depletion of fresh water
- Assess problems of water quality and propose solutions to address water pollution
- Explain how waste water is treated

About 8% of Canada's surface is covered by water, more than any other nation, and 18% of the world's total available fresh water resides in the Great Lakes, seen here in a satellite image.

Hudson Bay

CANADA

Great Lakes

UNITED STATES

TURNING THE TAP: THE PROSPECT OF CANADIAN BULK WATER EXPORTS

"Water promises to be to the twenty-first century what oil was to the twentieth century: the precious commodity that determines the wealth of nations."
—*FORTUNE MAGAZINE*, MAY 2000

"The wars of the twenty-first century will be fought over water."
—WORLD WATER COMMISSION CHAIRMAN ISMAIL SERAGELDIN

"I predict that the United States will be coming after our fresh water aggressively within three to five years. I hope that when the day comes, Canada will be ready."
—PETER LOUGHEED, FORMER PREMIER OF ALBERTA

There are few topics more emotional or more controversial for Canadians than the subject of fresh water. Some argue that water is our legacy, our natural

capital, and that its abundance defines us as Canadians. They fear that we will place our sovereignty at risk if we allow large-scale diversions of fresh water, or bulk water exports, from Canadian water bodies. Once bulk water exports are allowed to begin flowing to the thirsty southwestern United States, they maintain, they will be impossible to stop.

For others, access to fresh water is a fundamental human right. They argue that those who possess it in abundance have the moral duty to provide water to those who lack it. As the stewards of 25% of the world's wetlands, 7% of the world's renewable flowing water, and 18% of the world's surface fresh water (mainly in the Great Lakes),[1] Canada truly has abundant resources to manage.

For some, water is a valuable, marketable commodity, which Canadians possess in surplus, and for which prices will continue to increase in the coming decades. Canada could be in an enviable position of economic and strategic strength in a world water market.

Others maintain that we should not even consider exporting our water to serve those who have mistreated, mismanaged, and depleted their own water supplies. Transporting large quantities of water from Canadian water bodies would cause massive changes, perhaps even permanent damage, to our natural ecosystems. And to what end, if those who would import our water have such a poor track record in appropriately managing this precious resource?

For example, desert areas of the southwestern United States are home to the enormous and rapidly increasing populations of cities like Los Angeles, Phoenix, and Las Vegas. The Imperial Valley of California—a natural desert (the sand dune scenes from *Star Wars: Return of the Jedi* were filmed there)—is one of the most fertile agricultural areas in the world, turning out water-intensive fruits like strawberries all winter. This is possible only because vast quantities of water are transported to the area from the Colorado River, via the 132-km All-American Canal. These deserts could never, under natural circumstances, sustainably support such large populations and water-dependent human activities.

Finally, there are those who reason that the very thirsty states of the American Southwest will be coming for our water before long anyway and that perhaps we would be wise to sell it to them before they contemplate taking it by force.

As an environmental issue and a political issue it is confusing, complicated, and controversial, but it is crucially important for us as humans, as Canadians, and as citizens of North America and the world. Canada possesses some of the most enviable water resources in the world, but we also are some of the most wasteful users of water; per capita daily use of water in Canada (about 343 L/day) is surpassed only by the United States.

Water is already exported to the United States from Canada. The 66 bottlers of water in Canada produced more than 2.3 billion litres of bottled water in 2006; more than a third of it was exported, mostly to the United States.[2] Significant *interbasin transfers*—the transportation of water from one drainage basin to another—already occur between Canada and the United States. Most of this—about 97% of the volume—is for electrical power production.[3]

However, Canada has not yet approved the wholesale bulk export or massive diversion of water to the United States. The North American Free Trade Agreement (NAFTA) identifies water as a marketable and tradable commodity, which effectively means that Canada is prohibited from restricting water for use exclusively within its national boundaries. Interestingly, Simon Reisman, Canada's chief trade negotiator for NAFTA, was a director of the GRAND Canal Company, a private-sector proponent of bulk water diversion.[1] The "GRAND" (Great Recycling and Northern Development) Canal scheme would involve damming James Bay and diverting the 20 rivers that flow into it toward the south. Another large-scale bulk water export plan, NAWAPA (North American Water and Power Alliance), would divert the Yukon, Peace, and Liard rivers through an 800-km-long canal running along the Rocky Mountain Trench and into the United States.

For the moment, Canada's fresh water is protected against bulk exports by a watershed-based approach in which each province and territory individually prohibits bulk water exports under the *International Boundary Waters Treaty Act*. Because Canada's position on bulk water exports has been relatively firm, some American companies are eyeing the significant water resources in Alaska as an alternative source.

This discussion is ongoing, and it will continue in the coming decades. What is **your** position on bulk water exports? You may be called upon, before too long, to decide.

Freshwater Systems

"Water, water, everywhere, nor any drop to drink." The well-known line from Coleridge's poem *The Rime of the Ancient Mariner* describes the situation on our planet quite well. Water may seem abundant to us, but water that we can drink is actually quite rare and limited (**FIGURE 12.1**). Roughly 97.5% of Earth's water resides in the oceans and is too salty to drink or use to water crops. Only 2.5% is considered **fresh water**, water that is relatively pure, with few dissolved salts. Because most fresh water is tied up in glaciers, icecaps, and underground aquifers, just over 1 part in 10 000 of Earth's water is easily accessible for human use.

Water is constantly moving among the reservoirs specified in **FIGURE 12.1** via the hydrologic cycle. As water moves, it redistributes heat, erodes mountain ranges, builds river deltas, maintains organisms and ecosystems, shapes civilizations, and gives rise to political conflicts. Let us first examine the portions of the hydrologic cycle that are most conspicuous to us—surface water bodies—and take stock of the ecological systems they support.

Rivers and streams wind through landscapes

Water from rain, snowmelt, or springs runs downhill and converges where the land dips lowest, forming streams,

roots

WATER

The word *water* was used in its present-day spelling by English poet Geoffrey Chaucer in the 1300s. Prior to that, it was spelled *wæter* in Old English. The origin was probably the Proto-Indo-European word *wodōr*. Among the many relatives of this word are the Greek *húdōr* (from which is derived the English prefix *hydro-*), the Latin *unda* (meaning "wave"), and the Gaelic *uisge* (from which is derived the English word *whiskey*).

creeks, or brooks. These watercourses merge into rivers, whose water eventually reaches the ocean (or sometimes ends in a landlocked water body). A smaller river flowing into a larger one is a **tributary**, and the area of land drained by a river and all its tributaries is that river's **drainage basin** or **watershed**.

Rivers shape the landscape through which they run. The force of water rounding a river's bend gradually eats away at the outer shore, eroding soil from the bank. Meanwhile, sediment is deposited along the inside of the bend, where water currents are weaker. In this way, over time, river bends become exaggerated in shape (**FIGURE 12.2**). Eventually, a bend may become such an extreme

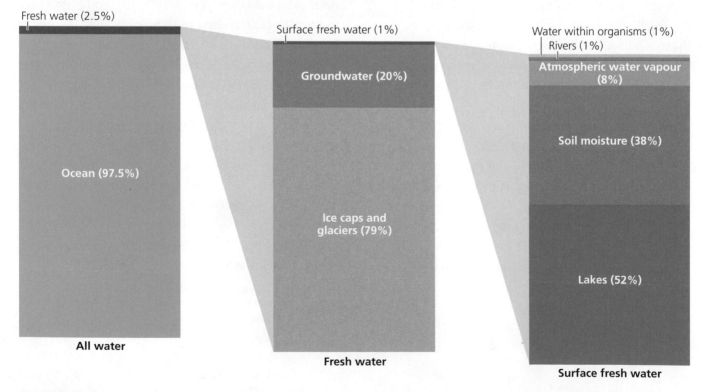

FIGURE 12.1   The world ocean is by far the largest reservoir in the hydrosphere, and it is a saltwater reservoir. Only 2.5% of Earth's water is fresh water. Of that 2.5%, most is tied up in glaciers and ice caps. Of the 1% that is surface water, most is in lakes and soil moisture. Data from United Nations Environment Programme (UNEP) and World Resources Institute.

FIGURE 12.2
Rivers and streams flow downhill, shaping landscapes, as shown by an oxbow of this meandering river in Alberta.

FIGURE 12.3
Shallow, ephemeral or seasonal water bodies with ample vegetation are called wetlands and include swamps, bogs, and marshes, such as this one in Botswana, Africa.

loop (called an *oxbow*) that water erodes a shortcut from one end of the loop to the other, pursuing a direct course. The bend is cut off and remains as an isolated U-shaped water body called an *oxbow lake*.

Over thousands or millions of years, a river may shift from one course to another, back and forth over a large area, carving out a flat valley. Areas nearest a river's course that are flooded periodically are said to be within the river's **floodplain**. Frequent deposition of silt from flooding makes floodplain soils especially fertile. As a result, agriculture thrives in floodplains, and **riparian** (riverside) forests are productive and species-rich.

The water of rivers and streams hosts diverse ecological communities. Algae and detritus support many types of invertebrates, from water beetles to crayfish. Insects as diverse as dragonflies, mayflies, and mosquitoes develop as larvae in streams and rivers before maturing into adults that take to the air. Fish consume aquatic insects, and birds, such as kingfishers, herons, and ospreys, dine on fish. Many amphibians spend their larval stages in streams, and some live their entire lives in streams. Salmon migrate from oceans up rivers and streams to spawn.

Wetlands include marshes, swamps, and bogs

Systems that combine elements of fresh water and dry land are enormously rich and productive. Often lumped under the term **wetlands**, such areas include different types of systems. In freshwater **marshes** (**FIGURE 12.3**), shallow water allows plants to grow above the water's surface. Cattails and bulrushes are plants typical of North American marshes. **Swamps** also consist of shallow water

rich in vegetation, but they occur in forested areas. The cypress swamps of the southeastern United States, where cypress trees grow in standing water, are an example. Swamps are also created when beavers build dams across streams with limbs from trees they have cut, flooding wooded areas upstream. **Bogs** are ponds thoroughly covered with thick floating mats of vegetation and can represent a stage in aquatic succession; an example is the Mer Bleue Bog in Ontario.

Wetlands are extremely valuable as habitat for wildlife. They also provide important ecosystem services by slowing runoff, reducing flooding, recharging aquifers, and filtering pollutants. Despite these vital roles, people have drained and filled wetlands extensively, largely for agriculture. It is estimated that southeastern Canada has lost well over half of all wetlands since European colonization, with up to 90% loss in some areas. The Potholes region of the Canadian Prairies is the most highly productive agricultural region of the country, as well as the host of about 4.5 million hectares of wetlands. The vast grasslands and small wetlands of the Potholes region have been widely converted to agricultural production, such that only about half of the wetlands that were present in the late 1700s (prior to European settlement) remain today.[5]

Lakes and ponds are ecologically diverse systems

Lakes and ponds are bodies of open standing water. Their physical conditions and the types of life within them vary with depth and the distance from shore. As a result, scientists have described several zones typical of lakes and ponds (**FIGURE 12.4**).

Sunlight

Littoral zone

Limnetic zone

Profundal zone

Benthic zone

Photic

Aphotic

Note that in the "real world" a lake this small—a pond—would not have an aphotic profundal zone; only deeper lakes have profundal zones, where sunlight does not penetrate

FIGURE 12.4 In lakes and ponds, emergent plants grow around the shoreline in the littoral zone. The limnetic zone is the layer of open, sunlit water, where photosynthesis takes place. Sunlight does not reach the deeper profundal (aphotic) zone. The benthic zone, which is the bottom of the water body, often is muddy, rich in detritus and nutrients, and low in oxygen.

The region ringing the edge of a water body is named the **littoral zone**. Here the water is shallow enough that aquatic plants grow from the mud and reach above the water's surface. The nutrients and productive plant growth of the littoral zone make it rich in invertebrates—such as insect larvae, snails, and crayfish—on which fish, birds, turtles, and amphibians feed. The **benthic zone** extends along the bottom of the entire water body, from shore to the deepest point. Many invertebrates live in the mud on the bottom, feeding on detritus or preying on one another.

In the open portion of a lake or pond, away from shore, sunlight penetrates the shallow waters of the **limnetic zone**. Because light in the *photic* zone enables photosynthesis and plant growth, the limnetic zone supports phytoplankton, which in turn support zooplankton, both of which are eaten by fish. Within the limnetic zone, sunlight intensity (and therefore water temperature) decreases with depth. The water's turbidity affects

the depth of this zone; water that is clear allows sunlight to penetrate deeply, whereas turbid water does not. Below the limnetic zone is the **profundal zone**, the volume of open water that is in the *aphotic zone*, that is, the depth below which sunlight does not reach. This zone lacks plant life and thus is lower in dissolved oxygen and supports fewer animals. Aquatic animals rely on dissolved oxygen, and its concentration depends on the amount released by photosynthesis and the amount removed by animal and microbial respiration, among other factors. Note that the profundal zone is, by definition, aphotic, whereas the benthic zone may be photic or aphotic; "benthic" simply refers to "the bottom" of the water body, which may or may not be shallow enough for light to penetrate.

Ponds and lakes change over time naturally as streams and runoff bring them sediment and nutrients. **Oligotrophic** lakes and ponds, which have low-nutrient and high-oxygen conditions, may slowly give way to the high-nutrient, low-oxygen conditions of **eutrophic** water bodies (jump ahead to see **FIGURE 12.20**). Eventually, water bodies may fill in completely by the process of aquatic succession. As lakes or ponds change over time, species of fish, plants, and invertebrates adapted to oligotrophic conditions may give way to those that thrive under eutrophic conditions.

Some lakes are so large that they differ substantially in their characteristics from small lakes. These large lakes are sometimes known as inland seas; the Great Lakes are prime examples. Because they hold so much water, most of their biota is adapted to open water. Major fish species of the Great Lakes include lake sturgeon, lake whitefish, northern pike, alewife, bass, walleye, and perch. Lake Baikal in Asia is the world's deepest lake, at 1637 m deep, and the Caspian Sea is the world's largest enclosed body of water, at 371 000 km².

Groundwater plays key roles in the hydrologic cycle

Any precipitation reaching Earth's land surface that does not evaporate, flow into waterways, or get taken up by organisms infiltrates the surface. Most percolates downward through the soil to become **groundwater** (**FIGURE 12.5**). Groundwater makes up one-fifth of Earth's freshwater supply and plays a key role in meeting human water needs.

Groundwater is contained within **aquifers**: porous formations of rock, sand, or gravel that hold water. An aquifer's upper layer, or *zone of aeration*, contains pore spaces partly filled with water. In the lower layer, or *zone of saturation*, the spaces are completely filled with water. The boundary between these two zones is the **water table**. Below the level of the water table, all pore spaces and fractures in the rock or sediment are completely filled with water; above the water table, typically some water is present in the pore spaces, but the ground is not completely saturated. Picture a sponge resting partly submerged in a tray of water; the lower part of the sponge is completely saturated, whereas the upper portion may be moist but contains plenty of air in its pores. Any area where water infiltrates Earth's surface and reaches an aquifer below is known as an aquifer **recharge zone**.

There are two broad categories of aquifers. A **confined aquifer**, or *artesian aquifer*, exists when a water-bearing porous layer of rock, sand, or gravel is trapped between upper and lower layers of less permeable substrate (often clay). In such a situation, the water is under great pressure. In contrast, an **unconfined aquifer** has no impermeable upper layer to confine it, so its water is under less pressure and can be readily recharged by surface water.

Just as surface water becomes groundwater by infiltration and percolation, groundwater becomes surface water through springs (and human-drilled wells), sometimes keeping streams flowing when surface conditions are

FIGURE 12.5

Groundwater may occur in unconfined aquifers above impermeable layers or in confined aquifers under pressure between impermeable layers. Water may rise naturally to the surface at springs and through the wells we dig. Artesian wells tap into confined aquifers to mine water under pressure.

otherwise dry. Groundwater flows downhill and from areas of high pressure to areas of low pressure, emerging to join surface water bodies at **discharge zones**. A typical rate of groundwater flow might be only about 1 m per day, so groundwater may remain in an aquifer for a long time. In fact, groundwater can be ancient. The average age of groundwater has been estimated at 1400 years, and some is many tens of thousands or even millions of years old.

The world's largest known aquifer is the Ogallala Aquifer, which underlies the Great Plains of the United States. Water from this massive aquifer has enabled American farmers to create a bountiful grain-producing region. The volumes, the specific characteristics, and even the exact areal extents of the major aquifers in Canada are not yet thoroughly known; they are being studied under the Natural Resources Canada (NRCAN) Groundwater Mapping Program (**FIGURE 12.6**).[6]

Among the most significant aquifers in Canada— both in terms of extent or volume of water and in terms of the areas and populations they service—are the Paskapoo Formation, which covers more than 10 000 km² of south-western Alberta; the Oak Ridges Moraine, a series of glacial deposits that cover 1900 km² and provide much of the Greater Toronto area with water; and the Annapolis– Cornwallis Valley Aquifers in Nova Scotia, covering a surface area of 2400 km² in a valley running parallel to the Bay of Fundy.[7] Groundwater is of particular impor-

tance on Prince Edward Island, which draws nearly all of its water from aquifers that underlie most of the island.

Water is unequally distributed across Earth's surface

Different regions, even different areas within the same country, can possess vastly different amounts of ground-water, surface water, and precipitation. For example, even though the region of the southwestern United States is very dry, the country as a whole actually has water resources roughly equivalent to those of Canada; however, the main concentration of water resources in the United States is in Alaska. In terms of global extremes, precipitation ranges from a high of about 1200 cm per year at Mount Waialeale on the Hawaiian island of Kauai to virtually zero in Chile's Atacama Desert. Some polar areas also receive very little precipitation; thus, they qualify as deserts, even though they are cold rather than hot.

People are not distributed across the globe in accor-dance with water availability. Many areas with high popu-lation density are water poor, leading to inequalities in per capita water resources among and within nations (**FIGURE 12.7**). For example, Canada has 20 times as much water for each of its citizens as China does. The Amazon River carries 15% of the world's runoff, but its

FIGURE 12.6   Some of the significant aquifers that are being studied in the Groundwater Mapping Program include the Paskapoo Formation, Oak Ridges Moraine, and Annapolis–Cornwallis Valley aquifers.

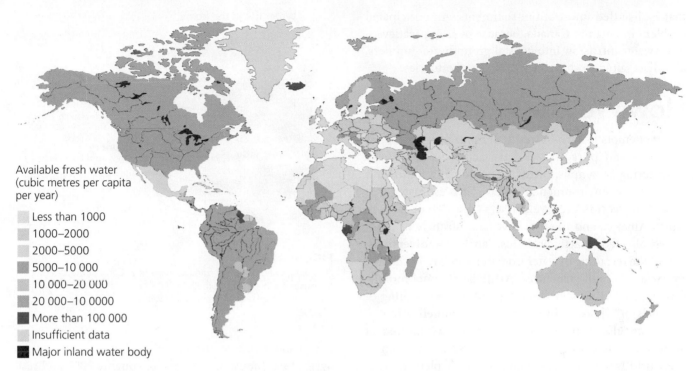

Available fresh water
(cubic metres per capita
per year)

- Less than 1000
- 1000–2000
- 2000–5000
- 5000–10 000
- 10 000–20 000
- 20 000–10 0000
- More than 100 000
- Insufficient data
- Major inland water body

FIGURE 12.7 Nations vary tremendously in the amount of fresh water per capita available to their citizens. For example, Iceland, Papua New Guinea, Gabon, and Guyana (dark blue in this map) each have more than 100 times as much water per person as do many Middle Eastern and North African countries. *Source:* Data from U.N. Environment Programme and World Resources Institute, as presented by Harrison, P., and F. Pearce. (2000). *AAAS Atlas of Population and the Environment.* Berkeley, CA: University of California Press.

watershed holds less than half a percent of the world's human population. Asia possesses the most water of any continent but has the least water available per person, whereas Australia, with the least amount of water, boasts the most water available per person. Because of this mismatched distribution of water and population, one challenge has always been to transport fresh water from its source to where people need it.

Fresh water is distributed unevenly in time as well as space. India's monsoon season brings concentrated storms in which half of a region's annual rain may fall in a few hours. Northwest China receives three-fifths of its annual precipitation during three months when crops do not need it. The uneven distribution of water across time is one reason people have erected dams to store water, so that it can be distributed when needed.

Climate change will cause water problems and shortages

As if the existing mismatches between water availability and human need were not enough, global climate change will worsen conditions in many regions by altering precipitation patterns, melting glaciers, causing early-season runoff, and intensifying droughts and flooding.

Environment Canada reports that climate change is expected to affect fresh water and the hydrologic cycle in Canada in four main ways:[8]

1. The present midlatitude rain belt will shift northward.
2. Snowmelt and spring runoff will occur earlier than at present.
3. There will be more evapotranspiration, which will start earlier and continue longer.
4. The interior continental region will experience drier summers.

The last major drought in the Prairies occurred in 2001–2002, but if climate model predictions of warmer temperatures and decreasing precipitation in interior continental regions come to pass, it may mean that droughts will become more common, more severe, and more extended.

Additional impacts of global climatic warming in Canada could include warmer river temperatures, which would damage aquatic ecosystems and freshwater fish. Water temperatures in the Great Lakes are expected to increase and water levels to decrease.[9]

There also are several potential secondary problems. For example, if water levels drop, it may be necessary to dredge channels to accommodate shipping. This would stir up and re-suspend sediments, increasing the turbidity of the water and potentially reactivating toxic chemicals that had settled into bottom sediments. An anticipated problem in Atlantic Canada, because of rising sea levels, is saltwater intrusion into coastal groundwater aquifers, as well as saltwater disturbance of coastal estuaries.

How We Use Water

In our attempts to harness freshwater sources for countless purposes and pursuits, we have achieved impressive engineering accomplishments. In so doing, we also have altered many environmental systems. It is estimated that 60% of the world's largest 227 rivers (and 77% of those in North America and Europe) have been strongly or moderately affected by artificial dams, canals, and **diversions**; that is, the rerouting of water from its natural river channel by means of built structures. Artificial channel modifications, including straightening and concrete-lining of channels, are collectively referred to as **channelization**.

We are also using too much water. Data indicate that at present our consumption of fresh water in much of the world is unsustainable, and we are depleting many sources of surface water and groundwater. One-third of the world's people are already (in 2011) affected by water scarcity (with less than 1000 m^3 of water per person per year), according to the World Health Organization.

Water supplies our households, agriculture, and industry

We all use water at home for drinking, cooking, and cleaning (**FIGURE 12.8**). Farmers and ranchers use water to irrigate crops and water livestock. Most manufacturing and industrial processes require water. The proportions of each of these three types of use—residential/municipal, agricultural, and industrial—vary dramatically among nations (**FIGURE 12.9**). Nations with arid climates tend to use more fresh water for agriculture, and heavily industrialized nations use a great deal for industry. Globally, we

Water use in the home

Showers and baths 35%
Toilet flushing 30%
Laundry 20%
Kitchen and drinking 10%
Cleaning 5%

FIGURE 12.8
According to Environment Canada, this is how Canadians apportion their use of water in the home.
Source: Data from Environment Canada, Water Use: Withdrawal Uses (as of 2006).

spend about 70% of our annual freshwater allotment on agriculture. Industry accounts for roughly 20%, and residential and municipal uses for only 10%.

When we remove water from an aquifer or surface water body and do not return it, this is called *consumptive use*. A large portion of agricultural irrigation and of many industrial and residential uses is consumptive. *Nonconsumptive use* of water does not remove, or only temporarily removes, water from an aquifer or surface water body. Using water to generate electricity at hydroelectric dams is an example of nonconsumptive use; water is taken in, passed through dam machinery to turn turbines, and released downstream.

We have erected thousands of dams

A **dam** is any obstruction placed in a river or stream to block the flow of water so that water can be stored in a

FIGURE 12.9
Nations apportion their freshwater consumption differently. Industry consumes most water used in Canada, agriculture uses the most in India, and most water in Lithuania goes toward domestic use. The largest category of water withdrawal in Canada (more than 60% of the total) is that for water used in the production of electricity. This category includes only withdrawals, not in-stream use. Withdrawals for power production are not included in the data shown in this diagram. *Source: Data are based on information from U.N. Food and Agriculture Organization (FAO, 2000) and from Environment Canada, (2005), The Management of Water: Water Use.*

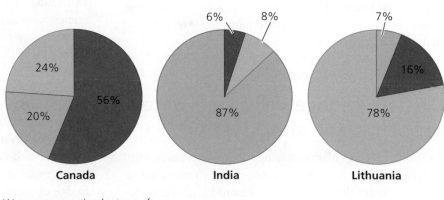

reservoir. We build dams to prevent floods, provide drinking water, facilitate irrigation, and generate electricity (**FIGURE 12.10**; **TABLE 12.1**). Power generation with hydroelectric dams is discussed in greater detail in the chapter on Energy Alternatives.

Worldwide, we have erected more than 45 000 large dams (greater than 15 m high) across rivers in more than 140 nations, and tens of thousands of smaller dams. In the Prairie provinces alone there are almost 800 dams.[10] Only a few major rivers in the world remain undammed and free-flowing; these run through the tundra and taiga of Canada, Alaska, and Russia and in remote regions of Latin America and Africa.

Our largest dams are some of humanity's greatest engineering feats. The Gardiner Dam in Saskatchewan is the largest in Canada in terms of water-holding capacity; the Mica Dam in British Columbia is the tallest. The two behemoths in the United States are the Hoover and Glen Canyon dams. The Hoover Dam, probably the most recognizable icon of the great dam-building period in the United States, holds 35.2 km³ of water in a reservoir that is 177 km long and 152 m deep. The Glen Canyon's reservoir is almost as large; together they store four times as much water as flows in the river in an entire year.

China's Three Gorges Dam is the world's largest

The complex mix of benefits and costs that dams produce is exemplified by the world's largest dam project, the Three Gorges Dam on China's Yangtze River. (It is worth noting that the second-largest dam in the world is not a water dam but the Syncrude tar sand tailings dam in Alberta.) The Three Gorges Dam, 186 m high and 2 km wide, was completed in 2006 (**FIGURE 12.11A**). When completely filled in 2010, its reservoir reached 616 km in length (as long as Lake Superior), holding more than

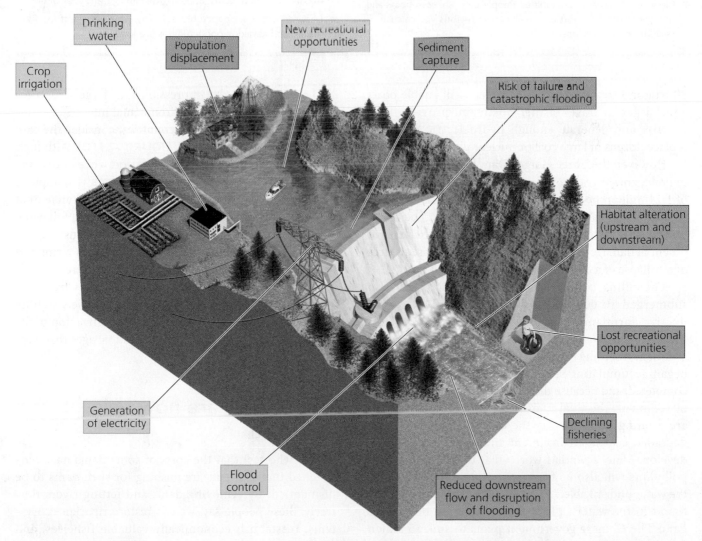

FIGURE 12.10 Damming rivers has diverse consequences for people and the environment. The generation of clean and renewable electricity is one of several major benefits (green boxes) of hydroelectric dams. Habitat alteration is one of several negative impacts (red boxes).

Table 12.1   Major Benefits and Costs of Dams

Benefits

- Power generation. Hydroelectric dams (pp. 595–598) provide inexpensive electricity.
- Emissions reduction. Hydroelectric power produces no greenhouse gases in its operation (although some are produced during construction and maintenance of infrastructure). By replacing fossil fuel combustion as an electricity source, hydropower reduces air pollution and climate change, and their health and environmental consequences.
- Crop irrigation. Reservoirs can release irrigation water when farmers most need it and can buffer regions against drought.
- Drinking water. Many reservoirs store plentiful, reliable, and clean water for municipal drinking water supplies, provided that watershed lands draining into the reservoir are not developed or polluted.
- Flood control. Dams can prevent floods by storing seasonal surges, such as those following snowmelt or heavy rain.
- Shipping. By replacing rocky river beds with deep placid pools, dams enable ships to transport goods over longer distances.
- New recreational opportunities. People can fish from boats and use personal watercraft on reservoirs in regions where such recreation was not possible before.

Costs

- Habitat alteration. Reservoirs flood riparian habitats and displace or kill riparian species. Dams modify rivers downstream. Shallow warm water downstream from a dam is periodically flushed with cold reservoir water, stressing or killing many fish.
- Fisheries declines. Salmon and other fish that migrate up rivers to spawn encounter dams as a barrier. Although "fish ladders" at many dams allow passage, most fish do not make it.
- Population displacement. Reservoirs generally flood fertile farmland and have flooded many human settlements. An estimated 40–80 million people globally have been displaced by dam projects over the past half century.
- Sediment capture. Sediment settles behind dams. Downstream floodplains and estuaries are no longer nourished, and reservoirs fill with silt.
- Disruption of flooding. Floods create productive farmland by depositing rich sediment. Without flooding, topsoil is lost, and farmland deteriorates.
- Risk of failure. There is always risk that a dam could fail, causing massive property damage, ecological damage, and loss of life.
- Lost recreational opportunities. Tubing, whitewater rafting, fly-fishing, and kayaking opportunities are lost.

38 trillion litres of water. This project will enable boats and barges to travel farther upstream, provide flood control, and generate enough hydroelectric power to replace dozens of large coal or nuclear plants.

However, the Three Gorges Dam has cost $25 billion to build, and its reservoir flooded 22 cities and the homes of 1.24 million people, requiring the largest resettlement project in China's history (**FIGURE 12.11B**). The major earthquake in southern China in 2008 raised fears of potential damage to the great structure; the consequences of a collapse of a dam this large would be devastating.

The filling of the reservoir behind the dam also submerged 10 000-year-old archaeological sites, productive farmlands, and wildlife habitat. Moreover, the reservoir slows the river's flow so that suspended sediment is settling behind the dam. Indeed, the reservoir began accumulating sediment as soon as the dam was completed, and because the river downstream is deprived of sediment, the tidal marshes at the Yangtze's mouth are eroding away, leaving the city of Shanghai with a degraded coastal environment and less coastal land to develop. Many scientists worry that the Yangtze's many pollutants will also be trapped in the reservoir, making the water undrinkable. In fact, high levels of bacteria were found in the water as it began building up behind the dam. The Chinese government plans to sink $5 billion into building hundreds of sewage treatment and waste disposal facilities.

Lest you have the impression that large structures with extensive social and environmental impacts are constructed only in developing countries, consider the case of the St. Lawrence Seaway (**FIGURE 12.11C**). Although it took more than 50 years of discussion, once under way the St. Lawrence Seaway took only 5 years to complete; it opened in 1959. The seaway is a series of canals that connects the Great Lakes to the Atlantic Ocean, following the route of the St. Lawrence River. Its construction required the displacement of 6500 people from farms and homes along the canal route; whole villages were flooded, as well as historically important battlefields from the War of 1812. The Lost Villages Historical Society website (http://lostvillages.ca/) documents the construction of the St. Lawrence Seaway and the farms and villages that were affected.

Some dams are now being removed

People who feel that the costs of some dams have outweighed their benefits are pushing for such dams to be dismantled. By removing dams and letting rivers flow freely, these people say, we can restore riparian ecosystems, reestablish economically valuable fisheries, and revive river recreation, such as fly-fishing and rafting. Another common reason for the decommissioning of

(a) The Three Gorges Dam in Yichang, China

(c) **Archival photo of the construction of the St. Lawrence Seaway**

FIGURE 12.11
China's Three Gorges Dam, completed in 2003, is the world's largest dam **(a)**. Well over a million people were displaced, archaeological treasures were lost forever, and whole cities were levelled for its construction, as shown here in Sichuan Province **(b)**. The filling of the reservoir began in 2003 and was completed in 2010. The construction of the St. Lawrence Seaway **(c)** from 1954 to 1959 required the displacement of 6500 people and caused the flooding of 14 000 hectares of land, 7 villages, and 225 farms

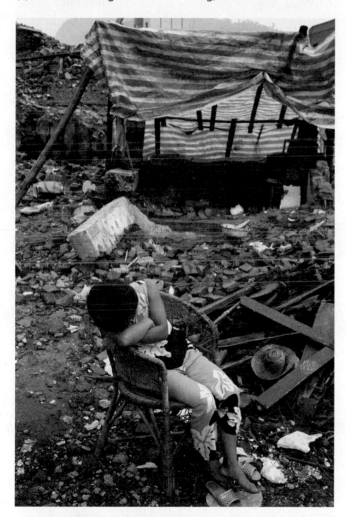

(b) Displaced people in Sichuan Province, China

study of the response of the river and aquatic communities to changes in flow rate, water temperature, sedimentation, and other factors that accompany decommissioning.

Dikes and levees are meant to control floods

Flood prevention ranks high among reasons we control the movement of fresh water. People have always been attracted to riverbanks for their water supply and for the flat topography and fertile soil of floodplains. Flooding is a normal, natural process caused by snowmelt or heavy rain, and floodwaters spread nutrient-rich sediments over large areas, benefiting both natural systems and human agriculture.

In the short term, however, floods can do tremendous damage to the farms, homes, and property of people who choose to live in floodplains. To protect against floods, individuals and governments have built **dikes** and levees (long raised mounds of earth) along the banks of rivers to hold rising water in main channels. Many dikes are small and locally built, but some are massive. In Canada, the flood diversion wall that protects the city of Winnipeg from the Red River is a major example of a flood protection structure (**FIGURE 12.12**). In the United States the

dams is that many aging dams are in need of costly repairs or have outlived their economic usefulness.

Roughly 500 dams have been removed in the United States in recent years, and more will soon follow. In Canada only a handful of dams have been decommissioned so far, but the concept of dam removal for river restoration and ecological recovery is beginning to take hold. Dam removals also provide opportunities for scientific

FIGURE 12.12

A flood diversion wall protected the city of Winnipeg during the 1997 Red River flood but may have exposed other villages to flooding. In this satellite image, the water appears blue, and the diversion wall can be seen in the upper righthand corner of the photograph, keeping the water from entering the core of the city of Winnipeg. A similar situation, necessitating controlled flooding of a small area to save a large area, occurred in 2011 when the Assiniboine River flooded.

Army Corps of Engineers has constructed thousands of kilometres of massive levees along the banks of major waterways (those that failed in New Orleans after Hurricane Katrina are examples). Although these structures prevent flooding at most times and places, they can sometimes worsen flooding because they force water to stay in channels and accumulate, building up enormous energy and leading to occasional catastrophic overflow events.

We divert—and deplete—surface water to suit our needs

People have long diverted water from rivers, streams, lakes, and ponds to farm fields, homes, and cities. *Diversion* refers to the process of removing water from its channel or modifying its flow for the purpose of using it elsewhere.

The Colorado River in the southwestern United States is one of the world's classic examples of diversion and overallocation of water from a major river. Early in its course, some Colorado River water is piped through a mountain tunnel and down the Rockies' eastern slope to supply the city of Denver. More is removed for Las

Vegas and other cities and for farmland as the water proceeds downriver. When it reaches Parker Dam on the California–Arizona state line, large amounts are diverted into the Colorado River Aqueduct, which brings water to millions of people in the Los Angeles and San Diego areas via a long open-air canal. From Parker Dam, Arizona also draws water, transporting it in the large canals of the Central Arizona Project. Farther south at Imperial Dam, water is diverted into the Coachella and All-American Canals, destined for agriculture, mostly in California's Imperial Valley. To make this desert bloom, Imperial Valley farmers soak the soil with subsidized water for which they pay one penny per 795 L.

What water is left in the Colorado River after all the diversions is just a trickle making its way to the Gulf of California and Mexico. On some days, water does not reach the gulf at all. This reduction in flow (**FIGURE 12.13**) has drastically altered the ecology of the lower river and the once-rich delta, changing plant communities, wiping out populations of fish and invertebrates, and devastating fisheries. It also led to a tense international incident between the United States and Mexico in the 1970s, necessitating high-level international talks and agreements concerning water reallocation, which improved the situation somewhat.

Nowhere are the effects of surface water depletion so evident as at the Aral Sea. Once the fourth-largest lake on Earth, just larger than Lake Huron, it has lost more than four-fifths of its volume in just 45 years (**FIGURE 12.14**). This dying inland sea, on the border of present-day Uzbekistan and Kazakhstan, is the victim of irrigation

FIGURE 12.13

Flow at the mouth of the Colorado River has greatly decreased over the past century as a result of withdrawals, mostly for agriculture. The river now often runs dry at its mouth.

Source: Data from Postel, S. 2005. Liquid assets: The critical need to safeguard freshwater ecosystems. *Worldwatch Paper 170. Washington, DC: Worldwatch Institute.*

(a) Ships stranded by the Aral Sea's fast-receding waters

Russia

Kazakhstan

Uzbekistan

Black Sea   Iran
Caspian Sea   Turkmenistan

100 km

North
Aral Sea

Aral Sea

South
Aral
Sea

1960   **2006**

(c) The shrinking Aral Sea, then and now

(b) Satellite view of Aral Sea, 2002

FIGURE 12.14
Ships lie stranded in the sand **(a)** because the waters of Central Asia's Aral Sea have receded so far and so quickly **(b)**. The Aral Sea was once the world's fourth-largest lake. However, it has been shrinking for the past four decades **(c)** because of overwithdrawal of water to irrigate cotton crops. Today restoration efforts are beginning to reverse the decline in the northern portion of the sea, and waters there are slowly rising.

practices. The former Soviet Union instituted large-scale cotton farming in this region by flooding the dry land with water from the two rivers leading into the Aral Sea. For a few decades this action boosted Soviet cotton production, but it caused the Aral Sea to shrink, and the irrigated soil became waterlogged and salinized.

Today 60 000 fishing jobs are gone, winds blow pesticide-laden dust up from the dry lake bed, and what cotton grows on the blighted soil cannot bring the regional economy back. However, all may not be lost: Scientists, engineers, and local people struggling to save the northern portion of the Aral Sea and its damaged ecosystems may now have finally begun reversing its decline.

Inefficient irrigation wastes water

The Green Revolution required significant increases in irrigation, and 70% more water is withdrawn for irrigation today than in 1960. During this period, the amount of land under irrigation has doubled. Expansion of irrigated agriculture has kept pace with population growth; irrigated area per capita has remained stable for at least four decades at around 460 m^2.

Irrigation can more than double crop yields by allowing farmers to apply water when and where it is needed. The world's 274 million hectares of irrigated

weighing the issues

FLOOD PROTECTION AT WHAT COST?

In May 2011, during record high-water levels on the Assiniboine River, the government of Manitoba deliberately breached a dike near Portage-la-Prairie, with the goal of releasing pressure in the Portage Reservoir and averting a much larger, uncontrolled flood. The controlled release put 150 homes and a considerable area of farmland at risk. In the end, the controlled breach worked, and no homes in the threatened area were significantly harmed.

A similar situation occurred during the Red River flood of 1997, during which the Red River Floodway diverted floodwater to protect the city of Winnipeg, but perhaps at the cost of flooding in smaller communities such as St. Agathe. Both events caused significant stress for those in the path of diverted floodwaters.

If you were a decision maker in Manitoba, would you have reached the same decision? Is it worthwhile to protect certain areas, even if it means risking others? What might you do to compensate those who were at risk?

cropland make up only 18% of world farmland but yield fully 40% of world agricultural produce, including 60% of the global grain crop. Still, most irrigation remains highly inefficient. Only about 45% of the fresh water we use for irrigation actually is taken up by crops. Inefficient "flood and furrow" irrigation, in which fields are liberally flooded with water that may evaporate from standing pools, accounts for 90% of irrigation worldwide. Overirrigation leads to waterlogging and salinization, which affect one-fifth of farmland today and reduce world farming income by $11 billion.

Many national governments have subsidized irrigation to promote agricultural self-sufficiency. Unfortunately, inefficient irrigation methods in arid regions, such as the Middle East, are using up huge amounts of groundwater for little gain. Worldwide, roughly 15–35% of water withdrawals for irrigation are thought to be unsustainable. In areas where agriculture is demanding more fresh water than can be sustainably supplied, *water mining*—withdrawing water faster than it can be replenished—is taking place (**FIGURE 12.15**). In these areas, aquifers are being depleted or surface water is being piped in from other regions.

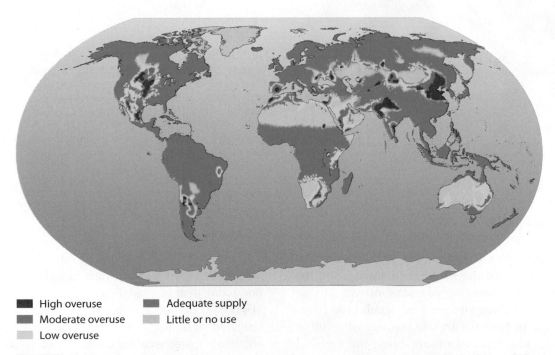

■ High overuse	■ Adequate supply
■ Moderate overuse	■ Little or no use
■ Low overuse	

FIGURE 12.15 Irrigation for agriculture is the main contributor to unsustainable water use. Mapped are regions where overall use of fresh water (for agriculture, industry, and domestic use) exceeds the available supply, requiring groundwater depletion or diversion of water from other regions. The map understates the problem because it does not reflect seasonal shortages.　Source: *Data from UNESCO. 2006. Water: A Shared Responsibility. World Water Development Report 2. Paris and New York: UNESCO and Berghahn Books.*

Wetlands have been drained for a variety of reasons

Throughout recent history, governments have encouraged laborious efforts to drain wetlands in order to promote settlement and farming. Many of today's crops grow on the sites of former wetlands—swamps, wooded marshes, bogs, and river floodplains—that people have drained and filled in (**FIGURE 12.16**). Wetlands also have historically been seen as "swamps"—insect-infested, smelly, and useless for any kind of industrial or agricultural development. In the 1930s the governor of Florida announced his intention to drain the entire Everglades, a unique cypress, mangrove, and tropical hardwood wetland that occupies much of the southern portion of the state. This attitude began to change dramatically in North America with the rise of the modern environmental movement in the 1970s and has continued to change as a result of research efforts to determine the economic value of services provided by wetlands.

In 1971, an international agreement was reached in Ramsar, Iran, concerning the documentation and protection of wetlands around the world. It is known as the *Ramsar Convention*, or more accurately, the *Convention on Wetlands of International Importance, Especially as Waterfowl Habitat*. The Ramsar Convention, to which Canada is a signatory, demonstrates the global concern regarding wetland loss and degradation. The mission of the treaty is the "conservation and wise use of all wetlands through local, regional, and national actions and international cooperation."[11] Today a large portion—perhaps 90%—of the original wetlands in southern Canada has been lost, but Canada as a whole still has the largest area of wetlands of any country in the world, according to Ramsar Convention data (**FIGURE 12.17**).[12]

Many people now have a different view of wetlands. Rather than seeing them as worthless swamps, science has made it clear that wetlands are valuable ecosystems. This scientific knowledge, along with a preservation ethic, has induced policy makers to develop regulations to safeguard remaining wetlands. Yet, because of loopholes, differing laws, development pressures—and even debate over the legal definition of wetlands—many of these vital ecosystems are still being lost.

We are depleting groundwater

Groundwater is more easily depleted than surface water because most aquifers recharge very slowly. If we compare an aquifer to a bank account, we are making more withdrawals than deposits, and the balance is shrinking. Today we are extracting 160 km³ more water each year than is finding its way back into the ground. This is a major problem because one-third of Earth's human population—including 26% of the population of Canada—relies on groundwater for its needs. As aquifers are depleted, water tables drop. Groundwater becomes more difficult and expensive to extract, and eventually it may run out. In parts of Mexico, India, China, and other Asian and Middle Eastern nations, water tables are falling 1–3 m per year.

When groundwater is overpumped in coastal areas, saltwater can intrude into aquifers, making water undrinkable. This has occurred widely in the Middle East

FIGURE 12.16
Most of North America's wetlands have been drained and filled, and the land converted to agricultural use. The northern Great Plains region of Canada was pockmarked with thousands of "prairie potholes," water-filled depressions that served as nesting sites for most of the continent's waterfowl. Today many of these wetlands have been lost; shown are farmlands encroaching on prairie potholes.

FIGURE 12.17
The Columbia Wetlands, seen here, is Ramsar site number 1463—a wetland of international significance and the largest of its kind in British Columbia.

and in localities as varied as Florida, Turkey, and Bangkok. Moreover, as aquifers lose water, their substrate can become weaker and less capable of supporting overlying strata, and the land surface above may subside. For this reason, cities from Venice to Bangkok to Shanghai are slowly sinking. Mexico City's downtown has sunk over 10 m since the time of Spanish arrival; streets are buckled, old buildings lean at angles, and underground pipes break so often that 30% of the system's water is lost to leaks.

Sometimes land subsides suddenly in the form of **sinkholes**, areas where the ground gives way with little warning, occasionally swallowing people's homes (**FIGURE 12.18**). Once the ground subsides, soil can undergo *compaction*, becoming compressed and losing the porosity that enabled it to hold water. Recharging a depleted aquifer may thereafter become much more difficult.

Falling water tables also do vast ecological harm. Permanent wetlands exist where water tables are high

FIGURE 12.18
When too much groundwater is withdrawn too quickly, especially in areas underlain by soluble rocks such as limestone, the land above it may collapse in sinkholes.

enough to reach the surface, so when water tables drop, wetland ecosystems dry up. In Jordan, the Azraq Oasis covered 7500 ha and enabled migratory birds and other animals to find water in the desert. The water table beneath this oasis dropped 2.5–7 m during the 1980s because of increased well use by the city of Amman. As a result, the oasis dried up altogether during the 1990s. Today international donors are collaborating with the Jordanian government to try to find alternative sources of water and restore this oasis.

Our thirst for bottled water seems unquenchable

It seems to fit our busy lifestyle. Canadians' use of bottled water is surpassed only by that of Americans. Statistics Canada reports that almost 3 in 10 households in Canada today utilize bottled water as their main source for domestic drinking water. The proportion of households dependent on bottled water increases with household income, although the relationship between income and bottled water consumption is complex. Interestingly, in a 2008 study by Statistics Canada, university-educated households were shown to be *less* likely to consume bottled water.[13]

For the nation as a whole, some 820 million litres of water were bottled for Canadian consumption in 2000; by 2003 the amount had increased to almost 1.5 billion litres. This means that the average per capita consumption of 17.9 L of bottled water per year in 1995 had risen to 27.6 L by 2000, and then jumped to almost 50 L by 2003![14]

An interesting thing about bottled water is that much of it is just ordinary tap water—in fact, it has been estimated that as much as a quarter of all bottled water comes straight from a municipal water tap, sometimes with additional filtering or other treatment. Advertising and labelling legislation prohibits bottling companies from misrepresenting what is in the bottle, of course, so if you read the label carefully you should be able to determine whether the water has come from a "natural" source, such as groundwater or a spring, or from a municipal supply.

But is bottled water from a natural source necessarily more healthful or safer for you? Although most people think so, in fact there are fewer checks on bottled water and the bottling process than on municipal water supplies, which are rigorously monitored and regulated. Canada's *Food and Drugs Act* does not require a manufacturer to obtain a licence in order to bottle water (although the water itself is expected to meet the requirements established for food products). From an environmental perspective, it also takes a considerable amount of energy to produce bottled water, and there are some concerns about

weighing the issues

THE PRICE OF A LITRE

Do you drink bottled water? Why? (Do you think it is safer than municipal water? Do you prefer the taste? Is it more convenient?) What do you pay for a litre of bottled water? What do you pay for a litre of gas at the pump? What do you think *should* be reflected in these prices? What price do you think was paid for the water by the company that bottled it? What about the source of the water you consume—is it groundwater, and if so, is its source adequately protected? And what about the plastic waste that it generates?

the sustainability of groundwater withdrawal and lack of protection of the source water. Finally, concerns have been raised, even by Health Canada, about chemicals that might leach into water from plastic bottles under some circumstances.

So the next time you reach for a bottle of water, consider what's in the bottle, where it came from, how it was extracted and monitored, and exactly what you are paying for. *Then* decide whether you think it is worth generating an empty plastic bottle.

Will we see a future of water wars?

Depletion of fresh water leads to shortages, and resource scarcity can lead to conflict, as shown by the research of Thomas Homer-Dixon and others. Many predict that water's role in regional conflicts will increase as human population continues to grow in water-poor areas and as climate change alters regional patterns of precipitation. A total of 261 major rivers, whose watersheds cover 45% of the world's land area, are *transboundary* waterways—that is, they cross or flow along national borders, and disagreements are common. Water is already a key element in the hostilities among Israel, the Palestinian people, and neighbouring nations.

On the positive side, many nations have cooperated with neighbours to resolve water disputes. India has struck cooperative agreements over management of transboundary rivers with Pakistan, Bangladesh, Bhutan, and Nepal. In Europe, international conventions have been signed by multiple nations along the Rhine and the Danube rivers. The international agreements between Canada and the United States, governing the Great Lakes and other water bodies that straddle the boundary between our two nations, have been examples of largely successful water management agreements. Such progress gives reason to hope that future water wars will be few and far between.

Solutions to Depletion of Fresh Water

Human population growth, expansion of irrigated agriculture, and industrial development doubled our annual freshwater use between 1960 and 2000. We now use an amount equal to 10% of total global runoff. The hydrologic cycle makes fresh water a renewable resource, but if our usage exceeds what a lake, a river, or an aquifer can provide, we must reduce our use, find another water source, or be prepared to run out of water.

Solutions can address supply or demand

To address depletion of fresh water, we can aim either to increase supply or to reduce demand. Strategies for reducing demand include conservation and efficiency measures. Lowering demand is more difficult politically in the short term but may be necessary in the long term. In the developing world, international aid agencies are increasingly funding demand-based solutions over supply-based solutions because demand-based solutions offer better economic returns and cause less ecological and social damage.

To increase supply in a given area, people have transported water through pipes and aqueducts from areas where it is more plentiful or accessible. In many instances, water-poor regions have forcibly appropriated water from communities too weak to keep it for themselves. For instance, Los Angeles grew by using water it appropriated from other, less-inhabited regions of California. In so doing, it desertified the environments of those areas, creating dust bowls and destroying rural economies. In 1941, Los Angeles needed water and decided to divert streams feeding into Mono Lake, more than 565 km away in northern California. As the lake level fell 14 m over 40 years, salt concentrations doubled and aquatic communities suffered. Other desert cities in the American Southwest—such as Las Vegas, Phoenix, and Denver—are expected to double in population in the coming decades. Today Las Vegas is trying to win approval for a 450-km pipeline to import groundwater from sparsely populated eastern Nevada, where local residents and wildlife advocates oppose the diversion plan.

Desalination "makes" more water

Another supply-side strategy is to develop technologies to find or "make" more water. The best known technological approach to generate fresh water is **desalination**, or *desalinization*, the removal of salt from seawater or other water of marginal quality. One method of desalination mimics the hydrologic cycle by hastening evaporation from allotments of ocean water with heat and then condensing the vapour—essentially *distilling* fresh water. Another method involves forcing water through membranes to filter out salts; the most common process of this type is called *reverse osmosis*.

More than 7500 desalination facilities are operating worldwide, most in the arid Middle East and some in small island nations that lack groundwater. The largest plant, in Saudi Arabia, produces 485 million litres of fresh water every day (**FIGURE 12.19**). However, desalination is expensive, requires large inputs of fossil fuel energy, and generates concentrated salty waste.

Agricultural demand can be reduced

Because most water is used for agriculture, it makes sense to look first to agriculture for ways to decrease demand. Farmers can improve efficiency by lining irrigation canals to prevent leaks, levelling fields to minimize runoff, and adopting efficient irrigation methods. Low-pressure spray irrigation directs water downward toward plants, and drip irrigation systems target individual plants and introduce water directly onto the soil. Both methods reduce water lost to evaporation and surface runoff. Low-pressure precision sprinklers in use in a number of arid localities have efficiencies of 80–95% and have resulted in water savings of 25–37%. Experts have estimated that drip irrigation, which has efficiencies as high as 90%, could cut water use in half while raising yields by 20–90% and giving developing-world farmers $3 billion in extra annual income.

Choosing crops to match the land and climate in which they are being farmed can save huge amounts of water. Currently, crops that require a great deal of water, such as cotton, rice, and alfalfa, are often planted in arid areas with government-subsidized irrigation. As a result of the subsidies, the true cost of water is not part of the costs of growing the crop. Eliminating subsidies and growing crops in climates with adequate rainfall could greatly reduce water use. Finally, selective breeding and genetic modification can result in crop varieties that require less water.

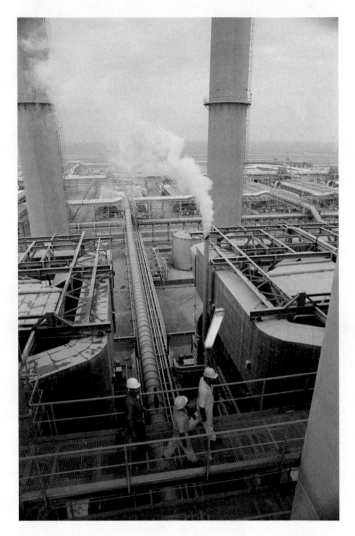

FIGURE 12.19
The Jubail Desalinization Plant in Saudi Arabia is the largest facility in the world that turns saltwater into fresh water.

We can lessen residential and industrial water use in many ways

We can each help reduce agricultural water use by decreasing the amount of meat we eat because producing meat requires far greater water inputs than producing grain or vegetables. In households, we can reduce water use by installing low-flow faucets, showerheads, washing machines, and toilets. Automatic dishwashers, a European study showed, can use less water than does washing dishes by hand.[15] If your home has a lawn, it is best to water it at night, when water loss from evaporation is minimal. Better yet, you can replace a water-intensive lawn with native plants adapted to the region's natural precipitation patterns. An example is *xeriscaping*—landscaping with plants that are well adapted to a dry environment.

Industry and municipalities can take water-saving steps as well. Manufacturers are shifting to processes that use less water and in doing so are reducing their costs. Some cities are recycling municipal waste water for irrigation and industrial uses, or capturing excess surface runoff during their rainy seasons and pumping it into aquifers. Finding and patching leaks in pipes has saved some cities and companies large amounts of water—and money. A program of retrofitting enabled Massachusetts to reduce water demand by 31% and avoid an unpopular $500 million river diversion scheme.

Economic approaches to water conservation are being debated

Economists who want to use market-based strategies to achieve sustainable water use have suggested ending government subsidies of inefficient practices and letting water become a commodity whose price reflects the true costs of its extraction. Others worry that making water a fully priced commodity would make it less available to the world's poor and increase the gap between rich and poor. Because industrial use of water can be 70 times as profitable as agricultural use, market forces alone might favour uses that would benefit wealthy and industrialized people, companies, and nations at the expense of the poor and less industrialized.

Similar concerns surround another potential solution, the privatization of water supplies. In the past two decades, many public water systems were partially or wholly privatized, with their construction, maintenance, management, or ownership being transferred to private companies. This was done in the hope of increasing the systems' efficiency, but many firms have little incentive to allow equitable access to water for rich and poor alike. Already in some developing countries, rural residents without access to public water supplies, who are forced to buy water from private vendors, end up paying on average 12 times more than those connected to public supplies.

Other experiences indicate that decentralization of control over water, from the national level to the local level, may help conserve water. In Mexico, the effectiveness of irrigation systems improved dramatically once they were transferred from public ownership to the control of 386 local water user associations.

Regardless of how demand is addressed, the ongoing shift from supply-side to demand-side solutions is beginning to pay dividends. A new focus on demand (through government mandates and public education) has decreased public water consumption, and industries are becoming more water-efficient.

Freshwater Pollution and Its Control

The quantity and distribution of fresh water poses one set of environmental and social challenges. Safeguarding the *quality* of water involves another collection of environmental and human health dilemmas. To be safe for consumption by human beings and other organisms, water must be relatively free of disease-causing organisms and toxic substances.

Although developed nations have made admirable advances in cleaning up water pollution over the past few decades, the World Commission on Water concluded that more than half the world's major rivers are "seriously depleted and polluted, degrading and poisoning the surrounding ecosystems, threatening the health and livelihood of people who depend on them." The largely invisible pollution of groundwater, meanwhile, has been termed a "covert crisis."

Water pollution takes many forms

The term **pollution** describes the release into the environment of matter or energy that causes undesirable impacts on the health and well-being of humans or other organisms. Pollution can be physical, chemical, or biological and can affect water, air, or soil.

Water pollution comes in many forms and can cause diverse impacts on aquatic ecosystems and human health. We can categorize pollution into several types, including nutrient pollution, biological pollution by disease-causing organisms, toxic chemical pollution, physical pollution by sediment, and thermal pollution.

Nutrient pollution You learned in previous chapters how nutrient pollution from fertilizers and other sources can lead to eutrophication and hypoxia in coastal

roots

POLLUTION

The word *pollution* comes from the Latin verb *polluere*, which means, "to soil, defile, or contaminate" and, in earlier Latin, "to desecrate or defile." It was used in its present sense, referring to contamination of the environment, as early as 1860, but it was not commonly used in this way until the middle 1950s.

marine areas. Eutrophication proceeds in a similar fashion in freshwater systems, where phosphorus is usually the nutrient that spurs growth. When excess phosphorus enters surface waters, it fertilizes algae and aquatic plants, boosting their growth rates and populations. Although such growth provides oxygen and food for other organisms, algae can cover the water's surface, depriving deeper-water plants of sunlight. As algae die off, they provide food for decomposing bacteria. Decomposition requires oxygen, so the increased bacterial activity drives down levels of dissolved oxygen. These levels can drop too low to support fish and shellfish, leading to dramatic changes in aquatic ecosystems.

Eutrophication (**FIGURE 12.20**) is a natural process, but excess nutrient input from runoff from farms, golf courses, lawns, and sewage can dramatically increase the rate at which it occurs. We can reduce nutrient pollution by treating waste water, reducing fertilizer application, planting vegetation to increase nutrient uptake, and purchasing phosphate-free detergents.

Pathogens and waterborne diseases   Disease-causing organisms (pathogenic viruses, protists, and bacteria) can enter drinking water supplies when these are contaminated with human waste from inadequately treated sewage or with animal waste from feedlots. Specialists monitoring water quality can tell when water has been contaminated by waste when they detect fecal coliform bacteria, which live in the intestinal tracts of people and other vertebrates. These bacteria are usually not pathogenic themselves, but they serve as indicators of fecal contamination, which may mean that the water holds other pathogens that can cause ailments, such as giardiasis, typhoid, or hepatitis A.

Biological pollution by pathogens causes more human health problems than any other type of water pollution. According to the World Health Organization in 2010, despite advances in many parts of the world, major problems still exist. On the positive side, 5.9 billion people (87% of the population) have access to safe water as a result of some form of improvement in their water supply—an increase from 4.1 billion (79% of the population) in 1990. However, more than 1.1 billion people are still without safe water supplies. In addition, 2.6 billion people have no sewer or sanitation facilities. Most of these are Asians and Africans, and four-fifths of the people without sanitation live in rural areas. These conditions contribute to widespread health impacts and 5 million deaths per year.

Treating sewage constitutes one approach to reducing the risks that waterborne pathogens pose. Another is using chemical or other means to disinfect drinking water. Others include hygienic measures, such as public

(a) Oligotrophic water body

(b) Eutrophic water body

FIGURE 12.20
An oligotrophic water body **(a)** with clear water and low nutrient content may eventually become a eutrophic water body **(b)** with abundant algae and high nutrient content. Pollution of freshwater bodies by excess nutrients accelerates the process of eutrophication.

education to encourage personal hygiene and government enforcement of regulations to ensure the cleanliness of food production, processing, and distribution.

Toxic chemicals   Our waterways have become polluted with toxic organic substances of our own making, including pesticides, petroleum products, and other synthetic chemicals. Many of these can poison animals and plants, alter aquatic ecosystems, and cause a wide array of human health problems, including cancer. In addition, toxic metals (such as arsenic, lead, and mercury) and acids (from acid precipitation and acid drainage from mine sites) also cause negative impacts on human health and the environment.

Legislating and enforcing more stringent regulations of industry can help reduce releases of these toxic inorganic chemicals. Better yet, we can modify our industrial processes and our purchasing decisions to rely less on these substances.

Suspended matter   Although floods build fertile farmland, sediment and other suspended matter that is transported by rivers can also impair aquatic ecosystems. Mining, clear-cutting, land clearing for housing development, and careless cultivation of farm fields all expose soil to wind and water erosion. Some water bodies, such as China's Yellow River, are naturally sediment-rich, but many others are not. When a clear-water river receives a heavy influx of eroded sediment, aquatic habitat can change dramatically, and fish adapted to clear-water environments may not be able to adjust. We can reduce sediment pollution by better managing farms and forests and avoiding large-scale disturbance of vegetation.

Thermal pollution   Water's ability to hold dissolved oxygen decreases as temperature rises, so some aquatic organisms may not survive when human activities raise water temperatures. When we withdraw water from a river and use it to cool an industrial facility, we transfer heat energy from the facility back into the river where the water is returned. People also raise surface water temperatures by removing streamside vegetation that shades water.

Too little heat can also cause problems. On many dammed rivers, water at the bottoms of reservoirs is colder than water at the surface. When dam operators release water from the depths of a reservoir, downstream water temperatures drop suddenly. These low water temperatures may favour cold-loving invasive species over endangered native species.

physical, chemical, and biological properties of water to characterize **water quality**. Biological properties include the presence of fecal coliform bacteria and other disease-causing organisms, as discussed above. Algae and aquatic invertebrates are also commonly used as biological indicators of water quality.

Chemical properties include nutrient concentrations, pH, taste and odour, and hardness. "Hard" water contains naturally high concentrations of calcium and magnesium ions, which prevent soap from lathering and leave chalky deposits behind when heated or boiled. An important chemical characteristic is dissolved oxygen content. Dissolved oxygen is an indicator of aquatic ecosystem health because surface waters low in dissolved oxygen are less capable of supporting aquatic life.

Among physical characteristics, *turbidity* measures the density of suspended particles in a water sample. If scientists can measure only one parameter, they will often choose turbidity because it tends to correlate with many others and is thereby a good indicator of overall water quality. Fast-moving rivers that cut through arid or eroded landscapes, like the Yellow River, carry a great deal of sediment and are turbid and muddy looking as a result. The colour of the water can reveal particular substances present in a sample. Some forest streams run the colour of iced tea because of chemicals called tannins that occur naturally in decomposing leaf litter. Finally, temperature can be used to assess water quality. High temperatures can interfere with some biological processes, and warmer water holds less dissolved oxygen.

Water pollution comes from point and non-point sources

Some water pollution is emitted from **point sources**—discrete locations, such as a factory or sewer pipe. In contrast, **non-point-source** pollution arises from multiple cumulative inputs over larger areas, such as farms, city streets, and residential neighbourhoods (**FIGURE 12.21**).

Many common activities give rise to non-point-source water pollution, such as applying fertilizers and pesticides to lawns, applying salt to roads in winter, and changing automobile oil. To minimize non-point-source pollution of drinking water, governments can limit development on watershed land surrounding reservoirs.

Scientists use several indicators of water quality

Most forms of water pollution are not very visible to the human eye, so scientists and technicians measure certain

Groundwater pollution is a serious problem

Most efforts at pollution control have focused on surface water. Yet increasingly, groundwater sources once assumed to be pristine have been contaminated by pollution from industrial and agricultural practices. Groundwater pollution is largely hidden from view and is extremely difficult to monitor (**FIGURE 12.22**); it can be out-of-sight, out-of-mind for decades until widespread contamination of drinking supplies is discovered.

Groundwater pollution is also more difficult to manage than surface water pollution. Rivers flush their pollutants fairly quickly, but groundwater retains its contaminants until they decompose, which in the case of persistent pollutants can be many years or decades. The long-lived pesticide DDT, for instance, is still found widely in aquifers in North America, even though it was banned 40 years ago. Moreover, chemicals break down much more slowly in aquifers than in surface water or soils. Groundwater generally contains less dissolved

| Non-point sources of water pollution | Pollutant | Point sources of water pollution |

Farms, lawns, and golf courses → Fertilizers, herbicides, and pesticides

Animal feedlots (also non-point source)

Nutrients, waste, and bacteria

Sewage treatment plants

Residential neighbourhoods and urban streets → Salt on winter roads; oil, grease, and chemicals from urban runoff

Industrial waste and toxic chemicals ← Factories and disposal sites

Construction sites, and deforested and overgrazed land → Eroded soil

Oil spills

Abandoned mines (also point source) → Acid drainage

Oil tankers

FIGURE 12.21 Point-source pollution comes from discrete facilities or locations, usually from single outflow pipes. Non-point-source pollution (such as runoff from streets, residential neighbourhoods, lawns, and farms) originates from numerous sources spread over large areas.

FIGURE 12.22

Groundwater supplies must be closely monitored, especially in areas where the potential for contamination is high. It is much easier to prevent contamination of groundwater than to remediate after contamination has occurred.

oxygen, microbes, minerals, and organic matter, so decomposition is slower. For instance, concentrations of the herbicide alachlor decline by half after 20 days in soil, but in groundwater this takes almost 4 years.

There are many sources of groundwater pollution, including some natural sources

Some chemicals that are toxic at high concentrations, including aluminum, fluoride, nitrates, and sulphates, occur naturally in groundwater. After all, water that resides in aquifers is surrounded by rocks—the natural sources for many chemical compounds, both benign and toxic— for hundreds to tens of thousands of years. During that time of close contact many compounds are leached from the rocks into the groundwater (including the calcium and magnesium that lead to water "hardness," mentioned above). The poisoning of Bangladesh's wells by arsenic is one case of natural contamination (see "The Science Behind the Story: Arsenic in the Waters of Bangladesh").

However, there is no escaping the fact that groundwater pollution from human activity is widespread. Industrial, agricultural, and urban wastes—from heavy metals to petroleum products to industrial solvents to pesticides—can leach through soil and seep into aquifers. Pathogens and other pollutants can enter groundwater through improperly designed wells and from the pumping of liquid hazardous waste below ground.

Leakage from underground septic tanks, tanks of industrial chemicals, and tanks of oil and gas also pollutes groundwater (**FIGURE 12.23**). According to Environment Canada, without adequate corrosion protection, more than half of underground gasoline storage tanks can be expected to begin leaking by the time they are 15 years old, and just 1 L of gasoline can contaminate up to 1 million L of groundwater.[16] Intercepting carcinogenic or otherwise toxic pollutants, such as chlorinated solvents and gasoline, before they reach aquifers is vital because once an aquifer is contaminated, it is extremely difficult to remediate.

Agriculture also contributes to groundwater pollution. Nitrate from fertilizers has leached into groundwater in agricultural areas throughout Canada and in 49 of the 50 U.S. states. Nitrate in drinking water has been linked to cancers, miscarriages, and "blue baby syndrome," which reduces the oxygen-carrying capacity of infants' blood. Agriculture can also contribute pathogens, primarily

originating from animal wastes. In 2000, the groundwater supply of Walkerton, Ontario, became contaminated with the bacterium *Escherichia coli*, or *E. coli*. Two thousand people became ill, and seven died (see "The Science Behind the Story: When Water Turns Deadly: The Walkerton Tragedy").

Legislative and regulatory efforts have helped reduce pollution

As numerous as our freshwater pollution problems may seem, it is important to remember that many of them were worse a few decades ago, when Lake Erie was declared officially "dead."

Citizen activism and government response during the 1960s and 1970s resulted in fundamental changes in environmental practices and legislation that made it illegal to discharge pollution from a point source without a permit, set standards for industrial waste water and for contaminant levels in surface waters, and funded construction of sewage treatment plants. In Canada most such legislation is enacted and enforced at the provincial level, although the federal government sets environmental guidelines through the *Canadian Environmental Protection Act* and other federal legislation, and regulates any interprovincial transfers of hazardous materials. However, probably the single most powerful act that serves to protect water quality in Canada is a federal law, the *Fisheries Act*, which makes it illegal to damage any water body that serves as a habitat for fish (although mining companies are exempt from this Act under some circumstances). Thanks to such legislation, point-source pollution has been reduced, and rivers and lakes in most parts of North America are cleaner than they have been in decades.

The Great Lakes represent a success story in fighting water pollution. Much of this work has been carried out through the International Joint Commission (IJC), the *Great Lakes Water Quality Agreement*, and the *International Boundary Waters Treaty Act*. In the 1970s the Great Lakes, which hold 18% of the world's surface fresh water, were badly polluted with waste water, fertilizers, and toxic chemicals. Today, coordinated efforts of the Canadian and U.S. governments have paid off. Releases of toxic chemicals are down, and phosphorus runoff has decreased. Bird populations are rebounding, and Lake Erie is now home to the world's largest walleye fishery.

The Great Lakes' troubles are by no means over— sediment pollution is still heavy, PCBs and mercury still settle on the lakes from the air, and fish are not always safe to eat. However, the progress so far shows how conditions can improve when citizens push their governments to take action.

FIGURE 12.23
Leaky underground gasoline storage tanks have been a major source of groundwater pollution. They are particularly problematic in the Atlantic provinces, where reliance on groundwater is very high.

THE SCIENCE BEHIND THE STORY

Arsenic in the Waters of Bangladesh

These skin lesions were caused by arsenic poisoning in Bangladesh.

In the 1970s, UNICEF, with the help of environmental scientists at the British Geological Survey, launched a campaign to improve access to fresh water in Bangladesh. By digging thousands of small artesian wells, the designers of the program hoped to reduce Bangladeshis' dependence on disease-ridden surface waters. In the mid-1990s, however, scientists began to suspect that the wells dug to improve Bangladeshis' health were contaminated with arsenic, a poison that, if ingested frequently, can cause serious skin disorders and other illnesses, including cancer.

A medical doctor sounded the first alarm. In 1983, dermatologist K. C. Saha of the School of Tropical Medicine in Calcutta, India, saw the first of many patients from West Bengal, an area of India just west of Bangladesh, who showed signs of arsenic poisoning. Through a process of elimination, contaminated well water was identified as the likely cause of the poisoning. The hypothesis was confirmed by groundwater testing and by the work of epidemiologists, among them Dipankar Chakraborti of Calcutta's Jadavpur University.

However, it was not until the late 1990s that large-scale testing of Bangladesh's wells began. By 2001, when the British Geological Survey and the government of Bangladesh published their final report, 3524 wells had been tested. Of the shallow wells—those less than 150 m deep—46% exceeded the World Health Organization's maximum recommended level of 10 µg/L of arsenic. Extrapolating across all of Bangladesh, the scientists estimated that as many as 2.5 million wells serving 57 million people were contami-

nated. As the figure shows, arsenic contamination is most prevalent in southern Bangladesh, but localized hot spots are found in northern regions of the country.

Scientists have not yet reached consensus on the chemical processes by which Bangladesh's shallow aquifers became contaminated. All agree that the arsenic is of natural origin; what remains unclear is how the low levels of arsenic naturally present in soils were dissolved in the aquifers in elemental and highly toxic form. One initial explanation, suggested by Chakraborti and his colleagues, placed most of the blame on agricultural irrigation. By drawing large amounts of water out of aquifers during Bangladesh's dry season, they argued, irrigation had permitted oxygen to enter the aquifers and prompted the release of arsenic from pyrite, a common mineral.

Other scientists contend that pyrite oxidation cannot explain most cases of arsenic contamination. In a 1998 paper in the journal Nature, Ross Nickson of the University College London and his colleagues suggested that arsenic was being released from iron oxides carried into Bangladesh by the Ganges River. They pointed to results of a hydrochemical survey that measured the chemical composition of aquifers throughout Bangladesh. Contrary to the predictions of the pyrite oxidation hypothesis, the survey found that arsenic concentrations tended to increase with aquifer depth and to be inversely correlated with concentrations of sulphur, a component of pyrite. Nickson and his colleagues concluded that highly reducing chemical conditions created by buried organic matter, such as peat, had probably leached arsenic from iron oxides over thousands of years.

Massachusetts Institute of Technology hydrologist Charles Harvey and colleagues have suggested that irrigation may contribute to the arsenic problem after all but not because of pyrite oxidation. In a 2002 paper in the journal Science, they described an experiment in which more than a dozen wells were dug near the capital city of Dhaka. Contrary to the pyrite oxidation hypothesis, and in agreement with Nickson and his colleagues, they found little evidence of a connection between sulphur or oxygen and arsenic.

However, they also found that they could increase arsenic concentrations by injecting organic matter, such as molasses, into their experimental wells. In the process of being metabolized by microbes, the molasses appeared to be freeing arsenic from iron oxides. A similar process might take place naturally, Harvey's team argued, when runoff from rice paddies, ponds, and rivers recharges aquifers that have been depleted by heavy pumping for irrigation. In support of this hypothesis, they found that much of the carbon in the shallow wells was of recent origin. Other scientists, however, have found arsenic in much older waters. This finding suggests that Bangladesh's arsenic problem may be caused by multiple hydrological and geological factors.

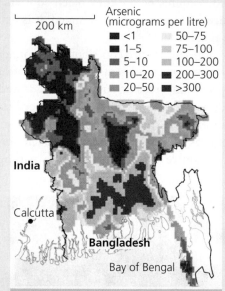

In a modern tragedy, thousands of wells dug for drinking water in Bangladesh at the urging of international aid workers turned out to be contaminated with arsenic. This map shows that arsenic concentrations are highest in the southern portion of the country.
Source: Kinniburgh, D. G., and P. L. Smedley, eds. (2001). Arsenic Contamination of Groundwater in Bangladesh. Department of Public Health Engineering Bangladesh, British Geological Survey Report.

Other developed nations have also reduced water pollution. In Japan, Singapore, China, and South Korea, legislation, regulation, enforcement, and investment in wastewater treatment have brought striking water quality improvements. However, non-point-source pollution, eutrophication, and acid precipitation remain major challenges.

We treat our drinking water

Technological advances have also improved our ability to control pollution. The treatment of drinking water and the treatment of waste water are mainstream practices in developed nations today. Health Canada publishes standards for drinking water contaminants, which local governments and water suppliers are obligated to meet. Categories for standards include microbiological parameters (viruses, bacteria, protozoa, turbidity); chemical and physical parameters (including both health and esthetic guidelines); and radiological parameters. More than 80 characteristics are considered in these guidelines; some have numerical standards associated with them, while others do not. The guidelines are set by the Federal Provincial–Territorial Committee on Drinking Water, which includes members from Health Canada, Environment Canada, and the Council of Environment Ministers, as well as the Canadian Advisory Council on Plumbing.

Before being sent to your tap, water from a reservoir or aquifer is treated with chemicals to remove particulate matter; passed through filters of sand, gravel, and charcoal; and/or disinfected with small amounts of an agent, such as chlorine.

It is better to prevent pollution than to mitigate the impacts after it occurs

In many cases, solutions to pollution will need to involve prevention, not simply **"end-of-pipe"** treatment and cleanup. With groundwater contamination, preventing pollution in the first place is by far the best strategy when one considers the other options for dealing with the problem: Filtering groundwater before distributing it can be extremely expensive; pumping water out of an aquifer, treating it, and then injecting it back in, repeatedly, takes an impracticably long time; and restricting pollutants on lands above selected aquifers would simply shift pollution elsewhere.

There are many things ordinary people can do to help minimize freshwater pollution. One is to exercise the power of consumer choice in the marketplace by purchas-

ing phosphorus-free detergents and other "environmentally friendly" products. Another is to become involved in protecting local waterways. Locally based "riverwatch" groups or watershed associations enlist volunteers to collect data and help provincial and federal agencies safeguard the health of rivers and other water bodies. Such programs are proliferating as citizens and policy makers increasingly demand clean water.

Waste Water and Its Treatment

Waste water refers to water that has been used by people in some way. It includes water carrying sewage; water from showers, sinks, washing machines, and dishwashers; water used in manufacturing or cleaning processes by businesses and industries; and stormwater runoff.

Although natural systems can process moderate amounts of waste water, the large and concentrated amounts generated by our densely populated areas can harm ecosystems and pose threats to human health. Thus, attempts are now widely made to treat wastewater before releasing it into the environment.

Municipal wastewater treatment involves several steps

In rural areas, **septic systems** are the most popular method of waste water disposal. In a septic system, waste water runs from the house to an underground septic tank, inside which solids and oils separate from water. The clarified water proceeds downhill to a drain field of perforated pipes laid horizontally in gravel-filled trenches underground. Microbes decompose the waste water these pipes emit. Periodically, solid waste needs to be pumped from the septic tank and taken to a landfill.

In more densely populated areas, municipal sewer systems carry waste water from homes and businesses to centralized treatment locations. There, pollutants in waste water are removed by physical, chemical, and biological means (**FIGURE 12.24**).

At a treatment facility, *primary treatment*, the physical removal of contaminants in settling tanks or clarifiers, generally removes about 60% of suspended solids from waste water. Waste water then proceeds to *secondary treatment*, in which water is stirred and aerated so that aerobic bacteria degrade organic pollutants. Roughly 90% of suspended solids may be removed after secondary treatment. Finally, the clarified water is treated with chlorine, and sometimes ultraviolet light, to kill bacteria.

(*text continued on page 369*)

Raw sewage enters
treatment facility

1 Screens and grit tank
Solid objects and grit removed

2 Primary clarifier
Oils, greases, and solids removed

Oils and greases float to the top

Solids sink to the bottom

Solids disposed at landfill

Gases chemically treated to reduce odour

3 Aeration basin
Microbes consume organic matter

4 Secondary clarifier
Remaining oils, greases, and solids removed

Some solids returned to seed aeration basin with new microbes

Sludge sent to anaerobic digester

5 Filtering and disinfection
Water filtered with coal and sand, and/or disinfected with chlorine or UV light

Effluent discharged into waterways

Gas to generate electricity

Biosolids for cropland

FIGURE 12.24 Shown here is a generalized process from a modern, environmentally sensitive wastewater treatment facility. Waste water initially passes through screens to remove large debris and into grit tanks to let grit settle **(1)**. It then enters tanks called primary clarifiers **(2)**, in which solids settle to the bottom and oils and greases float to the top for removal. Clarified water then proceeds to aeration basins **(3)** that oxygenate the water to encourage decomposition by aerobic bacteria. Water then passes into secondary clarifier tanks **(4)** for removal of further solids and oils. Next, the water may be purified by chemical treatment with chlorine, passage through carbon filters, and/or exposure to ultraviolet light **(5)**. The treated water (called *effluent*) may then be piped into natural water bodies, used for urban irrigation, flowed through an artificial wetland, or used to recharge groundwater. In addition, most treatment facilities control odour in the early steps and use anaerobic bacteria to digest sludge removed from the waste water. Sludge from digesters may be sent to farm fields as fertilizer, and gas from digestion may be used to generate electric power.

THE SCIENCE BEHIND THE STORY

When Water Turns Deadly: The Walkerton Tragedy[17]

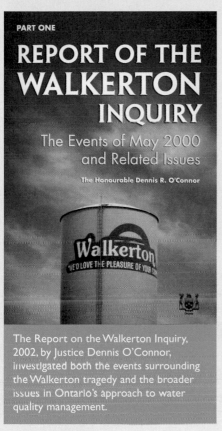

PART ONE

REPORT OF THE WALKERTON INQUIRY

The Events of May 2000 and Related Issues

The Honourable Dennis R. O'Connor

The Report on the Walkerton Inquiry, 2002, by Justice Dennis O'Connor, investigated both the events surrounding the Walkerton tragedy and the broader issues in Ontario's approach to water quality management.

Until May 2000, there was little to distinguish Walkerton from dozens of small towns in southern Ontario.[18]

That's how Justice Dennis O'Connor started his 2002 report entitled *Report of the Walkerton Inquiry: The Events of May 2000 and Related Issues.* He continued with a matter-of-fact summary of events:

In May 2000, Walkerton's drinking water system became contaminated with deadly bacteria, primarily Escherichia coli O157:H7. Seven people died, and more than 2,300 became ill. The community was devastated. The losses were enormous. There were widespread feelings of frustration, anger, and insecurity.[19]

In response to these events the Ontario government ordered the public inquiry, which found that contaminants entered Walkerton's municipal water wells around May 12, via any of a number of pathways. The transport of contaminants and their eventual entry into three wells were probably facilitated by heavy rains. The main source for the contaminants was animal wastes from livestock on a nearby farm. The farmer had followed appropriate procedures, the inquiry concluded, and was not at fault.

The contaminants were *Escherichia coli* and, less importantly, *Campylobacter jejuni.* Both are short, curved, rod-shaped bacteria (see photo) that occur commonly in the feces of birds, bats, and other warm-blooded animals. Symptoms of infection in humans include bloody diarrhea and stomach pain.

Some strains of *E. coli,* including the O157:H7 strain found at Walkerton, can be deadly. *C. jejuni* also has been linked to the development of a debilitating and sometimes fatal condition, Guillain-Barré syndrome. These are seriously pathogenic organisms.

Events began to unfold in Walkerton about six days after the initial contamination. Twenty children missed school on May 18; two were admitted to hospital. Multiple cases of intestinal illness prompted the medical officer of health, Dr. Murray McQuigge, to inquire about the safety of the water supply. Three times he was assured of its safety by Stan Koebel, manager of the Walkerton Public Utilities Commission (PUC). On May 21, Dr. McQuigge issued a boil-water advisory, in spite of the PUC's assurances.

The inquiry later concluded that Ontario's procedures for water safety testing were faulty and inadequate, and that PUC operators were insufficiently trained, had not done the daily testing they were supposed to do, and falsified data entries to give the impression that testing had taken place.

The inquiry concluded that chlorine residual testing and turbidity monitoring would have allowed for the detection and resolution of the problem. Chlorine residual testing is a simple approach that indicates whether sufficient chlorine has been added to the water to inactivate all the bacteria. If no "leftover" or residual chlorine remains in the water, then all of the added chlorine was used up and it is possible that some bacteria remain active. *Turbidity* refers to lack of clarity in the water; sometimes this is caused by suspended sediment, but a concentration of microorganisms can also cause turbidity. If chlorine residual testing and turbidity monitoring had been done on a daily basis, the problems would have been detected earlier and the outbreak could have been contained.

If a problem had been detected, further testing would have been triggered to identify the cause. This would have included technologies that detect an enzyme called beta-glucuronidase, which is produced by almost all forms of *E. coli* and very few other bacteria.

The sample is placed in a medium that changes colour or fluoresces if it is exposed to the enzyme. Sometimes it is necessary to culture the bacteria for a few days to have a sufficient concentration in the sample.

Most tests reveal the presence of *E. coli* but neither the exact amount nor the strain. Professor Ulrich Krull and colleagues at the University of Toronto Mississauga have developed a detection technology based on DNA. These *biosensors* contain short sequences of single-stranded DNA or *ssDNA,* which link or *hybridize* with complementary sequences of ssDNA in the sample, if they are present. An indicator, such as a fluorescing gel, shows that hybridization has occurred. Biosensors are useful because they instantly reveal not only the presence of the bacteria, but also the specific strain.

In his report, Justice O'Connor brought forward some pressing concerns about Ontario's approach to drinking water. Health Canada sets guidelines for drinking water quality; the provinces and territories have the responsibility to meet these guidelines and ensure drinking water safety. In some provinces this responsibility falls to the health ministry, in others the environment ministry. In 2002 Ontario passed the *Safe Drinking Water Act* to address the concerns raised by Justice O'Connor through the Walkerton Inquiry.

The contaminants found in the municipal water supply in Walkerton in 2000 included the bacteria *C. jejuni* and the deadly O157:H7 strain of *E. coli,* shown here.

CANADIAN ENVIRONMENTAL PERSPECTIVES

David Schindler

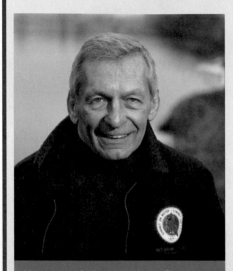

University of Alberta ecologist David Schindler warns that Canadian freshwater resources are under stress.

- ■ **Ecosystem ecologist** and Killam Memorial **Professor** of Biological Sciences at the University of Alberta
- ■ **Limnologist** and **biogeochemist**
- ■ **Freshwater advocate**

Although his is not a "household name," it is probable that no other environmental scientist in Canada today is better known or more highly regarded for his commitment to freshwater resources and ecosystems than the University of Alberta's David Schindler.

Schindler is an ecologist and a *limnologist*—a scientist who studies ponds, lakes, wetlands, and freshwater ecology. He received a D. Phil. in ecology from Oxford University, where he attended as a Rhodes Scholar in the late 1960s. After serving two years as an Assistant Professor at Trent University, Schindler joined the Fisheries Research Board of Canada, which later became the Department of Fisheries and Oceans, as the founding director of the Experimental Lakes Area (ELA), one of the most successful and productive long-term research programs on freshwater

systems. (You will learn more about the ELA in "Central Case: The Rain and the Big Nickel," which looks at the impacts of acid rain on northern lakes.)

Through his work at ELA, Schindler contributed significantly to the scientific understanding of the effects of phosphorus and acid rain on lake ecosystems. This understanding helped lead to restrictions on the phosphorus content of detergents and sewage, as well as changes in air quality legislation in Canada, the United States, and the European Union. In recognition of his contributions to the scientific understanding of freshwater ecosystems, Schindler has received many prizes, awards, medals, and honorary degrees, including the first Stockholm Water Prize, the Volvo International Environment Prize (he is the only Canadian to win either prize), the Tyler Environmental Prize, and the Gerhard Herzberg Canada Gold Medal for Science and Engineering, which came with a research grant of $1 million.

Professor Schindler has most recently turned his attention to the Alberta tar sand developments and their intensive use of water. In an article entitled *The Myth of Abundant Canadian Water* he wrote, "It is perhaps ironic that Alberta, the province most vociferously opposed to controlling greenhouse gases in order to protect its pampered petrochemical industries, will almost certainly be the first to suffer from freshwater shortages."[20] In the same article he continued, "To a water expert, looking ahead is like the view from a locomotive, 10 seconds before the train wreck. Sometime in the coming century, the increasing human demand for water, the increasing scarcity of water due to climate warming, and one of the long droughts of past centuries will collide, and Albertans will learn first-hand what water scarcity is all about."[21] Schindler is also now making important contributions to the scientific understanding of the effects of global warming and of stratospheric ozone depletion on northern lakes.

Dr. Schindler's instruction at the University of Alberta is somewhat out of the ordinary for a typical science professor. He co-teaches a graduate course entitled Limnology: The Philosophy, Sociology, and Politics of Science and Public Policy in Canada; Environmental Decision Making.[22] The course is consistent with what is perhaps his most important achievement, which goes beyond the science. It lies instead in his success at communicating the scientific message about freshwater vulnerability to those who most need to hear it. In a profile of Schindler's achievements, the Natural Sciences and Engineering Research Council of Canada noted that he has "succeeded in conveying his knowledge and its importance to legislators in Canada and around the world and to the general public,"[23] and that through his work and teaching he has inspired many students to become involved with research and careers in environmental science. This contribution will have a lasting impact on Canada and Canadians.

"The time to make these decisions is now, not after our water is gone."[24]**—David Schindler**

Thinking About Environmental Perspectives

David Schindler is widely recognized as a model for active, engaged science, and it is often noted that he has inspired many students to enter the field of environmental science. Is there a professor in your college or university who has inspired you to continue in your studies? How do you think Professor Schindler manages to balance his scientific research with his political activism on behalf of freshwater resources? Compare Schindler's story to the Environmental Profile on David Suzuki in the first chapter of the book, recalling that Suzuki chose to give up doing science on a daily basis in order to focus more exclusively on environmental activism.

Most often, the treated water, called **effluent**, is piped into rivers or the ocean following primary and secondary treatment. Sometimes, however, "reclaimed" water is used for lawns and golf courses, for irrigation, or for industrial purposes, such as cooling water in power plants.

As water is purified throughout the treatment process, solid material called *sludge* is removed. Sludge is sent to digesting vats, where microorganisms decompose much of the matter. The result, a wet solution of "biosolids," is then dried and disposed of in a landfill, incinerated, or used as fertilizer on cropland. Methane-rich gas created by the decomposition process is sometimes burned to generate electricity, helping to offset the cost of the treatment facility.

Artificial wetlands can aid treatment

Natural wetlands already perform the ecosystem service of water purification, and wastewater treatment engineers are now manipulating wetlands and even constructing wetlands *de novo* to employ them as tools to cleanse waste water. The practice of treating waste water and other types of polluted runoff with so-called **constructed** (or **artificial**) **wetlands** is growing quickly. For example, the government of Nova Scotia and the Nova Scotia Agricultural College are constructing a test series of three artificial wetlands that will be used to filter agricultural runoff from livestock operations. Generally in this approach, waste water that has gone through primary treatment

at a conventional facility is pumped into the wetland, where microbes living amid the algae and aquatic plants decompose the remaining pollutants. Water cleansed in the wetland can then be released into waterways or allowed to percolate underground.

Constructed wetlands also serve as havens for wildlife and areas for human recreation. Restored and artificial wetlands in Ontario, Alberta, Nova Scotia, and many other locations in Canada are serving as wetland habitats for birds and wildlife, while helping to recharge depleted aquifers.

Conclusion

Citizen action, government legislation and regulation, new technologies, economic incentives, and public education are all enabling us to confront what will surely be one of the great environmental challenges of the new century: ensuring adequate quantity and quality of fresh water for ourselves and for the planet's ecosystems.

Accessible fresh water is only a minuscule percentage of the hydrosphere, but we generally take it for granted. With our expanding population and increasing water usage, we are approaching conditions of widespread scarcity. Water depletion and water pollution are already taking a toll on the health, economies, and societies of the developing world, and they are beginning to do so in arid areas of the developed world. There is reason to hope that we may yet attain sustainability in our water usage, however. Potential solutions are numerous, and the issue is too important to ignore.

REVIEWING OBJECTIVES

You should now be able to:

Explain the importance of water and the hydrologic cycle to ecosystems, human health, and economic pursuits

- We depend utterly on drinkable water, and a functioning hydrologic cycle is vital to maintaining ecosystems and our civilization.

Delineate the distribution of fresh water on Earth

- Of all the water on Earth, only about 1% is readily available for our use.
- Water availability varies in space and time, and regions vary greatly in the amounts they possess.

Describe major types of freshwater ecosystems

- The main types of freshwater ecosystems include rivers and streams, wetlands, and lakes and ponds.

Discuss how we use water and alter freshwater systems

- We use water for agriculture, industry, and residential use. The ratio of these uses varies among societies, but globally 70% is used for agriculture.
- Most of the world's rivers are dammed. Dams bring a diverse set of benefits and costs. Increasingly, people are proposing dam removal.
- We divert water with canals and irrigation ditches and attempt to control floods with dikes and levees.
- We pump water from aquifers and surface water bodies, sometimes at unsustainable rates.

Assess problems of water supply and propose solutions to address depletion of fresh water

- Water tables are dropping worldwide from unsustainable groundwater extraction. Surface water extraction has caused rivers to run dry and water bodies to shrink.
- Unequal water distribution amid shrinking supplies may heighten political tensions over water in the future.
- Solutions to expand supply, such as desalination, are worth pursuing, but not to the exclusion of finding ways to decrease demand.
- Solutions to reduce demand include technology, approaches, and consumer products that increase efficiency in agriculture, industry, and the home.

Assess problems of water quality and propose solutions to address water pollution

- Water pollutants include excessive nutrients, microbial pathogens, toxic chemicals, sediment, and thermal pollution.

- Water pollution stems from point sources and non-point sources.
- Scientists who monitor water quality use biological, chemical, and physical indicators.
- Groundwater pollution can be more persistent than surface water pollution.
- Legislation and regulation have improved water quality in developed nations in recent decades.
- Preventing water pollution is better than mitigation.

Explain how waste water is treated

- Septic systems are used to treat waste water in rural areas.
- Waste water is treated physically, biologically, and chemically in a series of steps at municipal wastewater treatment facilities.
- Artificial wetlands enhance wastewater treatment while restoring habitat for wildlife.

TESTING YOUR COMPREHENSION

1. Define *groundwater*. What role does groundwater play in the hydrologic cycle?
2. Why are sources of fresh water unreliable for some people and plentiful for others?
3. Describe three benefits of damming rivers and three costs. What particular environmental, health, and social concerns has China's Three Gorges Dam and its reservoir raised?
4. Why do the Colorado, Rio Grande, Nile, and Yellow rivers now slow to a trickle or run dry before reaching their deltas?
5. Why are water tables dropping around the world? What are some environmental costs of falling water tables?

6. Name three major types of water pollutants, and provide an example of each. List three properties of water that scientists use to determine water quality.
7. Why do many scientists consider groundwater pollution a greater problem than surface water pollution?
8. What are some anthropogenic (human) sources of groundwater pollution?
9. Describe how drinking water is treated. How does a septic system work?
10. Describe and explain the major steps in the process of wastewater treatment. How can artificial wetlands aid such treatment?

THINKING IT THROUGH

1. Discuss possible strategies for equalizing distribution of water throughout the world. Consider supply and transport issues. Have our methods of drawing, distributing, and storing water changed very much throughout history? How is the scale of our efforts affecting the availability of water supplies?

2. How can we lessen agricultural demand for water? Describe some ways in which we can reduce household water use. How can industrial uses of water be reduced?
3. Discuss some of the methods we can adopt, in addition to "end-of-pipe" solutions, to prevent contamination and ensure "water security."

4. How might desalination technology help "make" more water? Describe two methods of desalination. Where is this technology being used?

5. Let's say that you have been put in charge of water policy for your region. The aquifer beneath your region has been overpumped, and many wells have already run dry. Agricultural production last year decreased for the first time in a generation, and farmers are clamouring for you to do something. Meanwhile, the region's largest city is growing so fast that more water is needed for its burgeoning urban population. What policies would you consider to restore your region's water supply? Would you try to

take steps to increase supply, to decrease demand, or both? Explain why you would choose such policies.

6. Having solved the water depletion problem in your region, your next task is to deal with pollution of the groundwater that provides the region's drinking water supply. Recent studies have shown that one-third of the province's groundwater has levels of pollutants that violate international standards for human health. Citizens are fearful for their safety, and the provincial government is threatening enforcement. What steps would you consider taking to safeguard the quality of your region's groundwater supply, and why?

INTERPRETING GRAPHS AND DATA

Close to 75% of the fresh water used by people is used in agriculture, and about 1 of every 14 people lives where water is scarce. By the year 2050, scientists project that two-thirds of the world's population will live in water-scarce areas, including most of Africa, the Middle East, India, and China. How much water is required to feed 7 billion people a basic dietary requirement of 2700 calories (11.3 kJ) per day? The answer depends on the efficiency with which we use water in agricultural production and on the type of diet we consume.

1. How many litres of water are needed to produce 2300 calories (9.6 kJ) of vegetable food? How many litres of water are needed to produce 400 calories (1.7 kJ) of animal food? How many litres of water are needed daily to provide this diet? Annually?

2. How many litres of water would be saved daily, compared to the diet in the graph, if the 2700 calories were provided entirely by vegetables? Annually?

3. Reflect on one of the quotes at the beginning of this chapter: "Water promises to be to the twenty-first century what oil was to the twentieth century: the precious commodity that determines the wealth of nations." How do you think the demographic

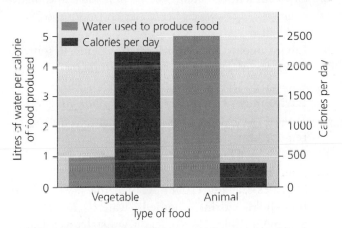

Amount of water needed to produce **vegetable** and **animal** food (orange), and global average calories per day consumed of vegetable and animal food (red) (1000 calories = 0.004184 kJ).
Source: Data from Wallace, J. S. (2000). Increasing agricultural water use efficiency to meet future food production. Agriculture, Ecosystems and Environment 82:105–119.

pressure on the water supply could affect world trade, particularly trade of agricultural products? Do you think it could affect prospects for peace and stability in and among nations? How so?

CHAPTER ENDNOTES

1. Environment Canada, *Fresh Water: Quick Facts*, www.ec.gc.ca/water/en/e_quickfacts.htm

2. Agriculture and Agri-Foods Canada, *The Canadian Bottled Water Industry*, www4.agr.gc.ca/AAFC-AAC/display-afficher.do?id=1171644581795&lang=e#sig

3. Quinn, F. (2007) *Water Diversion, Export, and Canada–U.S. Relations: A Brief History* (August). Program on Water Issues (POWI), Munk Centre for International Studies at the University of Toronto, www.powi.ca

4. Quinn, F. (2007) *Water Diversion, Export, and Canada–U.S. Relations: A Brief History* (August). Program on Water Issues (POWI), Munk Centre for International Studies at the University of Toronto, www.powi.ca

5. Prairie Pothole Joint Venture, *Introduction to the Prairie Pothole Region, 2005 Implementation Plan Section I*, www.ppjv.org

6. Natural Resources Canada, *Groundwater Mapping Program: Overview*, http://ess.nrcan.gc.ca/gm-ces/overview_e.php

7. Coté, François (2006) *Freshwater Management in Canada IV: Groundwater*. Library of Parliament, Parliamentary Information and Research Service, Science and Technology Division, February 2006, www.parl.gc.ca/information/library/PRBpubs/prb0554-e.html#aquifers

8. Environment Canada, *Water—Vulnerable to Climate Change*, www.ec.gc.ca/water/en/info/pubs/FS/e_FSA9.htm

9. Environment Canada, Informational and Resources Services, *Water—Vulnerable to Climate Change*, www.ec.gc.ca/water/en/info/pubs/FS/e_FSA9

10. Environment Canada, *Fresh Water, Bulk Removal of Water*, www.ec.gc.ca/water/en/manage/removal/e_remove.htm

11. Ramsar Convention, www.ramsar.org

12. Ramsar Convention, www.ramsar.org

13. Statistics Canada (2008) Against the flow: Which households drink bottled water? *EnviroStats*, Summer, Vol. 2, No. 2, www.statcan.ca/Daily/English/080625/d080625c.htm

14. Statistics Canada (2008) Against the flow: Which households drink bottled water? *EnviroStats*, Summer, Vol. 2, No. 2, www.statcan.ca/Daily/English/080625/d080625c.htm

15. Stamminger, R. (May/June 2006). "Is a machine more efficient than the hand?". Home energy, http://www.homeenergy.org/show/article/nav/kitchen/id/180

16. Environment Canada, *The Management of Water: Leaking Underground Storage Tanks and Pipelines*, www.ec.gc.ca/water/en/manage/poll/e_tanks.htm

17. Based partly on information from O'Connor, Dennis R. (2002) *Report of the Walkerton Inquiry: The Events of May 2000 and Related Issues*. Toronto: Government of Ontario.

18. O'Connor, Dennis R. (2002) *Report of the Walkerton Inquiry: The Events of May 2000 and Related Issues*. Toronto: Government of Ontario.

19. O'Connor, D. R. (2002) *Report of the Walkerton Inquiry: The Events of May 2000 and Related Issues*. Toronto: Government of Ontario.

20. Schindler, D. (2006) *The Myth of Abundant Canadian Water*, March, www.innovationcanada.ca/en/articles/the-myth-of-abundant-canadian-water

21. Schindler, D. (2006) *The Myth of Abundant Canadian Water*, March, www.innovationcanada.ca/en/articles/the-myth-of-abundant-canadian-water

22. University of Alberta, Faculty of Science, Department of Biological Sciences, www.biology.ualberta.ca/faculty/david_schindler/?Page=1023

23. NSERC News Releases, *David Schindler*, www.nserc.gc.ca/news/2000/aoe_schindler_e.htm

24. Schindler, D. (2006) *The Myth of Abundant Water*, Canada Foundation for Innovation, March 1, 2006; www.innovationcanada.ca/en/articles/the-myth-of-abundant-canadian-water

MyEnvironmentPlace

Go to **www.myenvironmentplace.ca** where you will find quizzes, animations, your Pearson eText, and more.

13 Marine and Coastal Systems and Fisheries

Cod fishers haul in a dwindling catch.

Upon successfully completing this chapter, you will be able to

- Identify physical, geographical, chemical, and biological aspects of the marine environment
- Describe major types of marine ecosystems
- Outline historic and current human uses of marine resources

- Assess human impacts on marine environments
- Review the current state of ocean fisheries and reasons for their decline
- Evaluate marine protected areas and reserves as innovative solutions

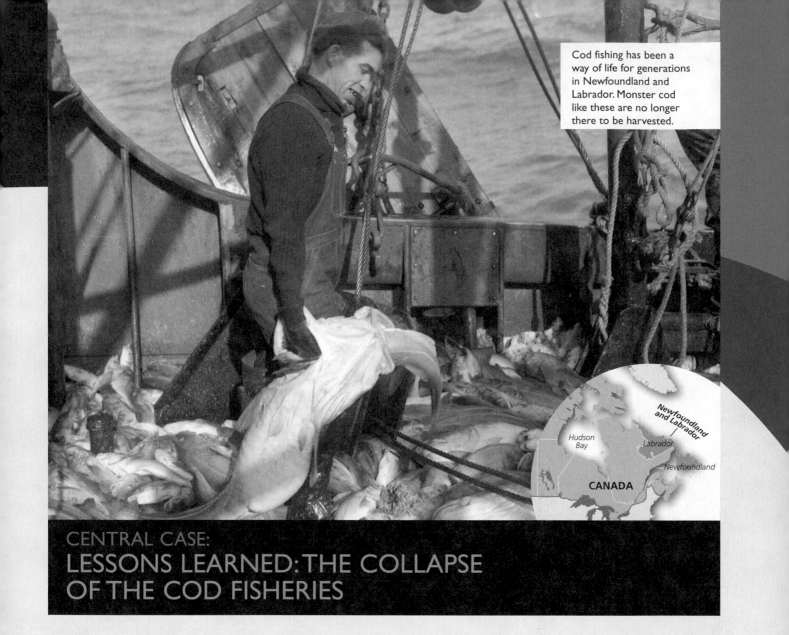

Cod fishing has been a way of life for generations in Newfoundland and Labrador. Monster cod like these are no longer there to be harvested.

CENTRAL CASE:
LESSONS LEARNED: THE COLLAPSE OF THE COD FISHERIES

"All of a sudden they just crashed."
—DONALD PAUL, NEWFOUNDLAND FISHER, IN 1997

"Either we have sustainable fisheries, or we have no fishery."
—CANADIAN FISHERIES MINISTER DAVID ANDERSON, IN 1998

No fish has had more impact on human civilization than the Atlantic cod. Europeans exploring the coasts of North America 500 years ago discovered that they could catch these abundant fish by dipping baskets over the railings of their ships, and the race to harvest this resource helped lead to the colonization of the New World. Starting in the early 1500s, schooners captured countless millions of cod, and the fish became a dietary staple on both sides of the Atlantic.

Since then, cod fishing has been the economic engine for hundreds of coastal communities in eastern Canada and New England. In many Canadian coastal villages, cod fishing has been a way of life for generations (see photo). So it came as a shock when the cod all but disappeared, and governments had to step in and close the fisheries.

The Atlantic cod (*Gadus morhua*) is a type of *groundfish*, a fish that lives or feeds along the bottom. People have long coveted groundfish, such as halibut, pollock, haddock, and flounder. Adult cod eat smaller fish and invertebrates, commonly grow to 60–70 cm long, and can live 20 years. A mature female cod can produce several million eggs.

Atlantic cod inhabit cool ocean waters on both sides of the North Atlantic and occur in 24 discrete populations, called *stocks*. One stock inhabits the Grand

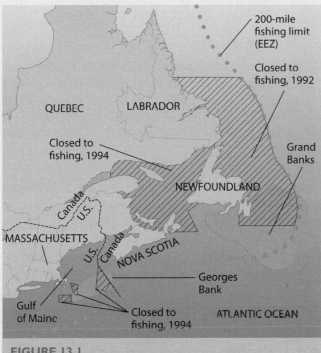

FIGURE 13.1
Ten stocks of Atlantic cod inhabit areas of the northwestern Atlantic Ocean, including the Grand Banks and Georges Bank, regions of shallow water that are especially productive for groundfish. Portions of these areas have been closed to fishing because cod populations have collapsed after being overfished.

Banks off the Newfoundland coast, and another lives on Georges Bank off Massachusetts (**FIGURE 13.1**).

The Grand Banks provided ample fish for centuries. With advancing technology, however, ships became larger and more effective at finding fish. By the 1960s, massive industrial trawlers from Europe were vacuuming up unprecedented numbers of groundfish. In 1977, Canada exercised its legal right to the waters 200 nautical miles from shore, the **Exclusive Economic Zone** established by the U.N. Convention on the Law of the Sea. Foreign fleets were expelled from most of the Grand Banks, and Canada's fishing industry was revved up like never before.

Catches began to dwindle in the 1980s. Too many fish had been taken, and trawling had destroyed much underwater habitat. Environmental factors also played a role. By 1992 the situation was dire: Scientists reported that mature cod were at just 10% of their long-term abundance. On July 2, Fisheries Minister John Crosbie announced a two-year ban on commercial cod fishing off of Newfoundland and Labrador, where the $700 million fishery supplied income to 16% of the province's

workforce. To compensate fishers, the government offered 10 weekly payments of $225, along with training for new job skills and incentives for early retirement. Over the next two years, 40 000 fishers and processing plant workers lost their jobs. Some coastal communities faced economic ruin; for generations, fishing had been their reason for being.

Cod stocks did not rebound by 1994, so the government extended the moratorium, enacted bans on all other major cod fisheries, and scrambled to offer more compensation, eventually spending more than $4 billion. In 1997–1998, Canada partially reopened some fisheries, but data soon confirmed that the stocks were not recovering. In April 2003, the cod fisheries were closed indefinitely, to recreational as well as commercial fishing. Today it remains illegal, for the most part, to fish for cod in these areas, and the Committee on the Status of Endangered Wildlife in Canada has placed Newfoundland cod populations on its endangered list. Fishers challenging the ban have been arrested, fined, and jailed.

Across the border in U.S. waters, cod stocks were collapsing in the Gulf of Maine and Georges Bank. In 1994, the National Marine Fisheries Service (NMFS) closed three prime fishing areas. Over the next several years, NMFS designed a number of regulations, but these steps were too little, too late. A 2005 report revealed that the cod were not recovering as hoped, and scientists are struggling to explain why. Research suggests that once the mature cod were eliminated, the species they preyed upon proliferated. Now those species compete with and prey on young cod, preventing the population from rebuilding.

The closures have allowed some other species to rebound. Seafloor invertebrates have begun to recover in the absence of trawling; spawning stocks of haddock and yellowtail flounder have risen; and sea scallops have increased in biomass fourteenfold in the Georges Bank fishery. Such recoveries in no-fishing areas show scientists, fishers, and policy makers that protecting areas of ocean can help save dwindling marine populations. In the Grand Banks, however, research has shown that the fundamental nature of the ecosystem has shifted from a bottom-oriented fauna to a shallow-water fauna. There are no signs that a complete recovery will ever be achievable.

The Ocean

It has been said that our planet Earth should more properly be named "Ocean." After all, ocean water covers the vast majority of our planet's surface. Moreover, the oceans strongly influence how our planet's systems work. They influence global climate, teem with biodiversity, facilitate transportation and commerce, and provide us with resources. Even landlocked areas far from the coasts are affected. The oceans provide fish for people to eat in Saskatchewan, supply oil to power cars in Ontario, and influence the weather in Manitoba. In this chapter you will learn about **oceanography**, the scientific study of the physics, chemistry, biology, and geology of the oceans.

Ocean covers most of Earth's surface

Although we generally speak of oceans (**FIGURE 13.2**) in the plural, giving each major basin a name—Pacific, Atlantic, Indian, Arctic, and Southern—all these oceans are connected, composing a single vast body of water. This one "world ocean" covers 71% of Earth's surface and contains about 97.5% of its surface water. The ocean takes up most of the hydrosphere, influences the atmosphere and lithosphere, and encompasses much of the biosphere, including at least 250 000 species. The world ocean touches and is touched by virtually every environmental system and every human endeavour.

The ocean contains more than water

Ocean water contains approximately 96.5% H_2O by mass; most of the remainder consists of ions from dissolved salts (**FIGURE 13.3**). Ocean water is salty primarily because ocean basins are the final repositories for water that runs off the land. Rivers carry sediment and dissolved salts from the continents into the ocean, as do winds. Evaporation from the ocean surface then removes pure water, leaving a higher concentration of salts. If we were able to evaporate all the water from the oceans, the empty basins would be covered with a layer of dried salt 63 m thick.

The **salinity**—basically, the saltiness—of ocean water generally ranges from 33 to 37 parts per thousand (ppt, also denoted ‰ or "per mil"), varying from place to place because of differences in evaporation, precipitation, and freshwater runoff from land and glaciers. Salinity near the

roots
SALINITY

The term **salinity** likely derives from the Latin words *salinum* ("salt cellar") or *salinae* ("salt pit"), both of which have the Latin root *sal*, meaning "salt." The suffix *-ity* derives from the Latin *-itatem*, which is used to denote a state or condition of being.

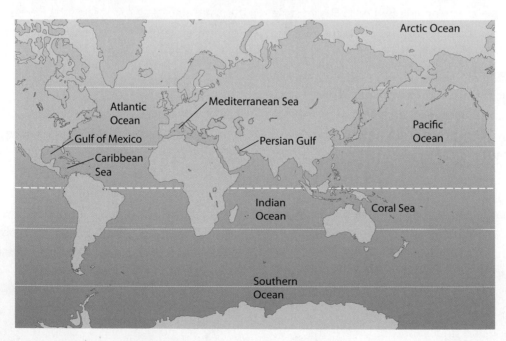

FIGURE 13.2   The world ocean is connected in a single vast body of water, with different names. The Pacific Ocean is the largest and, like the Atlantic and Indian Oceans, includes both tropical and temperate waters. The smaller Arctic and Southern Oceans include the waters in the north and south polar regions, respectively. Many smaller bodies of water are named as seas or gulfs; a selected few are shown here.

FIGURE 13.3
Ocean water consists of 3.5% salt, by mass, as shown by the proportionally thin coloured slices of the cube in this diagram. Most of this salt is NaCl in solution, so sodium and chloride ions are abundant. A number of other ions and trace elements are also present.

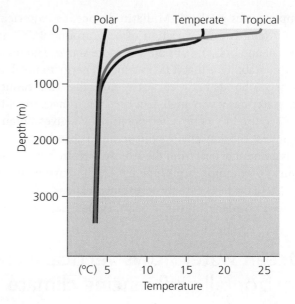

FIGURE 13.4
Ocean water varies in temperature with depth. Water temperatures near the surface are warmer because of daily heating by the Sun, and within the top 1000 m they become rapidly colder with depth. This temperature differential is greatest in the tropics because of intense solar heating and is least in the polar regions. Deep water at all latitudes is equivalent in temperature.
Source: Garrison, T. (2005). Oceanography, 5th ed. Belmont, CA: Brooks/Cole.

equator is low because this region has a great deal of precipitation, which is relatively salt free. In contrast, surface salinity is high at latitudes roughly 30–35 degrees north and south, where evaporation exceeds precipitation.

Besides the dissolved salts shown in **FIGURE 13.3**, nutrients such as nitrogen and phosphorus occur in seawater in trace amounts (well under one part per million) and play essential roles in nutrient cycling in marine ecosystems. Another aspect of ocean chemistry is dissolved gas content. Roughly 36% of the gas dissolved in seawater is oxygen, which is produced by photosynthetic plants, bacteria, and phytoplankton, and by diffusion from the atmosphere. Marine animals depend on this oxygen, and oxygen concentrations are highest in the upper layer of the ocean, reaching 13 ml/L of water.

Ocean water is vertically structured

Surface waters in tropical regions receive more solar radiation and therefore are warmer than surface waters in temperate or polar regions. In all regions, however, temperature declines with depth (**FIGURE 13.4**). Water density increases as salinity rises and as temperature

falls. These relationships give rise to different layers of water; heavier (colder and saltier) water sinks, and lighter (warmer and less salty) water remains nearer the surface. Waters of the surface zone are heated by sunlight each day and are stirred by wind such that the properties are fairly uniform throughout the zone. The salinity of surface water is influenced by a variety of interacting factors, some of which contribute to greater salinity (e.g., evaporation and sea ice formation, both of which remove freshwater from the surface layer) and some of which contribute to reduced salinity (e.g., precipitation, melting of sea ice, and the influx of river water, all of which bring freshwater into the surface layer).

Below the zone of warm, salty surface water is the **thermocline**, a zone in which temperature decreases rapidly with depth, toward the much colder deep layer. The salinity of the water also changes, increasing with depth along the *halocline*. In response to the changes in temperature and salinity, the density of the water also changes rapidly with depth, increasing along the *pycnocline*. The transitional zone marked by the thermocline, halocline, and pycnocline contains about 18% of ocean water by volume, compared with the surface zone's 2%. The remaining 80% resides in the ocean's vast deep layer. The dense, dark, cold water in this zone is sluggish and unaffected by winds, storms, sunlight, or daily temperature fluctuations.

Despite the daily heating and cooling of surface waters, ocean temperatures are much more stable than temperatures on land. Midlatitude oceans experience yearly temperature variation of only around 10°C, and tropical and polar oceans are still more stable. The reason for this stability is that it takes a lot of energy to break the hydrogen bonds between water molecules; the result is that water has a very high *heat capacity*, a measure of the heat required to increase temperature by a given amount. High heat capacity enables the ocean to absorb a tremendous amount of heat from the atmosphere. In fact, the heat content of the entire atmosphere is equal to that of just the top 2.6 m of the ocean. By absorbing heat and releasing it to the atmosphere, the ocean helps regulate Earth's climate.

Ocean water flows vertically and horizontally, influencing climate

Surface winds and heating in seawater create huge vertical flows of water, or **currents. Upwelling**, the vertical flow of cold, deep water toward the surface, occurs where horizontal currents diverge, or flow away from one another. Because upwelled water is rich in nutrients from the bottom, upwellings are often sites of high primary productivity and lucrative fisheries. Upwellings also occur where strong winds blow away from or parallel to coastlines (**FIGURE 13.5**). An example is the western coast of Vancouver Island, where north winds and the Coriolis effect move surface waters away from the shore, raising nutrient-rich water from below and creating a biologically rich region. The cold water also chills the air along the coast, giving Vancouver Island its famous cool, rainy summers.

In areas where surface currents converge, or come together, surface water sinks and **downwelling** occurs. Downwelling transports water rich in dissolved gases,

providing an influx of oxygen for deep-water life. Vertical currents also occur in the deep zone, where differences in water density can lead to rising and falling convection currents, similar to those seen in molten rock and in air.

The **thermohaline circulation** is the global oceanic circulation system of upwelling and downwelling currents. It connects surface water flows to deeper water flows, with far-reaching effects on global climate. The term *thermohaline* comes from root words that mean "heat" and "salinity." In this worldwide circulatory system, warmer, fresher water moves along the surface and water in the deep zones, which is colder, saltier, and denser, circulates far beneath the surface.

In the Atlantic Ocean, warm surface water flows northward from the equator in the Gulf Stream, carrying heat to high latitudes and keeping Europe warmer than it would otherwise be. As the surface water of this conveyor belt system releases heat energy and cools, it becomes denser and sinks, creating **North Atlantic Deep Water (NADW)**. The sinking of this cold, dense water keeps the northern part of the Atlantic basin connected to the global thermohaline circulation system; without it, the climate in areas bordering the North Atlantic would be very different (see "The Science Behind the Story: Tip Jets and NADW off the Coast of Greenland"). A similar phenomenon happens in the Southern Ocean, where extremely cold, salty water sinks to form **Antarctic Bottom Water (AABW)**. Without or with weaker thermohaline circulation, Earth would be a very different place: The climate of France would be similar to that of Newfoundland; tropical regions would become even hotter, as their heat would not be moved north by the Gulf Stream; the deep ocean could become lifeless, lacking the oxygen-rich waters provided by the thermohaline circulation; biological productivity in the Pacific and Indian Oceans would suffer, as

FIGURE 13.5
Upwelling is the movement of bottom waters upward. This type of vertical current often brings nutrients up to the surface, creating rich areas for marine life. For example, north winds blow along the western coast of Vancouver Island (1), while the Coriolis effect draws wind and water away from the coast (2). Water is then pulled up from the bottom (3) to replace the water that moves away from shore.

North

South

1 Wind blows from the north along coastline

Surface water

2 Coriolis effect causes surface water to move away from the coast

Cold, deep water rich in nutrients

Upwelling

3 Upwelling of cold, nutrient-rich water replaces surface water that has moved away from the coast

THE SCIENCE BEHIND THE STORY

Tip Jets and NADW off the coast of Greenland

Dr. Kent Moore of the University of Toronto in a research plane over the North Atlantic.

The formation of North Atlantic Deep Water (NADW), in which extremely cold water sinks in the northern part of the Atlantic to join the deep oceanic circulation, is an integral part of the global thermohaline circulation. It is also crucial for keeping the northern Atlantic basin connected to the rest of the global circulation system. If NADW formation were suppressed, the warm Gulf Stream current—responsible for the relatively mild climate of northeastern North America and Western Europe—could be cut off from entering the North Atlantic, with devastating climatic consequences for this region and globally.

Given its importance, it is surprising to learn that ocean water sinks to form NADW only under extremely specific conditions, and these conditions occur in just a handful of geographic locations in the North Atlantic. What's more, as Professor Kent Moore from the University of Toronto and his colleagues have discovered, the sinking of cold ocean water is also dependent upon highly specialized conditions in the atmosphere off the coast of Greenland.

To investigate the conditions under which NADW forms, Dr. Moore deploys scientific buoys in the North Atlantic, which measure the temperature and other characteristics of ocean water (yes, pretty much like the buoys in the first part of the movie *The Day After Tomorrow*). With data from these buoys, he is able to pinpoint the exact locations where ocean water

becomes cold and dense enough to sink, becoming NADW.

Dr. Moore, an atmospheric physicist, and colleagues have also investigated the role of the atmosphere in oceanic circulation in this part of the Atlantic. They do this by comparing satellite imagery and buoy data to information they collect by flying aboard a research plane equipped with scientific instruments for measuring a wide variety of atmospheric conditions. The aircraft, a modified four-engine passenger jet, is nicknamed FAAM (Facility for Airborne Atmospheric Measurements).

The scientists have discovered that the topography of Greenland plays a fundamental role in oceanic circulation in the North Atlantic, and specifically determines the locations where NADW circulation can be triggered. High speed wind events, with wind speeds greater than 25 m/sec, are common near the southern end of Greenland, which acts as a massive topographic barrier. The topographic barrier funnels and directs the winds in one direction or another, forming very narrow

high-speed wind streams over the adjacent ocean. These events are called *tip jets* (or *reverse tip jets*, depending on the direction of flow) and Dr. Moore describes the experience of flying through one of these high-speed wind streams as "rough."

What Dr. Moore and his colleagues have discovered, in particular, is that tip jets and related wind events are intimately associated with the formation of NADW. The high-speed winds have the effect of drawing warmth away from surface ocean water, cooling it sufficiently to increase its density and trigger sinking. The locations where this occurs are extremely localized because of the narrow channeling of winds that must pass either around or over the topographic barriers formed by the coast of Greenland.

Given the importance of NADW and the thermohaline circulation system in regulating climate, particularly around the North Atlantic, Professor Moore agrees that there is much fundamental research that needs to be carried out to improve our understanding of these atmospheric and oceanic processes and connections.

Extremely focused, high-speed wind events called tip jets, like this one off Cape Farewell on the southern coast of Greenland, are crucial in the formation of North Atlantic Deep Water because they draw heat away from surface water. In this figure, based on satellite imagery from February 2007, wind speeds are shown in metres per second.

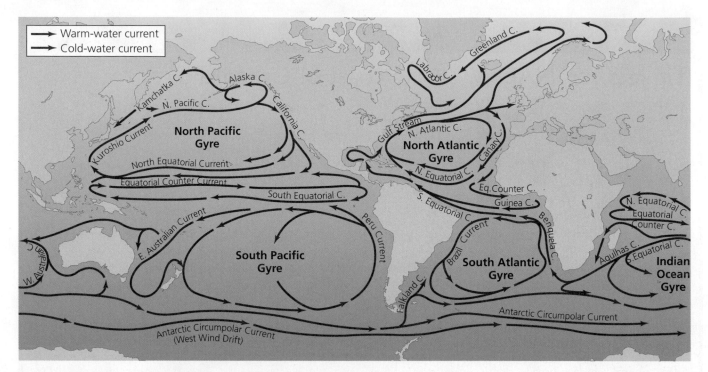

FIGURE 13.6   The upper waters of the oceans flow in currents, which are long-lasting and predictable global patterns of water movement. Warm- and cold-water currents interact with the planet's climate system, and people have used them for centuries to navigate the ocean.   *Source: Garrison, T. (2005). Oceanography, 5th ed. Belmont, CA: Brooks/Cole.*

fewer nutrients from depth would make it to the surface layer where photosynthesis happens; and the removal of greenhouse gases from the atmosphere to the deep ocean would cease, thus accelerating global climate change.

Ocean water also flows horizontally, in vast riverlike flows (**FIGURE 13.6**), driven mainly by wind systems and differences in air pressure. These surface currents flow within the upper 400 m of water, horizontally and for great distances. Long-lasting patterns in surface currents influence global climate, and play key roles in the phenomena known as El Niño and La Niña. They have also been crucial in navigation and human history; currents helped carry Polynesians to Easter Island, Darwin to the Galápagos, and Europeans to the New World. Currents transport heat, nutrients, pollution, and the larvae of many marine species from place to place.

Some horizontal surface currents are very slow; others, like the Gulf Stream, are rapid and powerful. From the Gulf of Mexico, the Gulf Stream moves up the U.S. Atlantic coast and flows past the eastern edges of Georges Bank and the Grand Banks at a rate of 160 km per day (nearly 2 m/s). Averaging 70 km across, the Gulf Stream continues across the North Atlantic, bringing warm water to Europe and moderating that continent's climate, which otherwise would be much colder.

Some of the ocean's surface currents take the form of enormous gyres. A **gyre** is an oceanic current that flows in a circular motion as a result of the *Coriolis force* (an artifact of Earth's rotation, which we will discuss in

greater detail in the chapter on atmospheric science and air pollution). There are five great gyres in the world ocean: the North Atlantic, South Atlantic, North Pacific, South Pacific, and Indian Ocean gyres (see **FIGURE 13.6**).

La Niña and El Niño demonstrate the atmosphere–ocean connection

Horizontal ocean currents can have far-reaching impacts on climate. An example is the La Niña–El Niño cycle, which demonstrates the linkages between the oceanic and atmospheric systems. Under normal conditions, prevailing winds blow from east to west along the equator, from a region of high pressure in the eastern Pacific to one of low pressure in the western Pacific, forming a large-scale convective loop, or atmospheric circulation pattern (**FIGURE 13.7A**). The winds push surface waters westward, causing water to "pile up" in the western Pacific. As a result, water near Indonesia can be 50 cm higher and 8°C warmer than water near South America. The westward-moving surface waters allow cold water to rise up from the deep in a nutrient-rich upwelling along the coast of Peru and Ecuador.

El Niño conditions are triggered when air pressure increases in the western Pacific and decreases in the eastern Pacific, causing the equatorial winds to weaken. Without these winds, the warm water that collects in the

(a) Normal conditions

(b) El Niño conditions

FIGURE 13.7
In these diagrams, red and orange colours denote warmer water, and blue and green colours denote colder water. Under normal conditions **(a)**, prevailing winds push warm surface waters toward the western Pacific. Under El Niño conditions **(b)**, the winds weaken and the warm water flows back across the Pacific toward South America, like water sloshing in a bathtub. This shuts down upwelling along the American coast and alters precipitation patterns regionally and globally.
Source: Adapted from National Oceanic and Atmospheric Administration, Tropical Atmospheric Ocean Project.

western Pacific flows eastward (**FIGURE 13.7B**), suppressing upwellings along the Pacific coast of South, Central, and North America, and shutting down the delivery of nutrients that support marine life and fisheries. Coastal industries, such as Peru's anchovy fisheries, are devastated by each El Niño event; the 1982–1983 event caused more than $8 billion in economic losses worldwide. El Niños alter weather patterns around the world, creating rainstorms and floods in areas that are generally dry (such as southern California), and causing drought and fire in regions that are typically moist (such as Indonesia). In Canada, El Niño tends to produce weather that is drier and warmer than normal, with more frequent droughts.

La Niña events are the opposite of El Niño; under these conditions, cold surface waters extend far westward in the equatorial Pacific, and weather patterns are affected in opposite ways. La Niña–influenced weather tends to be abnormally cool and wet all the way from British Columbia to southern Québec. These cycles, called the **El Niño–Southern Oscillation (ENSO)**, are periodic but irregular, occurring every two to eight years. Scientists are getting better at deciphering the triggers for these events, and predicting their impacts on weather. They are also investigating whether globally warming air and sea temperatures may be increasing the frequency and strength of these cycles.

Seafloor topography can be rugged and complex

Although oceans are depicted on most maps and globes as smooth, blue swaths, portions of the ocean floor are complex. As you learned in the context of the tectonic and rock cycles, underwater volcanoes shoot forth enough magma to build islands above sea level, such as the Hawaiian Islands. Steep canyons similar in scale to the Grand Canyon lie just offshore of some continents. The lowest spot in the oceans—the Mariana Trench in the South Pacific—is deeper than Mount Everest is high, by more than 2.1 km. Our planet's longest mountain range also is under water—the Mid-Atlantic Ridge, which runs the length of the Atlantic Ocean, is just part of it (**FIGURE 13.8**).

Georges Bank and the Grand Banks are essentially huge underwater mounds formed from the debris

FIGURE 13.8
The seafloor can be rugged. The spreading margin between tectonic plates at the Mid-Atlantic Ridge gives rise to a vast underwater volcanic mountain chain.

FIGURE 13.9
A stylized bathymetric profile shows key geologic features of the submarine environment. Shallow regions of water exist around the edges of continents over the continental shelf, which drops off at the shelf–slope break. The relatively steep dropoff called the continental slope gives way to the more gradual continental rise, all of which are underlain by sediments from the continents. Vast areas of seafloor are flat abyssal plain. Seafloor spreading occurs at oceanic ridges, and oceanic crust is subducted in trenches. Volcanic activity along trenches often gives rise to island chains, such as the Aleutian Islands. Features on the left side of this diagram are more characteristic of the Atlantic Ocean, and features on the right are more characteristic of the Pacific Ocean.
Source: Adapted from Thurman, H. V. (1990). Essentials of Oceanography, 4th ed. New York: Macmillan.

dumped by glaciers at their southernmost extent. As climate warmed and the glaciers retreated, sea level rose and this hilly terrain became submerged. The 200-nautical-mile fishing limit established by the Convention on the Law of the Sea is particularly problematic here because of the underwater topography—about 10% of the Grand Banks lies outside of Canada's Exclusive Economic Zone, which makes it very difficult to regulate the entire fishery as a system.

We can gain an understanding of underwater geographic features by examining a stylized map (**FIGURE 13.9**) that reflects *bathymetry* (the measurement of ocean depths) as well as topography. In bathymetric profile, gently sloping **continental shelves** underlie the shallow waters bordering the continents. Continental shelves vary in width from 100 m to 1300 km, averaging 70 km wide, with an average slope of 1.9 m/km. These shelves drop off with relative suddenness at the *shelf–slope break*. From there, the **continental slope** angles more steeply downward to the *continental rise*, the gentling slope that connects the continental shelf to the **abyssal plain**, the flat bottom of the deep ocean.

Most of the abyssal plain is flat, but volcanic peaks that rise above the ocean floor provide physical structure for marine animals and are often the site of productive fishing grounds. Some island chains, such as the Florida Keys, are formed by the development of reefs and lie atop the continental shelf. Others, such as the Aleutian Islands, which curve across the North Pacific from Alaska toward Russia, are volcanic in origin. The Aleutians are also the site of a deep trench that, like the Mariana Trench, formed

at a convergent tectonic plate boundary, where one slab of crust dives beneath another in the process of subduction. These trenches are the deepest places on Earth.

Marine and Coastal Ecosystems

With their variation in topography, temperature, salinity, nutrients, and sunlight, marine and coastal environments feature a variety of ecosystems. Most marine and coastal ecosystems are powered by solar energy, with sunlight driving photosynthesis by phytoplankton in the photic zone. Yet even the darkest ocean depths host life.

Regions of ocean water differ greatly, and some zones support more life than others. The uppermost 10 m of water absorb 80% of the solar energy that reaches the water's surface. For this reason, nearly all of the oceans' primary productivity occurs in the well-lit top layer, or **photic zone**. Generally, the warm, shallow waters of continental shelves are most biologically productive and support the greatest species diversity. Habitats and ecosystems occurring between the ocean's surface and floor are termed **pelagic**, whereas those that occur on the ocean floor are called **benthic**.

Open-ocean ecosystems vary in their biological diversity

Biological diversity in pelagic regions of the open ocean is highly variable in its distribution. Primary productiv-

roots

NEKTON AND PLANKTON

Nekton, referring to marine animals that actually swim, was coined by German biologist Ernst Haeckel in 1890 and was derived from the Greek *nektos*, meaning "swimming." **Plankton**, referring to microscopic organisms that float rather than swim, was coined by German physiologist Viktor Hensen in 1891 and is derived from the Greek *planktos*, meaning "wandering, drifting, roaming."

ity and animal life near the surface are concentrated in regions of nutrient-rich upwelling. Marine animals that actively swim are referred to as **nekton**. They are contrasted with **plankton**, microscopic organisms that float rather than swim, including *phytoplankton* (typically algae and other protists, rather than plants, even though the prefix *phyto-* means "plant") and *zooplankton* (animals).

Phytoplankton are particularly important, because they constitute the base of the marine food chain in the pelagic zone. These photosynthetic algae, protists, and cyanobacteria feed zooplankton, which in turn become food for nektonic fish, jellyfish, whales, and other free-swimming animals (**FIGURE 13.10**). Predators at higher trophic levels include larger fish, sea turtles, and sharks. Many fish-eating birds, such as puffins, petrels, and shearwaters, feed at the surface of the open ocean, returning periodically to nesting sites on islands and coastlines.

FIGURE 13.10
The uppermost reaches of ocean water contain billions upon billions of phytoplankton—tiny photosynthetic algae, protists, and bacteria that form the base of the marine food chain—as well as zooplankton, small animals and protists that dine on phytoplankton and comprise the next trophic level.

FIGURE 13.11
Life is scarce in the dark depths of the deep ocean, but the creatures that do live there can appear bizarre. The anglerfish lures prey toward its mouth with a bioluminescent (glowing) organ that protrudes from the front of its head.

In recent years biologists have been learning more about animals of the very deep ocean, although tantalizing questions remain. In deep-water ecosystems, animals have adapted to deal with extreme water pressures and to live in the dark without food from photosynthetic organisms. Some of these often bizarre-looking creatures scavenge carcasses or organic detritus that falls from above. Others are predators, and still others attain food from symbiotic mutualistic bacteria. Some species carry bacteria that produce light chemically by *bioluminescence* (**FIGURE 13.11**).

Some ecosystems form around hydrothermal vents, where heated water spurts from the seafloor, often carrying minerals that precipitate to form large rocky structures. Tubeworms, shrimp, and other creatures in these recently discovered systems use symbiotic bacteria to derive their energy by chemosynthesis from chemicals in the heated water, rather than from sunlight. They manage to thrive within amazingly narrow zones between scalding-hot and icy cold water.

Shallow-water systems are highly productive

Large brown algae, or **kelp**, grow from the floor of continental shelves, reaching upward toward the sunlit surface. Some kelp reaches 60 m in height and can grow 45 cm in a single day. Dense stands of kelp form underwater "forests" along many temperate coasts (**FIGURE 13.12**). Kelp forests supply shelter and food for invertebrates and fish, which in turn provide food for higher trophic level predators, such

FIGURE 13.12
"Forests" of tall brown algae known as *kelp* grow from the floor of the continental shelf. Numerous fish and other creatures eat kelp or find refuge among its fronds.

as seals and sharks. Sea otters, a keystone species, control sea urchin populations; when otters disappear, urchins overgraze the kelp, destroying the forests and creating "urchin barrens." Kelp forests also absorb wave energy and protect shorelines from erosion. People eat some types of kelp, and kelp provides compounds known as alginates, which serve as thickeners in a wide range of consumer products, including cosmetics, paints, paper, and soaps. In shallow subtropical and tropical waters, coral reefs occur. A **coral reef** is a mass of calcium carbonate composed of the skeletons of tiny colonial marine organisms. A coral reef may occur as an extension of a shoreline, along a barrier island paralleling a shoreline, or as an *atoll*, a ring around a submerged island.

Corals themselves are tiny invertebrate animals related to sea anemones and jellyfish. They remain attached to rock or existing reef and capture passing food with stinging tentacles. Corals also derive nourishment from microscopic symbiotic algae, known as *zooxanthellae*, which inhabit their bodies and produce food

through photosynthesis. Most corals are colonial, and the colourful surface of a coral reef consists of millions of densely packed individuals. As the corals die, their skeletons remain part of the reef while new corals grow atop them, increasing the reef's size.

Like kelp forests, coral reefs protect shorelines by absorbing wave energy. They also host tremendous biodiversity (**FIGURE 13.13A**). Reefs provide complex physical structure (and thus many varied habitats) in shallow nearshore waters, which are regions of high primary productivity. Besides the staggering diversity of anemones, sponges, hydroids, tubeworms, and other sessile (stationary) invertebrates, innumerable molluscs, flatworms, sea stars, and urchins patrol the reefs, while thousands of fish species find food and shelter in reef nooks and crannies.

Coral reefs are experiencing worldwide declines, however. Many have undergone **coral bleaching**, a process

(a) Coral reef community

(b) Bleached coral

FIGURE 13.13
Corals reefs provide food and shelter for a tremendous diversity **(a)** of fish and other creatures. However, these reefs face multiple environmental stresses from human impacts, and many corals have died as a result of coral bleaching **(b)**, in which corals lose their zooxanthellae. Such bleaching is evident in the whitened portion of this coral.

that occurs when the coloured symbiotic zooxanthellae leave the coral, depriving it of nutrition. Corals lacking zooxanthellae lose colour and frequently die, leaving behind ghostly white patches in the reef (**FIGURE 13.13B**). Coral bleaching is not entirely understood. For example, it is not known exactly why the zooxanthellae leave during coral bleaching—or even *if* they leave; it has been hypothesized, alternatively, that they may lose their pigmentation (hence the "bleaching"), possibly as a result of *photodamage* caused by exposure to ultraviolet radiation.[1]

Coral bleaching may result from stress caused by increased sea surface temperatures associated with global climate change, from changes in light levels in some shallow-water areas, from an influx of pollutants, or from some combination of these and other unknown factors, both natural and anthropogenic. In addition, coral reefs sustain significant damage when divers stun fish with cyanide or by throwing explosives over the side of the boat, a common fishing and fish collection practice (for the pet trade) in the waters of Indonesia and the Philippines. Tourism also has been a significant burden on coral reefs globally; each scuba diver who breaks off a small piece of a reef contributes to its demise. Even with the advent of ecotourism, which of course advocates taking only photographs, the traffic of

divers' feet and hands on the reefs continues to take a toll. Finally, as global climate change proceeds, the oceans are becoming more acidic, as excess carbon dioxide from the atmosphere reacts with seawater to form carbonic acid. Acidification threatens to deprive corals of the carbonate ions they need to produce their structural parts.

A few coral species without symbiotic algae thrive in waters outside the tropics and build reefs on the ocean floor at depths of 200–500 m. These little-known reefs, which occur in cold-water areas off the coasts of Norway, Spain, the British Isles, and elsewhere, are only now beginning to be studied by scientists. Already, however, many have been badly damaged by trawling—the same practice that has so degraded the benthic habitats of groundfish, such as the Atlantic cod. Norway and other countries are now beginning to protect some of these deep-water reefs.

Intertidal zones undergo constant change

Where the ocean meets the land, **intertidal** or **littoral** ecosystems (**FIGURE 13.14**) spread between the uppermost

Tidal zones

— Supratidal zone (splash zone)

— Level of high tide

— Intertidal zone

— Level of low tide

— Subtidal zone

FIGURE 13.14 The rocky intertidal zone is the swath of a rocky shoreline between the lowest and highest reaches of the tides. This is an ecosystem rich in biodiversity, typically containing large invertebrates, such as sea stars (starfish), barnacles, crabs, sea anemones, corals, bryozoans, snails, limpets, chitons, mussels, nudibranchs (sea slugs), and sea urchins. Fish swim in tidal pools, and many types of algae cover the rocks. Areas higher on the shoreline are exposed to the air more frequently and for longer periods, so organisms that can best tolerate exposure specialize in the upper intertidal zone. The lower intertidal zone is exposed less frequently and for shorter periods, so organisms less able to tolerate exposure thrive in this zone.

reach of the high tide and the lowest limit of the low tide. **Tides** are the periodic rising and falling of the ocean's height at a given location, caused by the gravitational pull of the Moon and Sun. High and low tides occur roughly six hours apart, so intertidal organisms spend part of each day submerged in water, part of the day exposed to the air and sunlight, and part of the day being lashed by waves. Subject to tremendous extremes in temperature, moisture, light exposure, and salinity, these creatures must also protect themselves from marine predators at high tide and terrestrial predators—even opportunistic predators like crows, seagulls, and raccoons—at low tide.

The intertidal environment is a tough place to make a living, but it is home to a remarkable diversity of organisms. Rocky shorelines can be full of life among the crevices, which provide shelter and pools of water (*tidepools*) during low tides. Sessile animals, such as anemones, mussels, and barnacles, live attached to rocks, filter-feeding on plankton in the water that washes over them. Urchins, sea slugs, chitons, and limpets eat intertidal algae or scrape food from the rocks. Sea stars (starfish) creep slowly along, preying on the filter-feeders and herbivores at high tide. Crabs clamber around the rocks, scavenging detritus.

The rocky intertidal zone is so diverse because environmental conditions, such as temperature, salinity, and moisture, change dramatically from the high to the low reaches. This environmental variation gives rise to horizontal bands formed by dominant organisms as they array themselves according to their habitat needs. Sandy intertidal areas, such as those of Cape Cod, host less biodiversity, yet plenty of organisms burrow into the sand at low tide to await the return of high tide, when they emerge to feed.

Coastal ecosystems protect shorelines

Along many of the world's coasts at temperate latitudes, **salt marshes** occur where the tides wash over gently sloping sandy or silty substrates. Rising and falling tides flow into and out of channels called *tidal creeks* and at highest tide spill over onto elevated marsh flats (**FIGURE 13.15**).

Salt marshes boast very high primary productivity and provide critical habitat for shorebirds, waterfowl, and the adults and young of many commercially important fish and shellfish species. Salt marshes also filter out pollution (hence the use of constructed or artificial wetlands for wastewater management). Coastal marshes stabilize shorelines against **storm surges**, temporary increases in sea level that accompany the low atmospheric pressures of intense storms, and storm waves, the very wind-driven large waves that crash onto the shore during a major

FIGURE 13.15

Salt marshes, like the Malbay salt marsh in the Gaspé Peninsula, shown here, occur in temperate intertidal zones where the substrate is muddy, allowing salt-adapted grasses to grow. Tidal waters generally flow through marshes in channels called *tidal creeks*, amid flat areas called *benches*, sometimes partially submerging the grasses.

storm. However, people like to live along coasts, and coastal sites are desirable for commerce. As a result, vast expanses of salt marshes have been altered to make way for coastal development. When salt marshes are destroyed, we lose the ecosystem services they provide. When Hurricane Katrina struck the Gulf Coast of Louisiana, for instance, the flooding was made worse because vast areas of salt marshes had vanished because of development, subsidence from oil and gas drilling, and dams that had held back marsh-building sediment. In tropical and subtropical latitudes, mangrove forests replace salt marshes along gently sloping sandy and silty coasts. The **mangrove** is a tree with a unique type of root system that curves upward (like a snorkel) to obtain oxygen lacking in the mud in which the tree grows, and curves downward like stilts to support the tree in changing water levels (**FIGURE 13.16**). Fish, shellfish, crabs, snakes, and other organisms thrive among the root networks, and birds feed and nest in the dense foliage of these coastal forests. Besides serving as nurseries for fish and shellfish that people harvest, mangroves also provide materials that people use for food, medicine, tools, and construction.

Mangrove forests in tropical areas have been destroyed as people have developed coastal areas for residential, commercial, and recreational uses. Shrimp farming in particular has driven the conversion of large areas of mangroves. We have eliminated half the world's mangrove forests, and their area continues to decline by 2%–8% per year. When mangroves are removed, coastal areas lose the ability to slow runoff, filter pollutants, and retain soil. As a result, offshore systems, such as coral reefs, are more readily degraded.

Moreover, mangrove forests protect coastal communities against storm surges and tsunamis (tidal waves), as

FIGURE 13.16
Mangrove forests are important ecosystems along tropical and subtropical coastlines throughout the world. Mangrove trees, such as these at Lizard Island, Australia, show specialized adaptations for growing in saltwater and provide habitat for many types of fish, birds, crabs, and other animals.

was shown when the 2004 Indian Ocean tsunami devastated areas where mangroves had been removed but caused less damage where mangroves were intact. The loss of coastal mangroves may also have played a role in the scale of devastation from Hurricane Nargus in Burma (Myanmar), a disaster that was greatly exacerbated by political stubbornness after the fact. Despite these important ecosystem services provided by mangroves, we have granted only about 1% of the world's remaining mangroves protection against development.

Freshwater meets saltwater in estuaries

Many salt marshes and mangrove forests occur in or near **estuaries**, water bodies where rivers flow into the ocean, mixing freshwater with saltwater. Estuaries are biologically productive ecosystems that experience fluctuations in salinity as tides and freshwater runoff vary daily and seasonally. For shorebirds and for many commercially important shellfish species, estuaries provide critical habitat. For *anadromous* fishes (fishes, such as salmon,

weighing the issues

COASTAL DEVELOPMENT

A developer wants to build a large marina on an estuary in your coastal town. The marina would boost the town's economy but eliminate its salt marshes. As a homeowner living adjacent to the marshes, how would you respond?

that spawn in freshwater and mature in saltwater), estuaries provide a transitional zone where young fish make the passage from freshwater to saltwater.

Estuaries around the world have been affected by urban and coastal development, water pollution, habitat alteration, and overfishing. The Gaspé Peninsula of Québec—where the St. Lawrence River flows into the Gulf of St. Lawrence and from there into the Atlantic Ocean—is one area in Canada where estuaries and salt marshes are important ecosystems. Florida Bay, where freshwater from the Everglades system mixes with saltwater, provides another example. This estuary has suffered pollution and a reduction in freshwater flow caused by irrigation and fertilizer use by sugarcane farmers, housing development, septic tank leakage, and other human impacts. Coastal ecosystems have borne the brunt of human impact because two-thirds of Earth's people choose to live within about 150 km of the ocean.

Human Use and Impact

Our species has a long history of interacting with the ocean. We have long travelled across ocean waters, clustered our settlements along coastlines, and been fascinated by the beauty, power, and vastness of the seas. We have also left our mark upon them by exploiting the ocean for resources and polluting the waters with our waste.

The ocean provides transportation routes

We have used the ocean for transportation for thousands of years, and the ocean continues to provide affordable means of moving people and products over vast distances. Ocean shipping has accelerated the global reach of some cultures and has promoted interaction among long-isolated peoples. It has had substantial impacts on the environment as well. The thousands of ships plying the world's oceans today carry everything from cod to cargo containers to crude oil. Ships transport ballast water, which, when discharged at ports of destination, may transplant aquatic organisms picked up at ports of departure. Some of these species, such as the zebra mussel, establish themselves and become invasive.

We extract energy and minerals

We mine the ocean for commercially valuable energy. Worldwide, about 30% of our crude oil and nearly half of our natural gas come from seafloor deposits. Most offshore oil and gas is concentrated in petroleum-rich regions, such as the North Sea and the Gulf of Mexico, but energy companies extract smaller amounts of oil and gas from diverse locations, among them the Grand Banks and adjacent Canadian waters. Proposals to drill for oil and gas in Georges Bank, however, have been stalled until recently by the Canadian government, in large part because of fears that spilled oil could damage the region's valuable fisheries.

Ocean sediments also contain a novel potential source of fossil fuel energy. **Methane hydrate** is an icelike solid consisting of molecules of methane (CH_4, the main component of natural gas) embedded in a crystal lattice of water molecules. Methane hydrates are stable at temperature and pressure conditions found in many sediments on the Arctic seafloor and the continental shelves. It is estimated that the world's deposits of methane hydrates may hold twice as much carbon as all known deposits of oil, coal, and natural gas combined.

Could methane hydrates be developed as an energy source to power our civilization through the twenty-first century and beyond? Perhaps, but a great deal of research remains before scientists and engineers can be sure how to extract these energy sources safely. Destabilizing a methane hydrate deposit could lead to a catastrophic release of gas. This could cause a massive landslide and tsunami, and would release huge amounts of methane, a potent greenhouse gas, into the atmosphere, exacerbating global climate change.

Fortunately, the ocean also holds potential for providing renewable energy sources that do not emit greenhouse gases. Engineers have developed ways of harnessing energy from waves, tides, and the heat of ocean water. These promising energy sources await further research, development, and investment.

We can extract minerals from the ocean floor, as well. By using large vacuum cleaner–like hydraulic dredges, miners collect sand and gravel from beneath the sea. Also extracted are sulphur from salt deposits in the Gulf of Mexico and phosphorite from offshore areas near the California coast and elsewhere. Other valuable minerals found on or beneath the seafloor include calcium carbonate (used in making cement) and silica (used as fire-resistant insulation and in manufacturing glass), as well as rich deposits of manganese, copper, zinc, silver, and gold ore. Many minerals are concentrated in manganese nodules, small ball-shaped accretions that are scattered across parts of the ocean floor. More than 1.5 trillion tonnes of manganese nodules may exist in the Pacific Ocean alone, and their reserves of metal may exceed all terrestrial reserves.

The logistical difficulty of mining the ocean floor has kept it only marginally economical or uneconomical so far, but that is changing very rapidly. A Canadian company called Nautilus Minerals has developed approaches that make use of existing offshore oil exploration technologies to mine the seafloor. In 2010 it opened the world's first underwater gold, silver, copper, and zinc mine, offshore from Papua New Guinea.

Seafloor mineral development has been one of the most controversial factors in the very long history of attempts to convene a comprehensive, binding Law of the Sea, an international legal discussion that actually began as early as the 1600s. To this day, the United States abstains from participating in some aspects of the Law of the Sea, primarily because of proposed restrictions on seafloor mining. The existing Law of the Sea, or **United Nations Convention on the Law of the Sea (UNCLOS)**, is based on a series of international conferences that took place between 1973 and 1982. This version of UNCLOS established the 200-nautical-mile Exclusive Economic Zones of nations (replacing the previous 12-mile zone), which greatly enhanced the ability of nations to control and manage their own coastal zones.

Marine pollution threatens resources and marine life

People have long used the ocean as a sink for waste and pollution. Even into the mid-twentieth century, it was common for coastal cities to dump trash and untreated sewage along their shores. Halifax only began to treat municipal sewage outflow into Halifax Harbour—approximately 181 million litres per day[2]—in the early 2000s. A surprising number of Canadian towns continue to discharge raw sewage into coastal and inland waters, even today. Fort Bragg, a bustling town on the northern

Californian coast, boasts of its Glass Beach, an area where beachcombers collect sea glass, the colourful surf-polished glass sometimes found on beaches after storms. But Glass Beach is in fact the site of the former town dump, and besides well-polished glass, the perceptive visitor may also spot old batteries, rusting car frames, and other trash protruding from the bluffs above the beach.

Oil, plastic, industrial chemicals, and excess nutrients all eventually make their way from land into the oceans. Raw sewage and trash from cruise ships and abandoned fishing gear from fishing boats add to the input. The scope of trash in the sea can be gauged by the amount picked up each September by volunteers who trek beaches in the Ocean Conservancy's International Coastal Cleanup. In this nonprofit organization's 25th annual cleanup, almost 500 000 people from more than 100 nations picked up 16 million kilograms of trash.

Plastic bags and bottles, cigarette butts, discarded fishing nets, gloves, fishing line, buckets, floats, abandoned cargo, and much else that people transport on the sea or deposit into it can harm marine organisms. Because most plastic is not biodegradable, it can drift for decades before washing up on beaches. Marine mammals, seabirds, fish, and sea turtles may mistake floating plastic debris for food and can die as a result of ingesting material they cannot digest or expel. Fishing nets and crab and lobster traps that are lost or intentionally discarded can continue snaring animals for decades (**FIGURE 13.17**). The "Great Pacific Garbage Patch" is a large mass of plastics and other anthropogenic debris (roughly 20 million km^2) that is floating in the pelagic zone, trapped in the circular currents of the North Pacific gyre. Its existence and extent were documented in 1988 by the U.S. National Oceanic and Atmospheric Administration.

Of 115 marine mammal species, 49 are known to have eaten or become entangled in marine debris, and 111 of 312 species of seabirds are known to ingest plastic. All five species of sea turtle in the Gulf of Mexico have died from consuming or contacting marine debris. Marine debris affects people, as well. Surveys of fishers have shown that more than half have encountered equipment damage and other problems from plastic debris.

Corals and other marine organisms that build their shells out of calcium carbonate ($CaCO_3$) also are susceptible to negative effects from **ocean acidification**. This refers to a decrease in the acidity (pH) of ocean water caused by the uptake of atmospheric carbon dioxide by surface water. Carbon dioxide mixed with water can react to form carbonic acid, which can cause calcium carbonate shells to dissolve. The carbon dioxide content of the atmosphere is increasing, and this increase appears to be causing ocean acidification. Surface ocean water, acting as a "sink" for carbon dioxide, may therefore mitigate some changes in the chemistry of the atmosphere that are associated with global climate change, but with potentially serious negative consequences for corals and other marine organisms.

Oil pollution comes from many sources

Major oil spills, such as the *Exxon Valdez* spill in Prince William Sound, Alaska, and the massive BP *Deepwater Horizon* spill of 2010 in the Gulf of Mexico, make headlines and cause serious environmental problems. However, the majority of oil pollution in the oceans comes not from large spills in a few particular locations but from the accumulation of innumerable, widely spread small sources (non-point sources), including leakage from small boats and runoff from human activities on land. Moreover, the amount of petroleum spilled into the oceans in a typical year is equalled by the amount that seeps into the water from naturally occurring seafloor deposits (**FIGURE 13.18**). (This was not the case in 2010, when the massive spill from the BP *Deepwater Horizon* rig exceeded all other human sources of oil spilled that year.)

Minimizing the amount of oil we release into coastal waters is important, because petroleum pollution is detrimental to marine life and to our economies. Petroleum can physically coat and kill marine organisms and can poison them when ingested. In response to headline-grabbing oil spills, governments worldwide have begun to implement more stringent safety standards for tankers, such as requiring industry to pay for tugboat escorts in sensitive and hazardous coastal waters, double hulls to preclude punctures, and the development of prevention

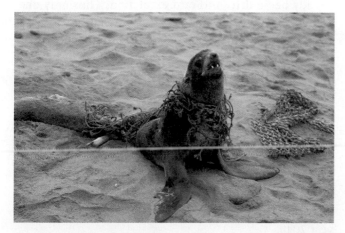

FIGURE 13.17
This northern fur seal became entangled in a discarded fishing net. Each year, many thousands of marine mammals, birds, and turtles are killed by plastic debris, abandoned nets, and other trash that people have dumped in the ocean.

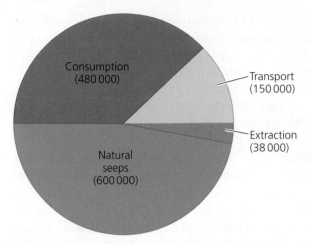

Sources of petroleum input into oceans (metric tonnes)

FIGURE 13.18
Of the 1.3 million metric tonnes of petroleum entering the world's oceans in a typical year, nearly half is from natural seeps. Petroleum consumption by people accounts for 38% of total input, and this includes numerous diffuse non-point sources, especially runoff from rivers and coastal communities and leakage from two-stroke engines. Spills during petroleum transport account for 12%, and leakage during petroleum extraction accounts for 3%. For comparison, in 2010 the BP *Deepwater Horizon* spill released about 800 000 metric tonnes of oil into the Gulf of Mexico.
Source: Data from National Research Council. (2003). Oil in the Sea III. Inputs, Fates, and Effects. *Washington, DC: National Academies Press.*

and response plans for major spills. The oil industry has resisted many such safeguards. Today, the ship that oiled Prince William Sound is still plying the world's oceans, renamed the *Sea River Mediterranean* and still featuring only a single hull.

Pollutants can contaminate seafood

Marine pollution can make some fish and shellfish unsafe for people to eat. One prime concern today is mercury contamination. Mercury is a toxic heavy metal that is emitted in coal combustion and from other sources. After settling onto land and water, mercury bioaccumulates in animals' tissues and biomagnifies as it makes its way up the food chain. As a result, fish and shellfish at high trophic levels can contain substantial levels of mercury. Eating seafood high in mercury is particularly dangerous for young children and for pregnant or nursing mothers, because the fetus, baby, or child can suffer neurological damage as a result.

Pollution from fertilizer runoff or other nutrient inputs can spur unusually rapid growth of phytoplankton, causing eutrophication and hypoxia. Excessive nutrient concentrations sometimes give rise to popula-

tion explosions among several species of marine algae that produce powerful toxins that attack the nervous systems of vertebrates. Blooms of these algae occur periodically on both the east and west coasts of Canada. Some algal species produce reddish pigments that discolour surface waters, and blooms of these species are nicknamed **red tides** (**FIGURE 13.19**). Harmful algal blooms can cause illness and death among zooplankton, birds, fish, marine mammals, and people as their toxins are passed up the food chain. They also cause economic loss for communities dependent on fishing or beach tourism. Reducing nutrient runoff into coastal waters can lessen the frequency of these outbreaks. When they occur, we can minimize their health impacts by monitoring to prevent human consumption of affected organisms.

As severe as the impacts of marine pollution can be, however, most marine scientists concur that the more worrisome dilemma is overharvesting. Unfortunately, the old cliché that "there are always more fish in the sea" is not true; the ocean today has been overfished, and like the groundfish of the Northwest Atlantic, many stocks have been largely depleted.

Emptying the Ocean

The ocean and its biological resources have provided for human needs for thousands of years, but today we are placing unprecedented pressure on marine resources. Half the world's marine fish populations are fully exploited, meaning that we cannot harvest them more intensively without depleting them, according to the U.N. Food and Agriculture Organization (FAO). An additional one-quarter of marine fish populations are overexploited and already being driven toward extinction. Thus only one-quarter of the world's marine fish populations can yield more than they are already yielding without being driven into decline.

The total global fisheries catch, after decades of increases, levelled off after about 1988 (**FIGURE 13.20**), despite increased fishing effort. Fishery collapses, such as those off Newfoundland and Labrador and New England, are ecologically devastating and also take a severe economic toll on human communities that depend on fishing. If current trends continue, predicted a comprehensive 2006 study in the journal *Science*, populations of *all* ocean species that we fish for today will collapse by the year 2048.

As our population grows, we will become even more dependent on the oceans' bounty. This makes it vital, say many scientists and fisheries managers, that we turn immediately to more sustainable fishing practices.

(a) Dinoflagellate (*Gymnodinium*)

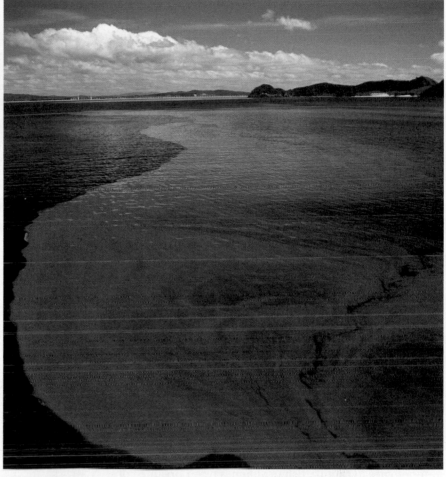

FIGURE 13.19
In a harmful algal bloom, certain types of algae multiply to great densities in surface waters, producing toxins that can bioaccumulate and harm organisms. Red tides are a type of harmful algal bloom in which the algae, such as dinoflagellates of the genus *Gymnodinium* **(a)**, produce pigment that turns the water red **(b)**.

(b) Red tide, Gulf of Carpentaria, Australia

We have long overfished

People have always harvested fish, shellfish, turtles, seals, and other animals from the oceans. Although much of this harvesting was sustainable, scientists are learning that people began depleting some marine species centuries or millennia ago. Overfishing then accelerated during the colonial period of European expansion and intensified further in the twentieth century.

A recent synthesis of historical evidence reveals that ancient overharvesting likely affected ecosystems in ways we only partially understand today. Several large animals, including the Caribbean monk seal, Steller's sea cow, and Atlantic grey whale, were hunted to extinction prior to the twentieth century—before scientists were able to study them or the ecological roles they played. Overharvesting of the vast oyster beds of the Chesapeake Bay led to the collapse of its oyster fishery in the late nineteenth century.

World capture and aquaculture production

China
World excluding China

FIGURE 13.20
The total global fisheries catch has increased over the past half-century, but in recent years growth has stalled, and many fear that a global catch decline is imminent if conservation measures are not taken soon. The figure shows trends with and without data on China's substantial fishing industry, which had been withheld from international scrutiny for many years.
Source: Data from U.N. Food and Agricultural Organization (FAO), 2009.

Eutrophication and hypoxia resulted, because there are no longer oysters to filter algae and bacteria from the water. In the Caribbean, green sea turtles ate sea grass and likely kept it cropped low, like a lawn. But with today's turtle population a fraction of what it was, sea grass grows thickly, dies, and rots, giving rise to disease, such as sea grass wasting disease, which ravaged sea grass in the 1980s. The best-known case of historical overharvesting is the near-extinction of many species of whales. This resulted from commercial whaling that began centuries ago and was curtailed only in 1986. Since then, some species have been recovering, but others have not.

Groundfish in the Northwest Atlantic historically were so abundant that the people who harvested them never imagined they could be depleted. Yet careful historical analysis of fishing records has revealed that even in the nineteenth century, fishers repeatedly experienced locally dwindling catches and each time needed to introduce some new approach or technology to extend their reach and restore their catch rate.

Fishing has become industrialized

Today's commercial fishing fleets are highly industrialized, employing fossil fuels, huge vessels, and powerful new technologies to capture fish in volumes never dreamed of by nineteenth-century mariners. So-called *factory fishing* vessels even process and freeze their catches while at sea. The global reach of today's fleets makes our impacts much more rapid and intensive than in past centuries.

The modern fishing industry uses a number of methods to capture fish at sea. Some vessels set out long *driftnets* that span large expanses of water (**FIGURE 13.21A**). These strings of nets are arrayed strategically to drift with currents so as to capture passing fish, and are held vertical by floats at the top and weights at the bottom. Driftnetting usually targets species that traverse the open water in immense schools (flocks), such as herring, sardines, and mackerel. Specialized forms of driftnetting are used for sharks, shrimp, and other animals.

Longline fishing (**FIGURE 13.21B**) involves setting out extremely long lines with up to several thousand baited hooks spaced along their lengths. Tuna and swordfish are among the species targeted by longline fishing.

Trawling entails dragging immense cone-shaped nets through the water, with weights at the bottom and floats at the top to keep the nets open. Trawling in open water captures pelagic fish, whereas *bottom-trawling* (**FIGURE 13.21C**) involves dragging weighted nets across the floor of the continental shelf to catch groundfish and other benthic organisms, such as scallops.

(a) Driftnetting

(b) Longlining

(c) Bottom-trawling

FIGURE 13.21
Commercial fishing fleets use several main methods of capture. In driftnetting **(a)**, huge nets are set out to drift through the open water to capture schools of fish. In longlining **(b)**, lines with numerous baited hooks are set out in open water. In bottom-trawling **(c)**, weighted nets are dragged along the floor of the continental shelf. All methods result in the capture of nontarget animals. The illustrations above are schematic for clarity and do not capture the immense scale that these technologies can attain; for instance, industrial trawling nets can be large enough to engulf multiple jumbo jets.

Some fishing practices kill nontarget animals and damage ecosystems

Unfortunately, some fishing practices catch more than just the species they target. **By-catch** refers to the accidental capture of animals, and it accounts for the deaths of many thousands of fish, sharks, marine mammals, and birds each year. For example, the FAO reports that in South and Central American shrimp fisheries in the 1990s, for each 1 kg of shrimp caught, 10–33 kg of other animals were caught; 30% of the by-catch was used, while the rest was discarded as trash.[3]

Driftnetting captures substantial numbers of dolphins, seals, and sea turtles, as well as countless nontarget fish. Most of these end up drowning (mammals and turtles need to surface to breathe) or dying from air exposure on deck (fish breathe through gills in the water). Many nations have banned or restricted driftnetting because of excessive by-catch. The widespread death of dolphins in driftnets motivated consumer efforts to label tuna as "dolphin-safe" if its capture uses methods designed to avoid dolphin by-catch. Such measures helped reduce dolphin deaths from an estimated 133 000 per year in 1986 to fewer than 2000 per year since 1998.

Similar by-catch problems exist with longline fishing, which kills turtles, sharks, and albatrosses, magnificent seabirds with wingspans up to 3.6 m. Several methods are being developed to limit by-catch from longline fishing, but an estimated 300 000 seabirds of various species die each year when they become caught on hooks while trying to ingest bait.

Bottom-trawling can destroy entire communities and ecosystems. The weighted nets crush organisms in their path and leave long swaths of damaged sea bottom. Trawling is especially destructive to structurally complex areas, such as reefs, that provide shelter and habitat for many animals. In recent years, underwater photography has begun to reveal the extent of structural and ecological disturbance done by trawling (**FIGURE 13.22**). Trawling is often likened to clear-cutting and strip-mining, and in heavily fished areas, the bottom may be damaged more than once. At Georges Bank, it is estimated that the average expanse of bottom has been trawled three times.

We can see the effects of large-scale industrialized fishing in the catch records of groundfish from the Northwest Atlantic. Although cod had been harvested since the 1500s on the Grand Banks, catches more than doubled once immense industrial trawlers from Europe, Japan, and the United States appeared in the 1960s (**FIGURE 13.23A**). These record-high catches lasted only a decade; the industrialized approach removed so many fish that the stock has not recovered. Likewise, on Georges Bank, cod catches rose greatly in the 1960s, remained high for 30 years, and then collapsed (**FIGURE 13.23B**).

Throughout the world's oceans, today's industrialized fishing fleets are depleting marine populations quickly. In a 2003 study, Canadian fisheries biologists Ransom Myers and Boris Worm analyzed fisheries data from FAO archives, looking for changes in the catch rates of fish in various regions of ocean since they were first exploited by industrialized fishing. For one region after another, they found the same pattern: Catch rates dropped precipitously, with 90% of large-bodied fish and sharks eliminated within only a decade (**FIGURE 13.24**). Following that, populations stabilized at 10% of their former levels. This means, Myers and Worm concluded, that the oceans today contain only one-tenth of the large-bodied animals they once did.

(a) Before trawling

(b) After trawling

FIGURE 13.22 Bottom-trawling causes severe structural damage to reefs and benthic habitats, and it can decimate underwater communities and ecosystems. A photo of an untrawled location **(a)** on the seafloor of Indonesia shows bottom-dwelling fish and a vibrant and diverse coral reef community. A photo of a trawled location **(b)** nearby shows a flattened and lifeless expanse of broken coral.

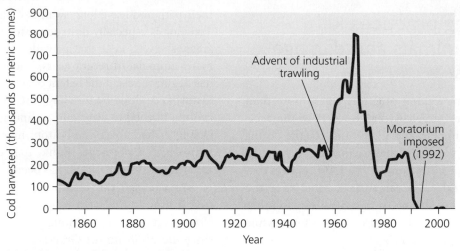

(a) Cod harvested from Grand Banks

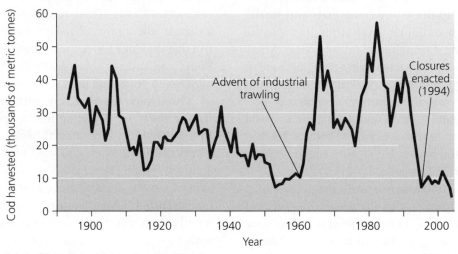

(b) Cod harvested from Georges Bank

FIGURE 13.23   In the North Atlantic off the coast of Newfoundland and Labrador, commercial catches of Atlantic cod **(a)** increased with intensified fishing by industrial trawlers in the 1960s and 1970s. The fishery subsequently crashed, and moratoria imposed in 1992 and 2003 have not brought it back. A similar pattern is seen in the cod catches at Georges Bank **(b)**; industrial fishing produced 30 years of high catches, followed by a collapse and the closure of some areas to fishing. Note also that in each case, there is one peak before 1977 and one after 1977. The first peak and decline resulted from foreign fishing fleets, whereas the second peak and decline resulted from Canadian and U.S. fleets, respectively, after they laid claim to their 200-nautical-mile Exclusive Economic Zones.   *Source: Data in (a) from Millennium Ecosystem Assessment, 2005. Data in (b) from O'Brien, et al. 2005. Georges Bank Atlantic Cod. In Mayo, R. K. and M. Terceiro, eds. Assessment of 19 Northeast Groundfish Stocks Through 2004. Woods Hole, MA: Northeast Fisheries Science Center.*

As we have seen, when animals at high trophic levels are removed from a food web, the proliferation of their prey can alter the nature of the entire community. Many scientists now conclude that most marine communities may have been very different prior to industrial fishing.

Several factors mask declines

Although industrialized fishing has depleted fish stocks in region after region, the overall global catch has remained roughly stable for two decades (see **FIGURE 13.20**). The seeming stability of the total global catch can be explained by several factors that mask population declines. One is that fishing fleets have been travelling longer distances to reach less-fished portions of the ocean. They also have been fishing in deeper waters; average depth of catches was 150 m in 1970 and 250 m in 2000. Moreover, fishing fleets have been spending more time fishing and have been setting out more nets and lines—expending increasing effort just to catch the same number of fish.

Improved technology also helps explain large catches despite declining stocks. Today's Japanese, European, Canadian, and U.S. fleets can reach almost any spot on the globe with vessels that attain speeds of 80 km/h. They have access to an array of technologies that militaries have developed for spying and for chasing enemy submarines, including advanced sonar mapping equipment, satellite navigation, and thermal sensing systems. Some fleets

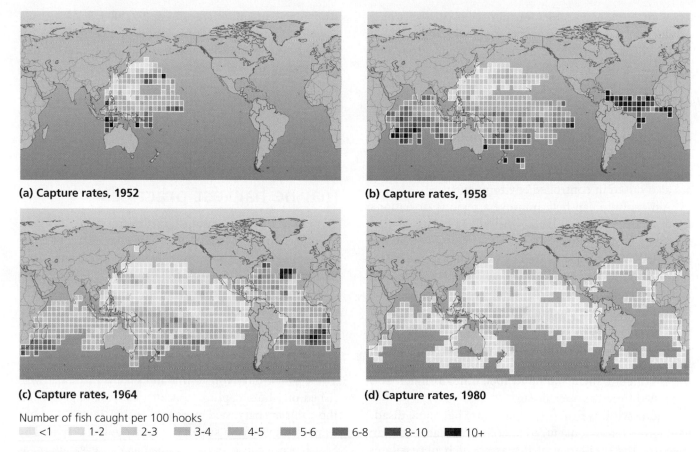

(a) Capture rates, 1952

(b) Capture rates, 1958

(c) Capture rates, 1964

(d) Capture rates, 1980

Number of fish caught per 100 hooks

<1   1-2   2-3   3-4   4-5   5-6   6-8   8-10   10+

FIGURE 13.24 As industrial fishing fleets reached each new region of the world's oceans, capture rates of large predatory fishes were initially high and then within a decade declined markedly. In the figure, darker colours signify high capture rates, and lighter colours signify low capture rates. High capture rates in the southwestern Pacific in 1952 **(a)** gave way to low ones in later years. Excellent fishing success in the tropical Atlantic and Indian Oceans in 1958 **(b)** had turned mediocre by 1964 **(c)** and poor by 1980 **(d)**. High capture rates in the north and south Atlantic in 1964 (c) gave way to low capture rates there in 1980 (d). *Source: Adapted from Myers, R. A. and B. Worm. 2003. Rapid worldwide depletion of predatory fish communities. Nature 423:280–283.*

rely on aerial spotters to find schools of commercially valuable fish, such as bluefin tuna. One final cause of misleading stability in global catch numbers is that not all data supplied to international monitoring agencies may be accurate, for a variety of reasons, including economic pressure to falsify data.

We are "fishing down the food chain"

Overall figures on total global catch tell only part of the story, because they do not relate the species, age, and size of fish harvested. Careful analyses of fisheries data have revealed in case after case that as fishing increases, the size and age of fish caught decline. Cod caught in the Northwest Atlantic today are on average *much* smaller than they were decades ago, and it is now rare to find a cod more than 10 years of age, although cod of this age formerly were common. The reproductive potential of today's smaller cod is much less—an

order of magnitude less—than that of the giant cod of previous decades.

In addition, as particular species become too rare to fish profitably, fleets begin targeting other species that are in greater abundance. Generally this means shifting from large, desirable species to smaller, less desirable ones. Fleets have time and again depleted popular food fish (such as cod) and shifted to species of lower value (such as capelin, smaller fish that cod eat). Because this often entails catching species at lower trophic levels, this phenomenon has been termed "fishing down the food chain," a concept proposed by UBC fisheries scientist Daniel Pauly and colleagues in 1998.

Aquaculture has benefits and drawbacks

There has been a dramatic increase in farm fisheries, or **aquaculture**, over the past few decades. From a small percentage of the total fish harvest only 20 years ago, aquaculture now accounts for more than 30% of world production. Freshwater fish species—including rainbow trout, brook trout, arctic char, and tilapia, as well as Atlantic, coho, and chinook salmon—are currently farmed in Canada. Canada is the fourth-largest producer of farmed salmon in the world[4] and the economic value of the aquaculture industry is now well over a half-billion dollars annually. Shellfish—including clams, oysters, scallops, and mussels, as well as some types of marine plants, algae, and oysters for pearl production—are also raised in controlled environments.

Aquaculture can help improve a region's or nation's food security by increasing overall amounts of fish available. It also reduces pressure on overharvested and declining wild stocks, as well as reducing by-catch and providing employment for fishers who can no longer fish from depleted natural stocks. Aquaculture also relies far less on fossil fuels than do fishing vessels, and provides a safer work environment. Fish farming can be remarkably energy-efficient, producing as much as 10 times as much fish per unit area as is harvested from oceanic waters on the continental shelf, and up to 1000 times as much as is harvested from the open ocean.

Along with its benefits, aquaculture has some disadvantages. Dense concentrations of farmed animals can increase the incidence of disease, which necessitates antibiotic treatment and results in additional expense. If farmed aquatic organisms escape into ecosystems where they are not native, they may spread disease to native stocks or may outcompete native organisms for food or habitat. The opposite has also occurred—recent research suggests that wild Pacific salmon swimming near aquaculture pens may pass parasites, which then spread rapidly as a result of the high population densities in the pens.

The high-density fish populations involved in aquaculture also produce a significant amount of waste, both from the farmed organisms and from the feed that goes uneaten and decomposes in the water column. Farmed fish often are fed grain, and growing grain to feed animals that we then eat can reduce the energy efficiency of food production and consumption. In other cases, farmed fish are fed fishmeal made from wild ocean fish, such as herring and anchovies, whose harvest may place additional stress on wild fish populations.

Aquaculture has also led to damaging landscape changes in some coastal ecosystems, including the removal of protective mangrove forests. Coastlines evolve geologically as natural barriers to the battering of storm waves and winds. When these barriers are removed or disrupted, shorelines are left defenceless. The world saw the effects of shoreline modification graphically illustrated during the devastating Sumatra–Andaman tsunami of December 24, 2004, a seismic sea wave generated by a major submarine earthquake off the coast of Indonesia. Many of the coastlines in this part of South Asia and the Pacific had been significantly altered for aquaculture pen construction. The tsunami met with little natural resistance as it rushed onshore.

Consumer choice can influence marine harvest practices

To most of us, marine fishing practices may seem a distant phenomenon over which we have no control. Yet by exercising careful choice when we buy seafood, consumers can influence the ways in which fisheries function. Purchasing ecolabelled seafood, such as dolphin-safe tuna, is one way to exercise choice, but in most cases consumers have no readily available information about how their seafood was caught.

Several nonprofit organizations have recently devised concise guides to help consumers make informed choices. These guides differentiate fish and shellfish that are overfished or whose capture is ecologically damaging from those that are harvested more sustainably. **TABLE 13.1** has some examples from such a consumer guide, prepared by SeaChoice, a consortium of Canadian conservation organizations, which also provides a wealth of information about sustainable fisheries for the public on its website.

Modern whaling provides an interesting example of consumer influences on marine harvesting practices. Whaling has been carried out for centuries (possibly millennia) by traditional societies from Scandinavia to northern Canada to Japan. Modern whaling began in the nineteenth century off the eastern coast of North America, in response to the demand for whale oil and, later, for meat. By the middle of the twentieth century, the catch was so large that it exceeded sustainable limits, and some species were close to extinction. In 1986 the International Whaling Commission banned whaling in an effort to allow stocks to replenish; this moratorium probably averted the extinction of several species, at least temporar-

weighing the issues

EATING SEAFOOD

After reading this chapter, do you plan to alter your decisions about eating seafood in any way? If so, how? If not, why not? Do you think consumer buying choices can exert an influence on fishing practices? On mercury contamination in seafood?

Table 13.1   Seafood Choices for Consumers

Best Choices

- Abalone (U.S. Farmed)
- Arctic Char (Farmed in Recirculating Systems)
- Barramundi (U.S. Farmed in Fully Recirculating Systems)
- Capelin (Iceland)
- Catfish (U.S. Farmed)
- Clams (Farmed)
- Clams, Softshell/Steamers (Wild-caught)
- Cobia (U.S. Farmed)
- Cod, Atlantic (Hook-and-line from Iceland and Northeast Arctic)
- Cod, Pacific (U.S. Bottom Longline, Jig and Trap)
- Crab, Dungeness (California, Oregon and Washington)
- Crab, Kona (Australia)
- Crab, Stone
- Crawfish/Crayfish (U.S. Farmed)
- Croaker, Atlantic (U.S. Non-trawl)
- Giant Clam/Geoduck (Wild-caught)
- Haddock (Hook-and-line from U.S. Atlantic)
- Halibut, Pacific (U.S.)
- Lobster, California Spiny (California)
- Lobster, Caribbean Spiny (Florida)
- Lobster, Spiny (Baja California, Mexico)
- Mackerel, Atlantic (Canada)
- Mackerel, King (U.S. Atlantic and U.S. Gulf of Mexico)

- Mackerel, Spanish (U.S. Atlantic and U.S. Gulf of Mexico)
- Mahi Mahi (Troll/Pole from U.S. Atlantic)
- Mullet, Striped
- Mussels (Farmed)
- Oysters (Farmed)
- Perch, Yellow (Lake Erie)
- Pollock, Atlantic (Gillnet and Purse Seine from Norway)
- Prawn, Freshwater (U.S. Farmed)
- Prawn, Spot (Canadian Pacific)
- Rockfish, Black (Hook-and-line from California, Oregon and Washington)
- Sablefish/Black Cod (Alaska and Canadian Pacific)
- Salmon (Drift Gillnet, Purse Seine and Troll, from Alaska)
- Salmon Roe (Drift Gillnet, Purse Seine and Troll, from Alaska)
- Salmon, Freshwater Coho (U.S. Farmed in Tank Systems)
- Sardines, Pacific (U.S.)
- Scad, Big-eye (Hawaii)
- Scad, Mackerel (Hawaii)
- Scallops (Farmed)
- Scallops, Sea (Diver-caught in Laguna Ojo de Liebre and Guerrero Negro, Baja California Sur, Mexico)
- Sea Urchin Roe (Canada)
- Seatrout, Spotted (Wild-caught from Florida and Louisiana)

- Shrimp (U.S. Farmed in Fully Recirculating Systems or Inland Ponds)
- Shrimp, Pink (Oregon)
- Squid, Longfin (U.S. Atlantic)
- Striped Bass (U.S. Wild-caught)
- Striped Bass (U.S. Farmed or Wild-caught)
- Swordfish (Hawaii Harpoon, Handline)
- Swordfish (Harpoon & Handline-caught from Canada, the U.S., North Atlantic & East Pacific)
- Tilapia (U.S. Farmed)
- Trout, Rainbow/Steelhead (U.S. Farmed)
- Tuna, Albacore (Troll/Pole from the Canadian and U.S. Pacific)
- Tuna, Albacore ("White" Canned) (Troll/pole from the Canadian and U.S. Pacific)
- Tuna, Bigeye (Troll/Pole from the U.S. Atlantic)
- Tuna, Skipjack (Worldwide Troll, Pole-and-line)
- Tuna, Skipjack ("Light" Canned) (Troll/Pole)
- Tuna, Yellowfin (Troll/Pole from the Pacific and U.S. Atlantic)
- White Seabass (Hook-and-line from California)
- Whitefish, Lake (Lake Huron and Lake Superior)
- Whitefish, Lake (Trap-net from Lake Michigan)
- Wreckfish

Source: Monterey Bay Aquarium Seafood Watch (2012). Buyer's Guide: All Regions Guide. "Best Choices," www. montereybayaquarium.org/cr/SeafoodWatch/web/sfw_regional.aspx

---

ily. There is a large market for whale meat in Japan, with the result that Japan officially objected to the moratorium. Japan continues whaling today, ostensibly for scientific research purposes, although it is quite widely believed that this is a front for commercial whaling. Whaling is carried out legally by Inuit communities in Canada's North, where whale meat is part of the traditional diet.

Marine biodiversity loss erodes ecosystem services

Overfishing, pollution, habitat change, and other factors that deplete biodiversity can threaten the ecosystem services we derive from the oceans. In the 2006 study in

Science that predicted global fisheries' collapse by 2048, the study's 14 authors analyzed all existing scientific literature to summarize the effects of biodiversity loss on ecosystem function and ecosystem services. They found that across 32 different controlled experiments conducted by various researchers, systems with less species diversity or genetic diversity showed less primary and secondary production and were less able to withstand disturbance.

The team also found that when biodiversity was reduced, so were habitats that serve as nurseries for fish and shellfish. Moreover, biodiversity loss was correlated with reduced filtering and detoxification (as from wetland vegetation and oyster beds), which can lead to harmful algal blooms, dead zones, fish kills, and beach closures.

Marine Conservation

Because we bear responsibility and stand to lose a great deal if valuable ecological systems collapse, marine scientists have been working to develop solutions to the problems that threaten the oceans. Many have begun by taking a hard look at the strategies used traditionally in fisheries management.

Fisheries management has been based on maximum sustainable yield

Fisheries managers conduct surveys, study fish population biology, and monitor catches. They then use that knowledge to regulate the timing of harvests, the techniques used to catch fish, and the scale of harvests. The goal is to allow for maximal harvests of particular populations while keeping fish available for the future—the concept of **maximum sustainable yield**. If data indicate that current yields are unsustainable, managers might limit the number or total biomass of that species that can be harvested, or they might restrict the type of gear fishers can use.

Despite such efforts, several fish and shellfish stocks have plummeted, and many scientists and managers now feel it is time to rethink fisheries management. One

key change these reformers suggest is to shift the focus away from individual species and toward viewing marine resources as elements of larger ecological systems. This means considering the impacts of fishing practices on habitat quality, on species interactions, and on other factors that may have indirect or long-term effects on populations. One key aspect of such an *ecosystem-based management* approach is to set aside areas of ocean where systems can function without human interference.

We can protect areas in the ocean

Hundreds of **marine protected areas (MPAs)** have been established, most of them along the coastlines of developed countries[5] (**FIGURE 13.25**). However, despite their name, marine protected areas do not necessarily protect all their natural resources, because nearly all MPAs allow fishing and other extractive activities. As a recent report from an environmental advocacy group put it, even national marine sanctuaries "are dredged, trawled, mowed for kelp, crisscrossed with oil pipelines and fibre-optic cables, and swept through with fishing nets."

Because of the lack of true refuges from fishing pressure, many scientists—and some fishers—want to establish areas where fishing is prohibited. Such "no-take" areas have come

National Park (with marine component)
National Marine Conservation Area
Oceans Act Marine Protected Area
National Marine Wildlife Area
Migratory Bird Sanctuary (with a marine component)
Species at Risk Act, Critical Habitat (Aquatic Species)
Fisheries Act Fishery Closure
UNESCO Biosphere Reserve
Voluntary Fishery Closure
Notice to Mariners
Important Bird Area

Legislation   **Voluntary stewardship**
(a)

(b) Endeavour Hydrothermal Vents Marine Protected Area

FIGURE 13.25   There are numerous tools that can be used to protect marine areas in Canada, which range from legislated to voluntary measures **(a)**. Canada's first official marine protected area, designated in 2003, was the Endeavour Hydrothermal Vents area on the Juan da Fuca Ridge off the west coast of Vancouver Island **(b)**.

to be called **marine reserves**. Designed to preserve entire ecosystems intact without human interference, marine reserves are also intended to improve fisheries. Scientists argue that marine reserves can act as production factories for fish for surrounding areas, because fish larvae produced inside reserves will disperse outside and stock other parts of the ocean. Proponents maintain that by serving both purposes, marine reserves are a win–win proposition for environmentalists and fishers alike.

Many fishers dislike the idea of no-take reserves, however, just as most were opposed to the Canadian groundfish moratoria and the Georges Bank closures. Nearly every marine reserve that has been established or proposed has met with pockets of intense opposition from people and businesses that use the area for fishing or recreation. Opposition comes from commercial fishing fleets as well as from individuals who fish recreationally. Both types of fishers are concerned that marine reserves will simply put more areas off-limits to fishing. In some parts of the world, protests have become violent. For instance, to protest fishing restrictions, fishers in the Galápagos Islands destroyed offices at Galápagos National Park and threatened researchers and park managers with death.

Reserves can work for both fish and fishers

In the past decade, data synthesized from marine reserves around the world have been indicating that reserves *do* work as win–win solutions that benefit ecosystems, fish populations, and fishing economies. In 2001, 161 prominent marine scientists signed a "consensus statement" summarizing the effects of marine reserves. Besides boosting fish biomass, total catch, and record-sized fish, the report stated, marine reserves yield several benefits. Within reserve boundaries, they

■ Produce rapid and long-term increases in abundance, diversity, and productivity of marine organisms
■ Decrease mortality and habitat destruction
■ Lessen the likelihood of extirpation of species

Outside the reserve boundaries, marine reserves

■ Can create a "spillover effect" when individuals of protected species spread outside reserves
■ Allow larvae of species protected within reserves to "seed the seas" outside reserves

The consensus statement was backed up by research into reserves worldwide. At Apo Island in the Philippines,

biomass of large predators increased eightfold inside a marine reserve, and fishing improved outside the reserve. At two coral reef sites in Kenya, commercially fished and keystone species were up to 10 times as abundant in the protected area as in the fished area. At Leigh Marine Reserve in New Zealand, snapper increased fortyfold, and spiny lobsters were increasing by 5%–11% yearly. Spillover from this reserve improved fishing and ecotourism, and local residents who once opposed the reserve now support it.

The review of data from existing marine reserves as of 2001 revealed that just one to two years after their establishment, marine reserves

■ Increased densities of organisms on average by 91%
■ Increased biomass of organisms on average by 192%
■ Increased average size of organisms by 31%
■ Increased species diversity by 23%

Since that time, further research has shown that reserves create a fourfold increase in catch per unit of effort in fished areas surrounding reserves and that they can greatly increase ecotourism by divers and snorkelers.

On Georges Bank, once commercial trawling was halted in 1994, populations of many organisms began to recover. As benthic invertebrates began to come back, numbers of groundfish, such as haddock and yellow-tail flounder, rose inside the closed areas, and scallops increased by 14 times. Moreover, fish from the closure areas appear to be spilling over into adjacent waters, because fishers have been catching more and more groundfish from Georges Bank as a whole since the late 1990s. From these and other data sets, increasing numbers of scientists, fishers, and policy makers are advocating the establishment of fully protected marine reserves as a central management tool.

How should reserves be designed?

If marine reserves work in principle, the question becomes how best to design reserves and arrange them into networks. Scientists today are asking how large reserves need to be, how many there need to be, and where they need to be placed. Involving fishers directly in the planning process is crucial for coming up with answers to such questions. In Canada, marine reserves are managed by Parks Canada through the National Marine Conservation Areas Program, and their management plans are designed as partnerships among coastal communities; Aboriginal people; provincial, territorial, and federal government agencies; and other stakeholders.

CANADIAN ENVIRONMENTAL PERSPECTIVES

Farley Mowat

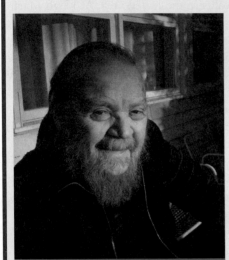

Canadian author Farley Mowat has written extensively about his experiences in the Arctic. Books like *A Whale for the Killing* and *Sea of Slaughter* led the Sea Shepherd Conservation Society to name one of its fleet of "eco-piracy" boats after him.

■   **Author**
■   **Conservationist** and **naturalist**
■   **Animal welfare activist**

He is a "natural storyteller," a gifted writer, and a Canadian icon. His books—more than 18 million of them sold, in many languages—have helped familiarize readers with wildlife and life in wild places. They have raised awareness and changed attitudes, and have even influenced Canadian government policies. Books like *Never Cry Wolf* (1963) are fixtures in Canadian classrooms. Some of his books have brought controversy and criticism, and one, *Sea of Slaughter* (1984), apparently contributed to his being barred from entering the United States.[6]

Farley Mowat was born in Ontario but grew up in Saskatoon during the Great Depression. As a child he was fascinated with nature and kept numerous wild animals and even insects as household pets. Mowat's first formal writing as a young teenager was an article on birds. Several of his later books, such as *Owls in the Family* (1961), were based on reminiscences of animals and nature experiences from his childhood. Mowat served in active combat duty during the Second World War. His

intense battlefield experiences eventually provided material and inspiration for some of his later writings, such as *My Father's Son: Memories of War and Peace* (1992).

After returning from the war he studied biology at the University of Toronto, which eventually led him to a two-year sojourn in the Arctic. His first book, *People of the Deer* (1952), was based on his frustration upon becoming aware of the destitute situation of the Ihalmiut, an Inuit band who, he felt, had been misunderstood and exploited by white people.

A number of Mowat's subsequent books also were based on his experiences in the Arctic. He won the Governor General's Award for *Lost in the Barrens* (1956), which tells the story of two young people—one white, the other Cree—who are lost in the Arctic wilderness. They manage to survive for part of the winter, but ultimately are rescued by an Inuit boy whose extensive knowledge of the Arctic environment saves them.

Mowat's relationship with the people of Newfoundland and Labrador, where he lived for eight years, is complex. His 1968 book *This Rock Within the Sea: A Heritage Lost* tells of a noble people with a calling to the sea. By 1972, however, *A Whale for the Killing* dramatically illustrated his disillusionment after an unfortunate beached whale was inhumanely shot to death. The book is also a plea for action to save whales from extinction.

In 1984, *Sea of Slaughter* was published, providing an overview of animal life in the North Atlantic since the early days of European fishing and whaling. Roger Tory Peterson compared the environmental significance of *Sea of Slaughter* to that of Rachel Carson's *Silent Spring*, saying, "In this masterpiece, Canada's most beloved naturalist-author is as angry about the assault on the living sea as Rachel Carson was about the land in *Silent Spring*."[7] On a promotional tour for *Sea of Slaughter*, Mowat attempted to enter the United States but was barred. He explored the possible reasons for this in his next book, *My Discovery of America* (1985).

Mowat has the distinction—perhaps dubious—of having a ship named after him. The *R/V Farley Mowat* is one of a small fleet

of vessels that belong to the Sea Shepherd Conservation Society, of which Mowat is the international chair. Sea Shepherd, founded by Paul Watson (a co-founder of Greenpeace), is an eco-activist organization that has pledged to sink or sabotage any vessels it believes to have violated international whaling laws. Greenpeace, also an activist environmental group, has repeatedly distanced itself from Sea Shepherd because of the extreme nature of its approach.

On April 12, 2008, the Department of Fisheries and Oceans, Transport Canada, Canadian Coast Guard, and RCMP took possession of the *Farley Mowat* for alleged violations of the *Marine Mammal Regulations*.[8] The Sea Shepherd Conservation Society, which claims the charges to be false, says of the *Farley Mowat*, "She is a protector, and a symbol of hope for a better, more humane, and more ecologically conscious future."[9] The vessel has since been sold and will be used for scientific research expeditions.

"So ends the story of how the Sea of Whales became a Sea of Slaughter as, one by one, from the greatest to the least, each in turn according to its monetary worth, the several cetacean nations perished in a roaring holocaust fuelled by human avarice." —**Farley Mowat, Sea of Slaughter (1984)**

Thinking About Environmental Perspectives

The Sea Shepherd Conservation Society, of which Farley Mowat is the international chair, has been criticized for extremism. Its anti-whaling actions have included ramming, disabling, and otherwise confronting whaling vessels from the Faeroe Islands (in the North Atlantic) to Antarctica. Sea Shepherd maintains the position that standing by and observing illegal activities that endanger ocean life is not an acceptable pathway, and it pledges to take whatever actions are necessary to protect sea life and habitats. What do you think? Are extreme and potentially dangerous actions, like ramming a vessel, acceptable, or perhaps even necessary, in some circumstances?

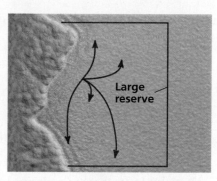

FIGURE 13.26   Marine reserves of different sizes may have varying effects on ecological communities and fisheries. Young and adult fish and shellfish of different species can disperse different distances, as indicated by the red arrows in the figure. A small reserve (left panel) may fail to protect animals because too many disperse out of the reserve. A large reserve (right panel) may protect fish and shellfish very well but will provide relatively less "spillover" into areas where people can legally fish. Thus medium-sized reserves (middle panel) may offer the best hope of preserving species and ecological communities while also providing adequate fish to fishers and human communities.   *Source: Halpern, B. S., and R. R. Warner. 2003. Matching marine reserve design to reserve objectives. Proceedings of the Royal Society of London B 270:1871–1878.*

Of several dozen studies that have estimated how much area of the ocean should be protected in no-take reserves, estimates range from 10% to 65%, with most falling between 20% and 50%. Other studies are modelling how to optimize the size and spacing of individual reserves so that ecosystems are protected, fisheries are sustained, and people are not overly excluded from marine areas (**FIGURE 13.26**). If marine reserves are designed strategically to take advantage of ocean currents, many scientists say, then they may well seed the seas and help lead us toward solutions to one of our most pressing environmental problems.

Conclusion

The ocean covers most of our planet and contains diverse topography and ecosystems, some of which we are only now beginning to explore and understand. We are learning more about the ocean and coastal environments while intensifying our use of their resources and causing these areas more severe impacts. In so doing, we are coming to understand better how to use these resources without depleting them or causing undue ecological harm to the marine and coastal systems on which we depend.

Today, scientists are demonstrating that setting aside protected areas of the ocean can serve to maintain natural systems and also to enhance fisheries. This is vital at a time when we are depleting many of the world's marine fish stocks. As historical studies reveal more information on how much biodiversity the ocean formerly contained and has now lost, we may increasingly look beyond simply making fisheries stable and instead consider restoring the ecological systems that once flourished in our waters.

REVIEWING OBJECTIVES

You should now be able to:

Identify physical, geographical, chemical, and biological aspects of the marine environment

- The ocean covers 71% of Earth's surface and contains more than 97% of its surface water.
- Ocean water contains 96.5% H_2O by mass and various dissolved salts.
- Colder, saltier water is denser and sinks. Water temperatures vary with latitude, and temperature variation is greater in surface layers.
- Persistent currents move horizontally through the oceans, driven by density differences, sunlight, and wind.

- Vertical water movement includes upwelling and downwelling, which affect the distribution of nutrients and life.
- Seafloor topography can be complex.

Describe major types of marine ecosystems

- Major types of marine and coastal ecosystems include pelagic and deep-water open ocean systems, kelp forests, coral reefs, intertidal zones, salt marshes, mangrove forests, and estuaries.
- Many of these systems are highly productive and rich in biodiversity. Many also suffer heavy impacts from human influence.

Outline historic and current human uses of marine resources

■ For millennia, people have fished the ocean and used ocean waters for transportation.

■ Today we extract energy and minerals from the ocean.

Assess human impacts on marine environments

■ People pollute ocean waters with trash, including plastic and nets that harm marine life.

■ Marine oil pollution results from non-point sources on land, as well as from tanker spills at sea.

■ Heavy metal contaminants in seafood affect human health, and nutrient pollution can lead to harmful algal blooms.

■ Overharvesting is perhaps the major human impact on marine systems.

Review the current state of ocean fisheries and reasons for their decline

■ Half the world's marine fish populations are fully exploited, 25% are already overexploited, and only 25% can yield more without declining.

■ Global fish catches have stopped growing since the late 1980s, despite increased fishing effort and improved technologies.

■ People began depleting marine resources long ago, but impacts have intensified in recent decades.

■ Commercial fishing practices include driftnetting, longline fishing, and trawling, all of which capture nontarget organisms, called by-catch.

■ Today's ocean holds only one-tenth the number of large animals that it did before the advent of industrialized commercial fishing.

■ As fishing intensity increases, the fish available become smaller.

■ Marine biodiversity loss affects ecosystem services.

■ Consumers can encourage good fishery practices by shopping for sustainable seafood.

■ Traditional fisheries management has not stopped declines, so many scientists feel that ecosystem-based management is needed.

Evaluate marine protected areas and reserves as innovative solutions

■ We have established far fewer protected areas in the ocean than we have on land, and most marine protected areas allow many extractive activities.

■ Marine reserves can protect ecosystems while also boosting fish populations and making fisheries sustainable.

TESTING YOUR COMPREHENSION

1. What proportion of Earth's surface does the ocean cover? What is the average salinity of ocean water? How are density, salinity, and temperature related in each layer of ocean water?

2. What factors drive the system of ocean currents? In what ways do these movements affect conditions for life in the oceans?

3. Where in the ocean are the most productive areas of biological activity located?

4. Describe three kinds of ecosystems found near coastal areas and the kinds of life they support.

5. Why are coral reefs biologically valuable? How are they being degraded by human impact?

6. What is causing the disappearance of mangrove forests and salt marshes?

7. Discuss three ways in which people are combating pollution in the oceans and on our coasts.

8. Describe an example of how overfishing can lead to ecological damage and fishery collapse.

9. Name three industrial fishing practices, and explain how they create by-catch and harm marine life.

10. How does a marine reserve differ from a marine protected area? Why do many fishers oppose marine reserves? Explain why many scientists say no-take reserves will be good for fishers.

THINKING IT THROUGH

1. What benefits do you derive from the ocean? How does your behaviour affect the ocean, both directly and indirectly? Give specific examples.

2. We have been able to reduce the amount of oil we spill into the ocean, but petroleum-based products, such as plastic, continue to litter the ocean and shorelines. Discuss some ways that we can reduce this threat to the marine environment.

3. Describe the trends in global fish capture over the past 50 years, and explain several factors that account for these trends.

4. Consider what you know about biological productivity in the ocean, about the scientific data on marine reserves, and about the social and political issues surrounding the establishment of marine reserves. What ocean regions do you think it would be particularly appropriate to establish as marine reserves? Why?

5. Image that you make your living fishing on the ocean, just as your father and grandfather did, and as most of your neighbours do in your small coastal village. Your region's fishery has just collapsed, however, and everyone is blaming it on overfishing. The government has closed the fishery for three years, and scientists are pushing for a permanent marine reserve to be established on your former fishing grounds. You have no desire to move away from your village, so what steps will you take now? Will you protest the closure? What compensation will you ask of the government if it prevents you from fishing? Will you work with scientists to establish a reserve that improves fishing in the future, or will you oppose their attempts to create a reserve? What data and what assurances will you ask of them?

6. Let's say that you are mayor of a coastal town where some residents are employed as commercial fishers and others make a living serving ecotourists who come to snorkel and scuba dive at the nearby coral reef. In recent years, several fish stocks have crashed, and ecotourism is dropping off as fish disappear from the increasingly degraded reef. Scientists are urging you to help establish a marine reserve around portions of the reef, but most commercial and recreational fishers are opposed to this idea. What steps would you take to restore your community's economy and environment?

INTERPRETING GRAPHS AND DATA

The accompanying graph presents trends in the status of North Atlantic swordfish, a highly migratory species managed directly by the U.S. National Marine Fishery Service. The solid red line shows the mortality rate from fishing. The solid blue line indicates the biomass of the stock. The graph also indicates the date when an international recovery plan was implemented.

1. Describe the trends in swordfish stocks (1) before the adoption of an international management plan and (2) since the plan was adopted. Describe the interactions between fishing mortality and biomass as illustrated by the graph.

2. Based on the data in the graph, predict the likely trend in swordfish production over the next 10 years, assuming no change to the status quo.

3. This graph illustrates an effort that is succeeding, but not all rebuilding plans lead to stock recovery. Beyond the existence of a plan, what actions might play a role in supporting stock recovery efforts?

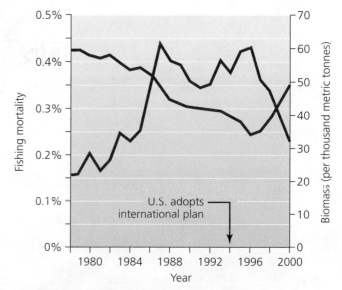

Trends in fishing mortality and stock biomass for North Atlantic swordfish, 1978–2000.

Source: Adapted from Rosenberg, A., et al. (2006). Rebuilding U.S. fisheries: Progress and problems. Frontiers in Ecology and the Environment 4(6).

CHAPTER ENDNOTES

1. NOAA Coral Health and Monitoring Program, *Coral Bleaching*, www.coral.noaa.gov/cleo/coral_bleaching.shtml

2. Halifax Regional Municipality, Halifax Harbour Project, www.halifax.ca/harboursol/WhatistheHarbourSolutionsProject.html

3. Clucas, I. (1997) *A Study of the Options for Utilization of Bycatch and Discards from Marine and Capture Fisheries*, Fishery Industries Division, FAO Fisheries Department, http://www.fao.org/docrep/W6602E/w6602E10.htm#10

4. Fisheries and Oceans Canada, Aquaculture Fact Sheets, *Fin Fish*, www.dfo-mpo.gc.ca/aquaculture/finfish_e.htm

5. Parks Canada, Fisheries and Oceans Canada, and Environment Canada (2005) *Canada's Marine Protected Areas Strategy*, www.dfo-mpo.gc.ca/oceans-habitat/oceans/mpa-zpm/fedmpa-zpmfed/pdf/mpa_e.pdf

6. The Canadian Encyclopedia *Historica*, Farley Mowat, www.thecanadianencyclopedia.com/index.cfm?PgNm=TCE&ArticleId=A0005502

7. Amazon.com, *Sea of Slaughter* by Farley Mowat (Reviews), www.amazon.com/Sea-Slaughter-Farley-Mowat/dp/1576300196

8. Department of Fisheries and Oceans, News Releases 2008, *Enforcement Actions Taken Against Farley Mowat—Update*, www.dfo-mpo.gc.ca/media/npress-communique/2008/20080414-eng.htm; the vessel remains in custody as of late 2008

9. Sea Shepherd Conservation Society, *Neptune's Navy*, www.seashepherd.org/fleet/fleet.html

MyEnvironmentPlace

Go to **www.myenvironmentplace.ca** where you will find quizzes, animations, your Pearson eText, and more.

14

Atmospheric Science and Air Pollution

This is Earth's atmosphere, from space.

Upon successfully completing this chapter, you will be able to

- Describe the composition, structure, and function of Earth's atmosphere
- Outline the scope of outdoor air pollution and assess potential solutions
- Explain stratospheric ozone depletion and identify steps taken to address it

- Define *acidic deposition* and illustrate its consequences
- Characterize the scope of indoor air pollution and assess potential solutions

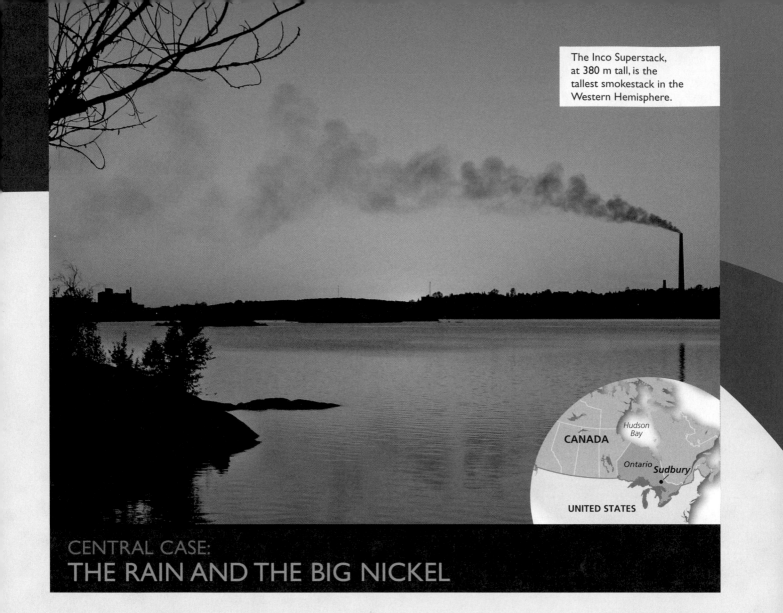

The Inco Superstack, at 380 m tall, is the tallest smokestack in the Western Hemisphere.

CANADA

Hudson Bay

Ontario Sudbury

UNITED STATES

CENTRAL CASE:
THE RAIN AND THE BIG NICKEL

"Despite Canada's success at reducing acid-causing emissions, acid deposition is still affecting our environment."
—ENVIRONMENT CANADA, *2004 CANADIAN ACID DEPOSITION SCIENCE ASSESSMENT*

"The problem [of acid rain] has not gone away."
—GENE LIKENS, DIRECTOR OF THE INSTITUTE OF ECOSYSTEM STUDIES IN MILLBROOK, NEW YORK

Sudbury, Ontario, is home to some of the world's largest nickel and copper deposits. These are not ordinary mineral deposits—they were formed by rock melting that resulted from the impact of a meteorite 15 km in diameter more than 2 billion years ago. The impact left a crater almost 600 km in diameter and 40 km deep, in which the massive ore deposits were localized. A "sister" meteorite impact left a smaller crater, now filled by the deep, clear waters of Lake Wanapitei.

Sudbury also claims to be the "blueberry capital of the world," but here a downside becomes apparent. Blueberries thrive in highly acidic soils, but the soils of the Sudbury area are not naturally so acidic. What happened to create this blueberry-friendly environment?

Nickel mining and refining happened. Mining started in the Sudbury area in the late 1800s and continues today. The mining and, particularly, refining of ores (through *smelting*, in which the ore is crushed and heated to a very high temperature to segregate the metals of interest) generate emissions high in sulphur dioxide (SO_2). These sulphur-rich emissions, if released to the atmosphere, combine with water vapour to form sulphuric acid, which ultimately falls as *acidic deposition*. The rocks and soils of the Sudbury area are naturally susceptible to acidification because of their chemical composition.

As early as the 1920s, the degradation of the natural environment around Sudbury was recognized as a problem. Acid rain devastated the area's forests and water bodies. Pollution stained the treeless soil black. In 1969—quite early in the modern environmental movement (recall that the first Earth Day was in 1970)—the government of Ontario informed Inco, the principal mining company and main polluter in the area at the time, that it would be required to substantially decrease emissions from its facilities. Inco's response, cutting-edge in its day, was to build a "Superstack," 380 m tall, to carry emissions from the smelter far away from the immediate Sudbury area (see photo). The Superstack was completed in 1972, and to this day it remains the tallest smokestack in the Western Hemisphere.

Today we know that the Superstack was only a partial solution. It did disperse the sulphurous emissions, but rather than ending the acidic deposition it just spread the problem farther afield. Environment Canada estimates that 7000 lakes in northern Ontario and Québec were damaged by acid-causing emissions from smelters in Sudbury.[1] The sensitivity of the underlying granitic rocks contributed to the acidification problem, which affected not only forests and soils, but also fish and the sport fishing industry in an area of approximately 17 000 km^2.[2] Sulphur emissions from the Superstack were dispersed over a much broader area than they would have been, had the stack height been less.

Beginning in the early 1980s, Inco and Falconbridge (the other major producer of smelter emissions in the area) undertook vigorous efforts to clean their emissions prior to releasing them to the atmosphere. The result is that SO_2 emissions today have been reduced by as much as 90%. Lakes, forests, and soils in the region have shown significant biological and chemical improvements in the more than 30 years since the Superstack was constructed. However, many of the damaged lakes are still acidic and contaminated with metals.[3]

The Experimental Lakes Area in northwestern Ontario, set up in 1968 and maintained by Fisheries and Oceans Canada, is one facility where scientific research on lake acidification and recovery takes place. The area consists of 58 small lakes and their watersheds, with a permanent field research station. Here scientists carry out research on the impacts of acidification, investigate the process of recovery, and test a variety of remediation approaches. For example, many of the fish in a sulphur-acidified lake died of starvation as a result of the impacts of acidification on their food sources (see photo). When the lake was remediated, the fish population was able to recover. This kind of research gives scientists a better idea of the recovery process and the robustness of aquatic systems undergoing chemical and biological changes.[4]

The most important legacy of the Superstack is that it ushered in an era of ecological awareness, recovery, and restoration in Ontario, and of pride in the natural environment in the Sudbury area. Partners in the Regional Land Reclamation Program, launched in 1978, continue to carry out environmental research on acidification and the recovery process, which may prove useful in other parts of the world where acidification has caused ecological damage.

In the Experimental Lakes Area of northwestern Ontario, many of the trout in an experimentally acidified lake died of starvation as a result of the loss of their food sources (top). When the lake was remediated, the fish population was able to recover (bottom).

The Atmosphere and Weather

Every breath we take reaffirms our connection to the **atmosphere**, the thin layer of gases that surrounds Earth. We live at the bottom of this layer, which provides us with oxygen, absorbs hazardous solar radiation, burns up incoming meteors, transports and recycles water and nutrients, and moderates climate.

The atmosphere consists of roughly 78% nitrogen gas (N_2) and 21% oxygen gas (O_2). The remaining 1% is composed of argon gas (Ar) and minute concentrations of several other gases (**FIGURE 14.1**). These include *permanent gases* that remain at stable concentrations and *variable gases* that vary in concentration from time to time or place to place as a result of natural processes or human activities.

Over Earth's long history, the atmosphere's chemical composition has changed. Oxygen gas began to build up in an atmosphere dominated by carbon dioxide (CO_2), nitrogen, carbon monoxide (CO), and hydrogen (H_2) about 2.7 billion years ago, with the emergence of autotrophic microbes that emitted oxygen as a by-product of photosynthesis. Today, human activity is altering the quantities of some atmospheric gases, such as carbon dioxide, methane (CH_4), and ozone (O_3). In this chapter we will explore some of the atmospheric changes brought about by artificial pollutants, but we must first begin with an overview of Earth's atmosphere.

The atmosphere is layered

The atmosphere that stretches so high above us and seems so vast is actually just a thin coating about 1/100 of Earth's diameter, like the fuzzy skin of a peach. This coating consists of four layers that atmospheric scientists recognize by measuring differences in temperature, density, and composition (**FIGURE 14.2**).

The bottommost layer, the **troposphere**, blankets Earth's surface and provides us with the air we need to live. The movement of air within the troposphere is also largely responsible for the planet's weather. Although it is thin (averaging 11 km high) relative to the atmosphere's other layers, the troposphere contains three-quarters of the atmosphere's mass because air is denser near Earth's surface. On average, tropospheric air temperature declines by about 6°C for each kilometre in altitude, dropping to roughly –52°C at its highest point. At the top of the troposphere, however, temperatures cease to decline with altitude, marking a boundary called the *tropopause*. The tropopause acts like a cap, limiting mixing

FIGURE 14.1
Earth's atmosphere consists mostly of nitrogen, secondarily of oxygen, and lastly of a mix of gases at dilute concentrations. Permanent gases are fixed in concentration. Variable gases vary in concentration as a result of either natural processes or human activities.
Source: Data from Ahrens, C. D. (2007). Meteorology Today, *8th ed. Belmont, CA: Brooks/Cole.*

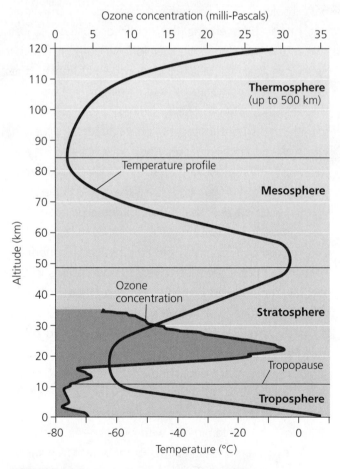

FIGURE 14.2
Temperature drops with altitude in the troposphere, rises with altitude in the stratosphere, drops in the mesosphere, and then rises again in the thermosphere. The tropopause separates the troposphere from the stratosphere. Ozone reaches a peak in a portion of the stratosphere, giving rise to the term *ozone layer*.
Source: Adapted from Jacobson, M. Z. (2002). Atmospheric Pollution: History, Science, and Regulation. *Cambridge: Cambridge University Press; and Parson, E. A. (2003).* Protecting the Ozone Layer: Science and Strategy. *Oxford: Oxford University Press.*

between the troposphere and the atmospheric layer above it, the stratosphere.

The **stratosphere** extends from 11 km to 50 km above sea level. Although similar in composition to the troposphere, the stratosphere is 1000 times as dry and less dense. Its gases experience little vertical mixing, so once substances (including pollutants) enter it, they tend to remain for a long time. The stratosphere attains a maximum temperature of –3°C at its highest altitude but is colder in its lower reaches. The reason is that ozone and oxygen absorb and scatter the Sun's ultraviolet (UV) radiation, so that much of the UV radiation penetrating the upper stratosphere fails to reach the lower stratosphere. Most of the atmosphere's minute amount of ozone concentrates in a portion of the stratosphere roughly from 17 km to 30 km above sea level, a region that has come to be called Earth's **ozone layer**. The ozone layer greatly reduces the amount of UV radiation that reaches Earth's surface. Because UV light can damage living tissue and induce mutations in DNA, the ozone layer's protective effects are vital for life on Earth.

Above the stratosphere lies the **mesosphere**, which extends from 50 km to 80 km above sea level. Air pressure is extremely low here, and temperatures decrease with altitude, reaching their lowest point at the top of the mesosphere. From here, the **thermosphere**, our atmosphere's top layer, extends upward to an altitude of 500 km.

Atmospheric properties include temperature, pressure, and humidity

Although the lower atmosphere is stable in its chemical composition, it is dynamic in its movement; air movement within it is due to differences in the physical properties of air masses. Among these properties are pressure and density, relative humidity, and temperature.

Gravity pulls gas molecules toward Earth's surface, causing air to be most dense near the surface and less so as altitude increases. **Atmospheric pressure**, the force per unit of area produced by a column of air, also decreases with altitude because at higher altitudes fewer molecules are pulled down by gravity (**FIGURE 14.3**). At sea level, atmospheric pressure is 1013 millibars (mb). Mountain climbers trekking to Mount Everest, the world's highest mountain, can look up and view their destination from Kala Patthar, a nearby peak, at roughly 5.5 km in altitude. At this altitude, pressure is 500 mb—half the atmosphere's air molecules are above the climber, and half are below. A climber who reaches Everest's peak (8.85 km), where the "thin air" is just more than 300 mb, stands above two-thirds of the molecules in the atmosphere. When we fly on

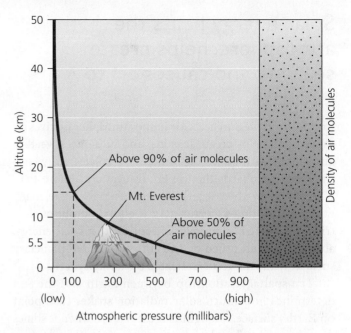

FIGURE 14.3
As one climbs higher through the atmosphere, gas molecules become less densely packed. As density decreases, so does atmospheric pressure. Because most air molecules lie low in the atmosphere, one needs to be only 5.5 km high to be above half the planet's air molecules. *Adapted from Ahrens, C. D. (2007).* Meteorology Today, *8th ed. Belmont, CA: Brooks/Cole.*

a commercial jet airliner at a cruising altitude of 11 km, we are above roughly 80% of the atmosphere's molecules.

Another property of air is **relative humidity**, the ratio of water vapour a given volume of air contains to the maximum amount it *could* contain at a given temperature. Average daytime relative humidity in June in the desert at Phoenix, Arizona, is only 31% (meaning that the air contains less than a third of the water vapour it possibly can at its temperature), whereas on the tropical island of Guam, relative humidity rarely drops below 88%. People are sensitive to changes in relative humidity because we perspire to cool our bodies. When humidity is high, the air is already holding nearly as much water vapour as it can, so sweat evaporates slowly and the body cannot cool itself efficiently. This is why high humidity makes it feel hotter than it really is. Low humidity speeds evaporation and makes it feel cooler.

The temperature of air also varies with location and time. At the global scale, temperature varies over Earth's surface because the Sun's rays strike some areas more directly than others. At more local scales, temperature varies because of topography, plant cover, proximity of land to water, and many other factors. Sometimes these local variations are striking—the side of a hill that is sheltered from wind or direct sunlight can have a totally different weather pattern, or **microclimate**, from the side facing into the wind or sunlight.

Solar energy heats the atmosphere, helps create seasons, and causes air to circulate

Energy from the Sun heats air in the atmosphere, drives air movement, helps create seasons, and influences weather and climate. An enormous amount of solar energy continuously bombards the upper atmosphere—more than 1000 watts/m^2 where it hits directly, at a right angle, many thousands of times greater than the total output of electricity generated by human society. Of that solar energy, about 70% is absorbed by the atmosphere and planetary surface, while the rest is reflected back into space.

The spatial relationship between Earth and the Sun determines how much solar radiation strikes each point on Earth's surface. Sunlight is most intense when it shines directly overhead and meets the planet's surface at a perpendicular angle. At this angle, sunlight passes through a minimum of energy-absorbing atmosphere, and Earth's surface receives a maximum of solar energy per unit of surface area. Conversely, solar energy that approaches Earth's surface at an oblique angle loses intensity as it traverses a longer distance through the atmosphere, and it is less intense when it reaches the surface, where the oblique angle of the incoming solar energy also is spread over a larger surface area. This is why, on average, solar radiation intensity is highest near the equator and weakest near the poles (**FIGURE 14.4**).

Because Earth is tilted on its *axis* (an imaginary line connecting the poles) by about 23.5°, the Northern and Southern Hemispheres each tilt toward the Sun for half the year, resulting in the change in seasons (**FIGURE 14.5**). Regions near the equator are largely unaffected by this tilt; they experience about 12 hours each of sunlight and darkness every day throughout the year. Near the poles, however, the effect is strong, and seasonality is pronounced.

Land and surface water absorb solar energy, re-radiating heat and causing water to evaporate. Air near Earth's surface therefore tends to be warmer and moister than air at higher altitudes. These differences set into motion a process of convective circulation (**FIGURE 14.6**). Warm air, being less dense, rises and creates vertical currents. As air rises into regions of lower atmospheric pressure, it expands and cools. Once the air cools, it descends and becomes denser, replacing warm air that is rising. The air picks up heat and moisture near ground level and prepares to rise again, continuing the process. Similar convective circulation patterns occur in ocean waters and in magma beneath Earth's surface.

The atmosphere drives weather and climate

Weather and climate involve the physical properties of the troposphere, including temperature, pressure, humidity, cloudiness, and wind. **Weather** specifies atmospheric conditions over short time periods, typically hours or days, and within relatively small geographic areas. **Climate** describes the pattern of atmospheric conditions found across large geographic regions over long periods—seasons, years, or millennia. Writer Mark Twain once noted the distinction

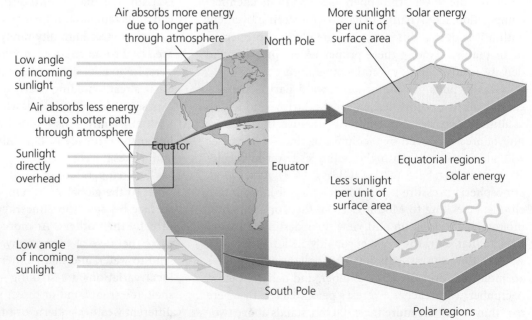

FIGURE 14.4
Because of Earth's curvature, polar regions receive, on average, less solar energy than equatorial regions. One reason is that sunlight gets spread over a larger area when striking the surface at an angle. Another reason is that sunlight approaching at a lower angle near the poles must traverse a longer distance through the atmosphere, during which more energy is absorbed or reflected. These patterns represent year-round averages; the latitude at which radiation approaches the surface perpendicularly varies with the seasons (see **FIGURE 14.5**).

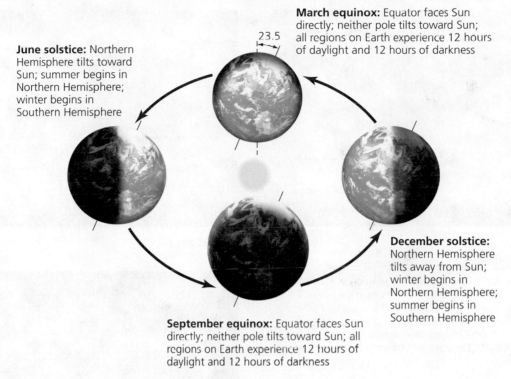

March equinox: Equator faces Sun directly; neither pole tilts toward Sun; all regions on Earth experience 12 hours of daylight and 12 hours of darkness

June solstice: Northern Hemisphere tilts toward Sun; summer begins in Northern Hemisphere; winter begins in Southern Hemisphere

December solstice: Northern Hemisphere tilts away from Sun; winter begins in Northern Hemisphere; summer begins in Southern Hemisphere

September equinox: Equator faces Sun directly; neither pole tilts toward Sun; all regions on Earth experience 12 hours of daylight and 12 hours of darkness

FIGURE 14.5 The seasons occur because Earth is tilted on its axis by 23.5 degrees. As Earth revolves around the Sun, the Northern Hemisphere tilts toward the Sun for one half of the year, and the Southern Hemisphere tilts toward the Sun for the other half of the year. In each hemisphere, summer occurs during the period in which the hemisphere is tilted toward the Sun.

Heat radiates to space

Cool, dry air

Condensation and precipitation

Air sinks, compresses, and warms

Air rises, expands, and cools

Warm, dry air

Hot, moist air

Air picks up moisture and heat (moist surface warmed by Sun)

FIGURE 14.6

Weather is driven in part by the convective circulation of air in the atmosphere. Air being heated near Earth's surface picks up moisture and rises. Once aloft, this air cools, and moisture condenses, forming clouds and precipitation. Cool, drying air begins to descend, compressing and warming in the process. Warm, dry air near the surface begins the cycle anew.

between climate and weather by saying, "Climate is what we expect; weather is what we get."

Air masses interact to produce weather

Weather can change quickly when air masses with different physical properties meet. The boundary between air masses that differ in temperature and moisture (and therefore density) is called a **front**. The boundary along which a mass of warmer, moister air replaces a mass of colder, drier air is termed a **warm front** (**FIGURE 14.7A**). Some of the warm, moist air behind a warm front rises over the cold air mass and then cools and condenses to form clouds that may produce light rain. A **cold front** (**FIGURE 14.7B**) is the boundary along which a colder, drier air mass displaces a warmer, moister air mass. The colder air, being denser, tends to wedge beneath the warmer air. The warmer air rises, expands, and then cools to form clouds that can produce thunderstorms and even tornadoes (**FIGURE 14.7C**). Once a cold front passes through, the sky usually clears, and the temperature and humidity drop.

Adjacent air masses may also differ in atmospheric pressure. A **high-pressure system** contains air that

(a) Warm front

(b) Cold front

FIGURE 14.7
When a warm front approaches **(a)**, warmer air rises over cooler air, causing light or moderate precipitation as moisture in the warmer air condenses. When a cold front approaches **(b)**, colder air pushes beneath warmer air, and the warmer air rises, resulting in condensation and heavy precipitation. **(c)** Cold fronts often spawn thunderstorms and even tornadoes, like this one in the U.S. Midwest's "Tornado Alley," 2011.

(c) Active weather

moves outward away from a centre of high pressure as it descends. High-pressure systems typically bring fair weather. In a **low-pressure system**, air moves toward the low atmospheric pressure at the centre of the system and spirals upward. The air expands and cools, and clouds and precipitation often result.

Under most conditions, air in the troposphere decreases in temperature as altitude increases. Because warm air rises, vertical mixing results. Occasionally, however, a layer of cool air occurs beneath a layer of warmer air. This departure from the normal temperature profile is known as a temperature inversion, or **thermal inversion (FIGURE 14.8)** because the normal direction of temperature change is inverted. The cooler air at the bottom of the inversion layer is denser than the warmer air at the top, so it resists vertical mixing and remains stable. Thermal inversions can occur in different ways, sometimes involving cool air at ground level and sometimes producing an inversion layer higher above the ground (as shown in **FIGURE 14.8B**). One common type of inversion occurs in mountain valleys where slopes block morning sunlight, keeping ground-level air within the valley shaded and cool.

Vertical mixing normally allows air pollution to be diluted upward, but thermal inversions trap pollutants near the ground. A thermal inversion sparked a "killer smog" crisis in London, England, in 1952. A high-pressure system settled over the city, acting like a cap on the pollution; at least 4000 people—possibly as many as 12 000—died as a result of this event. Inversions regularly cause smog buildups in large metropolitan areas in valleys ringed by mountains, such as Los Angeles, Mexico City, Seoul, and Rio de Janeiro.

Large-scale circulation systems produce global climate patterns

At larger geographic scales, convective air currents contribute to broad climatic patterns **(FIGURE 14.9A)**. Near the equator, solar radiation sets in motion a pair of convective cells known as **Hadley cells**. Here, where sunlight is most intense, surface air warms, rises, and expands. As it does so, it releases moisture, producing the heavy rainfall that gives rise to tropical rainforests near the equator.

After releasing much of its moisture, this air diverges and moves in currents heading northward and southward. The air in these currents cools and descends back to Earth at about 30° latitude north and south. Because the descending air has low relative humidity, the regions

(a) Normal conditions

(b) Thermal inversion

FIGURE 14.8 A thermal inversion is a natural atmospheric occurrence that can worsen air pollution locally. Under normal conditions **(a)**, tropospheric temperature decreases with altitude. Air of different altitudes mixes, dispersing pollutants upward and outward from their sources. During a thermal inversion **(b)**, cool air remains near the ground underneath a layer of air that warms with altitude. Little mixing occurs, and pollutants are trapped near the surface.

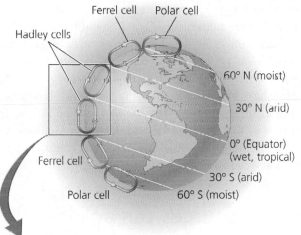

FIGURE 14.9
A series of large-scale convective cells **(a)** helps determine global patterns of humidity and aridity. Warm air near the equator rises, expands, and cools, and moisture condenses, giving rise to a wet climate in tropical regions. Air travels toward the poles and descends around 30° latitude. This air, which loses its moisture in the tropics, causes regions around 30° latitude to be arid. This convective circulation, a Hadley cell, occurs on both sides of the equator. Between roughly 30° and 60° latitude north and south, Ferrel cells occur; and between 60° and 90° latitude, polar cells occur. Air rises around 60° latitude, creating a moist climate, and falls around 90°, creating a dry climate. Global wind currents **(b)** show latitudinal patterns as well. Trade winds between the equator and 30° latitude blow westward, whereas westerlies between 30° and 60° latitude blow eastward. Global air circulation patterns are further modified by the influence of continental land masses and by the Coriolis force, which causes freely moving objects to be deflected to the right in the Northern Hemisphere and to the left in the Southern Hemisphere.

(a) Convection currents

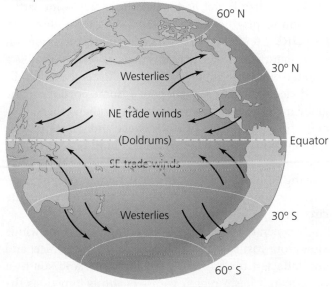

(b) Global wind patterns

roots

TRADE WINDS

Most people think that the term *trade winds*, the prevailing easterly surface winds in the tropics, originated because sailing ships used them to traverse the Atlantic for the purpose of trade in the fifteenth and sixteenth centuries. Sailing ships did make use of the trade winds, both for trade and for exploration, but the word itself originated in the early 1600s from the Old English word *tredan*, which meant "one's traditional business." In this sense, the term *trade* is not specifically related to commerce, but rather to the idea of something "habitual" or "regular," which certainly applies to the trade winds.

around 30° latitude are quite arid, giving rise to deserts. Two pairs of similar but less intense convective cells, called **Ferrel cells** and **polar cells**, lift air and create precipitation around 60° latitude north and south and cause air to descend at around 30° latitude and in the polar regions.

These three pairs of cells account for the latitudinal distribution of moisture across Earth's surface: warm, wet climates near the equator; arid climates and major deserts near 30° latitude; moist, temperate regions near 60° latitude; and dry, cold conditions near the poles. These patterns, combined with temperature variation, also help explain why biomes tend to be arrayed in latitudinal bands.

The Hadley, Ferrel, and polar cells interact with Earth's rotation to produce the global wind patterns shown in **FIGURE 14.9B**. As Earth rotates on its axis, locations on the equator spin faster than locations near the poles. As a result, the north–south air currents of the convective cells are deflected from a straight path as some portions of the globe move beneath them more quickly than others. This deflection is called the **Coriolis effect**, and it results in the curving global wind patterns evident in **FIGURE 14.9B**. The Coriolis effect influences the circulation of any freely moving fluid on Earth's surface, including ocean water, but its influence is not noticeable unless the scale of the circulation is quite large.

Between the equator and 30° latitude, the **trade winds** blow from east to west. Where the trade winds meet and are deflected toward the west, just north and south of the equator, lies a region with few winds known as the *doldrums*. Farther from the equator, between 30° and 60°

north and south latitude, the *westerlies* originate from the west and blow east. People used these global circulation patterns for centuries to facilitate ocean travel by wind-powered sailing ships.

The atmosphere interacts with the oceans to affect weather, climate, and the distribution of biomes. For instance, winds and convective circulation in ocean water together maintain ocean currents. Trade winds weaken periodically, leading to El Niño conditions. The atmosphere's interactions with other systems of the planet are complex, but even a basic understanding of how the atmosphere functions can help us comprehend how our pollution of the atmosphere can affect ecological systems, economies, and human health.

Outdoor Air Pollution

Throughout human history, we have made the atmosphere a dumping ground for airborne wastes. Whether from primitive wood fires or modern coal-burning power plants, people have generated air pollutants, gases and particulate material added to the atmosphere that can affect climate or harm people or other organisms. **Air pollution** refers to the release of air pollutants. In recent decades, government policy and improved technologies have helped us to substantially diminish outdoor air pollution, usually called *ambient air pollution*, in countries of the developed world. However, outdoor air pollution remains a problem, particularly in developing nations and in urban areas.

Natural sources can pollute

When we think of outdoor air pollution, we tend to envision smokestacks belching black smoke from industrial plants. However, natural processes produce a great deal of the world's air pollution. Some of these natural impacts can be exacerbated by human activity and land use policies.

Winds sweeping over arid terrain can send huge amounts of dust aloft. In 2001, strong westerlies lifted soil from deserts in Mongolia and China. The dust blanketed Chinese towns, spread to Japan and Korea, travelled eastward across the Pacific Ocean to the United States, then crossed the Atlantic, and left evidence atop the French Alps. Every year, hundreds of millions of tons of dust are blown westward by trade winds across the Atlantic Ocean from northern Africa to the Americas (**FIGURE 14.10A**). These dust storms bring nutrients to the Amazon basin, causing algal blooms off the west coast of Africa, as well as fungal and bacterial spores that have been linked to die-offs in Caribbean coral reef systems.

(a) Dust storm off west coast of Africa

(b) Grimsvötn volcano eruption, 2011

(c) Forest fire in Alberta

FIGURE 14.10
Massive dust storms, such as this one blowing across the Atlantic Ocean from Africa to the Americas **(a)**, are one type of natural air pollution. Volcanic eruptions are another source, as shown by Grimsvötn volcano in Iceland **(b)**, which erupted in 2011, causing air travel delays. A third natural cause of air pollution is fires in forests and grasslands **(c)**. Often, pollution from natural sources is made worse by human influence, such as when poor agricultural practices lead to soil erosion by wind or when fire suppression leads to more devastating fires.

Although dust storms are natural, the immense scale of these events is exacerbated by unsustainable farming and grazing practices that strip vegetation from the soil, promote wind erosion, and lead to desertification.

Volcanic eruptions release large quantities of particulate matter, as well as sulphur dioxide and other gases, into the troposphere. In 2010 and again in 2011, Icelandic volcanoes erupted voluminous clouds of ash, which shut down airports and delayed air travel in many parts of Britain and Europe. (**FIGURE 14.10B**). Major eruptions may blow matter into the stratosphere, where it can circle the globe and remain aloft for months or years.

Sulphur dioxide reacts with water and oxygen, and then condenses into fine droplets called **aerosols**, which reflect sunlight back into space and thereby cool the atmosphere and surface. The 1991 eruption of Mount Pinatubo in the Philippines ejected nearly 20 million tonnes of ash and aerosols and cooled global temperatures by roughly 0.5°C.

Burning vegetation also pollutes the atmosphere with soot and gases. More than 60 million hectares of forest and grassland burn in a typical year (**FIGURE 14.10C**). Fires occur naturally, but many are made more severe by human action. In North America, fuel buildup from decades of fire suppression has caused damaging forest fires in recent years. In the tropics, many fires result from the clearing of forests for farming and grazing by "slash-and-burn." In 1997, a severe drought brought on by the twentieth century's strongest El Niño event caused forest fires in Indonesia to rage out of control. Their smoke sickened 20 million Indonesians and caused a plane to crash and ships to collide. Combined with tens of thousands of fires in drought-plagued Mexico, Central America, and Africa, these fires released more carbon monoxide into the atmosphere during 1997–1998 than did our worldwide combustion of fossil fuels.

We create various types of outdoor air pollution

Since the onset of industrialization, human activity has introduced a variety of sources of air pollution. As with water pollution, air pollution can emanate from mobile or stationary sources, and from *point sources* or *non-point sources*. A point source describes a specific spot where large quantities of pollutants are discharged. Non-point sources are more diffuse, often consisting of many small sources. Power plants and factories act as stationary point sources, whereas millions of automobiles on the roadways—each one a tiny point source—together create a massive, mobile non-point source of pollutants.

Once pollutants are in the atmosphere in sufficient concentrations, they may do harm directly, or they may induce chemical reactions that produce harmful compounds. **Primary pollutants**, such as soot and carbon monoxide, are pollutants emitted into the troposphere in a form that can be directly harmful or that can react to form harmful substances. Harmful substances produced when primary pollutants interact or react with constituents of the atmosphere are called **secondary pollutants**. Secondary pollutants include tropospheric ozone, sulphuric acid, and other examples we will explore below.

Arguably the greatest human-induced air pollution problem today is our emission of greenhouse gases that contribute to global climate change. Addressing our release of excess carbon dioxide, methane, and other gases that warm the atmosphere stands as one of our civilization's primary challenges. We will discuss this issue separately and in depth in the next chapter, *Global Climate Change*.

CEPA identifies harmful airborne substances

The *Canadian Environmental Protection Act (CEPA)* (1999) provides a list of air pollutants that are subject to legislative control and management. These pollutants differ widely in their chemical composition, chemical reactivity, emission sources, residence time (how long they remain in various environmental reservoirs, including organisms), persistence (how long they last before breaking down), transportability (their ability to be moved long or short distances), and impacts on the natural and built environments, and on human and ecosystem health. Environment Canada groups the pollutants of greatest concern into four categories:[5]

1. Criteria air contaminants
2. Persistent organic pollutants
3. Heavy metals
4. Toxic air pollutants

Criteria air contaminants   Criteria air contaminants (CACs) are produced in varying quantities by a number of processes, including the burning of fossil fuels. In Canada, the list of CACs includes sulphur oxides, nitrogen oxides, particulate matter, volatile organic compounds, carbon monoxide, ammonia, and tropospheric ozone They are referred to as "criteria" contaminants because they were the first to come under government regulations, because of concerns about their potential impacts on human health.

Sulphur dioxide (SO_2) is a colourless gas with a strong odour. The vast majority of SO_2 and other sulphur oxide (SO_x or SOX) pollution results from the combustion of coal for electricity generation and industry. During combustion, elemental sulphur (S) in coal reacts with oxygen gas (O_2) to form SO_2. Once in the atmosphere, SO_2 may react to form sulphuric acid (H_2SO_4), which may then fall back to Earth as acid precipitation.

Nitrogen dioxide (NO_2) is a highly reactive, foul-smelling reddish brown gas that contributes to smog and acid precipitation. Along with nitric oxide (NO), NO_2 belongs to a family of compounds called *nitrogen oxides* (NO_x or NOX). Nitrogen oxides result when atmospheric nitrogen and oxygen react at the high temperatures created by combustion engines. More than half of NO_x emissions result from combustion in motor vehicle engines; electrical utility and industrial combustion accounts for most of the rest.

Particulate matter (PM) is composed of solid or liquid particles small enough to be suspended in the atmosphere. References to PM often include a number, specifying the size of the particles. PM_{10}, for example, refers to particles less than 10 μm (microns) in diameter; $PM_{2.5}$ refers to extremely fine particles, with diameters less than 2.5 μm; and so on. Particulate matter (which can also be called *suspended particulates, SP*) includes primary pollutants, such as dust and soot, as well as secondary pollutants, such as sulphates and nitrates, which form as a result of the alteration of primary sulphur and nitrous oxides. Particulates can damage respiratory tissues when inhaled. Most particulate matter (60%) in the atmosphere is wind-blown dust; human activity accounts for much of the rest. Along with SO_2, it was largely the emission of particulate matter from coal combustion that produced London's 1952 killer smog.

Volatile organic compounds (VOCs or VOX) are carbon-containing chemicals used in and emitted by vehicle engines and a wide variety of solvents and industrial processes, as well as many household chemicals and consumer items. One group of VOCs consists of hydrocarbons, such as methane (CH_4, the primary component of natural gas), propane (C_3H_8, used as a portable fuel), butane (C_4H_{10}, found in cigarette lighters), and octane (C_8H_{18}, a component of gasoline). Human activi-

weighing the issues

BAD AIR DAYS

Are you sensitive to smog? Do you suffer from itchy eyes, burning lungs, or other symptoms on "bad air days"? Do you think there is a smog problem in your area?

If you visit the website of the National Air Pollution Surveillance Network (NAPS), maintained by Environment Canada, you can watch animations of severe smog events in which ground-level ozone exceeded the accepted air quality standard levels over very large areas of both Canada and the United States (www.etc-cte.ec.gc.ca/NAPS/naps_smog_e.html).

ties account for about half of VOC emissions, and the remainder comes from natural sources. For example, plants produce isoprene (C_5H_8) and terpene ($C_{10}H_{15}$).

Carbon monoxide (CO) is a colourless, odourless gas produced by the incomplete combustion of fuel. Vehicles and engines are the main source, but others include industrial processes, combustion of waste, and residential wood burning. Carbon monoxide poses risk to humans and other animals, even in low concentrations. It can bind to hemoglobin in red blood cells, preventing it from becoming oxygenated.

Ammonia (NH_3) is a colourless gas with a pungent odour—it is the smell associated with urine. Most NH_3 is generated from livestock waste and fertilizer production. Ammonia is poisonous if inhaled in great quantities and is irritating to the eyes, nose, and throat in lesser concentrations. In the atmosphere it combines with sulphates and nitrates to form secondary fine particulate matter ($PM_{2.5}$). NH_3 can also contribute to the nitrification and eutrophication of aquatic systems.

Tropospheric ozone (O_3) is also called *ground-level ozone* to distinguish it from the ozone in the stratosphere, which shields us from the dangers of UV radiation. In contrast to stratospheric ozone, O_3 from human activity forms and accumulates at ground level as a pollutant. In the troposphere, this colourless gas results from the interaction of sunlight, heat, nitrogen oxides, and carbon-containing chemicals; it is therefore a secondary pollutant. A major component of smog, ozone can pose health risks because of its instability as a molecule; this triplet of oxygen atoms will readily release one, leaving a molecule of oxygen gas (O_2) and a free oxygen atom. The free oxygen atom may then participate in reactions that can injure living tissues and cause respiratory problems. Tropospheric ozone is the pollutant that most frequently exceeds its air quality standard.

Persistent organic pollutants   Persistent organic pollutants (POPs) can last in the environment for long periods of time. They are capable of travelling great distances by air because they are *volatile*, which means that they evaporate readily. The term **persistent** refers to substances that have long residence times, because they remain in environmental reservoirs for a long time, or because they take a long time to degrade or break down, or both.

POPs are of particular concern because they can enter the food supply, bioaccumulate in body tissues, and have significant impacts on human health and the environment, even in low concentrations. They have few natural sources and come primarily from human activity. Examples include industrial chemicals, such as PCBs (polychlorinated biphenyls); pesticides, such as DDT (dichloro-diphenyl-trichloroethane, **FIGURE 14.11**), chlordane, and toxaphene; and contaminants and by-products, such as dioxins and furans, which come from incomplete combustion processes.

The indiscriminate spraying and persistent buildup of DDT caused widespread deaths of birds and other fauna in the 1950s and 1960s, leading Rachel Carson to write her famous book *Silent Spring*, one of the pivotal events in the modern environmental movement. DDT was banned for agricultural use in most developed nations in the 1970s and 1980s, but its use continues today in some parts of the developing world. As recently as 2002, DDT and its by-products were still widely detectable in human blood, tissue, and breast milk samples from subjects in North America.[6]

Heavy metals   **Heavy metals** can be transported by the air, enter our water and food supply, and reside for long periods in sediments. Metals tend to be associated with

FIGURE 14.11
Learning about the persistence and negative ecological impacts of some chemical pesticides catalyzed the public and helped launch the modern environmental movement in the late 1960s and early 1970s. Here, a farmer sprays pesticide on his field without adequate personal protection against chemical exposure.

particulate matter, either occurring in particulate form or attaching to small particles that can then be transported atmospherically. Heavy metals are poisonous, even in low concentrations, and can bioaccumulate in body tissues. These pollutants occur even in Canada's far north—they are carried from the industrial south by continent-scale atmospheric currents—where they are deposited on land and water surfaces. This is called *long-range transport of atmospheric pollutants (LRTAP)*, and it has been a concern in Canada since at least the early 1970s.

Mercury is a heavy metal of considerable concern in Canada. Mercury is *volatile* (evaporates readily) and occurs in a number of different chemical forms, some more toxic than others. It has natural as well as human sources. It has been used for a variety of industrial purposes, partly because of its unusual property of remaining liquid at surface temperatures and pressures. Like other heavy metals, mercury can enter the food chain, accumulate in body tissues, and cause central nervous system malfunction and other ailments. Mercury is *lipophilic*, which can be translated as "fat-loving"; it is chemically capable of binding to fatty tissues in organisms. Mercury is also of concern as a pollutant in surface water bodies.

Lead, also a heavy metal, enters the atmosphere as a particulate pollutant. The lead-containing compounds tetraethyl lead and tetramethyl lead, when added to gasoline, improve engine performance. However, exhaust from the combustion of leaded gasoline emits lead into the atmosphere, from which it can be inhaled or deposited on land or water. Like mercury, lead is bioaccumulative and can cause damage to the central nervous system. Once people recognized the dangers of lead, leaded gasoline began to be phased out in most industrialized nations in the 1970s. The use of leaded gas ended in Canada in 1993.[7] Today the greatest source of atmospheric lead pollution in developed nations is industrial metal smelting. However,

many developing nations still add lead to gasoline and experience significant lead pollution.

Toxic air pollutants   **Toxic air pollutants** are a broad category of "other" pollutants identified by *CEPA* as being harmful or toxic, and therefore subject to regulation, control, and monitoring. They include substances known to cause cancer, reproductive defects, or neurological, developmental, immune system, or respiratory problems in people. Some also negatively affect the health of animals and plants. This category overlaps with the other types of air pollutants (for example, lead, mercury, dioxins, furans, and ozone all appear on the list of toxic pollutants, as well as in their other categories), but it includes additional substances such as asbestos. Chlorofluorocarbons (CFCs) are also on the list. Most toxic air pollutants are produced by human activities, such as metal smelting, sewage treatment, and industrial processes.

Government agencies share in dealing with air pollution

In Canada the management of air-related issues is the responsibility of the federal government—primarily, but not exclusively, Environment Canada—and the provincial and territorial governments, through their environment ministries. For the most part, municipal governments do not have direct regulatory control over activities that affect air quality. However, municipal governments manage so many activities that influence air quality that their role is central to the collaborative effort.

Federal   The principal federal legislation under which air quality is regulated is the *Canadian Environmental Protection Act* (1999), described officially as "an Act respecting pollution prevention and the protection of the environment and human health in order to contribute to sustainable development."[8] Although *CEPA* gives the lead responsibility for air quality to Environment Canada, it also defines an important role for Health Canada, which we will investigate in greater detail in the chapter on *Environmental Health and Hazards*. Federal agencies, such as Transport Canada and Natural Resources Canada, also have programs and activities with important linkages to air quality issues.

The federal government is also responsible for entering Canada into international agreements concerning air quality. The *Montreal Protocol* and the *Kyoto Protocol* are examples of multilateral agreements that address air pollution issues of global concern (stratospheric ozone depletion and global warming, respec-

weighing the issues

INVESTIGATING YOUR REGION'S AIR QUALITY

How polluted is the air near where you live? Go to the National Pollutant Release Inventory (NPRI) website at www.ec.gc.ca/pdb/npri/npri_home_e.cfm. Use the *Google Earth* mapping tool to check on the amounts of pollutants released in your own province or local area. Are there any specific facilities in your area that are major emitters of atmospheric pollutants?

tively). In 2011 Canada became the first signatory nation from the developed world to announce that it would withdraw from the Kyoto Protocol.

Canada has a long history of international agreements with the United States to control transboundary pollution. For air quality, these date back to agreements made in the early 1900s, although the modern era began in 1979 with agreements concerning the long-range transport of pollutants related to acid deposition. The present bilateral international agreement on transboundary air pollution, coordinated primarily through the International Joint Commission, is the *Canada–United States Air Quality Agreement*, signed in 1991. This agreement has three annexes, the first dealing with acid rain precursors, the second with coordination of international scientific research, and the third with ground-level ozone.

Provincial/territorial   Each provincial and territorial government approaches air quality issues with its own agenda and set of rules, through its environment ministry. This makes sense—not just politically but scientifically, too—since issues vary dramatically from one region to another. For example, as discussed in "Central Case: The Rain and the Big Nickel," acid deposition caused by both local pollution and pollutants transported from the industrial midwestern states is the major air pollution issue in Ontario. In Saskatchewan, in contrast, air quality issues associated with the handling of grain, feed, and livestock are of greater concern.

Regional differences in the handling of air quality issues can lead to problems, though. For example, in the past the standards for acceptable levels and the protocols of measurement for pollutants have varied significantly from one jurisdiction to another. The government has been trying to bring these standards into conformity across the nation, by working through the Canadian Council of Ministers of the Environment (CCME). In 1998 the federal government, provinces, and territories signed an agreement to enhance effectiveness, accountability, and clarity in the management of environmental issues throughout Canada. Roles and responsibilities are assigned, on a case-by-case basis, to the government agency best situated to deal with the matter, but each level of government still retains its legal authority in the matter. The CCME has signed several agreements on harmonized standards for water quality, but those for air quality, the *National Ambient Air Quality Objectives*, have yet to be formally enacted.[9]

Municipal   Only two municipalities in Canada—Montreal and Greater Vancouver—have been given direct regulatory authority over sources of air pollution by their respective provincial governments. However, all munici-palities manage programs and activities that directly influence air quality on a daily basis—public transportation and land use zoning come to mind, for example.

Therefore, most municipalities have programs aimed at improving air quality and raising public awareness of air quality issues. The top concerns differ from one location to another, and air quality may or may not be the top issue in a given municipality. For example, in Mississauga, Ontario—a geographically spread-out, largely suburban city—transportation and related air quality concerns are the central environmental issue, both for government decision makers and for the general public. In Halifax, with a smaller population, shorter travel distances, and fewer cars, wastewater management takes priority over air quality concerns. Pollution sources differ, too, from one locality to another. In Sudbury, smelters are a central concern; in Mississauga, the issue is cars and coal-fired power plants. Elsewhere, pulp-and-paper mills are of primary concern, or grain-handling operations, or large feedlots, or dust from cement manufacturers.

Monitoring shows that many forms of air pollution have decreased

CEPA not only lists the pollutants of interest but also requires that any releases of these pollutants be reported to the National Pollutant Release Inventory (NPRI), which is maintained by Environment Canada. The NPRI is thus one important vehicle that can be used to keep track of air quality in Canada. The data on NPRI are submitted, under law, directly by those who emit harmful substances into the atmosphere.

Pollutants also are measured and monitored through a nationwide network of monitoring stations that compose the National Air Pollution Surveillance (NAPS) Network, coordinated by Environment Canada (**FIGURE 14.12**). Many of the stations in the network are NAPS-designated sites; however, stations managed by other federal agencies (such as the Meteorological Service of Canada), as well as provincial, territorial, municipal, or other types of agencies (such as universities), also contribute data to the network.

The main focus of air quality monitoring is on the criteria air contaminants, but other categories of pollutants are monitored at some stations. Specialized and regional networks often contribute to the monitoring of these other pollutants. Examples include the Canadian Air and Precipitation Monitoring Network (non-urban air quality); Surface Ozone Monitoring Network; and Mercury Deposition Network.

FIGURE 14.12   This map shows the network of real-time air quality monitoring stations across Canada.

In the decades since the first modern anti-pollution actions in North America in the early 1970s, emissions of some criteria air contaminants have decreased substantially. This has resulted in declining levels of these pollutants, as measured at air quality monitoring stations throughout Canada (**FIGURE 14.13**). The most dramatic decrease can be seen in atmospheric lead. Even though Canada did not phase out leaded gas until 1993, the cessation of leaded gas use in the United States in the early 1970s had a clear impact on atmospheric lead in Canada. In contrast, O_3 shows an increase over the same period, whereas NO_2 and PM show only minimal decreases (see also **FIGURE 14.14** on page 422). Not surprisingly, these three pollutants are the core indicators for Canada's Air Quality Health Index.

There are several reasons for the declines in some pollutants, which have occurred in spite of increases in population, energy use, vehicle use, and economic productivity in North America. Cleaner-burning motor vehicle engines and automotive technologies such as catalytic converters have played a large part in decreasing emissions of carbon monoxide and several other pollutants. Sulphur dioxide permit-trading and clean coal technologies have reduced SO_2 emissions. Technologies, such as electrostatic precipitators and **scrubbers** (**FIGURE 14.15** on page 422), which chemically convert or physically remove airborne pollutants before they are emitted

from smokestacks, have allowed factories, power plants, and refineries to decrease emissions of several pollutants.

Other industrialized nations have also succeeded in reducing emissions and improving air quality, thanks to improved technologies and targeted federal policies. Between 1996 and 2005, London, England, achieved a 56% reduction in CO emissions, a 41% drop in NO_x emissions, a 28% decline in particulate matter release, and an impressive 73% decrease in SO_2 emissions. Only tropospheric ozone showed an increase, rising 33%.

We will complete our look at outdoor air pollution with an examination of three specific issues: photochemical smog; acidic deposition; and stratospheric ozone depletion, along with a brief consideration of air quality issues in rural areas and in the rapidly industrializing nations of the developing world.

Smog is the most common, widespread air quality problem

In response to the increasing incidence of fogs polluted by the smoke of Britain's Industrial Revolution, an early British scientist coined the term **smog**. Today the term is used worldwide to describe unhealthy mixtures of air pollutants that often form over urban areas.

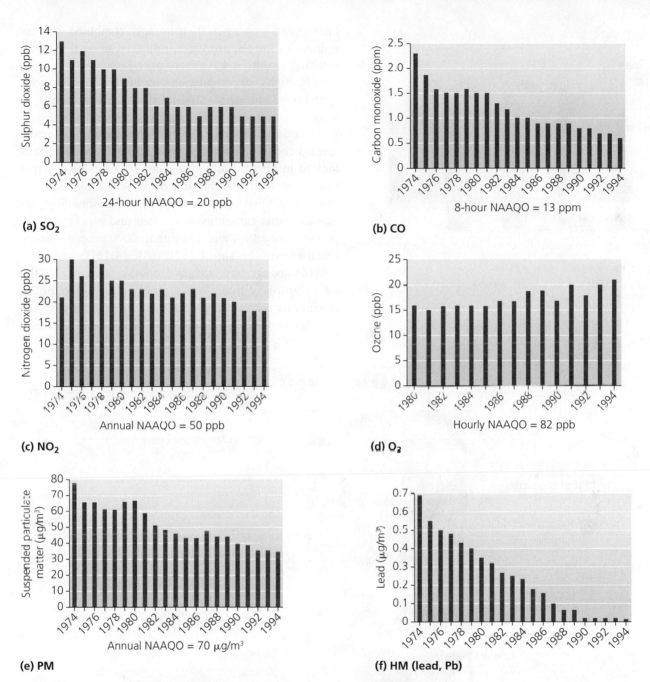

FIGURE 14.13 Mean annual levels of some criteria air contaminants have declined since the early 1970s; others show little to no improvement. NAAQO stands for the National Ambient Air Quality Objectives, given for comparison in each case.

The deadly smog that enveloped London in 1952 was what we today call **industrial smog**, or grey-air smog. When coal or oil is burned, some portion is completely combusted, forming CO_2; some is partially combusted, producing CO; and some remains unburned and is released as soot, or particles of carbon. Moreover, coal contains varying amounts of contaminants, including mercury and sulphur. Sulphur reacts with oxygen to form sulphur dioxide, which can undergo a series of reactions to form sulphuric acid and ammonium sulphate (**FIGURE 14.16A** on page 423). These chemicals and

others produced by further reactions, along with soot, are the main components of industrial smog and give the smog its characteristic grey colour.

Industrial smog is far less common today in developed nations than it was 50–100 years ago. In the wake of the 1952 London episode and others, the governments of most developed nations began regulating industrial emissions to minimize the external costs they impose on citizens. However, in regions that are industrializing today, such as China, India, and Eastern Europe, heavy reliance on coal burning (by industry and by citizens

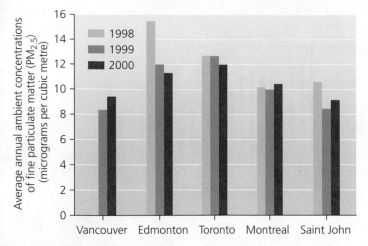

FIGURE 14.14
Levels of fine particulate matter are still a problem in Canadian cities. Based on data from National Air Pollution Surveillance Network, Environment Canada.

heating and cooking in their homes), combined with lax pollution controls, produces industrial smog that poses significant health risks in many areas.

Although coal combustion supplies the chemical constituents for industrial smog, weather also plays a role, as it did in London in 1952. A similar event occurred four years earlier in Donora, Pennsylvania. Here, air near the ground cooled during the night, and because Donora is located in hilly terrain, too little morning sun reached the valley floor to warm and disperse the cold air. The resulting thermal inversion trapped smog containing particulate matter emissions from a steel and wire factory; 21 people were killed, and more than 6000 people—nearly half the town—became ill (**FIGURE 14.16B**).

Hilly topography, such as Donora's, is a factor in the air pollution of many other cities where surrounding mountains trap air and create inversions. This is true for Mexico City, which has long symbolized the smog

FIGURE 14.15
In this spray-tower wet scrubber, polluted air (1) rises through a chamber while arrays of nozzles spray a mist of water mixed with lime or other active chemicals (2). The falling mist captures pollutants and carries them to the bottom of the chamber (3), essentially washing them out of the air. Excess mist is captured on a screen (4), and air emitted from the scrubber has largely been cleansed (5). Periodically, the dirty water is drained from the chamber (6), cleansed in a settling tank, and recirculated (7) through the spray nozzles. The resulting sludge must be disposed of (8) as hazardous waste. Scrubbers and other pollution control devices come in many designs; the type shown here typically removes at least 90% of particulate matter and gases, such as sulphur dioxide.

Coal and oil

Sulphur (S) in coal and oil

Carbon (C)

—Oxygen (O₂)

—Oxygen (O₂)

Burning

Burning

Sulphur dioxide (SO₂)

Carbon monoxide (CO) and carbon dioxide (CO₂)

—Oxygen (O₂)

Sulphur trioxide (SO₃)

—Water vapour (H₂O)

Sulphuric acid (H₂SO₄)

—Ammonia (NH₃)

Ammonium sulphate ((NH₄)₂SO₄)

(a) Burning sulphur-rich oil or coal without adequate pollution control technologies

(b) Smog event of 1948, midday in Donora, Pennsylvania

FIGURE 14.16

Emissions from the combustion of coal and oil in plants without pollution control technologies can create industrial smog. Industrial smog consists primarily of sulphur dioxide and particulate matter, as well as carbon monoxide and carbon dioxide from the carbon component of fossil fuels. When fossil fuels are combusted, sulphur contaminants give rise to sulphur dioxide, which in the presence of other chemicals in the atmosphere can produce several other sulphur compounds **(a)**. Under certain weather conditions, industrial smog can blanket whole towns or regions, as it did in Donora, Pennsylvania, shown here in the daytime during its deadly 1948 smog episode **(b)**.

problems of modern cities. Modern-day Mexico City, however, suffers from a different type of smog, called photochemical smog.

Photochemical smog is produced by a complex series of reactions

A photochemical process is one whose activation requires light. **Photochemical smog**, or brown-air smog, is formed through light-driven chemical reactions of primary pollutants and normal atmospheric compounds that produce a mix of more than 100 different chemicals, tropospheric ozone often being the most abundant among them (**FIGURE 14.17A**). High levels of NO₂ cause photochemical smog to form a brownish haze over cities (**FIGURE 14.17B**). Hot, sunny, windless days in urban areas provide perfect conditions for the formation of pho-

tochemical smog. Exhaust from morning traffic releases large amounts of NO and VOCs into a city's air. Sunlight then promotes the production of ozone and other constituents of photochemical smog. Levels of photochemical pollutants in urban areas typically peak in midafternoon and can irritate people's eyes, noses, and throats.

The cities most afflicted by photochemical smog are those with weather and topography that promote it. The geographic area associated with a particular air mass is called an **airshed**. People who live within the same airshed tend to experience similar weather and "bad air" days. Airsheds that are topographically constrained, such as those that occupy topographical basins or valleys, allow less natural circulation and renewal of the air, and are more prone to inversions and prolonged smog events.

Some provinces have cut emissions leading to photochemical smog through vehicle inspection programs, such as AirCare in British Columbia or Drive Clean in Ontario, where drivers are required to have their vehicle exhaust inspected regularly at check stations to maintain their registrations. Although a failed "smog check" means inconvenience for the car owner, these programs help maintain vehicle condition and make the air measurably cleaner for all of us.

(b) Photochemical smog over Mexico City

(a) Formation of photochemical smog

FIGURE 14.17

Nitric oxide, a key element of photochemical smog, can start a chemical chain reaction **(a)** that results in the production of other compounds, including nitrogen dioxide, nitric acid, ozone, and peroxyacyl nitrates (PANs). PANs can induce further reactions that damage living tissues in animals and plants. Nitric acid contributes to acidic deposition as well as photochemical smog. Photochemical smog is common today over many urban areas, especially those with hilly topography or frequent inversion layers. Mexico City **(b)** frequently experiences photochemical smog.

In 2003, London, England, instituted a "congestion-charging" program. People driving into central London during weekdays were required to pay £8 (about $15) per day. The money was to be used to enhance bus service and encourage transport by rail, taxi, bicycle, and foot. Many citizens were outraged, arguing that the fees were too high or that the system discriminated against poor people. Others complained that it would not work or that the promised improvements in public transport were too slow in coming. However, many Londoners supported the program, and business support grew as the benefits became clearer. Traffic congestion in the zone decreased by nearly 30%, and there were 40–70 fewer injuries from traffic accidents per year. The air became cleaner, as well. In the first year, particulate matter in the charging zone declined by 15.5%, nitrogen oxide emissions decreased by 13.4%, and carbon dioxide emissions fell by 16.4%. The charges are still in place, although the congestion charge zone is now smaller. Similar congestion-charging schemes have been successfully implemented in other cities, such as Singapore. London's most recent (2010) Air Quality Strategy focuses on getting older, more polluting vehicles off the roads, and utilizing cleaner hybrid vehicles for transit routes.

Air quality is a rural issue, too

Air quality is not only an urban issue. In rural areas, people suffer from drift of airborne pesticides from farms, as well as industrial pollutants transported from cities, factories, and power plants. A great deal of rural air pollution emanates from feedlots, where cattle, hogs, or chickens are raised in dense concentrations. The huge numbers of animals at feedlots and the voluminous amounts of waste they produce release dust as well as methane, hydrogen sulphide, and ammonia. These gases create objectionable odours, and the ammonia contributes to nitrogen deposition across wide areas. Studies have shown that people working at and living near feedlots have high rates of respiratory problems.

Industrializing nations are suffering increasing air pollution

Although industrialized nations have been improving their air quality, outdoor air pollution is growing worse in many industrializing countries. In these societies, rapidly proliferating factories and power plants are releasing emissions with little effort to control pollution, and citizens continue to burn traditional sources of fuel, such as wood and charcoal, for cooking and home heating. Thus, just as occurred in England during its period of industrialization, new pollution sources are added to traditional sources while populations rise.

China has some of the world's worst air pollution. Four out of five Chinese cities surveyed by the World Bank in 2000 experienced SO_2 or NO_2 emissions above the threshold set by the World Health Organization. Air pollution became a serious concern for both the health and the performance of athletes during the Beijing Olympics of 2008. Together, China and India suffer 58% of the 1.8 million premature deaths that the World Bank estimates occur each year globally as a result of outdoor air pollution.

Southern Asia has a persistent 3-km-thick layer of pollution that hangs over the subcontinent throughout the dry season each December through April. Dubbed the *Asian Brown Cloud*, this massive layer of pollution is thought to reduce the sunlight reaching Earth's surface in that region by 10–15%, influence climate, decrease rice productivity by 5–10%, and account for many thousands of deaths each year.

Synthetic chemicals deplete stratospheric ozone

A pollutant in the troposphere, ozone is a highly beneficial gas at altitudes of about 25 km in the lower stratosphere, where it is concentrated in the stratospheric *ozone layer* (**SEE FIGURE 14.2**). Here, concentrations of ozone are only about 12 parts per million. However, ozone molecules are so effective at absorbing incoming ultraviolet radiation from the Sun that this concentration helps to protect life on Earth's surface from the damaging effects of ultraviolet (UV) radiation.

In the 1960s, atmospheric scientists began wondering why their measurements of stratospheric ozone were lower than theoretical models predicted. Researchers hypothesizing that natural or artificial chemicals were depleting ozone finally pinpointed a group of human-made compounds derived from simple hydrocarbons, such as ethane and methane, in which hydrogen atoms are replaced by chlorine, bromine, or fluorine. One class of such compounds, **chlorofluorocarbons (CFCs)**, was being mass-produced by industry at a rate of 1 million metric tons per year in the early 1970s, and this rate was growing by 20% a year.

Soon researchers showed that CFCs could deplete stratospheric ozone by releasing chlorine atoms that split ozone molecules, creating from each of them an O_2 molecule and a ClO molecule (see "The Science Behind the Story: Identifying CFCs as the Main Cause of Ozone Depletion"). Then in 1985, scientists announced that stratospheric ozone levels over Antarctica had declined by 40–60% in the previous decade, leaving a thinned ozone concentration that was soon dubbed the **ozone hole** (**FIGURE 14.18**).

Research over the next few years confirmed the link between CFCs and ozone loss in the Antarctic and indicated that depletion was also occurring in the Arctic and perhaps globally. The depletion was shown to be growing both in severity and in areal extent, almost without exception, year to year. Already concerned that increased UV radiation would lead to more skin cancer, scientists were becoming anxious over possible ecological effects as well, including harm to crops and to the productivity of ocean phytoplankton, the base of the marine food chain.

roots

OZONE

The word *ozone*, coined in 1840 by German chemist Christian Friedrich Schönbein, derives from the Greek (and later, German) word *ozon* (from *ozein*), meaning "to smell." The name was chosen to reflect the pungent smell of ozone, which some people liken to an electrical smell, like sparks from fireworks, and others to clean bed sheets or a forest. You can smell ozone immediately after a lightning storm.

There are still many questions to be resolved about ozone depletion

Although significant progress has been made in understanding stratospheric ozone depletion since the initial

(a) October mean ozone levels at the South Pole

(b) The largest recorded "ozone hole" over Antarctica, September 24, 2006

FIGURE 14.18
The "ozone hole" consists of a region of thinned ozone density in the stratosphere over Antarctica and the southernmost ocean regions. It has reappeared seasonally each September in recent decades. Data from Antarctica **(a)** show a steady decrease in stratospheric ozone concentrations from the 1960s to 1990. Ozone-depleting CFCs began to be regulated under the Montreal Protocol in 1987, and ozone concentrations stopped declining. Satellite imagery from September 24, 2006 **(b)**, shows the "ozone hole" (blue) at its largest-ever recorded extent to date. Data in (a) Earth System Research Laboratory Global Monitoring Division, NOAA www.esrl.noaa.gov

discovery of the role of CFCs, many questions remain. For example, will ozone depletion spread from the polar regions, where it is most severe, to encompass mid-latitude and even low-latitude regions (and if so, how quickly)? What is the actual relationship between ozone depletion and human health impacts, such as skin cancer? What are the other potential impacts of ozone depletion, for example, on marine and terrestrial ecosystems and on other types of materials? And—importantly, for policy decisions—are the substitute chemicals that are being proposed in international agreements definitely less damaging to the stratospheric ozone layer, or do they raise concerns of their own?

The question of polar ozone depletion is of particular interest, especially to Canadian scientists working in the Arctic. The answer to why ozone depletion is most severe over the poles probably lies in a more refined understanding of the physical processes involved in ozone-depleting reactions. For example, scientists now believe that the ozone-depleting chemical reactions may find ideal sites on tiny ice crystals that are found only where the air is extremely cold. These conditions are optimal over Antarctica, where a circular wind pattern called the *polar vortex* traps extremely cold air over the pole.

There are many other interesting questions waiting to be answered. For example, Dr. Ralf Staebler and colleagues from the Air Quality Research Division of Environment Canada are investigating a unique form of ozone depletion that occurs near the ground in the polar regions, as the sun rises in the spring after the long darkness of winter. Here, a sudden loss of ozone is caused by reactions with bromine, another type of halogen, which can deplete ozone at ground level in much the same manner as the chlorine from the CFCs in the upper atmosphere. The scientists measure this ozone loss using a mobile measurement platform—basically, a temperature-controlled box full of instruments and a meteorological mast mounted on a sled—which they call OOTI ("Out On The Ice") (**FIGURE 14.19**). They wanted a platform that would be self-contained, self-sufficient, and mobile, with which to measure ozone, the chemicals implicated in ozone-destroying chemistry, and the associated *micrometeorology*. As part of the Canadian contribution to the International Polar Year, this sled has been deployed near Alert, NU, Barrow, AK, and Kuujjuarapik (Hudson Bay) and from the Canadian icebreaker Amundsen on the frozen ocean south of Banks Island.

The researchers are particularly interested in finding out whether the ozone-depleting chemistry is occurring near the ground or directly at the ice–

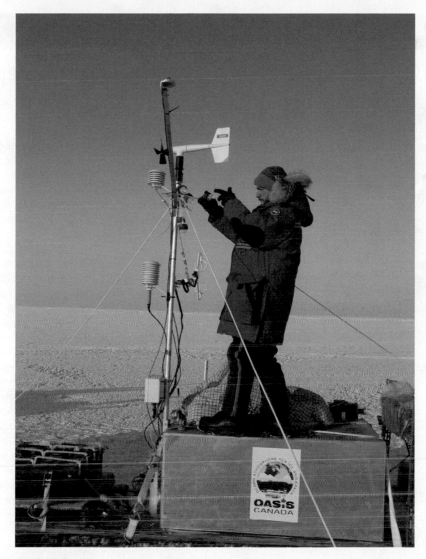

FIGURE 14.19
Researchers from the Air Quality Research Division of Environment Canada employ a mobile lab-on-a-sled called OOTI to measure ozone and ozone-depleting chemicals in the Arctic environment.

atmosphere interface. The OOTI sleds, combined with instruments operated by other researchers on the Amundsen Icebreaker, have allowed them to measure ozone depletion processes. Ozone-depleting reactions are of further interest to these researchers because they have an impact on the fate of mercury (Hg) in the Arctic. Ozone controls the oxidation state of the atmosphere. Once the ozone is gone, a new chemical regime is entered in which halogens emitted from the ocean take over this role. In an ozone-controlled atmosphere, the residence time of Hg vapour is quite long (on the order of a year). In a halogen-controlled regime, Hg is more efficiently converted to more chemically reactive forms, which can then enter the snow and ice and possibly the biosphere, with ensuing negative consequences.

The Montreal Protocol addressed ozone depletion

Scientists all over the world continue to address problems like these in an attempt to refine our understanding of the complex chemical process of ozone depletion. In the meantime, though, the international community has been unwilling to wait for catastrophe and has moved forward to strike an agreement to reduce and eventually eliminate the production of known ozone-depleting substances, also known as *ODS*.

In response to the scientific concerns, international policy efforts to restrict CFC production finally bore fruit in 1987 with the **Montreal Protocol**. In this treaty, signatory nations (eventually numbering 197) agreed to

THE SCIENCE BEHIND THE STORY

Identifying CFCs as the Main Cause of Ozone Depletion

Drs. F. Sherwood Rowland (left), Mario Molina (centre), and Paul Crutzen (right) jointly received the 1995 Nobel Prize in chemistry.

Ozone was discovered in 1839, and its presence in the upper atmosphere was first proposed in the 1880s. In 1924, British scientist G. M. B. Dobson built an instrument that could measure ozone concentrations by sampling incoming sunlight at ground level and comparing the intensities of wavelengths that ozone does and does not absorb. By the 1970s, the Dobson ozone spectrophotometer was being used by a global network of observation stations.

Research on CFCs has also had a long history. First invented in 1928, CFCs were useful as refrigerants, fire extinguishers, and propellants for aerosol spray cans. Starting in the 1960s, CFCs also found wide use as cleaners for electronics and as a part of the process of manufacturing rigid polystyrene foams. Research on the chemical properties of CFCs showed that they were almost completely inert; that is, they rarely reacted with other chemicals. Therefore, scientists surmised that, at trace levels, CFCs would be harmless to both people and the environment.

However, in June 1974, chemists F. Sherwood Rowland and Mario Molina published a paper in the journal *Nature*, arguing that the inertness that made CFCs so ideal for industrial purposes could also have disastrous consequences for the ozone layer.

Whereas reactive chemicals are broken down in the lower atmosphere, CFCs reach the stratosphere unchanged. Once CFCs reach the stratosphere, intense ultraviolet radiation from the Sun breaks them into their constituent chlorine and carbon atoms. In a two-step chemical reaction (see the figure), a chlorine atom can split an ozone molecule and then ready itself to split another one. Over its lifetime, each free chlorine atom, it was calculated, can catalyze the destruction of as many as 100 000 ozone molecules.

Rowland and Molina were the first to assemble a complete picture of the threat posed by CFCs, but they could not have reached their conclusions without the contributions of other scientists. British researcher James Lovelock had developed an instrument to measure extremely low concentrations of atmospheric gases. American scientists Richard Stolarski and Ralph Cicerone had shown that chlorine atoms can catalyze the destruction of ozone. Dutch meteorologist Paul Crutzen had shown that naturally produced nitrous oxide breaks down ozone. And American researcher James McDonald had predicted that ozone loss, by allowing more UV radiation to reach the surface, would result in thousands more skin cancer cases each year.

Rowland and Molina's analysis earned them the 1995 Nobel Prize in chemistry jointly with Crutzen. It also helped spark discussion among scientists, policy makers, and industry leaders over limits on CFC production. As a result, several nations banned the use of CFCs in aerosol spray cans in 1979. Other uses continued, however, and by the early 1980s global production of CFCs was increasing.

Then, a new finding shocked scientists and spurred the international community to take further action. Scientists at a British

cut CFC production in half. Five follow-up agreements strengthened the pact by deepening the cuts, advancing timetables for compliance, and addressing related ozone-depleting chemicals. Today the production and use of ozone-depleting compounds has fallen by 95% since the late 1980s, and scientists can discern the beginnings of long-term recovery of the stratospheric ozone layer. Industry has been able to shift to alternative chemicals that have largely turned out to be cheaper and more efficient.

There are still challenges to overcome. Much of the 5 billion kilograms of CFCs emitted into the troposphere has yet to diffuse up into the stratosphere, and CFCs are slow to dissipate or break down. Thus, we can expect a considerable lag time between the implementation of policy and the desired environmental effect. (This is one reason scientists often argue for proactive policy guided by the precautionary principle, rather than reactive policy that may respond too late.) Moreover, nations can plead for some ozone-depleting chemicals to be exempted from the ban; for example, the United States recently was allowed to continue using methyl bromide, a fumigant used to control pests on strawberries.

Despite the remaining challenges, the Montreal Protocol and its follow-up amendments are widely considered the biggest success story so far in addressing any global environmental problem. Environmental scientists have attributed this success primarily to two factors:

1. Policy makers engaged industry in helping to solve the problem, and government and industry worked

UV radiation

Ozone

CFC

Chlorofluorocarbons

Chlorine

Stratosphere

Oxygen

Chlorine

Chlorine monoxide

Refrigerators, aerosol
spray cans, air conditioners
(sources of chlorofluorocarbons)

Oxygen

Oxygen atom

A chlorine atom released from a CFC molecule in the presence of UV radiation reacts with an ozone molecule, forming one molecule of oxygen gas and one chlorine monoxide (ClO) molecule. The oxygen atom in the ClO molecule will then bind with a stray oxygen atom to form oxygen gas, leaving the chlorine atom to begin the destructive cycle anew. In this way, any given chlorine atom may destroy up to 100 000 ozone molecules.

research station in Antarctica had been recording ozone concentrations since the 1950s. In May 1985, Joseph Farman and colleagues reported in *Nature* that Antarctic ozone concentrations had declined dramatically since the 1970s. The decline exceeded even the worst-case predictions.

To determine what was causing the "ozone hole" over Antarctica, expeditions were mounted in 1986 and 1987 to measure trace amounts of atmospheric gases by using ground stations and high-altitude balloons and aircraft. Together with other researchers, Crutzen analyzed data col-

lected on the expeditions and concluded that the ozone hole resulted from a combination of Antarctic weather conditions and human-made chemicals.

In the frigid Antarctic winter, high-altitude—or polar stratospheric—clouds form. In the spring, those clouds provide ideal conditions for CFC-derived chlorine and other chemicals to catalyze the destruction of massive amounts of ozone. The problem is made worse by the fact that prevailing air currents largely isolate Antarctica's atmosphere from the rest of Earth's atmosphere.

In subsequent years, scientists used data from ground stations and satellites to show that ozone levels were declining globally. In 1987, those findings helped convince the world's nations to agree on the Montreal Protocol, which aimed to cut CFC production in half by 1998. Within two years, however, further scientific evidence and computer modelling showed that more drastic measures would be needed if serious damage to the ozone layer was to be avoided. In 1990, the Montreal Protocol was strengthened to include a complete phaseout of CFCs by 2000. By 1998, the amount of chlorine in the atmosphere appeared to be levelling off.

together on developing replacement chemicals. This cooperation reduced the battles that typically erupt between environmentalists and industry.

2. Implementation of the Montreal Protocol followed an adaptive management approach, altering strategies midstream in response to new scientific data, technological advances, or economic figures.

Because of its success in addressing ozone depletion, the Montreal Protocol is widely seen as a model for international cooperation in addressing other pressing global problems, such as persistent organic pollutants, climate change, and biodiversity loss.

Acidic deposition is another transboundary pollution problem

As discussed in "Central Case: The Rain and the Big Nickel," **acidic deposition** refers to the settling, or deposition, of acidic or acid-forming pollutants from the atmosphere onto Earth's surface. This can take place either by **acidic precipitation** (commonly referred to as **acid rain**, but also including acid snow, sleet, and hail), by fog, by gases, or by the deposition of dry particles. Acidic deposition is one type of **atmospheric deposition**, which refers more broadly to the wet or dry deposition on land of a wide variety of pollutants, including mercury, lead, nitrates, organochlorides, and others.

Acidic deposition originates primarily with the emission of sulphur dioxide and nitrogen oxides, largely through fossil fuel combustion by automobiles, electric utilities, and industrial facilities like the Inco and Falconbridge smelters in Sudbury. Once airborne, these primary pollutants can react with water, oxygen, and oxidants to produce secondary compounds of low pH, primarily sulphuric acid and nitric acid. Suspended in the troposphere, droplets of these acids may travel for days or weeks, sometimes covering hundreds or thousands of kilometres in a particular airshed before falling in precipitation (**FIGURE 14.20**).

Natural rainwater is not neutral; in fact, it is slightly acidic, with a typical pH of around 5.6. This is mainly because rainwater reacts with naturally occurring carbon dioxide in the air, forming carbonic acid. Rain and other forms of precipitation with pH less than about 5.1 are considered to be acidified. Acidification can occur as a result of natural processes, such as sulphur-rich volcanic eruptions, but the main cause of acid precipitation is human-generated air pollution.

Acidic deposition can have wide-ranging, cumulative detrimental effects on ecosystems and on our built environment (**TABLE 14.1**). Acids leach nutrients, such as calcium, magnesium, and potassium, from the topsoil, altering soil chemistry and harming plants and soil organisms. This occurs because hydrogen ions from

Table 14.1   Effects of Acidic Deposition on Ecosystems in Northeastern North America

Acidic deposition in northeastern forests has

- Accelerated leaching of base cations (ions that counteract acidic deposition) from soil
- Allowed sulphur and nitrogen to accumulate in soil
- Increased dissolved inorganic aluminum in soil, hindering plant uptake of water and nutrients
- Caused calcium to leach from needles of red spruce, leading to tree mortality from wintertime freezing
- Increased mortality of sugar maples because of leaching of base cations from soil and leaves
- Acidified many lakes, especially those situated on soils and bedrock of granitic composition
- Lowered lakes' capacity to neutralize further acids
- Elevated aluminum levels in surface waters
- Reduced species diversity and abundance of aquatic life, and negatively affected entire food webs

Source: Adapted from Driscoll, C.T., et al. (2001). Acid rain revisited. Hubbard Brook Research Foundation.

acidic precipitation take the place of calcium, magnesium, and potassium ions in soil compounds, and these valuable nutrients leach into the subsoil, where they become inaccessible to plant roots.

FIGURE 14.20   Acidic deposition can have consequences long distances downwind from its source. Sulphur dioxide and nitric oxide emitted by industries and utilities can be transformed into sulphuric acid and nitric acid through chemical reactions in the atmosphere. These acidic compounds then descend to Earth's surface in rain, snow, fog, and dry deposition.

Acidic precipitation also "mobilizes" toxic metal ions, such as aluminum, zinc, mercury, and copper, by chemically converting them from insoluble forms to soluble forms. Elevated soil concentrations of metals, such as aluminum, hinder water and nutrient uptake by plants. In some regions of Britain and the United States, acid fog with a pH of 2.3 (equivalent to vinegar) has enveloped forests for extended periods, leading to widespread tree mortality.

When acidic water runs off from land, it affects streams, rivers, and lakes. In fact, thousands of lakes in Canada, Scandinavia, the United States, and elsewhere now have lost their fish because acid precipitation leaches aluminum out of soil and rock and into waterways in a form that can be deadly to aquatic life. Aluminum can kill fish by damaging their gills and disrupting their salt balance, water balance, breathing, and circulation.

Besides altering natural ecosystems, acid precipitation also damages agricultural crops. Moreover, it erodes stone buildings, corrodes cars, and erases the writing from tombstones. Ancient cathedrals, monuments, temples, and stone statues in many parts of the world are experiencing irreversible damage as their features gradually wear away.

Because the pollutants leading to acid deposition can travel long distances, their effects may be felt far from their sources—a situation that has led to political bickering among the leaders of states and nations. For instance, much of the pollution from power plants and factories in Pennsylvania, Ohio, and Illinois falls out in southeastern Canada, as well as in states farther to the east. The bedrock geology and soil chemistry of the area that is receiving the acidic deposition also play a large role in the acid tolerance and the ecological response to acidification. As **FIGURE 14.21** shows, many regions in southeastern Canada have experienced acid deposition in excess of their critical loads.

FIGURE 14.21 The maximum amount of acid deposition that a region can receive without damage to its ecosystems—its critical load—depends on the acid rain neutralizing capacity of water, rocks, and soils. This map shows areas of eastern Canada where the levels of acid deposition have exceeded the capacity of the soils to neutralize the acid. From Environment Canada, *Acid Rain and Forests*, www.ec.gc.ca/acidrain/images/Exceedance_E.jpg

Acid deposition has not been reduced as much as scientists had hoped

Reducing acid precipitation involves reducing the pollution that contributes to it. New technologies, such as scrubbers, have helped. As a result of declining emissions of SO_2, average sulphate precipitation has decreased in northeastern North America since the early 1980s (**FIGURE 14.22A**). However, because of increasing NO_x emissions, average nitrate precipitation has changed little in the same period (**FIGURE 14.22B**). This may partly account for the trends in **FIGURE 14.23**, which suggest that although sulphate levels in many lakes in Ontario, Québec, and Atlantic Canada have declined, acidification has continued or even worsened in some of the lakes.

A report by scientists at Hubbard Brook Experimental Forest has disputed the notion that the problem of acid

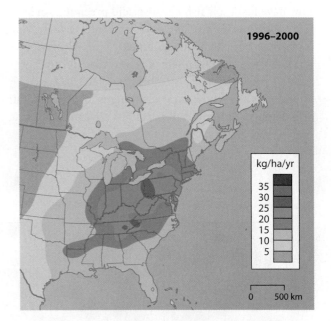

(a) Wet sulphate deposition down since early 1980s

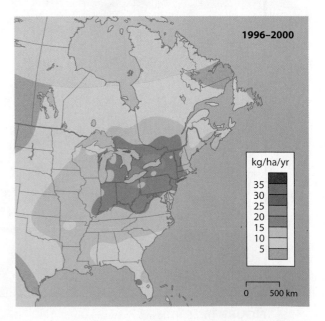

(b) Wet nitrate deposition shows little change since early 1980s

FIGURE 14.22   Acidic deposition of wet sulphates **(a)** and wet nitrates **(b)** has declined slightly in recent years in eastern North America. From Canadian National Atmospheric Chemistry Database, Meteorological Service of Canada, Environment Canada.

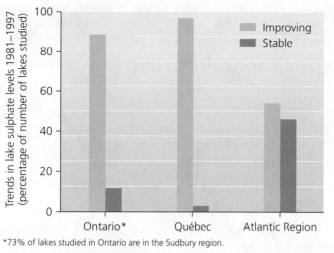

*73% of lakes studied in Ontario are in the Sudbury region.

(a) Trends in lake sulphate levels

(b) Trends in lake acidity

FIGURE 14.23 Although sulphate levels in many lakes in Ontario, Québec, and Atlantic Canada have shown improvement **(a)**, acid conditions in many of the lakes have not improved, and some have even continued to deteriorate **(b)**.
Source: State of the Environment Infobase Acid Rain, Environment Canada, Ontario, Atlantic, and Quebec Regions, adapted by National Indicators and Reporting Office, www.cc.gc.ca/soer-ree/English/Indicator_series/new_issues.cfm?issue_id=3&tech_id=10#bio_pic

deposition is being solved (see "The Science Behind the Story: Acid Rain at Hubbard Brook Experimental Forest"). Instead, the report said, the effects are worse than first predicted, and existing clean air legislation and limits on sulphate and nitrate emissions will be insufficient to solve the problem.

Indoor Air Pollution

Indoor air generally contains higher concentrations of pollutants than does outdoor air. As a result, the health effects from indoor air pollution in workplaces, schools, and homes outweigh those from outdoor air pollution. One estimate, from the U.N. Development Programme (2009) attributes almost 2 million deaths worldwide to indoor air pollution and 500 000 deaths to outdoor air pollution. Indoor air pollution alone, then, takes roughly 5500 lives each day.

If the impact of indoor air pollution seems surprising, consider that the average person in North America is indoors at least 90% of the time. Then consider that in the past half century a dizzying array of consumer products have been manufactured and sold, many of which we keep in our homes and offices and use extensively in our daily lives. Many of these products are made of synthetic materials that are not comprehensively tested for health effects before being brought to

market. Products as diverse as insecticides, cleaning fluids, plastics, and chemically treated wood can all exude volatile chemicals into the air.

In an ironic twist, some attempts to be environmentally prudent during the "energy crisis" of 1973–1974 worsened indoor air pollution in developed countries. To reduce heat loss and improve energy efficiency, building managers sealed off most ventilation in existing buildings, and building designers constructed new buildings with limited ventilation and with windows that did not open. These steps may have saved energy, but they also worsened indoor air pollution by trapping stable, unmixed air—and its pollutants—inside.

Indoor air pollution in the developing world arises from fuelwood burning

Indoor air pollution has the greatest impact in the developing world. Millions of people in developing nations burn wood, charcoal, animal dung, or crop waste inside their homes for cooking and heating with little or no ventilation (**FIGURE 14.24**). In the process, they inhale dangerous amounts of soot and carbon monoxide. In the air of such homes, concentrations of particulate matter are commonly 20 times as

THE SCIENCE BEHIND THE STORY

Acid Rain at Hubbard Brook Experimental Forest

Dr. Gene E. Likens is with the Institute of Ecosystem Studies.

Over the past 40 years, precipitation at the Hubbard Brook Experimental Forest has become slightly less acidic. However, it is still far more acidic than natural precipitation. Data from Likens, G. E. (2004). *Ecology* 85:2355–2362.

Acidic deposition involves subtle and incremental changes in pH levels that take place over long periods, so no single experiment can give us a complete picture of acidic deposition's effects. Nonetheless, one long-term study conducted in the Hubbard Brook Experimental Forest in New Hampshire's White Mountains has been critically important to our understanding of acidic deposition.

Established by the U.S. Forest Service in 1955, Hubbard Brook was initially devoted to research on hydrology, the study of water flow through forests and streams. In 1963, Hubbard Brook researchers broadened their focus to include a long-term study of nutrient cycling in forest ecosys-tems. Since then, they have collected and analyzed weekly samples of precipitation. The measurements make up the longest-running North American record of acid precipitation.

Throughout Hubbard Brook's 3160 ha, small plastic collecting funnels chan-nel precipitation into clean bottles, which researchers retrieve and replace each week. Hubbard Brook's laboratory mea-sures acidity and conductivity, which indi-cates the amounts of salts and other electrolytic contaminants dissolved in the water. Concentrations of sulphuric acid,

FIGURE 14.24

In the developing world, many people build fires inside their homes for cooking and heating, as seen here in a South African kitchen. Indoor fires expose family members to particulate matter and carbon monoxide. In most regions of the developing world, indoor air pollution is estimated to cause upward of 3% of all health risks.

nitrates, ammonia, and other compounds are measured elsewhere.

By the late 1960s, ecologists Gene Likens, F. Herbert Bormann, and others had found that precipitation at Hubbard Brook was several hundred times as acidic as natural rainwater. By the early 1970s, a number of other studies had corroborated their findings. Together, these studies indicated that the precipitation had pH values averaging around 4 and that individual rainstorms showed values as low as 2.1—almost 10 000 times as acidic as ordinary rainwater.

The most severe problems were found to be in the northeastern United States, where prevailing west-to-east winds were blowing emissions from fossil-fuel-burning power plants in the Midwest. Scientists hypothesized that when sulphur dioxide, nitrogen oxides, and other pollutants arrived in the Northeast, they were absorbed by water droplets in clouds, converted to acidic compounds such as sulphuric acid, and deposited on farms, forests, and cities in rain or snow.

Clean air legislation has helped reduce acidic deposition. At an area of Hubbard Brook known as Watershed 6, average pH increased slightly between 1965 and 1995, from about 4.15 to about 4.35 (see the first figure). Nonetheless, acidic deposition continues to be a serious problem in the northeastern United States and southeastern Canada.

Acidic deposition killed these trees on Mount Mitchell in western North Carolina.

Some long-term consequences of acidic deposition are now becoming clear. In 1996, researchers reported that approximately 50% of the calcium and magnesium in Hubbard Brook's soils had leached out. Meanwhile, acidic deposition had increased the concentration of aluminum in the soil, which can prevent tree roots from absorbing nutrients. The resulting nutrient deficiency slows forest growth and weakens trees, making them more vulnerable to drought and insects (see the second figure). It also reduces the ability of soil and water to neutralize acidity, making the ecosystem increasingly vulnerable to further inputs of acid.

In October 1999, researchers used a helicopter to distribute 50 tons of a calcium-containing mineral called wollastonite over one of Hubbard Brook's watersheds. Their objective was to raise the concentration of base cations to estimated historical levels. Over the next 50 years, scientists plan to evaluate the impact of calcium addition on the watershed's soil, water, and life. By providing a comparison with watersheds in which calcium remains depleted, the results should provide new insights into the consequences of acid rain and the possibilities for reversing its negative effects.

---

high as World Health Organization (WHO) standards. Poverty forces fully half the population and 90% of rural residents of developing countries to heat and cook with indoor fires.

Indoor air pollution from fuelwood burning, the WHO estimates, kills 1.6 million people each year, causing more than 5% of all deaths in some developing nations and 2.7% of the entire global disease burden. Many people who tend indoor fires are not aware of the health risks. They do not have access to the statistics showing that chemicals and soot released by burning coal, plastic, and other materials indoors can increase risks of pneumonia, bronchitis, allergies, sinus infections, cataracts, asthma, emphysema, heart disease, cancer, and premature death. Many who are aware of the health risks are too poor to have viable alternatives.

Tobacco smoke and radon are the most dangerous indoor pollutants in the developed world

In developed nations, the top risks associated with indoor air pollution are cigarette smoke and radon, a naturally occurring radioactive gas. The health effects of smoking cigarettes are well known, but only recently have scientists quantified the risks of inhaling secondhand smoke. *Secondhand smoke*, or environmental tobacco smoke, is smoke inhaled by a nonsmoker who is nearby or shares an enclosed airspace with a smoker. Secondhand smoke has been found to cause many of the same problems as directly inhaled cigarette smoke, ranging from irritation of the eyes, nose, and throat, to exacerbation of asthma and other respiratory ailments, to lung cancer. This hardly seems surprising when one considers that environmental tobacco smoke consists of a brew of more than 4000 chemical compounds, many of which are known or suspected to be toxic or carcinogenic.

Although smoking remains common in many parts of the developing world, its popularity has declined greatly in developed nations in recent years. Many public and private venues now ban smoking. In Canada, smoking is now prohibited in all indoor workplaces and public places, such as airports. The last of the provinces or territories to implement the ban was Yukon, in 2008.

After cigarette smoke, radon gas is the second-leading cause of lung cancer in the developed world. The WHO estimates that radon may account for 15% of lung cancer cases worldwide. Radon is a radioactive gas resulting from the natural decay of uranium in soil, rock, or water, which seeps up from the ground and can infiltrate buildings. Radon is colourless and odourless, and it can be impos-

sible to predict where it will occur without knowing details of an area's underlying geology (**FIGURE 14.25**). As a result, the only way to determine whether radon is entering a building is to measure radon with a test kit.

Indoor radon is taken very seriously in the United States, where it is difficult to purchase a home without tests showing that radon is not a problem. The U.S. Environmental Protection Agency (EPA) has recommended a maximum acceptable level of radon that is essentially the same as the ambient outdoor level. This has brought thousands of houses into the unacceptable range; the EPA has estimated that 6% of U.S. homes exceed the maximum recommended level.

Historically, Health Canada has taken the approach that some indoor concentration of naturally occurring soil gases, such as radon, is unavoidable. The maximum acceptable, or "action," level for indoor radon in homes and other non-occupational settings recommended by Health Canada is 0.02 WL (a Working Level is a unit of

FIGURE 14.25
One's risk from radon depends largely on underground geology. This map shows how the potential for elevated levels of radon can be estimated on the basis of the amount of naturally occurring uranium in rocks and soils. However, there is much fine-scale geographic variation from place to place, and construction materials and techniques also have an impact on the processes that can concentrate radon indoors. Testing is the only sure means of determining whether this colourless, odourless gas could be a problem in your home.
Source: Natural Resources Canada, www. geoscape.nrcan.gc.ca/ottawa/radon_e. php?p=1

measurement that is specific to radon and its daughter by-products), which is roughly equivalent to 200 Bq/m³ air (a Becquerel is a unit that measures the number of radioactive disintegrations per second), or 5.4 pCi/L air (picoCurie also measures the number of radioactive disintegrations per second). This is the same as the maximum permissible annual average concentration of radon daughters from the operation of a nuclear facility. The actionable level defined by the U.S. EPA is equivalent to 0.016 WL (about 4 pCi/L, or 150 Bq/m³ of air), considerably lower than the permissible level defined by Health Canada.

Many VOCs pollute indoor air

In our daily lives at home, we are exposed to many indoor air pollutants (**FIGURE 14.26**). The most diverse indoor pollutants are volatile organic compounds (VOCs). These airborne carbon-containing compounds are released by everything from plastics to oils to perfumes to paints to cleaning fluids to adhesives to pesticides. VOCs evaporate from furnishings, building materials, colour film, carpets, laser printers, fax machines, and sheets of paper. Some products, such as chemically treated furniture, release large amounts of VOCs when new and progressively less

FIGURE 14.26   The typical North American home contains a variety of potential sources of indoor air pollution. Shown are some of the most common sources, the major pollutants they emit, and some of the health risks they pose.

as they age. Other items, such as photocopying machines, emit VOCs each time they are used. Seemingly innocent indoor activities, like cooking, can even contribute pollutants; dioxins and furans, the toxic by-products of incomplete combustion that are problematic outdoor pollutants, can come from burning foods during meal preparation.

Although we are surrounded by products that emit VOCs, they are released in very small amounts. Studies have found overall levels of VOCs in buildings nearly always to be less than 0.1 parts per million. This is, however, a substantially greater concentration than is generally found outdoors, and indoor sources are suspected for most of these compounds.

The implications for human health of chronic exposure to VOCs are not well known. Because they exist in such low concentrations and because individuals are regularly exposed to mixtures of many different types, it is extremely difficult to study the effects of any one pollutant. An exception is formaldehyde, which does have clear and known health impacts. This VOC, one of the most common synthetically produced chemicals, irritates mucous membranes, induces skin allergies, and causes other ailments. Formaldehyde is used in numerous products, but health complaints have mainly resulted from its leakage from pressed wood and insulation. The use of plywood has decreased in the last decade because of health concerns over formaldehyde.

VOCs also include pesticides. Three-quarters of U.S. homes use at least one pesticide indoors during an average year, but most are used outdoors. Thus it may seem surprising that the U.S. Environmental Protection Agency found in a 1990 study that 90% of people's pesticide exposure came from indoor sources. Households that the agency tested had multiple pesticide volatiles in their air, at levels 10 times above levels measured outside. Some of the pesticides had apparently been used years earlier against termites and then seeped into the houses through floors and walls. DDT, banned 15 years before the study, was found in five of eight homes, probably having been brought in from outdoors on the soles of occupants' shoes.

Living organisms can pollute indoor spaces

Tiny living organisms can pollute; in fact, they may be the most widespread source of indoor air pollution in the developed world. Dust mites and animal dander can worsen asthma in children. Some fungi, mould, and mildew (in particular, their airborne spores) can cause severe health problems, including allergies, asthma, and other respiratory ailments. Some airborne bacteria can cause infectious disease. One example is the bacterium that causes Legionnaires' disease. Heating and cooling systems in buildings make ideal breeding grounds for microbes, providing moisture, dust, and foam insulation as substrates, as well as air currents to carry the organisms aloft. Microbes that induce allergic responses are thought to be a major cause of sicknesses produced by indoor pollution. When the cause of such an illness is a mystery, and when symptoms are general and nonspecific, it is often called **sick-building syndrome**.

We can reduce indoor air pollution

Using low-toxicity materials, monitoring air quality, keeping rooms clean, and providing adequate ventilation are the keys to alleviating indoor air pollution in most situations. In the developed world, we can try to limit our use of plastics and treated wood where possible and to limit our exposure to pesticides, cleaning fluids, and other known toxicants by keeping them in a garage or outdoor shed rather than in the house. Health Canada recommends that we test our homes and offices for mould and radon and monitor continuously for carbon monoxide. Because carbon monoxide is so deadly and so hard to detect, many homes are equipped with detectors that sound an alarm if incomplete combustion produces dangerous levels of CO. In addition, keeping rooms and air ducts clean and free of mildew and other biological pollutants will reduce potential irritants and allergens. Finally, it is important to keep our indoor spaces as well ventilated as possible to minimize concentrations of the pollutants among which we live.

Remedies for fuelwood pollution in the developing world include drying wood before burning (which

weighing the issues

HOW SAFE IS YOUR INDOOR ENVIRONMENT?

Think about the amount of time you spend indoors. Name the potential indoor air quality hazards in your home, work, or school environment. What could you do to make the indoor spaces you use safer?

CANADIAN ENVIRONMENTAL PERSPECTIVES

David Phillips

David Phillips has become a spokesperson on climatic change.

- Senior **climatologist** for Environment Canada
- **Meteorologist, weather researcher**, and Canada's "weather ambassador"
- Author and **science writer**

We all know his face and his voice. He is the go-to person for answers to any and all questions about the weather in Canada. He has a fascination with extreme weather trivia and especially for the role that weather has played in shaping the Canadian psyche. David Phillips is the official spokesperson for Environment Canada's Meteorological Service and Canada's unofficial "weather ambassador."

As a senior climatologist, Phillips is responsible for activities related to the study, promotion, and understanding of Canadian weather and climate.[10] Phillips claims that his interest in the weather wasn't sparked by any significant weather event, like a dramatic thunderstorm or lightning display; he says he grew up, like everyone else, as "just someone who hated and loved the weather."[11]

Phillips started as a researcher at Environment Canada, working on a Climatic Severity Index for Canadians. The study assessed 150 locations in Canada to determine where the worst weather occurs. The index ranges from 1 to 100, with 1 being the least severe and 100 the most severe. It combines weather-related stressors, such as extremes of heat and cold, wetness or dryness, windiness, poor air quality, darkness, fog, restricted visibility, lightning, thunderstorms, blowing snow, and freezing precipitation. It also accounts for factors that are responsible for human discomfort caused by the weather, such as mobility limitations, psychological factors, safety and hazardous conditions, and discomfort factors, such as wind chill.

When Phillips was interviewed on national TV about this study, his career as a spokesperson got its start. Phillips has been a voice of reason in the sometimes confusing public discourse about global climatic change. He often reminds people that just because we might be having an unusually hot (or cold) day, month, season, year, or even decade, it doesn't necessarily mean that this is an indicator of long-term climatic change.

"The atmosphere has . . . a beauty and fragility that requires us to better understand, enjoy, and protect it." —**David Phillips**

Thinking About Environmental Perspectives

When he first started working at Environment Canada, David Phillips was a researcher working on the Climatic Severity Index. That was back in the 1980s. Today there are numerous versions of such weather-, climate-, and atmosphere-related indexes. Examples include the Air Quality Index, the Palmer Drought Severity Index, and the Winter Severity Index, but there are many others. Choose one example of a weather-related index and find out (1) what the components of the index are (in other words, what weather-related factors are accounted for in the index and how they are combined and weighted), and (2) how this index has been used in Canada in the past (give some examples of extreme events to which the index has been applied).

---

reduces the amount of smoke produced), cooking outside, shifting to less-polluting fuels (such as natural gas), and replacing inefficient fires with cleaner stoves that burn fuel more efficiently. For example, the Chinese government has invested in a program that has placed more fuel efficient stoves in millions of homes in China. Installing hoods, chimneys, or cooking windows can increase ventilation for little cost, alleviating the majority of indoor smoke pollution.

Conclusion

Indoor air pollution is a potentially serious health threat; however, by keeping informed of the latest sci-entific findings and taking appropriate precautions, we as individuals can significantly minimize the risks to our families and ourselves. Outdoor air pollution has been addressed more effectively by government legislation and regulation. In fact, reductions in outdoor air pollution in Canada, the United States, Great Britain, and other developed nations represent some of the greatest strides made in environmental protection to date. Much room for improvement remains, however, particularly in reducing acidic deposition and the pho-tochemical smog that results from urban congestion. Avoiding unhealthy pollutant levels in the developing world will continue to pose a challenge as less-wealthy nations industrialize.

REVIEWING OBJECTIVES

You should now be able to:

Describe the composition, structure, and function of Earth's atmosphere

- The atmosphere consists of 78% nitrogen gas, 21% oxygen gas, and a variety of other gases in minute concentrations.
- The atmosphere includes four principal layers: the troposphere, stratosphere, mesosphere, and thermosphere. Temperature and other characteristics vary across these layers. Ozone is concentrated in the stratosphere.
- The Sun's energy heats the atmosphere, drives air circulation, and helps determine weather, climate, and the seasons.
- Weather is a short-term phenomenon, whereas climate is a long-term phenomenon. Fronts, pressure systems, and the interactions among air masses influence weather.
- Global convective cells called Hadley, Ferrel, and polar cells create latitudinal climate zones.

Outline the scope of outdoor air pollution and assess potential solutions

- Natural sources such as windblown dust, volcanoes, and fires account for much atmospheric pollution, but human activity can worsen some of these phenomena.
- Human-emitted pollutants include primary and secondary pollutants from point and non-point sources.
- To safeguard public health, Environment Canada and various other federal, provincial, and territorial agencies monitor a number of air contaminants, including sulphur oxides, nitrogen oxides, particulate matter, volatile organic compounds, carbon monoxide, ammonia, and tropospheric ozone.
- The principal legislation under which air quality and emissions are regulated in Canada is the *Canadian Environmental Protection Act* (1999).
- Industrial smog is produced by fossil fuel combustion and is still a problem in urban and industrial areas of many developing nations.
- Photochemical smog is created by chemical reactions of pollutants in the presence of sunlight. It impairs visibility and human health in urban areas.

- Rural areas suffer air pollution from feedlots and other sources.
- Industrializing nations, such as China and India, are experiencing some of the world's worst air pollution today.

Explain stratospheric ozone depletion and identify steps taken to address it

- CFCs destroy stratospheric ozone, and thinning ozone concentrations pose dangers to life because they allow more ultraviolet radiation to reach Earth's surface.
- The Montreal Protocol and its follow-up agreements have proven remarkably successful in reducing emissions of ozone-depleting compounds.
- The long residence time of CFCs in the atmosphere means a time lag between the protocol and the actual restoration of stratospheric ozone.

Define acidic deposition and illustrate its consequences

- Acidic deposition results when pollutants, such as SO_2 and NO_x, react with water in the atmosphere to produce strong acids that are deposited on Earth's surface.
- Acidic deposition may occur a long distance from the source of pollution.
- Water bodies, soils, trees, animals, and ecosystems all experience negative impacts from acidic deposition.

Characterize the scope of indoor air pollution and assess potential solutions

- Indoor air pollution causes far more deaths and health problems worldwide than outdoor air pollution.
- Indoor burning of fuelwood is the developing world's primary indoor air pollution risk.
- Tobacco smoke and radon are the deadliest indoor pollutants in the developed world.
- Volatile organic compounds and living organisms can pollute indoor air.
- Using low-toxicity building materials, keeping spaces clean, monitoring air quality, and maximizing ventilation are some of the steps we can take to reduce indoor air pollution.

TESTING YOUR COMPREHENSION

1. How thick is Earth's atmosphere? Name one characteristic of each of the four atmospheric layers.

2. Where is the "ozone layer" located? How and why is stratospheric ozone beneficial for people and tropospheric ozone harmful?

3. How does solar energy influence weather and climate? How do Hadley, Ferrel, and polar cells help to determine long-term climatic patterns and the location of biomes?

4. Describe a thermal inversion. How can thermal inversions contribute to the severity of pollution episodes?

5. Name three natural sources of outdoor air pollution and three sources caused by human activity.

6. What is the difference between a primary and a secondary pollutant? Give an example of each.

7. What is smog? How is smog formation influenced by the weather? By topography? How does photochemical smog differ from industrial smog?

8. How do chlorofluorocarbons (CFCs) deplete stratospheric ozone? Why is this depletion considered a long-term international problem? What has been done to address this problem?

9. Why are the effects of acidic deposition often felt in areas far from where the primary pollutants are produced? List three impacts of acidic deposition.

10. Name five common sources of indoor pollution. For each, describe one way to reduce one's exposure to this source.

THINKING IT THROUGH

1. Describe several factors that make it difficult to determine the specific causes of air pollution and to develop solutions. How did London try to improve its air quality? Are there any cities near you that have tried different approaches to mitigating air pollution?

2. Name one type of natural air pollution, and discuss how human activity can sometimes worsen it. What potential solutions can you think of to minimize this human impact?

3. Describe how and why emissions of some major pollutants have been reduced in North America since the 1970s, despite increases in population and economic activity.

4. International regulatory action has produced reductions in CFCs, but other transboundary pollution issues, including acidic deposition, have not yet been addressed as effectively. What types of actions do you feel are appropriate for pollutants that cross political boundaries?

5. Let's say that you have just been elected mayor of the largest city in your province. Your city's residents are complaining about photochemical smog and traffic congestion. Traffic engineers and city planners project that population and traffic will grow by 20% in the next decade. A citizens' group is urging you to implement a congestion-charging program like London's, but businesses are fearful of losing money if shoppers are discouraged from visiting. Consider the particulars of your city, and then decide whether you will pursue a congestion-charging program. If so, how would you do it? If not, why not, and what other steps would you take to address your city's problems?

6. You have just become the head of your region's office of public health and the environment ministry has informed you that your jurisdiction has failed to meet recommended air quality standards for ozone, sulphur dioxide, and nitrogen dioxide. The area is partly rural but is home to a city of 200 000 people, with sprawling suburbs. There are several large and aging coal-fired power plants, a number of factories with advanced pollution control technology, and no public transportation system. What steps would you urge the municipal or provincial government to take to meet the air quality standards? Explain how you would prioritize these steps.

INTERPRETING GRAPHS AND DATA

The U.S. National Oceanographic and Atmospheric Administration maintains an active website with ozone monitoring data at www.ozonelayer.noaa.gov/. If you go to the website and choose "Data" from the menu, you can investigate the data yourself.

Try going to "Current Data," click on "Antarctic (South Pole)," and then choose "Size of Ozone Hole (CPC)."

You should get a graph that looks something like this:

This graph shows the areal extent of the Southern Hemisphere ozone hole during the austral spring of 2010 (coloured lines), compared to values for the past ten years (black lines).

1. On the basis of this graph, what was the area (in millions km²) of the Southern Hemisphere ozone hole at the beginning of October 2010 (or the most recent year displayed on the graph)?
2. Was the ozone hole larger or smaller at the beginning of October in 2008? What about 1998?
3. How did the size of the ozone hole in October 2010 compare to the mean (average) size of the ozone hole for the years 2000–2009?
4. The Antarctic ozone undergoes its onset every year during the austral (Southern Hemisphere) spring. Which months constitute spring in the Southern Hemisphere?
5. Try clicking on other parts of the website to see what you can find. Under "Current" you will find summaries of recent data, and under "Historical" you will find archives of data from various organizations involved in both stratospheric and tropospheric ozone monitoring.

CHAPTER ENDNOTES

1. Environment Canada Green Lane, *Acid Rain and . . . Case Studies*, www.ec.gc.ca/acidrain/acidcase.html

2. Environment Canada Green Lane, *Acid Rain and . . . Case Studies*, www.ec.gc.ca/acidrain/acidcase.html

3. Environment Canada National Water Research Institute, www.nwri.ca/sande/jul_aug_2001-e.html

4. Department of Fisheries and Oceans, *Experimental Lakes Area*, www.dfo-mpo.gc.ca/regions/central/pub/ela-rle/index_e.htm

5. This section partially based on information from Environment Canada, *Clean Air Online*, www.ec.gc.ca/cleanair-airpur/Pollutants-WSBCC0B44A-1_En.htm

6. Centers for Disease Control, Agency for Toxic Substances and Disease Registry, *Division of Toxicology ToxFAQs*, September 2002, www.atsdr.cdc.gov/tfacts35.pdf

7. UNEP, *Phasing Lead Out of Gasoline: An Examination of Policy Approaches in Different Countries*, 1999.

8. Environment Canada, *CEPA Environmental Registry*, www.ec.gc.ca/CEPARegistry/the_act/

9. Environment Canada, *Clean Air Online*, www.ec.gc.ca/cleanair-airpur/Taking_Action/Canadian_Governments-WS3067CF5B-1_En.htm

10. Meteorological Service of Canada, Environment Canada, David Phillips www.msc-smc.ec.gc.ca/cd/biographies/david_phillips_e.html

11. Environment Canada, Canada's Weather Guru: A Chat with David Phillips, *Envirozine*, Issue 78, www.ec.gc.ca/EnviroZine/english/issues/78/feature_1_e.cfm

MyEnvironmentPlace

Go to **www.myenvironmentplace.ca** where you will find quizzes, animations, your Pearson eText, and more.

Global Climate Change

This is the toe of the Athabasca Glacier of the Columbia Icefield in the Canadian Rockies.

Upon successfully completing this chapter, you will be able to

- Describe Earth's climate system and explain the many factors influencing global climate
- Characterize human influences on the atmosphere and global climate

- Summarize modern methods of climate research
- Outline current and future trends and impacts of global climate change
- Suggest ways we can respond to climate change

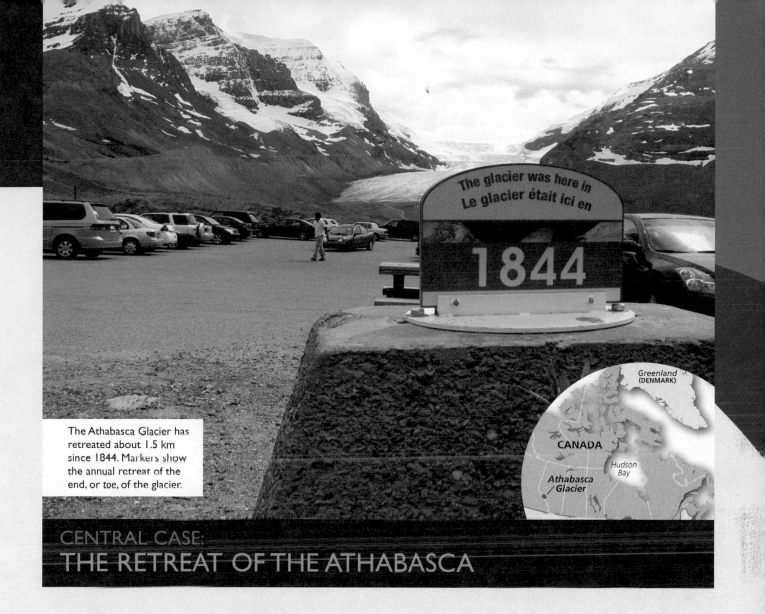

The Athabasca Glacier has retreated about 1.5 km since 1844. Markers show the annual retreat of the end, or *toe*, of the glacier.

CENTRAL CASE:
THE RETREAT OF THE ATHABASCA

"Warming of the climate system is unequivocal."
—INTERGOVERNMENTAL PANEL ON CLIMATE CHANGE, *FOURTH ASSESSMENT REPORT*

"We're in a giant car heading towards a brick wall and everyone's arguing about where they're going to sit."
—DAVID SUZUKI

The Athabasca Glacier is one of six valley glaciers that flow like huge rivers of ice from the Columbia Icefield, which straddles the border between Jasper and Banff National Parks. The Columbia Icefield, which sits among some of the highest peaks in the Canadian Rockies, is a remnant of the massive glacial ice that covered much of Canada during the Pleistocene glaciation. The Athabasca Glacier itself is about 6 km long and between 90 and 300 m in thickness.

Glaciers, although they consist of solid ice, flow (very slowly) under the influence of gravity. There are two main mechanisms for glacial flow. The first involves *internal deformation* of the crystals of ice. This is something like what would happen if you were to press down and slightly sideways on a deck of cards; the cards would slide past one another. Similarly, the ice crystals in the glacier slide translationally along internal planes of weakness. The second main flow mechanism is called *basal sliding*. This happens when a layer of meltwater lubricates the contact between the glacial ice and the underlying rock. Both mechanisms are probably at work in the Athabasca Glacier, which is moving downslope at a rate of a few centimetres per day.

Glaciers also grow and shrink in both volume and area, driven by changes in temperature and precipitation. When more snow falls than can melt in a year, the snow becomes compressed by additional snowfall and

This archival photo shows the Athabasca Glacier in 1919. By this time, the toe of the glacier had already been retreating from its maximum historical extent (in 1844) for 75 years. The blue box shows the approximate location of the chapter-opening photo.

eventually recrystallizes to form glacial ice. This process, called *accumulation*, is the mechanism by which glaciers grow in both volume and extent. However, if the annual snowfall melts entirely, the glacier will either remain constant or will slowly recede in volume and extent (through both melting and *sublimation*, in which the ice evaporates without actually melting); this loss of ice volume is called *ablation*.

The Athabasca Glacier has been retreating since 1844, when it was at its maximum historical extent (see photos). Since that time, the glacier has lost half of its volume and has retreated more than 1.5 km.[1] In 1844 the end, or *toe*, of the glacier extended well past the area where the Icefields Parkway (Hwy. 93) is now located. The glacier is currently retreating at a rate of about 2 to 3 metres per year.

This area of the Rockies was of significant interest during the 1800s for scientific research (mainly geology) and for fur trading, carried out chiefly by the Hudson's Bay Company. Wilcox Pass was discovered in 1896 by an exploration party that included Walter Wilcox, for whom the pass and Wilcox Peak were eventually named; Robert Lemoyne Barrett, one of the founders of the American Association of Geographers; and William Peyto, for whom Peyto Glacier was named.[2] At that time, the toe of the Athabasca butted right up against the steep slopes of Wilcox Peak. Although they attempted to find easier routes through the valley (where Hwy. 93 now lies), explorers and fur traders were blocked by the glacier and were forced to follow steep mountain trails such as the Wilcox Pass and the Athabasca Pass.

Is the retreat of the Athabasca Glacier a recent side effect of global warming caused by human activity? Or is it just the natural continuation of the retreat of glacial ice that began 12 000 years ago with the end of the Pleistocene glaciation? Like most climate-related questions, this is difficult to answer. By definition, *climate* is a long-term phenomenon. Records that span a few decades are insufficient to reveal true climatic trends. However, evidence is very clear now that mountain glaciers throughout the world have been in retreat since the end of the Little Ice Age, a geologically brief period (300 years) of unusually cold weather that ended in the mid-1800s (see **FIGURE 15.17**.) This has led some scientists to predict that the Rockies will be ice-free by the end of this century.

This satellite image shows part of the Columbia Icefield, the Athabasca Glacier, Icefields Parkway, and Wilcox Peak. The rest of the Columbia Icefield is off the left side of the photo.

Our Dynamic Climate

Climate influences virtually everything around us, from the day's weather to major storms, from crop success to human health, from national security to the ecosystems that support our economies. If you are a student in your twenties, climate change may well be the major event of your lifetime and the phenomenon that most shapes your future.

The 2007 release of the *Fourth Assessment Report* of the Intergovernmental Panel on Climate Change (IPCC) made clear to the world the strong scientific consensus that climate is changing, that we are the cause, and that climate change is already exerting impacts that will become increasingly severe if we do not take action.

Climate change is the fastest-moving area of environmental science today. New scientific papers that refine our understanding of climate are published every week, and policy makers and businesspeople make headlines with decisions and announcements just as quickly. By the time you read this chapter, new issues will have developed, and new problems and solutions may have been found. We urge you to explore further, with your instructor and on your own, the most recent information on climate change and the impacts it will have on your future.

What is climate change?

Climate describes an area's long-term atmospheric conditions, including temperature, moisture content, wind, precipitation, barometric pressure, solar radiation, and other characteristics. As you have learned, climate differs from weather in that weather specifies conditions at localized sites over hours or days, whereas climate describes conditions across broader regions over seasons, years, or millennia. **Global climate change** describes trends and

roots

CLIMATE

Climate is a fourteenth-century Scottish word that originates from the Old French *climat* and Latin *clima*. The original root is the ancient Greek *klima*, meaning "slope" or "incline." Greek geographers defined various zones (*klima*) of Earth's surface according to the angle (or slope) of the Sun's rays in that area. (The same root is found in the word *thermocline*.) With this meaning, "latitudinal zone," the word passed into Latin, where it eventually came to mean "region," more broadly, and then "weather associated with a particular region."

variations in Earth's climate, involving such aspects as temperature, precipitation, and storm frequency and intensity. People often use the term **global warming** synonymously in casual conversation, but global warming refers specifically to an increase in Earth's average surface temperature; it is thus only one aspect of global climate change.

Our planet's climate varies naturally through time, but the climatic changes taking place today are unfolding at an exceedingly rapid rate. Moreover, scientists agree that human activities, notably fossil fuel combustion and deforestation, are largely responsible. Understanding how and why climate is changing requires understanding how our planet's climate functions. Thus, we first will survey the fundamentals of Earth's climate system—a complex and finely tuned system that has nurtured life for billions of years.

The Sun and atmosphere keep Earth warm

Three factors exert more influence on Earth's climate than all others combined. The first is the Sun; without it, Earth would be dark and frozen. The second is the atmosphere; without it, Earth would be as much as 33°C colder on average, and temperature differences between night and day would be far greater than they are. The third is the ocean, which shapes climate by storing and transporting heat and moisture.

The Sun supplies most of our planet's energy. Earth's atmosphere, clouds, land, ice, and water together absorb about 70% of incoming solar radiation and reflect the remaining 30% back into space (**FIGURE 15.1**); the reflectivity of a surface is called **albedo**. The 70% that is absorbed into the system powers a wide variety of Earth's processes, from photosynthesis to winds, waves, and evaporation.

Greenhouse gases warm the lower atmosphere

As Earth's surface absorbs the incoming short-wavelength solar radiation, surface materials increase in temperature and emit **infrared radiation**, radiation with longer wavelengths than visible light. In this longer-wavelength form, the radiation emitted by Earth's surface begins to make its way back to outer space.

However, some gases that are naturally present in the lower part of the atmosphere (the troposphere) absorb this infrared radiation very effectively. These include water vapour, ozone (O_3), carbon dioxide (CO_2), nitrous oxide (N_2O), and methane (CH_4), as well as halocarbons, a diverse group that includes chlorofluorocarbons

Incoming solar radiation 342

Reflected solar radiation 107

Outgoing longwave radiation 235

Reflected by clouds, aerosols, and atmosphere 77

Emitted by atmosphere and clouds 195

Emitted by surface and passing through atmosphere 40

Absorbed by atmosphere 67

Greenhouse gases in atmosphere

Thermals 24

Evapo-transpiration 78

Reflected by surface 30

Radiation emitted by surface 390

Back radiation 324

Absorbed by surface 324

Absorbed by surface 168

FIGURE 15.1 Our planet absorbs nearly 70% of the solar radiation it receives from the Sun and reflects the rest back into space (yellow arrows). About 30% is reflected off of the top of the atmosphere, clouds, and the surfaces of icecaps, ocean, and land. Absorbed radiation is then reemitted (orange arrows) as heat. Greenhouse gases in the atmosphere absorb some of this radiation and reemit it again, sending some downward to warm the atmosphere and the surface through the greenhouse effect. This illustration, showing major pathways of energy flow in watts per square metre, indicates that our planet naturally emits and reflects 342 watts/m², the same amount it receives from the Sun. Arrow thicknesses in the diagram are proportional to flows of energy in each pathway. *Source: Data from Kiehl, J. T., and K. E. Trenberth. (1997). Earth's annual global mean energy budget. Bulletin of the American Meteorological Society 78:197–208.*

(CFCs). Such gases are known as **greenhouse gases (GHGs)** or, technically, **radiatively active gases**. After absorbing radiation emitted from the surface, greenhouse gases subsequently reemit infrared energy of slightly different wavelengths. Some of this reemitted energy is lost to space, but some travels back downward, warming the troposphere and the planet's surface in a phenomenon known as the **greenhouse effect**.

The greenhouse effect is a natural phenomenon, and greenhouse gases have been present in our atmosphere for all of Earth's history. It's a good thing, too; without the natural greenhouse effect, our planet would have a much colder surface temperature—probably an average of around –18°C—and life on Earth would be impossible, or at least very, very different. Thus, it is not the natural greenhouse effect that is the cause of current concerns, but the **anthropogenic**—human-generated—contribution to the greenhouse effect.

There are both natural and anthropogenic sources for almost all greenhouse gases—with the exception of chlorofluorocarbons (CFCs) and other halocarbons, such as HFC-23, which are wholly anthropogenic. However, human activities have increased the concentrations of many greenhouse gases in the past 250–300 years, thereby enhancing the greenhouse effect.

Greenhouse gases differ not only in their concentrations in the atmosphere but also in their ability to warm the troposphere and the surface. **Global warming potential** refers to the relative ability of one molecule of a given greenhouse gas to contribute to warming. **TABLE 15.1** shows the global warming potentials for several greenhouse gases. Values are expressed in relation to carbon dioxide, which is assigned a global warming potential of 1. Thus, a molecule of methane is 25 times as potent as a molecule of carbon dioxide, and a molecule of nitrous oxide is 298 times as potent as a CO_2 molecule.

Carbon dioxide is the anthropogenic greenhouse gas of primary concern

Carbon dioxide (CO_2) is not the most potent greenhouse gas on a per-molecule basis (**TABLE 15.1**), but it is far more abundant in the atmosphere than the other GHGs. Emissions of greenhouse gases from human activity in Canada and other economically developed countries consist mostly of carbon dioxide. Even after accounting for the greater global warming potential of molecules of the other gases, carbon dioxide's abundance in our emissions makes it the major anthropogenic contributor to global warming.

The main natural source of carbon dioxide moving into the atmosphere is the decay of organic material; volcanoes also emit a significant amount of CO_2. Natural sources greatly outweigh the human contribution; however, human activities have boosted the atmospheric concentration of carbon dioxide from around 280 parts per million (ppm), as recently as the late 1700s, to 389 ppm in 2010[3] (**FIGURE 15.2**). The atmospheric CO_2 concentration is now higher than at any time in the entire ice-core record of data going back 800 000 years, and likely the highest in the last 20 million years. More importantly, researchers have established a very strong link between atmospheric carbon dioxide and temperature, as you will see. When atmospheric GHGs are high, so is temperature.

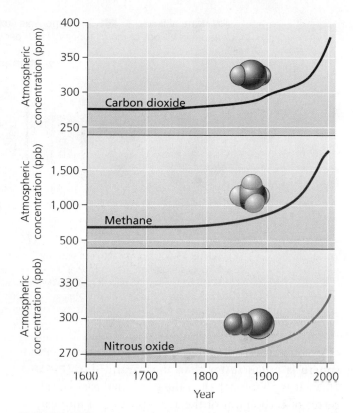

FIGURE 15.2
Since the start of the Industrial Revolution, global atmospheric concentrations of carbon dioxide, methane, and nitrous oxide have increased markedly.
Source: Data from Intergovernmental Panel on Climate Change (2007) Fourth Assessment Report.

Human activity has released carbon from sequestration in long-term reservoirs

Why has atmospheric CO_2 increased by so much, if the natural sources still outweigh the human sources? The simple answer is that the natural fluxes (inputs and outputs) cancel each other out. Human sources, which

do not cancel out, have thus shifted the overall balance of fluxes in the carbon cycle.

Recall our discussion of the carbon cycle and other biogeochemical cycles, where we examined the idea that human activities often accelerate the movements or **fluxes** of material from one **reservoir** to another in biogeochemical cycles. Through the biogeochemical cycling of carbon, some carbon is stored or **sequestered** for long periods in the lithosphere. The deposition, partial decay, and compression of organic matter (mostly plants) that grew in wetland or marine areas led to the formation of coal, oil, and natural gas in sediments. It takes millions of years for the organic precursors of fossil fuels to be buried, chemically altered, and trapped deep underground in their rock hosts; the main chapter of fossil fuel formation occurred during the Carboniferous Period, 290–354 million years ago.

In the absence of human activity, these lithospheric carbon reservoirs would be practically permanent. However, over the past two centuries we have extracted fossil fuels and burned them in our homes, factories, and automobiles, transferring large amounts of carbon from one reservoir (the long-term underground deposits) to another (the atmosphere). This human-modified flux

Table 15.1 Global Warming Potentials of Four Greenhouse Gases

Greenhouse gas	Relative heat-trapping ability (in CO_2 equivalents)
Carbon dioxide	1
Methane	25
Nitrous oxide	298
HFC-23	14 800

Source: Data are for a 100-year time horizon, from Intergovernmental Panel on Climate Change (2007) Fourth Assessment Report. Climate change 2007: The physical science basis.

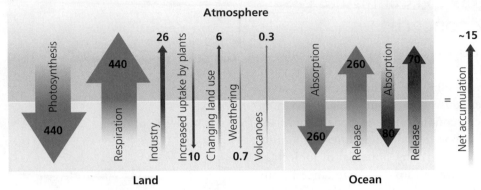

FIGURE 15.3 Human activities since the Industrial Revolution have sent more carbon dioxide from Earth to its atmosphere than is moving back from the atmosphere to Earth. Shown here are all the current fluxes of carbon dioxide, with arrows sized according to their mass of CO_2. Green arrows indicate natural fluxes, and red arrows indicate anthropogenic fluxes. *Source: Adapted from Intergovernmental Panel on Climate Change (2007) Fourth Assessment Report.*

of carbon from lithospheric reservoirs into the atmosphere is much faster than the natural flux (**FIGURE 15.3**). It is also faster than the combined total of all the fluxes of carbon out of the atmosphere and into carbon **sinks** (reservoirs that accept more of the material than they release), such as, notably, the ocean. The release of carbon from long-term reservoirs and the acceleration of the carbon flux from the lithospheric reservoir to the atmospheric reservoir are the main reasons atmospheric carbon dioxide concentrations have increased so dramatically since the Industrial Revolution.

At the same time, people have cleared and burned forests to make room for crops, pastures, villages, and cities. Forests, soils, and crops also serve as storage reservoirs and sinks for carbon—in this case, for recently active carbon in the short-term carbon cycle. Their removal reduces the biosphere's ability to absorb carbon dioxide from the atmosphere. In this way, deforestation also has modified the flux of carbon from terrestrial reservoirs to the atmospheric reservoir and has contributed to rising atmospheric CO_2 concentrations.

Other greenhouse gases contribute to warming

Carbon dioxide is not the only greenhouse gas increasing in concentration in the atmosphere as a result of our activities. We release **methane (CH$_4$)** by tapping into fossil fuel deposits, by raising livestock that emit methane as a metabolic waste product, by disposing of organic matter in landfills, and by growing certain crops, such as rice. Since 1750, atmospheric methane concentrations have risen 250% (see **FIGURE 15.2**), and today's concen-

tration is the highest by far in more than 800 000 years. Buried organic matter and natural gas deposits are the main natural sources of methane.

Human activities have also augmented atmospheric concentrations of *nitrous oxides*. These greenhouse gases, by-products of feedlots, chemical manufacturing plants, auto emissions, and synthetic nitrogen fertilizers, have risen by 18% since 1750 (**FIGURE 15.2**). The atmosphere is the largest nitrogen reservoir, but soils and soil-forming processes are the principal drivers of the nitrogen biogeochemical cycle. This is one reason that environmental scientists are taking a great interest in the impacts of climatic warming on soils.

Ozone—so important for life on Earth because of its function in the stratosphere as a UV filter—is also a radiatively active gas, contributing to warming both near the surface and up in the stratosphere. The concentration of ozone in the troposphere has risen roughly 36% since 1750, also contributing to photochemical smog. In a confusing twist of chemistry, CFCs and HFCs—the anthropogenic group of chemicals known as *halocarbons*, which have been implicated in stratospheric ozone depletion—are also radiatively active. The contribution of halocarbons to global warming has begun to slow as a result of the Montreal Protocol and subsequent controls on their production and release.

Water vapour is by far the most abundant naturally occurring greenhouse gas in our atmosphere, and contributes most to the natural greenhouse effect. Its concentrations vary locally, but its global concentration has not changed much over recent centuries, so it is not viewed as having driven industrial-age climate change. However, the concentration of water in the atmosphere is connected to temperature; as tropospheric temperatures continue to increase, Earth's water bodies should transfer more water vapour into the atmosphere, contributing to higher atmospheric concentrations. This could have a number of effects on climate, weather, and ecosystems. It also means that the effects of other greenhouse gases are amplified by the influence of added water vapour, contributing to further greenhouse warming.

There are many feedback cycles in the climate system

If global warming leads to an increase in the concentration of water vapour in the atmosphere, this can be expected to cause further warming because water is a radiatively active gas. This additional warming, in turn, could cause still more evaporation, leading to further increases in water vapour in the atmosphere, and so on. This is called a **positive feedback loop** or positive feedback cycle, and the climate system is loaded with them.

The climate system also has lots of **negative feedback loops**. For example, if global warming leads to increased evaporation and more water vapour in the atmosphere, it could give rise to increased cloudiness. Increased cloudiness could slow global warming by reflecting more solar radiation back into space. But the complexity of cloud cover doesn't end there; depending on whether low- or high elevation clouds resulted, they might shade and cool Earth's surface (a negative feedback), or contribute to warming, thus accelerating evaporation and further cloud formation (a positive feedback).

Water vapour is not the only natural constituent involved in feedbacks in the climate system. For example, warming of soils could cause an accelerated flux of soil gases to the atmosphere; some of these are GHGs, and their release could lead to further warming (a positive feedback). On the other hand, soil formation is accelerated by warmer, wetter weather, and soils function as a major sink for organic matter, removing carbon from the atmospheric reservoir (a negative feedback).

Aerosols—microscopic droplets and particles suspended in the air—also can have either a warming or cooling effect. Soot, or black carbon aerosols, can cause warming by absorbing solar energy, but most tropospheric aerosols are whiter and cool the atmosphere by reflecting the Sun's rays. When sulphur dioxide enters the atmosphere, it undergoes various reactions, some of which lead to acid precipitation. These reactions, along with volcanic eruptions, can contribute to the formation of a sulphur-rich aerosol haze in the upper atmosphere, which reduces the amount of sunlight that reaches Earth's surface. Aerosols released by major volcanic eruptions also can exert short-term cooling effects on Earth's climate over periods of up to several years.

Because of the complexity of these competing effects and feedbacks in the climate system, and the interactions among the various processes, minor modifications of components of the atmosphere can potentially lead to major effects on climate. Sorting out feedbacks and their relative importance and influence on one another is one of the greatest challenges in modern climate science.

Radiative forcing expresses change in energy input over time

Scientists have made quantitative estimates of the degree of influence that aerosols, greenhouse gases, and other factors exert over Earth's energy balance (**FIGURE 15.4**). The amount of change in energy that a given factor causes is called its **radiative forcing**. Positive forcing warms the surface, whereas negative forcing cools it. Scientists' best estimate is that Earth today compared with the pre-industrial Earth of the year 1750 is experiencing overall radiative forcing of about 1.6 watts/m². For context, look

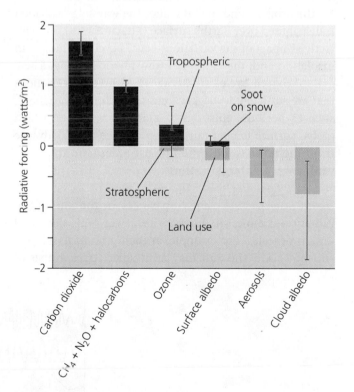

FIGURE 15.4
For each emitted gas or other human impact on the atmosphere since the Industrial Revolution, we can estimate the warming or cooling effect on Earth's climate. We express this as radiative forcing, which in this graph is shown as the amount of influence on climate today relative to 1750, in watts per square metre. Red bars indicate positive forcing (warming), and blue bars indicate negative forcing (cooling). A number of more minor influences are not shown. In total, scientists estimate that human impacts on the atmosphere exert a cumulative radiative forcing of 1.6 watts/m².

back at **FIGURE 15.1** and note that Earth is estimated to receive and give off 342 watts/m² of energy. Although 1.6 may seem like a small proportion of 342, it is enough to alter climate significantly.

The atmosphere is not the only factor that influences climate

Our climate is influenced by factors other than atmospheric composition. Among these are cyclic changes in Earth's rotation and orbit, variation in energy released by the Sun, absorption of carbon dioxide by the oceans, and oceanic circulation patterns. We will look at each of these factors in turn.

Milankovitch cycles   During the 1920s, Serbian mathematician Milutin Milankovitch described the influence of periodic changes in Earth's rotation and orbit around the Sun on **insolation**, the amount of solar energy that reaches Earth's surface. These variations, which include wobbling (or *precession*) of Earth's rotational axis, tilt of the axis (or *obliquity*), and change in the shape of Earth's orbit around the Sun, alter the way solar radiation is distributed over Earth's surface (**FIGURE 15.5**). The collective impact of the variations causes cyclical changes in insolation and, therefore, in atmospheric heating. These **Milankovitch cycles** (**FIGURE 15.6**) involve variations that are sufficient to trigger long-term climate variations, such as periodic episodes of **glaciation**, during which global surface temperatures drop and ice sheets advance from the poles toward the mid-latitudes, and the intervening warm **interglaciations**.

Solar output   The Sun varies in the amount of radiation it emits (its luminosity), over both short and long timescales. For example, at each peak of its 11-year sunspot cycle, the Sun may emit solar flares, bursts of

(a) Axial wobble (or *precession*)   **(b) Variation of tilt (or *obliquity*)**

(c) Variation of orbit (or *eccentricity*)

FIGURE 15.5
There are three orbital factors whose variations have a significant influence on climate. The first is an axial wobble **(a)** that occurs on a 19 000- to 23 000-year cycle. The second is a 3° shift in the tilt of Earth's axis **(b)** that occurs on a 41 000-year cycle. The third is a variation in Earth's orbit from almost circular to more elliptical **(c)**, which repeats itself every 100 000 years. These variations affect the intensity of solar radiation that reaches portions of Earth at different times, contributing to long-term changes in global climate.

energy strong enough to disrupt satellite communications. However, scientists are concluding that the variation in solar energy reaching our planet in recent centuries has simply not been great enough to drive significant temperature change on Earth's surface. Estimates place the radiative forcing of natural changes in solar output at only about 0.12 watts/m²—less than any of the anthropogenic causes shown in **FIGURE 15.4**.

FIGURE 15.6
The collective influence of variations in axial tilt, wobble, and orbital shape causes cyclical variations in solar insolation and heating of Earth's atmosphere and surface, which force cooling and warming trends in global climate on a variety of timescales and initiate major climatic shifts, such as glaciations.

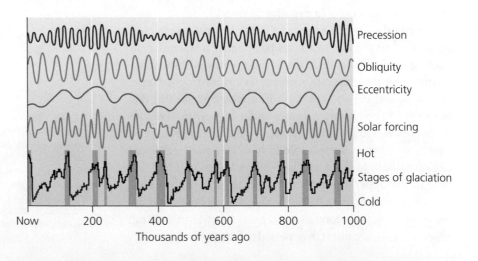

Ocean absorption   The ocean, acting as a sink, holds 50 times as much carbon as the atmosphere holds and absorbs carbon dioxide from the atmosphere, both through direct solubility of gas in water, and through uptake by marine phytoplankton for photosynthesis. As the concentration of carbon dioxide in the atmosphere increases, ocean water absorbs more carbon dioxide, but the rate of absorption increases more slowly than does the concentration in the atmosphere. Thus, carbon absorption by the ocean is slowing global warming but not preventing it. Futhermore, as ocean water warms, it absorbs less CO_2 because gases are less soluble in warmer water—a positive feedback effect that accelerates warming. The absorption of excess CO_2 by the ocean is also problematic because it causes the acidification of ocean water.

Ocean circulation   Ocean water exchanges tremendous amounts of heat with the atmosphere, and ocean currents move energy from place to place. In equatorial regions, the oceans receive more heat from the Sun and atmosphere than they emit. Near the poles, ocean water emits more than it receives. Because cooler water is denser than warmer water, the cool water at the poles tends to sink, and the warmer surface water from the equator moves poleward to take its place. This is one of the principles underlying global ocean circulation patterns.

One ocean–atmosphere interaction that influences climate is the El Niño–Southern Oscillation (ENSO), a systematic shift in atmospheric pressure, sea surface temperature, and ocean circulation in the tropical Pacific Ocean. El Niño conditions are triggered when air pressure increases in the western Pacific and decreases in the eastern Pacific, causing the equatorial winds to weaken. La Niña events are the opposite; under these conditions, cold surface waters extend far westward in the equatorial Pacific. Both El Niño and La Niña have dramatic influences on global weather patterns. ENSO cycles are periodic but irregular, occurring every two to eight years. Scientists are getting better at deciphering the triggers for these events and predicting their impacts on weather. They are also investigating whether globally warming air and sea temperatures may be increasing the frequency and strength of these cycles.

Ocean currents and climate also interact through the **thermohaline circulation**, a worldwide current system in which warmer, fresher water moves along the surface and colder, saltier water (which is more dense) moves deep beneath the surface (**FIGURE 15.7**). In the Atlantic Ocean, warm surface water flows northward from the equator in the Gulf Stream, carrying heat to high latitudes and keeping Europe warmer than it would otherwise be. As the surface water of this conveyor belt system releases heat energy and cools, it becomes denser and sinks, creating *North Atlantic Deep Water* (*NADW*).

Scientists hypothesize that interruptions in the thermohaline circulation could trigger rapid climate change. If global warming causes much of Greenland's ice sheet to melt, freshwater runoff into the North Atlantic would dilute surface waters, making them less dense (because fresh water is less dense than saltwater). This could potentially stop NADW formation and shut down the thermohaline circulation and the associated northward flow of

FIGURE 15.7   Warm surface currents carry heat from equatorial waters of the ocean north toward Europe and Greenland, where they release heat into the atmosphere and then cool and sink, forming the North Atlantic Deep Water. Scientists debate whether rapid melting of Greenland's ice sheet could interrupt the flow of warm water from equatorial regions and cause Europe to cool dramatically.

warm equatorial water (that is, the Gulf Stream), causing Europe to cool rapidly. Such a change may have had a role in the "Little Ice Age," a period of unusually cold climate that began in the fifteenth century. This scenario also inspired the 2004 film *The Day After Tomorrow*, although the filmmakers chose entertainment value over science and grossly exaggerated the potential impacts and the speed with which the effect might occur.

Some data suggest that the thermohaline circulation and formation of NADW in the North Atlantic is already slowing; other researchers argue that Greenland's runoff will not be enough to cause a shutdown this century. However, the possibility is worrisome; there is some evidence that interruptions of the thermohaline circulation have historically been responsible for extremely rapid shifts in climate in the areas bordering the North Atlantic. These climatic "flip-flops" are now thought to have occurred in the geologic past in periods as short as a decade or so. (See ''The Science Behind the Story: Tip Jets and NADW off the Coast of Greenland,'' in the chapter on Marine and Coastal Systems and Fisheries.)

The Science of Climate Change

To comprehend any phenomenon that is changing, we must study its past and present, and try to project its future. Climate scientists monitor present-day climatic conditions, but they also have devised clever means of inferring past change and have developed sophisticated methods to predict future change.

Proxy indicators tell us about the past

To understand how climate is changing today, and to predict future change, scientists must learn what climatic conditions were like thousands or millions of years ago. Evidence about climate in the geologic past—**paleoclimate**—is extremely important, because it gives us a baseline against which to measure the changes that we see happening in the climate system on a shorter timescale. The record of actual measurements of temperature, precipitation, and other indicators of climate is not very long—only a few hundred years' worth of data. Environmental scientists have developed a number of methods to decipher clues from the past. **Proxy indicators** are types of indirect evidence that serve as proxies, or substitutes, for direct measurement and that shed light on past climate.

Some human records of historical events can contribute to a longer database of weather information. For example,

roots

PROXY

A **proxy** is the authority to represent someone, to take care of someone's interests, or to act on someone's behalf as a "stand-in." In climatology, this term refers to measurements that "stand in" for direct measurements of climatic changes that happened too long ago for scientists to measure directly. The English word *proxy* comes originally from the Latin *procuration*, "caring for" or "taking care of." It originally entered English in the thirteenth century as *procuracy* and gradually became contracted to its present form *proxy*.

fishers have recorded the timing of sea ice formation for hundreds of years, and wine makers have kept meticulous records of precipitation and the length of the growing season.

To go back farther in time, we must begin to rely on the record-keeping ability of the natural world. For instance, growth rings in trees can give information about conditions of temperature and precipitation—they act as a proxy, or a stand-in, for actual measurements. The width of each ring of a tree trunk cut in cross-section reveals how much the tree grew in a particular growing season; a wide ring means more growth, generally indicating a wetter year. Long-lived trees, such as bristlecone pines, can provide records of precipitation and drought going back hundreds or thousands of years. Tree rings are also used to study fire history, since a charred ring indicates that a fire took place in that year.

The significance of annual growth rings is simple: Without the rings, scientists would have no way to know when a particularly cold or warm or dry or wet growth season occurred. With growth rings, scientists can count back to determine the age of the tree (or any other organism that accumulates material in annual growth cycles). Researchers can gather data on past ocean conditions from corals, for example, which accumulate material in annual rings. As they grow and build their reefs, the living corals take in trace elements from ocean water, incorporating these chemical clues into their rings.

Scientists continue to search for ways to extend the climate record back even farther. In arid regions, packrat middens are a valuable source of climate data. Packrats are rodents that carry seeds and plant parts back to their middens, or dens, in caves and rock crevices sheltered from rain. In an arid location, plant parts may last for centuries, allowing researchers to study the past flora of the region. Researchers also drill cores into sediments that lie beneath bodies of water. Sediments often preserve pollen grains and other remnants from plants that grew in the past, and analyzing these materials can illuminate the history of past vegetation. Because climate influences the types of plants that grow in an area, knowing what plants lived in a location at a given time can tell us much about the climate at that place and time.

Earth's icecaps, ice sheets, glaciers, and sediments hold clues to the much longer-term climate history. Over the ages, these huge expanses of snow and ice have accumulated to great depths, preserving within their layers tiny bubbles of the ancient atmosphere (**FIGURE 15.8**). Scientists can examine these trapped air bubbles by drilling into the ice and extracting long columns, or cores. The layered ice, accumulating season after season over thousands of years, provides a timescale, something like the growth rings of the tree. From these ice cores, scientists can determine atmospheric composition, greenhouse gas concentrations, temperature trends, snowfall, solar activity, and even (from trapped soot particles) frequency of forest fires and volcanic eruptions.

(a) Ice core

(b) Micrograph of ice core

FIGURE 15.8
In Greenland and Antarctica, scientists have drilled deep into ancient ice sheets and removed cores of ice like this one **(a)** to extract information about past climates. Bubbles trapped in the ice **(b)** contain small samples of the ancient atmosphere.

By extracting ice cores from Greenland and Antarctica, scientists have now been able to go back in time more than 800 000 years, reading Earth's global climatic history across eight glacial cycles (see "The Science Behind the Story: Reading History in the World's Longest Ice Core.") During 2007–2009, such research was funded and promoted as part of the International Polar Year, a large international scientific program coordinating research in the Arctic and Antarctic. The main approach to these studies makes use of the fact that the chemistry of the H_2O in the ice itself holds clues about climatic conditions at the time when it first formed as precipitation.

Stable isotope geochemistry is a powerful tool for the study of paleoclimate

Clues about paleoclimates can be partly uncovered through the study of the **stable isotope geochemistry** of the ice. (You learned about stable isotopes in the chapter on matter, energy, and the physical environment.) Stable isotopes are naturally occurring variations of elements, which vary just slightly from one another in mass but not in other chemical characteristics. This means, for example, that deuterium—a naturally occurring isotope of hydrogen that is heavier than simple hydrogen—behaves chemically like hydrogen. However, because of the difference in its mass, deuterium is separated from hydrogen and becomes differently concentrated in Earth materials (like ice) when acted upon by any process that is influenced by mass.

Consider, for example, the process of precipitation. Water that falls as precipitation is naturally enriched in the heavier isotopes of its components, hydrogen and oxygen. Water that remains behind in cloud form, on the other hand, will tend to be enriched in the lighter isotopes of its chemical constituents. The scientific term for the separation and differential concentration of isotopes of slightly different mass is *fractionation*. Many natural fractionation processes are temperature dependent—that is, they are controlled by variations in temperature. Sampling and analysis of Earth materials—not just ice but any natural material that incorporates isotopes and is affected by temperature-dependent fractionation processes—can reveal the past temperature history of those materials.

Proxy indicators like stable isotopes often give us information about local or regional areas, but to get a global perspective scientists need to combine multiple records from various areas. In fact, one of the most interesting challenges in stable isotope studies of paleoclimate has been to explain the slight mismatch in timing (*asynchronicity*) between major climatic events recorded in ice core records from Antarctic and Greenland ice cores. Because the number of available records decreases the farther back in time we go (because there isn't very much million-year-old ice left on Earth), estimates of global climate conditions for the recent past tend to be more reliable than those for the distant past.

Direct atmospheric sampling tells us about the present

Studying present-day climate is much more straightforward, because scientists can measure atmospheric conditions directly. As mentioned above, our records of direct measurements of temperature and precipitation date back several hundred years, although the more recent records are obviously the most reliable. Atmospheric carbon dioxide concentrations have been measured continuously at the Mauna Loa Observatory in Hawaii, starting in 1958 (**FIGURE 15.9**). These data show that atmospheric CO_2 concentrations have increased from 315 ppm in 1958 to 392 ppm in 2011. Today scientists at Mauna Loa continue to make these measurements, building upon the best long-term data set we have of direct atmospheric sampling of any greenhouse gas.

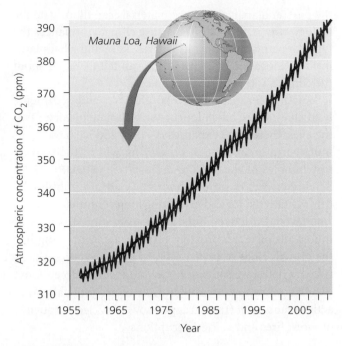

FIGURE 15.9

Atmospheric concentrations of carbon dioxide have risen steeply since these measurements began to be taken at the Mauna Loa Observatory in 1958. The jaggedness is caused by seasonal variations in photosynthetic uptake. The Northern Hemisphere has more land area and thus more vegetation than the Southern Hemisphere. Thus, more carbon dioxide is absorbed during the northern summer, when Northern Hemisphere plants are more photosynthetically active.

Source: Data from National Oceanic and Atmospheric Administration, Earth System Research Laboratory, Global Monitoring Division (2010).

FIGURE 15.10

Modern climate models incorporate many factors, including processes involving the atmosphere, land, ocean, ice, and biosphere. Such factors are shown graphically here, but the actual models deal with them as mathematical equations in computer simulations, carried in each individual element of a detailed geographical grid.

Models help us understand climate

To understand how climate systems function and to predict future climate change, scientists simulate climate processes with sophisticated computer programs. *Climate models* are programs that combine what is known about atmospheric circulation, ocean circulation, atmosphere–ocean–land interactions, and feedback mechanisms to simulate climate processes (**FIGURE 15.10**). They couple, or combine, the climate influences of the atmosphere and oceans into a single simulation. This requires manipulating vast amounts of data and complex mathematical equations repeated in each element of a detailed geographical grid, with both horizontal and vertical variations—it was simply not possible until the advent of modern computers.

Canadian scientists are internationally recognized as leaders in the development of such models, also called *general circulation models* or **global climate models (GCMs)**. Research utilizing climate models developed at the Canadian Centre for Climate Modelling and Analysis (CCCma), part of Environment Canada, has contributed to reports by the Intergovernmental Panel on Climate Change (IPCC). Scenarios based on Canadian models have also been used by the government of the United States in its *National Assessment of the Potential Consequences of Climate Variability and Change*, providing a basis for strategic planning for managing the consequences of climate change.

Researchers develop different climate models for different purposes. You can think of these models as being sort of like very sophisticated versions of computer simulation games, like *SimEarth*, *SimCity*, *SimAnt*, and so on. If you have played any of these games (especially the earlier versions, which required more hands-on intervention by the gamer), then you know something about how they work. You provide some starting information to the game (or computer model), setting up the preconditions for the simulation, and then you let it run. You can tweak it as the game goes on—constructing more buildings, taking away food sources, or adding more predators to the ant colony—but eventually the model will run to its natural completion.

That is something like how climate models work. Researchers construct models that are as realistic as possible, building in as much information as they can from what is understood about the functioning of the climate system. They can test the effectiveness of the models by entering past climate data and running the model toward the present. If a model produces accurate reconstructions of our current climate, based on well-established data from the past, then we have reason to believe that it simulates climate mechanisms realistically and that it may accurately predict future climate.

FIGURE 15.11 shows temperature results from three such simulations, as reported by the IPCC. Model results in **FIGURE 15.11A** are based on natural climate-changing factors alone (such as volcanic activity and variation in solar energy). Model results in **FIGURE 15.11B** are based on anthropogenic factors only (such as human emissions

(a) Natural factors only

(b) Anthropogenic factors only

(c) All factors

FIGURE 15.11
Scientists test climate models by entering climate data from past years and comparing model predictions (blue areas) with actual observed data (red lines). Models that incorporate only natural factors **(a)** or only human-induced factors **(b)** do not predict real climate trends as well as models that incorporate both natural and anthropogenic factors **(c)**. *Source: Data from the Intergovernmental Panel on Climate Change. 2001. Fourth Assessment Report.*

THE SCIENCE BEHIND THE STORY

Reading History in the World's Longest Ice Core

An EPICA researcher prepares a Dome C ice core sample for analysis.

Snow falling year after year compresses into ice and stacks up into immense sheets that scientists can mine for clues to Earth's climate history. The ice sheets of Antarctica and Greenland trap tiny air bubbles, dust particles, and other proxy indicators of past conditions. By drilling boreholes and extracting ice cores, researchers can tap into these valuable archives.

Recently, researchers drilled and analyzed the deepest core ever. At a remote, pristine site in Antarctica named Dome C, they drilled down 3270 m to bedrock and pulled out more than 800 000 years' worth of ice. The longest previous ice core (from Antarctica's Vostok station) had gone

back 420 000 years. Ice near the top of these cores was laid down recently; ice at the bottom is oldest. By analyzing ice at intervals along the core's length, researchers can generate a timeline of environmental change.

The Dome C core was drilled by the European Project for Ice Coring in Antarctica (EPICA), a consortium of researchers from 10 European nations. Antarctic operations are expensive and logistically complicated: Ice drilling requires powerful technology, and the analysis requires a diverse assemblage of experts. When the team published its results in the journal *Nature* in 2004, the landmark paper had 56 authors.

The researchers obtained data on surface air temperature going back 740 000 years by measuring the ratio of deuterium isotopes to normal hydrogen in the ice. This ratio is temperature dependent (top panel of figure).

By examining dust particles, they could tell when arid and/or windy climates sent more dust aloft. By analyzing air bubbles trapped in the ice, the researchers were later able to quantify atmospheric concentrations of carbon dioxide, methane, and nitrous oxide, across 800 000 years.

One finding was expected—yet crucial. The researchers documented that temperature swings in the past were tightly correlated with concentrations of carbon dioxide (middle panel of figure), as well as methane and nitrous oxide. Also clear and expected from the data was that temperature varied with swings in solar radiation caused by Milankovitch cycles; the Dome C core spanned eight glacial cycles.

A tight correlation between greenhouse gas concentrations and temperature does not prove causality: It doesn't prove that high atmospheric GHG concentrations caused warming, nor does it prove that warming caused GHG concentrations to increase.

What the correlation does demonstrate is that there is a close relationship between atmospheric GHGs and climatic warming: When atmospheric GHG concentrations are high, so is temperature, and vice versa. This is crucially important.

The EPICA data also demonstrate that by increasing greenhouse gas concentrations since the Industrial Revolution, we have brought them well above the highest levels they reached naturally in 650 000 years. Today's carbon dioxide concentration (392 ppm in 2011) is far above previous

---

of greenhouse gases and sulphate aerosols). Model results in **FIGURE 15.11C** are based on natural and anthropogenic factors combined, and this produces the closest match between predictions and actual climate.

Such results as those in **FIGURE 15.11C** clearly support the hypothesis that both natural and human factors contribute to climate dynamics, and they also indicate that global climate models can produce reliable predictions. As computing power increases and we glean more and better data from proxies, these models become increasingly reliable. They also are improving in resolution and are beginning to predict climate change region by region for various areas of the world.

Current and Future Trends and Impacts

Evidence that climate conditions have changed worldwide since industrialization is now overwhelming and indisputable. Climate change in recent years has already had numerous effects on the physical properties of our planet, on organisms and ecosystems, and on human well-being. If we continue to emit greenhouse gases into the atmosphere, the impacts of climate change will only grow more severe.

Future impacts of climate change are subject to regional variation, so the way each of us experiences these impacts over the coming decades will vary tremendously, maximum values. Present-day concentrations of methane and nitrous oxide are likewise the highest in 800 000 years. These data show that we as a society have brought ourselves deep into uncharted territory.

Other findings from the ice core are not as easily explained. Intriguingly, earlier glacial cycles differ from recent cycles. For recent cycles, the Dome C core showed that glacial periods were long and interglacial periods were brief, with rapid rise and fall of temperature. Interglacials thus appear on a graph of temperature through time as tall, thin spikes. However, in older cycles the glacial and interglacial periods were of more equal duration, and the warm extremes of interglacials were not as great. This change in the nature of glacial cycles through time had been noted by researchers working with oxygen isotope data from the fossils of marine organisms (bottom panel of figure). But why glacial cycles should be different before and after the 450 000-year mark, no one knows.

Today scientists are searching for a site that might provide an ice core stretching back more than 1 million years. Data from marine isotopes tell us that glacial cycles at that time switched from a periodicity of roughly 41 000 years (conforming to the influence of planetary tilt) to about 100 000 years (more similar to orbital changes). An ice core that captures cycles on both sides of the 1 million-year divide might help clarify the influence of Milankovitch cycles.

The Dome C ice core research shows that we still have plenty to learn about our complex climate history. The close correlation between greenhouse gases and temperature evident in the EPICA data provides a strong indication that we would do well to bring greenhouse emissions under control before it is too late.

Data from the EPICA ice core reveal changes in surface temperature (black line), atmospheric methane concentration (green line), and atmospheric carbon dioxide concentration (red line), across 800 000 years. High peaks in temperature indicate warm interglacial periods, and low troughs indicate cold glacial periods. Atmospheric concentrations of carbon dioxide and methane rise and fall in tight correlation with temperature. Today's current values are included at the far top right of the graph, for comparison.

Source: Adapted by permission of Macmillan Publishers Ltd: Brook, E. (2008). Paleoclimate: Windows on the greenhouse. Nature 453:291–291, Fig 1a. www.nature.com

depending on where we live. The impacts on Canada could be particularly severe. According to the CCCma,

Over the next century, the Canadian climate model indicates that the most northerly regions of the Earth will experience the greatest warming, with potentially serious impacts on Arctic communities and ecosystems. Major changes in climate are also expected in the Prairies, the east and west coasts and the Great Lakes basin. Many communities and climate-sensitive industries will be profoundly affected, including forestry, agriculture, marine transportation, fishing and oil and gas development . . . The magnitude and rate of change projected for the twenty-first century will put enormous pressure on our environment, our infrastructure and our social fabric. Climate modelling can help us avoid aggravating the situation by providing a glimpse of the future.[4]

The IPCC summarizes evidence of climate change and predicts future impacts

In recent years, it seems that virtually everyone is detecting climatic changes around us. A fisher in the Indian Ocean island of the Maldives notes the seas encroaching on his home island. A rancher in Alberta suffers a multi-year drought. A homeowner in Florida finds it impossible to obtain insurance against the hurricanes and storm surges that increasingly threaten. Residents of Montreal marvel over freakish winter weather events. But can we conclude that all of these impressions are part of a real pattern, or are they just ephemeral fluctuations in the data?

A true trend is a pattern that persists within a data set, even after short-term fluctuations, background noise, and local anomalies have been removed or accounted for. Is there solid scientific evidence to confirm that we are seeing a trend, and that the global climate is indeed already changing? A wide variety of data sets do appear to show significant trends in climate conditions over the past century and particularly in recent years. The most thoroughly reviewed and widely accepted synthesis of scientific information concerning climate change is a series of reports issued by the **Intergovernmental Panel on Climate Change (IPCC)**. This international panel of scientists and government officials was established in 1988 by the United Nations Environment Programme (UNEP) and the World Meteorological Organization.

In 2007 the IPCC released its Fourth Assessment Report, which represents the consensus of scientific climate research from around the world. (The next report is due in 2014 and will be released in stages.) This report summarizes many thousands of scientific studies, and it documents observed trends in surface temperature, precipitation patterns, snow and ice cover, sea levels, storm intensity, and other factors. It also predicts future changes in these phenomena after considering a range of potential scenarios for future greenhouse gas emissions. The report addresses impacts of current and future climate change on wildlife, ecosystems, and human societies. Finally, it discusses possible strategies we might pursue in response to climate change. **FIGURE 15.12** summarizes a selection of the IPCC report's major observed and predicted trends and impacts.

The IPCC report is authoritative, but—like all science—it deals in uncertainties. Its authors have therefore taken great care to assign statistical probabilities to its conclusions and predictions. In addition, its estimates regarding impacts of change on human societies are conservative, because its scientific conclusions had to be approved by representatives of the world's national governments, some of which are reluctant to move away from a fossil-fuel-based economy.

Temperature increases will continue

The IPCC report concludes that average surface temperatures on Earth increased by an estimated 0.74°C in the century from 1906 to 2005 (**FIGURE 15.13**), with most of this increase occurring in the last few decades. The fifteen years from 1997 to 2011 were, without exception, among the 20 warmest years on record since regular global instrumental measurements have been maintained (since the late 1800s). The numbers of extremely hot days and heat waves have increased, whereas the number of cold days has decreased.

Temperature changes are greatest in the Arctic, and climate scientists anticipate that this will likely continue to be the case throughout the rest of this century (**FIGURE 15.14**). Here, ice sheets are melting, sea ice is thinning, storms are increasing, and altered conditions are posing challenges for people and wildlife. As sea ice melts earlier, freezes later, and recedes from shore, it becomes harder for Inuit and for polar bears alike to hunt the seals they each rely on for food. Thin sea ice is dangerous for people to travel and hunt upon, and in recent years, polar bears have been dying of exhaustion and starvation as they try to swim long distances between ice floes. **Permafrost** (perennially frozen ground) is thawing in the Arctic, destabilizing countless buildings. The strong Arctic warming is contributing to sea-level rise by melting icecaps and ice sheets.

In the future, we can expect average surface temperatures on Earth to rise roughly 0.2°C per decade for the next 20 years, according to IPCC analysis. If we were to cease greenhouse gas emissions today, temperatures would still rise 0.1°C per decade because of the time lag from gases already in the atmosphere that have yet to exert their full influence. At the end of the twenty-first century, the IPCC predicts global temperatures will be

weighing the issues

CLIMATE CHANGE AND HUMAN RIGHTS

In December 2005, a group representing North America's Inuit sent a legal petition to the Inter-American Commission on Human Rights, demanding that the United States restrict its greenhouse gas emissions, which the Inuit maintained were destroying their way of life in the Arctic. After a year, the commission dismissed the petition with a terse three-sentence letter.

Do you think Arctic-living people deserve compensation from industrialized nations whose emissions have caused climate change that has disproportionately affected the Arctic? Do you think climate change can be viewed as a human rights issue? What ethical issues, if any, do you think climate change presents? How could these best be resolved?

Major Trends and Impacts of Climate Change, from IPCC *Fourth Assessment Report*, 2007

Global physical indicators

Earth's average surface temperature increased 0.74° C in the past 100 years, and will rise 1.8–4.0° C in the 21st century.

Eleven of the years from 1995 to 2006 were among the 12 warmest on record.

Atmospheric water vapour increased since at least the 1980s.

Oceans absorbed >80% of heat added to the climate system, and warmed to depths of at least 3000 m.

Glaciers, snow cover, ice caps, ice sheets, and sea ice will continue melting, contributing to sea-level rise.

Sea level rose by an average of 17 cm in the 20th century, and will rise 18–59 cm in the 21st century.

Ocean water became more acidic by about 0.1 pH unit, and will decrease in pH by 0.14–0.35 units more by century's end.

Storm surges increased, and will increase further.[1]

Sea level rise will worsen coastal erosion and degrade wetlands.

Carbon uptake by terrestrial ecosystems will likely peak by the mid-21st century and then weaken or reverse, amplifying climate change.[2]

Social indicators

Farmers and foresters have had to adapt to altered growing seasons and disturbance regimes.

Temperate-zone crop yields will rise until temperature warms beyond 3° C, but in the dry tropics and subtropics, crop productivity will fall and lead to hunger.[5]

Timber production may rise slightly in the near-term, but will vary by region.[5]

Impacts on biodiversity will cause losses of food, water, and other ecosystem goods and services.[2]

Sea-level rise will displace people from islands and coastal regions.[3]

Melting of mountain glaciers will reduce water supplies to millions of people.[2]

Economic costs will outweigh benefits as climate change worsens;[2] costs could average 1–5% of GDP globally for 4° C of warming.

Poorer nations and communities suffer more from climate change, because they rely more on climate-sensitive resources and have less capacity to adapt.[2]

Human health will suffer as increased warm-weather health hazards outweigh decreased cold-weather health hazards.[2]

Regional physical indicators

Arctic areas warmed fastest. Future warming will be greatest in the Arctic and greater over land than over water.

Summer Arctic sea ice thinned by 7.4% per decade since 1978.

Average Northern Hemisphere temperatures of the past 50 years were the highest in at least 1300 years.[1]

Thawing decreased area of Arctic permafrost in spring by 15% since 1900.

Precipitation increased in e. North America, e. South America, n. Europe, and n. and c. Asia since 1900.

Precipitation decreased in the Sahel, the Mediterranean, s. Africa, and parts of s. Asia since 1900.

Precipitation will generally increase at high latitudes and decrease at subtropical latitudes, often making wet areas wetter and dry ones drier.[1]

Heavy precipitation events increased over most land areas.[1]

Droughts became longer, more intense, and more widespread since the 1970s, especially in the tropics and subtropics.[1]

Droughts and flooding will increase, leading to agricultural losses.[2]

Over most land areas, cold and frost days decreased[3] and will continue to decrease[4] while hot days and heat waves increased[3] and will continue to increase.[3]

Hurricanes intensified in the North Atlantic since 1970,[1] and will continue to intensify.[1]

The thermohaline circulation will slow, but will not shut down and chill Europe in the 21st century.[3]

Antarctica will continue accumulating snow, but may also continue losing ice around its edges.

Biological indicators

Species ranges are shifting toward the poles and upward in elevation, and will continue to shift.

The timing of seasonal phenomena (such as migration and breeding) is shifting, and will continue to shift.

About 20–30% of species studed so far will face extinction risk if temperature rises more than 1.5–2.5° C.[5]

Species interactions and ecosystem structure and function could change greatly, resulting in biodiversity loss.

Corals will experience further mortality from bleaching and ocean acidification.[5,4]

FIGURE 15.12   Climate change has had consequences already and is predicted to have many more. Listed here are some of the main observed and predicted trends and impacts described in the Intergovernmental Panel on Climate Change's *Fourth Assessment Report*. For simplicity, this figure expresses mean estimates only; the IPCC report provides ranges of estimates as well. [1]Certainty level = 66%–90% probability of being correct. [2]Certainty level = ~80% probability of being correct. [3]Certainty level = 90%–99% probability of being correct. [4]Certainty level = > 99% probability of being correct. [5]Certainty level = ~50% probability of being correct.   *Source: Data from the Intergovernmental Panel on Climate Change (IPCC). 2007. Fourth Assessment Report.*

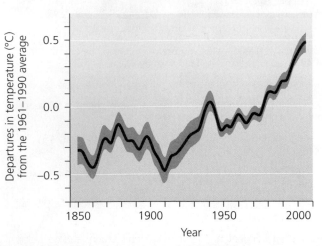

(a) Global temperature measured since 1850

(b) Northern Hemisphere temperature over the past 1000 years

FIGURE 15.13   Data from thermometers **(a)** show changes in Earth's average surface temperature since 1850. Grey shaded area indicates range of uncertainty. In **(b)**, proxy indicators (blue line) and thermometer data (red line at right) together show average temperature changes in the Northern Hemisphere over the past 1000 years. The grey-shaded zone represents the 95% confidence range. This record shows that twentieth-century warming has eclipsed the magnitude of change during both the "Medieval Warm Period" (tenth to fourteenth centuries) and the "Little Ice Age" (fifteenth to nineteenth centuries).   *Source: Data in (a) from the Intergovernmental Panel on Climate Change. (2007). Fourth Assessment Report. Data in (b) from and IPCC. (2001). Third Assessment Report.*

1.8°C–4.0°C higher than today's, depending upon the emission scenario. Unusually hot days and heat waves will become more frequent. Temperature change is predicted to vary from region to region in ways that parallel existing regional differences (**FIGURE 15.15**).

Sea surface temperatures are also increasing as the oceans absorb heat. The record number of hurricanes and tropical storms in 2005—Katrina and 27 others—left many people wondering whether global warming was to blame. Are warmer ocean temperatures spawning

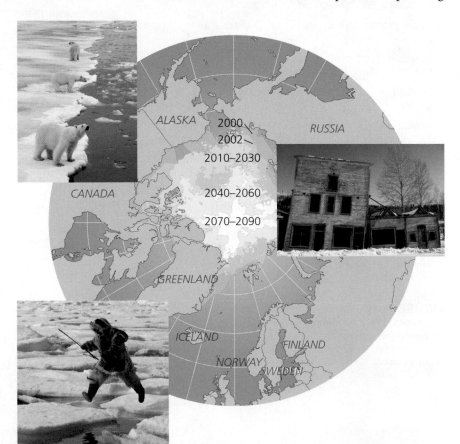

FIGURE 15.14

The Arctic has borne the brunt of climate change's impacts so far. As Arctic sea ice melts it recedes from large areas, as shown by the map indicating the mean minimum summertime extent of sea ice for the recent past, present, and future. Inuit find it difficult to hunt and travel in their traditional ways, and polar bears starve because they are less able to hunt seals. As permafrost thaws beneath them, human-made structures are damaged: phone poles topple and buildings can lean, buckle, crack, and fall. *Source: Map data from National Center for Atmospheric Research and National Snow and Ice Data Center.*

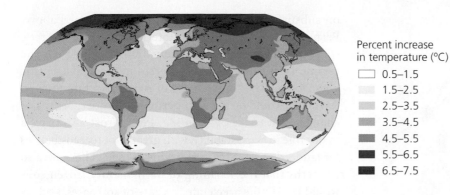

FIGURE 15.15
This map shows projected increases in surface temperature for the decade 2090–2099, relative to temperatures in 1980–1999. Land masses will warm more than the ocean, and the Arctic will warm the most, up to 7.5°C. The IPCC uses multiple climate models when predicting regional variation in how temperature will change, and this map was generated by using an emission scenario that is intermediate in its assumptions, involving an average global temperature rise of 2.8°C by 2100.
Source: Data from Intergovernmental Panel on Climate Change. (2007). Fourth Assessment Report.

Percent increase in temperature (°C)

☐ 0.5–1.5
1.5–2.5
2.5–3.5
3.5–4.5
4.5–5.5
5.5–6.5
6.5–7.5

more hurricanes, or hurricanes that are more powerful or long lasting? However, the 2006 hurricane season, in contrast, was quieter than usual. Recent analyses of storm data suggest that warmer seas may not be increasing the number of storms but could be increasing the power of storms and possibly their duration.

Changes in precipitation will vary by region

A warmer atmosphere holds more water vapour, but changes in precipitation patterns have been complex, with some regions of the world receiving more precipitation than usual and others receiving less. In regions from the African Sahel to the Western Prairies, droughts have become more frequent and severe, harming agriculture, promoting soil erosion, reducing drinking water supplies, and encouraging forest fires. Meanwhile, in both dry and humid regions, heavy rain events have increased, contributing to damaging floods.

Precipitation changes are predicted to vary among different regions (**FIGURE 15.16**). In general, precipitation will increase at high latitudes and decrease at low and middle latitudes, magnifying differences in rainfall that already exist and worsening water shortages in many developing countries of the arid subtropics. In many areas, heavy precipitation events will become more frequent, increasing the risk of flooding.

Melting ice and snow have far-reaching effects

As the world warms, mountaintop glaciers are disappearing (**FIGURE 15.17**). Since 1980, the World Glacier Monitoring Service estimates, major glaciers have each lost an average of 13 m in vertical thickness of water mass equivalent. Many glaciers on tropical mountaintops have disappeared altogether. As discussed in "Central Case: The Retreat of the Athabasca," the Athabasca Glacier has retreated 1.5 km since the late nineteenth century, with the rate of retreat accelerating dramatically after 1980. Peyto Glacier in Banff National Park, Alberta, retreated rapidly during the first half of the twentieth century, stabilized briefly in 1966, and then resumed its retreat in 1979. Illecillewaet Glacier in Glacier National Park, British Columbia, has retreated 2 km in the past century.

Mountains accumulate snow in the winter and release meltwater gradually during the summer. Throughout high-elevation areas of the world, however, warming temperatures will continue to melt mountain glaciers, posing risks of sudden floods as ice dams burst, and reducing summertime water supplies to millions of people. More

Percent change in precipitation

>20% decrease
10–20% decrease
5–10% decrease
5% decrease to 5% increase
5–10% increase
10–20% increase
>20% increase

FIGURE 15.16
This map shows projected changes in June–August precipitation for the decade 2090–2099, relative to precipitation levels in 1980–1999. Browner shades indicate less precipitation, and bluer shades indicate more precipitation. White indicates areas for which models could not agree. This map was generated by using an emission scenario that is intermediate in its assumptions, involving an average global temperature rise of 2.8°C by 2100.
Source: Data from Intergovernmental Panel on Climate Change. 2007. Fourth Assessment Report.

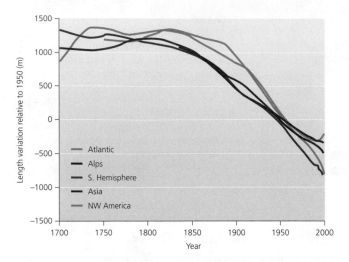

FIGURE 15.17

This is a collection of length records for glacial tongues from different parts of the world, grouped by region and portrayed in terms of change relative to 1950 (which is set at zero). The geographical distribution of the data is also shown.

Source: Intergovernmental Panel on Climate Change, Fourth Assessment Report (2007), Physical Science Basis Working Group, Figure 4.13. www.ipcc.ch/publications_and_data/ar4/wg1/en/ch4s4-5-2.html

than one-sixth of the world's people live in regions supplied by mountain meltwater, and some of these people are already beginning to face water shortages. If this water vanishes during drier months, whole communities will be forced to look elsewhere for water, or to move.

Warming of temperatures will have an impact not only on surface snow and ice (**FIGURE 15.18**) but also

on subsurface ice and permafrost, as mentioned above. Permafrost is the most characteristic feature of Arctic soils, and its expected behaviour in a changing climate regime is not thoroughly understood from a scientific perspective. The foundations of roads and buildings in the north would be at risk if permafrost undergoes major changes as a result of warming. Permafrost also plays a major role in slope stability, with greatly increased chances for landslides as permafrost begins to melt. There are also concerns that the warming of permanently frozen soils would lead to the accelerated release of soil gases, such as methane, which could contribute to a positive feedback cycle in the climate system, leading to further warming.

The Arctic is changing dramatically

Warming temperatures are already reducing snow cover, affecting permafrost stability at high latitudes, and melting the immense ice sheets of the Arctic. Recent research reveals that melting of the Greenland ice sheet is accelerating (see "The Science Behind the Story: Greenland's Glaciers Race to the Sea"). At the other end of the world, in Antarctica, ice shelves almost the size of Prince Edward Island have disintegrated as a result of contact with warmer ocean water, but increased precipitation has so far supplied the continent with enough extra snow to compensate for the loss of ice around its edges.

According to Dr. Luke Copland of the University of Ottawa, the area of Canada's ice shelves has shrunk by

FIGURE 15.18

The Canadian Regional Climate Model, developed by Environment Canada and the University of Québec at Montreal, shows the projected change, to the middle of this century, in snow cover. As the climate warms, winter snow could decrease by 50% in much of southern Canada and increase slightly in the high Arctic.

Source: CCma Environment Canada.

approximately 90% over the past 100 years. One major event that contributed to this loss was the collapse of the Ayles Ice Shelf in 2005 (FIGURE 15.19). The Ayles Ice Shelf was one of Canada's six major ice shelves, located off the northern coast of Ellesmere Island, Nunavut, about 800 km south of the North Pole. On August 13, 2005, it broke off, creating an ice island 14 km by 5 km, and 37 m in thickness. The oldest ice in the ice island is more than 3000 years old. This ice breakup was so large that it was detected by seismometers. The breakup happened

very quickly, lasting less than an hour according to reconstructions based on satellite images. Since the breakup, the ice island has drifted, becoming temporarily locked in place during winter freeze-ups and then breaking free and drifting again, and it has broken into two large parts. The large ice island fragments could pose a risk to oil rigs and drilling in the Beaufort Sea.

One reason warming is accelerating in the Arctic is that as snow and ice melt, darker, less-reflective surfaces are exposed, and Earth's albedo, or capacity to reflect

(a) Ayles Ice Shelf before breakup

(b) Ayles ice island after breakup

FIGURE 15.19
As seen in these satellite images, the Ayles ice shelf **(a)**, one of Canada's major ice sheets north of Ellesmere Island, collapsed in 2005 **(b)**, forming a huge ice island 14 km by 5 km in size.

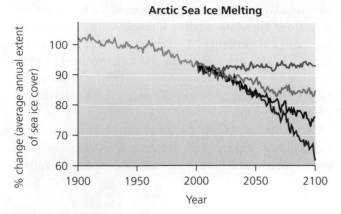

Future rapid growth, slow technological change (Scenario A2)
Mixed future of "green" energy & fossil fuel use (Scenario A1)
A future "green" world, with clean energy (Scenario B1)
Already committed future change
Model reproduction of past change

FIGURE 15.20
The various curves on this graph show climate model simulations of several of the future scenarios described by the IPCC. Scenario A2, in which population growth is rapid and technological advancement to lower-emission energy technologies is slow, yields the most dramatic decrease in areal extent of Arctic sea ice.

light, decreases. As a result, more of the Sun's rays are absorbed at the surface, fewer reflect back into space, and the surface warms. In a positive feedback, this warming causes more ice and snow to melt, which in turn causes more absorption of radiation and more warming.

Near the poles, snow cover, permafrost, and ice sheets are projected to decrease, and sea ice will continue to shrink in both the Arctic and the Antarctic (**FIGURE 15.20**). Some climate scenarios show Arctic sea ice disappearing completely from the Northwest Passage by the late twenty-first century, creating new shipping lanes for commerce (and likely a rush to exploit underwater oil and mineral reserves that may exist in Arctic waters).

Rising sea levels will affect millions of people in coastal zones and on islands

As glaciers and ice sheets melt, increased runoff into the oceans causes sea levels to rise. Sea levels also are rising because ocean water is warming, and water expands in volume as its temperature increases. In fact, recent sea-level rise has resulted primarily from the thermal expansion of seawater. Worldwide, average sea levels rose an estimated 17 cm during the twentieth century (**FIGURE 15.21**). Seas rose by an estimated 1.8 mm/year during 1961–2003 and 3.1 mm/year during 1993–2006. Note that these numbers represent vertical rises in water

weighing the issues

AN ICE-FREE NORTHWEST PASSAGE AND CANADA'S ARCTIC SOVEREIGNTY

Now that the Northwest Passage—the long-coveted sea route from the Atlantic to the Pacific via the Arctic Ocean—may soon be ice-free, northern nations are anxious to confirm their territorial influence in the region. Canada reaffirmed its sovereignty over Arctic waters at an international conference held in Greenland recently, and Prime Minister Stephen Harper pledged to spend billions of dollars defending Canada's interests in the Arctic if necessary. In addition to the sea route, the Arctic subsurface may hold as much as 25% of the world's undiscovered oil and gas reserves. The U.S. argues that the Arctic does not belong to Canada, or to anyone else. What do you think? Who should control Arctic Ocean waters, and for what purposes? How much of Canadian taxpayers' money should be spent to assert and maintain Canada's sovereignty in the Arctic?

level, and on most coastlines a vertical rise of centimetres means metres of horizontal incursion inland.

Higher sea levels lead to beach erosion, coastal flooding, intrusion of saltwater into aquifers, and other impacts. In 1987, unusually high waves struck the island nation of the Maldives and triggered a campaign to build a large seawall around Male, the nation's capital. Known as "The Great Wall of Male," the seawall is intended to protect buildings and roads by dissipating the energy of incoming waves during storm surges. A storm surge is a temporary and localized rise in sea level brought on by the

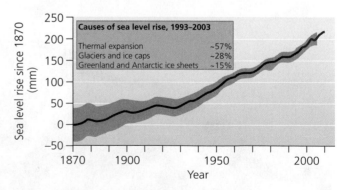

FIGURE 15.21
Data from tide gauges (black line) and satellite observations (red line) show that global average sea level has risen about 200 mm since 1870. Grey shaded area indicates range of uncertainty. Thermal expansion of water accounts for most sea-level rise.
Source: Data from Intergovernmental Panel on Climate Change. 2007. Fourth Assessment Report.

low atmospheric pressure and winds associated with storms. The higher sea level is to begin with, the farther inland a destructive storm surge can reach. "With a mere one-metre rise [in sea level]," Maldivian president Maumoon Abdul Gayoom warned in 2001, "a storm surge would be catastrophic, and possibly fatal to the nation."

The Maldives is not the only nation with such concerns. In fact, among island nations, the Maldives has fared better than many others. It saw a sea-level rise of about 2.5 mm per year throughout the 1990s, but most Pacific islands are experiencing greater changes. Regions experience differing amounts of sea-level change because land elevations may be rising or subsiding naturally, depending on local geologic conditions.

The IPCC predicts that at the end of the twenty-first century mean sea level will be 18–59 cm higher than today, depending upon the emission scenario. However, these estimates do not take into account findings on accelerated ice melting in Greenland, because that research is so new that it has not yet been incorporated into climate models. If Greenland's melting continues to accelerate, then sea levels will rise more quickly.

Rising sea levels will force hundreds of millions of people to choose between moving upland or investing in costly protections against high tides and storm surges. Canada's coastal regions will be variably affected, as shown in **FIGURE 15.22**. Low-lying coastal locations, such as parts of the St. Lawrence estuary, Nova Scotia, Cape Breton, and Prince Edward Island, are particularly vulnerable to flooding. Some areas of the far north, including the coasts of the Beaufort Sea, and low-lying areas of the B.C. coast are also at risk of both flooding and accelerated coastal erosion.

Worldwide, densely populated regions on low-lying river deltas, such as the Ganges–Brahmaputra Delta in Bangladesh and the Irrawaddy Delta of Burma, will be most affected. So will storm-prone regions, coastal cities, and areas around the world where land is subsiding. Many Pacific islands will need to be evacuated, and some nations, such as Tuvalu and the Maldives, fear for their very existence. In the meantime, they may suffer from shortages of fresh water because rising seas threaten to bring saltwater into the nation's wells, as the 2004 tsunami did. The contamination of groundwater and soils by seawater threatens not only island nations but also coastal areas that depend on small lenses of fresh water floating atop saline groundwater in coastal aquifers.

FIGURE 15.22

This map shows the sensitivity of the coastlines of Canada to the expected rise in sea level as a result of climate change. Sensitivity is the degree to which a coastline may experience physical changes, such as flooding, erosion, beach migration, and coastal dune destabilization. Two major regions of high sensitivity are identified: Atlantic Canada and parts of the Beaufort Sea coast.
Source: The Atlas of Canada, NRCAN, Coastal Sensitivity to Sea-Level Rise, http://atlas.nrcan.gc.ca/site/english/index.html

THE SCIENCE BEHIND THE STORY

Greenland's Glaciers Race to the Sea

Outlet glaciers melt into Scoresby Sund, Greenland's largest fjord.

Scientists have known for years that the Arctic is bearing the brunt of global warming and that the massive ice sheet covering Greenland is melting around its edges. But data from 1993 to 2003 showed Greenland's ice loss accounting for only 4–12% of global sea-level rise, about 0.21 mm/yr. And as authors of the IPCC's Fourth Assessment Report used results from climate models to predict Greenland's future contributions to sea-level rise, the models told them to expect more of the same.

However, some brand-new research hadn't made it into the models. Scientists studying how ice moves were learning that ice sheets can collapse more quickly than expected and that Greenland's ice loss is accelerating. As a result, they said, the IPCC report underestimates the likely speed and extent of future sea-level rise.

Greenland's ice sheet is massive, nearly 3 km at its thickest point, and covers approximately 1.7 million km^2—an area larger than the entire province of Québec. If the entire ice sheet were to melt, global sea level would rise by a whopping 7 m. The ice sheet, like all perennial ice masses, gains mass by accumulating snow during cold weather, which becomes packed into ice over time. It loses mass as surface ice melts in warm weather, generally at the periphery, where ice is thinnest or contacts seawater. If melting and runoff outpace accumulation, the ice sheet shrinks.

Researchers are now learning that the internal physical dynamics of how ice moves may be even more important. These dynamics can speed the flow of immense amounts of ice in outlet glaciers downhill toward the coast, where erod-ing ice sloughs off and melts into the sea. The first good indication of this process came in 2002 when a team of researchers noted that ice in outlet glaciers flows more quickly during warm months, when pools of meltwater form on the surface and leak down through crevasses and vertical tunnels called moulins to the bottom of the glacier. There, the water runs downhill in a layer between bedrock and ice, lubricating the bedrock surface and enabling the ice to slide downhill like a car hydroplaning on a wet road. In addition, the meltwater weakens ice on its way down and warms the base of the glacier, melting some of it to create more water (see the figure).

Other scientists have proposed that warming ocean water melts ice shelves along the coast, depriving outlet glaciers of the buttressing support that holds them in place. Without a floating ice tongue at its terminus, a glacier slides into the ocean more readily. These physical dynamics represent positive feedback, researchers said; once global warming initiates these processes, they encourage further melting. As such, it is likely that Greenland's melting will accelerate.

Researchers have determined that Greenland lost a total of 91 km^3 of ice in 1996, 138 km^3 in 2000, and 224 km^3 in 2005. This last amount exceeds all the water consumed in Canada in almost two decades! More recent studies continue to show that Greenland's ice losses are accelerating. Scientists will be keeping a close eye on the ice sheet to see whether it continues to discharge water more and more quickly. If it does, climate modellers will have several years in which to incorporate into their models the new and evolving understanding of the physical dynamics of ice—just in time for the next IPCC report, scheduled for 2014.

Snowmelt exposes darker ice, which absorbs more sunlight

Snow

Ice

Outlet glacier

Bedrock

Moulin

Meltwater lake

Crevasse

Warm ocean water breaks up floating ice tongue

Disintegration of ice tongue weakens support for glacier

Meltwater cascades down through ice in moulins and crevasses

Water flows beneath ice, lubricating bedrock surface

Outlet glaciers from Greenland's ice sheet are accelerating their slide into the ocean because meltwater is descending through moulins and crevasses, lubricating the bedrock surface. Moreover, melting snow exposes darker ice, which absorbs sunlight and speeds melting. Finally, breakup of floating ice tongues weakens support for the glacier.

Coastal and island residents also worry about damage to the marine ecosystems that are critical for their economy, including coral reefs. Coral reefs provide habitat for important food fish that are consumed locally and exported; offer snorkelling and scuba diving sites for tourism; and reduce wave intensity, protecting coastlines from erosion. Around the world, rising seas will eat away at the coral reefs, mangrove forests, and salt marshes that serve as barriers protecting our coasts.

Climate change poses two additional threats to coral reefs: warmer waters are causing coral bleaching, and enhanced CO_2 concentrations in the atmosphere are changing ocean chemistry. As ocean water absorbs atmospheric CO_2, it becomes more acidic, which impairs the growth of coral and other organisms whose exoskeletons consist of calcium carbonate. Ocean water has already decreased by 0.1 pH unit overall (a fairly large amount), and is predicted to decline in pH by 0.14–0.35 more units over the next 100 years. This could easily be enough to destroy all or most of our planet's living coral reefs.

Climate change affects organisms and ecosystems

The many changes in Earth's physical systems have direct consequences for life on our planet. Organisms are adapted to their environments, so they are affected when those environments are altered. As global warming proceeds, it modifies temperature-dependent biological phenomena. For instance, in the spring, birds are migrating earlier, insects are hatching earlier, and animals are breeding earlier. Plants are leafing out earlier, too— an effect confirmed by satellite photography that records whole landscapes "greening up" each year.

These changes in seasonal timing are expected to continue, and they are having complex effects. For instance, European birds known as great tits time their breeding cycle so that their young hatch and grow at the time of peak caterpillar abundance. However, as plants leaf out earlier and insects emerge earlier, research shows that great tits are not breeding earlier. As a result of the mismatch in timing, fewer caterpillars are available when young birds need them, and fewer birds survive. Although some organisms will no doubt adapt to such changes in seasonal timing, research so far shows that in most cases mismatches occur.

A similar situation provided an unexpected benefit and is helping to prevent outbreaks of the invasive parasitic spruce budworm on Vancouver Island. Budworm development is triggered by temperature, while the development of the Douglas fir, the preferred food of the budworm larva, is triggered more by light and day length. As a result of a 90-year increase in winter temperatures on southern Vancouver Island, the budworm larvae are emerging from their shelters earlier, at a time when the Douglas fir, their main food source, is not yet available.

Biologists have recorded spatial shifts in the ranges of organisms, with plants and animals moving toward the poles or upward in elevation (toward cooler regions) as temperatures warm. As these trends continue, some organisms will not be able to cope, and as many as 20–30% of all plant and animal species could be threatened with extinction, the IPCC estimates. Trees may not be able to shift their distributions fast enough. Animals adapted to montane environments may be forced uphill until there is nowhere left to go. Rare species finding refuge in protected preserves may be forced out of preserves into developed areas, making such refuges far less effective tools for conservation.

The American pika (*Ochotona princeps*), a small mammal that lives on rocky slopes near mountain glaciers in southern Canada, may be the first animal in North America to become extinct as a result of climatic warming. The pika (**FIGURE 15.23**), while clearly not the only animal likely to suffer from warming (polar bears come to mind), is extremely sensitive to environmental conditions, especially temperature. Pikas cannot survive if temperatures are too high. Their favoured habitat, in the vicinity of glaciers, is also threatened as a result of rapidly changing conditions in the glacial environment.

These changes will greatly affect species interactions, and scientists foresee major modifications in the structure and function of communities and ecosystems. In regions where precipitation and stream flow increase, erosion and flooding will pollute and alter aquatic systems. In regions where precipitation decreases, lakes, ponds, wetlands,

FIGURE 15.23
Pikas live near glaciers in southern Canada. They are extremely sensitive to temperature, and may become one of the first animals to be driven to extinction by climatic warming.

weighing the issues

ENVIRONMENTAL REFUGEES?

The Pacific island nation of Tuvalu has been losing 9 cm of elevation per decade to rising seas. Appeals from Tuvalu's 11 000 citizens were heard by New Zealand, which began accepting them in small numbers as of 2003, although the government has not officially categorized them as **environmental refugees**—people driven from their homelands as a result of environmental change or natural disaster. Tuvaluans have been particularly vocal about global warming, but several other small Pacific island nations have joined in voicing their concerns.

   Will there come a time when neighbouring countries should begin to treat people who leave small island nations as environmental refugees? Should they be doing it now? What will happen to these people after relocation—do you think a national culture can survive if its entire population is relocated?

and streams will diminish, affecting aquatic organisms, as well as human health and well-being. Acidification of the oceans may pose major threats for corals and other marine animals. Given that corals will likely also suffer increased bleaching from thermal stress, the world's coral reefs are expected to decline substantially. This would reduce marine biodiversity significantly, because so many other organisms depend on living coral reefs for food and shelter.

   Effects on plant communities are an important component of climate change (**FIGURE 15.24**). By drawing in CO_2 for photosynthesis, plants act as sinks

for carbon. If climate change increases vegetative growth, this could help mitigate carbon emissions, in a process of negative feedback. However, if climate change decreases plant growth (through drought or fire, for instance), then positive feedback could increase carbon flux to the atmosphere. The many impacts on ecological systems will reduce the ecosystem goods and services we receive from nature and that our societies depend on, from food to clean air to drinking water.

Climate change exerts societal impacts—and vice versa

Human society has begun to feel the impacts of climate change. Damage from drought, flooding, hurricanes, storm surges, and sea-level rise, as discussed above, has already taken a toll on the lives and livelihoods of millions of people. However, climate change will have additional consequences for humans, including impacts on agriculture, forestry, economics, and health. **FIGURE 15.25** gives an overview of the complex interactions between human systems and the systems of the natural world in determining and reacting to climatic change.

   Let us look in a bit more detail at some of the most important human drivers and impacts of climate change.

Agriculture   For farmers, earlier springs require earlier crop planting. For some crops in the temperate zones, production may increase slightly with moderate warming, because growing seasons become longer and because more carbon dioxide is available to plants for photosynthesis. However, rainfall will shift in space and time, and in areas where droughts and floods become

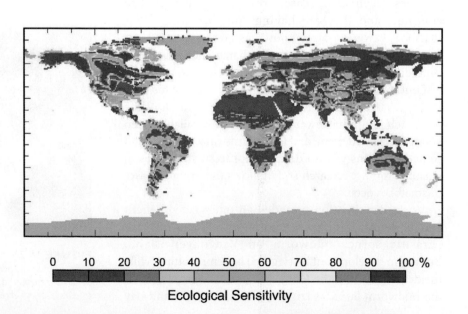

FIGURE 15.24
This map shows the predicted percentage of the ecological landscape that is being driven toward changes in plant species as a result of projected human-induced climate change, by 2100, assuming a climate system in which atmospheric CO_2 has doubled.
Source: NASA–JPL/Caltech http://www.nasa.gov/topics/earth/features/climate20111214i.html

0   10   20   30   40   50   60   70   80   90   100 %

Ecological Sensitivity

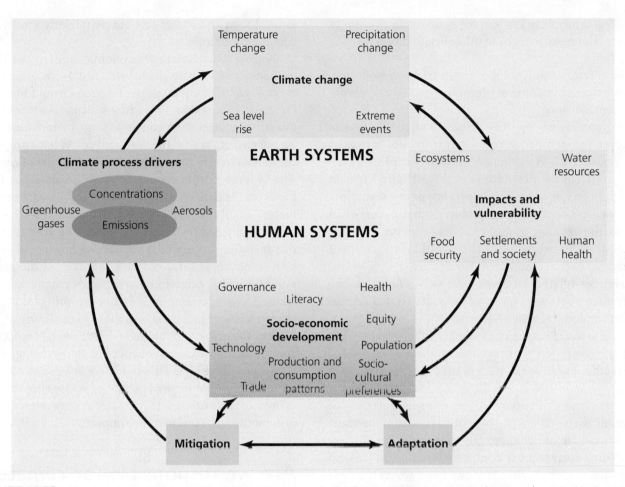

FIGURE 15.25 Human and natural systems interact in complex ways to both influence and react to climatic change, as shown in this diagram from the Fourth Assessment Report of the IPCC. *Source: Intergovernmental Panel on Climate Change. 2007. Fourth Assessment Report.*

more severe, these will cut into agricultural productivity. Overall, global crop yields are predicted to increase somewhat, but beyond a rise of 3°C, the IPCC expects crop yields to decline. In seasonally dry tropical and subtropical regions, growing seasons may be shortened, and harvests may be more susceptible to drought and crop failure. Thus, scientists predict that crop production will fall in these regions even with minor warming. This would worsen hunger in many of the world's developing nations.

It is tempting to think that a warmer North would mean that Canada's agricultural region would expand, or, at worst, shift toward the north. This is unlikely to happen. It takes a very long time for weathering and the accumulation of organic material to lead to the formation of soil profiles. Much of Canada's North is bare rock, covered by a thin, rocky, immature soil. The rock of the Canadian Shield was scraped clean by advancing glaciers during the last major glaciation in the Pleistocene epoch. The Pleistocene glaciers retreated from Canada's North more than 10 000 years ago, but in all that time there has been no significant development of a tillable soil horizon over much of the land area. In

other words, our breadbasket, the Prairies, will still have good soils but will become too hot and dry for successful farming, while Canada's North, although warmer and wetter, won't have the soil to take advantage of the better climatic conditions.

Forestry Forest managers increasingly find themselves having to battle insect and disease outbreaks, invasive species, and catastrophic fires, which are mostly caused by decades of fire suppression but are also promoted by longer, warmer, drier fire seasons (**FIGURE 15.26**). For timber and forest products, enriched atmospheric CO_2 may spur greater growth in the near term, but this will vary substantially from region to region. Other climatic effects, such as drought, may eliminate these gains. For instance, droughts brought about by a strong El Niño in 1997–1998 allowed immense forest fires to destroy millions of hectares of rainforest in Indonesia, Brazil, Mexico, and elsewhere.

Health As a result of climate change, we will face more heat waves—and heat stress can cause death, especially among older adults. A 2003 heat wave killed at least 35 000 people in Europe, for example. In addition, a warmer climate exposes us to other health problems:

- Respiratory ailments that result from air pollution, as hotter temperatures promote formation of photochemical smog
- Expansion of tropical diseases, such as dengue fever, into temperate regions as vectors of infectious disease (such as mosquitoes) move toward the poles; the advent of mosquito-borne West Nile Virus in southern Canada may be a preview of this scenario
- Disease and sanitation problems that occur when floods overcome sewage treatment systems
- Injuries and drownings that will likely increase if storms become more frequent or intense
- Hunger-related ailments that will worsen as the human population grows and climate-related stresses on agricultural systems increase
- Health hazards from cold weather will likely decrease, but researchers feel that the increase from warm-weather hazards will more than offset these gains

Economics   People will experience a variety of economic costs—and some benefits, too—from the many impacts of climate change. On the whole, researchers predict that costs will outweigh benefits and that this gap will widen as climate change grows more severe. Climate change will also widen the gap between rich and poor, both within and among nations. Poorer people have less wealth and technology with which to adapt to climate change, and poorer people rely more on resources (such as local food and water) that are particularly sensitive to climatic conditions.

From a wide variety of economic studies, the IPCC estimated that climate change will cost 1–5% of GDP on average globally, although poor nations would lose proportionally more than rich nations. Economists trying to quantify damages from climate change by measuring the "social cost of carbon" (i.e., external costs) have proposed costs of anywhere from $10 to $350 per tonne of carbon. The highest-profile economic study to date has been the Stern Review commissioned by the British government. This study maintained that climate change could cost roughly 5–20% of world GDP by the year 2200 but that investing just 1% of GDP starting now could enable us to avoid these future costs. Regardless of the precise numbers, many economists and policy makers are concluding that spending money now to mitigate climate change will save us a great deal more in the future.

All these physical, biological, and social impacts of climate change are consequences of the warming effect of our greenhouse gas emissions. We are bound to experience further consequences, but by addressing the root causes of anthropogenic climate change we can still prevent the most severe future impacts.

Are we responsible for climate change?

The IPCC's 2007 report concluded conservatively that it is more than 90% likely that most of the global warming recorded over the past half-century is due to the well-documented increase in greenhouse gas concentrations in our atmosphere. Scientists agree that this increase in greenhouse gases results primarily from our combustion of fossil fuels for energy and transportation, and secondarily from land use changes, including deforestation and agriculture (**FIGURE 15.27**).

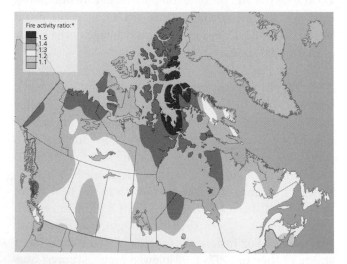

FIGURE 15.26
This map shows fire activity (Maximum Seasonal Severity Rating) in 2060 compared to current fire activity, derived from the Canadian Climate Model. Values greater than 1.0 mean there will be more fire activity in the future, whereas values less than 1.0 would mean less fire activity in the future.
Source: Flannigan, M.D., B.J. Stocks, and B.M. Wotton (2000) Climate Change and Forest Fires, The Science of the Total Environment, 262:221–229.

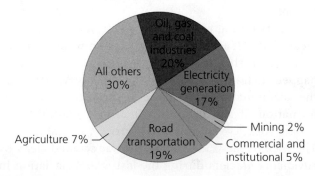

FIGURE 15.27
Greenhouse gas emissions in Canada come primarily from the use of fossil fuels for both energy and transportation.
Source: Environment Canada. www.ec.gc.ca/pdb/ghg/newsrelease2006_e.cfm

By the time the IPCC's *Fourth Assessment Report* came out, many scientists had already become concerned enough to put themselves on record urging governments to address climate change. In June 2005, as the leaders of the G8 industrialized nations met, the national academies of science from 11 nations (Canada, Brazil, China, France, Germany, India, Italy, Japan, Russia, the United Kingdom, and the United States) issued a joint statement urging these political leaders to take action. Such a broad consensus statement from the world's scientists was virtually unprecedented, on any issue. The statement read, in part,

> *The scientific understanding of climate change is now sufficiently clear to justify nations taking prompt action. It is vital that all nations identify cost-effective steps that they can take now, to contribute to substantial and long-term reduction in net global greenhouse gas emissions . . . A lack of full scientific certainty about some aspects of climate change is not a reason for delaying an immediate response that will, at a reasonable cost, prevent dangerous anthropogenic interference with the climate system.*

Despite the overwhelming evidence for climate change and its impacts, many people have tried to deny that it is happening. Many of these naysayers now admit that the climate is changing but a few still doubt that we are the cause. Most of the world's nations have moved forward to confront climate change through international dialogue, leaving behind outdated debates over whether climate change is real and whether humans are to blame. These debates were fanned by people—some quietly representing interests in the oil industry—who aimed to cast doubt on the scientific consensus. Their views were amplified by the news media, which seeks to present two sides to every issue, even when the arguments are not equally supported by evidence.

For many, former U.S. Vice President Al Gore's 2006 movie and book, *An Inconvenient Truth*, presented an eye-opening summary of the science of climate change and a compelling call to action. Awareness of climate change grew as the 2007 IPCC report was made publicly available on the Internet and was widely covered in the media, and later as Gore and the IPCC were jointly awarded the Nobel Peace Prize.

Then in 2009, a hacker illegally broke into computers at the University of East Anglia, U.K., and made public several thousand documents, including over 1000 private e-mails among a handful of climate scientists. A few of these messages appeared to show questionable behaviour in the use of data and the treatment of other researchers. Climate-change deniers named the incident "Climategate" and used it to accuse the entire scientific establishment of wrongdoing and conspiracy. The news media disseminated the story widely.

Subsequent investigations into the affair by independent panels exonerated the climate scientists, concluding that there was no evidence of wrongdoing. The panels pointed out that many media accounts trumpeting the news had misrepresented the content of the e-mails. The panels concluded that hacked e-mails among a few individuals in no way called into question the vast array of research results that have been compiled by thousands of hard-working independent climate scientists over several decades. Unfortunately, the exoneration was too little and too late: too little, because these findings, unlike the original accusations, never made the front pages of most of the news media; and too late, because the likely goal of the "Climategate" campaign—to sabotage the 2009 climate talks in Copenhagen—had already been achieved.

Today, most of the world's people accept that our fossil fuel consumption is altering the planet that our children will inherit. As a result of this shift in public opinion, and in response to demand from their shareholders, many corporations and industries began offering support for reductions in greenhouse gas emissions. These corporate leaders joined ranks with the insurance industry, which many years earlier had grown concerned with climate change as it foresaw increased payouts for damage caused by coastal storms, drought, and floods.

Responding to Climate Change

Today we possess a broadened consensus that climate change is a clear and present challenge to our society. Precisely how we should respond to climate change is a difficult question, however, and one we will likely be wrestling with for decades. The strategy that we choose, as a society, will determine how successful we are at curbing climate change, and how quickly (or *if*) we can make it happen. The IPCC bases its climate predictions on four groups of potential scenarios of human response to climate change, and variations of these four basic scenarios (they are called the SRES scenarios, which stands for *Special Report on Emissions Scenarios*):

1. Scenario "A1" assumes a world of very rapid economic growth, a global population that peaks in mid-century, and rapid introduction of new and more efficient technologies. A1 is divided into three groups that describe alternative directions of technological change: fossil-intensive energy resources, non-fossil energy resources, and a mix of energy sources.

2. Scenario "B1" describes a world with the same global population as A1 but with more rapid changes in economic structures toward a service- and information-based economy.

3. Scenario "A2" describes a world with high population growth, slow economic development, and slow advancement to lower-emission energy technologies.

4. Scenario "B2" describes a world with intermediate population and economic growth, emphasizing local solutions to economic, social, and environmental sustainability.[5]

Three of these scenarios are represented in **FIGURE 15.20** showing the potential for major changes in Arctic ice. As shown in **FIGURE 15.28**, each set of scenarios represents a different set of human responses to climate change, with different implications for the rapidity and vigour—and thus the specific outcomes and success—of the response.

Shall we pursue mitigation, adaptation, or intervention?

We can respond to climate change in two fundamental ways: mitigation or adaptation. A third, which many climate scientists are reluctant to consider, is direct intervention in the global climate system.

For **mitigation**, the aim is to mitigate, or alleviate, the problem. In this case we would choose to pursue actions that reduce greenhouse gas emissions, in order to lessen the severity of future climate change. For example, mitigation strategies can focus on reducing greenhouse gas emissions by improving energy efficiency, switching to clean and renewable energy sources, encouraging farm practices that protect soil quality, recovering landfill gas, and preventing deforestation.

The second type of response is to accept that climate change is happening and to pursue strategies to minimize its impacts on us. This strategy is called **adaptation** because the goal is to adapt to change by finding ways to cushion oneself from its blows. Erecting a seawall, like Maldives residents did with the Great Wall of Male, is an example of adaptation using technology and engineering. The people of Tuvalu also adapted, but with a behavioural choice—some chose to leave their island and make a new life in New Zealand. Other examples of adaptation include restricting coastal development; adjusting farming practices to cope with drought; and modifying water management practices to deal with reduced river flows, glacial outburst floods, or salt contamination of groundwater.

James Ford from McGill University, along with other Canadian researchers, has studied Inuit adaptation to climate change in Canada's North. Ford is a geographer, with an interest in global environmental change and natural hazards. He focuses his research specifically on the Arctic, where his doctoral thesis work investigated the vulnerability of a particular community in Nunavut to the effects of climate change. This included, for example, working with hunters to determine how they have been

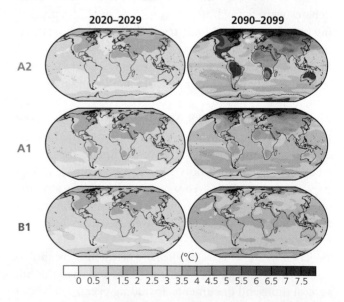

FIGURE 15.28   Here are three of the scenarios (A2, A1, and B1) studied by the IPCC for emissions of carbon dioxide and related warming. The dark red line shows projected temperature change if carbon dioxide emissions could be held at year 2000 levels, rather than being allowed to increase with population and economic growth; the black line represents historical data for the 20th century. The bars show the range of temperature increases predicted for each of the scenarios. The maps show the timing and distribution of temperature changes resulting from the various scenarios. These predictions are compilations based on data from a large number of climate models.   *Source: Data from Intergovernmental Panel on Climate Change. 2007. Fourth Assessment Report.*

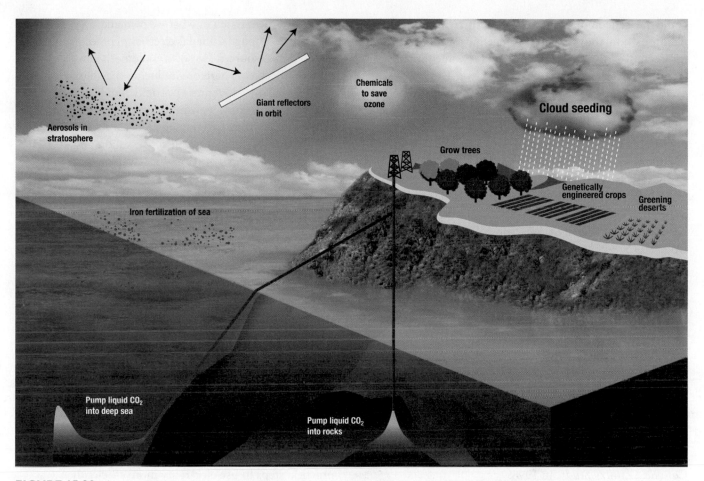

FIGURE 15.29 Intervention strategies involve grand-scale geo-engineering of the climate system. Proposals have included putting huge reflecting mirrors in orbit and fertilizing the ocean surface with iron to enhance photosynthesis in oceanic phytoplankton. *Source: Figure is based on Lawrence Livermore National Laboratory,* Geoengineering could slow down the global water cycle, *News Release NR-08-05-04, May 27, 2008 https://www.llnl.gov/news/newsreleases/2008/NR-08-05-04.html*

affected by changes in the extent and thickness of sea ice, and in the migratory behaviour of wildlife.[6] This research has contributed to adaptation plans aimed at reducing the vulnerability of communities in Nunavut and elsewhere in the Arctic to the effects of climate change.

The third category of possible responses, **intervention**, is one that you won't hear as much about. This refers to a set of possible large-scale technological modifications to the global climate system (**FIGURE 15.29**). This option makes climate scientists extremely nervous. For one thing, interfering with global-scale Earth systems—especially a system as complex and riddled with feedbacks as the climate system—could lead to all sorts of unanticipated and unwanted side effects. And scientists fear that even the suggestion that the climate system could be engineered to "fix" human-induced climate change would cause people to abandon efforts at mitigation.

However, intervention strategies have been quietly discussed for years, and some scientists feel that we need to begin discussing them more seriously and openly, so that we can be ready if the day ever comes when these strategies are needed. Grand-scale climate intervention strategies, often referred to as **geo-engineering**, fall into two main categories: (1) strategies that aim to increase fluxes of greenhouse gases out of the atmosphere, and (2) strategies that aim to reduce the incoming solar radiation.

An example of the first set of strategies is *ocean fertilization*. We know that the ocean serves as a sink for carbon dioxide. It has been hypothesized that adding iron to ocean water would boost the primary productivity of oceanic phytoplankton, increasing their ability to intake carbon dioxide through photosynthesis and thus enhancing the ability of the ocean to act as a sink for atmospheric carbon dioxide. Experimentation around this concept remains inconclusive. Similar approaches that could be applied on land include the planting of billions of trees to act as a carbon sink and genetic modification of plants to become more active photosynthesizers.

The second set of strategies revolves around technologies that aim to increase the albedo of Earth's atmosphere, so that a greater proportion of incoming solar radiation could be reflected. Huge rotatable mirrors orbiting in fixed position above Earth's surface have been proposed, for example. Another proposition is to alter the composition of Earth's atmosphere by injecting a mist of water or sulphur aerosols to increase atmospheric reflectivity. Sulphur aerosols would have the additional unwanted side effect of causing acidic precipitation, and would certainly do nothing to help ease the problem of ocean acidification.

Intervention through geo-engineering remains wholly hypothetical. Many environmental advocates have criticized intervention and even adaptation strategies, because they view them as escapist—a way of sidestepping the hard work that must be done to protect future generations from climate change. However, adaptation and mitigation are not mutually exclusive approaches; a person or a nation can pursue both. Indeed, both approaches are necessary.

Adaptation strategies are needed; even if we were to halt all our emissions now, global warming would continue until the planet's systems reached a new equilibrium, with temperature rising an additional 0.6°C, and considerably more in such areas as Canada's North, by the end of this century. Because we will face this change no matter what we do, it is wise to develop ways to minimize its impacts. Canada produced a national assessment of climate change impacts and adaptation strategies, *The Canada Country Study*, in 1998.

Mitigation is also necessary. If we do nothing to slow climate change, it will eventually overwhelm any efforts at adaptation we could make. To leave a sustainable future for our civilization and to safeguard the living planet that we know, we will need to pursue mitigation. Moreover, the faster we begin reducing our emissions, the lower the level at which they will peak, and the less we will alter climate. We will spend the remainder of this chapter examining approaches to the mitigation of climate change.

We can look more closely at our lifestyle

In Canada, major sources of GHG emissions include power generation facilities that produce electricity, heat, or steam by using fossil fuels; oil and gas extraction; mining, smelting, and refining of metals, and steel production; pulp, paper, and saw mills; petroleum refineries; and chemical producers. Other activities that contribute significantly to GHG emissions include transportation, waste disposal, and agriculture-related activities.[7] Some of these are large-scale industrial causes, but many can be influenced by the simple choices we all make in our everyday lives.

The generation of electricity is one significant source of carbon dioxide emissions. From cooking and heating to the clothes we wear, much of what we own and do depends on electricity. Although Canada's electricity comes mainly from hydroelectric sources (58%), 25% comes from fossil-fuel-related processes. Therefore, reducing the volume of fossil fuels we burn to generate electricity would lessen greenhouse gas emissions, as would decreasing electricity consumption. There are two ways to reduce the amount of fossil fuels we use: (1) encouraging conservation and efficiency and (2) switching to cleaner and renewable energy sources.

Conservation and efficiency   Conservation and efficiency in energy use can arise from new technologies, such as high-efficiency light bulbs and appliances, or from individual ethical choices to reduce electricity consumption. For instance, replacing an old washing machine with an energy-efficient washer can cut your CO_2 emissions by 200 kg annually. Replacing standard light bulbs with compact fluorescent lights reduces energy use for lighting by 40%. Such technological solutions are popular, and they can be profitable for manufacturers while also saving consumers money.

Consumers can also opt for lifestyle choices. For nearly all of human history, people managed without the electrical appliances that most of us take for granted today. It is possible for each of us to choose to use fewer greenhouse gas–producing appliances and technologies and to take practical steps to use electricity more efficiently.

Sources of electricity   We can reduce greenhouse gas emissions by altering the types of energy we use. Among fossil fuels, natural gas burns more cleanly than oil, and oil is cleaner-burning than coal. Using natural gas instead of coal produces the same amount of energy with roughly one-half the emissions. Moreover, approaches to boosting the efficiency of fossil fuel use, such as cogeneration, produce fewer emissions per unit of energy generated.

Currently, interest in carbon capture, sequestration, and storage is intensifying. **Carbon capture and storage (CCS)** refers to technologies or approaches that remove carbon dioxide from power plant emissions. Successful carbon capture technology would allow power plants to continue using fossil fuels while cutting greenhouse gas pollution. The carbon would then be stored somewhere— perhaps underground, under pressure, in locations where it would not seep out. However, we are still a long way from developing adequate technology and secure storage space to accomplish this, and some experts doubt that we will ever be able to sequester enough carbon to make a dent in our emissions.

Technologies and energy sources that generate electricity without using fossil fuels represent another means of reducing greenhouse gas emissions. These include nuclear power, hydroelectric power, geothermal energy, photovoltaic cells, wind power, and ocean energy sources. These energy sources give off no emissions during their use (but some in the production of their infrastructure). We will examine these clean and renewable energy sources in detail in subsequent chapters.

Transportation is a significant source of greenhouse gases

The typical automobile is highly inefficient. Close to 85% of the fuel you pump into your gas tank does something other than move your car down the road (**FIGURE 15.30**). Although more aerodynamic designs, increased engine efficiency, and improved tire design could help reduce these losses, gasoline-fuelled automobiles may always remain somewhat inefficient.

Automotive technology The technology exists to make our vehicles more fuel-efficient than they currently are. Raising fuel efficiency will require government mandate and/or consumer demand. As gasoline prices rise, demand for more fuel-efficient automobiles will intensify. Advances in technology are also bringing us alternatives to the traditional combustion-engine automobile. These include hybrid vehicles that combine electric motors and gasoline-powered engines for greater efficiency. They also include fully electric vehicles, alternative fuels, such as compressed natural gas and biodiesel, and hydrogen fuel cells.

Driving less and using public transportation People can also opt to make lifestyle choices that reduce their reliance on cars. For example, some people are choosing to live nearer to their workplaces. Others use mass transit, such as buses, subway trains, and light rail. Still others bike or walk to work or for their errands (**FIGURE 15.31**). Canadians use public transportation

FIGURE 15.31

By choosing human-powered transportation methods, such as bicycles, we can greatly reduce our transportation-related greenhouse gas emissions. More people are choosing to live closer to their workplaces and to enjoy the dual benefits of exercise and reduced emissions by walking or cycling to work or school.

for approximately 7% of daily transportation needs. Increasing this level of use would be an extremely efficient way to reduce energy use and pollution. Unfortunately, reliable and convenient public transit is not available in many communities. Making automobile-based cities and suburbs more friendly to pedestrian and bicycle traffic and improving people's access to public transportation are central challenges for city and regional planners.

We can reduce emissions in other ways as well

Other pathways toward mitigating climate change include advances in agriculture, forestry, and waste management. In agriculture, sustainable land management that protects the integrity of soil on cropland and rangeland enables soil to store more carbon. Techniques have also been developed to reduce the emission of methane from

Gas 100% → 14% Moving car

62% Engine heat loss, friction, inefficiencies

17% Idling

5% Drive train friction and inefficiencies

2% Running accessories: water pump, stereo, etc.

FIGURE 15.30

Conventional automobiles are extremely inefficient. Almost 85% of useful energy is lost, and only 14% actually moves the car down the road.

rice cultivation and from cattle and their manure, and to reduce nitrous oxide emissions from fertilizer. We can also grow renewable biofuels, and this is an active area of current research.

In forest management, the rapid reforestation of cleared areas helps restore forests, which act as reservoirs that pull carbon from the air. Sustainable forestry practices and the preservation of existing forests can help to reverse the carbon dioxide emissions resulting from deforestation.

Waste managers are doing their part to cut greenhouse emissions by recovering methane seeping from landfills, treating wastewater, and generating energy from waste in incinerators. Individuals, communities, and waste haulers also help reduce emissions by encouraging recycling, composting, and the reduction and reuse of materials and products.

We will need to follow multiple strategies to reduce emissions

We should not expect to find a single magic bullet for mitigating climate change. Instead, reducing emissions will require many steps by many people and institutions across many sectors of our economy. The good news is that most reductions can be achieved by using current technology and that we can begin implementing these changes right away.

In the long term, any one approach will not be enough. To stop climate change, we will need to reduce emissions (as opposed to stabilizing them), and this may require us to develop new technology, further change our lifestyles, and/ or reverse our population growth. However, there is plenty we can do in the meantime to mitigate climate change simply by scaling up the technologies and approaches for emissions reductions that we already have developed.

How quickly and successfully we translate science and technology into practical solutions for reducing emissions depends largely on the policies we urge our leaders to pursue and on how government and the market economy interact. Governmental command-and-control policy has been vital in safeguarding environmental quality and promoting human well-being. However, government mandates are often resisted by industry, and market incentives can sometimes be more effective in driving change.

With climate change policy, we are in the midst of a dynamic period of debate and experimentation. At all levels—international, national, provincial/territorial, regional, and local—policy makers, industry, commerce, and citizens are searching for ways to employ government and the market to reduce emissions in ways that are fair, economically palatable, effective, and enforceable.

We began tackling climate change by international treaty

In 1992, the United Nations convened the U.N. Conference on Environment and Development Earth Summit in Rio de Janeiro, Brazil. Nations represented at the Earth Summit signed the U.N. Framework Convention on Climate Change (FCCC), which outlined a plan for reducing greenhouse gas emissions to 1990 levels by the year 2000 through a voluntary, nation-by-nation approach. By the late 1990s, it was already clear that the voluntary approach was not likely to succeed. After watching the seas rise and observing the failure of most industrialized nations to cut their emissions, nations of the developing world— the Maldives among them—helped initiate an effort to create a binding international treaty that would require all signatory nations to reduce their emissions. This effort led to the *Kyoto Protocol*. An outgrowth of the FCCC drafted in 1997 in Kyoto, Japan, the **Kyoto Protocol** mandated signatory nations, by the period 2008–2012, to reduce emissions of six greenhouse gases to levels below those of 1990 (**TABLE 15.2**). Canada was the 99th country to ratify the agreement, signing in 2002. The treaty took effect in 2005 after Russia became the 127th nation to ratify it.

The United States refused to ratify the Kyoto Protocol. U.S. leaders have called the treaty unfair because it requires industrialized nations to reduce emissions but does not require the same of rapidly industrializing nations, such as China and India, whose greenhouse emissions have risen more than 50% in the past 15 years.

Table 15.2 Emissions Reductions Required and Achieved		
Nation	**Required change 1990–2008/2012***	**Observed change 1990–2006†**
Russia	0.0%	−32.0%‡
Germany	−21.0%	−17.2%
United Kingdom	−12.5%	−14.3%
France	0.0%	−0.8%
Italy	−6.5%	+12.1%
Japan	−6.0%	+6.5%
United States	−7.0%	+15.8%
Canada	−6.0%	+29.1%

*Percentage decrease in emissions (carbon-equivalents of six greenhouse gases) from 1990 to period 2008–2012, as mandated under Kyoto Protocol.

†Actual percentage change in emissions (carbon-equivalents of six greenhouse gases) from 1990 to 2006. Negative values indicate decreases; positive values indicate increases. Values do not include influences of land use and forest cover.

‡Russia's substantial decrease was due mainly to economic contraction following the breakup of the Soviet Union.

Source: Data from U.N. Framework Convention on Climate Change, National Greenhouse Gas Inventory Reports, 2007.

Proponents of the Kyoto Protocol say the differential requirements are justified because industrialized nations created the current problem and therefore should take the lead in resolving it; furthermore, the average Canadian today still generates 3 times the GHG emissions of the average Chinese, and 14 times that of the average Indian.

Because resource use and per capita emissions are far greater in the industrialized world, governments and industries there often feel they have more to lose economically from restrictions on emissions. Ironically, industrialized nations are also the ones most likely to gain economically, because they are best positioned to invent, develop, and market new technologies to power the world in a post–fossil fuel era.

As a signatory to the Kyoto Protocol, Canada has been obliged to submit an inventory report of its GHG emissions on an annual basis, using an internationally agreed-to format. The National Inventory monitors six gases—carbon dioxide (CO_2), methane (CH_4), nitrous oxide (N_2O), sulphur hexafluoride (SF_6), perfluorocarbons (PFCs), and hydrofluorocarbons (HFCs)—and provides an analysis of the factors underlying the trends in emissions since 1990. Total greenhouse gas emissions in Canada fluctuate from year to year as a result of changes in the mix of sources used for electricity production (reduced coal and increased hydro and nuclear generation), lower emissions from fossil fuel production (as a result of fuel switching and a smaller volume of oil refined), and reduced demand for heating fuels because of warmer winters in 2004, 2005, and 2006.

Overall, however, emissions in 2008 were about 24.1% above the 1990 total (**FIGURE 15.32**), which is still about 31.5% above Canada's Kyoto target.[8] By some reckoning, 2009 emissions appear to have dropped; note, however, the reporting threshold at this point. Canada

is not just off-target; it would take radical technological and economic changes to fulfill the commitment we have made, as a nation, in signing the Kyoto Protocol. At the 15th Conference of the Parties (COP) of the Kyoto Protocol in Copenhagen in 2009, Canada received the so-called "Dinosaur Award" and was accused of obstructing global progress toward a solution for climate change, opting instead to protect the interests of the fossil fuel industry.

Then, in 2011 at the 17th COP in Durban, South Africa, Canada became the first nation to withdraw from the Kyoto agreement. Environment Minister Peter Kent cited Canada's liability to incur large financial penalties for failure to reach emission targets as the reason for the withdrawal.

For its part, the United States emits fully one-fifth of the world's greenhouse gases, so its refusal to join international efforts to curb greenhouse emissions has generated widespread resentment and has undercut the effectiveness of global efforts. At the 2007 COP in Bali, Indonesia, where 190 nations strove to design a road map for future progress, the delegate from Papua New Guinea drew thunderous applause and cheers when he requested of the U.S. delegation, "If for some reason you are not willing to lead . . . please get out of the way."

However, as of 2008 (the most recent year with full international data), nations that signed the Kyoto Protocol had decreased their emissions by 5.2% from 1990 levels. Much of this reduction was due to economic contraction in Russia and nations of the former Soviet Bloc following the breakup of the Soviet Union. When these nations are factored out, the remaining signatories showed a 7.9% *increase* in emissions from 1990 to 2008. Kyoto Protocol critics and supporters alike acknowledge that even if every nation complied with the treaty, greenhouse gas emissions would continue to increase—albeit

Canada's GHG Emissions 1990–2008

FIGURE 15.32 Total carbon dioxide emissions in Canada are considerably above Canada's Kyoto target. *Source: Environment Canada, National Inventory Report 1990-2008.*

more slowly than they would without the treaty. Nations are now looking ahead and negotiating over what will come next to supersede Kyoto.

Market mechanisms are being used to address climate change

Market tools such as permit trading programs represent a means of harnessing the economic efficiency of the free market to achieve policy goals while allowing business, industry, or utilities flexibility in how they meet those goals. Supporters of permit trading programs argue that they provide the fairest, least expensive, and most effective method of achieving emissions reductions. Polluters get to choose how to reduce their emissions and are given financial incentives for reducing emissions below the legally required amount. We will likely discover how successful these ventures are over the next decade as various carbon trading programs are implemented around the world.

The world's first emissions trading program for greenhouse gas reduction (operating since 2003) is the Chicago Climate Exchange, which now boasts hundreds of member corporations, institutions, and municipalities, mainly in the United States, Canada, and Brazil, but recently beginning to include other countries as well.

The world's largest *cap-and-trade* program is the European Union Emission Trading Scheme, which began on January 1, 2005. All EU member states participate, and each submits for approval a national allocation plan that conforms to the nation's obligations under the Kyoto Protocol. This market got off to a successful start, and carbon prices reached $30 per tonne in 2006. However, when investors determined that national governments had allocated too many emissions permits to their industries, the price of carbon fell. The overallocation gave companies little incentive to reduce emissions, so permits lost their value. By early 2007, prices in the market had fallen below $0.30. This drop is roughly equivalent to a stock valued at $40 falling to less than 40 cents. Proponents of emissions trading chalk up the freefall in the European market as a learning experience, but in the long run permits will be valuable and the market will work only if government policies are in place to limit emissions.

Carbon offsets are in vogue

Emissions trading programs have allowed participants who cannot or will not adequately reduce their own emissions to use carbon offsets instead. A *carbon offset* is a voluntary payment to another entity intended to enable that entity to reduce the greenhouse emissions that one is unable or unwilling to reduce oneself. The payment thus offsets one's own emissions. For instance, a coal-burning power plant could pay a reforestation project to plant trees that will soak up as much carbon as the coal plant emits. Or a university could fund the development of clean and renewable energy projects to make up for fossil fuel energy the university uses.

Carbon offsets are becoming popular among utilities, businesses, universities, governments, and individuals trying to achieve **carbon neutrality**, a state in which no net carbon is emitted. For time-stressed people with enough wealth, offsets represent a simple and convenient way to reduce emissions without investing in efforts to change one's habits. For example, you can go to the website of the company TerraPass, calculate your emissions for travel by car or plane or for your residence, and purchase offsets for those emissions. Your money funds renewable energy and efficiency projects, and you can advertise your donation with bumper stickers and decals.

In principle, carbon offsets seem a great idea, but in practice they often fall short. Without rigorous oversight to make sure that the offset money actually accomplishes what it is intended for, carbon offsets risk being no more than a way for wealthy consumers to assuage a guilty conscience. Efforts to create a transparent and enforceable offset infrastructure are ongoing. If these efforts succeed, then carbon offsets could become an effective and important key to mitigating climate change.

You can reduce your own carbon footprint

Carbon offsets, emissions trading schemes, national policies, international treaties, and technological innovations will all play roles in mitigating climate change. But in the end the most influential factor may be the collective decisions of millions of regular people. In our everyday lives, each one of us can take steps to approach a carbon-neutral lifestyle by reducing greenhouse emissions that result from our decisions and activities. Just as we each have an ecological footprint, we each have a **carbon footprint** that expresses the amount of carbon we are responsible for emitting.

You can apply many of the strategies discussed in this chapter in your everyday life—from deciding where to live and how to get to work to choosing appliances. You will encounter still more solutions in our discussions of energy sources, conservation, and renewable energy in subsequent chapters.

Global climate change may be the biggest challenge facing us and our children. Fortunately, it is still early enough that we may be able to avert the most severe impacts. Taking immediate, resolute action is the most important thing that we, personally and as a society, can do.

CANADIAN ENVIRONMENTAL PERSPECTIVES

Sheila Watt-Cloutier

Sheila Watt-Cloutier, former chair of the Inuit Circumpolar Council, has been widely honoured around the world for her work in bringing attention to climate change and its impacts in the Arctic.

- **Inuit educational and health care advocate**
- **Environmental activist** and **world leader on climate change and human rights**
- Former **chair of the Inuit Circumpolar Council**

Sheila Watt-Cloutier was born in the remote town of Kuujjuaq in northern Québec (the region known in Inuktitut as Nunavik). Even today there are no road connections between Kuujjuaq and the south. She grew up with a traditional Inuit way of life, travelling only by dogsled as a child, eating foods gathered from the wild, and participating in hunts with her family and other community members.

Through McGill University, Watt-Cloutier studied psychology and sociology, and subsequently worked as an educational and health care advocate in Nunavik. She was the Inuk advisor to a widely read report on Nunavik's education system, called *Silatunirmut: The Pathway to Wisdom*, and co-wrote, co-produced, and co-directed a video for Inuit youth, *Capturing Spirit: The Inuit Journey*. On the importance of raising youth awareness of traditional ways, she says that "the Inuit strength is our culture, and our young people need to stay in touch with tradition."[9]

In 1995, Watt-Cloutier helped oversee the administration of Inuit land claims under the James Bay and Northern Québec Agreement. She was elected president of the Inuit Circumpolar Council Canada in 1995, and through that post she became a spokesperson on the issue of persistent organic pollutants—chemicals that remain in the environment for a long time, become widely distributed geographically and accumulate in the fatty tissues of people and wildlife. She describes the contamination of the Arctic food chain by POPs as "a sign of the intrusive effects of globalization."[10] She later helped negotiate the Stockholm Convention on POPs, a global treaty intended to protect human health and the environment from persistent chemical contaminants.[11]

In 2002, Watt-Cloutier became the chair of the International ICC, which represents 150 000 Inuit in Canada, the United States, Russia, and Greenland.[12] In 2005, Watt-Cloutier and 62 other Inuit from Canada and Alaska filed a petition with the Inter-American Commission on Human Rights, seeking changes to policy for the impacts of climate change on the traditional Inuit way of life. Watt-Cloutier is listed on the petition as the principal plaintiff. The petition squarely blames "actions and omissions" of the United States, and provides a detailed scientific analysis of the damaging effects of climate change on temperature, wildlife, human health, and cultural well-being in the Arctic. "For every one degree the temperature increases per year globally, it's more like three to five degrees in the Arctic," she says. "For us, this is a monumental change."[13]

Watt-Cloutier feels that her efforts to make the rest of the world aware of the dramatic changes that northerners are already experiencing have put a human face on the impacts of environmental change and may ultimately help connect people to the environment. Watt-Cloutier, who now lives in Iqaluit, Nunavut, still draws her strength from the northern landscape and her deeply ingrained Inuit culture.

She has been widely recognized for her work. She is an Officer of the Order of Canada and a recipient of a Lifetime Achievement Award for Human Development from the United Nations. She has also received the Rachel Carson Prize, the Global Green Award, and an Aboriginal Achievement Award. She was nominated for the Nobel Peace Prize for her work on climate change, an honour many thought she might share with the eventual winner, former U.S. Vice President Al Gore.

"We are the early warning system for the entire planet."—**Sheila Watt-Cloutier**

Thinking About Environmental Perspectives

Sheila Watt-Cloutier has said that people in the Arctic are deeply and internally connected to the environment because they depend on it for their survival and that—in contrast—people from the south in Canada tend to be disconnected from nature. What do you think? Is it possible to experience a deep, almost spiritual, connection with the environment if you are not living and surviving in the wilderness?

Conclusion

Many factors influence Earth's climate, and human activities have come to play a major role. Climate change is well underway, and further greenhouse gas emissions will increase global warming and cause increasingly severe and diverse impacts. Sea-level rise and other consequences of global climate change will affect locations worldwide from the Maldives to Bangladesh to Ellesmere Island to the Canadian Prairies. As scientists and policy makers come to better understand anthropogenic climate change and its environmental, economic, and social consequences, more and more of them are urging immediate action. Reducing greenhouse gas emissions and taking other actions to mitigate and adapt to climate change represent the foremost challenge for our society in the coming years.

REVIEWING OBJECTIVES

You should now be able to:

Describe Earth's climate system and explain the many factors influencing global climate

- Earth's climate changes naturally over time, but it is now changing rapidly because of human influence.
- The Sun provides most of Earth's energy and interacts with the atmosphere, land, and oceans to drive climate processes.
- Earth absorbs about 70% of incoming solar radiation and reflects about 30% back into space.
- Greenhouse gases, such as carbon dioxide, methane, water vapour, nitrous oxide, ozone, and halocarbons, warm the atmosphere by absorbing infrared radiation and reemitting infrared radiation of different wavelengths.
- Milankovitch cycles influence climate in the long term.

Characterize human influences on the atmosphere and global climate

- Increased greenhouse gas emissions enhance the greenhouse effect.
- By burning fossil fuels, clearing forests, and manufacturing halocarbons, humans are increasing atmospheric concentrations of many greenhouse gases.
- Human input of aerosols into the atmosphere exerts a variable but slight cooling effect.

Summarize modern methods of climate research

- Geologic records, such as cores through ice or sediments, reveal information about past climatic conditions.
- Direct atmospheric sampling tells us about the current composition of the atmosphere.
- Coupled general circulation models serve to predict future changes in climate.

Outline current and future trends and impacts of global climate change

- The IPCC has comprehensively synthesized current climate research, and its periodic reports represent the consensus of the scientific community.

- Temperatures on Earth have warmed by an average of 0.74°C over the past century and are predicted to rise 1.8°C–4.0°C over the next century.
- Changes in precipitation vary by region.
- Sea level has risen an average of 17 cm over the past century.
- Other impacts include melting of glaciers and polar ice, frequency of extreme weather events, impacts on agriculture, forestry, and health, and effects on plants and animals.
- Climate change and its impacts will vary regionally.
- Despite some remaining uncertainties, the scientific community feels that evidence for humans' role in influencing climate is strong enough to justify governments' taking action to reduce greenhouse emissions.

Suggest ways we can respond to climate change

- Both adaptation and mitigation are necessary for responding to climate change. A much less desirable option, but one that we may need to consider one day, is direct intervention in the global climate system.
- Conserving electricity, improving efficiency of energy use, and switching to clean and renewable energy sources will help reduce fossil fuel consumption and greenhouse emissions.
- Encouraging new automotive technologies and investment in public transportation will help reduce greenhouse emissions.
- Solving the climate problem will require the deployment of multiple strategies.
- The Kyoto Protocol provided a first step for nations to begin addressing climate change, but has proven largely ineffective. In 2011, Canada exercised its legal right to withdraw from the international agreement.
- Emissions trading programs are providing a way to harness the free market and engage industry in reducing emissions.
- Individuals are increasingly exploring carbon offsets and other means of reducing personal carbon footprints.

TESTING YOUR COMPREHENSION

1. What happens to solar radiation after it reaches Earth? How do greenhouse gases warm the lower atmosphere?
2. Why is carbon dioxide considered the main greenhouse gas? How could an increase in water vapour create either a positive or negative feedback effect?
3. How do scientists study the ancient atmosphere?
4. Has simulating climate change with computer programs been effective in helping us predict climate? How do these programs work?
5. List five major trends in climate that scientists have documented so far. Now list five future trends or impacts that they are predicting.
6. Describe how rising sea levels, caused by global warming, can create problems for people. How may climate change affect marine ecosystems?
7. How might a warmer climate affect agriculture? How is it affecting distributions of plants and animals? How might it affect human health?
8. What are the main sources of greenhouse gas emissions in Canada? In what ways can we reduce these emissions?
9. What roles have international treaties played in addressing climate change? Give two specific examples.
10. Describe one market-based approach for reducing greenhouse emissions. Explain one reason it may work well and one reason it may not work well.

THINKING IT THROUGH

1. To determine to what extent current climate change is the result of human activity versus natural processes, which type of scientific research do you think is most helpful? Why?
2. Some people argue that we need "more proof," or "better science," before we commit to substantial changes in our energy economy. How much "science," or certainty, do you think we need before we should take action regarding climate change? How much certainty do you need in your own life before you make a major decision? Should nations and elected officials follow a different standard? Do you believe that the precautionary principle is an appropriate standard in the case of global climate change? Why or why not?
3. Describe several ways in which we can reduce greenhouse gas emissions from transportation. Which approach do you think is most realistic, which approach do you think is least realistic, and why?
4. Imagine that you would like to make your own lifestyle carbon neutral and that you aim to begin by reducing the emissions you are responsible for by 25%. What actions would you take first to achieve this reduction?
5. The IPCC predicts that slight warming could shift agricultural belts toward the poles and marginally increase global crop production. How might this shift affect Canada's North? Locate the nations of Russia and Argentina on a world map, and hypothesize how such a poleward shift of agriculture might affect these nations. Now locate India, Nigeria, and Ethiopia, and hypothesize how the shift might affect them. Given that many developing nations near the equator are already suffering from food shortages and soil degradation, what effects do you think that global warming may have? If climate change magnifies inequities between developed and developing nations, what could we do to alleviate this problem?
6. You have just been elected premier of a province. Polls show that the public wants you to take bold action to reduce greenhouse gas emissions. However, polls also show that the public does not want prices of gasoline or electricity to rise more than they already have. Carbon-emitting industries in your province are wary of emissions reductions being required of them but are willing to explore ideas with you. Your parliament will support you in your efforts as long as you remain popular with voters. The province to the west has just passed ambitious legislation mandating steep greenhouse gas emissions reductions. The province to the east has joined a new regional emissions-trading consortium. What actions will you take in your first year as premier?

INTERPRETING GRAPHS AND DATA

The graph illustrates Canada's GHG emissions (CO_2) between 1990 and 2002, with projections to 2015 according to a "business-as-usual" scenario and a "Kyoto-based" scenario. From the information provided on the graph, answer the following questions.

1. Calculate the approximate percentage change in CO_2 emissions between 1990 and 2008.

2. Between 1990 and 2008, the population of Canada increased from 27.7 million to 33.5 million and the inflation-adjusted gross domestic product (GDP) went from $825 billion to $1321 billion (inflation-adjusted, reported in 1997 dollars). Calculate the per capita GDP for 1990 and 2008, and then calculate the percentage increases in both population and GDP per capita over this time period.

3. What quantitative conclusions can you draw from these data about CO_2 emissions per capita? About CO_2 emissions per unit of total economic activity? Create a graph and sketch a trend line of CO_2 emissions per capita from 1990 to 2008. Now sketch a trend line of CO_2 emissions per unit of total economic activity from 1990 to 2008. Describe your graph, and speculate on its implications for Canada's economic and environmental future.

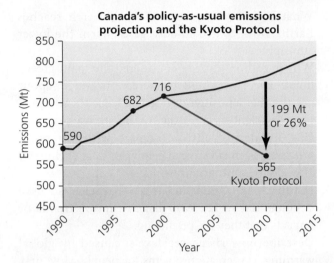

Based on the National GHG Inventory, this graph shows Canada's GHG emissions (CO_2) between 1990 and 2008, with projections based on a "business-as-usual" scenario and a "Kyoto-based" scenario.
Source: Data from National Inventory Report 1990-2008: Greenhouse Gas Sources and Sinks in Canada–Executive Summary, *Government of Canada, 2011.*

CHAPTER ENDNOTES

1. Parks Canada, Jasper National Park www.pc.gc.ca/eng/pn-np/ab/jasper/visit/visit32.aspx. Accessed 20 June 2011.

2. Dave Birrell, Peakfinder: People www.peakfinder.com/people.asp?PersonsName=Wilcox%2C+Walter+D. Accessed 20 June 2011

3. U.S. National Oceanic and Atmospheric Administration (NOAA), *Trends in Atmospheric Carbon Dioxide–Mauna Loa*, www.esrl.noaa.gov/gmd/ccgg/trends/

4. As Canada's climate changes, and weather patterns shift, Canadian climate models provide guidance in an uncertain future. CCCma Environment Canada, www.cccma.ec.gc.ca/20051116_brochure_e_pgs.pdf

5. Intergovernmental Panel on Climate Change, *Fourth Assessment Report*, 2007.

6. Dr. James Ford, *Geography—Global Environmental Change, Area of Specialization*, www.arcticnorth.com/JamesPersonalWebsite/specialization.html; and Ford, J. (2008) Emerging trends in climate change policy: The role of adaptation, *International Public Policy Review*, pp. 5–16.

7. Environment Canada, National GHG Inventory, www.ec.gc.ca/pdb/ghg/onlinedata/downloadDB_e.cfm#s5

8. Environment Canada, National Inventory Report 1990–2008: Greenhouse Gas Sources www.ec.gc.ca/ges-ghg

9. *Canadian Geographic*, Sheila Watt-Cloutier: Citation of Lifetime Achievement, from www.canadiangeographic.ca/cea/archives/archives_lifetime.asp?id=159

10. *Canadian Geographic*, Sheila Watt-Cloutier: Citation of Lifetime Achievement, from www.canadiangeographic.ca/cea/archives/archives_lifetime.asp?id=159

11. Stockholm Convention on Persistent Organic Pollutants (POPs), http://chm.pops.int/Default.aspx

12. Inuit Circumpolar Council, http://inuitcircumpolar.com/index.php?ID=1&Lang=En

13. *Canadian Geographic*, Sheila Watt-Cloutier: Citation of Lifetime Achievement, from www.canadiangeographic.ca/cea/archives/archives_lifetime.asp?id=159

MyEnvironmentPlace

Go to **www.myenvironmentplace.ca** where you will find quizzes, animations, your Pearson eText, and more.

Fossil Fuels: Energy Use and Impacts

16

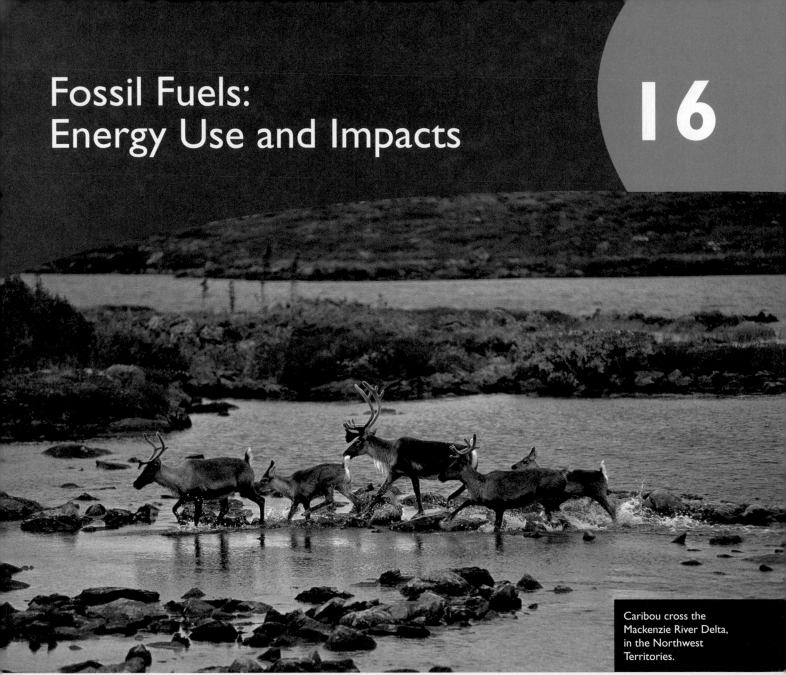

Caribou cross the Mackenzie River Delta, in the Northwest Territories.

Upon successfully completing this chapter, you will be able to

- Identify the principal energy sources that we use
- Describe the nature and origin of coal and evaluate its extraction and use
- Describe the nature and origin of natural gas and evaluate its extraction and use
- Describe the nature and origin of oil and evaluate its extraction, use, and future availability
- Describe the nature, origin, and potential of alternative fossil fuel types and technologies

- Outline and assess environmental impacts of fossil fuel use
- Evaluate political, social, and economic impacts of fossil fuel use
- Specify strategies for conserving energy and enhancing efficiency

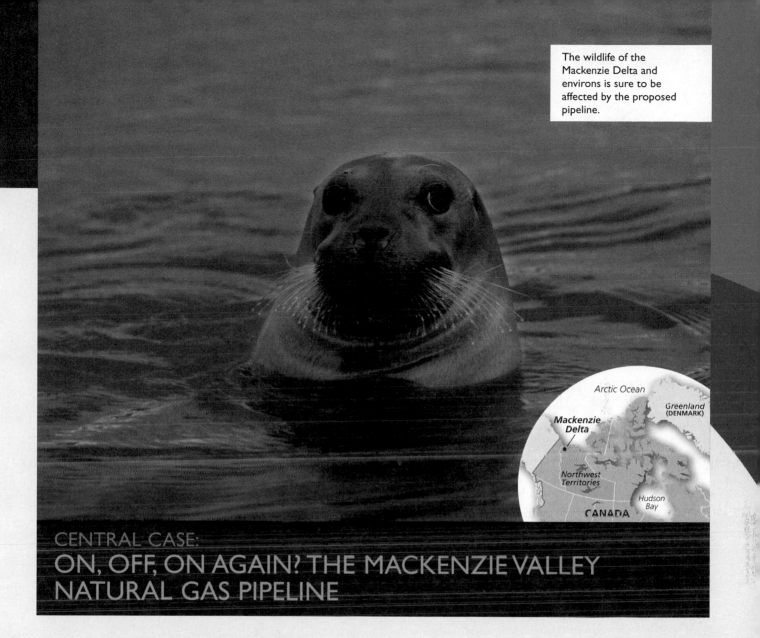

The wildlife of the Mackenzie Delta and environs is sure to be affected by the proposed pipeline.

Arctic Ocean

Greenland (DENMARK)

Mackenzie Delta

Northwest Territories

Hudson Bay

CANADA

ON, OFF, ON AGAIN? THE MACKENZIE VALLEY NATURAL GAS PIPELINE

"We've embarked on the beginning of the last days of the age of oil."

—MIKE BOWLIN, FORMER CEO (RETIRED), ARCO

"I listened to a brief by northern businessmen in Yellowknife who favour a pipeline through the North. Later, in a native village far away, I heard virtually the whole community express vehement opposition to such a pipeline. Both were talking about the same pipeline; both were talking about the same region—but for one group it is a frontier, for the other a homeland."

—JUSTICE THOMAS BERGER, *NORTHERN FRONTIER, NORTHERN HOMELAND*, 1977

The Mackenzie Valley Gas Project is a proposal to develop three major natural gas fields located in the Mackenzie Delta, Northwest Territories, and deliver the natural gas to southern markets through a 1196-km pipeline system to be constructed along the Mackenzie Valley (see maps).[1]

The idea of a major pipeline running from the Beaufort Sea down the Mackenzie Valley is not new. A pipeline was proposed and examined seriously in the early 1970s; it was called, at the time, "the biggest project in the history of free enterprise."[2]

In 1974 the federal government appointed Justice Thomas Berger to carry out an inquiry into the potential impacts of the project on the people of Canada's North, since the proposed route crosses four Aboriginal regions. Berger travelled throughout the North, meeting with Dene, Inuit, Métis, and white residents and leaders. The report of the inquiry (released in 1977) was called *Northern Frontier, Northern Homeland*. It recommended that pipeline development in the North be delayed by at least 10 years because of deep opposition by native

These maps show the location of the proposed Mackenzie River Valley natural gas pipeline.

leaders and the potential for negative impacts. The report further recommended that such development not proceed until native land claims in the area had been successfully resolved.

Among the main concerns were the potential impacts on people and animals that would result from the infrastructure (roads, airports, towns) likely to accompany the construction of the pipeline. As reported by CBC News, "Some dismissed the impact of a pipeline, saying it would be like a thread stretched across a football field. Those close to the land said the impact would be more like a razor slash across the Mona Lisa."[3]

In the end, the pipeline project was delayed for much longer than 10 years. The idea was on-again, off-again for many years, but was revitalized at the turn of the twenty-first century. Interestingly, many of the native leaders who vehemently opposed the pipeline in the 1970s had by that time become supporters, realizing that it would bring much-needed jobs and revenue to the North. Chief Frank T'Seleie of Fort Good Hope, Northwest Territories, was a vocal opponent of the project as a young man in the 1970s. He now supports the pipeline, since many of the land claims in the area have been settled. He even participated in project negotiations on behalf of native communities.[4]

The partners in the current project are four major Canadian oil and gas companies—Imperial Oil Resources Ventures, ConocoPhillips Canada, Shell Canada, and ExxonMobil Canada, known collectively as the "Producer Group"—and Aboriginal Pipeline Group, representing the interests of Aboriginal people in the project.[5]

The project has been equally controversial on its second go-around. In October 2006, Alternatives North (a social justice group based in Yellowknife) estimated that Imperial Oil and its partners will earn billions of dollars from the project and should not receive federal subsidization. However, principal partner Imperial Oil claims that the project is only marginally economic and will not proceed without assurance of at least $1.2 billion from the federal government. According to Imperial Oil, the cost of the project has increased to $16.2 billion, and the scheduled start date for production (originally 2010) has been delayed until 2014.[6]

According to Nature Canada, the pipeline has the potential to transform the valley into an industrial landscape; fragment habitat for bears, caribou, and wolves; harm fish and fish habitat by increasing sediment deposition into rivers; permanently damage breeding areas for millions of geese, tundra swans, and other migratory birds; require forests to be cut and heavy machinery deployed for infrastructure; trigger a rush of oil and gas development in the Mackenzie Valley (this was also predicted by the Berger report); and increase greenhouse gas emissions.[7] It remains to be scientifically proven or observed whether these impacts will occur, and to what degree.

An interesting side issue concerns the ultimate fate of the gas itself. Much of the natural gas produced in the Mackenzie Delta gas fields may never make it to the southern Canadian and American consumers for whom it was originally intended. This is because of the enormous acceleration in development of tar sand deposits in Alberta. Tar sand production requires significant inputs of energy, and the complete, successful development of these deposits is dependent on the production and delivery of natural gas from the North. The first 20 years' worth of natural gas from the Mackenzie Delta may go straight into the production of oil from Alberta's tar sands. The Mackenzie pipeline would transport natural gas, but pipelines are also used to transport oil. Oil pipelines are subject to at least as much controversy as natural gas pipelines, primarily because of the risk of leaks. In July of 2010 an oil pipeline owned by Enbridge, Inc., which carries oil from Griffith, Indiana, to Sarnia, Ontario, ruptured and spilled more than 800 000 U.S. gallons (about 3000 m³) of oil into a tributary of the Kalamazoo River in Michigan. In 2011

the U.S. State Department delayed indefinitely a decision to approve the construction of the Keystone XL oil pipeline, proposed to carry oil from the Alberta tar sands to oil refineries along the Gulf Coast of the United States. The planned route for the controversial pipeline was to cross a particularly sensitive ecosystem overlying an important aquifer in Nebraska, and many residents feared that a spill would permanently damage their principal source of water. Since then, the Government of Canada has actively pursued plans to move ahead with the construction of the Northern Gateway Pipelines, a set of twin pipelines that would carry natural gas to the east and oil to the west from Alberta to B.C., opening up new possibilities for the sale of oil from the tar sands to China and other Asian markets.

Sources of Energy

Humanity has devised many ways to harness the renewable and nonrenewable forms of energy available on our planet. We use a wide variety of energy sources to heat and light our homes, power our machinery, fuel our vehicles, and provide the comforts and conveniences to which we've grown accustomed in the modern industrial age.

We use a variety of energy sources

A great deal of energy emanates from Earth's core, making geothermal power available for our use. Energy also results from the gravitational pull of the Moon and Sun, and we are just beginning to harness the power from the ocean tides that these forces generate. An immense amount of energy resides within the bonds among protons and neutrons in atoms, and this energy provides us with nuclear power.

Most of our energy, however, comes ultimately from the Sun. We can harness energy from the Sun's radiation directly in a number of ways. Solar radiation also helps drive wind patterns and the hydrologic cycle, making possible such forms of energy as wind power and hydroelectric power. And of course, sunlight drives photosynthesis and the growth of plants, from which we take wood and other biomass as a fuel source. Finally, when plants die and are preserved in sediments under particular conditions, they may impart their stored chemical energy to **fossil fuels**, highly combustible substances formed from the remains of organisms from past geologic ages. The three fossil fuels we use widely today are oil, coal, and natural gas.

Since the Industrial Revolution, fossil fuels have replaced biomass as our society's dominant source of energy. Global consumption of the three main fossil fuels has risen steadily for years and is now at its highest level ever (**FIGURE 16.1A**). The high energy content of fossil fuels makes them efficient to burn, ship, and store. Besides providing for transportation, heating, and cooking, these fuels are used to generate *electricity*, a secondary form of energy that is easier to transfer over long distances and apply to a variety of uses.

Canada's energy stream is complex; we use energy in different forms for different purposes (**FIGURE 16.1B**). We also both import and export energy—in some cases, different grades of the same form of energy (such as coal, which is both imported and exported). But overall Canada is a net exporter of energy.

Energy sources such as sunlight, geothermal energy, and tidal energy are considered perpetually **renewable** or inexhaustible because their supplies will not be depleted by our use. Other sources, such as timber, are renewable

roots

ENERGY

The term **energy**, with the scientific meaning of "a source of power," first appeared in the late sixteenth century. Before that, the Middle French *énergie* meant "force or vigor of expression" and was used to describe writing or speaking. The word originates from the Latin *energia* and, earlier, Greek *en* ("at") plus *ergon* ("work").

(a) Global consumption of fossil fuels

FIGURE 16.1
Global consumption of fossil fuels **(a)** has risen greatly over the past half century. Oil use rose steeply during the 1960s to overtake coal, and today it remains our leading energy source. Canada's energy mix **(b)** illustrates our fundamental dependence on fossil fuels, as well as the importance of uranium (for nuclear energy) and hydropower in our energy mix. Data for (a) from U.S. Energy Information Administration and International Energy Agency. Graphic in (b) from Natural Resources Canada. (2006).
Source: Report of the National Advisory Panel on Sustainable Energy Science and Technology, Office of Energy Research and Development.

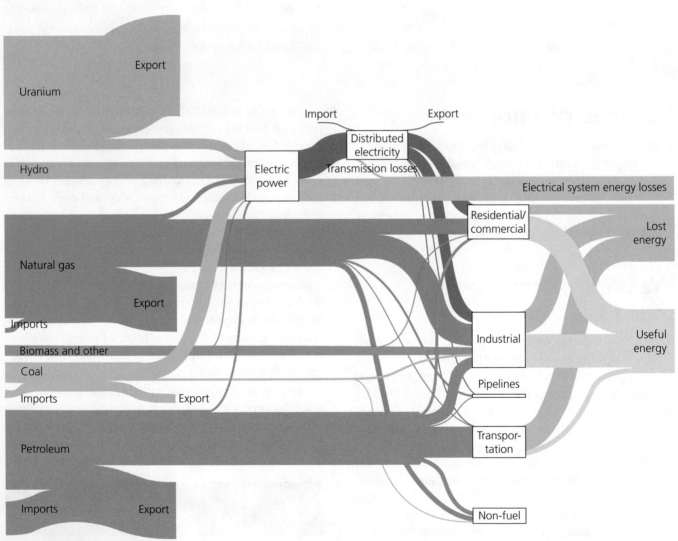

(b) Canada's energy stream

only if we do not harvest them at too great a rate. In contrast, such energy sources as oil, coal, and natural gas are considered **nonrenewable** because at our current rates of consumption we will use up Earth's accessible store of them in a matter of decades to centuries. Nuclear power as currently harnessed through fission of uranium can be

considered nonrenewable to the extent that uranium ore is in limited supply.

Although these nonrenewable fuels result from ongoing natural processes, the timescales on which they are created are so long that once the fuels are depleted, they cannot be replaced within any time span useful to our civilization. It takes a thousand years for the biosphere to generate the amount of organic matter that must be buried to produce a single day's worth of fossil fuels for our society. To replenish the fossil fuels we have depleted so far would take many millions of years. For this reason, and because fossil fuel use exerts severe environmental impacts, renewable energy sources increasingly are being developed as alternatives to fossil fuels, as we will see in a subsequent chapter.

Fossil fuels are indeed fuels created from "fossils"

The fossil fuels we burn today in our vehicles, homes, industries, and power plants were formed from the tissues of organisms that lived 100 million to 500 million years ago. The energy these fuels contain came originally from the Sun and was converted to chemical-bond energy as a result of photosynthesis. The chemical energy in these organisms' tissues then became concentrated as these tissues decomposed and their hydrocarbon compounds were altered and compressed.

Most organisms, after death, do not end up as part of a coal, gas, or oil deposit. A tree that falls and decays as a rotting log undergoes mostly **aerobic** decomposition; in the presence of air, bacteria and other organisms that use oxygen break down plant and animal remains into simpler carbon molecules that are recycled through the ecosystem. Fossil fuels are produced only when organic material is broken down in an **anaerobic** environment, one that has little or no oxygen. Such environments include the bottoms of shallow seas, deep lakes, and swamps (**FIGURE 16.2**).

Over millions of years, organic matter that accumulates at the bottoms of such water bodies undergoes decomposition, forming an oil precursor called **kerogen**. Geothermal heating then acts on the kerogen to create crude oil and natural gas. Natural gas can also be produced nearer the surface by anaerobic bacterial decomposition of organic matter. Oil and gas come to reside in porous rock layers beneath dense, impervious layers. Coal is formed when plant matter is compacted so tightly that there is little decomposition. The specific type of fuel that forms in any given place is dependent on the chemical composition of the starting material, the temperatures and pressures to which the material is subjected, the presence or absence of anaerobic decomposers, and the passage of time.

Fossil fuel reserves are unevenly distributed

Fossil fuel deposits are localized and unevenly distributed over Earth's surface, so some regions have substantial reserves of fossil fuels whereas others have very few. How

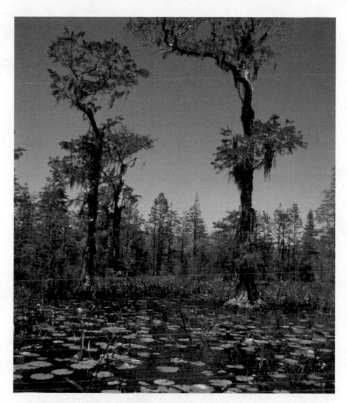

FIGURE 16.2

Tropical swamps, like the Okefenokee Swamp in Florida, shown here, are one type of environment in which the formation of fossil fuels would have begun 100 million to 150 million years ago. Fossil fuels begin to form when organisms die and end up in oxygen-poor conditions, such as when trees fall into bogs and are buried by sediment, or when marine phytoplankton and zooplankton drift to the seafloor and are buried.

long each nation's fossil fuel reserves will last depends on how much the nation extracts, how much it consumes, and how much it imports from and exports to other nations. Nearly two-thirds of the world's proven reserves of crude oil lie in the Middle East. The Middle East is also rich in natural gas, but Russia contains more than twice as much natural gas as any other country. Russia is also rich in coal, as is China, but the United States possesses more coal than any other nation (**TABLE 16.1**).

Table 16.1   Nations with the Largest Proven Reserves of Fossil Fuels

Oil (% world reserves)	Natural gas (% world reserves)	Coal (% world reserves)
Saudi Arabia, 19.8	Russian Federation, 23.7	United States, 28.9
Iran, 10.3		Russian Federation, 19.0
Iraq, 8.6	Iran, 15.8	China, 13.9
Kuwait, 7.6	Qatar, 13.5	Australia, 9.1
Venezuela, 6.6	Turkmenistan, 4.3	India, 7.1
	Saudi Arabia, 4.2	

Source: Data from British Petroleum. (2010). Statistical review of world energy 2010.

Developed nations consume more energy than developing nations

Citizens of developed regions generally consume far more energy than do those of developing regions (**FIGURE 16.3**). Per person, the most-industrialized nations use up to 100 times as much energy as do the least-industrialized nations. The United States, with only 4.6% of the world's population, accounts for 22.5% of the world's energy use. Even so, Canada's per capita energy use is higher. This is partly a result of the cold climate and long distances that characterize our nation, but careless use patterns are part of the story, too.

Moreover, developed and developing nations tend to apportion their energy use differently. Industrialized nations use roughly one-third of their energy on transportation, one-third on industry, and one-third on all other uses. Developing nations devote a greater proportion of their energy to subsistence activities, such as agriculture, food preparation, and home heating, and substantially less on transportation. In addition, people in developing countries often rely on manual or animal energy sources instead of automated ones. For instance, rice farmers in Bali plant rice by hand, but industrial rice growers in California use airplanes. Because industrialized nations rely more on equipment and technology, they use more fossil fuels. In Canada, where hydroelectric resources are particularly abundant,

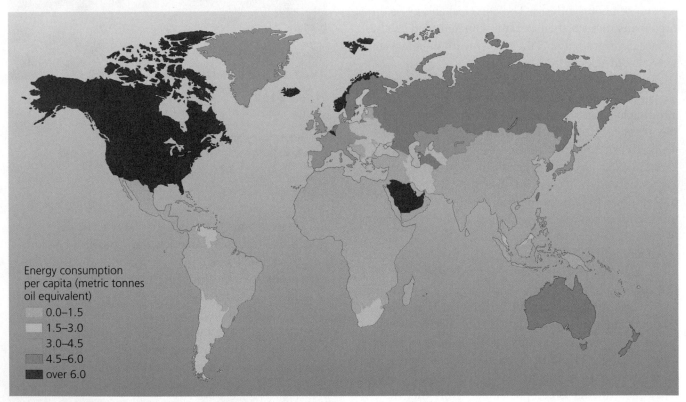

Energy consumption per capita (metric tonnes oil equivalent)

- 0.0–1.5
- 1.5–3.0
- 3.0–4.5
- 4.5–6.0
- over 6.0

(a) Map of energy consumption per person

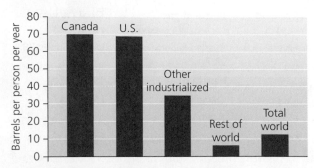

(b) Energy use per capita, in oil equivalents

FIGURE 16.3

Regions vary greatly in their consumption of energy per person **(a)**. People in industrialized nations consume the most. The map combines all types of energy, standardized to metric tonnes of "oil equivalent," that is, the amount of fuel needed to produce the energy gained from combusting one metric tonne of crude oil. The bar graph **(b)** compares energy use in oil equivalents in Canada and the United States—world "leaders" in energy use—to other nations of the world. *Source: Data from British Petroleum. 2007. Statistical review of world energy 2007.*

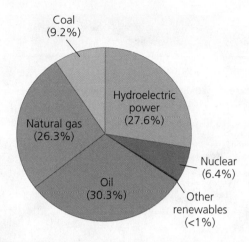

FIGURE 16.4
Fossil fuels dominate energy consumption in Canada, as in other industrialized nations.
Source: Data from BP 2010 Statistical Review of World Energy.

oil, coal, and natural gas still supply 66% of energy needs (**FIGURE 16.4**).

It takes energy to make energy

We don't simply get energy for free. To harness, extract, process, and deliver the energy that we use requires that we invest substantial inputs of energy. Drilling and extracting oil and natural gas requires the construction of an immense infrastructure of roads, wells, vehicles, storage tanks, pipelines, housing for workers, and more—which necessitates the use of energy. Piping and shipping the natural gas out of the Mackenzie River Delta and delivering it to the market for use would require further energy inputs. Thus, when evaluating the value of an energy source, it is important to subtract costs in energy invested from benefits in energy received. **Net energy** expresses the difference between energy returned (that is, the resulting consumable energy) and energy invested to achieve it:

Net Energy = Energy Returned – Energy Invested

When comparing energy sources, it is useful to use a ratio often denoted as **EROI**, or *energy returned on investment*. EROI ratios are calculated as follows:

EROI = Energy Returned/Energy Invested

Higher ratios mean that we receive more energy from each unit of energy that we invest; when EROI = 1, it means that the amount of energy invested is the same as the amount of energy extracted. Fossil fuels are widely used because their EROI ratios have historically been high. However, EROI ratios can change over time. For instance, those for oil and natural gas declined from more than 100:1 in the 1940s to about 30:1 in the 1970s, and today they are less than 15:1 globally. The EROI ratios have declined because we extracted the easiest deposits first and now must work harder and harder to extract the remaining amounts. Canadian tar sands, for comparison, have EROI ratios of 5:1 to 3:1; ethanol produced from corn has an EROI of less than 2:1. Solar panels have an EROI of approximately 1:1 unless the calculation extends for the lifetime of the technology, which greatly raises the EROI for technologies, like solar, that require the biggest energy (and financial) inputs up front.

Coal, Natural Gas, and Oil

The three principal fossil fuels, on which our modern industrial society has been founded, are coal, natural gas, and oil. Let us consider each of them, in turn.

Coal is the world's most abundant fossil fuel

The proliferation 300 million to 400 million years ago of swampy environments where organic material could be buried has resulted in substantial coal deposits throughout the world. The precursor to coal is *peat*, a moist soil composed of compressed organic matter. **Coal** is organic matter (generally woody plant material) that was compressed under very high pressure to form a dense, carbon-rich solid material (**FIGURE 16.5**). Coal is a rock, whereas peat is a soil. Coal typically results when little decomposition takes place within the parent organic material because it cannot be digested or because appropriate decomposers are not present. Coal provides one-quarter of the world's commercial energy consumption.

Coal use has a long history

People have used coal longer than any other fossil fuel. The Romans used coal for heating in the second and third centuries in Britain, as have people in parts of China for 2000–3000 years. Native Americans of the Hopi Nation still follow ancestral traditions by using coal to fire pottery, cook food, and heat their homes. Once commercial mining began in Europe in the 1700s, people began using coal widely as a heating source. Coal found an expanded market after the invention of the steam engine because it was used to boil water to produce steam. Coal-fired steam engines helped drive the Industrial Revolution, powering factories, agriculture, trains, and ships. The birth of the steel industry in 1875 increased demand still further because coal fuelled the furnaces used to produce steel.

FIGURE 16.5

Coal forms as a result of the compaction of ancient plant matter underground. Scientists categorize coal into several types, depending on the amount of heat, pressure, and moisture involved in its formation. Anthracite coal is formed under the greatest pressure, where temperatures are high and moisture content is low. Lignite coal is formed under conditions of much less pressure and heat but more moisture. Peat is also part of this continuum, representing plant matter that is minimally compacted.

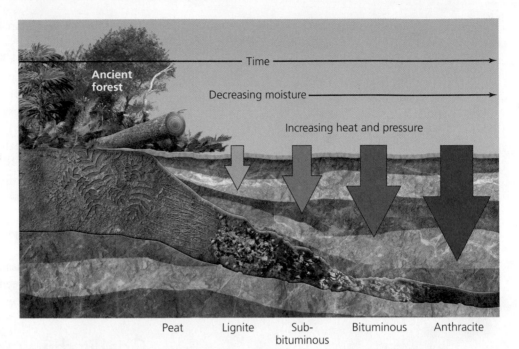

In the 1880s, people began to use coal to generate electricity. In coal-fired power plants, coal combustion converts water to steam, which turns a turbine to create electricity (see "The Science Behind the Story: Clean Coal for Electricity Generation"). Today coal provides more than 30% of the electrical-generating capacity of Canada. Canada hosts approximately 10 billion tonnes of coal reserves—more than our oil and natural gas reserves combined. China and the United States are the primary producers and consumers of coal (**TABLE 16.2**).

Coal is mined from the surface and from below ground

We extract coal by using two major methods. We reach underground deposits with **subsurface mining**. Shafts are dug deep into the ground, and networks of tunnels are dug or blasted out to follow coal seams. The coal is removed systematically and shipped to the surface. Today less than

2% of Canada's coal is extracted by underground mining. The history of underground mining in Nova Scotia demonstrates the hazards posed to miners who go deep under the ground to mine When coal deposits are at or near the surface, open-pit or strip-mining methods are used. Open-pit mining involves large excavations, which are deepened and widened as mining proceeds. This type of coal mining is common in Alberta and British Columbia. In **strip-mining**, heavy machinery removes earth in long, horizontal strips to expose the layers, or *seams*, and extract the coal. The pits are subsequently refilled with the soil that had been removed. Strip-mining is most common in the Prairies and in New Brunswick.[8] Strip-mining operations can occur on immense scales; in some cases entire mountaintops are lopped off.

Coal varies in its qualities

Coal varies from deposit to deposit in many ways, including in its water content and the amount of potential energy it contains. The starting material, peat, is essentially organic material that is broken down anaerobically but remains wet, near the surface, and not well compressed. Peat has been widely used as a fuel in Britain and other locations. Canada is home to some of the most extensive peat deposits in the world, and 90% of our exported peat goes to the United States. As you learned in our chapter on *Soil Resources*, peat is also of interest as a northern soil, and scientists are closely tracking its response to global climate change.

As peat decomposes further, as it becomes buried more deeply under sediment, as pressure and heat

Table 16.2 Top Five Producers and Consumers of Coal	
Production (% world production)	**Consumption (% world consumption)**
China, 45.6	China, 46.9
United States, 15.8	United States, 15.2
Australia, 6.7	India, 7.5
India, 6.2	Japan, 3.3
Indonesia, 4.6	South Africa, 3.0

Data from British Petroleum. (2010). Statistical review of world energy 2010.

increase, and as time passes, water is squeezed out of the material, and carbon compounds are packed more tightly together, forming coal. Scientists classify coal into four types: *lignite, sub-bituminous, bituminous,* and *anthracite.* Lignite is the least-compressed type of coal, and anthracite is the most-compressed type. The greater the compression, the greater the energy content per unit of volume.

Most coal contains impurities, including sulphur, mercury, arsenic, and other trace metals, and coal deposits vary in the amounts of impurities they contain. Sulphur content depends in part on whether the coal was formed in freshwater or saltwater sediment. Coal from eastern provinces of Canada tends to be relatively high in sulphur (e.g., 2%) because it was formed from marine sediment, where sulphur from seawater was present. In comparison, coal from Alberta and British Columbia is typically lower in sulphur content, ranging down to about 0.5%, whereas coal from China can be very sulphur-rich (and thus more polluting), ranging up to about 3%.

When high-sulphur coal is burned, it produces sulphate air pollutants, which contribute to industrial smog and acidic deposition; China's use of high-sulphur coal deposits has contributed to severe air-quality problems in that country. Combustion of coal high in mercury content emits mercury that bioaccumulates in organisms' tissues, poisoning animals as it moves up food chains. Such pollution problems commonly occur downwind of coal-fired power plants. Scientists and engineers are seeking ways to cleanse coal of its impurities so that it can continue to be used as an energy source while minimizing impact on health and the environment. Reducing pollution from coal is important because society's demand for this relatively abundant fossil fuel may soon rise as supplies of oil and natural gas decline.

Natural gas is the fastest-growing fossil fuel in use today

Natural gas consists primarily of methane (CH_4) and typically includes varying amounts of other volatile hydrocarbons. (Natural "gas" is actually something of a misnomer, as the material can be liquid at the ambient pressures and temperatures in subsurface reservoirs.) Natural gas provides one-quarter of global commercial energy consumption. It is a much cleaner-burning fuel than coal or oil, so it produces less pollution. World supplies of natural gas are projected to last for at least 60 more years (proven global reserves, at current levels of production), and much longer if more unconventional sources, such as shale gas, are brought into production.

Natural gas is formed in two main ways

Natural gas can arise from either of two processes. *Biogenic* gas is created at shallow depths by the anaerobic decomposition of organic matter by bacteria. An example is the "swamp gas" you can sometimes smell when stepping into the muck of a swamp.

In contrast, *thermogenic* gas results from compression of organic material, accompanied by heating deep underground. The organic precursor materials come most commonly from animal and plant matter, such as zooplankton and phytoplankton in shallow marine waters. As the organic matter is buried more and more deeply under sediments, the pressure exerted by the overlying sediments grows, and temperatures increase; this process is called *maturation.* Carbon bonds in the organic matter begin breaking, and the organic matter turns into kerogen, which acts as a source material for both natural gas and crude oil. Further heat and pressure act on the kerogen to degrade complex organic molecules into simpler hydrocarbon molecules. At very deep levels—below about 3 km—the high temperatures and pressures tend to form natural gas. Whereas biogenic gas is nearly pure methane, thermogenic gas contains small amounts of other gases as well as methane.

Thermogenic gas may be formed directly, along with coal or crude oil, or from coal or oil that is altered by heating. Most gas extracted commercially is thermogenic and is found above deposits of crude oil or seams of coal, so its extraction often accompanies the extraction of those fossil fuels. The natural gas found in the Mackenzie River Delta, discussed in "Central Case: On, Off, On Again? The Mackenzie Valley Natural Gas Pipeline," originated from the thermogenic decomposition of organic matter in shallow marine sediments.

Often, natural gas goes to waste as it escapes from coal mines or oil wells. Methane from coal seams, called *coalbed methane,* commonly leaks to the atmosphere during mining. To avoid this waste, and because methane is a potent greenhouse gas that contributes to climate change, mining engineers are now trying to capture more of this gas for energy. Likewise, in most remote oil-drilling areas, where the transport of natural gas remains prohibitively expensive, natural gas is flared—wasted by simply being burned off. Gas captured during oil drilling is expensive to export, but in some cases it can be reinjected into the ground for potential future extraction or to maintain the pressure needed to bring the oil to the surface.

One source of biogenic natural gas is the decay process in landfills, and many landfill operators are now capturing this gas to sell as fuel. This practice decreases

THE SCIENCE BEHIND THE STORY

Clean Coal for Electricity Generation

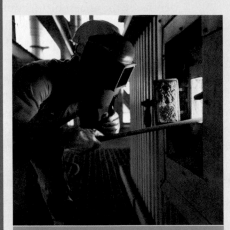

A worker checks a furnace at a coal-fired power plant.

We use coal—lots of it—to generate electricity, in a process that dates back more than a century (see the figure). Once mined, coal is hauled to power plants, where it is pulverized. The crushed coal is blown into a boiler furnace on a super-heated stream of air and burned in a blaze of intense heat—typical furnace temperatures often flare at 815°C.

Water circulating around the boiler absorbs the heat and is converted to high-pressure steam. This steam is injected into a **turbine**, a rotary device that converts the kinetic energy of a moving substance, such as steam, into mechanical energy. As steam from the boiler exerts pressure on the blades of the turbine, they spin, turning the turbine's drive shaft.

The drive shaft is connected to a generator, which features a *rotor* that rotates and a *stator* that remains stationary. Generators make use of a phenomenon that you may have experimented with in your high school physics class: Moving magnets adjacent to coils of copper wire causes electrons in the wires to move, generating alternating electric current. The current flows into transmission lines that travel from the power plant out to the customers who use the plant's electricity.

As we try to balance growing demand for electricity with rising concerns about environmental and health impacts of coal combustion, power plants continue to rely heavily on coal while scientists work to limit the pollution that use of this fuel creates. **Clean coal** technologies largely focus on approaches to rid the generation process of toxic chemicals before or after the coal is burned.

There are two principal clean-coal pathways being investigated by researchers internationally. These involve technologies that are aimed at (1) a cleaner combustion process and (2) *gasification* and the production of clean synthetic fuels from coal.[9]

Combustion-focused technologies start with the pulverized-coal process and apply improvements aimed at making combustion more efficient and more complete, and thus cleaner. One example is *fluidized bed* technologies, which bathe the finely pulverized coal in jets of air during combustion. This leads to a turbulent, fluid-like environment, which allows the temperature to be increased and raises the efficiency of the chemical reactions that occur during combustion. Gasification technologies are less well developed; they involve creating clean synthetic fuels, including hydrogen, from coal.

Either approach can be combined with technologies aimed at cleaning the coal prior to combustion; cleaning emissions after burning and before they leave the smokestack; cogeneration technologies; and carbon capture and storage technologies. For example, some precombustion technologies utilize sulphur-metabolizing bacteria to remove sulphur from the coal prior to burning. Technologies that clean emissions before they leave the stack include *scrubbers*, which utilize calcium- or sodium-based materials to absorb and remove sulphur dioxide (SO_2) from the emissions. Other types of scrubbers use chemical reactions to strip away nitrogen oxides (NO_X), breaking them down into elemental nitrogen and water. Multilayered filtering devices can be used to capture tiny ash particles before they leave the stack.

---

energy waste, can be profitable for the operator, and helps reduce the atmospheric release of methane.

Natural gas has only recently been widely used

Throughout history, naturally occurring seeps of natural gas would occasionally be ignited by lightning and could be seen burning in parts of what is now Iraq, inspiring the Greek essayist Plutarch around 100 CE. to describe their "eternal fires." The first commercial extraction of natural gas took place in 1821, but until recently its use was localized because technology did not exist to pipe gas safely over long distances. Natural gas was used to fuel streetlamps, but when electric lights replaced most gas lamps in the 1890s, gas companies began marketing gas for heating and cooking. The first major commercial natural gas development in Canada was at Bow Lake, Alberta, southwest of Medicine Hat, in 1908.[10] After the Second World War, wartime improvements in welding and pipe building made gas transport safer and more economical, and during the 1950s and 1960s, thousands of kilometres of underground pipelines were laid throughout North America.

Today natural gas is increasingly favoured because it is versatile and clean-burning, emitting just half as much carbon dioxide per unit of energy produced as coal and two-thirds as much as oil. Converted to a liquid at low temperatures (*liquefied natural gas*, or *LNG*), it can be shipped long distances in refrigerated tankers, although this poses risks of catastrophic explosions. Natural gas deposits are greatest in Russia and the Middle East, and Russia and the United States lead the world in gas production and gas

Coal is used as a fuel source to generate electricity. Coal is pulverized and blown into a high-temperature furnace. Heat from the combustion boils water, and the resulting steam turns a turbine, generating electricity by passing magnets past copper coils. The steam is then cooled and condensed in a cooling loop and returned to the furnace. "Clean coal" technologies make the combustion process more efficient, clean the coal prior to combustion, or filter out pollutants after combustion. Toxic ash residue is disposed of at hazardous waste disposal sites.

Some energy analysts and environmental advocates question a policy emphasis on clean coal. Coal, they maintain, is an inherently dirty means of generating power and should be replaced outright with cleaner energy sources. However, with coal-fired power plants still generating a significant proportion of Canada's electricity—as well as Canada's greenhouse gas emissions—the push to clean up coal-based technologies makes sense.

consumption, respectively (**TABLE 16.3**); Canada is the world's third-largest producer of natural gas.

Natural gas extraction becomes more challenging with time

To access some natural gas deposits, prospectors need only drill an opening because pressure and low molecular weight drive the gas upward naturally. The first gas fields to be tapped were of this type. Most fields remaining today, however, require that gas be pumped to Earth's surface. In Alberta as well as parts of the United States, it is common to see a device called a *horsehead pump* (**FIGURE 16.6**). This pump moves a rod in and out of a shaft, creating pressure to pull both natural gas and crude oil to the surface.

As with oil and coal, many of the most accessible natural gas reserves have already been exhausted, causing their production to decline. Thus, deposits located in more remote

Table 16.3 Top Five Producers and Consumers of Natural Gas

Production (% world production)	Consumption (% world consumption)
United States, 20.1	United States, 22.2
Russian Federation, 17.6	Russian Federation, 13.2
Canada, 5.4	Iran, 4.5
Iran, 4.4	Canada, 3.2
Norway, 3.5	China, 3.0

Source: Data from British Petroleum. (2010). Statistical review of world energy 2010.

FIGURE 16.6
Horsehead pumps, like this one in Drayton Valley, Alberta, are used to extract natural gas as well as oil. They are a common feature of the landscape in Alberta and parts of the United States. The pumping motion of the machinery draws gas and oil upward from below ground.

areas, such as the Mackenzie River Delta, are becoming more attractive economically. Much extraction today also makes use of sophisticated techniques to break into rock formations and pump gas to the surface. One such "fracturing technique" is to pump salt water or another fluid under high pressure into the rocks to crack them. Sand or small glass beads are inserted to hold the cracks open once the water is withdrawn. This type of extraction (called *fracking*) has extensive environmental impacts, and it is very water-intensive (**FIGURE 16.7**). Fracking is used to recover *shale gas*, natural gas produced from shale, which is the fastest growing part of the natural gas industry.

Offshore drilling produces much of our gas and oil

Drilling for natural gas, as well as for oil, takes place not just on land but also in the seafloor on the continental shelves. Offshore drilling has required developing tech-

FIGURE 16.7
Fracking is used to extract natural gas, some types of oil, and bitumen from tar sands, as shown here. It involves injecting a fluid (usually water) into the ground under pressure to induce the rock to fracture, as shown here, and release the petroleum that it holds.

FIGURE 16.8
The Hibernia Offshore Drilling Platform, shown here, is located in the North Atlantic about 300 km off the coast of Newfoundland in the Grand Banks. It is the world's largest offshore platform and began production in 1997.

Table 16.4   Top Ten Producers and Consumers of Oil

Production (% world production)	Consumption (% world consumption)
Russian Federation, 12.9	United States, 21.7
Saudi Arabia, 12.0	China, 10.4
United States, 8.5	Japan, 5.1
Iran, 5.3	India, 3.8
China, 4.9	Russian Federation, 3.2
Canada, 4.1	Saudi Arabia, 3.1
Mexico, 3.9	Germany, 2.9
Venezuela, 3.3	South Korea, 2.7
United Arab Emirates, 3.2	Brazil, 2.7
Iraq, 3.2	Canada, 2.5

Source: *Data from British Petroleum. (2010). Statistical review of world energy 2010.*

nology that can withstand the forces of wind, waves, and ocean currents. Some drilling platforms are fixed standing platforms built with unusual strength. Others are resilient floating platforms anchored in place above the drilling site. Most of the offshore gas and oil development in Canada is located in the Beaufort Sea and in the North Atlantic Ocean off the coasts of Newfoundland, Labrador and Nova Scotia (**FIGURE 16.8**). These are very risky environments because of stormy weather and icy waters, as well as the extreme depths of drilling (more than 2.5 km, in the case of Newfoundland).

Oil is the world's most-used fuel

Oil has dominated world energy use since the 1960s, when it eclipsed coal. It now accounts for 37% of the world's commercial energy consumption. Its use worldwide over the past decade has risen more than 17%.

People have used solid forms of oil (such as tar and asphalt) from deposits easily accessible at Earth's surface for at least 6000 years. The modern extraction and use of petroleum for energy began in the 1850s, when miners drilling for groundwater or salt occasionally encountered oily rocks instead. At first, entrepreneurs bottled the crude oil from these deposits and sold it as a healing aid, unaware that crude oil is carcinogenic when applied to the skin and poisonous when ingested. Soon, however, it was realized that this "rock oil" could be used to light lamps and lubricate machinery. Edwin Drake is generally credited with drilling the world's first oil well, in Titusville, Pennsylvania, in 1859. In fact, however, the first oil well was drilled a full year earlier, in 1858, at Oil Springs, Ontario, by James Miller Williams, who struck free liquid oil only 20 m below the surface while attempting to drill a water well.[11]

Today our global society produces and consumes nearly 750 L of oil each year for every man, woman, and child. The United States consumes nearly one-fourth of the world's oil and shows little sign of abating. For our part, Canadians—less than 0.5% of the world's population—consume 2.5% of the oil. **TABLE 16.4** shows the top oil-producing and oil-consuming nations.

Heat and pressure underground form petroleum

The sludgelike liquid we know as **oil**, **crude oil**, or **petroleum** (a term that includes both oil and natural gas) tends to form within a window of temperature and pressure conditions often found 1.5–3 km below the surface. Like natural gas, most of the crude oil we now extract was formed when dead plant material (and small amounts of animal material) drifted down through shallow coastal marine waters millions of years ago and was buried in sediments on the ocean floor.

Crude oil is a mixture of hundreds of different types of hydrocarbon molecules characterized by carbon chains of different lengths. The specific properties of the oil depend on the chemistry of the organic starting materials, the

roots

PETROLEUM

The word **petroleum**, which includes both oil and natural gas in its modern usage, comes from a combination of the Latin words *petra* ("rock") and *oleum* ("oil"). Until about 1300 CE, **oil** was used exclusively in reference to "olive oil," and it derived much earlier from the Greek *elaion*, "olive tree."

characteristics of the geologic environment of formation, and the details of the maturation process. A hydrocarbon chain's length affects its chemical properties, which has consequences for human use, such as whether a given fuel burns cleanly in a car engine. Oil refineries sort the various hydrocarbons of crude oil, separating those intended for use in gasoline engines from those, such as tar and asphalt, used for other purposes.

Petroleum geologists infer the location and size of deposits

Because petroleum forms only under certain conditions, it occurs in isolated deposits. Once geothermal heating separates hydrocarbons from their source material and produces crude oil, this liquid migrates upward through rock pores, sometimes assisted by seismic faulting. It tends to collect in porous layers beneath dense, impermeable layers.

Geologists searching for oil (or other fossil fuels) drill rock cores and conduct ground, air, and seismic surveys to map underground rock formations, understand geologic history, and predict where fossil fuel deposits might lie. One method is to create powerful vibrations (by exploding dynamite, thumping the ground with a large weight, or using an electric vibrating machine) at the surface in one location and then measure how long it takes the seismic waves to reach receivers at other surface locations. Density differences in the substrate cause waves to reflect off layers, refract, or bend. Scientists and engineers interpret the patterns of wave reception to infer the density, thickness, and location of underlying geologic layers—which in turn provide clues about the location and size of fuel deposits.

Over the past few decades, geologists have greatly improved their methods for locating new deposits; however, with their scientific understanding of Earth processes, geologists are generally quick to acknowledge that petroleum is ultimately a finite and nonrenewable resource.

Some portion of oil that is located by geologists will be impossible to extract by using current technology and will need to wait for future advances in extraction equipment or methods. Thus, estimates are generally made of *technically recoverable* oil. However, oil companies will not be willing to extract these entire amounts. Some oil would be so difficult to extract that the expense of doing so would exceed the income the company would receive from the oil's sale. Thus, the amount a company chooses to drill for will be determined by the costs of extraction (and transportation), together with the current price of oil on the world market. Because the price of oil fluctuates, the portion of oil from a given deposit that is *economically recoverable* fluctuates as well.

Thus, technology sets a limit on the amount that *can* be extracted, whereas economics determines how much *will* be extracted. The amount of oil, or any other fossil fuel, in a deposit that is technologically and economically feasible to remove under current conditions is the *proven recoverable reserve* of that fuel.

We drill to extract oil

Once geologists have identified an oil deposit, an oil company will typically conduct exploratory drilling. Holes drilled during this phase are usually small in circumference and descend to great depths. If enough oil is encountered, extraction begins. Just as you would squeeze a sponge to remove its liquid, pressure is required to extract oil from porous rock. Oil is typically already under pressure—from above by rock or trapped gas, from below by groundwater, or internally from natural gas dissolved in the oil. All these forces are held in place by surrounding rock until drilling reaches the deposit, whereupon oil will often rise to the surface of its own accord.

Once pressure is relieved, however, both oil and natural gas become more difficult to extract and may need to be pumped out. Even after pumping, a great deal of oil remains stuck to rock surfaces. As much as two-thirds of a deposit may remain in the ground after **primary extraction**, the initial drilling and pumping of available oil (**FIGURE 16.9A**). Companies may then begin **secondary extraction**, in which solvents are used or underground rocks are flushed with water or steam to remove additional oil (**FIGURE 16.9B**).

Even after secondary extraction, quite a bit of oil can remain; we lack the technology to remove every last drop. Secondary extraction is more expensive than primary extraction, so many oil deposits did not undergo secondary extraction when they were first drilled because the price of oil was too low to make the procedure economical. When oil prices rose in the 1970s, many drilling sites were reopened for secondary extraction. Still more are being reopened today, as prices rise again. As mentioned above, secondary extraction also can be harder on the environment than primary extraction.

Petroleum products have many uses

Once crude oil is extracted, it is put through **refining** processes (see "The Science Behind the Story: How Crude Oil Is Refined"). Because crude oil is a complex mix of hydrocarbons, we can create many types of petroleum products by separating its various components. Since the 1920s, refining techniques and chemical manufacturing have greatly expanded our uses of petroleum to include a

(a) Primary extraction of oil

(b) Secondary extraction of oil

FIGURE 16.9   In primary extraction **(a)**, oil is drawn up through the well by keeping pressure at the top lower than pressure at the level of the oil deposit. Once the pressure in the deposit drops, however, material must be injected into the deposit to increase the pressure. Thus, secondary extraction **(b)** involves injecting seawater beneath the oil and/or gases just above the oil to force more oil up and out of the deposit.

wide array of products and applications, from lubricants to plastics to fabrics to pharmaceuticals. Today, petroleum-based products are all around us in our everyday lives (**FIGURE 16.10**).

Because petroleum products have become so central to our lives, many fossil fuel experts today are voicing concern that oil production may soon decline as we continue to deplete the world's recoverable oil reserves.

FIGURE 16.10   Petroleum products are everywhere in our daily lives. Besides the gasoline and other fuels we use for transportation and heating, petroleum products include many of the fabrics that we wear and most of the plastics that help make up countless items we use every day.

THE SCIENCE BEHIND THE STORY

How Crude Oil Is Refined

These workers are at a Citgo oil refinery in Lemont, Illinois.

Crude oil is a complex mixture of thousands of kinds of hydrocarbon molecules. Through the process of *refining*, these hydrocarbon molecules are separated into classes of different sizes and chemically transformed to create specialized fuels for heating, cooking, and transportation and to create lubricating oils, asphalts, and the precursors of plastics and other petrochemical products. To maximize the production of marketable products while minimizing negative environmental impacts, petroleum engineers have developed a variety of refining techniques.

The first step in processing crude oil is *distillation*, or *fractionation*. This process is based on the fact that different components of crude oil boil at different temperatures. In refineries, the distillation process takes place in tall columns filled with perforated horizontal trays (see figure). The columns are cooler at the top than at the bottom. When heated crude oil is introduced into the column, lighter components rise as vapour to the upper trays, condensing into liquid as they cool, while heavier components sink to the lower trays. Light gases, such as butane, boil at less than 32°C, and heavier oils, such as industrial fuel oil, boil only at temperatures above 343°C.

Since the early twentieth century, light gasoline, used in automobiles, has been in much higher demand than most other derivatives of crude oil. The demand for high-performance, clean-burning gasoline has also risen. To meet these demands, refiners have developed several techniques to convert heavy hydrocarbons into gasoline.

The general name for processes that convert heavy oil into lighter oil is *cracking*. One of the simplest methods is thermal cracking, in which long-chained molecules are broken into smaller chains by heating in the absence of oxygen. (The oil would ignite if oxygen were present.) Catalytic cracking, a related method, uses *catalysts*—substances that promote chemical reactions without being consumed by them—to control the cracking process. The result is an increase in the amount of a desired lighter product from a given amount of heavy oil. The products of cracking are then fed into a distillation column.

Refiners can also change the chemical composition of oil through a process called *catalytic reforming*. Catalytic reforming uses catalysts to promote chemical reactions that transform certain hydrocarbons that are slightly heavier than gasoline so that they can be blended with gasoline to obtain higher octane ratings. The octane rating reflects the amount of compression gasoline can undergo before it spontaneously ignites.

Besides distilling crude oil and altering the chemical structure of some of its components, refineries also remove contaminants. Sulphur and nitrogen compounds, which can be harmful when released into the atmosphere, are the two most common contaminants in crude oil. Government regulations have forced refiners to implement scrubbers and other methods of removing such contaminants, particularly sulphur. Some methods successfully remove up to 98% of sulphur.

As a result of all these approaches, crude oil is eventually converted into gasoline and a wide variety of other petroleum products.

We may have already depleted half our oil reserves

Some scientists and oil industry analysts calculate that we have already extracted nearly half of the world's oil reserves. So far we have used up about 1.1 trillion barrels of oil, and most estimates hold that somewhat more than 1 trillion barrels remain. (A barrel is not a metric unit of measurement, but it is still commonly used in the oil industry. It is equivalent to 0.158987 cubic metres, or 159 litres, or 42 U.S. gallons.)

To estimate how long this remaining oil will last, analysts calculate the *reserves-to-production ratio*, or *R/P ratio*, by dividing the amount of total remaining reserves by the annual rate of production (i.e., extraction and processing). At current levels of production (30 billion barrels globally per year), 1.2 trillion barrels would last about 40 more years.

Unfortunately, this does not mean that we have a full 40 years in which to figure out what to do once the oil runs out. A growing number of scientists and analysts insist that we will face a crisis not when the last drop of oil is pumped, but when the rate of production first begins to decline. They point out that when production declines as demand continues to increase (because of rising global population and consumption), we will experience an oil shortage immediately. Because production tends to decline once reserves are depleted halfway, most of these experts calculate that this crisis will likely begin within the next several years.

To understand the basis of these concerns, we need to turn back the clock to 1956. In that year, Shell Oil geologist M. King Hubbert calculated that U.S. oil production would peak around 1970. His prediction was ridiculed at the time, but it proved to be accurate; U.S. production peaked in that very year and has continued

Distillation column

Boiling temp.   **Product**

Less than 5°C — Butane

20–180°C — Naphtha

20–200°C — Gasoline

180–260°C — Kerosene

260–340°C — Diesel

370–600°C — Lubricating oil

Over 330°C — Heavy gas oil

Crude oil

Boiler

Residue

(a) Distillation columns   **(b) Distillation process**

At crude petroleum refineries **(a)**, crude oil is boiled, causing its many hydrocarbon constituents to volatilize and proceed upward through a distillation column **(b)**. Constituents that boil at the highest temperatures and condense readily once the temperature drops will condense at low levels in the column. Constituents that volatilize at lower temperatures will continue rising through the column and condense at higher levels, where temperatures are lower. In this way, heavy oils (generally consisting of long hydrocarbon molecules) are separated from lighter oils (generally those with short hydrocarbon molecules).

to fall since then (**FIGURE 16.11A**). The peak in production came to be known as **Hubbert's peak**.

In 1974, Hubbert analyzed data on technology, economics, and geology, predicting that global oil production would peak in 1995. It grew past 1995, but many scientists using newer, better data today predict that at some point in the coming decade, production will begin to decline (**FIGURE 16.11B**). Oil geologist Kenneth Deffeyes even contends that we have already passed the peak—that we did so in December 2005—and he is not alone in this belief. Indeed, because of year-to-year variability in production, we will be able to recognize that we have passed the peak of oil production only several years after it has happened.

Predicting an exact date for **"peak oil"** and the coming decline in production is difficult. Many companies and governments do not reveal their true data on oil reserves, and estimates differ as to how much oil we can extract

secondarily from existing deposits. Moreover, a recent U.S. Geological Survey report estimated 2 trillion barrels remaining in the world, rather than 1 trillion, and some estimates predict still greater amounts. A report by the U.S. General Accounting Office reviewed 21 studies and found that estimates for the timing of the oil production peak ranged from 2005 through 2040. Regardless of the exact timing, it seems certain that a peak in global oil production will occur. Discoveries of new oil fields peaked 30 years ago, and since then we have been extracting and consuming more oil than we have been discovering. Meanwhile, global demand continues to rise, particularly as China and India industrialize rapidly.

The coming divergence of demand and supply will likely have momentous economic, social, and political consequences that will profoundly affect the lives of each and every one of us. Pessimists predict the collapse of modern industrial society as fossil fuel supplies become

FIGURE 16.11
Because fossil fuels are nonrenewable resources, supplies at some point pass the midway point of their depletion, and annual production begins to decline. U.S. oil production peaked in 1970, just as geologist M. King Hubbert predicted decades previously; this high point is referred to as Hubbert's peak **(a)**. Today many analysts believe global oil production is about to peak. Shown is the latest projection **(b)**, from a 2007 analysis by scientists at the Association for the Study of Peak Oil. Data in (a) from Deffeyes, K. S. (2001). *Hubbert's Peak: The Impending World Oil Shortage*. Princeton, NJ: Princeton University Press; and U.S. Energy Information Administration. Data in (b) from Campbell, C. J., and the Association for the Study of Peak Oil and Gas. (2007).

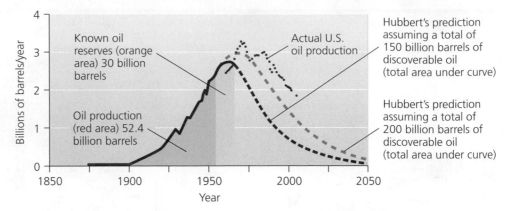

(a) Hubbert's prediction of peak in U.S. oil production, with actual data

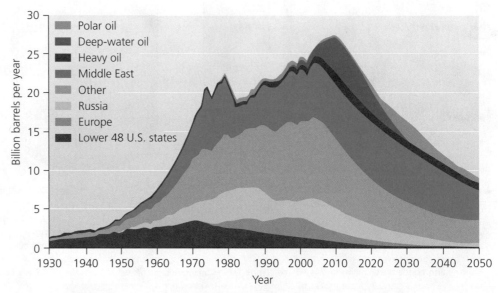

(b) Modern prediction of peak in global oil production

increasingly insufficient. More optimistic observers argue that as oil supplies dwindle, rising prices will create powerful incentives for businesses, governments, and individuals to conserve energy and develop alternative energy sources, and that these developments will save us from major disruptions caused by the coming oil peak.

weighing the issues

THE END OF OIL

How do you think your life would be affected if our society were to suffer a 50% decrease in oil availability over the next 10 years, as some observers have predicted? What steps would you take to adapt to these changes? What steps should our society take to deal with the coming depletion of oil? Do you think the recent surges in the price of oil and gasoline are an indication that such changes are beginning?

Indeed, to achieve a sustainable society, we will need to switch to renewable energy sources. Energy conservation can extend the time we have in which to make this transition. However, the research and development needed to construct the infrastructure for a new energy economy depend on having cheap oil, and the time we will have to make this enormous transition will be quite limited.

"Unconventional" Fossil Fuels

As oil production declines, we will rely more on natural gas and coal—yet these in turn will also peak and decline in future years. Are there other fossil fuels that can replace them and stave off our day of reckoning? At least three types of alternative fossil fuels exist in large amounts in deposits of tar sands, shale oil and gas, and methane hydrates.

FIGURE 16.12
In Alberta, companies strip-mine tar sands with the world's largest dump trucks and power shovels. On average, two metric tonnes of tar sands are required to produce one barrel of synthetic crude oil.

Canada owns massive deposits of tar sands

Tar sands (also called **oil sands**) are deposits of moist sand and clay containing 1–20% **bitumen**, a thick and heavy form of petroleum that is rich in carbon and poor in hydrogen. Tar sands represent crude oil deposits that have been degraded and chemically altered by water erosion and bacterial decomposition.

Because bitumen is too thick to extract by conventional oil drilling, tar sands are generally removed by strip-mining (**FIGURE 16.12**), using methods similar to coal strip-mining. For deposits 75 m or more below ground, a variety of *in situ* extraction techniques are being devised. Most of these involve fracking—injecting steam or chemical solvents to crack the rock and liquefy

the bitumen so it can be extracted through conventional wells. After extraction, bitumen may be sent to specialized refineries, where several types of chemical reactions that add hydrogen or remove carbon can upgrade it into more valuable synthetic crude oil.

Three-quarters of the world's tar sands lie in two areas: eastern Venezuela and northeastern Alberta. Tar sands in each region hold at least 175 billion barrels of oil. In Alberta, strip-mining began in 1967, but as rising crude oil prices make tar sands more profitable, dozens of companies are now angling to begin 100 or more mining projects in the region. In 2010, tar sands produced 1.5 million barrels of oil per day, contributing 54% of Canada's petroleum production. If all planned projects go through, production could reach 3.5 million barrels per day by 2025. The tar sands move Canada into a strong position for proven oil reserves in the international context (**FIGURE 16.13**).

Oil shale is abundant in the American West

Oil shale is sedimentary rock that contains abundant *kerogen*, which can be processed to produce liquid petroleum. Oil shale is formed by the same processes that form crude oil but occurs when kerogen was not buried deeply enough or subjected to enough heat and pressure to form oil.

Oil shale is mined by using strip-mines or subsurface mines. Once mined, oil shale can be burned directly like coal, or it can be baked in the presence of hydrogen and in the absence of air to extract liquid petroleum (a process called *pyrolysis*). Currently, industry is developing *in situ*

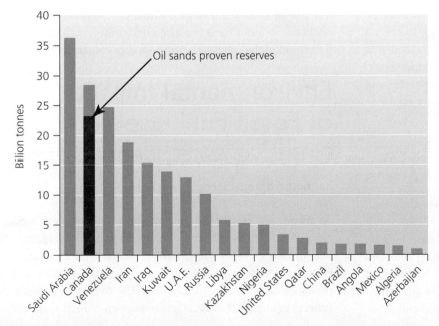

FIGURE 16.13   Canada's tar sands are a significant proven oil reserve, even in an international context.
Source: Based on BP Statistical Review of World Energy, 2010.

extraction processes in which rock is heated underground to liquefy and release oil into conventional wells.

The world's known deposits of oil shale may be able to produce more than 600 billion barrels of oil (roughly half as much as the crude oil remaining in the world). About 40% of global oil shale reserves are in the United States. Low prices for crude oil have kept investors away from the more costly oil shale, but as crude prices rise, oil shale is again attracting attention.

An increasingly important unconventional source of fossil fuel is **shale gas**. Natural gas can be produced from shale units by fracking, the same method used to extract oil from tar sands. When fracking is used for the extraction of shale gas, however, it is typical for a much larger horizontal area to be fractured, leading to significantly greater negative environmental impacts. It is likely that the amount of natural gas available to be extracted from shale and other unconventional sources will turn out to be overwhelmingly larger than the amount of oil that may be derived from these sources.

Methane hydrate is another form of natural gas

Methane hydrate (also called *methane clathrate* or *methane ice*) is a solid substance that consists of molecules of methane within a crystal lattice of water ice molecules. It occurs underground in some Arctic locations and more widely under the seafloor on the continental shelves. Most methane in these gas hydrates was formed by bacterial decomposition in anaerobic environments, but some results from thermogenic formation deeper below the surface. Scientists believe there to be immense amounts of methane hydrate on Earth—from perhaps as much as 20 times the amount of natural gas from all other sources.

However, there is currently no technology to extract methane hydrate safely, avoiding the risk of destabilizing these deposits during extraction. Such destabilization could lead to underwater landslides, tsunamis, and the release of large amounts of methane, a potent greenhouse gas.

Alternative fossil fuels have significant environmental impacts

Alternative and unconventional fossil fuels are abundant, but they are no panacea for our energy challenges. For one thing, their net energy values are low because they are expensive to extract and process. Thus the energy returned on energy invested (EROI) ratio is low. For instance, at least 40% of the energy content of oil shale is consumed in its production, and oil shale's EROI is only about 2:1 or

3:1, compared with a 5:1 or greater ratio for conventional crude oil. Natural gas extracted from the gas fields of the Mackenzie River Delta might never make it all the way to southern consumers if it must be sidetracked to support the extraction of oil from the Athabasca tar sands.

Second, these fuels exert severe environmental impacts. Tar sands and oil shale require extensive strip-mining and/or fracking, which utterly devastates landscapes over large areas and pollutes waterways that run into other areas. Although most governments require mining companies to restore mined areas to their original condition, regions denuded by the very first oil sand mine in Alberta 30 years ago have still not recovered.

Canadian environmentalists also are worried about the intensive water use that typically accompanies the extraction of unconventional fossil fuels through methods such as fracking, as well as the impacts on water quality in surrounding regions. The impacts on wildlife are also of concern; this concern was brought into stark focus in 2008 when hundreds of migratory birds died when their feathers became fouled with oil after landing on Syncrude's massive tailings pond near Fort McMurray, Alberta (**FIGURE 16.14**). A similar event happened in 2010, just days after Syncrude agreed to pay a penalty of $3 million for the previous event.

To give you an idea of the magnitude of these ponds, which can hold up to 540 000 000 m^3 of oily sludge, consider that the Syncrude tailings dam is the largest dam in Canada, and second in the world only to the Three Gorges hydroelectric dam in China. Canada's largest hydroelectric dam, the Gardiner, has just slightly more than one-tenth the capacity of the Syncrude tailings dam.[12]

Besides impacts from their extraction, our combustion of alternative fossil fuels would emit at least as much carbon dioxide, methane, and other air pollutants as does our use of coal, oil, and gas. Thus, they will worsen the effects that fossil fuels are already causing, including air pollution, global climate change, and ocean acidification.

Environmental Impact of Fossil Fuel Use

Our society's love affair with fossil fuels and the many petrochemical products we have developed from them has boosted our material standard of living beyond what our ancestors could have dreamed, has eased constraints on travel, and has helped lengthen our life spans. It has, however, also caused harm to the environment and human health. Concern over these impacts is a prime reason many scientists, environmental advocates, businesspeople, and policy makers are increasingly looking toward renewable sources of energy that exert less impact on natural systems.

FIGURE 16.14
Concerns about the impacts of tar sand exploitation on wildlife came to a head in 2008 when hundreds of migratory birds died after landing in an oily, toxic tailings pond at Fort McMurray, Alberta, similar to the one shown here **(a)**. Only a few of the oiled sea ducks managed to survive **(b)**.

(a) An oil sand tailings pond in Alberta

(b) Rescuing oiled sea ducks

Fossil fuel emissions cause pollution and drive climate change

When we burn fossil fuels, we alter flux rates in Earth's carbon cycle. We essentially take carbon that has been retired into a long-term reservoir underground and release it into the air. This occurs as carbon from within the hydrocarbon molecules of fossil fuels unites with oxygen from the atmosphere during combustion, producing carbon dioxide (CO_2). Carbon dioxide is a greenhouse gas, and CO_2 released from fossil fuel combustion warms our planet and drives changes in global climate. Because global climate change may have diverse, severe, and widespread ecological and socioeconomic impacts, carbon dioxide pollution (**FIGURE 16.15**) is becoming recognized as the greatest environmental impact of fossil fuel use.

Fossil fuels release more than carbon dioxide when they burn. Methane is a potent greenhouse gas, and other air pollutants resulting from fossil fuel combustion can have serious consequences for human health and the environment. Deposition of mercury and other pollutants from coal-fired power plants is increasingly recognized as a substantial health risk. The burning of fossil fuels in power plants and vehicles releases sulphur dioxide and nitrogen oxides, which contribute to industrial and photochemical smog and to acidic deposition.

We have already employed technologies, such as catalytic converters, to cut down on vehicle exhaust pollution. Gasoline combustion in automobiles releases

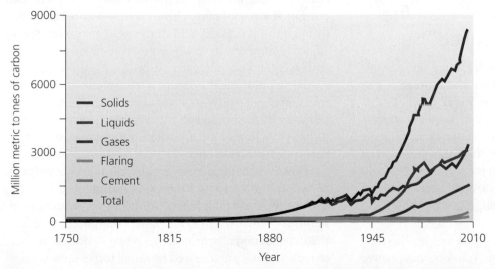

FIGURE 16.15 As industrialization has proceeded, and as population and energy consumption have grown, emissions from fossil fuels have risen dramatically. Here, worldwide emissions of carbon are subdivided by their source (liquid oil, solid coal, or natural gas). Also included are cement manufacture and flaring of natural gas. *Data are from Boden, T.A., G. Marland, and R.J. Andres (2010) Global, Regional, and National Fossil-Fuel CO_2 Emissions. Carbon Dioxide Information Analysis Center, Oak Ridge National Laboratory, U.S. Department of Energy, Oak Ridge, Tenn., U.S.A. doi 10.3334/CDIAC/00001_V2010*

pollutants that irritate the nose, throat, and lungs. Some hydrocarbons, such as benzene and toluene, are carcinogenic to laboratory animals and likely also to people. In addition, gases, such as hydrogen sulphide, can evaporate from crude oil, irritate the eyes and throat, and cause asphyxiation. Crude oil also often contains trace amounts of known poisons, such as lead and arsenic. As a result, workers at drilling operations, refineries, and other jobs that entail frequent exposure to oil or its products can develop serious health problems, including cancer.

Fossil fuels can pollute water as well as air. Atmospheric deposition of pollutants exerts many impacts on freshwater ecosystems. Moreover, oil from non-point sources—such as industries, homes, automobiles, gas stations, and businesses—runs off roadways and enters rivers and sewage treatment facilities to be discharged eventually into the ocean. Although most spilled oil results from these non-point sources, large catastrophic oil spills can have significant impacts on the marine environment. Crude oil's toxicity to most plants and animals can lead to high mortality. This was the case with the massive British Petroleum *Deepwater Horizon* oil spill and leak of 2010, which caused the immediate deaths and injuries of thousands of birds, turtles, fish, and shellfish, as well as harming marine mammals and corals. Longer-term concerns centre on the ultimate fate of the oil as well as the *dispersants*—chemicals (also toxic) that were used to induce the oil slicks to break up and disperse through the water column.

Oil can also contaminate groundwater supplies, such as when leaks from oil operations penetrate deeply into soil. Of even greater concern are the thousands of underground storage tanks containing petroleum products that have leaked, threatening drinking water supplies. In 2011, such concerns led the U.S. State Department to impose a significant delay on the multi-billion-dollar Keystone XL oil pipeline project.

Some emissions from fossil fuel burning can be "captured"

One relatively new technology for "cleaning up" carbon-based fuel sources is **carbon capture and storage (CCS)** or *carbon capture and sequestration*. Recall from our discussion of biogeochemical cycles that **sequestration** is a term that refers to the storage of materials in geologic reservoirs on a long timescale. In this case, the material of interest is carbon—primarily in the form of CO_2—and the goal is to prevent some of the carbon generated by the burning of fossil fuels from entering the atmosphere and contributing to global warming.

In a nutshell, what would happen is that the CO_2 emitted by, for example, a traditional coal-burning power plant would be captured before it reached the atmosphere and then diverted to a storage reservoir. The most likely reservoirs are the deep ocean, which already acts as a reservoir for atmospheric carbon dioxide, and geologic formations deep underground (**FIGURE 16.16**).

Industry analysts predict that 80–90% of the carbon dioxide emissions from large emitters like coal-fired generators could be captured and diverted, as compared with a power plant without CCS technology. This would go a long way toward helping Canada meet its commitments in the Kyoto Protocol—at least in the short term, while we attempt to transition to more renewable energy sources.

Many environmentalists are skeptical about CCS, arguing that the technology is unproven and that the true environmental impacts of reinjecting carbon dioxide into the ground or into ocean water are not known. Some point to the possibility of further acidification of ocean water (because carbon dioxide mixed with water yields carbonic acid). Additionally, underwater capture and storage would be temporary; deep water does not stay in place but moves, mixes, and ultimately upwells to the surface as part of the global thermohaline circulation. With regard to storage underground, some experts have expressed concern that extraction processes (fracking) have so extensively fractured rock units near Alberta's tar sands that they would no longer be suitable for the purpose of CCS. Still others argue that the approach is fundamentally flawed because it takes the burden off large emitters and serves only to prolong our dependence on fossil fuels rather than facilitating a shift to renewables.

Coal mining affects the environment

The mining of coal also has substantial impacts on natural systems and human well-being. Surface strip-mining can destroy large swaths of habitat and cause extensive soil erosion. It also can cause chemical runoff into waterways through the process of **acid drainage**. This occurs when sulphide minerals in newly exposed rock surfaces react with oxygen and rainwater to produce sulphuric acid. As the sulphuric acid runs off, it leaches metals from the rocks, many of which are toxic to organisms in high concentrations. Acid drainage is a natural phenomenon, but its rate accelerates greatly when mining exposes many new rock surfaces at once.

Government regulations require mining companies to restore strip-mined land following mining, but impacts can be severe and long-lasting just the same. Mountaintop removal (**FIGURE 16.17**) can have even greater impacts than conventional strip-mining. When countless tonnes of rock and soil are removed from the top of a mountain,

Coal-fired electricity

Chemical & fertilizer plants

Oil & gas production

Steel & cement production

CO₂

Impermeable cap rock

Groundwater

Enhanced oil recovery

Depleted oil or gas reservoir

Deep saline aquifer (2km)

FIGURE 16.16 CCS provides a possible mechanism for reducing the harmful environmental impacts of fossil fuel use.

it is difficult to keep material from sliding downhill, where immense areas of habitat can be degraded or destroyed and creek beds can be polluted and clogged.

Whereas mountaintop removal threatens the welfare of nearby residents, subsurface mining raises health concerns for miners. Underground coal mining is one of our society's most dangerous occupations. Besides risking injury or death from collapsing shafts and tunnels and from dynamite blasts and coal dust or methane explosions, miners constantly inhale coal dust in the enclosed spaces of mines, which can lead to respiratory diseases, including fatal black lung disease.

The costs of alleviating all these health and environmental impacts are high, and the public eventually pays

FIGURE 16.17
Strip-mining in some areas is taking place on massive scales, such that entire mountain peaks are levelled, as at this site in West Virginia. Such "mountaintop removal" can cause enormous amounts of erosion into waterways that flow into surrounding valleys, affecting ecosystems over large areas, as well as the people who live there.

them in an inefficient manner. The reason is that the costs are generally not accounted for in the market prices of fossil fuels, which are kept low through government subsidies to extraction companies.

Oil and gas extraction also alter the environment

Much more than drilling is involved in the development of an oil or gas field. Road networks must be constructed, and many sites may be explored in the course of prospecting. The extensive infrastructure needed to support a full-scale drilling operation typically includes housing for workers, access roads, transport pipelines, and waste piles for removed soil. Ponds may be constructed for collecting the toxic sludge that remains after the useful components of oil have been removed. At extraction sites for coalbed methane, groundwater is pumped out to free gas to rise, but salty groundwater dumped on the surface can contaminate soil and kill vegetation over large areas.

Many onshore North American oil reserves are located in Arctic or semi-arid areas. Plants grow slowly in tundra and semi-desert ecosystems, so even minor impacts can have long-lasting repercussions. Tundra vegetation at some northern oil developments, such as Prudhoe Bay in Alaska, still has not fully recovered from temporary roads last used 30 years ago during the exploratory phase of development. Studies at Prudhoe Bay also show that female caribou and their calves avoid all parts of the oil complex, including its roads, sometimes detouring many kilometres to do so. These studies also show that the reproductive rate of female caribou in the Prudhoe Bay region is lower than for those in undeveloped areas in

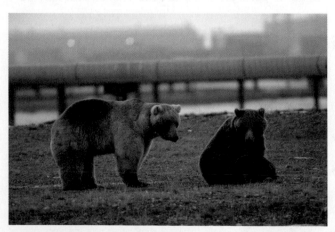

FIGURE 16.18
Like the Mackenzie River Valley, Alaska's North Slope is home to a variety of large mammals, including grizzly bears, polar bears, wolves, Arctic foxes, and large herds of caribou. How oil development may affect these animals is a controversial issue, and scientific studies are ongoing. Grizzly bears, such as the ones shown here, have been found near, or even walking atop, the Trans-Alaska Pipeline.

Alaska. As a result, although the herd near Prudhoe Bay has increased over the past 25 years, it has not increased as much as have herds in some other parts of Alaska.

There is no way of knowing how the Prudhoe Bay herd would have performed in the absence of development; that is, there is no control, as there would be for a manipulative experiment. It is difficult, therefore, to draw conclusions about the impacts of oil development on caribou and other wild animals, such as the grizzly bear (**FIGURE 16.18**), at remote oil developments in places like Prudhoe Bay or the Mackenzie River Valley. It can be anticipated that activities like road building, oil pad construction, worker presence, oil spills, accidental fires, trash buildup, permafrost melting, offroad vehicle trails, and dust from roads would have a significant impact on both vegetation and wildlife.

Political, Social, and Economic Aspects

The political, social, and economic consequences of fossil fuel use are numerous, varied, and far-reaching. Our discussion focuses on several negative consequences of fossil fuel use and dependence, but it is important to bear in mind that their use has enabled much of the world's population to achieve a higher material standard of living than ever before. It is also important to ask in each case whether switching to more renewable sources of energy would solve existing problems.

Oil supply and prices affect the economies of nations

Virtually all our modern technologies and services depend in some way on fossil fuels. Putting all of one's eggs in one basket is always a risky strategy. The fact that our economies are utterly tied to fossil fuels means that we are vulnerable to supplies' becoming suddenly unavailable or extremely costly. Nations that lack adequate fossil fuel reserves of their own are especially vulnerable. For instance, Germany, France, South Korea, and Japan consume far more energy than they produce and thus rely almost entirely on imports for their continued economic well-being (**FIGURE 16.19**). Canada is both an importer and an exporter of fossil fuels in different forms, but imports are outweighed by exports.

Reliance on foreign oil means that seller nations can control energy prices, forcing buyer nations to pay more and more as supplies dwindle. This became clear in 1973, when the *Organization of the Petroleum Exporting Countries (OPEC)* resolved to stop selling oil to the United

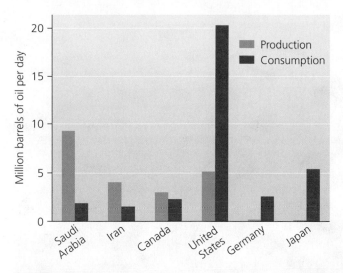

FIGURE 16.19
Japan, Germany, and the United States are among nations that consume far more oil than they produce. Iran, Saudi Arabia, and Canada are among countries that produce more oil than they consume and are able to export oil to high-consumption countries. Data from U.S. Energy Information Administration. 2007. *Annual Energy Review 2006.* Washington, DC.

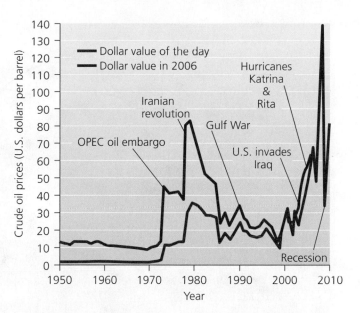

FIGURE 16.20
World oil prices have fluctuated greatly over the decades, often because of political and economic events in oil-producing countries. The greatest price hikes in recent times have resulted from wars and unrest in the oil-rich Middle East. Data from U.S. Energy Information Administration

States as a consequence of U.S. support of Israel. The embargo created panic in the West and caused oil prices to skyrocket (**FIGURE 16.20**), spurring inflation.

When Hurricanes Katrina and Rita slammed into the Gulf Coast in 2005, they damaged offshore platforms and refineries, causing oil and gas prices to spike significantly. The economic ripple effects served to remind us yet again how much we rely on a steady and ever-increasing supply of petroleum.

With the majority of world oil reserves located in the politically volatile Middle East, political instabilities there are a concern for policy makers. The world's third-largest holder of oil reserves, at 10%, is Iraq, which is why many people around the world believe that the American-led invasion of that nation in 2003 was motivated primarily to secure access to oil. Major petroleum trade relations among nations and regions of the world are depicted in **FIGURE 16.21**.

Residents may or may not benefit from fossil fuel resources

The extraction of fossil fuels can be extremely lucrative; many of the world's wealthiest corporations deal in fossil fuel energy or related industries. These industries provide jobs to millions of employees and supply dividends to millions of investors. Development can potentially yield economic benefits for people who live in petroleum-bearing areas, as well. In addition to the potential for jobs from the Mackenzie River Valley gas pipeline project,

for example, the federal government has promised at least $500 million in assistance to residents of the area. Supporters argue that income and federal assistance related to the project could pay for health care, police and fire protection, and other services that are currently scarce in this remote region.

In many parts of the world where fossil fuels have been extracted, local residents have not seen great benefits but instead have suffered. When multinational corporations extract oil or gas in developing countries, paying those countries' governments for access, the money often does not trickle down to residents of the regions where the extraction takes place. Moreover, oil-rich developing countries, such as Ecuador, Venezuela, and Nigeria, tend to have few environmental regulations, and existing regulations may go unenforced if a government does not want to risk losing the large sums of money associated with oil development.

In Nigeria, oil was discovered in 1958 in the territory of the Ogoni, one of Nigeria's native peoples, and the Shell Oil Company moved in to develop oil fields. Although Shell extracted $30 billion of oil from Ogoni land over the years, the Ogoni still live in poverty, with no running water or electricity. The profits from oil extraction on Ogoni land went to Shell and to the military dictatorships of Nigeria. The development resulted in oil spills, noise, and constantly burning gas flares, all of which caused illness among people living nearby. From 1962 until his death in 1995, Ogoni activist and leader Ken Saro-Wiwa worked for fair compensation to the Ogoni for oil extraction and environmental degradation on their land. After years of

FIGURE 16.21   The global trade in oil is lopsided; relatively few nations account for most exports, and some nations are highly dependent on others for energy. Canada imports some North Sea oil while exporting more to the United States. Numbers in the figure represent millions of metric tons. Data from British Petroleum. 2007. *Statistical review of world energy 2007.*

persecution by the Nigerian government, Saro-Wiwa was arrested in 1994, given a trial universally regarded as a sham, and put to death by a military tribunal.

We need to conserve energy and find renewable sources

Fossil fuel supplies are limited, and their use and our continued dependence on them have health, environmental, political, and socioeconomic consequences. Until our society makes the transition to renewable energy sources, we will need to find ways to minimize the expenditure of energy from our dwindling fossil fuel resources. **Energy conservation** is the practice of reducing energy use to extend the lifetimes of our nonrenewable energy supplies, to be less wasteful, and to reduce our environmental impact.

Many people first saw the value of conserving energy following the OPEC embargo of 1973–1974. In the subsequent three decades, however, many of the conservation initiatives that followed the oil crisis were abandoned. Without high market prices and an immediate threat of shortages, people lacked economic motivation to

conserve. Government funding for research into alternative energy sources decreased, speed limits increased, and countless proposals to raise the mandated average fuel efficiency of vehicles failed. The average fuel efficiency of new vehicles worsened, from 10.64 L/100 km in 1988 to 11.21 L/100 km in 2006, primarily as a result of increased sales of light trucks and sport utility vehicles (SUVs)(averaging 12.79 L/100 km) relative to cars (averaging 9.57 L/100 km).

All of this is changing, though, particularly in light of steadily increasing oil prices. In 2008, oil traded at a record high price of $147 per barrel (then declining, but soaring again in 2011), and increases were translated directly to gas station pumps. A 2008 survey of Canadian spending habits conducted by Investors Group, the largest mutual group company in Canada, revealed that 83% of Canadians planned to buy a more fuel-efficient car next time around, 51% had been cutting down on driving, and 44% planned to change their holiday plans in response to high fuel prices.[13] These types of consumer changes are happening with equal fury in the United States, and as a result the light truck and SUV industry in North America underwent a sudden, severe contraction, with a number of production facilities closing.

weighing the issues

MORE KILOMETRES, LESS GAS

If you drive an automobile, how many kilometres does it travel per 100 L of gasoline? If you drove 2400 km (the distance from Montreal to Winnipeg) in a car with a fuel efficiency of 8.33 L/100 km, instead of making the trip in an SUV with a fuel efficiency of 12.5 L/100 km, how much less gasoline would you have to buy? How much money would you save on the trip? How much would you save on the amount you typically drive in a year? Do you think that the government should raise taxes on gasoline sales as an incentive to consumers to conserve energy?

Transportation accounts for two-thirds of oil use and more than a quarter of energy use in Canada, and passenger vehicles consume more than half this energy. The vast distances of the Canadian landscape add to the problem. Thus, the failure to improve vehicular fuel economy over the past 20 years, despite the existence of technology to do so, has added greatly to oil consumption. This is unfortunate because the inefficient use of gasoline in auto engines wastes oil that we could put to better use in manufacturing countless products that enhance our lives. Transportation also accounts for about a third of Canada's greenhouse gas emissions, an increasing concern as we strive to meet our international commitments regarding climate change.[14]

Personal choice and increased efficiency are two routes to conservation

Energy conservation can be accomplished in two primary ways. As individuals, we can make conscious choices to reduce our own energy consumption. Examples include driving less, turning off lights when rooms are not being used, turning down thermostats, and investing in more-efficient machines and appliances. For any given individual or business, reducing energy consumption can save money while also helping to conserve resources.

As a society, we can conserve energy by making our energy-consuming devices and processes more efficient. Currently, more than two-thirds of the fossil fuel energy we use is simply lost, as waste heat, in automobiles and power plants. In the case of automobiles, we already possess the technology to increase fuel efficiency far above the current North American average of 900 km/100 L.

We could accomplish this with more efficient gasoline engines, lightweight materials, continuously variable transmissions, and alternative technology vehicles, such as electric/gasoline hybrids or vehicles that use hydrogen fuel cells.

We can also vastly improve the efficiency of our power plants. One way is to use **cogeneration**, in which excess heat produced during the generation of electricity is captured and used to heat workplaces and homes and to produce other kinds of power. Cogeneration can almost double the efficiency of a power plant. The same is true of *coal gasification* and *combined cycle* generation. In this process, coal is treated to create hot gases that turn a gas turbine, while the hot exhaust of this turbine heats water to drive a conventional steam turbine.

In homes and public buildings, a significant amount of heat is lost in winter and gained in summer because of inadequate insulation (**FIGURE 16.22**). Improvements in the design of homes and offices can reduce the energy required to heat and cool them. Such design changes can involve the building's location, the colour of its roof (light colours keep buildings cooler by reflecting the Sun's rays), and its insulation.

Among consumer products, scores of appliances, from refrigerators to light bulbs, have been reengineered through the years to increase energy efficiency. Energy-efficient lighting, for example, can reduce energy use by 80%, and new energy-efficient appliances have already reduced per-person home electricity use below what it was in the 1970s. Even so, there remains room for further improvement.

FIGURE 16.22
Many of our homes and offices could be made more energy-efficient. One way to determine how much heat a building is losing is to take a photograph that records energy in the infrared portion of the electromagnetic spectrum. In such a photograph, or *thermogram* (shown here), white, yellow, and red signify hot and warm temperatures at the surface of the house, whereas blue and green shades signify cold and cool temperatures. The white, yellow, and red colours indicate areas where heat is escaping.

CANADIAN ENVIRONMENTAL PERSPECTIVES

Mary Griffiths

Mary Griffiths spent much of her career at the Pembina Institute looking for ways to reduce the environmental impacts of fossil fuels and raise awareness about the need for wise management.

- ■ **Environmental policy analyst**
- ■ **Energy researcher**
- ■ **Author**

Circumstances and opportunities have led Mary Griffiths to "reinvent" herself and her career a number of times in her life. Throughout it all, however, she has maintained her childhood love of nature and her commitment to raising awareness about the interrelationships between people and the natural environment.

In the 1960s—before there was such as thing as a degree in environmental science—Griffiths earned a Ph.D. in geography and subsequently taught the subject for a number of years at the University of Exeter, England. She remembers teaching about the decline of the Ogallala Aquifer beneath the High Plains of the United States and thinking, at the time, how short-sighted it was to be depleting this critical resource. Many years later when she learned about the enormous quantities of

fresh water that were being used in Alberta to get oil out of the ground, she felt that it was very important to make sure that the aquifers were not being adversely affected.

Moving with her young family to the Netherlands, Griffiths helped set up a small environmental group to educate individuals and municipalities on the harmful effects of pesticides. "I have always believed in sound research as the basis for action, as well as in the power of leading by example. If one municipal authority could successfully manage its public open spaces without using pesticides, others could do it, too," she says.

The family's next move, to Canada this time, found Griffiths working with the environment and other portfolios for the Liberal Caucus at the Alberta Legislature. Occasionally she sought advice from staff at the Pembina Institute, whose mandate "is to advance sustainable energy solutions through innovative research, education, consulting and advocacy."[15] An opening at Pembina for a new policy analyst gave Griffiths the opportunity to focus entirely on environmental issues once more and to devote her research efforts to finding sustainable energy solutions.

As a senior policy analyst in the Energy Solutions group at Pembina, Griffiths became an expert on the environmental impacts of fossil fuel use, especially the impacts on water. She contributed to evaluations of the environmental impacts of energy projects, including oil sands developments and coal-fired power plants. She has written several books, including *When the Oilpatch Comes to Your Backyard: A Citizens' Guide* (2004), and has co-authored numerous reports on topics ranging from landowner rights to coalbed methane development, the use of water by the oil industry, and carbon

capture and storage. She has served on several government committees, including the Alberta Minister of the Environment's Environmental Protection Advisory Committee and Alberta Environment's Advisory Committee on Water Use Practice and Policy. In 2002, Griffiths received a Canadian Environment Award for her work on clean air issues and was awarded the Alberta Centennial Medal in 2005.[16]

Now retired from the Pembina Institute, Griffiths continues to carry out research on energy and water. She is convinced that water resources will come under increasing pressure in the future and hopes to encourage more and better research and the formulation of strong policies to ensure that freshwater aquifers are protected and managed in a sustainable manner. Her overall goal is to raise awareness about the need for wise management—in all sectors—to protect the environment. "We must scrutinize all our corporate, government, and individual planning decisions, to see if they meet our long-term goal of sustainability. And we should start planning for 2020 today."[17]

"Knowledge is the foundation for environmental action."[18]—**Mary Griffiths**

Thinking About Environmental Perspectives

Do you agree with Mary Griffiths that all environmental action should be founded on research and knowledge? Why is research so important in making environmental decisions and formulating environmental policies? How can researchers in science and social science communicate their findings to policy makers in understandable ways?

While manufacturers can improve the energy efficiency of appliances, consumers need to "vote with their wallets" by purchasing these energy-efficient appliances. Decisions by consumers to purchase energy-efficient products are crucial in keeping those products commercially available. For the individual consumer, studies show that the slightly higher cost of buying energy-

efficient washing machines is rapidly offset by savings on water and electricity bills. On the national level, France, Great Britain, and many other developed countries have standards of living equal to that of Canada, but they use much less energy per capita. This disparity indicates that Canadian citizens could significantly reduce their energy consumption without decreasing their quality of life.

Conclusion

It is often said that reducing our energy use is equivalent to finding a new oil reserve. Indeed, conserving energy is better than finding a new reserve because it lessens impacts on the environment while extending our access to fossil fuels.

However, energy conservation does not add to our supply of available fuel. Regardless of how much we conserve, we will still need energy, and it will need to come from somewhere. The only sustainable way of guaranteeing ourselves a reliable long-term supply of energy is to ensure sufficiently rapid development of renewable energy sources, which we will consider in greater detail in the next chapter.

Over the past 200 years, fossil fuels have helped us build the complex industrialized societies we enjoy today. However, we are now approaching a turning point in history: Our production of fossil fuels will begin to decline. We can respond to this new challenge in creative ways, encouraging conservation and developing alternative energy sources. Or we can continue our current dependence on fossil fuels and wait until they near depletion before we try to develop new technologies and ways of life. The path we choose will have far-reaching consequences for human health and well-being, for Earth's climate, and for our environment.

The ongoing debates over projects like the Mackenzie River Valley natural gas pipeline are microcosms of this debate over our energy future. Fortunately, there is not simply a trade-off between benefits of energy for us and harm to the environment, climate, and health. Instead, as evidence builds that renewable energy sources are becoming increasingly feasible and economical, it becomes easier to envision giving up our reliance on fossil fuels and charting a win–win future for humanity and the environment.

REVIEWING OBJECTIVES

You should now be able to:

Identify the principal energy sources that we use

- A variety of renewable and nonrenewable energy sources are available to us.
- Since the Industrial Revolution, nonrenewable fossil fuels—including oil, natural gas, and coal—have become our primary sources of energy.
- Fossil fuels are formed very slowly as buried organic matter is chemically transformed by heat, pressure, and/or anaerobic decomposition.
- In evaluating energy sources, it is important to compare the amount of energy obtained from them with the amount invested in their extraction and production.

Describe the nature and origin of coal and evaluate its extraction and use

- Coal is our most abundant fossil fuel. It results from organic matter that undergoes compression but little decomposition.
- The first fossil fuel to be widely used for heating homes and powering industry, coal is used today principally to generate electricity.
- Coal is mined underground and strip-mined from the land surface.
- Coal comes in different types and varies in its composition. Combustion of coal that is high in contaminants emits toxic air pollution.

Describe the nature and origin of natural gas and evaluate its extraction and use

- Natural gas consists mostly of methane and can be formed in two ways.
- Use of natural gas is growing rapidly, and it is cleaner burning than coal or oil.
- Natural gas often occurs with oil and coal deposits, is extracted in similar ways, and becomes depleted in similar ways.

Describe the nature and origin of oil and evaluate its extraction, use, and future availability

- Crude oil is a thick, liquid mixture of hydrocarbons that is formed underground under certain temperature and pressure conditions.
- Scientists locate fossil fuel deposits by analyzing subterranean geology. Geologists estimate total reserves, as well as the technically and economically recoverable portions of those reserves.
- Oil drilling often involves primary extraction followed by secondary extraction, in which gas or liquid is injected into the ground to help force up additional oil.
- Petroleum-based products, from gasoline to clothing to plastics, are everywhere in our daily lives.
- Components of crude oil are separated in refineries to produce a wide variety of fuel types.

- We have depleted nearly half the world's oil. Once we pass the peak and production slows, the gap between rising demand and falling supply may pose immense economic and social challenges for our society.

Describe the nature, origin, and potential of alternative fossil fuel types and technologies

- Tar sands, abundant in Canada's West, can be mined and processed into synthetic oil.
- Oil shale is abundant in the western United States.
- Methane hydrate is another type of methane gas.

Outline and assess environmental impacts of fossil fuel use

- Emissions from fossil fuel combustion pollute air, pose human health risks, and drive global climate change.
- Oil is a major contributor to water pollution.
- Strip-mining and mountaintop removal can devastate ecosystems locally or regionally, and acid drainage from coal mines pollutes waterways.
- Development for oil and gas extraction exerts various environmental impacts.

Evaluate political, social, and economic impacts of fossil fuel use

- Today's societies are so reliant on fossil fuel energy that sudden restrictions in oil supplies can have major economic consequences.
- Nations that consume more fossil fuels than they produce are especially vulnerable to supply restrictions.
- People living in areas of fossil fuel extraction do not always benefit from their extraction.

Specify strategies for conserving energy and enhancing efficiency

- Energy conservation involves both personal choices and efficient technologies. These two forces interact through the market power of consumer choice.
- Increases in automotive fuel efficiency and efficiency in power plant combustion could help us conserve immense amounts of oil.
- Conservation helps lengthen our access to fossil fuels and reduce environmental impact, but to build a sustainable society we will also need to shift to renewable energy sources.

TESTING YOUR COMPREHENSION

1. Why are fossil fuels our most prevalent source of energy today? Why are they considered nonrenewable sources of energy?
2. How are fossil fuels formed? How do environmental conditions determine what type of fossil fuel is formed in a given location? Why are fossil fuels often concentrated in localized deposits?
3. Describe how net energy differs from energy returned on investment (EROI). Why are these concepts important when evaluating energy sources?
4. Describe how coal is used to generate electricity.
5. Why is natural gas often extracted simultaneously with other fossil fuels? What constraints on its extraction does it share with oil?
6. How do geologists estimate the total amount of oil reserves that remain underground? How is the "tech-

nically recoverable" oil different from the "economically recoverable" oil?
7. How do we create petroleum products? Provide examples of several of these products.
8. What is Hubbert's peak? Why do many experts think we are about to pass the global production peak for oil? What consequences could there be for our society if we do not transition soon to renewable energy sources?
9. List three environmental impacts of fossil fuel production and consumption. Compare some of the contrasting views of scientists regarding the environmental impacts of the Mackenzie River Valley natural gas pipeline.
10. Describe two main approaches to energy conservation; give specific examples of each.

THINKING IT THROUGH

1. Roughly how much oil is left in the world, and how much longer can we expect to use it? What steps should we take to avoid energy shortages in the future?

2. Compare the effects of coal and oil consumption on the environment. Which process do you think has ultimately been more detrimental to the environment, oil extraction or coal mining, and why? What steps could governments, industries, and individuals take to reduce environmental impacts?

3. If Canada and other developed countries reduced dependence on foreign oil and on fossil fuels in general, do you think that their economies would benefit or suffer? Might your answer be different for the short term and the long term? What factors come into play in trying to make such a judgment?

4. Do some additional research and contrast the experiences of the Ogoni people of Nigeria with those of the citizens of the Northwest Territories. How have they been similar and different, thus far? Do you think businesses or governments should take steps to ensure that local people benefit from oil-drilling operations? How could they do so?

5. You have been elected to be a negotiator on behalf of Aboriginal interests in the ongoing discussions about the development of the Mackenzie River Valley natural gas pipeline. What will your position be? Explain it to another negotiator who disagrees with you.

6. Would it be more difficult to contain and remediate a major oil spill, like the BP *Deepwater Horizon* spill of 2010, if it were to happen in the Beaufort Sea or in deep water off the coast of Newfoundland, compared to the Gulf of Mexico? What would be some of the important differences?

7. Throughout this book we have asked you to imagine yourself in various roles. This time we ask you simply to be yourself. Given the information in this chapter on petroleum supplies, consumption, and depletion, what actions, if any, do you plan to take to prepare yourself for changes in our society that may come about as oil production declines? Describe in detail how you think your life may change, and suggest one thing you could do to help reduce negative impacts of oil depletion on our society.

INTERPRETING GRAPHS AND DATA

The fossil fuels that we burn today were formed long ago from buried organic matter. However, only a small fraction of the original organic carbon remains in the coal, oil, or natural gas that is formed. Thus, it requires approximately 90 metric tonnes of ancient organic matter—so-called paleoproduction—to result in just 3.8 L of gasoline. The graph presents estimates of the amount of paleoproduction required to produce the fossil fuels humans have used each year over the past 250 years.

1. Estimate in what year the annual consumption of paleoproduction, represented by our combustion of fossil fuels, surpassed Earth's current annual net primary production (NPP).

2. In 2000, approximately how many times greater than global NPP was our consumption of paleoproduction?

3. If on average it takes 7000 units of paleoproduction to produce 1 unit of fossil fuel, estimate the total carbon content of the fossil fuel consumed in 2000. How does this amount compare to global NPP?

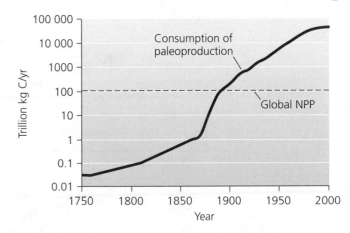

Annual human consumption of paleoproduction by fossil fuel combustion (red line), 1750–2000. The dashed line indicates current annual net primary production (NPP) for the entire planet.
Source: Data from Dukes, J. 2003. Burning buried sunshine: Human consumption of ancient solar energy. Climatic Change 61:31–44.

CHAPTER ENDNOTES

1. Mackenzie Gas Project, www.mackenziegasproject. com/theProject/index.html#

2. CBC News In-depth, *The Mackenzie Valley Pipeline*, www.cbc.ca/news/background/mackenzievalley_pipeline/index.html, updated March 12, 2007.

3. CBC News In-depth, *The Mackenzie Valley Pipeline*, www.cbc.ca/news/background/mackenzievalley_pipeline/index.html, updated March 12, 2007.

4. CBC News In-depth, *The Mackenzie Valley Pipeline*, www.cbc.ca/news/background/mackenzievalley_pipeline/index.html, updated March 12, 2007.

5. Mackenzie Gas Project, www.mackenziegasproject. com/whoWeAre/index.htm

6. CBC News In-depth, *The Mackenzie Valley Pipeline*, www.cbc.ca/news/background/mackenzievalley_pipeline/index.html, updated March 12, 2007.

7. Nature Canada: Take Action! The Mackenzie River Gas Project, www.naturecanada.ca/take_action_raise_voice_protect.asp

8. Coal Association of Canada, www.coal.ca/content/index.php?option=com_content&task=view&id=43&Itemid=40

9. CCTRM Canada's Clean Coal Technology Roadmap, Natural Resources Canada, 2005, www.cleancoaltrm. gc.ca

10. Petroleum History Society, *Six Historical Events in the First 100 Years of Canada's Petroleum Industry*, www. petroleumhistory.ca/history/wells.html#springs

11. Petroleum History Society, *Six Historical Events in the First 100 Years of Canada's Petroleum Industry*, www. petroleumhistory.ca/history/wells.html#springs

12. Tariq Piracha, Natural Resources Canada, *Natural Elements: Squeezing Water from Oil Sands—Resources Management in Petroleum Development*, modified 2008-05-06, www.nrcan-rncan.gc.ca/com/elements/issues/22/wateau-eng.php

13. Canwest News Service, June 17, 2008, as referenced in the *Montreal Gazette*.

14. The State of Energy Efficiency in Canada, *Office of Energy Efficiency Report 2006*, Natural Resources Canada, www.oee.nrcan.gc.ca/publications/statistics/see06/transportation.cfm?attr=0

15. The Pembina Institute, *About Pembina: Our Mission*, www.pembina.org

16. Pembina Institute, *Bio: Mary Griffiths*, http://re.pembina.org/author/43

17. *The Edmonton Journal*, p. 1, 2005, "What Will Edmonton Look Like in 2015?" posted on Pembina Institute Renewable Energy Op-Ed page, http://re.pembina.org/op-ed/1152

18. *Canadian Geographic*, from the citation for the Canadian Environment Award, Mary Griffiths, www.canadiangeographic.ca/cea/archives/archives_individual.asp?id=54

MyEnvironmentPlace

Go to **www.myenvironmentplace.ca** where you will find quizzes, animations, your Pearson eText, and more.

(a) Low tide

(b) High tide

The Bay of Fundy is shown here at low tide (a) and high tide (b).

Upon successfully completing this chapter, you will be able to

- Discuss the reasons for seeking alternatives to fossil fuels
- Summarize the contributions to world energy supplies of conventional alternatives to fossil fuels
- Describe the scale, methods, and environmental impacts of hydroelectric power, nuclear power, and biomass energy
- Outline the major "new renewable" alternative sources of energy and assess their potential for growth

- Describe a variety of new biomass, solar, wind, geothermal, and ocean energy technologies, and outline their advantages and disadvantages
- Explain the benefits of hydrogen and fuel cells and assess future options for energy storage and transportation

Water rushes from the sluice gates at the Annapolis Tidal Power Station in Nova Scotia.

Hudson Bay

CANADA

Bay of Fundy

CENTRAL CASE:
HARNESSING TIDAL ENERGY AT THE BAY OF FUNDY

"I believe that water will one day be employed as fuel, that hydrogen and oxygen which constitute it, used singly or together, will furnish an inexhaustible source of heat and light. . . . Water will be the coal of the future."

—JULES VERNE, IN *THE MYSTERIOUS ISLAND*, 1874

"Not only will atomic power be released, but someday we will harness the rise and fall of the tides and imprison the rays of the Sun."

—THOMAS A. EDISON, 1921

"EXTREME HAZARD," reads the posted sign. "Incoming tide rises 5 feet [1.5 m] per hour and may leave you stranded for 8 hours." Not only do ocean tidewaters rise quickly, but nowhere else in the world is the difference between low tide and high tide as great

as here, in the Bay of Fundy on Canada's Atlantic coast (see chapter-opening photo).

The Bay of Fundy is a long, narrow bay that separates the provinces of Nova Scotia and New Brunswick, just touching the U.S. state of Maine. The name "fundy" is thought to have come from early Portuguese explorers, who called it the "deep river," or *rio fundo*.

The long, narrow, deep configuration of the bay is responsible for its extreme tidal variation. When the tide comes in, a large volume of ocean water (about 100 billion tonnes) rushes in, against the outgoing freshwater flow, up the length of the narrowly constricted bay (see satellite photos). This phenomenon is called a *tidal bore*. The result is a very large vertical difference between high and low tide (up to 17 m near the extreme head of the bay, but more typically about 12 m in the main part of the bay). The large tidal range makes this one of the most suitable locations in the world for generating power from ocean tides.

(a) Low Tide   **(b) High Tide**

Satellite images show low tide (a) and high tide (b) in the Bay of Fundy.

The Bay of Fundy is the site of one of only three operating tidal power plants in the world. The Annapolis Royal Tidal Power Generating Station, owned by Nova Scotia Power, is located on a small side-basin on the Nova Scotia side of the main bay, by the town of Annapolis Royal. The power station, which opened in 1984, works on the same principle as normal hydro-electric power generation—the movement of rushing water turns the blades of a turbine, which, in turn, runs a generator to produce electricity.

In the case of tidal power, a *sluice*—like a dam with movable openings—is constructed across a narrow part of the water body. When the tide comes in, the sluice gates are opened and the water flows through. At high tide, the gates are closed. When the tide starts to go out, the water above the sluice is held behind the closed gates. Once there is a sufficient difference in water level (1 m, in the case of the Annapolis power station), the gates are opened. The water rushes out from behind the sluice to join the rest of the outgoing tide (see photo), turning the turbine blades in the process. At this station, Nova Scotia Power generates enough power to run about 4000 homes.[1]

Many of the negative impacts of traditional hydroelectric power generation are associated with the creation of large reservoirs of standing water behind dams; tidal power does not entail these negative impacts, because the water has to be retained behind the sluice gates only for brief periods. The few negative environmental impacts of tidal power generation are mainly associated with interference in the normal currents of the water body. In one case, for example, a whale is thought to have died after following some fish through the sluice gates and becoming trapped.

Nova Scotia Power and its partners are among those working on new *in-stream* tidal power technologies. These approaches involve underwater turbines—like underwater windmills—that would eliminate the need to construct a visible dam or sluice across the waterway. As new in-stream technologies are developed, the environmental impacts of tidal power will become even less significant.

Alternatives to Fossil Fuels

Fossil fuels helped drive the Industrial Revolution and create the unprecedented material prosperity we enjoy today. Our global economy is largely powered by fossil fuels: 80% of the world's energy comes from oil, coal, and natural gas, and these three fuels generate two-thirds of the world's electricity. However, these nonrenewable energy sources will not last forever. Oil production is thought to be peaking now, and easily extractable supplies of oil and natural gas may not last half a century more. Moreover, the use of coal, oil, and natural gas entails substantial environmental impacts.

For these reasons, most scientists and energy experts, and many economists and policy makers, accept that we will need to shift from fossil fuels to energy sources that are less easily depleted and gentler on our environment. Developing alternatives to fossil fuels has the added benefit of helping to diversify an economy's mix of energy, lessening price volatility and dependence on foreign fuel imports.

There is a wide range of alternatives to fossil fuels. Most of these energy sources are renewable, and most have less impact on the environment than oil, coal, or natural gas. However, at this time most remain more costly than fossil fuels, at least in the short term, and many depend on technologies that are not yet fully developed. In this chapter we will explore the "conventional" alternatives to fossil fuels; then we will look more closely at some "new renewable" alternatives.

Hydro, nuclear, and biomass are "conventional" alternatives

Three alternative energy sources are currently the most developed and widely used worldwide; they are hydro-electric power, nuclear power, and energy derived from biomass. Each of these well-established energy sources plays substantial roles in the energy and electricity budgets of nations today. We therefore call them "conventional" alternatives to fossil fuels.

Fuelwood and other biomass sources provide 10.0% of the world's energy; nuclear power provides 6.3%; and hydropower provides 2.2%. In some respects, this trio of conventional energy alternatives is an odd collection. They are generally considered to exert less environmental impact than fossil fuels, but more than the "new renewable" alternatives we will discuss later in this chapter. Yet, as you will see, they each involve a complex mix of benefits and drawbacks for human well-being and the environment.

Although their global contributions to overall energy supply are relatively minor, the conventional alternatives to fossil fuels contribute significantly to the generation of electricity. Nuclear and hydropower each account for nearly one-sixth of the world's electricity generation.

Canada's energy mix is somewhat different from that of the rest of the world, because almost 60% of our electricity is generated from hydroelectric power (**FIGURE 17.1**). In the United States, for comparison, it is much more common for electricity to be generated by coal-fired power plants or nuclear energy than by running water. Hydropower is the source of approximately 25% of Canada's total primary energy.

Hydroelectric Power

People worldwide draw more energy from the motion of water than from any other renewable source except biomass. In **hydroelectric power** (or *hydropower*), the kinetic energy of moving water is used to turn turbines and generate electricity.

Modern hydropower uses two approaches

People have long harnessed the power of moving water. Waterwheels spun by river water powered mills in past centuries. Today we utilize the kinetic energy of water in two major ways: with large dams and with "run-of-river" technologies.

(a) Electricity generation in Canada, by fuel type

(b) Total power generation by energy type, in 2003

FIGURE 17.1

(a) In Canada we depend heavily on abundant hydropower sources for electricity generation. **(b)** This map shows regional variations in the type of energy source used to generate electricity in Canada; the units are terrawatt hours (TWh).
Source: Energy Information Administration, U.S. Department of Energy, Country Analysis Briefs: Canada, www.eia.doe.gov/emeu/cabs/Canada/Full. html

Most hydroelectric power today comes from impounding water in reservoirs behind large concrete dams that block the flow of river water and then controlling the flow of water through the dam. Because the water is held in reservoirs behind dams, this approach is variously referred to as a *reservoir, storage,* or *impoundment* approach. If you have ever seen the Gardiner Dam on the South Saskatchewan River (Canada's largest hydroelectric dam), the Ottawa-Holden Dam on the Ottawa River (**FIGURE 17.2A**), the Hoover Dam on the Colorado River, or any other large dam, you have seen an impoundment approach being used for hydroelectric power generation.

When reservoir water passes through a dam, it turns the blades of turbines, causing a generator to generate electricity (**FIGURE 17.2B, C**). Electricity generated in the

(a) Beck II Generating Station

(b) Turbine generator

1 Water flows from the reservoir through the dam.

2 The flowing water turns the turbine.

3 The turbine turns the rotor, which consists of a series of magnets.

4 Electricity is produced as the rotor spins past the stator, which is the stationary part of the generator made of coils of copper wire.

Reservoir

Dam

Intake

Powerhouse

Powerlines

Stator ⎫
Rotor ⎬ Generator
        ⎭
Turbine

Outflow

(c) Hydroelectric power

FIGURE 17.2 Large dams, such as the Ottawa-Holden Dam on the Ottawa River between Ontario and Québec **(a)**, generate substantial amounts of hydroelectric power. Inside these dams, flowing water is used to turn turbines similar to the one shown here **(b)**. As shown in **(c)**, water is funnelled through a portion of the dam (1) to rotate the turbine (2), which turns rotors containing magnets (3). The spinning rotors generate electricity (4) as their magnets pass coils of copper wire. Electrical current is transmitted through power lines, and the river's water flows out through the base of the dam.

powerhouse of a dam is transmitted to the electric grid by transmission lines, and the water is allowed to flow into the riverbed below the dam to continue downriver. The amount of power generated depends on the distance the water falls and the volume of water released. By storing water in reservoirs, dam operators can ensure a steady and predictable supply of electricity at all times, even during seasons of naturally low river flow.

An alternative to large dams is the **run-of-river** (or *diversion*) approach, which generates electricity without

water impoundment and without greatly disrupting the flow of river water. On the one hand, this approach sacrifices the reliability of water flow that the storage approach guarantees, but on the other hand it minimizes many of the negative impacts of large dams. Run-of-river can use various methods, one of which diverts a portion of a river's flow through a pipe or channel, passing it through a powerhouse and then returning it to the river (**FIGURE 17.3**). The pipe or channel can be run along the surface or underground. Another method involves the river

FIGURE 17.3
Run-of-river systems divert a portion of a river's water for electricity generation. Some designs involve piping water downhill through a powerhouse and releasing it downriver, and some involve using water as it flows over shallow dams.

water flowing over a dam small enough not to impede fish passage, using the water to turn turbines and then returning the water to the river.

Run-of-river systems are particularly useful in areas remote from established electrical grids and in regions without the economic resources to build and maintain large dams. Run-of-river is often called *small hydro* or even *micro-hydro* (referring to installations that produce less than 1000 kW of power), in contrast to the *large hydro* of traditional hydroelectric dams. Some environmentalists worry that the impacts of run-of-river systems on water flow and other aspects of the aquatic system are not sufficiently understood, but the impacts are surely less than those of large dams.

Hydropower generates relatively little air pollution

The great age of dam building for hydroelectric power (as well as for flood control and irrigation) began in the 1930s, when the U.S. federal government constructed dams as public projects. Dam construction in the United States peaked in 1960, when 3123 dams were completed in a single year. American engineers subsequently exported dam-building technologies to the developing world. Indian Prime Minister Pandit Nehru commented in 1963 that "dams are the temples of modern India," referring to their central importance in the development of energy capacity in that nation.

Hydropower now accounts for 2.2% of the world's energy supply but 16.0% of electricity production (and considerably more than this in Canada). For nations with large amounts of river water and the economic resources to build dams, hydroelectric power has been a keystone of their development. The largest producing region is Europe but Eastern Asia, led by China, is rapidly developing its capacity (**FIGURE 17.4**).

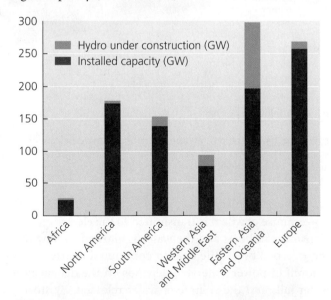

FIGURE 17.4
Europe currently has the highest installed capacity for hydropower, but Asia—led by China—is rapidly developing its capacity; units are gigawatts (GW).
Source: Data are for 2009. from International Hydropower Association Activity Report, *2010.*

Hydropower has two clear advantages over fossil fuels for the production of electricity. First, it is renewable: as long as precipitation falls from the sky and fills rivers and reservoirs, we can use water to turn turbines. The second advantage is cleanliness. Because no combustion is involved, no carbon dioxide or other pollutants are emitted during the production of hydropower. Fossil fuels *are* used in constructing and maintaining dams, and recent evidence indicates that large reservoirs release the greenhouse gas methane as a result of anaerobic decay in deep water. But overall, hydropower creates only a small fraction of the greenhouse gas emissions typical of fossil fuel combustion.

Hydropower is also efficient, with an EROI (*energy returned on investment*) of 10:1 or more, at least as high as any other modern-day energy source. Fossil fuels had higher EROI in the past, but as the cost of reaching remaining deposits has increased, their EROI values have dipped below that of hydropower.

Hydropower has many negative impacts, too

Although it is renewable, efficient, and produces little air pollution, hydropower does have other negative impacts. Damming rivers destroys habitat for wildlife as riparian areas above dam sites are submerged and those below are starved of water. Because water discharge is regulated to optimize electricity generation, the natural flooding cycles of rivers are disrupted. Suppressing floods prevents floodplains from receiving fresh nutrient-laden sediments. Instead, sediments become trapped behind dams, where they gradually fill the reservoir.

Dams also cause **thermal pollution**, because water downstream may become warmer if water levels are kept unnaturally shallow. Moreover, periodic flushes of cold water occur from the release of reservoir water; such thermal shocks, together with habitat alteration, have damaged many native fish populations in dammed waterways. Dams also block the passage of fish and other aquatic creatures, effectively fragmenting the river and reducing biodiversity.

The weight of water in a large reservoir can cause geological impacts, such as earthquakes, particularly where water has seeped into fractures in the bedrock underlying the reservoir. Dam collapses—whether as a result of earthquakes or landslides or from degradation of the construction materials—are regrettably not uncommon, and have resulted in many deaths in the decades since the great surge in large dam construction. These ecological and physical impacts also translate into negative social and economic impacts on local communities.

There has also been recent concern about the generation of greenhouse gases in large hydroelectric reservoirs. As mentioned above, large reservoirs release methane, as well as carbon dioxide, as a result of anaerobic decay in deep water, particularly in warm climates.

The most controversial hydroelectric installation in Canada is the James Bay Project in northern Québec, an extremely complicated, multi-phase project that began in 1970. James Bay has been controversial for environmental, political, social, and economic reasons, as well as being intimately connected with the modern history of Aboriginal land claims in Canada. The project has involved significant river diversions, resulting in the merging of several major watersheds on the eastern shore of the Hudson Bay, from the southern tip of James Bay to Ungava Bay in the north. Just two of these diversions, of the Caniapiscau and Eastmain rivers, inundated about 11 000 km^2 of boreal forest, with major impacts on water resources in nearby Cree villages.

Additional environmental impacts associated with the James Bay Project have included massive changes to the landscape, seismic tremors, fluctuating water levels, and loss of wetlands, with consequent ecological impacts. The decomposition of organic matter killed as a result of flooding has also proven problematic, and flooding is thought to have contributed to higher levels of methylmercury in local waterways. (*Methylmercury* is a particularly toxic and bioaccumulative form of mercury, which forms in aquatic systems through bacterially mediated processes. These occur most readily in oxygen-poor conditions, which are created by reservoir flooding and the subsequent decay of flooded organic matter.) The river diversions associated with the James Bay Project also have interfered with animal migration patterns (e.g., caribou) and fish spawning habitats (e.g., salmon).

Hydropower may not expand much more

China's recently completed Three Gorges Dam is the world's largest hydroelectric installation. When fully operational, Three Gorges will have 32 generators producing as much electricity as dozens of coal-fired or nuclear plants. The reservoir required the displacement of over a million people, and there are concerns about its ecological impacts.

Hydropower is not likely to expand much more in North America. One reason is that most of the large rivers that offer excellent opportunities for hydropower are already dammed. Another reason is that people have grown more aware of the negative environmental impacts of dams. In some regions residents are resisting dam construction, or even (primarily in the United States) proposing to dismantle some dams and restore river habitats. Hydropower will likely continue to increase substantially in Asia, however, as China develops its capacity.

Nuclear Power

Nuclear power—usable energy extracted from the force that binds atomic nuclei together—occupies a conflicted position in our modern debate over energy. It is free of the air pollution produced by fossil fuel combustion, so it has been put forth as an environmentally friendly alternative to fossil fuels. Yet nuclear power's great promise has been clouded by nuclear weaponry, by the challenge of radioactive waste disposal, and by the long shadow of Chernobyl and other power plant accidents. Public safety concerns and the costs of addressing them have constrained the development and spread of nuclear power in Canada and many other nations.

First developed commercially in the 1950s, nuclear power has expanded 15-fold worldwide since 1970. The United States generates the most electricity from nuclear power—nearly a third of the world's production—followed by France and Japan. Although the United States is the leader in quantity of electricity generated, only about 20% of its total electricity comes from nuclear sources. A number of other nations rely more heavily on nuclear power (**TABLE 17.1**); France leads the list, obtaining 75% of its electricity from nuclear power. Canada generates approximately 15% of its electricity with nuclear power. The province of Ontario leads the

Table 17.1 Top Producers of Nuclear Power			
Nation	**Nuclear power produced***	**Operating plants†**	**Percentage of electricity from nuclear power***
United States	796.8	104	20.2
France	390.0	58	75.2
Japan	260.1	54	28.9
Russia	153.0	32	17.8
South Korea	141.1	21	34.8
Germany	127.6	17	26.1
Canada	85.3	18	14.8
Ukraine	77.8	15	48.6
China	70.1	13	1.9
United Kingdom	62.9	19	17.9
World Total	2559.7	441	14.0

*In billion kilowatt-hours (BkWh) for 2009.

†As of August 2010. Data from the Nuclear Energy Institute (www.nei.org/).

roots

FISSION

The term **fission** was first used in physics to describe the splitting of a nucleus quite recently—in 1939. This was only a few years after the discovery of neutrons, and during a time when there was frantic scientific and political effort to manufacture and deploy the first atomic bomb. Previously the term had been used to apply to the process of cell division, and it derives much earlier than that from the Latin word *findere*, "to cleave, split, or divide."

nuclear industry in Canada, with about half of the electricity used in the province coming from its 16 operating nuclear generators; Québec and New Brunswick have one operating reactor each.

Fission releases nuclear energy

Strictly defined, *nuclear energy* is the energy that holds together protons and neutrons in the nucleus of an atom. We harness this energy by converting it to thermal energy, which can then be used to generate electricity.

The reaction that drives the release of nuclear energy in power plants is **fission**, the splitting apart of atomic nuclei (**FIGURE 17.5**). To induce fission, the nuclei of large, heavy atoms, such as uranium or plutonium, are bombarded with neutrons, causing them to break apart. Each split nucleus produces heat, radiation, and multiple

FIGURE 17.5

In nuclear fission, an atom of fissionable material (in this case, ^{235}U) is bombarded with a neutron. The collision splits the uranium atom into smaller atoms and releases two or three neutrons, radiation, and energy. The neutrons can continue to split other uranium atoms in a chain reaction. Engineers at nuclear plants use control rods to absorb excess neutrons and regulate the rate of the reaction.

neutrons, as well as the leftover fragments of the original nucleus. The emitted neutrons then bombard other nearby *fissionable* (or *fissile*) atomic nuclei, resulting in a self-sustaining chain reaction.

If not controlled, this chain reaction becomes a runaway process that releases enormous amounts of energy; it is responsible for the explosive power of a nuclear bomb. Inside a nuclear power plant, however, fission is controlled so that, on average, only one of the two or three neutrons emitted with each fission event goes on to induce another fission event. In this way, the chain reaction maintains a constant output of energy at a controlled rate.

Enriched uranium is used as fuel in nuclear reactors

We generate electricity from nuclear power by controlled fission in **nuclear reactors**, facilities contained within nuclear power plants. This is just one step in a longer process called the *nuclear fuel cycle*, which begins when the naturally occurring element uranium is mined from underground deposits.

Uranium minerals are uncommon, and uranium ore is in finite supply; it must be mined, which is why nuclear power is generally considered to be a nonrenewable energy source. However, Canada is particularly rich in uranium resources, and currently produces about one-third of the world's uranium. Canada also has developed reactor technologies that are used in many countries.

Uranium is useful for nuclear power because it is radioactive. Radioactive isotopes, or *radioisotopes*, emit subatomic particles and high-energy radiation as they decay into lighter radioisotopes, until they ultimately become stable isotopes. The isotope uranium-235 decays into a series of daughter isotopes, eventually forming stable lead-207. Each radioisotope decays at a rate determined by that isotope's *half-life*, the time it takes for half of the atoms to give off radiation and decay.

Over 99% of the uranium in nature occurs as the isotope uranium-238; uranium-235 (with three fewer neutrons) makes up less than 1% of the total. Because ^{238}U does not emit enough neutrons to maintain a chain reaction when it splits, ^{235}U is more commonly used for commercial nuclear power. Mined uranium ore therefore must be processed or *enriched*, so that the concentration of ^{235}U is at least 3%. The enriched uranium is formed into pellets of uranium dioxide (UO_2), which are then incorporated into *fuel rods* (**FIGURE 17.6**) that are used in nuclear reactors.

After several years in a reactor, the uranium fuel will have decayed to the point where it can no longer generate

FIGURE 17.6
Enriched uranium fuel is formed into pellets and then packaged into fuel rods, shown here. The fuel rods are encased in metal and inserted into the cores of nuclear reactors.

adequate energy, and must be replaced with new fuel. In some countries (not Canada and the United States), the spent fuel is reprocessed to recover what usable energy may be left. Most spent fuel, however, is disposed of as radioactive waste.

Fission takes place in nuclear power plants

The neutrons bombarding uranium fuel in a reactor are slowed down with a substance called a *moderator*, most often water. As fission proceeds, it becomes necessary to soak up the excess neutrons produced when uranium nuclei divide, so that on average only a single neutron from each nucleus goes on to split another nucleus. For this purpose, *control rods*, made of a material that absorbs neutrons, are placed into the reactor among the fuel rods. Engineers move these control rods into and out of the water to maintain the fission reaction at the desired rate.

All this takes place within the reactor core and is the first step in the electricity-generating process of a nuclear power plant (**FIGURE 17.7**). The reactor core is housed within a reactor vessel, and the vessel, steam generator, and associated plumbing are protected within a containment building. Containment buildings, with their metre-thick concrete and steel walls, are constructed to prevent leaks of radioactivity due to accidents or natural catastrophes such as earthquakes.

Instead of using ^{235}U-enriched fuel, some reactors (including the Canadian CANDU reactor) are designed to make use of ^{238}U and other fissile materials present in natural (unenriched) ores. Some of these are so-called

2 Water heated by fission circulates through the primary loop, which is pressurized to prevent boiling.

3 Water heated by fission in the primary loop boils water in the secondary loop, creating steam.

1 Fission occurs in the reactor core, where fuel rods are submerged in water. The water slows neutrons in order to initiate a chain reaction in uranium-235 in the fuel rods, while control rods absorb excess neutrons to regulate that reaction.

4 The steam drives turbines, which generate electricity.

Control rod   Primary loop   Secondary loop

Moderator (water)

Steam

Turbine

Generator

Reactor core

Reactor vessel   Nuclear fuel (uranium)   Steam generator

Condenser   Cooling loop

Cooling tower

Containment building

5 Cold water from the cooling tower circulates within the cooling loop, condensing steam in the secondary loop and converting it to liquid water, which then returns to be boiled by the heated pressurized water of the primary loop.

FIGURE 17.7   In a pressurized light water reactor, the most common type of nuclear reactor, uranium fuel rods are placed in water, a moderator that slows neutrons so fission can occur (1). Control rods are moved into and out of the reactor core to absorb excess neutrons and regulate the chain reaction. Water heated by fission circulates through the primary loop (2) and warms water in the secondary loop, which turns to steam (3). Steam drives turbines to generate electricity (4). The steam is then cooled in the cooling tower by water from an adjacent water body and returns to the containment building (5) to be heated again in the primary loop.

breeder reactors, which generate new fissile material at a faster rate than they use it up. Because 99% of all uranium is ^{238}U, breeder reactors make better use of fuel, produce less waste for a given amount of energy generation, and eliminate the costly necessity to enrich nuclear fuels. However, breeder reactors are more expensive to construct than conventional reactors, and some technologies may be more susceptible to explosive accidents.

Nuclear power generates little air pollution

Nuclear power plants generate electricity without creating air pollution from stack emissions. In contrast, combusting coal, oil, or natural gas emits sulphur dioxide that contributes to acidic deposition and particulate air pollution, as well as greenhouse gases.

Scientists from the International Atomic Energy Agency (IAEA) have calculated that nuclear power produces emissions up to 150 times lower than those from fossil fuel combustion. They conducted a "cradle-to-grave" analysis that included emissions not just from power generation, but also from the mining, processing, and transport of fuel; manufacturing of equipment; construction of power plants; disposal of wastes; and

decommissioning of plants. The results showed that, per unit of energy produced, fossil fuels produce much higher emissions than either renewable energy sources or nuclear energy.

Because the IAEA is responsible for promoting nuclear energy, critics point out that the agency is motivated to show nuclear power in a favourable light. However, few experts would argue with the conclusion that nuclear and renewable energy sources are cleaner than fossil fuels.

Nuclear power has additional environmental advantages over fossil fuels—coal in particular. Because uranium generates far more power than coal by weight or volume, less of it needs to be mined, so uranium mining (which is commonly done in underground mines) causes less damage to landscapes and generates less solid waste than coal mining (which is often, though not always, done at the surface by strip-mining). Moreover, in the course of normal operation, nuclear power plants are safer for workers than coal-fired plants.

Nuclear power also has serious drawbacks, though. One is that the waste it produces is radioactive; it must be handled with great care, and disposed of in a way that minimizes danger to present and future generations. A second major concern is that if an accident occurs at a power plant, or if a plant is sabotaged, or if a government were to use its nuclear capabilities for aggressive purposes,

Environmental Impacts of Coal-Fired and Nuclear Power		
Type of Impact	**Coal**	**Nuclear**
Land and ecosystem disturbance from mining	Extensive, on surface or underground	Less extensive
Greenhouse gas emissions	Considerable emissions	None from plant operation; much less than coal over the entire life cycle
Other air pollutants	Sulphur dioxide, nitrogen oxides, particulate matter, and other pollutants	No pollutant emissions
Radioactive emissions	No appreciable emissions	No appreciable emissions during normal operation; possibility of emissions during severe accident
Occupational health among workers	More known health problems and fatalities	Fewer known health problems and fatalities
Health impacts on nearby residents	Air pollution impairs health	No appreciable known health impacts under normal operation
Effects of accident or sabotage	No widespread effects	Potentially catastrophic widespread effects
Solid waste	More generated	Less generated
Radioactive waste	None	Radioactive waste generated
Fuel supplies remaining	Should last several hundred more years	Uncertain; supplies could last for a longer or shorter time than coal supplies

FIGURE 17.8 Coal-fired power plants and nuclear power plants pose very different risks and impacts to human health and the environment. This chart compares the major impacts of each mode of electricity generation. The more severe impacts are indicated by red boxes.

the consequences can be catastrophic. Given this mix of advantages and disadvantages (**FIGURE 17.8**), many governments (although not necessarily most citizens) have judged the good to outweigh the bad, and today the world has 436 operating nuclear plants in 30 nations.

Nuclear power poses small risk of large accidents

Although nuclear power poses fewer chronic health risks than does fossil fuel combustion, the possibility of catastrophic accidents has spawned a great deal of public anxiety over nuclear power. As plants around the world

weighing the issues

CHOOSE YOUR RISK

Given the choice of living next to a nuclear power plant or living next to a coal-fired power plant, which would you choose? What kinds of information would inform your choice?

age, they require more maintenance. New concerns have also surfaced that nuclear plants could become targets for terrorism, or radioactive material could be stolen and used in terrorist attacks. This possibility is especially worrisome in countries of the former Soviet Union, where former nuclear sites have gone without adequate security for years.

Three significant events have been most influential in shaping public opinion about nuclear energy. They are Three Mile Island, Chernobyl, and Fukushima Dai-ichi.

Three Mile Island The first took place at the Three Mile Island plant in Pennsylvania, where in 1979 the United States experienced its most serious nuclear power plant accident. Through a combination of mechanical failure and human error, coolant water drained from the reactor vessel, temperatures rose inside the reactor core, and metal surrounding the uranium fuel rods began to melt, releasing radiation. This process, called a **meltdown**, proceeded through half of one reactor core at Three Mile Island. Area residents stood ready to be evacuated, but fortunately most radiation remained trapped inside the containment building.

The accident was brought under control within days, the damaged reactor was shut down, and a multibillion-dollar cleanup lasted for years. Three Mile Island is regarded as a near-miss; the emergency could have been far worse had the meltdown proceeded through the entire stock of uranium fuel, or had the containment building not contained the radiation. Although residents have shown no significant health impacts in the years since, the event put safety concerns squarely on the map for both citizens and policy makers.

Chernobyl   In 1986 an explosion at the Chernobyl plant in Ukraine (then part of the Soviet Union) caused the most severe nuclear power plant accident the world has yet seen. Engineers had turned off safety systems to conduct tests. Human error, combined with technological failures and unsafe reactor design, led to explosions that destroyed the reactor and sent clouds of radioactive debris into the atmosphere. For 10 days radiation escaped from the plant while emergency crews risked their lives (some later died from radiation exposure) to put out fires. Most residents of the surrounding countryside remained at home for these 10 days, exposed to radiation, before the Soviet government belatedly began evacuating more than 100 000 people.

In the months and years afterwards, workers erected a gigantic concrete sarcophagus around the demolished reactor, scrubbed buildings and roads, and removed irradiated materials (**FIGURE 17.9**). However, the landscape for at least 30 km around the plant remains contaminated today. An international team plans to build a larger sarcophagus around the original one, which is seriously deteriorating.

The accident killed 31 people directly and sickened or caused cancer in thousands more. Exact numbers are uncertain because of inadequate data and the difficulty of determining long-term radiation effects. Health authorities estimate that most of the over 4000 cases of thyroid cancer since diagnosed in people who were children at the time resulted from the accident. Estimates for the total number of cancer cases attributable to Chernobyl, past and future, vary widely, ranging from several thousand, on the conservative side, to as many as 200 000 fatal cancers.

Atmospheric currents carried radioactive fallout from Chernobyl across much of the Northern Hemisphere, particularly Ukraine, Belarus, and parts of Russia and Europe (**FIGURE 17.10**). Fallout was greatest where rainstorms brought radioisotopes down from the radioactive cloud. Parts of Sweden received high amounts of fallout, and the accident reinforced the Swedish public's fears about nuclear power. A survey taken after the event asked, "Do you think it was good or bad for the country to invest in nuclear energy?" The proportion of respondents answering "bad" jumped from 25% before Chernobyl to 47% afterward.

(a) The Chernobyl sarcophagus

(b) Technicians measuring radiation

FIGURE 17.9
The world's worst nuclear power plant accident unfolded in 1986 at Chernobyl, in present-day Ukraine. As part of the extensive cleanup operation, the destroyed reactor was encased in a massive concrete sarcophagus **(a)** to contain further radiation leakage. Technicians scoured the landscape surrounding the plant **(b)**, measuring radiation levels, removing soil, and scrubbing roads and buildings.

Fukushima Dai-ichi   On Friday, March 11, 2011, a megathrust earthquake of magnitude 9.0—one of the largest earthquakes ever measured—struck in a subduction zone just off the northeast coast of Tōhoku, Japan. The earthquake, devastating in its own right, also generated a massive tsunami that swept ashore, killing more than 15 000 people, injuring many more, and wiping whole villages off the map.

The tsunami also inundated the Fukushima Dai-ichi power plant, located on the coast of Japan, not far from the earthquake's epicentre. (Nuclear power plants are commonly located near the ocean or large lakes, because they require large volumes of water to use as coolant fluid.) The nuclear reactors at Fukushima Dai-ichi shut down

FIGURE 17.10 Radioactive fallout from the Chernobyl disaster was deposited across Europe in complex patterns resulting from atmospheric currents and rainstorms in the days following the accident. Darker colours in this map of ^{137}Cs deposition indicate higher levels of radioactivity. Although Chernobyl produced 100 times more fallout than the U.S. bombs dropped on Hiroshima and Nagasaki in World War II, it was distributed over a much wider area. Thus, levels of contamination outside of Ukraine, Belarus, and western Russia were relatively low.   *Source: Data from Swiss Agency for Development and Cooperation, Bern, 2005.*

automatically as a result of the earthquake, as they were intended to do; however, fission continues in the reactor cores, requiring constant cooling to maintain a manageable temperature. The back-up generators that should have kept the coolant fluids circulating were flooded and incapacitated by the tsunami. The subsequent overheating of the reactor cores set off a series of fires, explosions, and core meltdowns, accompanied by several releases of radioactive materials (**FIGURE 17.11**). These events required significant interventions, and the radioactive releases resulted in public health warnings; for example, food grown in the area had to be taken off the market.

The International Atomic Energy Agency introduced a scale for the measurement of nuclear accidents, called the *International Nuclear and Radiological Event Scale.* The scale ranges from 0 (a "deviation" from normal procedures, with no safety significance), through 1–3 ("incidents" of increasing severity) and 4–7 ("accidents"). Three Mile Island is one of several events given a rating of

5, an "accident with wider consequences," which includes limited release of radioactive material and severe damage to the reactor core. Both Chernobyl and Fukushima (as a whole, although each reactor was given its own individual rating) have been rated as 7, the most severe level on this scale. A level 7 accident involves "major release of radioactive material with widespread health and environment effects, requiring implementation of planned and extended counter-measures."

Radioactive waste disposal remains problematic

Even if nuclear power generation could be made completely safe, and accidents like those at Chernobyl and Fukushima Dai-ichi were completely avoidable, we would be left with the conundrum of what to do with spent fuel rods and other radioactive waste. Recall that fission

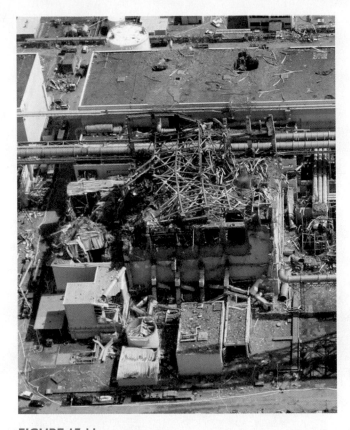

FIGURE 17.11
This photo from March, 2011, shows some of the nuclear reactor buildings at Fukushima Dai-ichi that were damaged by the massive Tōhoku earthquake and tsunami.

utilizes ^{235}U as fuel, leaving as waste the 97% of uranium that is ^{238}U. This ^{238}U, as well as all irradiated material and equipment that is no longer being used, is radioactive and must be disposed of in a location where radiation will not escape. Because the half-lives of uranium, plutonium, and many other radioisotopes are far longer than human lifetimes, this *high-level waste* will continue emitting radiation for many thousands of years. Thus, radioactive waste must be placed in unusually stable and secure locations and monitored for many, many years to protect future generations.

Currently, nuclear waste from power generation is held in temporary storage at nuclear power plants in Canada and other places around the world. Spent fuel rods are sunken in pools of cooling water to minimize radiation leakage (**FIGURE 17.12A**). However, plants have only a limited capacity for this type of on-site storage.

FIGURE 17.12
Spent uranium fuel rods are stored on-site at nuclear power plants and will likely remain at these scattered sites until a central repository for commercial radioactive waste is fully developed. Spent fuel rods are most often kept in "wet storage" in pools of water **(a)**, which keep them cool and reduce radiation release. Alternatively, radioactive waste may be kept in "dry storage" in thick-walled casks layered with lead, concrete, and steel **(b)**.

Many plants are now expanding their storage capacity by storing waste in thick casks of steel, lead, and concrete (**FIGURE 17.12B**).

In addition to keeping the waste dry, isolated from groundwater and the biosphere, and safe from geological disruptions such as earthquakes, another concern is that nuclear waste will need to be transported to its permanent repository. Because this would involve shipment by rail or truck, many people worry that the risk of an accident or of sabotage is unacceptably high.

(a) Wet storage

(b) Dry storage

Storing waste at many dispersed sites creates a large number of potential hazards, so it is desirable to send the waste to a central repository that can be heavily guarded. Even transporting high-level waste to a central repository poses risks, however; it is a dangerous cargo and derailments, accidents, and terrorist attacks are all concerns.

Sweden has established a single repository for low-level waste near one power plant, and is searching for a single disposal site deep within bedrock for spent fuel rods and other high-level waste. In the United States, a multi-year search for a disposal site homed in on Yucca Mountain, in the desert of southern Nevada; however, the project is now all but dead as a result of political delays and funding cutbacks. No site has yet been chosen in Canada, but at a research facility in Lac du Bonnet, Manitoba scientists are testing proposals for long-term storage deep underground in the stable, ancient crystalline rocks of the Canadian Shield. This approach is called **geological isolation** (**FIGURE 17.13**), and it is the disposal method of choice among nations that are seeking permanent repositories for high-level waste.

Multiple dilemmas have slowed nuclear power's growth

Dogged by concerns over waste disposal, safety, and cost overruns, nuclear power's growth has slowed. Many plants have been much more expensive than anticipated, and public anxiety in the wake of Chernobyl has made utilities less willing to invest in new plants. In addition, some plants have aged more quickly than expected because of problems that were underestimated, such as corrosion in coolant pipes. Decommissioning a plant can sometimes be more expensive than the original construction.

As a result of these economic issues, electricity from nuclear power today remains more expensive than electricity from coal and other sources. Nonetheless, nuclear power remains one of the few currently viable alternatives to fossil fuels with which we can generate large amounts of electricity in short order.

Many experts predict nuclear power will decrease because three-quarters of Western Europe's capacity is

FIGURE 17.13
There is no permanent repository for high-level radioactive waste in Canada. Scientific testing of various proposals is ongoing. At a site similar to the Lac du Bonnet research facility in Manitoba, waste could be buried in a network of tunnels deep underground in the stable, crystalline rocks of the Canadian Shield, as shown here.

scheduled to be retired by 2030, and Germany, Belgium, and Sweden have declared an intention to phase out nuclear power altogether. Asian nations, in contrast, are adding nuclear capacity. China, India, and South Korea are expanding their nuclear programs to help power their rapidly growing economies. Japan is so reliant on imported oil that it is eager to diversify its energy options. Asia hosts two-thirds of the most recent nuclear plants to go into operation, and more than half of the plants now under construction.

Fusion remains a dream

For as long as scientists and engineers have generated power from nuclear fission, they have tried to figure out how they might use nuclear fusion instead. **Fusion**—the

weighing the issues

MORE NUCLEAR POWER?

Do you think Canada as a whole, or your province in particular, should expand its nuclear power program? Why, or why not?

roots
FUSION

The term **fusion** was applied to the merging of two atomic nuclei by physicists researching these processes in the 1930s and 1940s. It comes from the Latin word *fusus*, "to spread out or flow," and it has the same root as the English word *fuse*, "to melt." Both probably come from a much earlier Indo-European root *gheu-*, meaning "to flow or pour." Interestingly, this root may also have something to do with the origins of the English word *god*.

process that drives our Sun's vast output of energy and the force behind hydrogen or thermonuclear bombs—involves forcing together the small nuclei of lightweight elements under extremely high temperature and pressure. The hydrogen isotopes deuterium and tritium can be fused together to create helium, releasing a neutron and a tremendous amount of energy.

Overcoming the mutually repulsive forces of protons in a controlled manner is difficult, and fusion typically requires extremely high temperatures. Researchers have not yet developed "cold" fusion for commercial power generation; fusion experiments still require scientists to input more energy than they produce from the process. Fusion's potentially huge payoffs, though, make many scientists eager to keep trying.

If one day we were to find a way to control fusion in a reactor, we could produce vast amounts of energy using water as a source of hydrogen for fuel. The process would create only low-level radioactive wastes, without polluting emissions or the risk of dangerous accidents, sabotage, or weapons proliferation. A consortium of industrialized nations, including Canada, is collaborating to build a prototype fusion reactor called the International Thermonuclear Experimental Reactor (ITER) in southern France. Even if this multibillion-dollar effort succeeds, however, power from fusion seems likely to remain a dream until many years in the future.

Traditional Biomass Energy

Although technologies for many renewable energy sources are still early in their stages of development, biomass energy is widely used. Worldwide, it is a "conventional" alternative to fossil fuels. Indeed, biomass was the very first source of energy used by our human ancestors, whose mastery of fire represents one of the first great steps toward the control of the environment. Today, traditional biomass accounts for about 10% of energy use globally.

Biomass energy means different things to different users

When people use the term **biomass energy**, they can mean very different things. To a subsistence farmer in Africa, biomass energy means cutting wood from trees or collecting livestock manure and burning it to heat and cook for her family. To an industrialized farmer in Saskatchewan, biomass energy might mean shipping his grain to a high-tech refinery that converts it into liquid fuel to run automobiles.

People harness biomass energy from many types of plant matter, including wood from trees, charcoal (which is actually charred wood, not coal), and agricultural crops, as well as combustible animal waste products such as cattle manure. Fossil fuels are not considered biomass energy sources because their organic matter has not been part of living organisms for millions of years and has undergone considerable chemical alteration.

Traditional biomass sources are widely used in the developing world

Over 1 billion people still use wood from trees as their principal energy source. In developing nations, especially in rural areas, families gather fuelwood to burn in their homes for heating and cooking (**FIGURE 17.14**). In these nations, the direct combustion of fuelwood, charcoal, and manure accounts for fully 35% of energy use—in the poorest nations, up to 90%.

Fuelwood and other traditional biomass sources constitute nearly 80% of all renewable energy used worldwide. Many new approaches and technologies are being developed to make biomass energy more efficient and most sustainable, but these still constitute a very small proportion of overall energy use. As developing nations industrialize, fossil fuels are replacing traditional energy sources (**FIGURE 17.15**); as a result, traditional biomass use is growing more slowly worldwide than overall energy use. However, the total use of fuelwood in the developing world continues to increase, and the International Energy Agency estimates that by the year 2030, 2.6 billion people will be using traditional fuels for heating and cooking in unsustainable ways.

Traditional biomass energy has environmental pros and cons

Biomass energy has one overarching environmental benefit: It is essentially *carbon-neutral*, releasing no net carbon into the atmosphere. Although burning biomass emits plenty of carbon, it is simply the carbon that photosynthesis had pulled from the atmosphere to create the biomass in the first place. That is, the carbon that biomass combustion emits is balanced by the carbon that photosynthesis had sequestered within the biomass just years, months, or weeks before. Therefore, when we replace fossil fuels with bioenergy, we reduce net carbon flux to the atmosphere, helping to mitigate global climate change.

However, this holds only if biomass sources are not overharvested. Harvesting fuelwood at an unsustainably rapid rate leads to deforestation, soil erosion, and desertification, damaging landscapes, diminishing biodiversity, and impoverishing human societies. Deforestation increases the carbon flux to the atmosphere, because less vegetation means less carbon uptake by plants for photosynthesis. In arid regions that are heavily populated and support meagre woodlands, fuelwood harvesting can have enormous impacts; such is the case with many regions of Africa and Asia. Burning fuelwood and other biomass in traditional ways for cooking and heating also leads to health hazards from indoor air pollution.

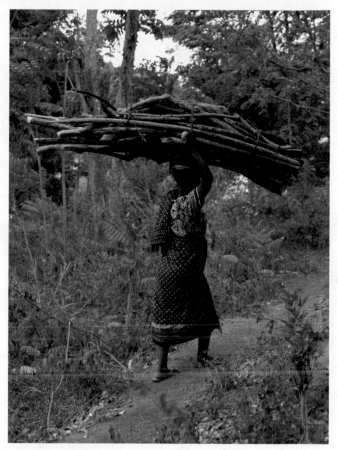

FIGURE 17.14
Over a billion people in developing countries rely on fuelwood for heating and cooking. Wood cut from trees remains the major source of biomass energy used in the world today. In theory, biomass is renewable; in practice, it may not be renewable if forests are overharvested.

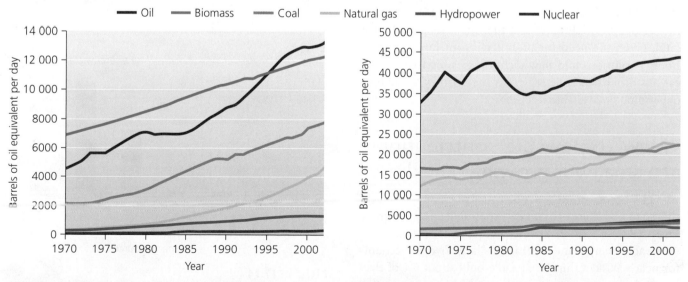

(a) Energy consumption in developing nations

(b) Energy consumption in industrialized nations

FIGURE 17.15 Energy consumption patterns vary greatly between developing nations **(a)** and wealthier industrialized nations, here represented by nations of the Organisation for Economic Cooperation and Development (OECD) **(b)**. Note the large role that traditional biomass (primarily fuelwood) plays in supplying energy to developing countries. Note also that the *y* axes differ; people in developing nations consume far less energy than those in industrialized nations. *Source: Data from Energy Information Administration, U.S. Department of Energy.*

"New" Renewable Energy Sources

Next we will explore a group of alternative energy sources that are often called the "new renewables." These include energy from sunlight, wind, Earth's geothermal heat, ocean water, and hydrogen, as well as new technologies for biomass energy. Most of these energy sources are not truly new; they are as old as our planet, and people have used them for millennia. They are referred to as "new" because they are not yet used on a wide scale in our modern industrial society. These energy sources are harnessed using technologies that are still in a rapid phase of development, and they will likely come to play a much larger role in the future.

There are three major applications for new renewables in the world's energy market today:

- Power generation (using wind, solar, and other energy sources to generate electricity)
- Space heating (using solar or terrestrial energy sources to heat buildings or factories) and *district heating/cooling* (distributing heated or cooled air to many buildings throughout a community or urban area)
- Fuel (using hydrogen fuels, or using crops, crop residues, or waste materials to manufacture ethanol and biodiesel for use in transportation)[2]

All of these applications are very important in Canada, and promising alternative energy resources are available for all three. Electricity generation powers our modern lifestyle and industry; space heating is important in our northern climate; and fuel for transportation is vital, given the need for mobility in our large country. Energy solutions and new technologies for these applications differ from one region of the country to another, depending on available resources.

"New" renewable contributions are small but growing quickly

As a global community, we obtain only half of one percent (0.5%) of our energy from new renewable energy sources. Only 18% of our electricity worldwide comes from renewable energy, and traditional "large hydro" accounts for nearly 90% of this. In Canada, only about 6% of electricity generation comes from renewable sources *other* than traditional large hydro (**TABLE 17.2**). Most non–large hydro renewable electricity generation in Canada now comes from wind, followed by small hydro (run-of-river) installations and biomass.

Table 17.2 Renewable* Generation Capacity in Canada† (2009)	
Technology	**Installed capacity (MW)**
Wind	3549
Small hydro	2000
Solar PV	95
Biomass	1628
Landfill gas	5
Geothermal	1 (experimental)
Tidal energy	20

*Not including large hydro

†Data sources: Canadian Wind Energy Association (www.canwea.ca); International Small Hydro Atlas (www.small-hydro.com); Canadian Solar Industries Association (www.cansia.ca); Pembina Institute (www.pembina.org); Centre for Energy (www.centreforenergy.com); Canadian Geothermal Energy Association (www.cangea.ca); Nova Scotia Power (www.nspower.ca).

Although they comprise only a minuscule proportion of our energy budget, the new renewable energy sources are growing at much faster rates than conventional energy sources. Over the past three decades, solar, wind, and geothermal energy sources have grown far faster than the overall energy supply (**FIGURE 17.16**). The leader in growth is wind power, which has expanded by nearly 50% *each year* since the 1970s. Because these sources started from such low levels of use, however, it will take them some time to catch up to conventional sources. For instance, the absolute amount of energy added by a 50% increase in wind power is still far less than the amount added by just a 1% increase in oil, coal, or natural gas.

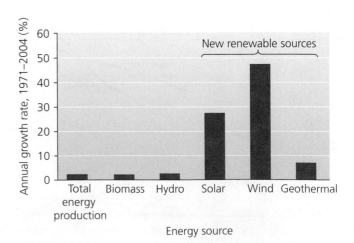

FIGURE 17.16

Globally, the "new" renewable energy sources are growing substantially faster than the total primary energy supply. Solar power has grown by 28% each year since 1971, and wind power has grown by 48% each year. Because these sources began from such low starting levels, however, their overall contribution to our energy supply is still small. *Source: Data from International Energy Agency Statistics, 2007.*

Use of new renewables has been expanding quickly because of growing concerns over diminishing fossil fuel supplies (causing both high prices and national security concerns) and the substantial environmental impacts of fossil fuel combustion. Unlike fossil fuels, renewable sources are inexhaustible on timescales relevant to human societies. Advances in technology are also making it easier and less expensive to harness renewable energy sources. Developing renewables can diversify an economy's mix of energy, lowering price volatility and protecting against supply restrictions.

New energy sources also can create employment opportunities and sources of income and property tax for communities, especially in rural areas passed over by other economic development. Developing technologies require more labour per unit of energy output than do established technologies, and it has been calculated that photovoltaic (PV) solar, wind, and biomass energy implementation supports more jobs than natural gas and coal, per unit of energy generated. This means that shifting to renewable energy could actually support more employment than remaining with a fossil fuel economy.[3]

Rapid growth in renewable energy sectors seems likely to continue as population and consumption grow, global energy demand expands, fossil fuel supplies decline, and people demand cleaner environments. More governments, utilities, corporations, and consumers are now promoting and using renewable energy, and, as a result, the prices of renewables are falling.

The transition won't happen overnight

We cannot switch to renewable energy sources overnight, because there are technological, economic, and social barriers. Currently, most renewables lack adequate technological development and infrastructure. However, rapid advances in recent years suggest that most remaining barriers are political. For decades, research and development of renewable sources have received far less in subsidies, tax breaks, and other incentives from governments than have conventional sources. For example, in the United States, by one estimate, of the $150 billion in federal government subsidies provided to nuclear, solar, and wind power in the past half century, the nuclear industry received 96%, solar received 3%, and wind less than 1%.

The funding situation has not been much different in Canada (**FIGURE 17.17**). As recently as 2006, the Report of the National Advisory Panel on Sustainable Energy Science and Technology[4] included the somewhat surprising statement that "renewable and nuclear technologies

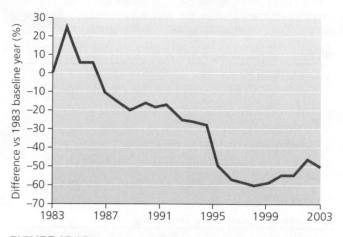

FIGURE 17.17
Federal funding for energy research and development (R&D) has plummeted in Canada over the past 20 years. Some of the gap has been filled by increases in funding from provinces and the private sector. Of federal energy R&D funds, a very small proportion has gone to the development of alternative energy technologies, primarily nuclear.

were not considered by the Panel to be key priorities for a national energy science and technology effort."

In light of continuing short-term profits and unclear policy signals, companies have not been eager to invest in the transition from fossil fuels to renewable energy. Under these circumstances, our best hope may be for a gradual shift driven largely by economic supply and demand. If the transition proceeds too slowly—if we wait for the market to do its work, without government encouragement—then fossil fuel supplies could dwindle faster than we are able to develop new sources, and we could find our economies disrupted and our environment highly degraded. Encouraging the development of renewable energy alternatives holds promise for a vigorous and sustainable energy economy without the environmental impacts of fossil fuels.

Biofuels and Biopower

As discussed earlier, biomass is widely used as a traditional energy source, especially in the developing world. Today biomass energy sources are becoming increasingly diverse and innovative (**TABLE 17.3**), providing great potential for addressing our energy challenges.

Biomass can be processed to make vehicle fuels

An important use of biomass energy is for conversion into **biofuels**. The two principal types of biofuels developed

Table 17.3   New Sources of Biomass Energy

Biofuels for powering vehicles

- Corn grown for ethanol
- *Bagasse* (sugarcane residue) grown for ethanol
- Soybeans, rapeseed (canola), and other crops grown for biodiesel
- Used cooking oil for biodiesel
- Plant matter treated with enzymes to produce cellulosic ethanol
- Algae fuels

Biopower for generating electricity

- Crop residues (such as cornstalks) burned at power plants
- Forestry residues (such as wood waste from logging) burned at power plants
- Processing wastes (such as solid or liquid waste from sawmills, pulp mills, and paper mills) burned at power plants
- "Landfill gas" burned at power plants
- Livestock waste from feedlots for gas from anaerobic digesters
- Organic components of municipal solid waste from landfills

FIGURE 17.18

An increasing proportion of the corn crop in Canada, as in the United States, is used to produce ethanol. Brazil produces most of the rest of the world's ethanol, from *bagasse* (sugarcane residue). Production of ethanol in Canada and worldwide has grown rapidly in the last decade.

so far are *ethanol* (for gasoline engines) and *biodiesel* (for diesel engines).

Ethanol is the alcohol that is in beer, wine, and liquor. It is produced as a biofuel by fermenting biomass, generally from carbohydrate-rich crops, in a process similar to brewing beer. The carbohydrates contained in the plants are converted to sugars and then to ethanol. Ethanol is now widely added to gasoline in the United States to reduce automotive emissions, spurred by the 1990 U.S. Clean Air Act. In 2008 in the United States, more than 9.2 billion litres of ethanol were produced, mostly from corn (**FIGURE 17.18**). The total production capacity for ethanol in Canada, as of 2009, was approximately 1.4 billion litres.

Any vehicle with a gasoline engine runs well on gasoline blended with up to 10% ethanol. Many automakers are now producing *flexible-fuel vehicles* that run on E-85, a mix of 85% ethanol and 15% gasoline. Few gas stations offer E-85, so drivers generally are forced to fill these cars with conventional gasoline; however, increasing infrastructure for ethanol will change this. In Brazil, for many years, sugarcane residue has been crushed to make *bagasse*, a material that is then used to make ethanol. Half of all new Brazilian cars are flexible-fuel vehicles, and ethanol from sugarcane accounts for 40% of all automotive fuel that Brazil's drivers use.

Vehicles with diesel engines can run on **biodiesel**, produced from vegetable oil mixed with small amounts of ethanol or methanol (wood alcohol). In Canada and in Europe, where most biodiesel is used, rapeseed (canola) oil is the oil of choice, whereas U.S. biodiesel producers use mostly soybean oil. Biodiesel producers can even utilize animal fats and used grease and cooking oil from restaurants.

Most frequently, biodiesel is mixed with conventional *petrodiesel* (petroleum-based diesel fuel); a 20% biodiesel mix (called B20) is common today. To run on straight vegetable oil, a diesel engine needs to be modified. Although the parts needed for these modifications can be bought for as little as $800, it remains to be seen whether using straight vegetable oil might entail further costs, such as reduced longevity or greater engine maintenance. Biodiesel cuts down on emissions compared with petrodiesel (**FIGURE 17.19**). Its fuel economy is almost as good, and it costs just slightly more, at today's oil prices. It is also nontoxic and biodegradable.

Growing crops specifically to produce ethanol or biodiesel may not be sustainable, so researchers are refining some new techniques for biofuel production. So-called second-generation biofuel technologies use enzymes to produce ethanol from the cellulose that gives structure to all plant material. If we can produce this *cellulosic ethanol* in commercially feasible ways, ethanol could be made from low-value crop waste (indigestible residues, such as corn stalks and husks), rather than from high-value crops (**FIGURE 17.20A**).

Other research projects are underway that aim to produce biofuels from algae, called third-generation biofuels. Lipids and carbohydrates from several species of photosynthetic algae can be converted into a variety of biofuels. Algae can be grown for the purpose in open ponds or in closed transparent tubes called *photobioreactors* (**FIGURE 17.20B**). Algae grow much faster than terrestrial crops, can be harvested every other day, and

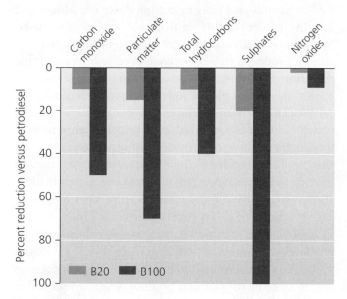

FIGURE 17.19
Burning biodiesel in a diesel engine emits less pollution than burning conventional petroleum-based diesel. Shown are the percentage reductions in several major automotive pollutants that one can attain by using B20 (a mix of 20% biodiesel and 80% petrodiesel) and B100 (pure biodiesel).
Source: Data from U.S. Environmental Protection Agency.

produce many times more biofuel than other crops. Algae farms can be set up just about anywhere, and can use waste water or saltwater. Because algae need nutrients, waste water from sewage treatment plants can be a good source of water. And because carbon dioxide is required for algal growth, algae farms can even be used to capture smokestack emissions. Production of algal fuels is still expensive, but the cost will likely come down as technologies improve.

Electricity can be generated from biomass

We can harness biomass energy by combusting biomass to generate electricity. Many of the sources used for this **biopower** are the waste products of existing industries. For instance, the forest products industry generates large amounts of woody debris in logging operations and at sawmills, pulp mills, and paper mills (**FIGURE 17.21A**), which can be used for biopower. Other waste sources include organic waste from municipal landfills, animal waste from agricultural feedlots, and crop residues (such as cornstalks and husks). Some crops are grown specifically to produce biopower. These include fast-growing trees, such as willows and poplars (**FIGURE 17.21B**), and fast-growing grasses, such as bamboo, fescue, and switchgrass.

(a) Switchgrass for cellulosic ethanol

(b) Algae for third-generation biofuels

FIGURE 17.20
(a) Switchgrass, a fast-growing plant native to the North American prairies, provides fuel for biopower and is being studied as a crop to provide cellulosic ethanol. **(b)** Algae are a leading candidate for a next-generation biofuel. Here algae are growing in networks of lighted tubes at a demonstration facility. Algae grow quickly, can be farmed in many places, and can be used to produce biodiesel, ethanol, and other fuels.

Power plants built to combust biomass operate similarly to those fired by fossil fuels; the combustion heats water, creating steam to turn turbines and generators, thereby generating electricity. Much of the biopower produced so far comes from power plants that generate both electricity and heating through *cogeneration*. These plants are often located where they can take advantage of forestry waste.

Biomass is also increasingly being combined with coal in coal-fired power plants in a process called *co-firing*. Wood chips, wood pellets, or other biomass is introduced with coal into a high-efficiency boiler that uses one of

(a) Forestry residues

(b) Fast-growing poplars

FIGURE 17.21
(a) Forestry residues (here from a Swedish logging operation on Vancouver Island) are a major source material for the production of biopower. **(b)** Hybrid poplars are specially bred for fast growth, and they are harvested for use in biopower production. The monocultural plantations, which may replace natural systems over large areas, do not function ecologically as forests.

several technologies. Biomass can substitute for up to 15% of the coal with only minor equipment modification and no appreciable loss of efficiency. Co-firing can be a relatively easy and inexpensive way for fossil-fuel-based utilities to expand their use of renewable energy.

The anaerobic bacterial breakdown of waste by microbes in landfills produces methane and other gases. This **landfill gas** is now being captured and used as fuel, generating both electricity and profits while avoiding harmful greenhouse gas emissions from the landfill (see "The Science Behind the Story: Energy from Landfill Gas at Beare Road"). Landfill gas utilization solves local environmental problems by cutting down on odours and limiting the possibility of fires and explosions caused by escaping methane gas. Methane and other gases can also be produced in a more controlled way in anaerobic digestion facilities. The resulting *biogas* can then be burned in a power plant's boiler to generate electricity.

We can also harness biopower through *gasification*, in which biomass is vaporized at extremely high temperatures in the absence of oxygen, creating a gaseous mixture that includes hydrogen, carbon monoxide, carbon dioxide, and methane. This mixture can generate electricity when used in power plants to turn a gas turbine to propel a generator. Gas from gasification can be treated in various ways to produce methanol, synthesize a type of diesel fuel, or isolate hydrogen for use in hydrogen fuel cells. An alternative method of heating biomass in the absence of oxygen can produce a liquid fuel called *pyrolysis oil*, which can be burned to generate electricity.

Biofuels have environmental and economic benefits

Adding biofuels such as ethanol and biodiesel to gasoline or petrodiesel helps those fuels to combust more completely, reducing pollution. Replacing gasoline or petrodiesel with biofuels reduces emissions of nitrogen oxides, greenhouse gases, and other pollutants. When used instead of coal in co-firing and direct combustion, biopower reduces emissions of sulphur dioxide because plant matter, unlike coal, contains no appreciable sulphur content.

Shifting from fossil fuels to biomass energy also can have economic benefits. The forest products industry in North America now obtains much of its energy by combusting the waste it recycles, including woody waste from pulp mill processing. Biomass tends to be the least expensive type of fuel for burning in power plants, and improved energy efficiency brings lower prices for consumers. As a resource, biomass tends to be well spread geographically, so using it should help support rural economies and reduce many nations' dependence on imported fuels.

Biofuels also have drawbacks

Growing crops to produce biofuels exerts tremendous impacts on ecosystems. Although crops grown for energy typically receive lower inputs of pesticides and fertilizers than those grown for food, cultivating biofuel crops is land-intensive and brings with it all the impacts of monocultural agriculture. Biofuel crops take up land that might

THE SCIENCE BEHIND THE STORY

Energy from Landfill Gas at Beare Road

Many municipalities utilize passive flaring systems like this one to dispose of landfill gases, preventing the gas from collecting and exploding catastrophically.

This is the landfill gas cleanup room at the Beare Landfill Power Plant, where particulates and moisture are removed from the methane gas, prior to bringing it to the furnaces.

Methane (CH_4) is the main component of **landfill gas**, gas generated by the decomposition of waste in landfills. (Carbon dioxide, CO_2, is typically a close second.) The capture, recovery, and use of landfill gas for electricity generation can yield from 50% to 70% of the energy of natural gas, in addition to cutting down greenhouse gas emissions that would otherwise result from its release into the atmosphere.[5] Capture is particularly important in the case of methane, which is approximately 21 times more effective than carbon dioxide as a greenhouse gas.

Municipalities around the world have long captured and burned off the gases that are naturally generated by garbage accumulating in landfills. In the past, this has been undertaken mainly to avoid odours, fires, and the potential for explosions. For

years at Beare Road Landfill in Toronto, as at many other sites, the gas was allowed to leak from the landfill via pipes called "candlesticks"—vertical pipes that allow the gas to flow passively out of the ground, with flames occasionally flaring from the tops of the pipes (see photo).

The passive flaring system at Beare Road has been replaced by over 80 vertical wells designed to extract approximately 40 m^3 of landfill gas per minute from the ground.[6] The gas—almost 50% methane—is brought to the Beare Landfill Power Plant, where particulate matter and moisture are removed (see second photo). The gas then goes to a series of reciprocating gas furnaces, where it is burned to generate electricity. Electricity generation began at the site in 1996.[7]

The Beare Landfill Power Plant currently produces enough electricity to service 4000 homes. The total cost of this *LFGTE (landfill gas-to-electricity)* facility was about $8.5 million. It has a 10-year anticipated life span, based on the amount of garbage in the landfill, and generates approximately $2 million in revenues each year for its owner, E.S. Fox, which has an agreement with Ontario Power Generation to purchase the electricity. Other LFGTE projects in Canada, including the Keele Valley Landfill in Toronto, Saint Michel Landfill near Montréal, and Clover Bar Landfill near Edmonton, have even higher gas and electricity outputs, longer projected life spans, and greater potential profits for the owners of the projects.

Although LFGTE sounds like a win-win idea (reusing waste materials, cutting back on greenhouse gas emissions and air pollution), some environmentalists are fundamentally opposed to its development. They fear that generating something positive from a pile of garbage will derail attempts to get people to cut down on the amount of waste that they generate. This is a reasonable concern. However, in the case of old sites like Beare Road, which hasn't received any new garbage since 1983, the pollution-reducing benefits seem to make it a winning proposition.

As of 2003 there were 44 LFGTE systems in Canada,[8] mostly in Ontario, British Columbia, and Québec. These facilities will likely play an increasingly important role as Canada strives to reduce greenhouse gas emission.

otherwise be left in its natural condition or developed for other purposes.

If we were to try to produce all the automotive fuel currently used in North America with ethanol from corn, we would need to expand the already immense corn acreage by more than 60%, with no loss of productivity and without producing any additional corn for food. Even at current levels of production, biofuel is competing with food production. As farmers shift more corn crops to ethanol, corn supplies for food have dropped, and international corn prices have skyrocketed. In Mexico,

where corn tortillas are a staple food, average citizens found themselves struggling and protests erupted across the country over the inflated price of corn.

Growing bioenergy crops also requires substantial inputs of energy. We currently operate farm equipment using fossil fuels, and farmers apply petroleum-based pesticides and fertilizers to increase yields. Moreover, fossil fuels are used in refineries to heat water so that we can distil pure ethanol. Thus, shifting from gasoline to ethanol for our transportation needs would not eliminate our reliance on fossil fuels.

Furthermore, growing corn for ethanol yields only a modest amount of energy relative to the energy that needs to be input. Recall our discussion of *energy returned on investment* (EROI). The EROI, or ratio of energy returned to energy invested, for corn-based ethanol is controversial, but the best recent estimates place it around 1.5:1. This means that to gain 1.5 units of energy from ethanol, we need to expend 1 unit of energy. The EROI of Brazilian *bagasse* ethanol is much higher, but the low ratio for corn-based ethanol makes this fuel quite inefficient. For this reason, many critics do not view ethanol as an effective path to sustainable energy use.

Future advances in cellulosic ethanol may ease the environmental impacts of biofuel crops considerably. Third-generation biofuels such as algal fuels are promising and should take up far less space than growing corn. In the meantime, until these technologies develop and costs decline, biomass energy use involves a complex mix of advantages and disadvantages.

Solar Energy

The Sun provides energy for almost all biological activity on Earth by converting hydrogen to helium through nuclear fusion. On average, each square metre of Earth's surface receives about 1 kilowatt of solar energy—17 times the energy of a light bulb. As a result, a typical house has enough roof area to generate all its power needs with rooftop panels that harness **solar energy**. The amount of energy Earth receives from the Sun *each day*, if it could be collected in full for our use, would be enough to power human consumption for a quarter of a century.

The potential for using sunlight to meet our energy needs is tremendous. However, we are still in the process of developing solar technologies and learning the most effective and cost-efficient ways to put the Sun's energy to use. Most solar technologies rely on the collection and, in some cases, concentration, of the Sun's rays. The principal uses for solar energy today are heating and cooling air; heating water for home and industrial uses; drying crops, such as tea, coffee, fruit, and others; generating electricity for off-grid and distributed energy applications; detoxifying water and air; cooking food; and, of course, daytime lighting.

Passive solar heating is simple and effective

The most commonly used way to harness solar energy is through **passive solar** energy collection. In this approach, buildings are designed and building materials are chosen to maximize absorption of sunlight in winter, even as they keep the interior cool in the summer.

Passive solar design usually involves installing south-facing windows to maximize sunlight capture in the winter (in the Northern Hemisphere; north-facing windows are used in the Southern Hemisphere). Overhangs block light from above, shading windows in the summer when the Sun is high in the sky and when cooling is needed. Passive solar techniques also include the use of heat-absorbing construction materials (called *thermal mass*) that absorb heat, store it, and release it later. Thermal mass made of straw, brick, concrete, or other materials most often is used in floors, ceilings, and walls.

Thermal mass is strategically located to capture sunlight in cold weather and radiate heat to the interior of the building. In warm weather the mass absorbs warm air in the interior to cool the building. Passive solar design can also involve planting vegetation in particular locations around a building. By heating buildings in cold weather and cooling them in warm weather, passive solar methods conserve energy and reduce energy costs.

Active solar energy can heat air and water in buildings

Active solar approaches make use of technological devices to focus, move, and store solar energy. One active technology involves using **solar panels** or *flat-plate solar collectors*, most often installed on rooftops. The panels generally consist of dark-coloured, heat-absorbing metal plates mounted in flat boxes covered with glass panes. Water, air, or antifreeze solutions are run through tubes that pass through the collectors, transferring heat throughout a building. Heated water can be pumped to tanks to store the heat for later use. Active solar systems are especially effective for heating water, and can be used even in remote areas (**FIGURE 17.22**).

We can magnify the strength of solar energy by gathering sunlight from a wide area and focusing it on a single point. This is the principle behind *solar cookers*, simple portable ovens that use reflectors to focus sunlight onto food and cook it. Such cookers are proving extremely useful in parts of the developing world.

Utilities have put the solar cooker principle to work in large-scale, high-tech approaches to generating electricity. In one approach, mirrors concentrate sunlight onto a receiver atop a tall "power-tower" (**FIGURE 17.23**). From the receiver, heat is transported by fluids that are piped to a steam-driven generator to create electricity. These solar power plants can harness light from large mirrors spread across many hectares of land. The largest such plant—a

FIGURE 17.22
Engineers in Gaviotas, a remote highland town in Colombia, developed inexpensive solar panels that provide residences and businesses active solar power for heating, cooling, and water purification.

collaboration among government, industry, and utility companies in the California desert—produces power for 10 000 households.

An interesting combination of active and passive solar technologies is the "Solarwall" that provides heating and cooling at the Bombardier's Canadair plant in Montreal. This is a south-facing cladding wall with millions of tiny holes, each about 1 mm in diameter, which allow outside air to pass through. Behind the cladding is a space for air flow. The air passing along the back of the wall absorbs solar-generated heat and rises to the roof, where it is

FIGURE 17.23
At the Solar Two facility in the desert of southern California, the largest such facility in the world, mirrors are spread across wide expanses of land to concentrate sunlight onto a receiver atop a "power-tower." Heat is then transported through fluid-filled pipes to a steam-driven generator that produces electricity.

collected and circulated through the building. This installation, the largest in the world, eliminated the need for fossil fuels at this facility, thereby cutting atmospheric emissions, and improved interior air quality in the plant as well.

Active solar technology dates from the eighteenth century, but it was pushed to the sidelines as fossil fuels came to dominate our energy economy. Largely because of lack of investment, solar energy contributes only a minuscule portion of energy production in Canada and worldwide. However, the growth in solar energy use worldwide has been second only to that of wind power. Since 1995, solar energy use in Canada has grown by an estimated 25% per year.[9] The federal government and some provincial/territorial governments have provided financial incentives for homeowners and business owners to switch to solar technologies.

PV cells generate electricity directly

A direct approach to producing electricity from sunlight involves **photovoltaic (PV) cells**, which collect sunlight and convert it to electrical energy by making use of the *photovoltaic* or *photoelectric effect*. This effect occurs when light strikes one of a pair of metal plates in a PV cell, causing the release of electrons, which are attracted by electrostatic forces to the opposing plate. The flow of electrons from one plate to the other creates an electrical current (direct current, DC), which can be converted into alternating current (AC) and used for residential and commercial electrical power (**FIGURE 17.24**).

The plates of a typical PV cell are made of silicon, which conducts electricity. One silicon plate (the *n-type layer*) is rich in electrons; the other (the *p-type layer*) is electron-poor. When sunlight strikes the PV cell, it knocks electrons loose from some of the silicon atoms. Connecting the two plates with wires generates electricity as electrons flow from the n-type layer back to the p-type layer. Photovoltaic cells can be connected to batteries that store the accumulated charge until it is needed.

You may be familiar with small PV cells that power your watch or solar calculator. Atop the roofs of homes and other buildings, PV cells can be arranged in arrays. Increasingly, PV roofing tiles are being used in place of these arrays. In some remote areas, PV systems are used in combination with wind turbines and a diesel generator to power entire villages. The use of PV cells is growing fast, and should continue to increase as prices fall, technologies improve, and governments enact economic incentives to spur investment.

FIGURE 17.24   A photovoltaic (PV) cell converts sunlight to electrical energy. When sunlight hits the silicon layers of the cell, electrons are knocked loose and move from layer to layer. Connecting the layers with wiring allows electrical current to flow between them. This direct current (DC) is converted to alternating current (AC) to produce usable electricity. PV cells are grouped in modules, which comprise panels that can be erected in arrays.

Solar power offers many benefits

The Sun is effectively inexhaustible as an energy source for human civilization. Moreover, the amount of solar energy reaching Earth's surface should be enough to power our civilization once the technology is adequately developed. These primary benefits of solar energy are clear, but the technologies themselves also provide benefits. PV cells and other solar technologies use no fuel, are quiet and safe, contain no moving parts, require little maintenance, and do not even require a turbine or generator to create electricity. An average unit can produce energy for 20 to 30 years.

Solar systems allow for local, decentralized power. Homes, businesses, and isolated communities can use solar power to produce their own electricity without being near a power plant or connected to the power grid. In developing nations, solar cookers enable families to cook food without gathering fuelwood, lessening the daily workload and reducing deforestation. The low cost of solar cookers has made them available to many impoverished areas.

In the developed world, most PV systems are connected to the regional electric grid. This may enable owners of houses with PV systems to sell their excess solar energy to their local power utility. In this process, called **net metering**, the value of the power the consumer sells to the utility is subtracted from the consumer's monthly utility bill. As of this writing, net metering is available in most Canadian provinces.

Another advantage of solar power is that its development is producing new jobs. Currently, among major energy sources, PV technology employs the most people per unit of energy output. Finally, a major advantage of solar power over fossil fuels is that once a PV system is up and running, it produces no greenhouse gases or other polluting emissions.

Location and cost can be drawbacks

Solar energy currently has two major disadvantages. One is that not all regions are sunny enough to provide adequate power, given current technology. Daily or seasonal variation in sunlight can also pose problems for stand-alone solar systems if storage capacity in batteries or fuel cells is not adequate or if backup power is not available from a municipal power grid. In far northern locations, for example, although the total number of bright sunshine hours is very high over the course of a year, seasonal variations in the number of hours of daylight can make solar power more difficult to utilize (**FIGURE 17.25**). Intermittent supply is an argument that is also commonly levied against wind and other alternative energy sources. This can be mitigated against by having backup systems available, and by coupling different energy sources together. The use of alternative energy sources doesn't have to be an all-or-nothing venture; even if solar is only supplying 50% of the energy to a building, for example, GHG emissions will still be cut in half.

The primary disadvantage of current solar technology is the up-front cost of equipment. Proponents of solar power argue that decades of government promotion of fossil fuels and nuclear power have made solar power unable to compete. However, decreases in price and improvements in energy efficiency of solar technologies so far are encouraging, even in the absence of significant financial commitment from government and industry.

At their advent in the 1950s, solar technologies had efficiencies of around 6% while costing $600 per watt (the cost is now closer to $7 per watt). Recent single-crystal silicon PV cells are showing 15% efficiency commercially and 24% efficiency in lab research, suggesting that future solar technologies may be more efficient than any energy technologies we have today. Solar systems have become much less expensive over the years and now can pay for themselves within 10 to 20 years. After that time, they provide energy virtually for free as long as the equipment lasts. With future technological advances, some experts believe that the time to recoup investment could fall to one to three years.

Wind Energy

Wind energy—energy derived from moving air masses—is an indirect form of solar energy, because it is the Sun's differential heating of air masses that causes wind to blow. We can harness power from wind using **wind turbines**, mechanical assemblies that convert wind's kinetic energy, or energy of motion, into electrical energy.

Today's wind turbines have their historical roots in Europe, where windmills have been used for 800 years to drain wetlands, irrigate crops, and grind grain into flour. Wind causes the windmill's blades to turn, driving a shaft connected to several cogs that turn wheels, which perform the required work. In North America, countless ranches in the Prairies and the Great Plains have long used windmills to draw groundwater up for thirsty cattle.

After the 1973 oil crisis, governments in North America and Europe began funding research and development for wind power. This moderate infusion of funding boosted technological progress, and the cost of wind power was

(a)

(b)

FIGURE 17.25 Because some locations receive more sunlight than others, harnessing solar energy is more profitable in some areas than in others. The yearly solar average of Canada's populated areas **(a)** exceeds that in both Germany and Japan, the world's solar leaders. Solar energy can be used to power remote applications, as in this solar installation in Nunavut **(b)**. *Source: Based on* The Canadian Atlas Online, *Canadian Geographic www. canadiangeographic.ca/atlas/themes.aspx?id=weather&sub=weather_power_solarpower&lang=En*

cut in half within 10 years. Today wind power at favourable locations generates electricity for nearly as little cost per kilowatt-hour as conventional sources. The first wind power producer in Canada was Cowley Ridge Wind Plant in Alberta, the first phase of which opened in 1993. The largest is the Le Nordais project in the Gaspé Peninsula.

Modern wind turbines convert kinetic energy to electrical energy

In modern wind turbines, the wind turns blades that rotate machinery inside a compartment called a *nacelle*, which sits atop a tall tower (**FIGURE 17.26**). Inside the nacelle are a gearbox, a generator, and equipment to monitor and control the turbine's activity. Most towers range from 40 to 100 m tall. Higher is generally better, to minimize turbulence and maximize wind speed. Most rotors consist of three blades and measure 42 to 80 m across. Turbines are designed to yaw, or rotate back and forth, in response to changes in wind direction, ensuring that the motor faces into the wind at all times. Turbines can be erected singly, but they are often erected in groups called **wind farms**. The world's largest wind farms contain hundreds of turbines spread across the landscape.

Slight differences in wind speed yield substantial differences in power output. The energy content of a given amount of wind increases as the square of its velocity; for this reason, if wind velocity doubles, energy quadruples. Some turbines are designed to generate low levels of electricity by turning in light breezes; others are programmed to rotate only in stronger winds, operating less frequently but generating large amounts of electricity in short time periods.

Wind power is the fastest-growing energy sector

Like solar energy, wind provides only a small proportion of the world's power needs, but wind power capacity is growing fast—by 26% per year globally between 2000 and 2005, and then quadrupling between 2006 and 2009. Germany has been the world leader in installed wind capacity; however, in Denmark a series of wind farms supplies over 20% of the nation's electricity needs, the highest proportion in the world. Experts agree that wind power's rapid growth will continue. Meteorological evidence suggests that wind power could be expanded in Canada to about 30 000 MW, sufficient to meet 15% of the nation's electrical needs. To date, Canada's wind power leaders are Québec, Alberta, and Saskatchewan.[10]

Offshore and high-altitude sites are particularly promising. Wind speeds on average are roughly 20% greater over water than over land, and there is less air turbulence over water. It is clear from **FIGURE 17.27** that wind conditions over Hudson's Bay are stronger than anywhere over land in Canada, for example. Costs to erect and maintain offshore wind turbines are higher, but the stronger, less turbulent winds produce more power and make them potentially more profitable. Currently, offshore wind farms are limited to shallow water, where towers are sunk into sediments to stabilize them. In the future, towers may be placed on floating pads anchored to the seafloor in deep water. There are as yet no operational offshore wind installations in Canada.

Winter weather also promotes stronger wind conditions, as do high elevations. Studies in the Yukon Territory, for example, have found many elevated sites suitable for wind power development, and the territory

FIGURE 17.26
A wind turbine converts wind's energy of motion into electrical energy. Wind causes the blades to spin, turning a shaft that extends into the nacelle, perched atop the tower. Inside the nacelle, a gearbox converts the rotational speed of the blades, which can be up to 20 revolutions per minute (rpm) or more, into much higher rotational speeds (over 1500 rpm). These high speeds provide motion for a generator inside the nacelle to produce electricity.

Mean Wind Speed at 50 m above ground
Vitesse moyenne du vent à 50 m au dessus du sol

Horizontal resolution of 5 km
Resolution horizontale de 5 km

(a) Distribution of wind in Canada

(b) Cowley Ridge Wind Plant, Alberta

FIGURE 17.27   Southern Alberta and Saskatchewan enjoy some of Canada's best conditions for wind power, but offshore wind speeds are highest **(a)**. Cowley Ridge Wind Plant in southwestern Alberta **(b)** was Canada's first commercial wind power plant, opened in 1993.   *Source: Based on Canadian Geographic, The Canadian Atlas Online, "Wind Power" www.canadiangeographic.ca/atlas/themes.aspx?id=WEATHER&sub=WEATHER_POWER_WINDPOWER&lang=En*

has recently invested in new installations (**FIGURE 17.28**). Wind turbines in cold climates face specific challenges, however, such as icing of the turbine blades.

Wind power has many benefits

Like solar power, wind produces no emissions once the necessary equipment is manufactured and installed. The graph in **FIGURE 17.29** shows emissions per kWh of

FIGURE 17.28
Winter winds and high elevations combine to make conditions that are appropriate for wind power generation in Yukon Territory, although icing of the turbine blades can be a challenge.

electricity produced over the entire installed lifetime of various technologies. Emissions of CO_2 (the main greenhouse gas associated with global warming), SO_2 (the main precursor of acid rain), and NO_x (the main precursor of photochemical smog) are significantly lower for wind and other renewables, as well as nuclear and hydro, compared to fossil-fuel-based electricity generation. Other types of harmful emissions also can be avoided; for example, the U.S. Environmental Protection Agency (EPA) calculates that running a 1-megawatt wind turbine for 1 year prevents the release of approximately 30 kg of mercury, in comparison to the generation of electricity by a typical coal-fired power plant.

Wind power, under optimal conditions, is considerably more efficient than conventional power sources in its energy returned on investment (EROI). One study found that wind turbines produce 23 times more energy than they consume. For nuclear energy, the ratio was 16:1; for coal it was 11:1; and for natural gas it was 5:1.

Wind turbine technology can be used on many scales, from a single tower for local use to fields of hundreds that supply large regions. Small-scale turbine development can help make local areas more energy self-sufficient. Farmers and ranchers can lease their land for wind development, which provides extra revenue while increasing property tax income for rural communities. Because each turbine takes up only a small area, most of the land can still be used for farming, ranching, or other uses.

FIGURE 17.29
The lifetime emissions of CO_2, SO_2, and NO_x from wind, solar PV, hydro, nuclear, and even biomass-sourced electricity generation are dramatically lower per kWh than for all of the fossil-fuel-based sources.
Source: Data from Power Generation in Canada: A Guide, *Canadian Electricity Association 2006.*

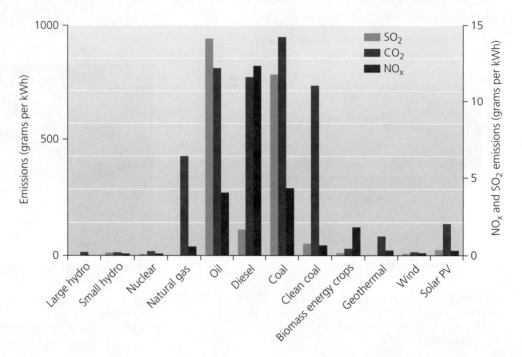

Wind power has some downsides—but not many

Wind is an intermittent resource; we have no control over when wind will occur, and this unpredictability is a major limitation in relying on it as an electricity source. However, this poses little problem if wind is only one of several sources contributing to a utility's power generation. Moreover, several new technologies are being developed to store energy generated by wind and release it later when needed.

Wind varies from place to place. Global and regional wind systems combine with local topography to create local wind patterns, and the best wind resources are not always near population centres that need the energy. Transmission networks would need to be greatly expanded to get wind power to where people live. When wind farms *are* proposed near population centres, local residents often oppose them. Some people object to wind farms for aesthetic reasons, feeling that the structures clutter the landscape. Although polls show wide public approval of existing wind projects and of the concept of wind power in general, newly proposed wind projects often elicit the **"not-in-my-backyard" (NIMBY)** syndrome among people living nearby.

Wind turbines may also pose a threat to birds and bats, which can be killed by flying into rotating blades or by encountering pockets of negative pressure in the lee side of the rotating blades. Studies at several sites suggest that bird deaths may be a less severe problem

weighing the issues

WIND AND NIMBY

How would you react if your electric utility proposed to build a wind farm atop a ridge running in back of your neighbourhood, such that the turbines would be visible from your house? Would you support or oppose the development? Why? If you would oppose it, where would you suggest the farm be located? Do you think anyone might oppose it in that location?

than was initially feared; for instance, one European study indicated that migrating seabirds fly past offshore turbines without problem. However, other data show that resident seabird densities decline near turbines. The key for protecting birds and bats may be selecting sites that are not on flyways or in the midst of prime habitat.

Geothermal Energy

Geothermal energy is one form of renewable energy that does not originate from the Sun; it is generated deep within Earth. The radioactive decay of elements deep in the interior of our planet generates heat that rises to the surface, heating rock and groundwater, and generating steam. Geysers and submarine hydrothermal vents are the surface manifestations of these processes.

One country that has abundant geothermal resources is Iceland (**FIGURE 17.30A**). It is an island built from magma that extruded above the ocean's surface and cooled—magma from the Mid-Atlantic Ridge, the area of volcanic activity along the spreading boundary of two tectonic plates. Because of the geothermal heat in this region, volcanoes and geysers are numerous in Iceland. In fact, the word *geyser* (a natural spring that discharges hot water or steam) originated from the Icelandic *Geysir*, the island's largest geyser.

Geothermal power plants use the energy of naturally heated underground water and steam for direct heating and to turn turbines and generate electricity (**FIGURE 17.30B**). Geothermal energy is renewable, in principle, because its use does not affect the amount of heat produced in Earth's interior.

However, geothermal power plants may not be capable of operating indefinitely. If a geothermal plant uses heated water more quickly than the groundwater is recharged, the plant will eventually run out of water. This is occurring at The Geysers, in Napa Valley, California, a very early geothermal application where the first generator was built in 1960. In response, operators have begun injecting municipal wastewater into the ground to replenish the supply. More geothermal plants are now reinjecting water after it is used, to help maintain pressure in the aquifer and thereby sustain the resource.

(a) Nesjavellir, Iceland

FIGURE 17.30

At the Nesjavellir geothermal power station in Iceland **(a)**, steam is piped from four wells to a condenser at the plant, where cold water pumped from lakeshore wells 6 km away is heated. The water, heated to 83°C, is sent through an insulated 270-km pipeline to Reykjavik, where residents use it for washing and space heating. **(b)** At a typical geothermal site, magma heats groundwater deep underground (1), some of which escapes naturally through surface vents such as geysers (2). Geothermal facilities tap into heated water below ground and channel steam through turbines in buildings to generate electricity (3). After being used, the steam is often condensed, and the water pumped back into the aquifer to maintain pressure (4).

2 Where natural fissures or cracks appear, heated water or steam surfaces in geysers or hot springs

3 Wells tap underground heated water or steam to turn turbines and generate power

Turbine and generator

Cooling tower

Recharge area

Geyser

Fault

Impermeable rock

Confined aquifer

Impermeable rock

Heat source (magma)

Steam

1 Magma heats groundwater

Injection well

4 Steam is cooled, condensed, and water is injected back into the aquifer to maintain pressure

(b) A geothermal power plant

We can harness geothermal energy for heating and electricity

Geothermal energy can be harnessed directly from geysers at the surface, but most often wells must be drilled down hundreds or thousands of metres toward heated groundwater. Water at temperatures of 150–370°C or more is brought to the surface and converted to steam by lowering the pressure in specialized compartments. The steam is then employed in turning turbines to generate electricity.

Hot groundwater can also be used directly for heating homes, offices, and greenhouses; for driving industrial processes; and for drying crops. Iceland heats most of its homes through direct heating with piped hot water. Iceland began using geothermal energy in the 1940s, and today 30 municipal district heating systems and 200 small private rural networks supply heat to 86% of the nation's residences.

Geothermal **ground-source heat pumps** (GSHPs) use thermal energy from near-surface land and water (see "The Science Behind the Story: Water and Earth Energy for Heating and Cooling in Toronto and Ottawa"). Soil varies in temperature from season to season less than air does, so the pumps heat buildings in the winter by transferring heat from the ground into buildings, and they cool buildings in the summer by transferring heat from buildings into the ground. Both types of heat transfer are accomplished by a network of underground plastic pipes that circulate water. Because heat is simply moved from place to place rather than being produced using outside energy inputs, heat pumps can be highly energy-efficient.

Natural Resources Canada estimates that there are at least 30 000 GSHPs making use of Earth energy to heat offices, institutions (such as hospitals and universities), factories, and residences in Canada. This is significant because more than half of the energy demand in institutional and commercial settings in Canada is for space heating. Compared to conventional electric heating and cooling systems, GSHPs heat spaces 50–70% more efficiently, cool them 20–40% more efficiently, can reduce electricity use by 25–60%, and can reduce emissions by up to 70%.

Use of geothermal power is growing

Geothermal energy provides less than 0.5% of the total energy used worldwide and remains largely unexploited in Canada. Worldwide it provides more power than solar and wind combined, but only a small fraction compared to hydropower and biomass. In Canada the geologic settings are such that true geothermal energy is commercially viable only in British Columbia because of its proximity to the boundary of the Juan da Fuca tectonic plate.

In the right setting, geothermal power can be among the cheapest sources of electricity. Currently Japan, China, and the United States lead the world in use of geothermal power. However, at the world's largest geothermal power plants, The Geysers in northern California, generating capacity has declined by more than 50% since 1989 as steam pressure has declined.

Geothermal power has benefits and limitations

Like other renewable sources, geothermal power greatly reduces polluting emissions, relative to fossil fuel combustion. Geothermal sources can release variable amounts of gases dissolved in their water, including carbon dioxide, methane, ammonia, and hydrogen sulphide. However, these gases are generally in very small quantities, and geothermal facilities using the latest filtering technologies produce even fewer emissions. By one estimate, each megawatt of geothermal power prevents the emission of 7.0 million kg of carbon dioxide emissions each year.

On the negative side, geothermal sources, as we have seen, may not always be truly sustainable. In addition, the water of many hot springs is laced with salts and minerals that corrode equipment. These factors may shorten the lifetime of plants, increase maintenance costs, and add to pollution. Moreover, use of geothermal energy is limited to areas where the energy can be tapped. Unless technology is developed to penetrate far more deeply into the ground, geothermal energy use will remain extremely localized. Nonetheless, many hydrothermal resources remain unexploited, awaiting improved technology and governmental support for their development.

Ocean Energy

The ocean hosts several underexploited energy sources. Each involves continuous natural processes that could potentially provide sustainable, predictable energy. Of the four approaches being developed, three involve motion, and one involves temperature.

THE SCIENCE BEHIND THE STORY

Water and Earth Energy for Heating and Cooling in Toronto and Ottawa

The Enwave Deep Lake Water Cooling Plant in Toronto takes advantage of the cold, deep waters of Lake Ontario to provide district cooling.

A forward-looking plan utilizes the cold, deep waters of Lake Ontario to provide air conditioning to more than 2.5 million m² of downtown office and living spaces in Toronto. The Enwave Deep Lake Water Cooling project is a district cooling technology that takes advantage of low-temperature lake water immediately adjacent to the downtown area. The project is coordinated by Enwave Energy, which was set up (originally as a nonprofit corporation) to develop the application more than 20 years ago.

The system works by taking cold water in through three large intake pipes that lie 83 m below the surface of the lake and extend 5.1 km from the shore. Each day, millions of litres of water at 4°C are pumped to the Toronto Island filtration plant, where the water is treated and circulated for normal distribution into the city drinking water supply via a pumping station. Before leaving the pumping station, the cold water is diverted through a series of heat exchangers. The coldness of the water is used to remove the thermal energy from warm water passing through pipes on the other side of the heat exchangers. The newly cooled water moves through a system of many kilometres of underground pipes, providing cooling to customers in more than 140 buildings. The water is then returned to the pumping station, and the circuit is repeated.

The chilled water and the city's drinking water always remain on opposite sides of the heat exchanger and thus never come into contact with each other. The chilled water is recirculated and recooled through a closed loop system (see diagram). By using the deep lake water to provide district cooling, the project saves approximately 128 million kWh annually in electricity, reducing CO_2 emissions by 79 000 tons and reducing electricity consumption by 90% compared to conventional air conditioning technologies.[11]

Geothermal or terrestrial ("Earth energy") heat pumps also utilize fluids to store, transport, and supply thermal energy. During the winter months, when the temperature just a few metres under the surface is considerably warmer than the air temperature, heat pumps are used to extract this near-surface thermal energy from groundwater travelling through underground pipes. This heat is primarily solar energy that was absorbed and stored in subsurface soil layers, rather than "true" geothermal energy originating from the hot inner layers of Earth.

Once extracted, the heat is distributed. The cooled fluid is then returned to its underground reservoir to be reheated. Heat pumps are reversible, so the same process can provide cooling. During the summer months, groundwater is used to cool buildings (in a process similar to the Enwave Deep Lake Water Cooling process) and is then returned to its underground reservoir to be recooled. Both heating and cooling by this method are cyclic processes that can be repeated indefinitely.

Closed-loop systems continuously recirculate the fluid through a pipeline circuit (see diagram) without discharging it back into the aquifer or water body from which it was obtained. In district heating systems in Canada, this fluid is typically a mixture of antifreeze and water, but plain water or air can work in some circumstances. In an *open-loop* system, in contrast, heat energy is acquired from the water via heat exchangers, and the water is then discharged back into the aquifer or water body. Open-loop systems can be less expensive, but they require a suitable water supply and must be designed to mitigate

Geothermal heat pump systems

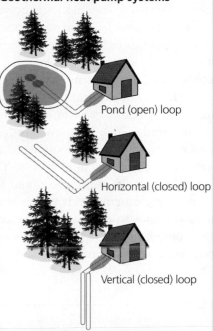

Pond (open) loop

Horizontal (closed) loop

Vertical (closed) loop

Geothermal heat pump systems operate on either closed-loop or open-loop systems, in which fluids are used to carry, supply, and store thermal energy. Heat pumps extract energy from the fluids, which are then returned to the underground reservoir.

environmental impacts.[12] Injecting water into an aquatic system at a temperature that differs from its original temperature may damage organisms in the ecosystem.

There are thousands of heat pump installations throughout Canada, some for individual buildings and others used in district heating or cooling. One example is the Underground Thermal Energy Storage (UTES) system, which relies on underground reservoirs to store heat during the summer and provide heat during the winter. The UTES technology has been in use at Carleton University in Ottawa since 1990. Environment Canada estimates that the UTES system reduces cooling costs by 80% and heating costs by 40% or more, in addition to significant reductions in the polluting emissions that would otherwise be associated with space heating and cooling.[13]

We can harness energy from tides, waves, and currents

Just as dams on rivers use the kinetic energy of flowing water to generate hydroelectric power, some scientists, engineers, businesses, and governments are developing ways to use the kinetic energy from the natural motion of ocean water to generate electrical power.

The rising and falling of ocean tides twice each day at coastal sites throughout the world moves large amounts of water past any given point on the world's coastlines (see "Central Case: Harnessing Tidal Energy at the Bay of Fundy"). Differences in height between low and high tides are especially great in long, narrow bays like the Bay of Fundy. Such locations are best for harnessing **tidal energy**, which is accomplished by erecting sluices across the outlets of tidal basins. The incoming tide flows through the sluice gates, and is trapped behind. Then, as the outgoing tide passes through the gates, it turns turbines to generate electricity (**FIGURE 17.31**). Some designs allow for generating electricity from water moving in both directions.

The world's largest tidal generating facility is the La Rance facility in France, which has operated for over 40 years. Smaller facilities operate in China and Russia and in Canada at the Bay of Fundy. Tidal stations release few or no pollutant emissions, but they can have impacts on the ecology of estuaries and tidal basins.

Wave energy, harnessed from wind-driven waves at the ocean's surface, could be developed at a variety of sites to produce electricity. Many designs for machinery to harness wave energy exist, but few have been adequately tested and no commercial facilities are operating yet. Some designs are for offshore facilities and involve floating devices that move up and down with the waves. Wave energy is greatest at deep-ocean sites, but transmitting the electricity to shore would be expensive. Other wave-energy technologies are designed for coastal installation. Some designs funnel waves into narrow channels and elevated reservoirs from which the water is then allowed to flow out, generating electricity in much the same manner as hydroelectric dams do. Other designs use rising and falling waves to push air into and out of chambers, turning turbines to generate electricity.

FIGURE 17.31   Energy can be extracted from the movement of the tides at coastal sites where tidal flux is great enough. One way of doing so involves using bulb turbines in concert with the outgoing tide. At high tide (1), ocean water is let through the sluice gates, filling an interior basin (2). At low tide (3), the basin water is let out into the ocean, spinning turbines to generate electricity (4). This technology is similar to what has been used at the Annapolis Tidal Power Station since 1984.

In addition to tides and waves, a third potential source of marine kinetic energy is the flow of ocean currents, such as the Gulf Stream. Devices that look essentially like underwater wind turbines have been erected in European waters to test the intriguing idea of harnessing the energy from the flow of surface currents.

The ocean stores thermal energy

Each day the tropical oceans absorb an amount of solar radiation equivalent to the heat content of 250 billion barrels of oil—enough to provide about 100 000 times the electricity used daily in Canada. The ocean's sun-warmed surface is higher in temperature than its deep water, and **ocean thermal energy conversion (OTEC)** is based on this gradient in temperature.

In a closed-cycle approach (similar to the systems discussed in "The Science Behind the Story: Water and Earth Energy for Heating and Cooling in Toronto and Ottawa"), warm surface water is piped into a facility to evaporate chemicals, such as ammonia, that boil at low temperatures. These evaporated gases spin turbines to generate electricity. Cold water piped in from ocean depths then condenses the gases so they can be reused. In the open-cycle approach, warm surface water is evaporated in a vacuum, and its steam turns turbines and then is condensed by cold water. Because ocean water loses its salts as it evaporates, the water can be recovered, condensed, and sold as desalinized fresh water for drinking or agriculture.

OTEC systems require not only a large temperature difference between the surface and deeper waters, but also a rapid dropoff of underwater topography near the coast, so that sufficiently cold temperatures can be accessed within a reasonable distance of the shore. Research on OTEC systems has been conducted in Hawaii and Japan, where conditions are optimal, but costs remain high, and as of yet no facility is commercially operational.

Hydrogen Fuel and Power Storage

At the beginning of the chapter we mentioned that there are three main categories of applications for renewables: electricity generation, space heating (and cooling), and fuels. All the renewable energy sources we have discussed so far can be used to generate electricity more cleanly than can fossil fuels. Many of them can be applied locally, to provide space heating or cooling for buildings and districts.

As useful as these applications are to us, however, a major drawback is that the energy and electricity generated by them cannot be stored and transported easily in large quantities for use when and where they are needed. This is why vehicles still rely on fossil fuels for power. The development of hydrogen shows fuel, fuel cells, and related energy storage technologies shows promise for storing and transporting energy conveniently.

In the "hydrogen economy" that many energy experts believe will be the next big energy wave worldwide, hydrogen fuel—together with electricity— believe will be the next big energy wave would serve as the basis for a clean, safe, and efficient energy system. This system would use as fuel the universe's simplest and most abundant element. Electricity generated from renewable sources that are intermittent, such as wind or solar energy, could be used to produce hydrogen. **Fuel cells**—which utilize chemical energy, like batteries—could then employ the hydrogen to produce electrical energy as needed to power vehicles, computers, cell phones, home heating, and countless other applications (**FIGURE 17.32**).

Basing an energy system on hydrogen could alleviate dependence on foreign fuels and help fight climate change. For these reasons, many governments, including the federal and provincial governments in Canada, are funding research into hydrogen and fuel cell technology. Automobile companies and other private corporations also are investing significant amounts in research and development to produce vehicles that run on hydrogen and to develop fuel cell technologies and infrastructure.

Hydrogen may be produced from water or from other matter

Hydrogen gas (H_2) does not tend to exist freely on Earth; rather, hydrogen atoms bind to other molecules, becoming incorporated in everything from water to organic molecules. To obtain hydrogen, we must force these substances to release their hydrogen atoms, and this requires an input of energy. Several ways of producing hydrogen are being studied. In **electrolysis**, electricity is input to split hydrogen atoms from the oxygen atoms of water molecules:

$$2H_2O \rightarrow 2H_2 + O_2$$

Whether this strategy for producing hydrogen would cause pollution over its entire life cycle depends on the source of the electricity used for the electrolysis. If coal is burned to create the electricity, then the process may not reduce emissions compared with fossil fuels. If, however,

FIGURE 17.32   Hydrogen fuel drives electricity generation in a fuel cell, creating water as a waste product. There are many different types of fuel cells. In this example, atoms of hydrogen first are stripped of their electrons (1). The electrons move from a negative electrode to a positive one, creating a current and generating electricity (2). Meanwhile, the hydrogen ions pass through a proton exchange membrane (3) and combine with oxygen to form water molecules (4).

the electricity is produced by a less-polluting renewable source, then hydrogen production by electrolysis would create much less pollution than fossil fuels. The "cleanliness" of a future hydrogen economy, therefore, depends largely on the source of electricity used in electrolysis.

The environmental impact of hydrogen production also depends on the source material for the hydrogen. Besides water, hydrogen can be obtained from biomass and fossil fuels. Obtaining hydrogen from these sources generally requires less energy input, but results in emissions of carbon-based pollutants. For instance, extracting hydrogen from the methane (CH_4) in natural gas entails producing one molecule of the greenhouse gas carbon dioxide for every four molecules of hydrogen gas:

$$CH_4 + 2H_2O \rightarrow 4H_2 + CO_2$$

Thus, whether a hydrogen-based energy system would be environmentally cleaner than a fossil fuel system will depend on how the hydrogen is extracted and on its source. Other questions about the lifetime environmental impacts of hydrogen fuel are still being investigated.

Fuel cells can be used to produce electricity

Once isolated, hydrogen gas can be used as a fuel to produce electricity within fuel cells. The chemical reaction involved in a fuel cell is simply the reverse of that shown for electrolysis; an oxygen molecule and two hydrogen molecules each split so that their atoms can bind and form two water molecules:

$$2H_2 + O_2 \rightarrow 2H_2O$$

The way this occurs in one common type of fuel cell is shown in **FIGURE 17.32**. Hydrogen gas (usually compressed and stored in an attached fuel tank) is allowed into one side of the cell, whose middle consists of two electrodes that sandwich a membrane that only protons (hydrogen ions) can move across. One electrode, helped by a chemical catalyst, strips the hydrogen gas of its electrons, creating two hydrogen ions that begin moving across the membrane. Meanwhile, on the other side of the cell, oxygen molecules from the open air are split into their component atoms along the other electrode. These oxygen ions soon bind to pairs of hydrogen ions travel-

CANADIAN ENVIRONMENTAL PERSPECTIVES

David Keith

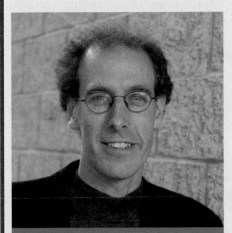

David Keith has made a lifetime commitment to solving problems related to energy and climate change.

- ■ **Sustainable energy advisor** and **energy systems expert**
- ■ **Physicist** and **Canada Research Chair in Energy and Environment** at the University of Calgary
- ■ **Canadian Geographic Environmental Scientist of the Year** for 2006

In 2001, *Canadian Geographic* created the Canadian Environment Awards, recognizing a variety of contributions to better understanding and management of the environment, from a wide spectrum of people. In 2006 the magazine also began to recognize the contributions of Canadian scientists, and the very first Canadian Environmental Scientist of the Year was David Keith.

As an undergraduate, Keith won first prize in Canada's National Physics Prize exam. As a graduate student, he won a departmental prize for excellence in

experimental physics at the Massachusetts Institute of Technology (MIT). He is now a professor appointed to both the Department of Chemical and Petroleum Engineering and the Department of Economics at the University of Calgary. These seemingly incongruent postings reflect the interdisciplinary nature of Keith's research interests, which lie at the intersections between climate science, energy technology, and public policy. His technical and policy work focuses on technologies for the capture and storage of CO_2, the economics and climatic impacts of large-scale wind power, the use of hydrogen as a transportation fuel, and the technology and implications of *geoengineering*[14]—that is, large-scale interventions in or modifications of Earth's climate system.

Keith, who chairs the Energy and Environmental Systems Group at the University of Calgary, has a reputation for being somewhat blunt, and for challenging entrenched beliefs. He has been known to reject some widely accepted ideas about energy and the environment—both those of the traditional energy sectors and those of the environmental movement. This prompted *Canadian Geographic* to call him a "contrarian" in his citation for Environmental Scientist of the Year.[15] For example, Keith spends a lot of time working out the economics of alternative, non–carbon-based energy technologies, such as wind power. "When it comes to climate change, I'm interested in technologies and social solutions that could take a big bite out of the problem," he says; but he also stresses that, in his opinion, "Economically, it's not even clear that global warming is all negative. It's just not true that the climate we have is automatically the best one—and you have to be straight about this."[16]

Much of Keith's commitment to solving problems related to climate change arises from his deep love of the Arctic. "One of the most fundamental reasons for working on the climate problem is to protect some remaining natural wilderness in the world . . . There are places, like the Arctic and Central Australia, we haven't yet messed with much. These are important, not just biologically but spiritually."[17] Keith comes by this commitment to environmental science naturally—his father, Anthony Keith, began his career as a Canadian Wildlife Service scientist in the 1960s, and was instrumental in convincing then-prime minister Pierre Trudeau to support a widespread ban on DDT use in Canada.

"We don't yet know how to manage the planet, and we don't have the institutions and governing structures for doing so."[18]
—*David Keith*

Thinking About Environmental Perspectives

David Keith's career has combined a number of seemingly unrelated disciplines (physics, economics, and engineering) into a research focus that makes a lot of sense in today's complicated environmental landscape. Try to identify some of your own cross-disciplinary interests. What about psychology and energy conservation (How do you get people to change their energy-using behaviour?)? Or ethics and waste disposal (Is it right to transport someone's garbage a long distance, to dispose of it in someone else's backyard?)? Or economics, political science, and water resources (Can you use laws or pricing structures to effect a change in the way we use and manage our water resources?)?

---

ling across the membrane, forming molecules of water that are expelled as waste, along with heat. While this is occurring, the electrons from the hydrogen atoms have travelled to a device that completes an electric current between the two electrodes. The movement of the hydrogen's electrons from one electrode to the other creates the output of electricity.

Hydrogen and fuel cells have many benefits

As a fuel, hydrogen offers a number of benefits. We will never run out of hydrogen; it is the most abundant element in the universe. It can be clean and nontoxic to use, and—depending on the source of the hydrogen and the source of electricity for its extraction—it may produce few greenhouse gases and other pollutants. Pure water and heat may be the only waste products from a hydrogen fuel cell, along with negligible traces of other compounds. In terms of safety for transport and storage, hydrogen can catch fire, but if kept under pressure it is probably no more dangerous than gasoline in tanks.

Hydrogen fuel cells are energy-efficient. Depending on the type of fuel cell, 35% to 70% of the energy released in the reaction can be used. If the system is designed to capture heat as well as electricity, then the energy efficiency of fuel cells can rise to 90%. These rates are comparable or superior to most nonrenewable alternatives.

Fuel cells are also silent and nonpolluting. Unlike batteries (which also produce electricity through chemical reactions), fuel cells will generate electricity whenever hydrogen fuel is supplied, without ever needing recharging. For all these reasons, hydrogen fuel cells are being used to power vehicles, including the buses now operating on the streets of many European, North American, and Asian cities.

Conclusion

The coming decline of fossil fuel supplies and the increasing concern over air pollution and global climate change have convinced many people that we will need to shift to renewable energy sources that will not run out and will pollute far less. Hydropower is a renewable, pollution-free alternative, but it is not without its own negative ecological impacts. Nuclear power showed promise, but high costs and public fears over safety stalled its growth. Biomass energy sources include traditional fuelwood, as well as newer biofuels and biopower. These sources can be carbon-neutral but are not all strictly renewable, especially if biomass sources are overharvested.

New renewable sources with promise for sustaining our civilization far into the future with gentler environmental impacts include solar energy, wind energy, geothermal energy, and ocean energy. By using electricity from renewable sources to produce hydrogen fuel, we may be able to use fuel cells to produce electricity when and where it is needed, helping to convert our transportation sector to a nonpolluting, renewable basis.

Most renewable energy sources have been held back by inadequate funding for research and development, and by artificially cheap market prices for nonrenewable resources that do not include external costs. Despite these obstacles, renewable technologies have progressed far enough to offer hope that we can shift from fossil fuels to renewable energy with a minimum of economic and social disruption. Whether we can also limit environmental impact will depend on how soon and how quickly we make the transition and to what extent we put efficiency and conservation measures into place.

REVIEWING OBJECTIVES

You should now be able to:

Discuss the reasons for seeking alternatives to fossil fuels

- Fossil fuels are nonrenewable resources, and we are gradually depleting them.
- Fossil fuel combustion causes air pollution that results in many environmental and health impacts and contributes to global climate change.

Summarize the contributions to world energy supplies of conventional alternatives to fossil fuels

- Biomass provides 10.0% of global primary energy use, nuclear power provides 6.3%, and hydropower provides 2.2%.
- Nuclear power generates 15.2% of the world's electricity, and hydropower generates 16.0%. In Canada, hydro accounts for almost 60% of electricity generation.

- "Conventional" energy alternatives are the alternatives to fossil fuels that are most widely used. They include hydroelectric power, nuclear power, and biomass energy.

Describe the scale, methods, and environmental impacts of hydroelectric power, nuclear power, and biomass energy

- Hydroelectric power is generated when water from a river runs through a powerhouse and turns turbines. Hydropower produces little air pollution, but dams and reservoirs can greatly alter riverine ecology. Run-of-river is an alternative approach.
- Nuclear power comes from converting the energy of subatomic bonds into thermal energy. Uranium is mined, enriched, processed, and used as fuel for controlled fission reactions. This process, carried out in nuclear reactors, produces heat that powers electricity generation.

■ Many advocates of "clean" energy support nuclear power because it lacks the polluting emissions of fossil fuels, but for many people the risks, costs, and challenges outweigh the benefits.

■ Traditional biomass energy sources, mainly fuelwood, charcoal, and animal waste, are widely used, especially in the developing world. Biomass can only be considered truly renewable if it is not overharvested.

Outline the major "new" renewable alternative sources of energy and assess their potential for growth

■ "New" renewable energy sources include solar, wind, geothermal, ocean, and new biomass technologies, as well as hydrogen fuels and fuel cells. Most of these are not truly "new," but they are currently in a stage of rapid development of modern technologies.

■ The new renewables currently provide far less energy and electricity than fossil fuels and other conventional energy sources. However, their use is growing quickly, and this growth is expected to continue as people move away from fossil fuels.

Describe a variety of new biomass, solar, wind, geothermal, and ocean energy technologies, and outline their advantages and disadvantages

■ Biofuels, including ethanol and biodiesel, are used to power automobiles. Some crops are grown specifically for this purpose, and waste oils are also used. There are some concerns about the impacts of using food crops to produce biofuels.

■ We use biomass to generate electrical power (biopower) from special crops, waste products from agriculture and forestry, and landfill gas. The use of biomass energy theoretically adds no net carbon to the atmosphere.

■ Energy from the Sun's radiation can be harnessed using passive methods or by active methods involving powered technology. Solar energy is perpetually renewable, creates no emissions, and enables decentralized power.

■ Wind energy is harnessed using turbines mounted on towers. They are often erected in arrays at wind farms on land or offshore, in locations with optimal wind conditions. Wind energy is renewable and creates no emissions. The cost is competitive with that of electricity from fossil fuels, but wind energy is an intermittent source and may face local opposition.

■ Thermal energy from inside the planet rises toward the surface and heats groundwater. Use of geothermal energy and Earth energy for direct heating of water, for electricity generation, and in heat pumps for space heating and cooling can be efficient and clean, but may be exhausted if water is overpumped.

■ Major ocean energy sources include the motion of tides, waves, and currents, and the thermal heat of ocean water. Ocean energy is perpetually renewable, but so far technologies have seen only limited development.

Explain the benefits of hydrogen and fuel cells and assess future options for energy storage and transportation

■ Hydrogen can serve as a fuel to store and transport energy, so that electricity generated by renewable sources can be made portable and used to power vehicles.

■ Hydrogen can be produced through electrolysis, or by using fossil fuels—in which case its environmental benefits are reduced.

■ Fuel cells create electricity by controlling an interaction between hydrogen and oxygen, and they produce only water as a waste product. Fuel cells are silent, nonpolluting, and do not need recharging.

TESTING YOUR COMPREHENSION

1. How much of our global energy supply do nuclear power, biomass energy, and hydroelectric power contribute? How much of our global electricity do these three conventional energy alternatives generate?

2. Describe how nuclear fission works. How do nuclear plant engineers control fission and prevent a runaway chain reaction? What has been done so far about disposing of radioactive waste?

3. In terms of greenhouse gas emissions, how does nuclear power compare to coal, oil, and natural gas? How do hydropower and biomass energy compare?

4. Contrast the two major approaches to generating hydroelectric power, and compare their environmental impacts.

5. List five sources of biomass energy. What is the world's most-used source of biomass energy? How

does biomass energy use differ between developed and developing nations?

6. About how much of our energy now comes from renewable sources? What is the most prevalent form of renewable energy we use? What form of renewable energy is most used to generate electricity? Which renewable source is experiencing the most rapid growth?

7. Contrast passive and active solar heating. Describe how each works, and give examples of each. What are the environmental and economic advantages and disadvantages of solar power?

8. How do modern wind turbines generate electricity? How does wind speed affect the process? What factors affect where wind turbines are placed? What are the environmental and economic benefits and drawbacks of wind power?

9. Define geothermal energy, and explain how it is used. In what ways is it renewable, or not renewable? How does it differ from what Natural Resources Canada calls "Earth energy"?

10. List and describe four approaches to obtaining energy from ocean water.

THINKING IT THROUGH

1. Given what you have learned about some of the conventional alternatives discussed in this chapter, do you think it is important for us to minimize our use of fossil fuels and maximize our use of these alternatives? What challenges or obstacles would we need to overcome, in order to transition smoothly to alternative sources of energy?

2. Nuclear power has by now been widely used for over three decades, and the world has experienced only one major accident (Chernobyl) responsible for a significant number of deaths. Would you call this a good safety record? Why might safety at nuclear power plants be better in the future? Why might it be worse?

3. There are many different sources of biomass and many ways of harnessing energy from biomass. Discuss one that seems particularly beneficial to you, and one with which you see problems. What biomass energy sources and strategies do you think our society should focus on investing in?

4. One of the greatest challenges in operationalizing new renewable energy sources is to find effective ways of storing and transporting the energy, to even out inconsistencies in supply. One possible solution is to convert solar, wind, or biomass energy into a fuel, such as hydrogen, that can be stored for later use. How is hydrogen fuel produced? Is it a clean process? What factors determine the amount of pollutants hydrogen production will emit?

5. Imagine that you are an investor, and you would like to invest in alternative energy. You are considering buying stock in companies that (1) construct nuclear reactors, (2) construct turbines for hydroelectric dams, (3) operate pulp mills, (4) build ethanol refineries, and (5) supply farm waste to co-fired power plants. What questions would you research about each of these companies before deciding how to invest your money? How do you expect you might apportion your investments, and why? Do you expect there may be ways in which you will feel torn between doing what seems financially wise and what seems best for the environment or for energy security? Explain.

6. Let's say that you are the CEO of a company that develops wind farms. Your staff is presenting you with three options, listed below, for sites for your next development. Describe at least one likely advantage and at least one likely disadvantage you would expect to encounter with each option. What further information would you like to know before deciding which to pursue?

   - Option A: A remote rural site in Yukon Territory
   - Option B: A ridge-top site among the suburbs of Saskatoon
   - Option C: An offshore site off the Nova Scotia coast

INTERPRETING GRAPHS AND DATA

It is not clear that growing crops such as corn for the purpose of producing ethanol is the most efficient use of crop lands. David Pimentel and Tad Patzek have estimated that replacing just one-third of the gasoline used in North America with ethanol would require more cropland than is needed to feed the population![19] They calculate that 0.6 hectares of corn will yield enough ethanol to displace one-third of the gasoline needed to run one average North American car for one year; for comparison, it would require 0.5 hectares of corn to feed one person for one year.

As shown on the graph, the area of corn planted in Canada peaked at about 1 315 000 hectares in 2001. Given that Pimentel and Patzek estimate that it would take 1.8 hectares of corn ethanol to displace the need for gasoline to run one car for a year, and given that there are approximately 12 650 000 cars in Canada, how much would the hectares planted in corn need to be increased in order to run all of the cars in Canada on ethanol? One-third of the cars? One-fourth of the cars?

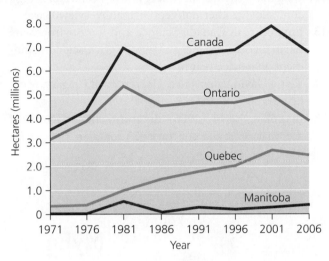

This graph shows the corn area planted in Canada, over time.
Source: Pimentel, David, and Tad W. Patzek (March 2005) Ethanol production using corn, switchgrass, and wood; Biodiesel production using soybean and sunflower. Natural Resources Research, 11(1).

CHAPTER ENDNOTES

1. Nova Scotia Power Environment > Renewable Energy > Tidal, www.nspower.ca/environment/green_power/tidal/technology.shtml

2. Pembina Institute, Renewable Energy, http://re.pembina.org/global/support

3. Worldwatch Institute and Center for American Progress (2006) *American Energy: The Renewable Path to Energy Security.* Washington, D.C.

4. *Powerful Connections: Priorities and Directions in Energy Science and Technology in Canada* (2006) The Report of the National Advisory Committee on Sustainable Energy Science and Technology, Office of Energy Research and Development, Natural Resources Canada, www.nrcan.gc.ca/eps/oerd-brde/report-rapport/toc_e.htm

5. Canadian Biogas Industry Overview, Ken Hogg (October 27, 2005) New Era Renewable Energy Solutions, www.ptac.org/eea/dl/eeaf0501p04.pdf

6. Canadian Biogas Industry Overview, Ken Hogg (October 27, 2005) New Era Renewable Energy Solutions, www.ptac.org/eea/dl/eeaf0501p04.pdf

7. Environment Canada, Municipal Solid Waste, Landfill Gas, Beare Road Project, www.ec.gc.ca/wmd-dgd/default.asp?lang=En&n=3438B2E7-1

8. Environment Canada, Methane to Markets Partnership Landfill Subcommittee (October 2005) Landfill Gas Management in Canada, www.methanetomarkets.org/resources/landfills/docs/canada_lf_profile.pdf

9. Canadian Geographic, The Canadian Atlas Online, *Solar Power,* www.canadiangeographic.ca/atlas/themes.aspx?id=weather&sub=weather_power_solarpower&lang=En

10. Canadian Geographic, The Canadian Atlas Online, *Wind Power,* www.canadiangeographic.ca/atlas/themes.aspx?id=WEATHER&sub=WEATHER_POWER_WINDPOWER&lang=En

11. C40 Large Cities Climate Summit 2007, *Case Studies: Energy*, www.nycclimatesummit.com/casestudies/energy/energy_CANADA.html

12. Canadian Centre for Energy, www.centreforenergy.com/silos/geothermal/geothermalOverview03.asp

13. Environment Canada Science and the Environment: Earth for Storing Energy, www.ec.gc.ca/science/sand-esept99/article5_e.html

14. Keith, David, *Homepage*, University of Calgary, www.ucalgary.ca/~keith/

15. Bergman, Brian (2006) Environmental scientist of the year: Climate contrarian, *Canadian Geographic* May/June, pp. 74–82.

16. Bergman, Brian (2006) Environmental scientist of the year: Climate contrarian, *Canadian Geographic* May/June, pp. 74–82.

17. Bergman, Brian (2006) Environmental scientist of the year: Climate contrarian, *Canadian Geographic* May/June, pp. 74–82.

18. Bergman, Brian (2006) Environmental scientist of the year: Climate contrarian, *Canadian Geographic* May/June, pp. 74–82.

19. Pimentel, David, and Tad W. Patzek (March 2005) Ethanol production using corn, switchgrass, and wood; Biodiesel production using soybean and sunflower. *Natural Resources Research*, 14(1).

MyEnvironmentPlace

Go to **www.myenvironmentplace.ca** where you will find quizzes, animations, your Pearson eText, and more.

18 Managing Our Waste

These containers are en route to a recycling facility.

Upon successfully completing this chapter, you will be able to

- Summarize and compare the types of waste we generate
- List the major approaches to managing waste
- Delineate the scale of the waste dilemma
- Describe conventional waste disposal methods: landfills and incineration

- Evaluate approaches for reducing waste: source reduction, reuse, composting, and recycling
- Discuss industrial solid waste management and principles of industrial ecology
- Assess issues in managing hazardous waste

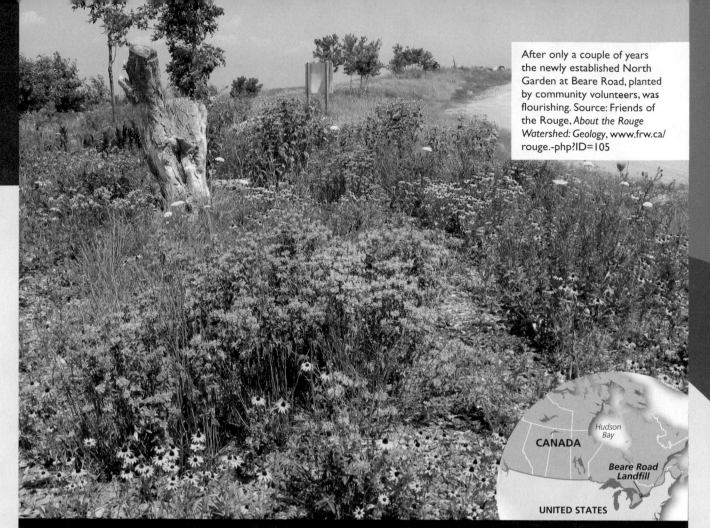

After only a couple of years the newly established North Garden at Beare Road, planted by community volunteers, was flourishing. Source: Friends of the Rouge, *About the Rouge Watershed: Geology*, www.frw.ca/rouge.-php?ID=105

CANADA

Hudson Bay

Beare Road Landfill

UNITED STATES

CENTRAL CASE:
THE BEARE ROAD LANDFILL: MAKING GOOD USE OF OLD GARBAGE

"An extraterrestrial observer might conclude that conversion of raw materials to wastes is the real purpose of human economic activity."

—GARY GARDNER AND PAYAL SAMPAT, WORLDWATCH INSTITUTE

"We can't have an economy that uses our air, water, and soil as a garbage can."

—DAVID SUZUKI

"The issue will never go away. It's going to be a crisis if we can't find another place for our trash."

—JANE PITFIELD, TORONTO CITY COUNCILLOR

In the eastern part of Toronto, not far from the University of Toronto Scarborough campus, there is a park with a grassy hill. On the hill there are trees, bike trails, and fields of wildflowers. This is the highest spot in the neighbourhood, overlooking the Rouge River. Visitors stroll, chat, admire the view, and walk their dogs. As you hike toward the top, there are few clues that beneath this grassy hill lie 9.6 million tonnes of garbage.[1] This is the old Beare Road Landfill.

The Beare Road site is located on gravel that was deposited some 12 000 years ago. At that time, when the last glaciation was drawing to a close, meltwater from the Laurentide Ice Sheet flowed into the Lake Ontario basin, creating a glacial lake much larger than the present-day Lake Ontario. Geologists refer to this ancient lake as Lake Iroquois (see map).

The coarse sandy and gravelly deposits of the former shoreline of Lake Iroquois are now bluffs, stranded high above the current lake level. These porous and permeable units host significant aquifers, including the aquifer of the Oak Ridges Moraine, as well as the headwaters for hundreds of streams and rivers. The

The location of the ancient shoreline of glacial Lake Iroquois is now marked by a series of gravel deposits and bluffs. Old gravel pits show the extent of aggregate extraction from these deposits over the past 100+ years. Many of the worked-out gravel pits were later utilized as dumpsites for municipal solid waste.

About 12 000 years ago, glacial Lake Iroquois formed a shoreline around the Lake Ontario basin while glacial Lake Algonquin formed its shoreline around the Lake Simcoe basin.

Former aggregate pits and landfills along Lake Iroquois shoreline.

deposits have also been profitable for producers of *aggregates*—gravel, sand, and crushed stone used for various construction purposes, including the building of roads and production of concrete. Many of the small towns scattered along the ancient shoreline in Ontario owe their economic beginnings to the exploitation of gravel and sand from these deposits.

Fast-forward to the latter half of the 1900s, when worked-out gravel pits scattered along the ancient shoreline sat empty. Some of the pits filled with water, serving as recreational lakes for fishing and swimming. In other cases, they beckoned to local residents—what better place to dispose of municipal solid waste? In that era, the negative impacts of tossing waste into such a porous and permeable medium were little known, and a number of the pits were used for this purpose (see maps), including the Beare Road gravel pit.

The Beare Road pit officially began receiving municipal garbage in 1968. It began with a capacity of 3 million tonnes, but this was increased several times over the years as the urgency grew for places to put Toronto's ever-increasing garbage. The final increase in capacity was accompanied by a promise of funding from the government to be used toward the rehabilitation of the landscape, ultimately making it available for recreational use by the community.[2]

The landfill was eventually closed down in 1983.[3] At that time a system for passive flaring of landfill gases was installed (see "The Science Behind the Story: Energy from Landfill Gas at Beare Road," Chapter 17). Some landscape restoration was undertaken, by the government and by local residents (see photo), and the site was opened as a park.

In 1996, E.S. Fox, in agreement with the City of Toronto (owner of the site) and Ontario Power Generation, began to collect the methane-rich gas being generated by the decomposing garbage at Beare Road. This type of operation is called *LFGTE (landfill gas-to-electricity)*, and it makes use of what would otherwise be a harmful by-product of the garbage. Methane gas smells bad, damages vegetation, and is explosive and flammable. It is also a highly effective greenhouse gas, which must be actively managed if Canada hopes to minimize GHG emissions to fulfill its commitment to control global warming in the future.

Some environmental problems persist at the site; they are typical of old dumpsites and will require active management for years. For example, early engineering installations designed to control the collection and movement of leachate failed years ago. The impermeable liner that had been installed to prevent leakage filled with leachate, which then began to seep from the side of the hill at the level where the liner topped out—a classic demonstration of the "bathtub effect." The possibility persists that leachate may one day threaten community developments immediately downstream from the site. The exact content and composition of the waste also are unknown.

In spite of these problems, the Beare Road project provides a hope-inspiring model for the management of old landfill sites. Gas collection and utilization has helped to resolve a number of local environmental problems (such as odour and damage to vegetation) and is contributing to the reduction of GHG emissions for Canada.

Approaches to Waste Management

As the world's human population rises, and as we produce and consume more material goods, we generate more waste. **Waste** refers to any unwanted material or substance that results from a human activity or process. The federal government of Canada has adopted a definition that states, in part, that waste is "any substance for which the owner/generator has no further use."[4] Another popular definition suggests that waste is "resources out of place," emphasizing the fact that most waste still contains a significant proportion of useful materials. These definitions represent a changing perception of waste—that there is much of value that can be recovered from our waste stream.

For management purposes, waste is divided into several main categories. *Municipal solid waste* is nonliquid waste that comes from homes, institutions, and small businesses. *Industrial solid waste* includes waste from production of consumer goods, mining, agriculture, and petroleum extraction and refining. *Hazardous waste* refers to solid or liquid waste that is toxic, chemically reactive, flammable, corrosive, or radioactive. It can include everything from paint and household cleaners to medical waste to industrial solvents. Another type of waste is *wastewater*, water we use in our households, businesses, industries, or public facilities and drain or flush down our pipes, as well as the polluted runoff from our streets and storm drains.

We have several aims in managing waste

Waste can degrade water quality, soil quality, and air quality, thereby degrading human health and the environment. Waste is also a measure of inefficiency, so reducing waste can potentially save industry, municipalities, and

consumers both money and resources. In addition, waste is unpleasant esthetically. For these and other reasons, waste management has become a vital pursuit.

There are three main components of **waste management**:

1. Minimizing the amount of waste we generate
2. Recovering waste materials and finding ways to recycle them
3. Disposing of waste safely and effectively

Minimizing waste at its source—called *source reduction*—is the preferred approach. There are several ways to reduce the amount of waste that enters the **waste stream**, the flow of waste as it moves from its sources toward disposal destinations (**FIGURE 18.1**). Manufacturers can use materials more efficiently. Consumers can buy fewer goods, buy goods with less packaging, and use those goods longer. Reusing goods you already own, purchasing used items, and donating your used items for others also help reduce the amount of material entering the waste stream.

Recovery (which includes recycling and composting) is widely viewed as the next best strategy in waste management. *Recycling* involves sending used goods to facilities that extract and reprocess raw materials to manufacture new goods. Newspapers, white paper, cardboard, glass,

roots

WASTE

The early uses of the word **waste**, around the year 1200, referred to a large, uninhabitable space. This makes sense when you consider that the word comes from the Latin root *vastus*; the same root is found in the words *vast* and *devastate*. The meaning "useless expenditure" dates from about 1300, and that of "garbage" from the early 1400s.

Waste stream with steps to reduce waste

Make industrial practices more efficient

Minimize packaging for products

Purchase "green" consumer products

Reuse items

Recycle items

Compost materials at home

Offer municipal composting

Waste stream without steps to reduce waste

Waste disposal (landfill, incinerator)

FIGURE 18.1
The most effective way to manage waste is to minimize the amount of material that enters the waste stream. To do this, manufacturers can increase efficiency, and consumers can buy "green" products that have minimal packaging, are designed to make recycling of components easy, or are produced in ways that minimize waste. Individuals can compost food scraps and yard waste at home and can reuse items rather than buying new ones. Many of us can recycle materials and compost yard waste through municipal recycling and composting programs. For all remaining waste, waste managers attempt to find disposal methods that minimize impact on human health and environmental quality.

metal cans, appliances, and some plastic containers have all become increasingly recyclable as new technologies have been developed and as markets for recycled materials have grown. Organic waste can be recovered through *composting*, or biological decomposition. Recycling is not a concept that humans invented; recall that all materials are recycled in ecosystems. Recycling is a fundamental feature of the way natural systems function.

Regardless of how effectively we reduce our waste stream, there will always be some waste left to dispose of. Disposal methods include burying waste in landfills and burning waste in incinerators. In this chapter we first examine how these approaches are used to manage municipal solid waste, and then we address industrial solid waste and hazardous waste.

Municipal Solid Waste

Municipal solid waste is waste produced by consumers, public facilities, and small businesses. It is what we commonly refer to as "trash" or "garbage." Everything from paper to food scraps to roadside litter to old appliances and furniture is considered municipal solid waste.

Patterns in the municipal solid waste stream vary from place to place

In Canada, paper, organics (mainly yard debris and food scraps), and plastics are the principal components of municipal solid waste, together accounting for more than 66% of the waste stream (**FIGURE 18.2**). Even after recycling, paper is the largest component of municipal solid waste. Patterns differ in developing countries; there, food scraps are often the primary contributor to solid waste, and paper makes up a smaller proportion.

Most municipal solid waste comes from packaging and nondurable goods (products meant to be discarded after a short period of use). In addition, consumers throw away old durable goods and outdated equipment as they purchase new products. As we acquire more goods, we generate more waste. According to Statistics Canada, which tracks a variety of social, economic, and environmental indicators, Canadian citizens produced more than 26 million tonnes of municipal solid waste in 2008, for a population of 33 million—almost 1 tonne per person for that year. This means that Canadians generated about

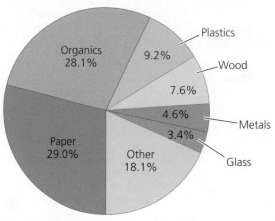

(a) Composition of municipal solid waste in Canada

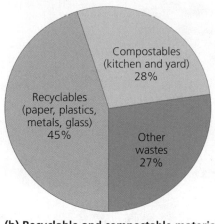

(b) Recyclable and compostable materials in municipal solid waste

FIGURE 18.2   Paper products are the largest component of the municipal solid waste stream in Canada (a), followed closely by organic wastes (yard trimmings and food scraps) and plastics. In total, each Canadian citizen generates more than 1 tonne (actually, 1037 kg in 2004, including both residential and industrial components)[5] of solid waste each year. Much of the waste generated by Canadians is, in principle, recyclable or compostable (b).   *Source: Data are for 2004, from Environment Canada, Waste Management, Municipal Solid Waste, www.ec.gc.ca/wmd-dgd/Default.-asp?lang=En&n=7623F633-1*

800 kg of trash per person that year, or 2.2 kg per person per day.[6]

Surpassing Canada in per capita solid waste generation is the United States, with about 3.3 kg per person per day.[7] Trailing behind is the Netherlands, with 1.4 kg per person per day. Among developed nations, Germany and Sweden produce the least waste per capita, generating just under 0.9 kg per person per day. Differences among nations result in part from differences in the cost of waste disposal; where disposal is expensive, people have incentive to waste less. The wastefulness of the North American lifestyle, with its excess packaging and reliance on nondurable goods, has caused critics to label this as "the throwaway society."

In developing nations, people consume less and generate considerably less waste. One study found that people of high-income nations waste more than twice as much as people of low-income nations. However, wealthier nations also invest more in waste collection and disposal, so they are often better able to manage their waste proliferation and minimize impacts on human health and the environment.

Waste generation is rising in all nations

In North America since 1960, waste generation has increased by almost 300%, and per capita waste generation has risen by about 70%. Plastics, which came into wide consumer use only after 1970, have accounted for the greatest relative increase in the waste stream during the

last several decades. In the past decade or so, waste generation in Canada has kept pace with the growth rate of the population but has lagged slightly behind the growth in real gross domestic product (GDP). This suggests a promising trend of waste diversion and producing more for less, perhaps because of recycling and a shift to more efficient waste management processes.

The intensive consumption that has long characterized wealthy nations is now increasing rapidly in developing nations. To some extent, this trend reflects rising material standards of living, but an increase in packaging is also to blame. Items made for temporary use and poor-quality goods designed to be inexpensive wear out and pile up quickly as trash, littering the landscapes of countries from Mexico to Kenya to Indonesia. Over the past three decades, per capita waste generation rates have more than doubled in Latin American nations and have increased more than fivefold in the Middle East. Like consumers in "the throwaway society," wealthy consumers in developing nations often discard items that can still be used. At many dumps and **landfills** throughout the developing world, in fact, poor people still support themselves by selling items they scavenge (**FIGURE 18.3**).

In many industrialized nations, per capita waste generation rates have levelled off or decreased in recent years. Waste generation has essentially kept pace with population in Canada since 1996, which means that per capita waste production has been essentially stable over this period. This is due largely to the increased popularity of recycling, composting, reduction, and reuse. We will examine these nondisposal approaches to waste management shortly, but let us first assess how we dispose of waste.

FIGURE 18.3
Tens of thousands of people used to scavenge each day from the dump at Payatas, outside Manila in the Philippines, finding items for themselves and selling material to junk dealers for 100–200 pesos ($2–$4) per day. That so many people could support themselves this way testifies to the immense amount of usable material needlessly discarded by wealthier portions of the population. The dump was closed in 2000 after an avalanche of trash killed hundreds of people.

Open dumping of the past has given way to improved disposal methods

Historically, people dumped their garbage wherever it suited them. Until the mid-nineteenth century, New York City's official method of garbage disposal was to dump it off piers into the East River. As population densities increased, municipalities took on the task of consolidating trash into open dumps at specified locations to keep other areas clean. This is how the worked-out gravel pits of the ancient Lake Iroquois shoreline in southern Ontario came to be used as dumpsites. To decrease the volume of trash, the dumps would be burned from time to time. Open dumping and burning still occur throughout much of the world.

As population and consumption rose in developed nations, more packaging and the use of nondegradable materials increased, waste production increased, and dumps accordingly grew larger. At the same time, expanding cities and suburbs forced more people into the vicinity of dumps and exposed them to the noxious smoke of dump burning. Reacting to opposition from residents living near dumps and to a rising awareness of health and environmental threats posed by unregulated dumping and burning, many nations improved their methods of waste disposal. Most industrialized nations now bury waste in lined and covered landfills and burn waste in incineration facilities.

Since the late 1980s, the recovery of materials for recycling has expanded, slightly decreasing the pressure on landfills (**FIGURE 18.4**). The total rate of diversion of municipal solid waste in Canada (that is, diversion away

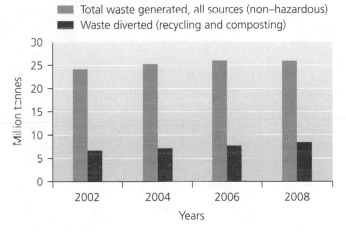

FIGURE 18.4
Waste generation may be levelling off in Canada. The diversion rate (to recycling and composting) has not changed much, hovering around 25–27%.
Source: Statistics Canada (2010) Cansim Table 153-0041.

from disposal or incineration, to recycling or composting) increased from 21% in 2000 to 27% in 2008. Over the same period, the rate of diversion of solid waste from residential sources increased more. Change has been slow, however, and an estimated $1.5 billion worth of recyclable materials were disposed of in 2004.[8]

Waste disposal is regulated by three levels of government

In Canada, municipal governments are responsible for the collection, diversion, and disposal of solid waste from residential and small commercial and industrial sources. If you put waste by the side of the road on garbage collection day and it is picked up by city garbage trucks, then it is municipal solid waste. Many municipalities now also provide drop-off facilities for special categories of waste, including household hazardous wastes, such as leftover paint.

Provincial and territorial governments have control over the movement of waste materials within the jurisdiction and over the licensing of treatment facilities and waste generators. Thus, each province or territory has its own legislation and guidelines regulating the design, siting, licensing, operations, and expansion of landfill sites. The federal government, meanwhile, is responsible for looking after international agreements about waste and regulating transboundary movements of waste materials. Federal involvement in waste management occurs mainly through the *Canadian Environmental Protection Act* and the *Fisheries Act*.

Sanitary landfills are engineered to minimize leakage of contaminants

In a modern **sanitary landfill**, waste is buried in the ground or piled up in large, carefully engineered mounds. In contrast to open dumps, sanitary landfills are designed to prevent waste from contaminating the environment and threatening public health (**FIGURE 18.5**). In a sanitary landfill, waste is partially decomposed by bacteria and compresses under its own weight to take up less space. Waste is typically interlayered with soil, a method that speeds decomposition, reduces odours, and reduces infestation by pests. Limited infiltration of rainwater allows for biodegradation by aerobic and anaerobic bacteria.

To protect against environmental contamination, landfills must be located away from wetlands and situated well above the local water table. The bottoms and sides of modern sanitary landfills are lined with heavy-duty plastic or other high-tech geo-engineered fabrics. They are typically underlain by a thick layer (a metre or more) of impermeable clay to help prevent contaminants from seeping into aquifers. Sanitary landfills also have systems of pipes, collection ponds, and treatment facilities to collect and treat **leachate**, the liquid that results when substances from the trash dissolve in water as rainwater percolates downward. Leachate collection systems must be maintained throughout the lifetime of the landfill and for many years after closure. Regulations also require that area groundwater and soils be monitored regularly for contamination.

After a landfill is closed, it is capped with an engineered cover that must be maintained. The cap usually consists of a hydraulic barrier that prevents water from seeping down and gas from seeping up; a gravel layer above the hydraulic barrier that drains water, lessening pressure on the hydraulic barrier; a soil barrier that stores water and protects the hydraulic layer from weather extremes; and a topsoil layer that encourages plant growth, helping to prevent erosion.

FIGURE 18.5

Sanitary landfills are engineered to prevent waste from contaminating soil and groundwater. Waste is laid in a large, lined depression, underlain by an impervious clay layer designed to prevent liquids from leaching out. Pipes of a leachate collection system draw out these liquids from the bottom of the landfill. Waste is layered along with soil until the depression is filled, and it continues to be built up until the landfill is capped. Landfill gas produced by anaerobic bacteria may be recovered, and waste managers monitor groundwater for contamination.

At the Beare Road Landfill, some underlying rock and sediment units are naturally clay-rich shales, creating a barrier that appears to slow the subsurface movement of leachate from the site. However, the Iroquois sand and gravel deposits—removed at an earlier stage for aggregate production, forming the pit itself—are much more permeable, providing a pathway for leachate migration.[9] Although it met provincial standards for landfill technology at the time of its construction, the Beare Road Landfill predated most current regulations and guidelines. As a result, it has caused some environmental contamination, and residents of adjacent areas continue to express some concerns about the possibility of gas and leachate migration. There is no functional engineering to control leachate migration at the site, aside from a collection ditch around the perimeter and the gas collection technologies. The refuse mound is surrounded by a number of wells installed for the purpose of monitoring groundwater for any signs of leachate migration into the surrounding areas.[10] The mound was covered after the closure of the site to inhibit the infiltration of rainwater and the production and migration of leachate.

Landfills can be transformed after closure

Today many landfills lie abandoned. One reason is that waste managers have closed many smaller landfills and consolidated the trash stream into fewer, much larger landfills. Meanwhile, growing numbers of cities have converted closed landfills into public parks (**FIGURE 18.6**), like the Rouge Park in Toronto, which includes the Beare Road Landfill site. Such efforts date back at least to 1938, when an ash landfill at Flushing Meadows, in Queens, New York, was redeveloped for the 1939 World's Fair, and subsequently the 1964–1965 World's Fair. Designated a park in 1967, today the site hosts Shea Stadium, the Queens Museum of Art, the New York Hall of Science, and the Queens Botanical Garden. Shutting down an industrial site and getting it ready for cleanup and post-industrial repurposing is called **decommissioning**.

The Fresh Kills redevelopment endeavour in New York will be the world's largest landfill conversion project. The largest landfill in the world, Fresh Kills was the primary repository of New York City's garbage for half a century. On March 22, 2001, New York City Mayor Rudolph Giuliani and New York Governor George Pataki were on hand to celebrate as a barge arrived on the western shore of New York City's Staten Island and dumped the final load of trash at Fresh Kills. The landfill's closure was a welcome event for Staten Island's 450 000 residents, who had long viewed the landfill as a bad-smelling eyesore, health threat, and civic blemish. The 890 ha landfill featured six gigantic mounds of trash and soil. The highest, at 69 m, was higher than the nearby Statue of Liberty.

New York City planned to transform the old landfill into a world-class public park—a verdant landscape of rolling hills and wetlands teeming with wildlife, a mecca for recreation for New York's residents. Later in 2001, however, the landfill had to be reopened temporarily. After the September 11, 2001, terrorist attacks, the 1.8 million tonnes of rubble from the collapsed World Trade Center towers, including unrecoverable human remains, were taken by barge to Fresh Kills, where the material was sorted and buried. A monument will be erected at the site as part of the new park. Today, plans for the park are forging ahead. The master plan for reclamation of the site involves everything from ecological restoration of the wetlands to construction of roads, ball fields, sculptures, and roller-blading rinks. People will be able to bicycle on trails parallelling tidal creeks of the region's largest estuary and reach stunning vistas atop the hills.

FIGURE 18.6
Residents and members of Friends of the Rouge plant wildflowers at the Beare Road North Garden.
Source: Friends of the Rouge, About the Rouge Watershed: Geology, *www.frw.ca/rouge.php?ID=105.*

Landfills have drawbacks

Despite improvements in liner and cover technology and landfill siting, many experts believe that leachate will eventually escape even from well-lined landfills. Liners can be punctured, and leachate collection systems eventually cease to be maintained. Moreover, landfills are kept dry to reduce leachate, but the bacteria that break down material thrive in wet conditions. Dryness, therefore, slows waste decomposition. In fact, it is surprising how slowly some materials biodegrade when they are tightly compressed in a landfill. Innovative archeological research has revealed that landfills often contain food that has not decomposed and 40-year-old newspapers that are still legible (see "The Science Behind the Story: Digging Garbage: The Archaeology of Solid Waste").

Another problem is finding suitable areas to locate landfills because most communities do not want them nearby. This *not-in-my-backyard* (*NIMBY*) *syndrome* is one reason why Toronto, New York, and many other cities export their waste and why residents of areas that are receiving the waste are increasingly protesting. The quote from a Toronto city councillor at the beginning of this chapter refers to the ongoing struggle to find somewhere to dispose of Toronto's waste. The past practice—to export Toronto's trash to Michigan—had become increasingly unpopular among residents there. In 2007 an average of 74 truckloads per day of solid waste (approximately 441 363 tonnes) went to a Michigan landfill from Toronto (down from 142 daily truckloads in 2003). This amount continued to decline as the city surpassed its waste export reduction targets. Toronto's agreement with the receiving landfill in Michigan (by which the city is contractually obligated to continue to deliver garbage to the privately maintained landfill) expired at the end of 2010. In 2007, the City of Toronto acquired the Green Lane Landfill site located southwest of London. This landfill is still about 200 km from downtown Toronto, but it provides an alternative to the Michigan exports. The site features the latest landfill engineering technology, including onsite leachate treatment and methane gas collection and flaring systems.[11]

As a result of the NIMBY syndrome, landfills are rarely sited in neighbourhoods that are home to wealthy and educated people with the political clout to keep them out. Instead, they are disproportionately sited in poor and minority communities, as environmental justice advocates have frequently made clear.

The unwillingness of most communities to accept waste became apparent with the famed case of the "garbage barge," the *Mobro4000*. In Islip, New York, in 1987, the town's landfills were full, prompting town administrators to ship waste by barge to a methane production plant

roots

GARBAGE

The word **garbage**, first used in the late 1500s to mean "refuse" or "filth," probably comes from the Old French word *garbe*, which refers to the entrails or waste parts of an animal. The term *garbology*, the study of garbage as a social science, was coined by William Rathje in the 1970s.

in North Carolina. Prior to the barge's arrival, it became known that the shipment was contaminated with medical waste, including syringes, hospital gowns, and diapers. Because of the medical waste, the methane plant rejected the entire load. The barge sat in a North Carolina harbour for 11 days before heading for Louisiana. However, Louisiana would not permit the barge to dock. The barge travelled toward Mexico, but the Mexican navy prevented it from entering that nation's waters. In the end, the barge travelled 9700 km before eventually returning to New York, where, after several court battles, the waste was finally incinerated at a facility in Queens.

Incinerating trash reduces pressure on landfills

Incineration, or combustion, is a controlled process in which mixed garbage is burned at very high temperatures (**FIGURE 18.7**). At incineration facilities, waste is generally sorted and metals removed. Metal-free waste is chopped into small pieces to aid combustion and then is burned in a furnace. Incinerating waste reduces its weight by up to 75% and its volume by up to 90%.

However, simply reducing the volume and weight does not rid trash of components that are toxic. The ash remaining after trash is incinerated therefore must be disposed of in special landfills for hazardous waste. Moreover, when trash is burned, hazardous chemicals—including dioxins, heavy metals, and PCBs—can be created and released into the atmosphere. Such releases caused a backlash against incineration from citizens concerned about health hazards. Opponents also feel that incineration is incompatible with the more sustainable path of reducing consumption, producing less waste, and diverting more of the waste we produce into recycling and composting.

Most developed nations now regulate incinerator emissions, and some have banned incineration outright. In Canada the ability to ban incineration rests with the provinces and territories. In some provinces where incineration is allowed, such as Ontario (where a previous ban was lifted in 1995), some municipalities continue to ban incineration in their own jurisdictions, or do not include incineration as part of their waste reduction and diversion plans. For example, the City of Toronto's aggressive plan for reducing the amount of waste produced and shipped to Michigan does not include incineration.

As a result of real and perceived health threats from incinerator emissions—and of community opposition to these plants—engineers have developed several technologies to mitigate emissions. *Scrubbers* chemically treat the gases produced in combustion to remove hazardous

FIGURE 18.7 Incinerators reduce the volume of solid waste by burning it but may emit toxic compounds into the air. Many incinerators are waste-to-energy (WTE) facilities that use the heat of combustion to generate electricity. In a WTE facility, solid waste (1) is burned at extremely high temperatures (2), heating water, which turns to steam. The steam turns a turbine (3), which powers a generator to create electricity. In an incinerator outfitted with pollution-control technology, toxic gases produced by combustion are mitigated chemically by a scrubber (4), and airborne particulate matter is filtered physically in a baghouse (5) before air is emitted from the stack (6). Ash remaining from the combustion process is disposed of (7) in a landfill.

components and neutralize acidic gases, such as sulphur dioxide and hydrochloric acid, turning them into water and salt. Scrubbers generally do this either by spraying liquids formulated to neutralize the gases or by passing the gases through dry lime.

Particulate matter is physically removed from incinerator emissions in a system of huge filters known as a *baghouse*. These tiny particles, called fly ash, often contain some of the worst dioxin and heavy metal pollutants. In addition, burning garbage at especially high temperatures can destroy certain pollutants, such as PCBs. Even all these measures, however, do not fully eliminate toxic emissions.

Many incinerators burn waste to create energy

Incineration was initially practised simply to reduce the volume of waste, but today it often serves to generate electricity as well. Most North American incinerators today are **waste-to-energy (WTE) facilities** that use the heat

produced by waste combustion to boil water, creating steam that drives electricity generation or fuels heating systems. When burned, waste generates about 35% of the energy generated by burning coal, per unit weight.

Revenues from power generation, however, are usually not enough to offset the considerable financial cost of building and running incinerators. Because it can take many years for a WTE facility to become profitable, many companies that build and operate these facilities require communities contracting with them to guarantee the facility a minimum amount of garbage. In a number of cases, such long-term commitments have interfered with communities' later efforts to reduce their waste through recycling and other waste-reduction strategies.

Landfills can produce gas for energy

Combustion in WTE plants is not the only means of gaining energy from waste. Deep inside landfills, bacteria decompose waste in an oxygen-deficient environment.

THE SCIENCE BEHIND THE STORY

Digging Garbage: The Archaeology of Solid Waste

This is Fresh Kills Landfill before its closure.

Garbage and *knowledge* are two words rarely put together. But when scientist William Rathje dons trash-flecked clothes and burrows into a city dump, he gleans valuable information about how we live. By pulling tonnes of trash out of disposal sites over the course of decades, Rathje has turned dumpster diving into a noteworthy field of scientific inquiry that he calls *garbology*. An archaeologist by training, Rathje has brought exacting archaeological techniques to the contents of trashcans.

As a professor at the University of Arizona in the early 1970s, Rathje wanted his students to learn a technique common among archaeologists—sorting through ancient trash mounds to understand past cultures. With few ancient civilizations or their trash close at hand, he arranged for his students to dig through their neighbours' garbage.

In 1973, he gave that effort a name, "The Garbage Project," and began a methodical study of the contents of modern trash. With rakes and notebooks, the researchers sorted, weighed, itemized, and analyzed the refuse. They then visited the homes of the people who had generated the trash and asked residents about their shopping and consumption habits.

Then in 1987, amid growing debates about how quickly landfills were filling up, Rathje decided to see what was taking up space in them. The Garbage Project headed to landfills with a truck-mounted bucket auger—a large drill commonly employed by geologists and construction crews to handle everything from excavating soil samples to creating new water wells. Rathje and his researchers dug into landfills around North America, boring as far as 30 m down in 15 to 20 garbage "wells" at each site, with each well yielding up to 25 tonnes of trash.

Once excavated, landfill contents were sorted, weighed, and identified. Rathje's teams sometimes froze the trash before they worked with it to make the garbage easier to separate and to limit odour and flies. Smaller bits of trash were put through sieves and sometimes washed with water to make them easier to label. Rathje has excavated at least 21 dumps, uncovering a host of interesting things in the process:

- *Not much rot.* Trash doesn't decay much in closed landfills, Rathje has found. In the dry, low-oxygen conditions inside most closed dumps, trash turns into a sort of time capsule. Rathje's teams have found whole hot dogs in most digs, intact pastries that are decades old, and grass clippings that are still green. Decades-old newspapers are legible and can be used to date layers of trash.
- *Paper rules.* Paper-based products make up more than 40% of most landfill content, and construction debris makes up about 20%. Newspapers are often a high-volume item, averaging about 14% of landfill space.
- *Diapers not a problem.* Rathje says that fast-food packaging, polystyrene foam, and disposable diapers aren't a major problem, making up only about 3% of landfill content. (There are other concerns about diapers contributing pathogens to the waste stream, however.) If all plastic packaging were to be replaced by containers made of glass, paper, steel, or similar materials, Rathje maintains, the packaging load to landfills (in weight) would more than double.
- *Poison in small bottles.* Toxic waste comes in all sizes. If nail polish were sold in large drums, its chemical composition would make it illegal to throw out in a regular dump. Nail polish, however, is discarded in small bottles—hundreds of thousands of them per year. Luckily, however, the potentially toxic ingredients in nail polish don't always spread far, he found. Paper, diapers, and other nontoxic garbage often absorb toxic materials in landfills and keep the poisons from leaching out.

Through garbology, Rathje has gleaned unique insights into how we can change our often wasteful habits. Now a consulting professor at Stanford University, Rathje has emerged as a leading expert on how to reduce waste.

"Garbologist" William Rathje has pioneered the study of our culture through the waste we generate.

weighing the issues
GARBAGE JUSTICE?

Do you know where your trash goes? Where is your landfill or incinerator located? Are the people who live closest to the facility wealthy, poor, or middle class? What race or ethnicity are they? Do you know whether the people of this neighbourhood protested against the introduction of the landfill or incinerator?

This anaerobic decomposition produces *landfill gas*, a mix of gases that consists of roughly half methane. Landfill gas can be collected, processed, and used in the same way as natural gas.

Today more than 40 operational projects in Canada, like the one at Beare Road, collect landfill gas and convert it into energy. Other countries take advantage of this resource as well. In Chile, four facilities in Valparaiso and Santiago supply 40% of the region's demand for natural gas. In the United States, more than 300 facilities convert landfill gas to energy. At landfill sites where gas is not collected for commercial use, it is typically allowed to flow out passively through candlestick pipes, where it is burned off in flares to reduce odours.

Reducing waste is a better option

Reducing the amount of material entering the waste stream avoids costs of disposal and recycling, helps conserve resources, minimizes pollution, and can often save consumers and businesses money. Preventing waste generation in this way is known as **source reduction**.

Much of our waste stream consists of materials used to package goods. Packaging serves worthwhile purposes—preserving freshness, preventing breakage, protecting against tampering, and providing information—but much packaging is extraneous. Consumers can give manufacturers incentive to reduce packaging by choosing minimally packaged goods, buying unwrapped fruit and vegetables, and buying food in bulk. In addition, manufacturers can use packaging that is more recyclable. They can also reduce the size or weight of goods and materials, as they already have with many items, such as aluminum cans, plastic soft drink bottles, and personal computers.

Some governments have recently taken aim at a major source of waste and litter—plastic grocery bags.

These lightweight polyethylene bags can persist for centuries in the environment, choking and entangling wildlife and littering the landscape. Several nations have now banned their use. When Ireland began taxing these bags, their use dropped 90%. The IKEA Company began charging for them and saw similar drops in usage. In 2007 the small Manitoba town of Leaf Rapids became the first municipality in Canada to ban plastic bags, and the City of Toronto approved a per-bag charge of five cents for new plastic bags, which went into effect in 2009.

Increasing the longevity of goods also helps reduce waste. Consumers generally choose goods that last longer, all else being equal. To maximize sales, however, companies often produce short-lived goods that need to be replaced frequently, particularly in electronics and fashion. Thus, increasing the longevity of goods is largely up to the consumer. If demand is great enough, manufacturers will respond.

Reuse is one main strategy for waste reduction

To reduce waste, you can save items to use again or substitute disposable goods with durable ones. Habits as simple as bringing your own coffee cup to coffee shops or bringing sturdy reusable cloth bags to the grocery store can, over time, have substantial impact. You can also donate unwanted items and shop for used items yourself at yard sales and resale centres. Besides doing good for the environment, reusing items is often economically advantageous. Used items are quite often every bit as functional as new ones, and much cheaper. **TABLE 18.1** presents a sampling of actions that we all can take to reduce the waste we generate.

weighing the issues
REDUCING PACKAGING: IS IT A WRAP?

Reducing packaging cuts down on the waste stream, but how, when, and how much should we reduce? Packaging can serve very worthwhile purposes, such as safeguarding consumer health and safety. Can you think of three products for which you would *not* want to see less packaging? Can you name three products for which packaging could easily be reduced without ill effect to the consumer? Would you be any more or less likely to buy these products if they had less packaging?

Table 18.1   Some Everyday Things You Can Do to Reduce and Reuse

Donate used items to charity.

Reuse boxes, paper, plastic wrap, plastic containers, aluminum foil, bags, wrapping paper, fabric, packing material, and so on.

Rent or borrow items instead of buying them, when possible ... and lend your items to friends.

Buy groceries in bulk.

Decline bags at stores when you don't need them.

Bring reusable cloth bags shopping.

Make double-sided photocopies.

Bring your own coffee cup to coffee shops.

Pay a bit extra for durable, long-lasting, reusable goods rather than disposable ones.

Buy rechargeable batteries.

Select goods with less packaging.

Compost kitchen and yard wastes in a compost bin or worm bin (often available from your community or waste hauler).

Buy clothing and other items at resale stores and garage sales.

Use cloth napkins and rags rather than paper napkins and towels.

Write to companies to tell them what you think about their packaging and products.

When solid waste policy is being debated, let your government representatives know your thoughts.

Support organizations that promote waste reduction.

Table 18.2   Composting in Canada, 2007

Composted either kitchen or yard waste

	Percent
Canada	**57**
Newfoundland and Labrador	46
Prince Edward Island	98
Nova Scotia	92
New Brunswick	56
Québec	35
Ontario	71
Manitoba	50
Saskatchewan	52
Alberta	54
British Columbia	59

Source: Statistics Canada, Households and the Environment Survey, 2007.

Composting recovers organic waste

Composting is the conversion of organic waste into mulch or humus through natural biological processes of decomposition. The resulting compost can then be used to enrich soil. Householders can place waste in compost piles, underground pits, or specially constructed containers. As wastes are added, heat from microbial action builds in the interior, and decomposition proceeds. Banana peels, coffee grounds, grass clippings, autumn leaves, and countless other organic items can be converted into rich, high-quality compost through the actions of earthworms, bacteria, soil mites, sow bugs, and other detritivores and decomposers. Home composting is a prime example of how we can live more sustainably by mimicking natural cycles and incorporating them into our daily lives.

Centralized composting programs—there are now more than 350 of them in Canada—divert food and yard waste from the waste stream to composting facilities, where they decompose into mulch that community residents can use for gardens and landscaping. Some municipalities now ban yard waste from the municipal

waste stream, helping accelerate the drive toward composting. Approximately 28% of the Canadian solid waste stream is made up of materials that can easily be composted (see **FIGURE 18.2**). Composting reduces landfill waste, enriches soil and helps it resist erosion, encourages soil biodiversity, makes for healthier plants and more pleasing gardens, and reduces the need for chemical fertilizers. According to Statistics Canada, 57% of Canadian households do some form of composting (**TABLE 18.2**).

Recycling consists of three steps

Recycling, too, offers many benefits. **Recycling** consists of collecting materials that can be broken down and reprocessed to manufacture new items. In 2008, 8.5 million tonnes of materials were prepared for recycling by waste management organizations and companies. Of this, paper was the main component.[12]

The recycling loop contains three basic steps (**FIGURE 18.8**). The first step is collecting and processing used recyclable goods and materials. Communities may designate locations where residents can drop off recyclables or receive money for them. Many of these have now been replaced by the more convenient option of curbside recycling, in which trucks pick up recyclable items in front of houses, usually in conjunction with municipal trash pickup. Curbside recycling has grown rapidly, and its convenience has helped boost household recycling rates across Canada.

Items collected are taken to *materials recovery facilities (MRFs)*, where workers and machines sort items, using

FIGURE 18.8
The familiar recycling symbol consists of three arrows to represent the three components of a sustainable recycling strategy: collection and processing of recyclable materials, use of the materials in making new products, and consumer purchase of these products.

automated processes including magnetic pulleys, optical sensors, water currents, and air classifiers that separate items by weight and size. The facilities clean the materials, shred them, and prepare them for reprocessing.

Once readied, these materials are used in manufacturing new goods. Newspapers and many other paper products use recycled paper, many glass and metal containers are now made from recycled materials, and some plastic containers are of recycled origin. Some large objects, such as benches and bridges in city parks, are now made from recycled plastics, and glass is sometimes mixed with asphalt (creating "glassphalt") for paving roads and paths. The pages in this textbook are made from recycled paper that is up to 20% post-consumer waste.

If the recycling loop is to function, consumers and businesses must complete the third step in the cycle by purchasing products made from recycled materials. Buying recycled goods provides economic incentive for industries to recycle materials and for new recycling facilities to open or existing ones to expand. In this arena, individual consumers have the power to encourage environmentally friendly options through the free market. Many businesses now advertise their use of recycled materials, a widespread instance of *ecolabelling*. As markets for products made with recycled materials expand, prices continue to fall.

Recycling has grown rapidly and can expand further

The thousands of curbside recycling programs and MRFs in operation today have sprung up only in the last 20 years. According to Statistics Canada, 95% of Canadian households had access to recycling programs by 2007, and most programs covered all four recyclables: paper, plastic, glass, and metal.[13]

Recycling rates vary greatly from one product or material type to another and from one location to another. Rates for different types of materials and products range from nearly zero to almost 100%. The increase in recycling has been propelled in part by economic forces as established businesses see opportunities to save money and as entrepreneurs see opportunities to start new businesses. It has also been driven by the desire of municipalities to reduce waste and by the satisfaction people take in recycling. These two forces have driven recycling's rise even though it has often not been financially profitable. In fact, many of the increasingly popular municipal recycling programs are run at an economic loss. The expense required to collect, sort, and process recycled goods is often more than recyclables are worth in the market. Furthermore, the more people recycle, the more glass, paper, and plastic are available to manufacturers for purchase, driving down prices.

Recycling advocates, however, point out that market prices do not take into account external costs—in particular, the environmental and health impacts of *not* recycling. For instance, it has been estimated that globally, recycling saves enough energy to power 6 million households per year. And recycling aluminum cans saves 95% of the energy required to make the same amount of aluminum from mined virgin bauxite, its source material.

As more manufacturers use recycled products and as more technologies and methods are developed to use recycled materials in new ways, markets should continue to expand, and new business opportunities may arise. We are still at an early stage in the shift from an economy that moves linearly from raw materials to products to waste to

weighing the issues

COSTS OF RECYCLING AND NOT RECYCLING

Should recycling programs be subsidized by governments even if they are run at an economic loss? What types of external costs—costs not reflected in market prices—do you think would be involved in not recycling, say, aluminum cans? Do you feel these costs justify sponsoring recycling programs even when they are not financially self-supporting? Why or why not?

an economy that moves circularly, using waste products as raw materials for new manufacturing processes. The steps we have taken in recycling so far are central to this transition, which many analysts view as key to building a sustainable economy.

Financial incentives can help address waste

Waste managers have employed economic incentives to reduce the waste stream. The "pay-as-you-throw" approach to garbage collection uses a financial incentive to influence consumer behaviour. In these programs, municipalities charge residents for home trash pickup according to the amount of trash they put out. The less waste the household generates, the less the resident has to pay.

Return-for-refund schemes ("bottle bills" in the United States) represent another approach that hinges on financial incentive. To date, all provinces and territories except Nunavut have such programs. Consumers pay a deposit, return bottles and cans to stores after use, and receive a refund—generally $0.05 to $0.20 per bottle or can. The first bottle bills were passed in the 1970s to cut down on litter, but they have also served to decrease the waste stream. Research by Melissa Felder, Clarissa Morawski, and others has shown that where they have been enacted, these laws have proven profoundly effective and resoundingly popular; they are recognized as among the most successful recycling programs of recent decades. Jurisdictions with bottle and can refund programs have reported that their beverage container litter has decreased by 69–84%, their total litter has decreased by 30–64%, and their per capita container recycling rate has risen 260%.

Edmonton showcases reduction and recycling

Edmonton, Alberta, has one of the world's most advanced waste management programs. As recently as 1998, fully 85% of the city's waste was being landfilled, and space was running out. Today, just 35% goes to the new sanitary landfill, whereas 15% is recycled, and an impressive 50% is composted. Edmonton's citizens are proud of the program, and 88% of them participate in its curbside recycling program. Where blue recycling bins are available at apartments and condominiums, the participation rate of residents is 91%. The goal is to divert 90% of the city's waste from landfill by 2012.[14]

When Edmonton's residents put out their trash, city trucks take it to their new *co-composting* plant, the largest in North America (**FIGURE 18.9A**). The waste is dumped on the floor of the facility, and large items, such as furniture, are removed and landfilled. The bulk of the waste is mixed with dried sewage sludge for one to two days in five large rotating drums, each the length of six buses. The resulting mix travels on a conveyor to a screen that removes nonbiodegradable items. It is aerated for several weeks in the largest stainless steel building in North America (**FIGURE 18.9B**). The mix is then passed through a finer screen and finally is left outside for four to six months. The resulting compost—80 000 tonnes annually—is made available to area farmers and residents. The facility even filters the air it emits with a 1-m layer of compost, bark, and wood chips, which eliminates the release of unpleasant odours into the community. Christmas tree composting and "grasscycling" programs are now included, as well.

(a) Composting facility, Edmonton, Alberta

(b) Aeration building, Edmonton composting facility

FIGURE 18.9
Edmonton boasts one of North America's most successful waste management programs. Edmonton's gigantic composting facility (a) is the size of eight football fields. Inside the aeration building (b), which is the size of 14 professional hockey rinks, mixtures of solid waste and sewage sludge are exposed to oxygen and composted for 14–21 days.

Edmonton's program also includes a state-of-the-art MRF, a leachate treatment plant, a research centre, public education programs, and a wetland and landfill reveg-etation program. In addition, 100 pipes collect enough landfill gas to power 4000 homes, bringing thousands of dollars to the city and helping power the new waste management centre. Five area businesses reprocess the city's recycled items, including e-wastes. Newsprint and magazines are turned into new newsprint and cellulose insulation, and cardboard and paper are converted into building paper and shingles. Household metal is made into rebar and blades for tractors and graders, and recycled glass is used for reflective paint and signs.

Industrial Solid Waste

In Canada, disposal of wastes from nonresidential sources (industrial, commercial, and institutional) increased from 14.6 million to 17.3 million tonnes between 2002 and 2008.[15] **Industrial solid waste** includes waste from factories, mining activities, agriculture, petroleum extraction, and more. Waste is generated at various points along the process from raw materials extraction to manufacturing to sale and distribution (**FIGURE 18.10**).

Regulation and economics each influence industrial waste generation

Most methods and strategies of waste disposal, reduction, and recycling by industry are similar to those for municipal solid waste. For instance, businesses that manage their own waste onsite most often dispose of it in landfills, and companies must design and manage their landfills in ways that meet provincial/territorial, local, or tribal guidelines. Other businesses pay to have their waste disposed of at municipal disposal sites. Regulation and enforcement vary across provinces and territories and from municipality to municipality.

The amount of waste generated by a manufacturing process is one measure of its efficiency; the less waste produced per unit or volume of product, the more efficient that process is, from a physical standpoint. However, physical efficiency is not always equivalent to economic efficiency. Often it is cheaper for industry to manufacture its products or perform its services quickly but messily. That is, it can be cheaper to generate waste than to avoid generating waste. In such cases, economic efficiency is maximized, but physical efficiency is not. The frequent mismatch between these two types of efficiency is a major reason that the output of industrial waste is so great.

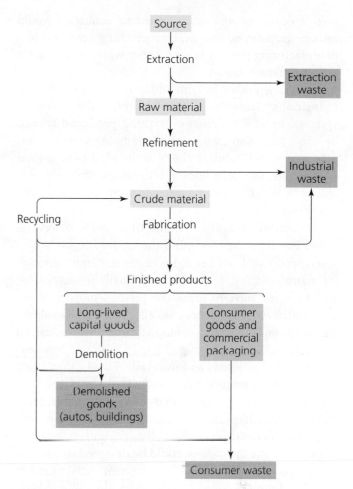

FIGURE 18.10
Industrial and municipal waste is generated throughout the life cycles of products. Waste is first generated when raw materials needed for production are extracted. Further industrial waste is produced as raw materials are processed and as products are manufactured. Waste results from the demolition or disposal of products by businesses and individuals. At each stage, there are opportunities for efficiency improvements, waste reduction, or recycling.

Rising costs of waste disposal, however, enhance the financial incentive to decrease waste and increase physical efficiency. Once either government or the market makes the physically efficient use of raw materials also economically efficient, businesses have financial incentives to reduce their own waste.

Industrial ecology seeks to make industry more sustainable

To reduce waste, growing numbers of industries today are experimenting with industrial ecology. A holistic approach that integrates principles from engineering, chemistry, ecology, and economics, **industrial ecology** seeks to redesign industrial systems to reduce resource inputs and to minimize physical inefficiency while maximizing economic efficiency. Industrial ecologists would reshape industry so that nearly everything produced in a manufacturing process is used, either within that process or in a different one.

The larger idea behind industrial ecology is that industrial systems should function more like ecological systems, in which almost everything produced is used by some organism, with very little being wasted. This principle brings industry closer to the ideal of ecological economists, in which human economies attain sustainability by functioning in a circular fashion rather than a linear one.

Industrial ecologists pursue their goals in several ways. For one, they examine the entire life cycle of a given product—from its origins in raw materials, through its manufacturing, to its use, and finally its disposal—and look for ways to make the process more ecologically efficient. This strategy is called **life-cycle analysis**. In addition, industrial ecologists examine industrial processes with an eye toward eliminating environmentally harmful products and materials. Finally, they study the flow of materials through industrial systems to look for ways to create products that are more durable, recyclable, or reusable. Goods that are currently thrown away when they become obsolete, such as computers, automobiles, and some appliances, could be designed to be more easily disassembled and their component parts reused or recycled. In this way, industrial ecology also helps to close the loop by minimizing wastes at both the industry end and the consumer end of the process.

By applying strategies aimed at reducing waste and preventing pollution at its source—commonly referred to as **pollution prevention (P2) strategies**—companies can significantly reduce their waste output.

Businesses are adopting industrial ecology

Businesses are taking advantage of the insights of industrial ecology to reduce waste and lessen their impact on health and the environment while saving money. A good example is the carpet tile company Interface, which asks customers to return used tiles for recycling and reuse as backing for new carpet. Interface also modified its tile design and its production methods to reduce waste. It adapted its boilers to use landfill gas for its energy needs and has the goal of sourcing all energy from renewable sources by 2020. Through such steps, the company has cut its waste generation by 80%, its fossil fuel use by 45%, and its water use by 70%—all while saving $30 million per year, holding prices steady for its customers, and raising profits by 49%.

Among many other initiatives are such programs as Canadian Tire's auto parts return initiatives and Xerox's take-back/lease programs for its used photocopiers. Programs like these are founded in good business principles, and they have the added benefit of building customer loyalty. An interesting variation of the take-back concept is the ENVIRx program run by the Pharmacists Association of Alberta, in which consumers are able to return unused medications to participating pharmacies for proper disposal. This helps prevent pharmaceuticals from entering the municipal waste stream.

The Swiss Zero Emissions Research and Initiatives (ZERI) Foundation sponsors dozens of innovative projects worldwide that attempt to create goods and services without generating waste. One example involving breweries is currently being pursued in Canada, Sweden, Japan, and Namibia. Brewers in these projects take waste from the beer-brewing process and use it to fuel other processes. Traditional breweries produce only beer while generating much waste, some of which goes toward animal feed. ZERI-sponsored breweries use their waste grain to make bread and to farm mushrooms. Waste from the mushroom farming, along with brewery wastewater, goes to feed pigs. The pigs' waste is digested in containers that capture natural gas and collect nutrients used to nourish algae for growing fish in fish farms. The brewer derives income from bread, mushrooms, pigs, gas, and fish, as well as beer, while producing little waste. Although most ZERI projects are not fully closed-loop systems, they attempt to approach this ideal.

An international initiative that has been adopted in Canada as an overriding strategy for industrial waste minimization is the Extended Producer Responsibility and Stewardship (or EPRS) program. The central goal of the program is to transfer a large part of the responsibility for waste minimization, both physical and financial, to producers.[16] This gives producers the economic incentives to design more environmentally efficient products and processes and to take greater responsibility for the product at the end of its life cycle. It also encourages producers to build the environmental costs of a product into its market price—one of the basic tenets of ecological economics.

Waste exchanges are an offshoot of industrial ecology

The concept of industrial ecology is based on a "closed loop" in which wastes are recycled back through the system. Following the definition of wastes as "resources out of place," industrial ecologists strive to find practical, economical uses for waste materials. To achieve this goal, they try to identify how waste products from one manufacturing process can be used as raw materials for a different process. For instance, used plastic beverage containers cannot be refilled because of the potential for contamination, but they can be shredded and reprocessed to make other plastic items, such as benches, tables, and decks.

Many network services have emerged with the goal of linking producers of waste with industries or individuals that can make use of the waste as raw materials. Such a network is called a **waste exchange**. You can check out an example of a nationwide waste exchange by visiting the website of The Waste Exchange of Canada at www. recyclexchange.net. Other waste exchanges operate locally or internationally.

For businesses, governments, and individuals alike, there are plenty of ways to reduce waste and mitigate the impacts of our waste generation—and quite often, doing so brings economic benefits. This is true both for solid waste and for hazardous waste.

Hazardous Waste

Hazardous wastes are diverse in their chemical composition and may be liquid, solid, or gaseous. In Canada, according to the *Canadian Environmental Protection Act (CEPA)* (1999), **hazardous waste** is waste that has one or more of the following properties:

- **Flammable**. Substances that easily catch fire (for example, natural gas or alcohol)
- **Corrosive**. Substances that corrode metals in storage tanks or equipment
- **Reactive**. Substances that are chemically unstable and readily react with other compounds, often explosively or by producing noxious fumes
- **Toxic**. Substances that harm the health of humans or other organisms when they are inhaled, are ingested, or come into contact with skin

Materials with these characteristics can harm human health and degrade environmental quality. Flammable and explosive materials can cause ecological damage and atmospheric pollution. For instance, fires at tire dumps, such as the one in Hagersville, Ontario, in 1990 (**FIGURE 18.11**), have caused air pollution and highway closures. Toxic wastes in lakes and rivers have caused fish die-offs, endangered aquatic mammals (see "Central Case: The Plight of the St. Lawrence Belugas"), and closed important domestic fisheries.

Certain categories of materials that are clearly "dangerous" are nevertheless not included in the official definition of hazardous waste. An example is biomedical waste, which includes things like human tissues and fluids,

FIGURE 18.11
In 1990 a pile of 15 million discarded tires in Hagersville, Ontario, caught fire and burned for 17 days, releasing thousands of litres of toxic chemicals, such as benzene and toluene, into the air and water.

and discarded medical sharps. These materials are excluded from the definition of hazardous waste not because they are without risk but because they require specialized handling, treatment, and disposal methods and are therefore controlled under different legislation. Similarly, radioactive waste requires a special set of management approaches.

Hazardous wastes have diverse sources

Industry, mining, households, small businesses, agriculture, utilities, and building demolition all create hazardous waste. Industry produces the largest amounts of hazardous waste, but in most developed nations industrial waste generation and disposal is highly regulated. This regulation has reduced the amount of hazardous waste entering the environment from industrial activities. As a result, households currently are the largest source of unregulated hazardous waste.

Household hazardous waste (HHW) includes a wide range of items, such as paints, batteries, oils, solvents, cleaning agents, lubricants, and pesticides. Nine categories of hazardous materials are commonly used by municipalities for the purpose of sorting and disposing of HHW (**TABLE 18.3**).[17]

Canadians improperly dispose of approximately 27 000 tonnes of HHW each year,[18] and the average home contains close to 45 kg of it in sheds, basements, closets, and garages (**TABLE 18.4**). Although many hazardous substances become less hazardous over time as they degrade chemically, two classes of chemicals are particularly hazardous because their toxicity persists over time: organic compounds and heavy metals.

Organic compounds and heavy metals can be hazardous

In our day-to-day lives, we rely on the capacity of synthetic organic compounds and petroleum-derived compounds to resist bacterial, fungal, and insect activity. Such items as plastic containers, rubber tires, pesticides, solvents, and wood preservatives are useful to us precisely because they resist decomposition. We use these substances to protect our buildings from decay, kill pests that attack crops, and keep stored goods intact. However, the resistance of these compounds to decay is a double-edged sword, for it also makes them persistent pollutants. Many synthetic organic compounds are toxic because they can be absorbed readily through the skin of humans and other animals and can act as mutagens, carcinogens, teratogens, and endocrine disruptors.

Heavy metals, such as lead, chromium, mercury, arsenic, cadmium, tin, and copper, are used widely in industry for wiring, electronics, metal plating, metal fabrication, pigments, and dyes. Heavy metals enter the environment when paints, electronic devices, batteries, and other materials are disposed of improperly. Lead from fishing weights and from hunters' lead shot has accumulated in many rivers, lakes, and forests. In older homes, lead from pipes contaminates drinking water, and lead paint remains a problem, especially for infants. Heavy metals that are fat-soluble and break down slowly are prone to bioaccumulating.

"E-waste" is a new and growing problem

When we first began to conduct much of our business, learning, and communication with computers and other electronic devices, many people predicted that our paper waste would decrease. Instead, the proliferation of computers, printers, VCRs, fax machines, cell phones, GPS devices, MP3 players, and other gadgets has created a substantial new source of waste. These products have short lifetimes before people judge them obsolete, and most are discarded after only a few years.

The amount of **electronic waste**—often called **e-waste**—is growing rapidly. Statistics Canada reports that in 2009, 36% of Canadian households had unwanted electronic devices.[19] Canadians discarded 74 000 tonnes of computer waste in 2002, including 1.7 million desktop computers, 1.9 million cell phones, 2 million television sets, and 1.1 million VCRs (see also **TABLE 18.4**). The U.S. Environmental Protection Agency reports that 70% of the heavy metals found in U.S. landfills came from discarded electronic products.[20]

Most e-waste is disposed of in landfills as conventional solid waste. However, most electronic products contain heavy metals and toxic flame retardants, and recent research suggests that e-waste should instead be

---

Table 18.3   Categories of Household Hazardous Waste

- *Antifreeze* (ethylene or propylene glycol used or intended for use as a vehicle engine coolant; materials and their containers)
- *Fertilizers* (materials registered under the Fertilizers Act, packaged in 30-kg quantities or less, including their containers)
- *Lubricating oils* (petroleum-derived or synthetic oils, crankcase, engine and gear oils, and hydraulic, transmission and heat transfer fluids, and lubricating fluids used in machinery; containers of 30 L and less)
- *Paints and coatings* (household and industrial use, including their containers)
- *Pesticides, fungicides, herbicides, insecticides* (and their containers, including domestic, commercial, agricultural, and restricted pesticides)
- *Pressurized containers* (such as propane tanks and cylinders, and oxygen tanks)
- *Single-use dry cell batteries* (alkaline and carbon zinc, mercuric-oxide, silver-oxide and zinc-air, and lithium, including cylindrical, regular and button batteries)
- *Solvents* (and their containers, including turpentine, isopropanol, ethanol, ketones, xylene, toluene, mineral spirits, linseed oils, naphtha, and methylene chloride; these are better known as paint thinners, lacquer thinners, automotive body resin solvents, contact cement thinners, paint strippers, and degreasers)
- *Used oil filters* (from hydraulic, transmission or internal combustion engine applications, including diesel fuel filters, household furnace fuel filter, coolant filter, storage tank diesel fuel filter, sump-type automatic transmission filter, and others)

Source: Stewardship Ontario, Municipal Hazardous or Special Waste, Do What You Can Program; for more information see "What's Included."

Table 18.4   Household Hazardous Waste in Canada, 2009

% of households

Had leftover or expired medication to dispose of	**39**
Put them in the garbage	22
Took or sent them to a depot or drop-off centre	6
Returned them to a supplier or retailer	57
Poured them down the drain, sewer, ground, toilet or sink	8
Still had them	15
Other	1
Had leftover paint or solvents to dispose of	**39**
Put them in the garbage	4
Took or sent them to a depot or drop-off centre	62
Returned them to a supplier or retailer	8
Still had them	31
Other	2
Had unwanted engine oil or antifreeze to dispose of	**15**
Put them in the garbage	1
Took or sent them to a depot or drop-off centre	61
Returned them to a supplier or retailer	19
Still had them	18
Other	4
Had dead or unwanted car batteries to dispose of	**12**
Put them in the garbage	[data unreliable]
Took or sent them to a depot or drop-off centre	46
Returned them to a supplier or retailer	31
Still had them	20
Other	5
Had other dead or unwanted batteries to dispose of	**58**
Put them in the garbage	42
Took or sent them to a depot or drop-off centre	35
Returned them to a supplier or retailer	7
Still had them	18
Other	5
Had unwanted electronic devices to dispose of	**36**
Put them in the garbage	11
Took or sent them to a depot or drop-off centre	45
Returned them to a supplier or retailer	5
Donated them or gave them away	22
Still had them	28
Other	2
Had dead or unwanted compact fluorescent lights (CFLs) to dispose of	**22**
Put them in the garbage	56
Took or sent them to a depot or drop-off centre	24
Donated them or gave them away	4
Still had them	13
Other	3

Source: Statistics Canada, Households and the Environment Survey, 2009.

treated as hazardous waste (**FIGURE 18.12**). For instance, more than 6% of a typical computer is composed of lead. The cathode ray tubes in televisions and computer screens can hold up to 5 kg of heavy metals, such as lead and cadmium. These represent the second-largest source of lead in landfills today, behind auto batteries. In Canada there are no federal programs or legislation aimed specifically at dealing with e-waste, although initiatives have been started in most provinces. More and more electronics are now being recycled. The devices are taken apart, and parts are either reused or disposed of more safely. Roughly one-fifth of the nearly 2 million tonnes of electronics discarded in 2005 in the United States was recycled, the EPA estimates.

There are serious concerns about the health risks that recycling may pose to workers doing the disassembly, and wealthy nations ship much of their e-waste to developing countries, where the disassembly is done by poor workers with minimal safety regulations. These environmental justice concerns need to be resolved, but if electronics recycling can be done responsibly, it seems likely to be the way of the future.

In many North American cities, businesses, nonprofit organizations, or municipal services now collect used electronics for reuse or recycling. The next time you upgrade to a new computer, TV, DVD player, VCR, or cell phone, find out about opportunities to recycle your old ones.

(a) Electronic waste

FIGURE 18.12

(a) Discarded electronic waste can leach heavy metals and should be considered hazardous waste, researchers say. **(b)** Some proportion of all electronic devices tested exceeded 5 mg/L, the U.S. EPA's regulatory threshold for lead leachate. (Canada'a threshold for drinking water is 0.010 mg/L.) Devices with higher ferrous metal content tended to leach less lead. Where both standard and modified TCLPs were used, results are averaged. *Source: Data from Townsend, T. G., et al. 2004. RCRA toxicity characterization of computer CPUs and other discarded electronic devices. July 15, 2004, report to the U.S. EPA.*

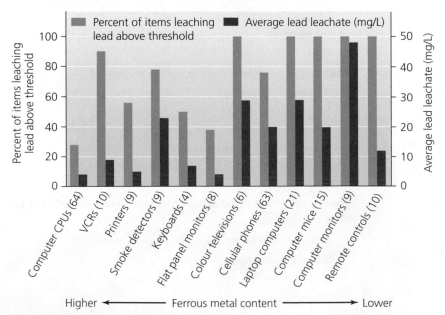

(b) Lead leaching from e-waste items

Several steps precede the disposal of hazardous waste

For many years we discarded hazardous waste without special treatment. In many cases, people did not know that certain substances were harmful to human health. In other cases, the danger posed by these substances was known or suspected, but it was assumed that the substances would disappear or be sufficiently diluted in the environment. The resurfacing of toxic chemicals in a residential area years after their burial at Love Canal in upstate New York provided a dramatic demonstration to the North American public that hazardous waste deserves special attention and treatment.

Since the 1980s, many communities have designated sites or special collection days to gather household hazardous waste or have designated facilities for the exchange and reuse of substances (**FIGURE 18.13**). Once consolidated in such sites, the waste is transported for treatment and ultimate disposal.

As for municipal solid waste, the management and control of hazardous waste and hazardous recyclable materials is a shared responsibility in Canada. The federal government regulates international agreements and transport. Provincial and territorial governments regulate intraprovincial transport and are responsible for licensing hazardous waste generators, carriers, and treatment facilities.[21] As hazardous waste is generated, transported, and disposed of, the producer, carrier, and disposal facility

FIGURE 18.14
Unscrupulous individuals or businesses sometimes dump hazardous waste illegally to avoid disposal costs.

must each report the type and amount of material generated; its location, origin, and destination; and its handling. This is intended to prevent illegal dumping and encourage the use of reputable waste carriers and disposal facilities. Because it can be quite costly to dispose of hazardous waste, irresponsible companies sometimes illegally and anonymously dump waste, creating health risks for residents and financial headaches for local governments forced to deal with the mess (**FIGURE 18.14**).

Hazardous waste from industrialized nations is also sometimes dumped illegally in developing nations—a major environmental justice issue. This practice occurs despite the *Basel Convention*, an international treaty to prevent such acts. In 2006, a ship secretly dumped toxic wastes in Abidjan, the capital of Ivory Coast, after being told by Dutch authorities that the Netherlands would charge money to dispose of the waste in Amsterdam. The waste caused several deaths and thousands of illnesses in Abidjan, and street protests forced the government to resign over the scandal. Some jail sentences and fines were eventually handed down in this case, although thousands of victims still have received no compensation for their suffering.

Fortunately, high costs of disposal have also encouraged conscientious businesses to invest in reducing their hazardous waste. Many biologically hazardous materials can be broken down by incineration at high temperatures in cement kilns. Some hazardous materials can be treated by exposure to bacteria that break down harmful components and synthesize them into new compounds. Besides bacterial bioremediation, phytoremediation is also used. Various plants have now been bred or engineered to take

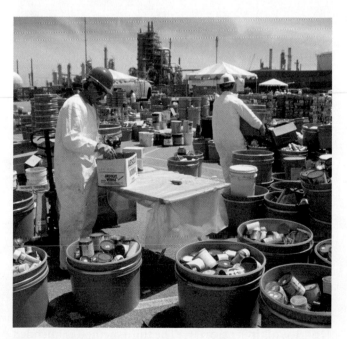

FIGURE 18.13
Many communities designate collection sites or collection days for household hazardous waste. Here, workers handle waste from an Earth Day collection event.

up specific contaminants from soil; they then break down organic contaminants into safer compounds or concentrate heavy metals in their tissues. The plants are eventually harvested and disposed of.

There are three disposal methods for hazardous waste

There are three primary means of hazardous waste disposal: secure landfills, surface impoundments, and injection wells. These do nothing to lessen the hazards of the substances, but they do help keep the waste isolated from people, wildlife, and ecosystems.

Secure landfills   Design and construction standards for landfills that receive hazardous waste are much stricter than those for ordinary sanitary landfills. Hazardous waste landfills, also called **secure landfills**, must have several impervious liners, leachate removal systems, and extensive monitoring wells, and they must be located far from aquifers. Dumping of hazardous waste in ordinary landfills is particularly problematic in closed-down landfills that received wastes prior to the advent of more-secure disposal options for hazardous materials.

Surface impoundments   Liquid hazardous waste, or waste in dissolved form, may be stored in ponds or **surface impoundments**, shallow depressions lined with plastic and an impervious material, such as clay. Water containing dilute hazardous waste is placed in the pond and allowed to evaporate, leaving a residue of solid hazardous waste on the bottom (**FIGURE 18.15**). This process is repeated until the dry material is removed and transported elsewhere for permanent disposal. Impoundments are not ideal. The underlying layer can crack and leak waste. Some material may evaporate or blow into surrounding areas. Rainstorms may cause waste to overflow and contaminate nearby areas. For these reasons, surface impoundments are used only for temporary storage.

The potential for problems with surface impoundment of hazardous wastes became abundantly clear in the small rural town of Elmira, Ontario, in the late 1980s. UniRoyal (now the Crompton Company) had operated a chemical production facility at Elmira since 1942. One of the substances produced at the plant was the so-called Agent Orange, an extremely powerful herbicide used by the United States during the Vietnam War to defoliate large areas of forest. (U.S. and Vietnamese soldiers and civilians later suffered serious health impacts as a result of exposure to this chemical.) Rubber and agrichemicals were also produced at the plant. The waste by-products

FIGURE 18.15

Surface impoundments are a strategy for temporarily disposing of liquid hazardous waste. The waste, mixed with water, is poured into a shallow depression lined with plastic and clay to prevent leakage. When the water evaporates, leaving a crust of the hazardous substance, new liquid is poured in and the process repeated. This method alone is not satisfactory because waste can potentially leak, overflow, evaporate, or blow away.

of chemical production were disposed of—legally, and within Ontario Ministry of Environment regulations for the day—in a clay-lined surface impoundment pit onsite, starting in the 1960s.

Then, in 1989, traces of chemical markers, notably the carcinogen N-nitrosodimethylamine (NDMA), began to appear in municipal drinking water wells, downslope of the impoundment site. Apparently the clay liner of the impoundment pit had failed, perhaps because it had become saturated, and contaminants were leaking out of the pit and joining the groundwater. The company undertook remediation of both the impoundment pit and the surrounding aquifers in the early 1990s. However, the town of Elmira no longer withdraws its drinking water from these aquifers; instead, it pipes water in from another municipality.

Deep-well injection   The third method is intended for long-term disposal. In **deep-well injection**, a well is drilled deep beneath the water table into porous rock,

Injection well

Unconfined aquifer

Impervious soil

Confined aquifer

Impervious soil

Porous rock

Injected hazardous waste

FIGURE 18.16
Liquid hazardous waste may be pumped deep underground, by deep-well injection. The well must be drilled below any aquifers, into porous rock separated by impervious clay. The technique is expensive, and waste may leak from the well shaft into groundwater.

and wastes are injected into it (**FIGURE 18.16**). The waste is meant to remain deep underground, isolated from groundwater and human contact. This idea seems attractive in principle, but in practice wells become corroded and can leak wastes into soil, allowing them to enter aquifers. Alberta accounts for approximately 90% of all deep-well injection of hazardous wastes in Canada.

Radioactive waste is especially hazardous

Radioactive waste is particularly dangerous to human health. It is, by definition, **radioactive** (that is, giving off energetic particles and radiation in the process of spontaneous radioactive decay) and thus potentially hazardous to human and animal health. In addition, some of it is highly toxic, and some of it is extremely persistent. The dilemma of disposal has dogged the nuclear energy industry for decades. There is as yet no identified permanent repository for radioactive waste in Canada. Yucca Mountain in Nevada was approved as the single-site repository for all nuclear waste in the United States but the licence application was withdrawn in 2010. Other countries, including Germany also have designated permanent disposal sites for radioactive waste.

Most proposals for permanent disposal of radioactive waste involve some form of **geologic isolation**; that is, using the absorptive capacity and impermeability of some naturally occurring rock units to block the movement of contaminants away from the disposal site. Canadian proposals focus on disposal in automated facilities located deep underground in the stable, ancient, plutonic igneous rocks of the Canadian Shield. Other geologic settings that are amenable to geologic isolation include salt domes and thick shale units.

Geologic isolation would be combined with the chemical immobilization of the waste, sophisticated engineering design of the facility itself, and multiple-layered impervious containers for storage of the waste. In Canada, this is referred to as a **multiple-barrier approach**—that is, engineering the entire facility to place as many barriers as possible, both physical and chemical, in the pathway of any escaping contaminants.

Contaminated sites are being cleaned up, slowly

Many thousands of former military and industrial sites remain contaminated with hazardous waste in Canada and virtually every other nation on Earth. For most nations, dealing with these messes is simply too difficult, time-consuming, and expensive. Some contaminated sites, especially in the United States, have reached iconic status for the roles they played in raising public awareness, spurring local residents to action, and kick-starting the modern environmental movement. In Love Canal, a residential neighbourhood in Niagara Falls, New York, families were evacuated after toxic chemicals buried by a company and the city in past decades rose to the surface, contaminating homes and an elementary school. In Missouri, the entire town of Times Beach—another name that is practically synonymous with poorly managed toxic waste—was evacuated and its buildings demolished after being contaminated by dioxin from waste oil sprayed on its roads. The beneficial outcome is that these horrific cases led to the establishment of the first legislation to deal with liability, compensation, and cleanup costs associated with contaminated sites in the United States.

In Canada, many contaminated sites have been abandoned and thus fall under federal jurisdiction. Approximately 18 000 sites are currently listed in Canada's Federal Contaminated Sites Inventory and have been assessed or classified under the National Classification System for contaminated sites, developed by the Canadian Council of Ministers of the Environment.[22] Examples of the nearly 1197 priority sites identified for cleanup include the following:[23]

- *Faro Mine, Yukon:* $14.6 million for the largest and highest priority of the federal contaminated sites, an old lead, zinc, silver, and gold mine that was shut down when the company went into receivership. There are now approximately 70 million tonnes of tailings and 320 million tonnes of waste rock at the site, with consequent acid drainage, wind-blown particulates, and other environmental hazards.[24]
- *Canadian Forces Base Esquimalt, British Columbia:* $4.56 million for remediation of hydrocarbon and heavy metal–contaminated soil, assessment, and risk management.
- *Port Radium Mine, Northwest Territories:* $7.1 million funding for sealing of mine openings, covering of areas of elevated radiation levels, stabilization of tailings areas, demolition, and hazardous waste disposal.
- *Belleville Small Craft Harbour, Ontario:* $6.8 million to treat contaminated soil and prevent contaminants in groundwater from discharging into the adjacent Bay of Quinte. Belleville Harbour was used for more than 50 years for the storage of coal and fuel products, which led to petroleum hydrocarbon and heavy metal contamination.

You can examine the complete Federal Contaminated Sites Inventory for yourself. It is maintained (interestingly, perhaps because of the enormous costs associated with remediation of these sites) by the Treasury Board of Canada Secretariat, and the website is www.tbs-sct.gc.ca/fcsi-rscf.

Sites that have been contaminated but have the potential to be cleaned up and remediated for other purposes are called **brownfields**. However, many sites are contaminated with hazardous chemicals we have no effective way to deal with. In such cases, cleanups simply involve trying to isolate waste from human contact, either by building trenches and clay or concrete barriers around a site or by excavating contaminated material, placing it in industrial-strength containers, and shipping it to a hazardous waste disposal facility. For all these reasons,

the current emphasis is on preventing hazardous waste contamination in the first place.

All three North American countries monitor industrial pollutants by using Pollutant Release and Transfer Registers (PRTRs), which combine reports from industrial facilities with information about transfers, off-site treatments, and disposal or recycling of pollutants. In Canada the PRTR is the National Pollutant Release Inventory (NPRI), established in 1992, which covers more than 300 chemicals plus the criteria air contaminants. In Mexico, it is the *Registro de Emisiones y Transferencia de Contaminantes (RETC)*, which covers 100 chemicals, and in the United States it is the Toxics Release Inventory (TRI), started in 1987, which tracks data for more than 600 chemicals.[25] By learning where these pollutants come from, where they end up, and how they are transferred, we may ultimately be in a better position to control them.

Conclusion

Our societies have made great strides in addressing our waste problems. Modern methods of waste management are far safer for people and gentler on the environment than past practices of open dumping and open burning. In many countries, recycling and composting efforts are making rapid progress. Canada has changed in a few decades from a country that did virtually no recycling to a nation in which nearly one-quarter of all solid waste is diverted from disposal. The continuing growth of recycling, composting, and pollution-prevention initiatives, driven by market forces, government policy, and consumer behaviour, shows potential to further alleviate our waste problems.

Despite these advances, our prodigious consumption habits have created more waste than ever before. Our waste management efforts are marked by a number of difficult dilemmas, including the cleanup of highly contaminated sites, safe disposal of hazardous and radioactive waste, and frequent local opposition to disposal sites. These dilemmas make clear that the best solution to our waste problem is to reduce our generation of waste. Finding ways to reduce, reuse, and efficiently recycle the materials and goods that we use stands as a key challenge for this century.

CANADIAN ENVIRONMENTAL PERSPECTIVES

Brennain Lloyd

Brennain Lloyd defends the North against the irresponsible dumping of garbage and other harmful waste materials.

- **Coordinator** of Northwatch
- **Peace and environmental activist**
- **Advisor** on natural resource management

Brennain Lloyd came to environmental activism from the peace movement, where she confronted issues such as poverty, injustice, and violence. As she explains it, "peace work in northeastern Ontario inevitably led to working with environmental groups" on such issues as the impacts of uranium mining and refining, the threat of a nuclear waste dumpsite in the area, and the establishment of a military testing and training corridor for the delivery of air-launched cruise missiles. "These issues had huge peace implications, but also impacts on forest health, wildlife, and human communities."

Lloyd—who is from North Bay, Ontario—is the coordinator of Northwatch, a coalition of citizen organizations and individual members. Founded in 1988, Northwatch brings a northern perspective to regional environmental issues, including waste dumping; natural resource management, especially mining and logging; and water and air quality concerns. Northwatch also provides support for local citizen groups working to address environmental issues in their communities. Three current focus areas are better forest management, greater community involvement in mine monitoring and management, and preventing northeastern Ontario from becoming a dumping ground.[26]

Today, Lloyd is ubiquitous—speaking about nuclear waste disposal in the Canadian Shield to the Canadian Environmental Assessment Agency; presenting a talk at the University of Waterloo on garbage dumping in the North, as part of the university's Environmentalist-in-Residence series; participating in a task force on mining sector sustainability or running a workshop on forest management for a local citizens' group or advisory committee to the Ministry of Natural Resources; and reviewing and analyzing a proposal for a new biodiesel plant.

A few years ago, she was central to a successful intervention in the City of Toronto's plan to ship municipal garbage hundreds of kilometres for disposal in the old Adams Mine site in Kirkland Lake, Ontario. Northwatch coordinated community opposition to this plan, through the Adams Mine Intervention Coalition. The plan, which would have endangered regional water bodies and groundwater, was eventually overturned by the Toronto City Council in 2000. In 2004, the Province of Ontario passed the *Adams Mine Lake Act*, which revoked all existing approvals for the use of the old mine site as a landfill, prevented the site from ever being used for that purpose, and extended the same protection to all large water bodies in the province.

In addition to the Adams Mine struggle, Lloyd and Northwatch have intervened in a number of other plans to import waste into Northern Ontario, including Ontario's biomedical waste and PCBs from around the world. Radioactive waste has been a long-term struggle; the coalition opposes any plans to develop a deep geologic isolation disposal site for nuclear waste in the Canadian Shield. It also works to ensure appropriate decommissioning of old mine sites in the North, such as the uranium mines of Elliot Lake (see "Central Case: Mining Denendeh").

Northwatch often finds itself in a reactive position, such as opposing plans to use the North as a dumping ground or withdraw resources in a harmful or negligent manner. But Lloyd and her coalition also take a proactive stance on northern development, stating that "the North must realize a long-term objective of diversifying the economy while maintaining the natural resource base and making best use of those resources which are extracted. To this end, economic and social decisions must be made with the priority of creating and contributing to a 'sustainable' North."

"My work on waste management has been of necessity, in response to repeated efforts to use northeastern Ontario as a dumping ground for 'foreign' wastes."[27]—**Brennain Lloyd**

Thinking About Environmental Perspectives

Toronto reversed its original plan to ship garbage to a dumpsite located in the old Adams Mine near Kirkland Lake, Ontario, partly in response to the enormous opposition from organizations like the Adams Mine Intervention Coalition and Northwatch. What do you think about a city like Toronto shipping its garbage far away? If Toronto or other large cities simply run out of room to dispose of their garbage within their own borders, what realistic alternatives do they have?

REVIEWING OBJECTIVES

You should now be able to:

Summarize and compare the types of waste we generate

- Municipal and industrial solid waste, hazardous waste, and wastewater are major types of waste.

List the major approaches to managing waste

- Source reduction, recovery, and disposal are the three main components of waste management.

Delineate the scale of the waste dilemma

- Developed nations generate far more waste than developing nations do.
- Waste everywhere is increasing as a result of growth in population and consumption.

Describe conventional waste disposal methods: landfills and incineration

- Sanitary landfills guard against contamination of groundwater, air, and soil. Nonetheless, such contamination can occur.
- Incinerators reduce waste volume by burning it. Pollution control technology removes most pollutants from emissions, but some escape, and highly toxic ash needs to be disposed of in landfills.
- We are harnessing energy from landfill gas and generating electricity from incineration.

Evaluate approaches for reducing waste: source reduction, reuse, composting, and recycling

- Reducing waste before it is generated is the best waste management approach. Recovery is the next-best option.

- Consumers can take simple steps to reduce their waste output.
- Composting reduces waste while creating organic matter for gardening and agriculture.
- Recycling has grown slowly in recent years and now removes about 25% of waste from the Canadian waste stream.

Discuss industrial solid waste management and principles of industrial ecology

- Regulations differ, but industrial waste management is similar to that for municipal solid waste.
- Industrial ecology urges industrial systems to mimic ecological systems and provides ways for industry to increase its efficiency.

Assess issues in managing hazardous waste

- Hazardous waste is flammable, corrosive, reactive, or toxic.
- Electronic waste may be considered hazardous.
- Hazardous waste is strictly regulated, yet illegal dumping remains a problem.
- No fully satisfactory method of disposing of hazardous waste has yet been devised.
- Cleanup of hazardous waste sites is a long and expensive process.

TESTING YOUR COMPREHENSION

1. Describe five major methods of managing waste. Why do we practise waste management?
2. Why have some people labelled modern North America as "the throwaway society"? How much solid waste do Canadians generate, and how does this amount compare with that of people from other countries?
3. Name several technologies designed to make sanitary landfills safe places for the disposal of waste. Describe three problems with landfills.

4. Describe the process of incineration or combustion. What happens to the resulting ash? What is one drawback of incineration?
5. What is composting, and how does it help reduce input to the waste stream?
6. What are the three elements of a sustainable process of recycling?
7. What are the goals of industrial ecology?
8. What four criteria are used to define hazardous waste? Why are heavy metals and synthetic organic compounds particularly hazardous?

9. What are the largest sources of hazardous waste? Describe three ways to dispose of hazardous waste.

10. How is waste regulated in Canada? What are some of the similarities and differences between the regulation of nonhazardous wastes and that of hazardous wastes?

THINKING IT THROUGH

1. How much waste do you generate? Look into your waste bin at the end of the day, and categorize and measure the waste there. List all other waste you may have generated in other places throughout the day. How much of this waste could you have avoided generating? How much could have been reused or recycled?

2. Some people have criticized current waste management practices as merely moving waste from one medium to another. How might this criticism apply to the methods now in practice? What are some potential solutions?

3. Of the various waste management approaches covered in this chapter, which ones are your community and campus pursuing, and which are they not pursuing? Would you suggest that your community or campus start pursuing any new approaches? If so, which ones, and why?

4. Could manufacturers and businesses benefit from source reduction if consumers were to buy fewer products as a result? How? Given what you know about industrial ecology, what do you think the future of sustainable manufacturing may look like?

5. You are the CEO of a major corporation that produces containers for soft drinks and a wide variety of other consumer products. Your company's shareholders are asking that you improve the company's image—while not cutting into profits—by taking steps to reduce waste. What steps would you consider taking?

6. Now let's say that you are the president of your college or university. Your trustees want you to engage with local businesses and industries in ways that benefit both the school and the community. Your faculty and students want you to make the school a leader in waste reduction and industrial ecology. Consider the industries and businesses in your community and the ways they interact with facilities on your campus. Bearing in mind the principles of industrial ecology, can you think of any novel ways in which your school and local businesses might mutually benefit from one another's services, products, or waste materials? Are there waste products from one business, industry, or campus facility that another might put to good use? Can you design an eco-industrial park that might work on your campus? What steps would you propose to take as president?

INTERPRETING GRAPHS AND DATA

In 2006, about 90% of all households in Canada reported using some sort of recycling program.[28] This sounds like fantastic news—the "reduce, reuse, recycle" message appears to have reached the population, and the work of protecting the environment is mostly done. Is this true? Find out by taking a closer look at Canadian statistics.

The following table shows how many kilograms of residential waste were produced per person and how much waste was diverted from landfill sites through recycling in 2006. It also shows the percentage of households that used any type of recycling program in 2006.

Definitions:

- **Waste disposed:** waste that is landfilled, incinerated, or treated for final disposal (does not include materials destined for recycling and composting)

- **Recyclable materials diverted:** materials diverted from the waste stream and remanufactured into a new product or used as a raw material substitute

- **Total materials discarded:** the combined total amount of waste disposed and recyclable materials diverted

Disposal and Diversion of Residential Waste and Household Use of Recycling Programs, by Province and Territory, 2006

	1	2	3	4	5
	Total residential waste disposed,[29] per capita	Residential recyclable materials diverted,[30] per capita	Total materials discarded, per capita (Column 1 + Column 2)	Diversion rate	Households that used any recycling program in 2006[31]
	Kilograms per capita			Percent %	
Newfoundland and Labrador	446	x^{32}			82
Prince Edward Island	x	x			98
Nova Scotia	181	149			95
New Brunswick	289	44			83
Québec[33]	285	122			86
Ontario	292	119			93
Manitoba	386	60			79
Saskatchewan	300	39			87
Alberta	289	98			85
British Columbia	222	145			93
Yukon	214	x			—
Northwest Territories	347	x			—
Nunavut	x	x			—
Canada	283	115			90

Use the table to answer these questions:

1. For each region, calculate the total materials discarded per capita, including waste disposed and recyclable materials diverted. Record your answers in column 3 of the table.

2. For each region, calculate the diversion rate (the amount of residential recyclable materials diverted, per capita, compared to total materials discarded per capita), using the following formula:

$$\text{Diversion rate} = \frac{\text{Column 2}}{\text{Column 3}} \times 100$$

Record your answers in column 4 of the table.

3. Which province had the highest diversion rate?

4. Do you think there is a connection between the diversion rate and the percentage of households that use a recycling program in the provinces and territories? Explain your answer.

5. Create a scatter plot to compare the percentages of households that used a recycling program (column 5 from the table above) with the diversion rates (column 4). Identify each data point by labelling it with the provincial or territorial abbreviation (e.g., MB for Manitoba, NB for New Brunswick).

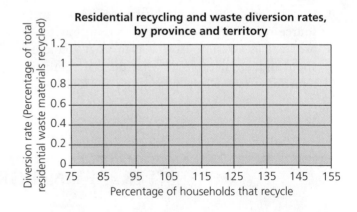

Residential recycling and waste diversion rates, by province and territory

6. Draw the line of best fit (the trend line that fits the majority of data points) for the above graph.

7. Describe the trend in the graph. Does this match your prediction in question 4?

8. How can you explain the connection between the percentage of households that recycle and the diversion rate?

Source: Statistics Canada, Contributed by Angela McCanny, Statistics Canada resource teacher, Ottawa, Ontario, www19.statcan.ca/02/02_051-eng.htm.

CHAPTER ENDNOTES

1. Canadian Biogas Industry Overview, Ken Hogg, October 27, 2005, *New Era Renewable Energy Solutions*, www.ptac.org/eea/dl/eeaf0501p04.pdf

2. City of Toronto Council and Committees, June 1, 1999, *Ontario Hydro Corridor Lands and Beare Road Ski Facility Trust Fund*, www.toronto.ca/legdocs/1999/agendas/committees/sc/sc990622/it035b.htm

3. Environment Canada, Waste Management, *Beare Road Project*, www.ec.gc.ca/wmd-dgd/default.asp?lang=En&n=3438B2E7-1

4. Government of Canada Depository Services Program, *Hazardous Waste Management: Canadian Directions, 1992*, http://dsp-psd.tpsgc.gc.ca/Collection-R/LoPBdP/BP/bp323-e.htm#A.%20Definitions%20and%20Classification(txt)

5. Environment Canada, Waste Management, *Municipal Solid Waste*, www.ec.gc.ca/wmd-dgd/Default.-asp?lang=En&n=7623F633-1

6. Statistics Canada, Environment Accounts and Statistics Product Catalogue (2011) No. 16-257.

7. Simmons, P., et al. (2006) The state of garbage in America. *BioCycle*, Vol. 47, p. 26.

8. Environment Canada, Waste Management, *Municipal Solid Waste*, www.ec.gc.ca/wmd-dgd/Default.-asp?lang=En&n=7623F633-1

9. Desrocher, S., and B. Sherwood-Lollar (1998) Isotopic constraints on off-site migration of landfill CH4, *Ground Water*, Vol. 36, No. 5, pp. 801–809. Research Library Core.

10. Desrocher, S., and B. Sherwood-Lollar (1998) Isotopic constraints on off-site migration of landfill CH4, *Ground Water*, Vol. 36, No. 5, pp. 801–809. Research Library Core.

11. City of Toronto Solid Waste Management, *Facts About Toronto's Trash*, updated November 1, 2007, www.toronto.ca/garbage/facts.-htm

12. Statistics Canada, Summary Tables: Disposal and Diversion of Waste, by Province and Territory www40.statcan.gc.ca/101/cst01/envir32c-eng.htm

13. Statistics Canada, Environment Accounts and Statistics Analytical and Technical Paper Series *Recycling by Canadian Housholds*, 2007.

14. City of Edmonton, 2011, *Recycling Facts*, www.edmonton.ca/for_residents/Environment/City_recycle_factsheet(web).pdf

15. Statistics Canada, Environment Accounts and Statistics Division, Cansim Table 153-0041.

16. Environment Canada, *EPR*, www.ec.gc.ca/epr/Default.-asp?lang=En&n=EEBCC813-1

17. Recycling Council of Ontario, *Household Hazardous Waste Fact Sheet, 1996*, www.rco.on.ca/RCO_files/HHW.pdf.

18. Canadian Institute for Environmental Law and Policy, *Understanding Hazardous Waste in Ontario, 2006*, www.cielap.org/pdf/HazWaste2007.pdf

19. Statistics Canada, Households and the Environment (2009), Highlights.

20. Canadian Institute for Environmental Law and Policy, *Understanding Hazardous Waste in Ontario, 2006*, www.cielap.org/pdf/HazWaste2007.pdf

21. Environment Canada, Waste Management, *Hazardous Waste*, www.ec.gc.ca/wmd dgd/dcfault.asp?lang=En&n=FDC36D83-1

22. Environment Canada, News Release, July 26, 2007, and Federal Contaminated Sites Inventory, www.tbs-sct.gc.ca/fcsi-rscf/home-accueil.aspx?Language=EN&sid=wu91133413870

23. Environment Canada, *Backgrounder: Federal Contaminated Sites Receiving Funds, 2007*, www.ec.gc.ca/default.asp?lang=En&n=714D9AAE-1&news=81941DCD-F8FA-4012-9266-CE-C4F186B0F7

24. Faro Mine Closure, *Challenges*, www.faromineclosure.yk.ca/project/challenges.html

25. Commission for Environmental Cooperation (2008) *The North American Mosaic: An Overview of Key Environmental Issues: Industrial Pollution and Waste*, www.cec.org/soe/files/en/SOE_IndustrialPollution_en.pdf

26. Northwatch, www.web.net/~nwatch/

27. Brennain Lloyd, from a delegation to the Canadian Environmental Assessment Agency, 2003, www.ceaa.gc.ca/010/0001/0001/0012/0002/0012/s6_e.htm

28. *EnviroStats* "Recycling in Canada" (July 1, 2007). As reported in *The Daily*. Retrieved June 29, 2008 www.statcan.ca/Daily/English/070713/d070713a.htm#tab2ftnote1

29. Statistics Canada (2006) *Waste Management Industry Survey: Business and Government Sectors*. Catalogue no. 16F0023X, Text Table 1: Disposal of waste, by source and by province and territory. Residential nonhazardous wastes disposed includes solid waste produced by all residences and includes waste that is picked up by the municipality (either using its own staff or through contracting firms) and waste

from residential sources that is self-hauled to depots, transfer stations, and disposal facilities.

30. Statistics Canada. Table 153-0042, Materials prepared for recycling, by source, Canada, provinces and territories, every 2 years (tonnes), CANSIM (database), Using E-STAT (distributor). This information covers only those companies and local waste management organisations that reported nonhazardous recyclable material preparation activities and refers only to that material entering the waste stream and does not cover any waste that may be managed on-site by a company or household. Additionally, these data do not include those materials transported by the generator directly to secondary processors such as pulp and paper mills while bypassing entirely any firm or local government involved in waste management activities.

31. Statistics Canada (2006) *Households and the Environment Survey*, Text table 3.7.

32. "x" means data is suppressed to meet the confidentiality requirements of the *Statistics Act*.

33. Waste diversion and residential sector disposal data are derived from a survey administered by RECYC. QUEBEC.

MyEnvironmentPlace

Go to **www.myenvironmentplace.ca** where you will find quizzes, animations, your Pearson eText, and more.

19 Environmental Health and Hazards

This is an open-pit asbestos mine in Thetford Mines, Québec.

Upon successfully completing this chapter, you will be able to

- Identify the major types of environmental health hazards and explain the goals of environmental health
- Describe the types, abundance, distribution, and movement of toxicants in the environment
- Discuss the study of hazards and their effects, including case histories, epidemiology, animal testing, and dose–response analysis

- Assess risk assessment and risk management
- Compare philosophical approaches to risk
- Describe policy and regulation in Canada and internationally

For many years, asbestos was valued and used widely in the built environment for its insulation, fire-resistance, and sound-muffling qualities. Here, asbestos was used as insulation around hot-water pipes.

Hudson Bay

Québec

CANADA

Eastern Townships

UNITED STATES

CENTRAL CASE:
THE ASBESTOS DILEMMA

"Over the past 50 years we have all been unwitting participants in a vast, uncontrolled, worldwide chemistry experiment involving the oceans, air, soils, plants, animals, and human beings."
—UNITED NATIONS ENVIRONMENT PROGRAMME, IN *A GUIDE TO THE STOCKHOLM CONVENTION ON PERSISTENT ORGANIC POLLUTANTS*

"Canada should hang its head in shame. We use tax dollars and foreign missions to host pro-asbestos conferences. We undermine the efforts of other countries to ban asbestos."
—PAT MARTIN, CANADIAN MEMBER OF PARLIAMENT

Some hazardous materials occur naturally but cause problems when they become concentrated in buildings where people are exposed to them on a daily basis. Asbestos is one of these. Therein lies a dilemma for Canada, which hosts some of the world's largest asbestos deposits. **Asbestos** is an industrial and commercial term encompassing several groups of minerals that occur in long, hairlike microscopic fibres (see photo). These fibres give asbestos some very useful characteristics, including thermal insulation, sound muffling, tensile strength, and fire resistance. Because of these qualities, asbestos has been used widely in buildings and in many products, beginning as early as the 1870s, when Canada was the world's largest producer and exporter.[1]

Two groups of minerals produce asbestos fibres— the amphibole group and the serpentine group. Canada produces asbestos only from the serpentine group, which includes only one asbestos-forming mineral, called *chrysotile*. Chrysotile accounts for about 99% of the world's asbestos trade today.[2]

Canada's asbestos deposits are clustered in the Eastern Townships of southern Québec, where the material is extracted from open-pit mines (see opening photo). People in this area spend their lives living and

Asbestos has been widely used in insulation and other products. The substance has now been removed from many buildings in which it was used because of human health risks related to exposure. Its removal poses risks as well, however, and removal workers must wear protective clothing and respirators.

working on top of chrysotile-bearing rocks. The town of Asbestos is the location of the world's largest asbestos deposit. In Asbestos, Thetford Mines, and other small towns of southeastern Québec, the asbestos mining and processing industry has been the principal employer.

Unfortunately, the fibrous structure of asbestos minerals that gives it its tensile strength and insulating properties also makes it dangerous when inhaled. When lodged in lung tissue, asbestos induces the body to produce acid to combat it. The acid scars the lung tissue but doesn't dislodge or dissolve the asbestos. Within a few decades the scarred lungs may cease to function, a disorder called *asbestosis*.

As early as the late 1800s, illnesses and fatalities associated with asbestos exposure were reported among British and European miners. In 1912, the link between asbestos and disease in miners was officially denied by the Canadian Department of Labour.[3] Then, in 1955, a medical officer from Thetford Mines reported that 128 of 4000 miners were confirmed to have asbestosis.[4]

In subsequent decades, many scientific studies confirmed the links between asbestos and asbestosis, as well as establishing connections with lung cancer and mesothelioma, a rare cancer of the lining of the chest cavity. One by one, international agencies and governments began to limit and regulate the use of asbestos-containing products.

However, controversy rages about the role of serpentine asbestos (i.e., chrysotile) in causing negative health impacts. There is widespread agreement that exposure to amphibole asbestos is extremely hazardous, but the government of Canada, supported by the asbestos industry, maintains that chrysotile asbestos is significantly less hazardous to human health. To some, this is purely a scientific discussion, requiring further studies to sort out the relative risks. To others, it is a clear case of the politicization of science, with federal and provincial government agencies ignoring and effectively overruling scientific consensus on the matter.

Risks from asbestos exposure are greatest for miners and those involved in the production of asbestos products. In the asbestos processing industry in India and other developing countries, exposure in the workplace with inadequate protection may worsen the problem. There are also concerns for residents of towns like Thetford Mines and Asbestos, where everyday, lifelong exposures have occurred. Asbestos-related health risks arise from inhalation of the fibres, so the risk depends on

- The concentration of fibres in the air
- How long your exposure lasts
- How often you are exposed
- The size of fibres inhaled
- The amount of time since the initial exposure (because some asbestos-related diseases are dormant for many years after the initial exposure)[5]

Because of these risks, asbestos has been removed from many schools and offices (see photo) throughout North America. In some cases, the dangers of exposure from asbestos removal may exceed the dangers of leaving it in place. This can occur, for example, if the asbestos would be exposed, disturbed, or displaced if removal were attempted. Once asbestos enters the air circulation system of a building it can be almost impossible to eliminate. To prevent this, the decision is sometimes taken to leave the material in place.

Today, Canada exports chrysotile asbestos to 60 countries, mainly developing nations in Asia, Africa, and Latin America. The federal and Québec provincial governments strongly support the asbestos industry, and have spent more than $40 million in the last few years to protect the asbestos market.[6] The value of Canadian asbestos exports in 2010 was almost $1 billion ($76 538 000, down from over $1 billion in 2008).[7]

Health Canada and National Resources Canada still do not support the conclusion that exposure to chrysotile asbestos is hazardous to human health or causes cancer, although the World Health Organization and even the Canadian Cancer Society do. Health Canada recommends wearing a respirator when dealing with asbestos-containing products and refers consumers to the Hazardous Products Act and the Canadian Environmental Protection Act.[8] In 2007, Health Canada began a study of the health risks of exposure to chrysotile asbestos. This study, which concluded that the cancer risk from chrysotile asbestos is real, although lower than for other types of asbestos, was released only in 2008 as a result of an inquiry under the Freedom of Information Act.

Canada is a party to the United Nations' Rotterdam Convention, which is intended to enforce the prior informed consent procedure in the context of international trade. Prior informed consent is based on the ethical principle that consent to an activity is not legally valid unless the consenting group has been adequately informed and can be shown to have a reasonable understanding of all potential impacts before giving consent. The application of prior informed consent to international trade involves the listing, by consensus of the parties, of certain hazardous substances, with the result that producers would have to obtain prior informed consent from receiving nations before exporting these substances.

Five types of asbestos are listed under the Rotterdam Convention. Chrysotile is not on the list; its inclusion has been blocked numerous times by a small group of nations, led by Canada. In June 2011, at the fifth meeting of the parties to the convention, Canada again blocked the inclusion of chrysotile on the prior informed consent list, in spite of widespread support for its inclusion from health and environmental organizations and experts around the world. According to an editorial in the Canadian Medical Association Journal in October 2008, "Canada is the only Western democracy to have consistently opposed international efforts to regulate the global trade in asbestos. And the government of Canada has done so with shameful political manipulation of science."[9]

In early 2012 there were two dramatic developments in the asbestos controversy. In a high-profile case in Italy, two construction executives were criminally convicted for negligence in the asbestos-related deaths of 2000 people. Around the same time, questions surfaced about whether some of the scientific studies that failed to link asbestos to cancer-related deaths might have been influenced by funding form the asbestos industry. The controversy about the health impacts of asbestos continues.

Environmental Health

Examining the impacts of human-made chemicals on wildlife and people is one aspect of the broad field of environmental health. The study and practice of **environmental health** assesses environmental factors that influence human health and quality of life. Those environmental factors include wholly natural aspects of the environment over which we have little or no control, as well as *anthropogenic* (human-caused) factors for which we ourselves are responsible. Practitioners of environmental health seek to prevent adverse effects on human health and on the ecological systems that are essential to environmental quality and human well-being.

Environmental hazards can be chemical, physical, biological, or cultural

There are innumerable environmental health threats, or hazards, in the world around us. People are exposed to environmental hazards every day. Some—like earthquakes, heat waves, poison ivy, and venomous snakes—occur naturally. Others arise from our exposure to activities and materials that are wholly anthropogenic, such as smoking or airplane flight, or the synthetic chemicals DDT, BPA, and PDBE.

For ease of understanding, we can categorize hazards into four main types: chemical, physical, biological, and

roots

HAZARD

The word **hazard** comes from an Old French word, *hasard*, which referred to "a game of dice." This, in turn, may have come originally from Arabic words meaning "to play at dice."

cultural. For each of these four types of hazards, there is some amount of risk that we cannot avoid—but there is also some amount of risk that we *can* avoid by taking precautions. Much of environmental health consists of taking steps to minimize the impacts of hazards and the risks of encountering them.

Chemical hazards   **Chemical hazards** include spills and other exposures to the many synthetic chemicals that our society produces, such as disinfectants, pesticides (**FIGURE 19.1A**), and pharmaceuticals. Chemicals produced naturally by organisms also can be hazardous. Following our overview of environmental health, much of this chapter will focus on chemical health hazards and the ways people study and regulate them.

Physical hazards   **Physical hazards** can arise from processes that occur naturally and pose risks to human life, health, and property (and to the natural environment, as well). These include earthquakes, volcanic

eruptions, fires, floods, blizzards, landslides, hurricanes, and droughts (**FIGURE 19.2**).

Most earthquakes are barely perceptible, but occasionally they are powerful enough to do tremendous damage to human life and property (**TABLE 19.1**). Damage is generally greatest where soils are loose or saturated with water—areas built on landfill are particularly susceptible, as witnessed during the 1995 earthquake in Kobe, Japan, and the 1989 earthquake in Loma Prieta, California. To minimize damage, engineers have developed ways to protect buildings from shaking. They do this by strengthening structural components while designing points at which a structure can move and sway harmlessly with ground motion. Just as a flexible tree trunk bends in a storm whereas a brittle one breaks, buildings with built-in flexibility are more likely to withstand an earthquake's violent shaking. Such designs are now an important part of building codes in quake-prone regions.

Erupting volcanoes affect both people and the natural environment. At some volcanoes, lava flows slowly downhill, such as Mount Kilauea in Hawaii, which has been erupting continuously since 1983. At other times, a volcano may let loose large amounts of ash and cinder in a sudden explosion, such as during the 1991 eruption of Mount Pinatubo in the Philippines. Besides affecting people, volcanic eruptions exert environmental impacts (**TABLE 19.2**). Ash blocks sunlight, and sulphur emissions lead to a sulphuric acid haze that blocks radiation and cools the atmosphere. Large eruptions can depress temperatures throughout the world. When Indonesia's Mount

(a) Chemical hazard

(b) Physical hazard

(c) Biological hazard

(d) Cultural hazard

FIGURE 19.1
Environmental health hazards can be divided into four types. Chemical hazards **(a)** include both artificial and natural chemicals. Much of our exposure comes from household chemical products, such as pesticides. The sun's ultraviolet radiation is an example of a physical hazard **(b)**. Excessive exposure increases the risk of skin cancer. Biological hazards **(c)** include exposure to organisms that transmit disease. Some mosquitoes are vectors for certain pathogenic microbes, including those that cause malaria. Cultural or lifestyle hazards **(d)** include decisions we make about how to behave, as well as constraints forced on us by socioeconomic factors. Smoking is a lifestyle choice that raises one's risk of lung cancer and other diseases.

FIGURE 19.2 This map shows the geographic distribution of significant natural disasters in Canada. The map, from Public Safety Canada, was prepared collaboratively with Natural Resources Canada, the Geological Survey of Canada, *The Atlas of Canada*, Environment Canada, and Statistics Canada.

Table 19.1 Examples of Large or Recent Earthquakes

Location	Year	Fatalities	Magnitude[1]
Shaanxi Province, China	1556	830 000	~8
Lisbon, Portugal	1755	70 000[2]	8.7
San Francisco, California	1906	3 000	7.8
Kwanto, Japan	1923	143 000	7.9
Anchorage, Alaska	1964	128[2]	9.2
Tangshan, China	1976	255 000+	7.5
Michoacan, Mexico	1985	9 500	8.0
Kobe, Japan	1995	5 502	6.9
Northern Sumatra	2004	228 000[2]	9.1
Kashmir, Pakistan	2005	86 000	7.6
Sichuan Province, China	2008	50 000+	7.9
Port-au-Prince, Haiti	2010	236 000	7.0
Maule, Chile	2010	521	8.8
Tōhoku, Japan	2011	15 365[2]	9.0

[1]Measured by moment magnitude; each full unit is roughly 32 times as powerful as the preceding full unit.

[2]Includes deaths from the resulting tsunami.

Tambora erupted in 1815, it cooled average global temperatures by 0.4°C to 0.7°C, enough to cause crop failures worldwide and make 1816 "the year without a summer."

Earthquakes, volcanic eruptions, and large coastal landslides can all displace huge volumes of ocean water instantaneously, triggering a massive tsunami. A massive tsunami devastated the coastlines of countries all around the Indian Ocean in 2004, killing about 228 000 people. Coral reefs, coastal forests, and wetlands were damaged, and salt water contaminated soil and aquifers. Those of us who live in Canada should not consider tsunamis to be something that occurs only in faraway places. A large tsunami struck North America's Pacific coast in 1700 following a huge earthquake in the Pacific Northwest, an event that could happen again if a large earthquake were to occur in the subduction zone of the Juan da Fuca Plate. Since the 2004 tsunami, nations and international agencies have stepped up efforts to develop systems to give coastal residents advance warning of approaching tsunamis. We can lessen the impacts of tsunamis if we preserve coral reefs and mangrove forests, which help protect coastlines by absorbing wave energy.

Aside from geologic hazards, people face other types of natural hazards. Heavy rains can lead to flooding that ravages low-lying areas near rivers and streams. Coastal erosion can eat away at beaches; wildfires can threaten life and property in fire-prone areas; tornadoes and hurricanes can cause extensive damage and loss of life.

We can do little to predict the timing of a natural disaster, such as an earthquake, and nothing to prevent one. However, scientists can map geologic faults to determine areas at risk of earthquakes, engineers can

Table 19.2 Examples of Notable Volcanic Eruptions

Location	Year	Impacts	Magnitude[2]
Yellowstone Caldera, Wyoming, United States	640,000 B.P.[1]	Most recent "mega-eruption" at site of Yellowstone National Park	8
Mount Mazama, Oregon, United States	6,870 B.P.	Created Crater Lake	7
Mount Vesuvius, Italy	C.E. 79	Buried Pompeii and Herculaneum	5
Mount Tambora, Indonesia	1815	Created "year without a summer"; killed at least 70 000 people	7
Krakatau, Indonesia	1883	Killed over 36 000 people; heard 5 000 km (3 000 mi) away; affected weather for 5 years	6
Mount Saint Helens, Washington, United States	1980	Blew top off mountain; sent ash 19 km (12 mi) into sky and into 11 U.S. states; 57 people killed	5
Kilauea, Hawaii, United States	1983–present	Continuous lava flow	1
Mount Pinatubo, Philippines	1991	Sulphuric aerosols lowered world temperature 0.5 °C	6
Eyjafjallajökull, Iceland	2010	Ash cloud disrupted air travel throughout Europe	1

[1]B.P. = years before the present.

[2]Measured by the Volcanic Explosivity Index, which ranges from 0 (least powerful) to 8 (most powerful).

design buildings in ways that help them resist damage, and citizens and governments can take steps to prepare for the aftermath of a severe quake. Other types of natural disasters are more amenable to prediction, forecasting, and early warning. Meteorologists have combined their skills and knowledge with sophisticated GIS-based terrain models to improve the forecasting of major storms and floods, for example.

Other physical hazards arise from our exposure to ongoing natural processes, such as ultraviolet (UV) radiation from sunlight (**FIGURE 19.1B**). Excessive exposure to UV radiation damages DNA and has been tied to skin cancer, cataracts, and immune suppression in humans. We can reduce UV exposure and risk by using clothing and sunscreen to shield our skin from intense sunlight.

Some regions are naturally prone to certain types of hazards, by virtue of their geology, topography, climate, and other physical characteristics. For example, you can see from **FIGURE 19.2** that the West Coast, southern Ontario, and south-central Québec are the most vulnerable to earthquakes, whereas the Rockies and West Coast are susceptible to landslides, and the Prairies and southern Ontario to tornadoes. However, some common practices increase our vulnerability to physical hazards:

- As our population grows, more people live in areas susceptible to natural disasters.
- Many of us choose to live in areas that are prone to hazards. For instance, coastlines are vulnerable to tsunamis and erosion by storms, and mountainous areas are prone to volcanoes and mass wasting.
- We engineer landscapes around us in ways that can increase the frequency or severity of natural hazards. Damming and diking rivers to control floods can sometimes lead to catastrophic flooding, and suppressing natural wildfire puts forests at risk of larger, truly damaging fires. Mining, clearing forests for agriculture, and clear-cutting on slopes can each induce mass wasting, increase runoff, compact soil, and change drainage patterns.
- As we change Earth's climate by emitting greenhouse gases, we alter patterns of precipitation, increasing risks of drought, fire, flooding, and mudslides locally and regionally. Rising sea levels induced by global warming increase coastal erosion. Some research suggests that warming ocean temperatures may increase the power and duration of hurricanes.

We can often reduce or mitigate the impacts of hazards through the thoughtful use of technology, engineering, and policy, informed by a solid understanding of geology and ecology. Examples include building earthquake-resistant structures, designing early warning systems for tsunamis and volcanoes, and conserving reefs and shoreline vegetation to protect against tsunamis and coastal erosion. In addition, better forestry, agriculture, and mining practices can help prevent mass wasting. Zoning regulations, building codes, and insurance incentives that discourage development in areas prone to landslides, floods, fires, and storm surges can help keep us out of harm's way and can decrease taxpayer expense in cleaning up after natural disasters. Finally, mitigating global climate change may help reduce the frequency of natural hazards in many regions.

Biological hazards **Biological hazards** result from ecological interactions among organisms (**FIGURE 19.1C**). When we become sick from a virus, bacterial infection, or other **pathogen**, we are suffering parasitism by other species that are simply fulfilling their ecological roles. This is *infectious disease*, also called *communicable* or *transmissible disease*. Infectious diseases, such as malaria, cholera, tuberculosis, and influenza (flu), all are considered environmental health hazards. As with physical and chemical hazards, it is impossible for us to avoid risk from biological agents completely, but we can take steps to reduce the likelihood of infection.

Cultural hazards Hazards that result from the place we live or our socioeconomic status, occupation, or behavioural choices can be thought of as **cultural hazards** or *lifestyle hazards*. For instance, choosing to smoke cigarettes, or living or working with people who smoke, greatly increases our risk of lung cancer (**FIGURE 19.1D**). Choosing to smoke is a personal behavioural decision, but exposure to secondhand smoke in the home or workplace may not be under one's control. Much the same might be said for drug use, diet and nutrition, crime, and

weighing the issues

RISKY BUSINESS

Do you live in a part of Canada that is "naturally" hazardous? Check your region on **FIGURE 19.2** to see if the natural disasters shown on the map match your experience of life in that part of the country. Can you determine which aspects of the natural environment make your region vulnerable to that particular type of hazard? Do you know what kinds of preparations have been undertaken by governments in your province or territory to minimize risk to the public?

mode of transportation. As advocates of environmental justice argue, such health factors as living in proximity to toxic waste sites or working unprotected with pesticides are often correlated with lack of education and awareness, and with socioeconomic deprivation.

Disease is a major focus of environmental health

Among the hazards people face, disease stands preeminent. Despite all our technological advances, we still find ourselves battling disease, which causes the vast majority of human deaths worldwide (**FIGURE 19.3A**). Many major killers, such as cancer, heart disease, and respiratory disorders, have genetic bases but are also influenced by environmental factors. For instance, whether a person develops asthma is influenced not only by genes but also by environmental conditions. Pollutants from fossil fuel combustion worsen asthma, and fewer children raised on farms suffer asthma than children raised in cities, studies have shown. Malnutrition can foster a wide variety of illnesses, as can poverty and poor hygiene. Moreover, lifestyle choices can affect risks of acquiring some noninfectious diseases: Smoking can lead to lung cancer and lack of exercise to heart disease, for example.

Infectious diseases account for 26% of deaths that occur worldwide each year—nearly 15 million people (**FIGURE 19.3B**). Some pathogenic microbes attack

us directly, and sometimes infection occurs through a **vector**, an organism that transfers the pathogen to the host. Mosquitoes are common disease vectors; so are rats. Many infectious agents are transported by water, or spend part or all of their life cycle in or near the water. Infectious diseases account for close to half of all deaths in developing countries but for very few deaths in developed nations. This discrepancy is due to differences in hygiene conditions and access to nutrition, health care, and medicine, which are tightly correlated with wealth.

Public health efforts have lessened the impact of infectious disease in developed nations and even have eradicated some diseases. Nevertheless, other diseases—among them tuberculosis, acquired immunodeficiency syndrome (AIDS), and West Nile virus—are increasing. Still others, such as the avian flu that began spreading worldwide in 2005–2006, remain as threats for a possible global epidemic.

Many diseases are spreading because of the mobility we have achieved in our era of globalization; a virus for influenza or SARS (Severe Acute Respiratory Syndrome), which paralyzed Toronto in 2003 after being imported from Hong Kong, can now hop continents in a matter of hours by airplane in its human host. Other diseases, such as tuberculosis and strains of malaria, are evolving resistance to antibiotics, in the same way as pests evolve resistance to pesticides. Tropical diseases, such as malaria, West Nile virus, dengue, cholera, and yellow fever, threaten to expand into the temperate zones with climatic

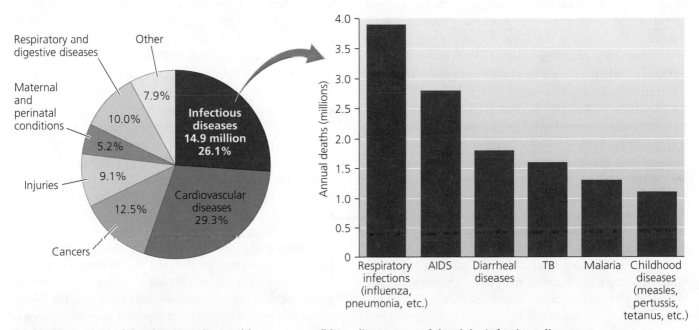

(a) Leading causes of death across the world

(b) Leading causes of death by infectious disease

FIGURE 19.3 Infectious diseases are the second-leading cause of death worldwide, accounting for more than one-quarter of all deaths per year **(a)**. Six types of diseases—respiratory infections, AIDS, diarrhea, tuberculosis (TB), malaria, and childhood diseases, such as measles—account for 80% of all deaths from infectious disease **(b)**. *Source: Data are for 2004, from World Health Organization.*

warming.[10] And habitat alteration can affect the abundance, distribution, and movement of certain disease vectors.

To predict and prevent infectious disease, environmental health experts deal with the often complicated interrelationships among technology, land use, and ecology. One of the world's leading infectious diseases, malaria (which takes nearly 1.3 million lives each year), provides an example. The microscopic organisms (four species of *Plasmodium*) that cause malaria depend on mosquitoes as a vector. These microorganisms can sexually reproduce only within a mosquito, and it is the mosquito that injects them into a human or other host. Thus the primary mode of malaria control has been to use insecticides, such as DDT, to kill mosquitoes. Large-scale eradication projects involving insecticide use and draining of wetlands have removed malaria from large areas of the temperate world where it used to occur, such as throughout the southern United States. However, types of land use that create pools of standing water in formerly well-drained areas can boost mosquito populations, potentially allowing malaria to reinvade.

Environmental health hazards exist indoors as well as outdoors

Outdoor hazards are generally more familiar to us, but we spend most of our lives indoors. Therefore, we must consider the spaces inside our homes and workplaces to be part of our environment and, as such, the sources of potential environmental hazards (**TABLE 19.3**). Asbestos, discussed in the Central Case, is one example of a naturally occurring material that is particularly hazardous when concentrated in products in the built environment. Radon is another indoor hazard. Radon is a highly toxic radioactive gas that is colourless and undetectable without specialized kits. It is naturally occurring; it seeps up from the ground in areas with certain types of bedrock and can build up inside basements and homes with poor air circulation. Exposure to radon over long periods is thought to be the second most important cause of lung cancer, after smoking.

Smoking—a lifestyle choice—exacerbates the effects of radon exposure. This type of combined factor also makes it complicated to estimate the number of deaths attributable to a single cause, such as radon exposure. The World Health Organization estimates that for a lifetime of exposure at 20 Bq/m³ of air,[11] the risk of developing cancer is about 3 people per 1000.[12] According to U.S. EPA calculations, if 1000 nonsmokers were exposed in the home over their lifetime to radon at the concentration of the EPA's "actionable" limit (the limit above which

Table 19.3	Selected Environmental Hazards

Air

Smoking and secondhand smoke

Chemicals from automotive exhaust

Chemicals from industrial pollution

Tropospheric ozone

Pesticide drift

Dust and particulate matter

Water

Pesticide and herbicide runoff

Nitrates and fertilizer runoff

Mercury, arsenic, and other heavy metals in groundwater and surface water

Food

Natural toxins

Pesticide and herbicide residues

Indoors

Asbestos

Radon

Lead in paint and pipes

Toxicants in paints, plastics, and consumer products

you should undertake remedial action, which is 4 pCi/L, or 150 Bq/m³),[13] about 7 of them would be expected to get lung cancer as a result; this is about the same as the risk of dying in a car crash. On the other hand, if those 1000 people were smokers, 62 of them would be expected to get lung cancer as a result; this is about seven times the risk of dying in a car crash.[14] This translates, according to the EPA and the Centers for Disease Control, into about 21 000 deaths per year in the United States from lung cancer caused by radon exposure.

Lead poisoning represents another indoor health hazard. When ingested, lead, a heavy metal, can cause damage to the brain, liver, kidney, and stomach; learning problems and behavioural abnormalities; anemia; hearing loss; and even death. It has been suggested that the downfall of ancient Rome was caused in part by chronic lead poisoning.

Today, lead poisoning can result from drinking water that has passed through the lead pipes common in older houses, especially those built before about 1950. Even in newer pipes, lead solder was widely used into the 1980s and is still sold in stores. Lead is perhaps most dangerous, however, to children through its presence in paint. Until 1976, most paints contained lead, and interiors in most houses were painted with lead-based paint. If you strip layers of paint from woodwork in an older home, you are likely to be exposed to airborne lead and should take appropriate precautions. Babies and young children often take an interest in peeling paint from walls and may ingest or inhale some of it. There is also a lot of lead in the environment, left over from previous use of leaded gasoline, which settled from the atmosphere onto land surfaces. This lead may be now ingested by children playing in yards, and brought indoors in the form of airborne dust, on shoes, and on clothing. About 5% of children in North America are thought to have been affected by lead poisoning; the number exposed may be much higher, as the health impacts from casual exposure may not be immediately apparent or easily diagnosed.

Lead in paint has been strictly limited in Canada since 1976 (and since 1972 in the United States). The government of Canada has responded to lead paint in imported toys and other items intended for children through legislation, such as the *Children's Jewellery Regulations*, which came into force in 2005. This law made it illegal to import, advertise, or sell children's jewellery or accessories that contain more than 600 mg/kg of total lead, or more than 90 mg/kg of migratable lead.[15] Lead that is *migratable* will leach from the item under certain circumstances; for children's toys, jewellery, and other accessories, the circumstance of greatest concern would occur when the child puts the item into his or her mouth.

In 2007 concerns were heightened when it was discovered that millions of children's toys, pieces of jewellery, baby bibs, and other items manufactured in China still contained lead-based paint. This included many toys sold under the popular Fisher-Price and Mattel brand names. Near the end of 2007, China agreed to limit the lead content of paint and to closely monitor the use of lead-based paints in manufacturing. Health Canada is working on further reducing the risk of children's exposure by limiting the lead contents of consumer products through the *Hazardous Products Act*. These limits will focus mainly on categories of products with which children are most likely to come into close contact, such as cribs and other children's furniture; toys; cooking utensils; candles; and other items.

One recently recognized hazard is a group of chemicals known as *polybrominated diphenyl ethers* (*PBDEs*). These compounds provide fire-retardant properties and are used in a diverse array of consumer products, including computers, televisions, plastics, and furniture. They appear to be released during production and disposal of products and also to evaporate at very slow rates throughout the lifetime of products. These chemicals persist and accumulate in living tissue, and their abundance in the environment and in people is doubling every few years. PBDEs appear to be *endocrine disruptors*, which means that they interfere with hormone levels; lab testing with animals shows them to affect thyroid hormones.

Animal testing also shows limited evidence that PBDEs may affect brain and nervous system development and might possibly cause cancer. Concern about PBDEs rose after a study showed that concentrations in the breast milk of Swedish mothers had increased exponentially from 1972 to 1997. The European Union decided in 2003 to ban PBDEs, and industries in Europe had already begun to phase them out. As a result, concentrations in breast milk of European mothers have fallen substantially. So far, Health Canada does not consider that the amounts of PDBEs consumed by Canadians pose a health risk.

Another common indoor air pollutant is formaldehyde (CH_2O), a colourless gas with a sharp, irritating odour. Health Canada states that some formaldehyde is present in the air in all Canadian homes, in varying concentrations.[16] It is widely used as a disinfectant and preservative. In the home, it can come from a wide variety of plastics and adhesives, textiles (such as permanent press clothing), and wood products—that "new furniture" or "new carpet" smell is often related to the presence of formaldehyde. Cigarette smoke also contributes formaldehyde to the indoor environment.

Toxicology is the study of poisonous substances

Studying the health effects of chemical agents suspected to be harmful, such as PBDEs, is the focus of the field of **toxicology**, the science that examines the effects of poisonous substances on humans and other organisms. Toxicologists assess and compare substances to determine their **toxicity**, the degree of harm a chemical substance can inflict. The concept of toxicity among chemical hazards is analogous to that of *pathogenicity* or *virulence* of the biological hazards that spread infectious disease. Just as types of microbes differ in their ability to cause disease, chemical hazards differ in their capacity to endanger us.

However, any chemical substance may exert negative effects if it is ingested in great enough quantities or if exposure is extensive enough. Conversely, a **toxic** agent (also known as a **toxin** or **toxicant**) in a minute enough quantity may pose no health risk at all. These facts are often summarized in the catchphrase, "The dose makes the poison." In other words, a substance's toxicity depends not only on its chemical identity but also on its quantity.

During the past century, our ability to produce new chemicals has expanded, concentrations of chemical contaminants in the environment have increased, and public concern for health and the environment has grown. These trends have driven the rise of *environmental toxicology*, which deals specifically with toxic substances that come from or are discharged into the environment. Environmental toxicology includes the study of health effects on humans, other animals, and ecosystems, and it represents one approach within the broader scope of environmental health.

Toxicologists generally focus on human health, using other organisms as models and test subjects. In environmental toxicology, animals are also studied out of concern for their welfare and because—like canaries in a coal mine—animals can serve as indicators of health threats that could soon affect humans.

As we review the effects of human-made chemicals throughout this chapter, it is important to keep in mind that artificially produced chemicals have played a crucial role in giving us the standard of living we enjoy today. These chemicals have helped create the industrial agriculture that produces our food, the medical advances that protect our health and prolong our lives, and many of the modern materials and conveniences we use every day. It is important to remember these benefits as we examine some of the unfortunate side effects of these advances, and look for better alternatives.

Toxic Agents in the Environment

The environment contains countless natural chemical substances that may pose health risks. These substances include oil oozing naturally from the ground; radon gas seeping up from bedrock; and toxic chemicals stored or manufactured in the tissues of living organisms—for example, toxins that plants use to ward off herbivores and toxins that insects use to defend themselves from predators. In addition, we are exposed to many synthetic (artificial, or human-made) chemicals.

Synthetic chemicals are ubiquitous in our environment

Synthetic chemicals are all around us in our daily lives (**FIGURE 19.4**). Hundreds of thousands of synthetic chemicals have been manufactured (**TABLE 19.4**), about 100 000 are in common use, and many have found their way into soil, air, and water. Synthetic chemicals that have been identified in Canadian lakes and streams include antibiotics, detergents, drugs, steroids, plasticizers, disinfectants, solvents, perfumes, and many other substances. The pesticides we use to kill insects and weeds on farms, lawns, and golf courses are some of the most widespread synthetic chemicals. As a result of all this exposure, every one of us carries traces of numerous industrial chemicals in our body.

FIGURE 19.4
Synthetic chemicals, such as those in household products, are everywhere around us in our everyday lives. Some of these compounds may potentially pose environmental or human health risks.

This should not *necessarily* be cause for alarm. Not all synthetic chemicals pose health risks, and relatively few are known with certainty to be toxicants. However, of the roughly 100 000 synthetic chemicals on the market today, very few (perhaps as low as 10%) have been thoroughly

Table 19.4 Estimated Numbers of Chemicals in Commercial Substances	
Type of chemical	**Estimated number**
Chemicals in commerce	100 000
Industrial chemicals	72 000
New chemicals introduced per year	2 000
Pesticides (21 000 products)	600
Food additives	8 700
Cosmetic ingredients (40 000 products)	7 500
Human pharmaceuticals	3 300

Source: Data from Harrison, P., and F. Pearce. 2000. AAAS Atlas of Population and Environment. Berkeley, CA: University of California Press.

tested for harmful effects. For the vast majority, we simply do not know what effects, if any, they may have.

Why are there so many synthetic chemicals around us? Let us consider pesticides and herbicides, made widespread by advances in chemistry and production capacity during and following the Second World War. As material prosperity grew in Westernized nations in the decades following the war, people began using pesticides not only for agriculture but also to improve the look of their lawns and golf courses and to fight termites, ants, and other insects inside their homes and offices. Pesticides were viewed as means toward a better quality of life.

It was not until the 1960s that people began to learn about the risks of exposure to pesticides. A key event was the publication of Rachel Carson's 1962 book, *Silent Spring*, which brought the pesticide dichloro-diphenyl-trichloroethane (DDT) to the public's attention.

Silent Spring began the public debate over synthetic chemicals

Rachel Carson was a naturalist, author, and government scientist. In *Silent Spring*, she brought together a diverse collection of scientific studies, medical case histories, and other data that no one had previously synthesized and presented to the general public. Her message was that DDT in particular and artificial pesticides in general were hazardous to people's health, the health of wildlife, and the well-being of ecosystems. Carson wrote at a time when large amounts of pesticides virtually untested for health effects were indiscriminately sprayed over residential neighbourhoods and public areas, on the assumption that the chemicals would do no harm to people (**FIGURE 19.5**). Most consumers had no idea that the store-bought

weighing the issues

THE CIRCLE OF POISON

It has been called the "circle of poison." Although Canada banned DDT in 1985 and the United States in 1972, U.S. companies still manufacture and export the compound to many developing nations. Thus, pesticide-laden food can be imported back into the United States and to other countries, including Canada. How do you feel about this? Is it unethical for one country to sell to others a substance that it has deemed toxic? Are there factors or circumstances that might change the view you take? Compare this with Canada's exportation of asbestos, discussed in the Central Case. What are the similarities and differences?

chemicals they used in their houses, gardens, and fields might be toxic.

Although challenged vigorously by spokespeople for the chemical industry, who attempted to discredit both the author's science and her personal reputation, Carson's book was a best-seller. Carson suffered from cancer as she finished *Silent Spring*, and she lived only briefly after its publication. However, the book helped generate significant social change in views and actions toward the environment. The use of DDT is now illegal in a number of nations and was banned in Canada in 1985. The United States banned DDT for almost all uses (except public emergencies) in 1972 but still manufactures and exports DDT to countries that do use it. Many developing countries with tropical climates use DDT to control human disease vectors, such as mosquitoes that transmit malaria. In these

FIGURE 19.5
Before the 1960s, the environmental and health effects of potent pesticides, such as DDT, were not widely studied or publicly known. Public areas, such as parks, neighbourhoods, and beaches, were regularly sprayed for insect control without safeguards against excessive human exposure. Here children on a beach are fogged with DDT from a pesticide spray machine in 1945.

countries, malaria represents a far greater health threat than do the toxic effects of the pesticide.

Toxicants come in several different types

Toxicants, whether they are natural or synthetic, can be classified into different types based on their particular effects on health. The best known are the **carcinogens**, which include chemicals and types of radiation that cause cancer. In cancer, malignant cells grow uncontrollably, creating tumours, damaging the body's functioning, and often leading to death. In our society today, the greatest number of cancer cases is thought to result from carcinogens contained in cigarette smoke. Carcinogens can be difficult to identify because there may be a long lag time between exposure to the agent and the detectable onset of cancer. Historically, much toxicological work focused on carcinogens. Now, however, we know that toxicants can produce many different types of effects, so scientists have many more endpoints, or health impacts, to look for.

Mutagens are chemicals that cause mutations in the DNA of organisms. Although most mutations have little or no effect, some can lead to severe problems, including cancer and other disorders. If mutations occur in an individual's sperm or egg cells, then the individual's offspring suffer the effects.

Chemicals that cause harm to the unborn are called **teratogens**. Teratogens that affect the development of human embryos in the womb can cause birth defects. One example involves the drug thalidomide, developed in the 1950s as a sleeping pill and to prevent nausea during pregnancy. Tragically, the drug turned out to be a powerful teratogen, and its use caused birth defects in thousands of babies (**FIGURE 19.6A**). Even a single exposure during pregnancy could result in limb deformities and organ defects. Thalidomide was banned in the 1960s once scientists recognized its connection with birth defects. Ironically, today the drug shows promise in treating a wide range of diseases, including Alzheimer's disease, AIDS, and various types of cancer.

The human immune system protects our bodies from disease. Some toxicants weaken the immune system, reducing the body's ability to defend itself against bacteria, viruses, allergy-causing agents, and other attackers. Others, called **allergens**, overactivate the immune system, causing an immune response when one is not necessary. One hypothesis for the increase in asthma in recent years is that allergenic synthetic chemicals are more prevalent in our environment.

(a) Thalamide poisioning

(b) Mercury poisioning

FIGURE 19.6 Two episodes of almost iconic status in the history of synthetic toxicants are the use of thalidomide by pregnant women in the late 1950s to early 1960s and the mercury poisoning of the residents of Minamata, Japan. The drug thalidomide turned out to be a potent teratogen **(a)**. It was banned in the 1960s but not before causing thousands of birth defects. Butch Lumpkin was an exceptional "thalidomide baby" who learned to overcome his short arms and deformed fingers, becoming a professional tennis instructor. To this day, the name of Minamata, Japan, is synonymous with the mercury poisoning that occurred there between the 1930s and 1960s **(b)**. The horrific impacts of mercury exposure are illustrated in this classic photograph of a victim, taken in 1972 by Eugene Smith.

Still other chemical toxicants, **neurotoxins**, assault the nervous system. Neurotoxins include various heavy metals, such as lead, mercury, and cadmium, as well as pesticides and some chemical weapons developed for use in war. A famous case of neurotoxin poisoning occurred in Japan, where a chemical factory dumped waste laden with mercury, a heavy metal, into Minamata Bay between the 1930s and 1960s. Thousands of people in and around the town on the bay were poisoned by eating fish contaminated with mercury (**FIGURE 19.6B**). People began to show symptoms that included slurred speech, loss of muscle control, disfiguring birth defects, and even death. The company and the government eventually paid about $5000 in compensation to each affected resident.

Endocrine disruption may be widespread

Scientists have recently begun to recognize the importance of **endocrine disruptors**, toxicants that interfere with the endocrine system. The endocrine system consists of chemical messengers (*hormones*) that travel through the body. Sent through the bloodstream at extremely low concentrations, these messenger molecules have many vital functions. They stimulate growth, development, and sexual maturity, and they regulate brain function, appetite, sex drive, and many other aspects of our physiology and behaviour.

Many endocrine disruptors are so similar to hormones in their molecular structure and chemistry that they "mimic" the hormone by interacting with receptor molecules just as the actual hormone would (**FIGURE 19.7**). Such effects were first noted as far back as the 1960s, with the pesticide DDT. Hormone-disrupting toxicants can affect an animal's endocrine system by blocking the action of hormones or accelerating their breakdown.

One common type of endocrine disruption involves the feminization of male animals, as shown by studies on alligators, fish, frogs, and other organisms. Feminization may be widespread because a number of chemicals appear to mimic the female sex hormone estrogen and bind to estrogen receptors. For example, when biologist Louis Guillette began studying the reproductive biology of alligators in Florida lakes in 1985, he discovered that alligators from one lake in particular, Lake Apopka northwest of Orlando, showed a number of bizarre reproductive problems. Females were having trouble producing viable eggs. Male hatchling alligators had severely depressed levels of the male sex hormone testosterone, and female hatchlings showed greatly elevated levels of the female sex hormone estrogen. The young animals had abnormal gonads, too, and smaller penises. Testes of the males

(a) Normal hormone binding

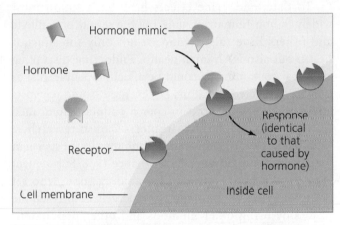

(b) Hormone mimicry

FIGURE 19.7
Many endocrine-disrupting substances mimic the structure of hormone molecules. Like a key similar enough to fit into another key's lock, the hormone mimic binds to a cellular receptor for the hormone, causing the cell to react as though it had encountered the hormone.

produced sperm at a premature age, and ovaries of the females contained multiple eggs per follicle instead of the expected one egg.

Guillette and his co-workers grew to suspect that environmental contaminants might be somehow responsible for the reproductive abnormalities. Lake Apopka had suffered a major spill of the pesticides dicofol and DDT in 1980, and yearly surveys thereafter showed a precipitous decline in the number of juvenile alligators in the lake. In addition, the lake received high levels of chemical runoff from agriculture and was experiencing eutrophication from nutrient input from fertilizers. Comparing alligators from heavily polluted Lake Apopka with those from cleaner lakes nearby, Guillette's team found that Lake Apopka alligators had abnormally low hatching rates in the years after the pesticide spill. Even as hatching rates recovered in the 1990s, the alligators continued to show aberrant hormone levels and bizarre gonad abnormalities.

Similar problems began cropping up in other lakes that experienced runoff of chemical pesticides. In the lab, researchers found that several contaminants detected in alligator eggs and young could bind to receptors for estrogen and exist in concentrations great enough to cause sex reversal of male embryos. One chemical in particular, atrazine—a widely used herbicide—appeared to disrupt hormones by inducing production of aromatase, an enzyme that converts testosterone to estrogen. In 2003, Guillette reported preliminary findings that nitrate from fertilizer runoff may also act as an endocrine disruptor; when nitrate concentrations in lakes are above the standard for drinking water, juvenile male alligators have smaller penises and 50% lower testosterone levels.

To date, endocrine effects have been found most widely in non-human animals, but the results of Guillette and others have raised concern not only for alligator health but also for human health. Endocrine-disrupting chemical contaminants could be affecting people, just as they have affected alligators. For example, some scientists attribute a striking drop in sperm counts among men worldwide to endocrine disruptors. Danish researchers reported in 1992 that the number and motility of sperm in men's semen had declined by 50% since 1938. Subsequent studies by other researchers—including some who set out to disprove the findings—have largely confirmed the results by using other methods and other populations (although there is tremendous geographic variation that remains unexplained).

Some researchers have also voiced concerns about rising rates of testicular cancer, undescended testicles, and genital birth defects in men. Other scientists have proposed that the rise in breast cancer rates (one in nine Canadian women alive today will develop breast cancer) may also be due to hormone disruption, because an excess of estrogen appears to feed tumour development in older women.

Endocrine disruptors can affect more than just the reproductive system. Some impair the brain and nervous system. North American studies have shown neurological problems associated with PCB contamination. In one study, mothers who ate Great Lakes fish contaminated with PCBs had babies with lower birth weights and smaller heads, compared with mothers who did not eat fish. These babies grew into children who showed weak and jerky reflexes and tested poorly in intelligence tests.

Endocrine disruption research has generated debate

Much of the research into hormone disruption has brought about strident debate. This is partly because a great deal of scientific uncertainty is inherent in any young and developing field. Another reason is that negative findings about chemicals pose an economic threat. Our society has invested heavily in some chemicals that now are suspect. One example is asbestos, the chrysotile form of which is still exported by Canada to the developing world, even as its health impacts are under increasing scrutiny, as discussed in the Central Case. Another example is bisphenol-A (see "The Science Behind the Story: Is Bisphenol-A Safe?"). A building block of polycarbonate plastic, bisphenol-A (BPA) occurs in a wide variety of plastic products we use daily, from drink containers to soft plastic toys, eating utensils, auto parts, CDs, and DVDs (**FIGURE 19.8**). It is used in epoxy resins, including those that coat metal food and drink cans. It is even used in dental sealants.

BPA leaches out of many products into water and food, and recent experimental evidence ties it to birth defects and other abnormalities in lab animals. The plastics industry vehemently protests that the chemical is safe, pointing to other research backing its contention. However, by one count through the end of 2006, 151 of the 178 published studies with lab animals report harm from even small amounts of bisphenol-A. Almost without exception, the studies reporting harm received public government funding, whereas those reporting no harm were industry funded. In 2008, Canada became the first country to declare bisphenol-A a dangerous substance. Many retailers responded by pulling BPA-containing products off their store shelves.[17]

Research results with bisphenol-A and mice, and those with atrazine and frogs, have both shown effects at extremely low levels of the chemical. This is also the case with research on other known or purported endocrine disruptors. The apparent reason is that the endocrine system is geared to respond to minute concentrations of substances (normally, hormones in the bloodstream). Because the endocrine system responds to minuscule amounts of chemicals, it is especially vulnerable to effects from environmental contaminants that are dispersed and diluted through the environment and that reach our bodies in very low concentrations.

Toxicants may concentrate in water

Toxicants are not evenly distributed in the environment, and they move about in specific ways (**FIGURE 19.9**). For instance, water, in the form of runoff, often carries toxicants from large areas of land and concentrates them in small volumes of surface water. If chemicals persist in pollution. When aquatic organisms become sick, we can take it as an early warning that something is amiss. This is why many scientists see findings that show impacts of low concentrations of pesticides on frogs, fish, and invertebrates as a warning that humans could be next. The contaminants that wash into streams and rivers also flow and seep into the water we drink and drift through the air we breathe.

Airborne toxicants can travel widely

Because many chemical substances can be transported by air (Chapter 13), the toxicological effects of chemical use can occur far from the site of direct chemical use. For instance, airborne transport of pesticides is sometimes termed *pesticide drift*. The Central Valley of California is widely considered the most productive agricultural region in the world. Because it is a naturally arid area, food production depends on intensive use of irrigation, fertilizers, and pesticides. Roughly 143 million kilograms of pesticide active ingredients are used in California each year, mostly in the Central Valley. The region's frequent winds often blow the airborne spray and dust particles containing pesticide residue for long distances. In the Sierra Nevada Mountains, research has associated pesticide drift from the Central Valley with population declines in four species of frogs. Families living in towns in the Central Valley have suffered health impacts, and activists for farm workers maintain that hundreds of thousands of residents are at risk.

Synthetic chemical contaminants are ubiquitous worldwide. Despite being manufactured and applied mainly in the temperate and tropical zones, contaminants appear in substantial quantities in the tissues of Arctic polar bears, Antarctic penguins, and people living in Greenland. Scientists can travel to the most remote and seemingly pristine alpine lakes in British Columbia and find them contaminated with foreign toxicants, such as PCBs. The surprisingly high concentrations in polar regions result from patterns of global atmospheric circulation that move airborne chemicals systematically toward the poles (FIGURE 19.10).

(a) Exposure through toys

(b) Exposure through cosmetics

FIGURE 19.8
Many soft plastic children's toys **(a)** and cosmetics **(b)** contain phthalates, a group of hormone-disrupting chemicals.

soil, they can leach into groundwater and contaminate drinking water supplies.

Many chemicals are soluble in water and enter organisms' tissues through drinking or absorption. For this reason, aquatic animals, such as fish, frogs, and stream invertebrates, are effective indicators of

Some toxicants are persistent

Once toxic agents arrive somewhere, they may degrade quickly and become harmless, or they may remain unaltered and persist for many months, years, or decades. Large numbers of such **persistent** synthetic

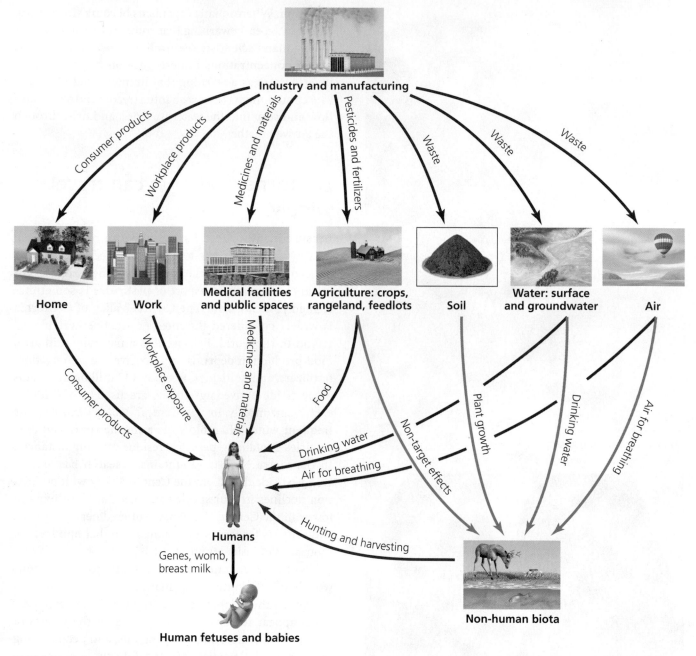

FIGURE 19.9   Synthetic chemicals take many routes in travelling through the environment. Although humans take in only a tiny proportion of these compounds, and although many compounds are harmless, humans—particularly babies—receive small amounts of toxicants from many sources.

chemicals exist in our environment today because we design them to persist. The synthetic chemicals used in plastics, for instance, are used precisely because they resist breakdown.

The rate at which chemicals degrade depends on such factors as temperature, moisture, and Sun exposure and on how these factors interact with the chemistry of the toxicant. Toxicants that persist in the environment have the greatest potential to harm many organisms over long periods of time. A major reason people have been so concerned about toxic chemicals,

such as DDT and PCBs, is that they have long persistence times. In contrast, the Bt toxin used for biocontrol of agricultural pests has a short persistence time.

Most toxicants eventually degrade into simpler compounds called **breakdown products**. Often these are less harmful than the original substance, but sometimes they are just as toxic as the original chemical, or more so. For instance, DDT breaks down into DDE, a highly persistent and toxic compound in its own right. A large number of chemical breakdown products have not been fully studied.

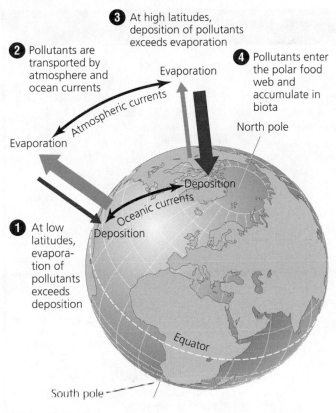

❸ At high latitudes, deposition of pollutants exceeds evaporation

❷ Pollutants are transported by atmosphere and ocean currents

Evaporation

❹ Pollutants enter the polar food web and accumulate in biota

North pole

Atmospheric currents

Evaporation

Deposition

Oceanic currents

❶ At low latitudes, evaporation of pollutants exceeds deposition

Deposition

Equator

South pole

FIGURE 19.10

In a process called *global distillation*, pollutants that evaporate and rise high into the atmosphere at lower latitudes, or are deposited in the ocean, are carried toward the poles by atmospheric currents of air and oceanic currents of water. For this reason, polar organisms take in more than their share of toxicants, despite the fact that relatively few synthetic chemicals are manufactured or used near the poles.

Toxicants may accumulate over time and up the food chain

Of the toxicants that organisms absorb, breathe, or consume, some are quickly excreted, and some are degraded into harmless breakdown products. However, others remain intact in the body. Toxicants that are fat-soluble or oil-soluble (often organic compounds, such as DDT and DDE) are absorbed and stored in fatty tissues. Others, such as methylmercury, may be stored in muscle tissue. If the rate of ingestion of such toxicants is greater than the rate of excretion, they may build up in an animal over time, in a process termed **bioaccumulation**.

Toxicants that bioaccumulate over time in the tissues of one organism may be transferred to other organisms when predators consume prey. When one organism consumes another, it takes in any stored toxicants and stores them itself, along with the toxicants it has received from eating other prey. Thus with each step up the food chain, from producer to primary consumer to secondary consumer and so on, concentrations of toxicants can be

greatly magnified. This process, called **biomagnification** or *food chain concentration*, occurred most famously with DDT. Top predators, such as birds of prey, ended up with high concentrations of the pesticide because concentrations were magnified as DDT moved from water to algae to plankton to small fish to bigger fish and finally to fish-eating birds (**FIGURE 19.11**).

Biomagnification caused populations of many North American birds of prey, such as the peregrine falcon, the bald eagle, the osprey, and the brown pelican, to decline precipitously from the 1950s to the 1970s. Eventually scientists determined that DDT was causing the birds' eggshells to grow thinner, so that eggs were breaking while in the nest.

All these birds' populations have rebounded since DDT was banned in North America, but such scenarios are by no means a thing of the past. The polar bears of Svalbard Island in Arctic Norway are at the top of the food chain and feed on seals that have biomagnified toxicants. Despite

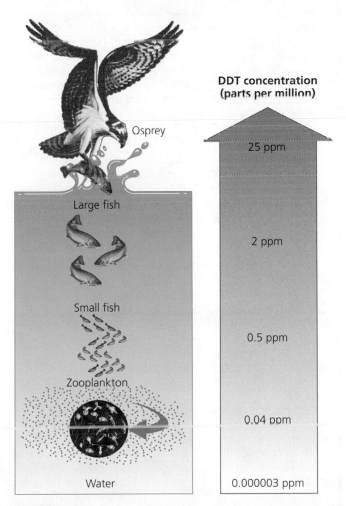

DDT concentration (parts per million)

Osprey

Large fish

25 ppm

2 ppm

Small fish

0.5 ppm

Zooplankton

0.04 ppm

Water

0.000003 ppm

FIGURE 19.11

Fat-soluble compounds, such as DDT, bioaccumulate in the tissues of organisms. As animals at higher trophic levels eat organisms lower on the food chain, the latter's load of toxicants passes up to each consumer. DDT moves from zooplankton through various types of fish, finally becoming highly concentrated in fish-eating birds, such as ospreys.

THE SCIENCE BEHIND THE STORY

Banning Bisphenol-A

(a) **(b)**

During normal cell division (a), chromosomes align properly. Exposure to bisphenol-A causes abnormal cell division (b), whereby chromosomes scatter and are distributed improperly and unevenly between daughter cells.

Can a compound in everyday products damage the most basic processes necessary for healthy pregnancies and births? Canada has been a leader in the international effort to determine whether bisphenol-A—found in plastic baby bottles, reusable water bottles, pitchers, tableware, storage containers, and other products—might be damaging the health of Canadians, especially children and infants.

Canada's *Chemicals Management Plan* was introduced in 2006 to review the safety of approximately 200 chemicals that have been on the market for many years without adequate scientific knowledge of their impacts. Bisphenol-A, or BPA, is one of these chemicals, and its potential for reproductive impacts made it a high priority for investigation.

The plastics industry produces more than 2.5 billion kilograms of BPA every year—more than a third of a kilogram for every person on the planet. BPA has been known to be an estrogen mimic since the 1930s and more recently has been linked to reproductive abnormalities in mice. Research has shown that BPA can leach out of plastic into water and food when the plastic is treated with extreme heat, acidity, or harsh soap. One study conducted by researchers for the magazine *Consumer Reports* found that BPA seeped out of the plastic walls of heated baby bottles into infant formula.

One early investigation took place almost by accident, at a laboratory at Case Western Reserve University in 1998. The

study was initiated when geneticist Patricia Hunt was making a routine check of female lab mice, which included extracting and examining developing eggs from the ovaries. The results on this occasion showed chromosome problems in about 40% of the eggs.

A bit of sleuthing revealed that a lab assistant had mistakenly washed the plastic mouse cages and water bottles with an especially harsh soap. The soap damaged the cages so badly that parts of them melted. The cages were made from plastic containing BPA. To recreate the accidental BPA exposure from the cage-washing incident, Hunt and other researchers washed the polycarbonate cages and water bottles by using varying levels of the harsh soap. They then compared mice kept in damaged cages with plastic water bottles with mice kept in undamaged cages with glass water bottles. The developing eggs of mice exposed to BPA through the damaged plastic showed significant problems during meiosis, the division of chromosomes during egg formation—just as they had in the original incident (see the photo). In contrast, the eggs of mice in the control cages were normal.

In additional tests, three sets of female mice were given oral doses of BPA over three, five, and seven days, and the same abnormalities were observed, although at lower levels (see the graph). The mice given BPA for seven days were most severely affected.

Published in 2003 in the journal *Current Biology*, Hunt's findings set off a wave of concern over the safety of bisphenol-A. Dozens of other studies have since come out; most have shown harmful effects in lab animals. A diversity of reproductive and other effects has been shown, and findings with obese mice have led some to suggest that bisphenol-A may be contributing to the current obesity epidemic. Health Canada's assessment of BPA did not support a link to obesity but did conclude that even low levels of exposure can affect neural development and behaviour if exposure occurs early in life.[18]

The result was a recommendation by Health Canada that BPA be declared a "toxic" substance as defined by the

Canadian Environmental Protection Act (1999). Health Canada maintains that typical BPA exposures for Canadians are far below harmful levels but urges caution for children and infants under 18 months. The assessment also concluded that BPA can harm fish and other organisms, and confirmed that the chemical has been identified in municipal wastewater.

In the United States and Europe, regulators have set safe intake levels for people at doses of 50 ng/g of body weight per day. The acceptable level in Canada has been set at half that amount, 25 ng/g of body weight per day. For comparison, lab tests show concentrations of 5–8 ng/mL of liquid in heated plastic baby bottles, 95% of which still are manufactured with BPA (as of 2007), suggesting significant potential for exposure at harmful levels.[19] Recent studies have found BPA in the urine of 91% of Canadians tested.[20] With a chemical that is so widely present in our lives, the scientific and social debate over bisphenol-A seems set to continue building.

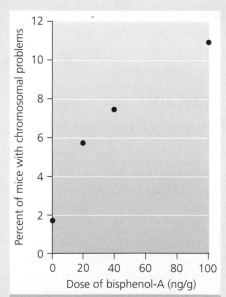

In this dose–response experiment, the percentage of mice showing chromosomal problems during cell division rose with increasing doses of bisphenol-A.
Source: Data from Hunt, P. A., et al. (2003). Bisphenol-A exposure causes meiotic aneuploidy in the female mouse. Current Biology *13:546–553.*

their remote Arctic location, Svalbard Island's polar bears show some of the highest levels of PCB contamination of any wild animals tested, as a result of biomagnification and the process of global distillation shown in **FIGURE 19.10**. The contaminants are likely responsible for the immune suppression, hormone disruption, and high cub mortality that the bears seem to be suffering. Cubs that survive receive PCBs in their mothers' milk, so the contamination persists and accumulates over generations.

Not all toxicants are synthetic

Although we have focused mainly on synthetic chemicals, chemical toxicants also exist naturally in the environment around us and in the foods we eat. We have good reason as citizens and consumers to insist on being informed about risks synthetic chemicals may pose, but it is a mistake to assume that all artificial chemicals are unhealthful and that all natural chemicals are healthful. In fact, the plants and animals we eat contain many chemicals that can cause us harm. Recall that plants produce toxins to ward off animals that eat them. In domesticating crop plants, we have selected for strains with reduced toxin content, but we have not eliminated these dangers. Furthermore, when we consume animal meat, we take in toxins the animals have ingested from plants or animals they have eaten.

Scientists are actively debating just how much risk natural toxicants pose. Some even maintain that the amounts of synthetic chemicals in our food from pesticide residues are dwarfed by the quantities of natural toxicants. However, others argue that natural toxicants are more readily metabolized and excreted by the body than synthetic ones, that synthetic toxicants persist and accumulate in the environment, and that synthetic chemicals expose people (such as farm workers and factory workers) to risks in ways other than the ingestion of food. In addition, our species may have been exposed to natural toxicants for millions of years, so we may have evolved partial resistance to some of them, which is not the case for the newer synthetic toxicants. What is clear is that more research is required in this area.

Studying the Effects of Hazards

Determining health effects of particular environmental hazards is a challenging job, especially because any given person or organism has a complex history of exposure to many hazards throughout life. Scientists rely on several different methods, including correlative surveys and manipulative experiments.

Wildlife studies use careful observations in the field and lab

When scientists were zeroing in on the impacts of DDT, one key piece of evidence came from museum collections of wild birds' eggs from the decades before synthetic pesticides were manufactured. Eggs from museum collections had measurably thicker shells than the eggs scientists were studying in the field from present-day birds. Scientists have pieced together the puzzle of toxicant effects on alligators by taking measurements from animals in the wild and then doing controlled experiments in the lab to test hypotheses. With frogs and atrazine, scientists first measured toxicological effects in lab experiments and then sought to demonstrate correlations with herbicide use in the wild.

Often the study of wildlife advances in the wake of some conspicuous mortality event. Off the California coast in 1998–2001, populations of sea otters fell noticeably, and many dead otters washed ashore. Field biologists documented the population decline, and specialists went to work in the lab performing autopsies to determine causes of death. The most common cause of death was found to be infection with the parasite *Toxoplasma*, which killed otters directly and also made them vulnerable to shark attack. *Toxoplasma* occurs in the feces of cats, so scientists hypothesized that sewage runoff containing waste from litter boxes was entering the ocean from urban areas and infecting the otters.

Human studies rely on case histories, epidemiology, and animal testing

In studies of human health, we gain much knowledge by studying sickened individuals directly. Medical professionals have long treated victims of poisonings, so the effects of common poisons are well known. Autopsies help us understand what constitutes a lethal dose. This process of observation and analysis of individual patients is known as a *case history* approach. Case histories have advanced our understanding of human illness, but they do not always help us infer the effects of rare hazards, newly manufactured compounds, or chemicals that exist at low environmental concentrations and exert minor long-term effects. Case histories also tell us little about probability and risk, such as how many extra deaths we might expect in a population because of a particular cause.

For such situations, which are common in environmental toxicology, epidemiological studies are necessary. Studies in the field of **epidemiology** involve large-scale comparisons among groups of people, usually contrasting a group known to have been exposed to some hazard and a group that has not. Epidemiologists track the fate of all people in the study, generally for a long period of time (often years or decades), and measure the rate at which deaths, cancers, or other health problems occur in each group. The epidemiologist then analyzes the data, looking for observable differences between the groups, and statistically tests hypotheses accounting for differences. When a group exposed to a hazard shows a significantly greater degree of harm, it suggests that the hazard may be responsible. For example, asbestos miners have been tracked for asbestosis, lung cancer, and mesothelioma rates. Survivors of the Chernobyl disaster in Ukraine have been monitored for thyroid and other cancers. Currently, levels of BPA in humans are being tracked as part of the Canadian Health Measures Survey.

This type of human tracking is part of an ongoing approach taken by Health Canada to the management and tracking of toxic chemicals, called *Human Biomonitoring of Environmental Chemical Substances*. The process is akin to a natural experiment, in which the experimenter takes advantage of the presence of groups of subjects made possible by some event or long-term exposure that has already occurred. A slightly different type of natural experiment was conducted by anthropologist Elizabeth Guillette (see "The Science Behind the Story: Pesticides and Child Development in Mexico's Yaqui Valley").

The advantages of epidemiological studies are their realism and their ability to yield relatively accurate predictions about risk. The drawbacks include the need to wait a long time for results and the inability to address future effects of new products just coming to market. In addition, participants in epidemiological studies encounter many factors that affect their health besides the one under study. Epidemiological studies measure a statistical association between a health hazard and an effect, but they do not confirm that the hazard *causes* the effect. It can also be difficult to disentangle the contributions of various factors to any observed negative health impacts. In cases where a number of factors are present, they may interact, affecting results. An example is smoking, which complicates the interpretation of epidemiological studies on the linkages between cancer and radon exposure. Smoking acts not only as an additional factor that may cause cancer in subjects but also as a reinforcing or *synergistic* factor.

Manipulative experiments are needed to establish causation. However, subjecting people to massive amounts of toxicants in a lab experiment would clearly be unethical. So researchers have traditionally used other animals as subjects to test toxicity. Foremost among these animal models have been laboratory strains of rats, mice,

and other mammals. Because of our shared evolutionary history, the bodies of other mammals function similarly to ours. The extent to which results from animal lab tests apply to humans varies from one study to the next.

Some people feel the use of rats and mice for testing is unethical, but animal testing enables scientific and medical advances that would be impossible or far more difficult otherwise. However, new techniques (with human cell cultures, bacteria, or tissue from chicken eggs) are being devised that may one day replace some live-animal testing.

Dose–response analysis is a mainstay of toxicology

The standard method of testing with lab animals in toxicology is dose–response analysis. Scientists quantify the toxicity of a given substance by measuring how much effect a toxicant produces at different doses or how many animals are affected by different doses of the toxic agent. The **dose** is the amount of toxicant the test animal receives or is exposed to and absorbs; the **response** is the type or magnitude of negative effects the animal exhibits as a result. The response is generally quantified by measuring the proportion of animals exhibiting negative effects. The data are plotted on a graph, with dose on the *x*-axis and response on the *y*-axis (**FIGURE 19.12A**). The resulting curve is called a **dose–response curve**.

Once they have plotted a dose–response curve, toxicologists can calculate a convenient shorthand gauge of a substance's toxicity: the amount of toxicant it takes to kill half the population of study animals used. This lethal dose for 50% of individuals is termed the **lethal-dose-50%** or **LD$_{50}$**. A high LD$_{50}$ indicates low toxicity, and a low LD$_{50}$ indicates high toxicity.

If the experimenter is instead interested in nonlethal health effects, he or she may want to document the level of toxicant at which 50% of a population of test animals is affected in some other way (for instance, what level of toxicant causes 50% of lab mice to lose their hair?). Such a level is called the **effective-dose-50%**, or **ED50**.

Sometimes responses occur only above a certain dose. Such a **threshold dose** (**FIGURE 19.12B**) might be expected if the body's organs can fully metabolize or excrete a toxicant at low doses but become overwhelmed at higher concentrations. It might also occur if cells can repair damage to their DNA only up to a certain point.

Sometimes responses *decrease* with increased dose. For example, the effectiveness of some vitamins, such as vitamin A, increases with increasing dose until a threshold is reached, beyond which the benefits cease to accrue. With still higher doses, however, a turning point is eventu-

(a) Linear dose-response curve

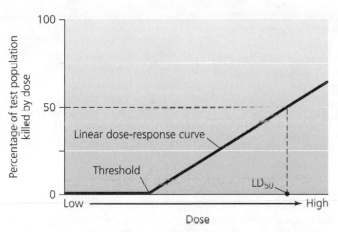

(b) Dose-response curve with threshold

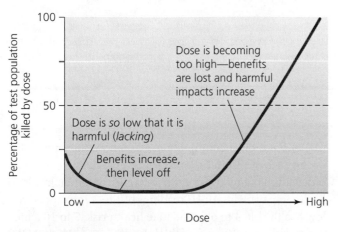

(c) U-shaped dose-response curve

FIGURE 19.12

In a classic linear dose–response curve **(a)**, the percentage of animals killed or otherwise affected by a substance rises with the dose. The point at which 50% of the animals are killed is labelled the lethal-dose-50, or LD_{50}. For some toxic agents, a threshold dose **(b)** exists, below which doses have no measurable effect. Some substances have dose–response curves shaped like a U. For example **(c)**, at low doses the benefits of vitamin A increase with dose, until a threshold is reached beyond which no further benefits accrue. With further increases, a dose is eventually reached beyond which negative impacts will begin to occur.

ally reached at which negative health effects begin to occur as dose is increased (**FIGURE 19.12C**). This type of dose–response curve is typical of materials that are harmful to health if they are missing altogether, but toxic if the dose is too high. Toxicologists are finding that some dose–response curves are U-shaped, J-shaped, or shaped like an inverted U. Such counterintuitive curves often occur with endocrine disruptors, likely because the hormone system is geared to function with extremely low concentrations of hormones and so is vulnerable to disruption by toxicants at extremely low concentrations. Complicated dose–response curves present a particular challenge for policy makers attempting to set safe environmental levels for toxicants. We may have underestimated the dangers of compounds that behave in these ways, because many such chemicals exist in very low concentrations over wide areas.

Knowing the shape of dose–response curves is crucial if one is planning to extrapolate from them to predict responses at doses below those that have been tested. Scientists generally give lab animals much higher doses relative to body mass than humans would receive in the environment. This is so that the response is great enough to be measured and so that differences between the effects of small and large doses are evident. Data from a range of doses help give shape to the dose–response curve. Once the data from animal tests are plotted, scientists extrapolate to estimate the effect of still-lower doses on a hypothetically large population of animals. This way, they can come up with an estimate of, say, what dose causes cancer in 1 mouse in 1 million. A second extrapolation is then required to estimate the effect on humans, with our greater body mass. Because these two extrapolations go beyond the actual data obtained, they introduce uncertainty into the interpretation of what doses are acceptable for humans. As a result, to be on the safe side, regulatory agencies set standards for maximum allowable levels of toxicants that are well below the minimum toxicity levels estimated from lab studies.

Individuals vary in their responses to hazards

Different individuals may respond quite differently to identical exposures to hazards. These differences can be genetically based or can be due to a person's current condition. People in poorer health are often more sensitive to biological and chemical hazards. Sensitivity also can vary with sex, age, and weight. Because of their smaller size (and thus higher concentration of toxin per kg of body weight for the same exposure) and rapidly developing organ systems, fetuses, infants, and young children tend to be much more sensitive to toxicants than are adults. Regulatory agencies,

THE SCIENCE BEHIND THE STORY

Pesticides and Child Development in Mexico's Yaqui Valley

Runoff from fields in the Yaqui Valley of Mexico carries agricultural chemicals.

With spindly arms and big, round eyes, one set of pictures resembles the stick figures drawn by young children everywhere. Next to them is another group of drawings, mostly disconnected squiggles and lines. Both sets of pictures are intended depict people. The main difference between the two groups of young artists: long-term pesticide exposure.

Children's drawings are not a typical tool of toxicology, but anthropologist Elizabeth Guillette wanted to try new methods. Guillette was interested in the effects of pesticides on children. She devised tests to measure childhood development based on techniques from anthropology and medicine. Guillette used the Yaqui Valley of northwestern Mexico as her study site.

The Yaqui Valley is farming country, worked for generations by the indigenous group that gives the region its name. Synthetic pesticides arrived in the area in the 1940s. Some Yaqui embraced the agricultural innovations, spraying their farms in the valley to increase their yields. Yaqui farmers in the surrounding foothills, however, generally chose to bypass the chemicals and to continue following more traditional farming practices. Although differing in farming techniques, Yaqui in the valley and foothills continued to share the same culture, diet, education system, income levels, and family structure.

At the time of the study, in 1994, valley farmers planted crops twice a year, applying pesticides up to 45 times from planting to harvest. A previous study conducted in the valley in 1990 had indicated high levels of multiple pesticides in the breast milk of mothers and in the umbilical cord blood of newborn babies. In contrast, foothill families avoided chemical pesticides in their gardens and homes.

To understand how pesticide exposure affects childhood development, Guillette and fellow researchers studied 50 preschoolers aged four to five—33 from the valley and 17 from the foothills. Each child underwent a half-hour exam, during which researchers showed a red balloon, promising to give the balloon later as a gift, and using the promise to evaluate long-

term memory. Each child was put through a series of physical and mental tests:

- Catching a ball from up to 3 m away, to test overall coordination
- Jumping in place for as long as possible, to assess endurance
- Drawing a picture of a person, as a measure of perception
- Repeating a short string of numbers, to test short-term memory
- Dropping raisins into a bottle cap from a height of about 13 cm, to gauge fine-motor skills

The researchers also measured each child's height and weight. When all tests were completed, each child was asked what he or she had been promised and then received the red balloon.

Although the two groups of children were not significantly different in height and weight, they differed markedly in other areas of development. Valley children were far behind the foothill children developmentally in coordination, physical endurance, long-term memory, and fine motor skills:

- From a distance of 3 m, valley children had great difficulty catching the ball.
- Valley children could jump for an average of 52 seconds, compared with 88 seconds for foothill children.
- Most valley children missed the bottle cap when dropping raisins, whereas

---

such as Health Canada, set standards for adults and then extrapolate downward for infants and children. However, in many cases the linear extrapolations still do not protect babies adequately. Many critics today contend that despite improvements, regulatory agencies still do not account explicitly enough for risks to fetuses, infants, children, older adults, and the immunocompromised.

Health Canada and Environment Canada collaborate on the *Air Quality Health Index (AQHI)*, a newly standardized national-level index that provides a measure of the level of air pollution at a given time and location, and translates this into the expected health impacts of the pollution. Air pollution is reported on a scale of 1 (very low) to 10+ (very high), based on measured concentrations of ozone (O_3), particulate matter ($PM_{2.5}$, PM_{10}), and nitrogen dioxide

(NO_2).[21] All these common air pollutants contribute to the occurrence of respiratory problems, especially in children, older adults, and those with allergies or other kinds of health impairment. AQHI readings of 1 to 3 correspond to a low health risk, 4 to 6 a moderate health risk, 7 to 10 a high health risk, and 10+ a very high health risk.[22] High AQHI readings can trigger policy responses, such as warnings for those who are most susceptible to remain indoors.

The type of exposure can affect the response

The risk posed by a hazard often varies according to whether a person experiences high exposure for short

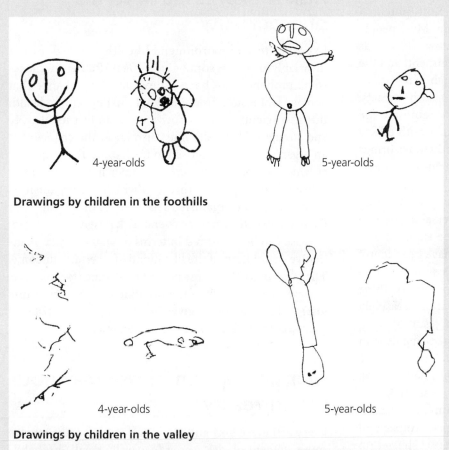

4-year-olds

5-year-olds

Drawings by children in the foothills

4-year-olds

5-year-olds

Drawings by children in the valley

Elizabeth Guillette's study in Mexico's Yaqui Valley offers a startling example of apparent neurological effects of pesticide poisoning. Young children from foothills areas where pesticides were not commonly used drew recognizable figures of people. Children the same age from valley areas where pesticides were used heavily in industrialized agriculture could draw only scribbles.

Source: Adapted from Guillette, E.A., M.M. Meza, M. G. Aquilar, A. D. Soto, and I. E. García, 1998. Anthropological Approach to the Evaluation of Preschool Children Exposed to Pesticides in Mexico. Environmental Health Perspectives 106(6):347-353.

foothill children dropped them into the caps far more often.

Each group did fairly well repeating numbers, but valley children showed poor long-term memory. At the end of the test, all but one of the foothill children remembered that they had been promised a balloon, and 59% remembered it was red. Of the valley children only 55% remembered they'd be getting a balloon, only 27% remembered the colour of the balloon, and 18% were unable to remember anything about the balloon.

The children's drawings exhibited the most dramatic differences (see the figure). The foothill children drew pictures that looked like people; in contrast, the scribbles of the valley children resembled little that looked like a person. By the standards of developmental medicine, the four- and five-year-old valley children drew at the level of a two-year-old.

Some scientists greeted Guillette's study with skepticism, pointing out that its sample size was too small to be meaningful. Others said that such factors as different parenting styles or unknown health problems could be to blame. Toxicologists argued that without blood or tissue tests on the children, the study results couldn't be tied to agrichemicals. Regardless of these criticisms, Guillette maintains that her findings show that nontraditional study methods are a valid way to track the effects of environmental toxins and that pesticides present a complex long-term risk to human growth and health.

periods of time, known as **acute exposure**, or lower exposure over long periods of time, known as **chronic exposure**. Incidences of acute exposure are easier to recognize, because they often stem from discrete events, such as accidental ingestion, an oil spill, a chemical spill, or a nuclear accident. Lab tests and LD$_{50}$ values generally reflect acute toxicity effects. However, chronic exposure is more common—and more difficult to detect and diagnose. Chronic exposure often affects organs gradually, as when smoking causes lung cancer, or when alcohol abuse induces liver or kidney damage. Pesticide residues on food or low levels of arsenic in drinking water also pose chronic risk. Because of the long time periods involved, relationships between cause and effect may not be readily apparent.

Mixes may be more than the sum of their parts

It is difficult enough to determine the impact of a single hazard on an organism, but the task becomes astronomically more difficult when multiple hazards interact. For instance, chemical substances, when mixed, may act in concert in ways that cannot be predicted from the effects of each in isolation. Mixed toxicants may sum each other's effects, cancel out each other's effects, or multiply each other's effects. Whole new types of impacts may arise when toxicants are mixed together.

Such interactive impacts—those that are more than or different from the simple sum of their constituent effects—are called **synergistic effects**. This creates one of the main problems associated with epidemiological studies that follow groups of people with potential exposure to hazards over a period of time. Most people are routinely exposed to a complex mixture of hazards from the home, the workplace, the environment, and the lifestyle choices they make, including such activities as smoking. In addition to its own negative health impacts, for example, smoking can synergistically reinforce the impacts of other factors. Disentangling the health effects of these various hazards is challenging and always brings a certain degree of uncertainty to the conclusions of epidemiological studies.

Lab experiments with alligators have indicated that DDE can either help cause or inhibit sex reversal, depending on the presence of other chemicals. Mice exposed to a mixture of nitrate, atrazine, and aldicarb have been found to show immune, hormone, and nervous system effects that were not evident from exposure to each of these chemicals alone. Wood frogs in the wild are increasingly suffering limb deformities, apparently the result of being parasitized by trematode flatworms. A frog's being near an agricultural field with pesticide runoff increases the rate of parasitic infection, because, as lab studies have shown, pesticides suppress the frog's immune response, making it more vulnerable to parasites. We saw examples of experiments designed to investigate the synergistic impacts of pesticides combined with other environmental stresses on frogs in "The Science Behind the Story: Climate Change, Disease, and the Amphibians of Monteverde."

Traditionally, environmental health has tackled effects of single hazards one at a time. In toxicology, the complex experimental designs required to test interactions, and the sheer number of chemical combinations, have meant that single-substance tests have received priority. This approach is changing, but scientists in environmental health and toxicology will never be able to test all possible combinations. There are simply too many hazards in the environment.

Risk Assessment and Risk Management

Policy decisions on whether to ban chemicals or restrict their use generally follow years of rigorous testing for toxicity. Likewise, strategies for combating disease and other health threats are often based on extensive research. Policy and management decisions reach beyond the scientific results on health to incorporate considerations about economics and ethics. And all too often, they are influenced by political pressure from powerful interests. The steps between the collection and interpretation of scientific data and the formulation of policy involve assessing and managing risk.

Risk is expressed in terms of probability

Exposure to an environmental health threat does not invariably produce some given effect. Rather, it causes some probability of harm, some statistical chance that damage will result. To understand the impact of a health threat, a scientist must know more than just its identity and strength. He or she must also know the chance that an organism will be exposed to the hazard, the frequency at which the organism may encounter it, the amount of substance or degree of threat to which the organism is exposed, and the organism's sensitivity to the threat. Such factors help determine the overall risk posed.

Risk can be measured in terms of *probability*, a quantitative description of the likelihood of a certain outcome. The probability that some harmful outcome (for instance, injury, death, environmental damage, or economic loss) will result from a given action, event, or substance expresses the **risk** posed by that phenomenon.

Our perception of risk may not match reality

Every action we take and every decision we make involve some element of risk, some (generally small) probability that things will go wrong. We try in everyday life to behave in ways that minimize risk, but our perceptions of risk do not always match statistical reality (**FIGURE 19.13**). People often worry unduly about negligibly small risks but happily engage in other activities that pose high risks. For instance, most people perceive flying in an airplane as a riskier activity than driving a car, but driving a car is statistically far more dangerous per km travelled.

Psychologists agree that this difference between risk perception and reality stems from the fact that we feel more at risk when we are not controlling a situation and

roots

RISK

The English word **risk** dates from the 1660s. It was derived from the older French word *risque* ("risk"), which was probably borrowed from the Italian *risco* (modern *rischio*), from *riscare*, "run into danger." Some possible related words include the Arabic *risq*, "something that has been given to you by God," and the Latin *risicum*, which describes the dangers posed to sailors by a barrier reef.

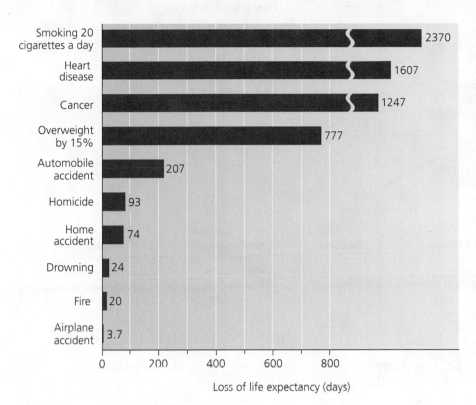

FIGURE 19.13
Our perceptions of risk do not always match the reality of risk. Listed here are several leading causes of death, along with a measure of the risk each poses. Risk is measured in days of lost life expectancy; that is, the number of days of life lost by people suffering the hazard, spread across the entire population—a measure commonly used by insurance companies. By this measure, one common source of anxiety, airplane accidents, poses 20 times less risk than home accidents, more than 50 times less risk than auto accidents, and more than 200 times less risk than being overweight by 15%. *Source: Data from Cohen, B. (1991). Catalogue of risks extended and updated.* Health Physics *61:317–335.*

more safe when we are "at the wheel"—regardless of the actual risk involved. When we drive a car, we feel we are in control, even though statistics show we are at greater risk than as a passenger in an airplane. This psychology can account for people's great fear of nuclear power, toxic waste, and pesticide residues on foods—environmental hazards that are invisible or little understood and whose presence in their lives is largely outside their personal control. In contrast, people are more ready to accept and ignore the risks of smoking cigarettes, overeating, and not exercising, all voluntary activities statistically shown to pose far greater risks to health.

Risk assessment analyzes risk quantitatively

The quantitative measurement of risk and the comparison of risks involved in different activities or substances together are termed **risk assessment**. Risk assessment is a way of identifying and outlining problems. In environmental health, it helps ascertain which substances and activities pose health threats to people or wildlife and which are largely safe.

Assessing risk for a chemical substance involves several steps. The first steps involve the scientific study of toxicity outlined above—determining whether a given substance has toxic effects and, through dose–response analysis, measuring how effects on an organism vary with the degree of toxicant exposure. Subsequent steps involve assessing the individual's or population's likely extent of exposure to the substance, including the frequency of contact, the concentrations likely encountered, and the length of time the substance is expected to be encountered. Risk assessment studies may be performed by scientists associated with the same industries that manufacture toxicants. This, in many people's minds, undermines the objectivity of the process.

Risk management combines science and other social factors

Accurate risk assessment is a vital step toward effective **risk management**, which consists of decisions and strategies to minimize risk (**FIGURE 19.14**). In most developed nations, risk management is handled largely by federal agencies, such as Environment Canada, Health Canada, Public Safety Canada, and Public Health Canada, as well as the Canadian Council of Ministers of the Environment (CCME), which comprises the federal, territorial, and provincial environment ministers. In risk management, scientific assessments of risk are considered in light of economic, social, and political needs and values. The costs and benefits of addressing risk in various ways are assessed with regard to both scientific and nonscientific concerns. Decisions whether to reduce or eliminate risk are then made.

Operational Activities
- research
- surveillance/monitoring
- corporate mgt. initiatives
- policy revision

Communications/Consultation
- strategy/approach; targeted activities
- proactive risk communication
- public education, consultation; polling

Legal Considerations
- duty of care
- accountability/responsibility
- international obligations

Context
- problem measurement
- technical quantification
- evaluation
- possibly inconclusive

Precautionary

Hazard Identification
- research findings
- international initiative
- legal mandate
- incident occurrence/crisis

Assessment

Policy Options
- choices/opportunities
- cost/benefits
- resources
- instrument choice
- consultation
- revision
- trade-offs required

Decision
- policy advice
- political input
- Cabinet/Parliament approval (as required)

Implementation
- communication
- administration
- testing/follow-up

Evaluation/Review
- results/effectiveness
- recommendations
- revision, adjustment, learning

Approach

Public Context
- values, ethics
- policy priorities (e.g., social, cultural, political, economic, international, etc.)
- public view of "acceptable risk"

Source: *Risk Management for Canada and Canadians: Report of the ADM Working Group on Risk Management* (PCO), Annex A.

FIGURE 19.14 The first step in addressing the risk of an environmental hazard is quantifying the hazard and its potential impacts. The precautionary approach is at the core of this integrated risk management strategy, from the report of the government of Canada's Working Group on Risk Management (2000). Once science identifies and measures the hazard, then risk management can proceed. In this process, economic accountability, political effectiveness, social responsiveness, and ethical issues and values are considered in light of the scientific data. The consideration of all these types of information is designed to result in policy decisions that minimize the risk of the environmental hazard. Citizen involvement is intended to be a central focus of this framework. *Source: Treasury Board of Canada Secretariat. (2000).* Results for Canadians—A Management Framework for the Government of Canada. *www.tbs-sct.gc.ca/report/res_can/rc-eng.asp*

In environmental health and toxicology, comparing costs and benefits can be difficult because the benefits are often economic, whereas the costs often pertain to health. Moreover, economic benefits are generally known, easily quantified, and of a discrete and stable amount, whereas health risks are hard-to-measure probabilities, often involving a very small percentage of people likely to suffer greatly and a large majority likely to experience little effect. When a government agency bans a pesticide, it may mean measurable economic loss for the manufacturer and the farmer, whereas the benefits accrue less predictably over the long term to some percentage of factory workers, farmers, and the public. Because of the lack of equivalence in the way costs and benefits are measured, risk management frequently stirs up debate.

Philosophical and Policy Approaches

Because we cannot know a substance's toxicity until we measure and test it, and because there are so many untested chemicals and combinations, science will never eliminate the many uncertainties that accompany risk assessment. In such a world of uncertainty, there are two basic philosophical approaches to categorizing substances as safe or dangerous.

Two approaches exist for determining safety

One approach is to assume that substances are harmless until shown to be harmful. We might nickname this the *innocent-until-proven-guilty approach.* Because thoroughly testing every existing substance (and combination of substances) for its effects is a hopelessly long, complicated, and expensive pursuit, the innocent-until-proven-guilty approach has the benefit of not slowing down technological innovation and economic advancement. However, it has the disadvantage of putting into wide use some substances that may later turn out to be dangerous.

The other approach is to assume that substances are harmful until they are shown to be harmless. This approach follows the **precautionary principle**. This more cautious approach should enable us to identify troublesome toxicants before they are released into the environment, but it may also significantly impede the pace of technological and economic advance.

These two approaches are actually two ends of a continuum of possible approaches. The two endpoints differ mainly in where they lay the burden of proof—specifically, whether product manufacturers are required to prove safety or whether government, scientists, or citizens are required to prove danger.

Philosophical approaches are reflected in policy

Because of the health and environmental consequences of hazardous substances, governments of developed nations have viewed regulatory oversight over manufactured substances as one solution to environmental health threats. One's philosophical approach has implications for policy, affecting what materials are allowed into our environment. Most nations follow a blend of the two approaches, but there is marked variation among countries. At the present time, European nations are embarking on a new policy course that largely incorporates the precautionary principle regarding the regulation of synthetic chemicals.

The precautionary principle has long been a foundation of Canada's approach to environmental management, perhaps more so in Environment Canada than in Health Canada, although Health Canada's move to declare BPA a toxic substance is a clear example of the use of the precautionary principle. The same is not true of the United States, where environmental and consumer advocates criticize policy makers and regulatory agencies for largely following the innocent-until-proven-guilty approach. For instance, compounds involved in cosmetics require no FDA review or approval before being sold to the public.

In Canada, several federal agencies are jointly responsible for tracking and regulating synthetic chemicals, emissions, and effluents. The centerpiece of the laws that govern the environment and environmental health issues in Canada, the *Fisheries Act,* which prohibits the introduction

of deleterious substances into any water body that provides habitat for fish, has proven to be one of the most powerful tools available for the protection of water quality in Canada.

Toxicants are also regulated internationally

Nations have sought to address chemical pollution with international treaties. One example is the *Basel Convention [of the United Nations] on the Control of Transboundary Movements of Hazardous Wastes and Their Disposal.* The Basel Convention (mentioned in the context of waste management) is probably the most comprehensive international agreement on hazardous materials. The convention came into effect in 1992 and has 170 parties (i.e., signatory nations that have ratified the agreement). Its central goal is to protect human health and the environment against the adverse effects of hazardous and other wastes.[23]

Another example of a U.N.-moderated vehicle is the *International Code of Conduct on the Distribution and Use of Pesticides.* This is not an international law but a set of voluntary guidelines and best practices for both private and public entities. The World Health Organization also plays a role in establishing these guidelines and monitoring adherence to them. The *Rotterdam Convention on the Prior Informed Consent Procedure for Certain Hazardous Chemicals and Pesticides in International Trade,* discussed in the Central Case, is an example of an international legal instrument that operates according to rules established by consensus of the parties.

The *Stockholm Convention on Persistent Organic Pollutants (POPs)* came into force in 2004 and has been ratified by roughly 140 nations. POPs are toxic chemicals that persist in the environment, bioaccumulate in the food chain, and often can travel long distances. The PCBs and other contaminants found in polar bears are a prime example. Because contaminants often cross international boundaries, an international treaty seemed the best way of dealing fairly with such transboundary pollution. The Stockholm Convention aims first to end the use and release of 12 of the POPs shown to be most dangerous, a group nicknamed the "dirty dozen" (**TABLE 19.5**).

It sets guidelines for phasing out these chemicals and encourages transition to safer alternatives. In September 2006, Canada completed the initial assessments of the 23 000 chemicals on its Domestic Substances List and derived a list of 2600 medium-priority substances, thereby becoming the first country to prioritize domestic chemicals as per the Stockholm agreement.[24]

The European Union is taking the world's boldest step toward testing and regulating manufactured chemicals. In 2007, the EU's REACH program went into effect (*REACH*

Table 19.5 The "Dirty Dozen" Persistent Organic Pollutants (POPs) Targeted by the Stockholm Convention

Toxicant	Type	Description
Aldrin	Pesticide	Kills termites, grasshoppers, corn rootworm, and other soil insects
Chlordane	Pesticide	Kills termites and is a broad-spectrum insecticide on various crops
DDT	Pesticide	Widely used in the past to protect against insect-spread diseases; continues to be applied in several countries to control malaria
Dieldrin	Pesticide	Controls termites and textile pests; also used against insect-borne diseases and insects in agricultural soil
Dioxins	Unintentional by-product	Produced by incomplete combustion and in chemical manufacturing; released in some kinds of metal recycling, pulp and paper bleaching, automobile exhaust, tobacco smoke, and wood and coal smoke
Endrin	Pesticide	Kills insects on cotton and grains; also used against rodents
Furans	Unintentional by-product	Result from the same processes that release dioxins; also are found in commercial mixtures of PCBs
Heptachlor	Pesticide	Kills soil insects, termites, cotton insects, grasshoppers, and mosquitoes
Hexachlorobenzene	Fungicide; unintentional by-product	Kills fungi that affect crops; released during chemical manufacture and from processes that give rise to dioxins and furans
Mirex	Pesticide	Combats ants and termites; also is a fire retardant in plastics, rubber, and electronics
PCBs	Industrial chemical	Used in industry as heat-exchange fluids, in electrical transformers and capacitors, and as additives in paint, sealants, and plastics
Toxaphene	Pesticide	Kills insects on crops; kills ticks and mites on livestock

Source: Data from United Nations Environment Programme (UNEP), 2001.

stands for Registration, Evaluation, Authorization, and Restriction of Chemicals). REACH shifts the burden of proof for testing chemical safety from national governments to industry and requires that chemical substances produced or imported in amounts of over one metric tonne per year be registered with a new European Chemicals Agency. This agency will evaluate industry research and decide whether the chemical seems safe and should be approved, whether it is unsafe and should be restricted, or whether more testing is needed.

Previous policy had required industry to test chemicals brought to market after 1981 (there are 4300 such chemicals) but required no such testing for chemicals already on the market in 1981 (which number more than 100 000). It is expected that REACH will require 30 000 substances to be registered. The REACH policy also aims to help industry by giving it a single streamlined regulatory system and by exempting it from having to file paperwork on substances under one metric tonne. By requiring stricter review of major chemicals already in use, exempting chemicals made only in small amounts, and providing financial incentives for innovating new chemicals, the EU hopes to help European industries research and develop safer new chemicals and products while safeguarding human health and the environment.

The EU expects that roughly 1500 substances may be judged harmful enough to be replaced with safer substances. These include carcinogens, mutagens, teratogens, persistent substances, and chemicals that bioaccumulate. (EU commissioners held off on including endocrine disruptors.) The EU also expects that 1–2% of substances may cease to be manufactured because their production will no longer be profitable.

EU commissioners estimated that REACH will cost the chemical industry and chemical users 2.8 billion to 5.2 billion euros over 11 years but that the health benefits to the public would be roughly 50 billion euros over 30 years. Changes in the program since then have made the predicted cost–benefit ratio even better.

Conclusion

International agreements, such as the Rotterdam and Stockholm Conventions, inspire hope that governments will act to protect the world's people, wildlife, and ecosystems from toxic chemicals and other environmental hazards. At the same time, solutions often come more easily when they do not arise from government regulation alone. To many minds, consumer choice, exercised through the market, may be the best way to influence industry's decision making. Consumers of products can make decisions that influence industry when they have full information from scientific research regarding the risks involved. Once scientific results are in, a society's philosophical approach to risk management will determine policy decisions.

CANADIAN ENVIRONMENTAL PERSPECTIVES

Wendy Mesley

Journalist Wendy Mesley became an environmental health crusader when she investigated the environmental causes of cancer for CBC's Marketplace.

- **Journalist** with strong interest in environmental issues
- **Cancer survivor**
- **Former co-host** of CBC's consumer program, *Marketplace*

Wendy Mesley isn't an obvious choice of a person to profile in a book about environmental science. She isn't a scientist at all, in fact—she is a journalist. She started out in high school answering the phone at CHUM Radio in Toronto and eventually moved on to earn a journalism degree at Ryerson. In recent years she has been a regular correspondent for CBC's evening news centrepiece, *The National*, as well as the anchor for *Sunday Report*. In 2002 she became the co-host of *Marketplace*, CBC's consumer watchdog show, and she has received several Gemini Awards for her work over the years.

Mesley has always taken an intelligent, investigative approach to her reporting. That is probably why, when she was diagnosed with breast cancer in 2005, she began to ask questions—lots of questions, some of them very difficult ones.

Of course she asked, "Why me?" Says Mesley, "I have been a health nut all my adult life, watching what I eat and exercising . . . and there is no history of it in my family."[25]

But more than that, she was determined to make some kind of sense about all of the *other* people who are ending up with cancer. Mesley was stunned to discover that the Canadian Cancer Society now predicts that almost one in every two people in Canada will get some form of cancer in their lifetimes. "The biggest shock was... to find out how common a club it really was. That was the big tragedy. Mine and everyone else's."[26]

Mesley eventually translated her investigative curiosity into a *Marketplace* series called *Chasing the Cancer Answer*. In the series, Mesley addressed what she calls "the elephant in the room"[27] that no one is talking about—the role of the myriad cancer-causing contaminants in the environment.

In the series, Mesley directed some pointed questions at the Canadian Cancer Society. She wondered, for example, why the society places such a huge financial emphasis on behavioural causes, like smoking and diet, while devoting virtually no attention, investigation, or funding to the environmental causes of cancer. She blasted the society for focusing so much attention on finding a cure and so little on prevention.[28] She questioned why there is so little awareness of common cancer-causing agents. For example, after taking birth control pills for most of her adult life, thinking she would only be at risk if she were also a smoker, Mesley was surprised to find out that in 2005 the World Health Organization had reclassified the synthetic hormones used in birth control pills as powerful (Class I) carcinogens.

The response to the series from some groups was immediate and vehement. The Physicians for a Smoke-Free Environment published an open letter to her, suggesting that highlighting environmental contaminants as a cause of cancer may have diverted valuable attention away from the cancer-causing role of human behaviour, especially smoking and secondhand smoke.

Today, more than seven years after being diagnosed with malignant tumours in her breast, Wendy Mesley is doing well. She is back at work, cancer free—at least for now—and maintaining the positive attitude that she has had from the very beginning of her cancer journey. She now does her best to avoid exposure to toxic chemicals, such as those found in cleaning products, for example, and is looking forward to spending many more years with her husband and young daughter.

"Talking about things in our environment that are making us sick means you have to do something about them. But it's easier to get out a message that will sell products than to take products off the shelf. There's no money in it."[29]—**Wendy Mesley**

Thinking About Environmental Perspectives

Wendy Mesley was criticized after her documentary on cancer aired on CBC television, for drawing attention away from the role of smoking and diet in causing cancer. What do you think? Has the Canadian Cancer Society focused too much of its efforts on quitting smoking, eating veggies, wearing sunblock, and living a healthy lifestyle, while ignoring the role of environmental exposure to carcinogenic chemicals? Do we need to consider both the behavioural and the environmental factors in the fight against cancer?

Whether the burden of proof is laid at the door of industry or of government, it is important to realize that we will never attain complete scientific knowledge of any risk. Rather, we must make choices based on the information available. Synthetic chemicals have brought us innumerable modern conveniences, a larger food supply, and medical advances that save and extend human lives. Human society would be very different without these chemicals. Yet a safer and happier future, one that safeguards the well-being of both humans and the environment, depends on knowing the risks that some hazards pose and on having means in place to phase out harmful substances and replace them with safer ones.

REVIEWING OBJECTIVES

You should now be able to:

Identify the major types of environmental health hazards and explain the goals of environmental health

- Environmental health seeks to assess and mitigate environmental factors that adversely affect human health and ecological systems.
- Environmental health threats include physical, chemical, biological, and cultural hazards.
- Many types of hazards occur naturally, but their occurrence and impacts can be worsened or mitigated by human activities.
- Disease is a major focus of environmental health.
- Environmental hazards exist indoors as well as outdoors.
- Toxicology is the study of poisonous substances.

Describe the types, abundance, distribution, and movement of toxicants in the environment

- Thousands of potentially toxic substances exist around us.
- Toxicants may be of human or natural origin. They include carcinogens, mutagens, teratogens, allergens, neurotoxins, and endocrine disruptors.
- Toxicants may enter and move through surface and groundwater reservoirs, or they may travel long distances through the atmosphere.
- Some chemicals break down very slowly and thus persist in the environment.
- Some organic poisons bioaccumulate and move up the food chain, poisoning consumers at high trophic levels through the process of biomagnification.

Discuss the study of hazards and their effects, including case histories, epidemiology, animal testing, and dose–response analysis

- In case histories, researchers study health problems in individual people.

- Epidemiology involves gathering data from large groups of people over long periods of time and comparing groups with and without exposure to the environmental health threat being assessed.
- In dose–response analysis, scientists measure the response of test animals to various doses of the suspected toxicant.
- Toxicity or strength of response may be influenced by the dose or amount of exposure, the nature of exposure (acute or chronic), individual variation, and synergistic interactions with other hazards.

Assess risk assessment and risk management

- Risk assessment involves quantifying and comparing risks involved in different activities or substances.
- Risk management integrates science with political, social, and economic concerns, in order to design strategies to minimize risk.

Compare philosophical approaches to risk

- An innocent-until-proven-guilty approach assumes that a substance is not harmful unless it is shown to be so.
- A precautionary approach entails assuming that a substance may be harmful unless proven otherwise.

Describe policy and regulation in Canada and internationally

- Health Canada, Environment Canada, and other federal and provincial/territorial agencies are jointly responsible for regulating environmental health threats under Canadian policy.
- Canada and European nations tend to take a more precautionary approach to environmental hazards and the testing of chemical products, as compared with the United States.

TESTING YOUR COMPREHENSION

1. What four major types of health hazards does research in the field of environmental health encompass?
2. In what way is disease the greatest hazard that people face? What kinds of interrelationships must environmental health experts study to learn about how diseases affect human health?

3. Where does most exposure to lead, asbestos, radon, and PBDEs occur? How has each been addressed?
4. When did concern over the effects of pesticides start to emerge? Describe the argument presented by Rachel Carson in *Silent Spring*. What impact did

it have on public perception of risk from synthetic chemicals? Is DDT still used?

5. List and describe the six types or general categories of toxicants described in this chapter.

6. How do toxicants travel through the environment, and where are they most likely to be found? What are the life spans of toxic agents? Describe the processes of bioaccumulation and biomagnification.

7. What are epidemiological studies, and how are they most often conducted?

8. Why are animals used in laboratory experiments in toxicology? Explain the dose–response curve. Why is a substance with a high LD_{50} considered safer than one with a low LD_{50}?

9. What factors may affect an individual's response to a toxic substance? Why is chronic exposure to toxic agents often more difficult to measure and diagnose than acute exposure? What are synergistic effects, and why are they difficult to measure and diagnose?

10. How do scientists identify and assess risks from substances or activities that may pose health threats?

THINKING IT THROUGH

1. Describe some environmental hazards that you think you may be living with indoors. How do you think you may have been affected by indoor or outdoor environmental hazards in the past? What philosophical approach do you plan to take in dealing with these toxicants in your own life?

2. Why is it that research on endocrine disruption has spurred so much debate? What steps do you think could be taken to help establish more consensus among scientists, industry, regulators, policy makers, and the public?

3. Do you feel that laboratory-bred animals should be used in experiments in toxicology? Why or why not?

4. Describe differences in the policies of Canada, the United States, and the European Union toward the study and management of the risks of synthetic chemicals. Which approach do you believe is best, and why?

5. Industry's critics say chemical manufacturers should bear the burden of proof for the safety of their products before they hit the market. Industry's supporters say that mandating more safety research will hamper the introduction of products that consumers want, increase the price of products as research costs are passed on to consumers, and cause companies to move to nations where standards are more lax. What do you think? Should government follow the precautionary principle and require proof of safety prior to a chemical's introduction to the market?

6. You are the parent of two young children, and you want to minimize the environmental health risks to your family as your kids grow up. Name five steps that you could take in your household and in your daily life that would reduce your children's exposure to environmental health hazards.

7. You have just been hired as the office manager for a high-tech startup company that employs bright and motivated young people but is located in an old, dilapidated building. Despite their youth, the company's employees seem perpetually sick with other unexplained illnesses. Looking into the building's history, you discover that the water pipes and ventilation system are many decades old, that there have been repeated termite infestations, and that part of the building was remodelled just before your company moved in but there are no records of what was done in the remodelling. Your company has all the latest furniture, computers, and other electronics. Most windows are sealed shut.

You want to figure out what is making the employees sick, and you want to convince your boss to give you a budget to hire professionals to examine the building for hazards. What hazards might you expect? What arguments will you use to convince your employer to fund tests and inspections? What questions will you ask employees to help focus and prioritize any funds you are granted for testing and inspections?

INTERPRETING GRAPHS AND DATA

To minimize exposure to ultraviolet (UV) radiation and thus the risk of skin cancer, people have increased their use of sunscreen lotions in recent decades. Recently,

however, some research has shown that chemicals in sunscreens may themselves pose some risk to human health. The compounds commonly used as UV protectants are fat soluble, environmentally persistent, and prone to bio-accumulation. Moreover, they exhibit estrogenic effects in laboratory rats (see Schlumpf et al., 2001, cited in the source note to the graph). Although the benefits of sunscreen use are substantial, the risks are not yet well understood. A hypothetical trade-off between the risk factors of UV exposure and those of sunscreen use illustrates the balancing act of risk management.

1. What dosage of applied sunscreen on the graph corresponds to the greatest risk caused by UV exposure? What dosage corresponds to the greatest risk caused by chemicals in the sunscreen? Which of these two points on the graph is associated with the greater risk?

2. What dosage of applied sunscreen on the graph corresponds to the least risk caused by UV exposure? What dosage corresponds to the least risk caused by chemicals in the sunscreen? Which of these two points is associated with the greater risk?

3. The total risk to the individual is the sum of the two individual risks. What point on the graph corresponds to the greatest total risk? What sunscreen dosage corresponds to the least total risk? (Is the answer unambiguous?) Based on the data shown

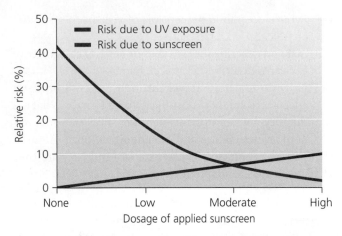

Hypothetical risk distributions for individuals using an estrogenic sunscreen to prevent skin cancer.
Source: Schlumpf, M., et al. 2001. In vitro and in vivo estrogenicity of UV screens. Environmental Health Perspectives 109:239–244.

here, how much sunscreen would you choose to apply the next time you go to the beach? Is there any other information you would like to know before you change the way you use sunscreen? Can you think of any other cases that illustrate this sort of trade-off between dose-dependent risk factors?

CHAPTER ENDNOTES

1. Greenberg, M. (2008) The defence of chrysotile, 1912–2007. *International Journal of Occupational Environmental Health*, Vol. 14, No. 1, pp. 57–66.

2. NRCAN, *Main Minerals and Metals Produced in Canada*, www.nrcan.gc.ca/mms/scho-ecol/main_e.htm#asbestos

3. Greenberg, M. (2008) The defence of chrysotile, 1912–2007. *International Journal of Occupational Environmental Health*, Vol. 14, No. 1, pp. 57–66.

4. Greenberg, M. (2008) The defence of chrysotile, 1912–2007. *International Journal of Occupational Environmental Health*, Vol. 14, No. 1, pp. 57–66.

5. Health Canada, *It's Your Health: Health Risks of Asbestos*, www.hcsc.gc.ca/hl-vs/iyh-vsv/environ/asbestos-amiante-eng.php

6. Greenberg, M. (2008) The defence of chrysotile, 1912–2007. *International Journal of Occupational Environmental Health*, Vol. 14, No. 1, pp. 57–66.

7. Industry Canada, Trade Data Online, Trade by Product, www.ic.gs.ca/sc_mrkti/tdst/tdo/tdo.php#tag Acessed June 11, 2011.

8. Health Canada, Consumer Product Safety: Asbestos, www.hc-sc.gc.ca/cps-spc/house-domes/decor/construct_asbestos_amiante-eng.php, and *It's Your Health: Health Risks of Asbestos*, www.hc-sc.gc.ca/hl-vs/iyhvsv/environ/asbestosamiante-eng.php

9. Attaran, Amir, David R. Boyd, and Matthew B. Stanbrook (2008) Asbestos mortality: A Canadian export, *CMAJ*, Vol. 179, No. 9, pp. 871–872.

10. West Nile Virus, *Canadian Family Physician*, www.cfpc.ca/cfp/2005/Jun/vol51-jun-cme-1.-asp

11. There are several units of measurement in common use for radon, and they are not directly convertible. WL (Working Level) is a measure of the concentration of the daughter products of radon; pCi (pico-Curie, usually measured per litre of air) and Bq (Becquerel, usually measured per cubic metre of air) are measures of the number of radioactive disintegrations or transformations per second. 1 Bq is equivalent to 27 pCi. 1 WL is approximately equivalent to 200 pCi/L.

12. World Health Organization, 2004, *Radon and Health Information Sheet,* www.who.int/phe/radiation/en/2004Radon.pdf

13. Health Canada's actionable limit is currently 200 Bq/m^3, or 5.4 pCi/L.

14. U.S. Environmental Protection Agency (2007) *A Citizen's Guide to Radon: The Guide to Protecting Yourself and Your Family from Radon,* www.epa.gov/radon/pubs/citguide.html

15. Health Canada Advises Canadians About Children's Potential Exposure to Lead, September 6, 2007, www.hc-sc.gc.ca/ahc-asc/media/advisories-avis/_2007/2007_114-eng.php

16. Health Canada, *It's Your Health: Formaldehyde and Indoor Air,* www.hcsc.gc.ca/hl-vs/iyh-vsv/environ/formaldehyde-eng.php

17. CBC News, *Health Canada, Bisphenol A: Announcement Imminent,* April 2008, www.cbc.ca/consumer/story/2008/04/15/bisphenol.html

18. Government of Canada, *Chemical Substances: An Eco-Action Initiative, Questions and Answers for Action on Bisphenol A Under the Chemicals Management Plan,* updated June 2008, www.chemicalsubstanceschimiques.-gc.ca/faq/bisphenol_a_qa-qr_e.html#14

19. Environmental Defence, *Toxic Nation: Toxic Baby Bottles in Canada,* 2008, www.toxicnation.ca/files/toxicnation/report/ToxicBabyBottleReport.pdf

20. Bushnik, T. et al. (2010) Lead and Bisphenol-A Concentrations in the Canadian Population. Statistics Canada, Health Reports. 82-003-X, Vol. 21, No. 3. http://www.statcan.gc.ca/pub/82-003-x/82-003-x2010003-eng.htm

21. Environment Canada, *About the Air Quality Health Index,* www.ec.gc.ca/cas-aqhi/default.asp?Lang=En&n=065BE995-1

22. Environment Canada, *About the Air Quality Health Index,* www.ec.gc.ca/cas-aqhi/default.asp?Lang=En&n=065BE995-1

23. Basel Convention on the Transboundary Movement of Hazardous Wastes and Their Disposal, www.basel.int

24. Chatterjee, Rhitu (2008) Hunting for persistent chemicals that might pollute the Arctic, *Environmental Science and Technology,* Vol. 42, No. 14, p. 5034, http://pubs.acs.org/subscribe/journals/esthag-w/2008/jun/science/rc_pops.html

25. Harvey, Robin (2008) Wendy Mesley: Cancer diagnosis compelled journalist to search for answers, *Being Well Magazine,* Winter, www.yorkregion.com/Health/beingwell%20magazine/article/67934

26. Harvey, Robin (2008) Wendy Mesley: Cancer diagnosis compelled journalist to search for answers, *Being Well Magazine,* Winter, www.yorkregion.com/Health/beingwell%20magazine/article/67934

27. Yates, Dana (2007) Moving On, *Ryerson University Alumni Magazine,* January, pp. 28–29, http://danayates.ca/samples/Wendy%20Mesley%20-%20winter%202007.pdf

28. Harvey, Robin (2008) Wendy Mesley: Cancer diagnosis compelled journalist to search for answers, *Being Well Magazine,* Winter, www.yorkregion.com/Health/beingwell%20magazine/article/67934

29. Yates, Dana (2007) Moving On, *Ryerson University Alumni Magazine,* January, pp. 28–29, http://danayates.ca/samples/Wendy%20Mesley%20-%20winter%202007.pdf

MyEnvironmentPlace

Go to **www.myenvironmentplace.ca** where you will find quizzes, animations, your Pearson eText, and more.

The Urban Environment: Creating Liveable Cities

20

Vancouver is said (by some) to be the world's most liveable city.

Upon successfully completing this chapter, you will be able to

- Describe the scale of urbanization
- Assess urban and suburban sprawl
- Outline city and regional planning and land use strategies
- Evaluate transportation options

- Describe the roles of urban parks
- Analyze environmental impacts and advantages of urban centres
- Assess the pursuit of sustainable cities

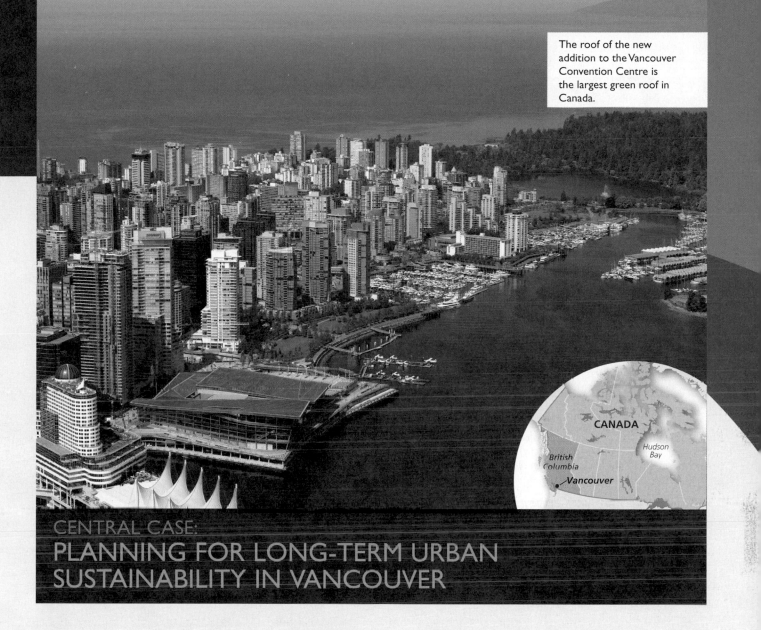

The roof of the new addition to the Vancouver Convention Centre is the largest green roof in Canada.

CANADA

Hudson Bay

British Columbia

Vancouver

CENTRAL CASE:
PLANNING FOR LONG-TERM URBAN SUSTAINABILITY IN VANCOUVER

"We have planning boards. We have zoning regulations. We have urban growth boundaries and 'smart growth' and sprawl conferences. And we still have sprawl."
—ENVIRONMENTAL SCIENTIST DONELLA MEADOWS, 1999

"No one will find out what works for our cities by looking at [them] . . . you've got to get out and walk."
—URBAN ACTIVIST JANE JACOBS

According to *The Economist*, Vancouver is "the world's most liveable city."[1] As it turns out, Vancouver has some credentials with which to back this up.

In 2002–2003, nine cities from Canada, Japan, Russia, Germany, India, Argentina, China, the United States, and Mexico participated in the International Sustainable Urban Systems Design competition. The competition

was designed to encourage cities to plan for the transition from a fossil-fuel–based economy to one based on alternative energy sources. The assigned task was to develop 100-year plans for urban sustainability.

The project that formed the basis for the Canadian entry that year was called cities*PLUS* (*Planning for Long-term Urban Sustainability*). Focusing on the Metro Vancouver area, the project involved sustainable transportation and urban greening, among other things. The Canadian team consisted of the Sheltair Group, a Vancouver-based urban planning and resource management company; the International Centre for Sustainable Cities (ICSC); Metro Vancouver; and the Liu Institute for Global Issues at UBC.

Some of the design teams came from industrialized nations; others came from the developing world. The projects were all different in scope, focus, and approach, but they all came to similar conclusions: Within 30 to

These maps, from the Vancouver Working Group Discussion Paper, compare the distribution of population in the Metro Vancouver area in 2000 with a "business-as-usual" projection to 2040. The paper concluded that unless the urban system is transformed, population spread will continue to encroach on green space, ultimately degrading both prosperity and quality of life.
Source: Vancouver Working Group of Western Economic Diversification Canada Discussion Paper, The Liveable City, www.wd.gc.ca/rpts/research/livable/2a_e.asp

50 years, without major changes, the energy, food, water, transportation, and other systems that support urban centres will begin to break down.

The citiesPLUS team produced Canada's first 100-year sustainability plan for a metropolitan area. At the competition's final event in Tokyo in 2003, the team was awarded the Grand Prize. In a discussion paper, the Vancouver Working Group of WEDC concluded that "business as usual" is not an acceptable scenario and that changes need to be put in place now if we hope to keep the urban environment liveable. The working group pointed to a projection of population distribution in the Metro Vancouver area to the year 2040 (see maps), concluding that "unless urban systems are transformed, expected population growth in the region will lead to

massive loss in natural amenities, and will undermine the region's prosperity and quality of life, long before 100 years from now."[2]

One outgrowth of the citiesPLUS project was the Sustainable Cities International Network, a resource-sharing network whose members are cities and regions engaged in long-term planning for urban sustainability. The purpose of the network is to transform the way cities approach planning decisions by placing them in a much longer timeframe—three generations.[3] Members share experiences, expertise, tools, and learning about long-term planning with other member cities. The network gives member communities an opportunity to learn from other cities' successes and setbacks. There are now 37 member cities from all over the world.

Meanwhile, Vancouver's city planners continue to try to incorporate the principles of sustainability into new urban developments. An interesting example (see photo) is the new addition to the Vancouver Convention Centre, which undertook its first duties during the 2010 Olympics. The roof of the building is the largest green roof in Canada. The rest of the addition has been built to meet high environmental standards, with efficient lighting, heating and cooling by thermal exchange with seawater, and an onsite desalinization plant.[4]

Will citiesPLUS, the Sustainable Cities International Network, and other similar urban sustainability initiatives change the world dramatically? Probably not; they likely will not even lead to any of the member cities' laying legitimate claim to the title of "Sustainable City." But taking steps to move the world's cities toward sustainability is more urgent than ever before, as the world's population becomes increasingly urbanized. If we want the cities of the future to provide a safe, healthy, liveable environment, then initiatives like those of citiesPLUS will need to become more common, more effective, and more widely adopted.

Our Urbanizing World

In 2008, a milestone was reached when 3.3 billion people—half the world's population—were city dwellers. This number is now over 3.5 billion and will likely increase

to 5 billion or more within the next two decades.[5] This shift from the countryside into towns and cities, or **urbanization**, is arguably the single greatest change our society has undergone since its transition from a nomadic hunter-gatherer lifestyle to a sedentary agricultural one. Even

roots

URBAN AND SUBURBAN

The word **urban**, first used in the early 1600s, is derived from the Latin word *urbanus*, "of or pertaining to a city or city life." Interestingly, the word **suburban** may have been used earlier, in the fourteenth century. It comes from the Latin *suburbium*, "an outlying part of a city."

though we commonly associate cities with noise, smog, garbage, and other negative environmental impacts, the truth is that cities offer many features that are beneficial—perhaps even crucial—to the environment. We will explore those features in this chapter.

Industrialization has driven the move to urban centres

Since 1950, the world's urban population has more than quadrupled. Urban populations are growing for two reasons: (1) The human population overall is growing, and (2) more people are moving from farms to cities than are moving from cities to farms.

The shift of population from country to city began long ago. Agricultural harvests that produced surplus food freed a proportion of citizens from farm life and allowed the rise of specialized manufacturing professions, class structure, political hierarchies, and urban centres. The earliest Canadian towns were administrative, military, and/or trading centres and were located for strategic purposes and for ease of access to waterways (**FIGURE 20.1A**). The earliest settlement in Canada that is still occupied today is probably St. John's, Newfoundland, founded as early as 1492.

In Canada, as elsewhere, the establishment of transportation routes for the shipment of raw materials and products was a central characteristic of the next stage of urban development (**FIGURE 20.1B**). Starting in the early 1800s, the Industrial Revolution spawned technological innovations that created jobs and opportunities in urban centres for people who were no longer needed on farms. Industrialization and urbanization bred further technological advances that increased production efficiencies, both on the farm and in the city.

Worldwide, the proportion of the population that is urban rose from 30% half a century ago to 50.5% in 2010. Between 1950 and 2005, the global urban population increased by 2.65% each year, whereas the rural population rose only by 1.12% annually. From 2005 to 2030, the United Nations projects that the urban population will

(a) Montréal

(b) Calgary

FIGURE 20.1

The city of Montreal **(a)**, originally an Iroquoian settlement, flourished as an early trade route because of its strategic port location at the confluence of the St. Lawrence and Ottawa rivers. Although there was a settlement at Fort Calgary prior to 1883 **(b)**, the actual town site was laid out by the Canadian Pacific Railway Company and was incorporated in 1884 as the first town in Alberta.

grow by 1.78% annually, whereas the rural population will decline by 0.03% each year.

Trends differ between developed and developing nations, however (**FIGURE 20.2**). In 1851, only 13% of Canadian citizens were urban dwellers; the percentage passed 50% shortly after 1920.[6] Following the industrialization of the 1800s and early 1900s, urban centres in both Canada and the United States continued to grow very rapidly through the early twentieth century and into the 1960s. Urban population growth then slowed dramatically—even reversing, in some cases—starting in the 1970s. This led to stagnancy and deterioration in the urban cores of many larger cities.

More recently there has been some recovery in city centres, but urban population growth remains slow throughout North America. This is partly because four of every five people already live in cities, towns, and suburbs.

FIGURE 20.2

In developing nations today, urban populations are growing quickly, whereas rural populations are levelling off and are expected to begin declining. Developed nations are already largely urbanized, so in these nations urban populations are growing more slowly, and rural populations are falling. Solid lines in the graph indicate past data, and dashed lines indicate projections of future trends.
Source: Data from Population Division of the Department of Economic and Social Affairs of the United Nations Secretariat (2010). World Urbanization Prospects: The 2009 Revision, Fig. 3. By permission.

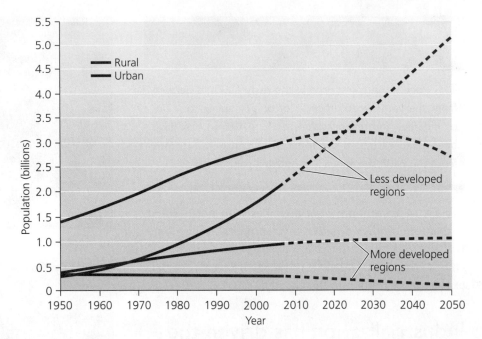

The proportion of Canada's population that is classified as "urban" now stands at more than 80% (**FIGURE 20.3**).

Although the population of Canada is as urbanized as that of the United States (also 80% urban), Canada has never been as heavily *sub*urban as the United States. Most U.S. urban dwellers reside in suburbs; fully 50% of the American population today is suburban. In Canada, 72% of the urban population lives in cities, with the remaining 28% in suburban areas.[7] In other words, only about 22% of the total Canadian population is suburban. Statistics Canada defines **suburbs** as areas that are peripheral to—and strongly "influenced by"—cities or towns.[8]

FIGURE 20.3

Canada's population has become increasingly urbanized, as shown in this graph based on census data from 1901 through 2006. Today, more than 80% of Canada's population lives in cities, towns, and suburbs.
Source: Statistics Canada. 2006. Portrait of the Canadian Population in 2006: Subprovincial population dynamics, Census Analytical Series, www12.statcan.ca/english/census06/analysis/popdwell/Subprov1.cfm

Today Ontario, Québec, and British Columbia are the most urbanized provinces in Canada. About 45% of Canada's population is housed in just six large urban centres, each with a population of more than 1 million: Toronto, Calgary, Edmonton, Montreal, Vancouver, and Ottawa–Gatineau. Canada's population is also highly concentrated in the south; according to the 2006 census, two out of three Canadians live within 100 km of the southern border, occupying only about 4% of the land area of the country.

Today's developing nations, where many people still reside on farms, are now urbanizing rapidly. In China, India, Nigeria, and other nations, rural people are streaming to cities in search of jobs and urban lifestyles. U.N. demographers estimate that virtually all the world's population growth over the next 25 years will be absorbed by urban areas of developing nations.

Today's urban centres are unprecedented in scale and rate of growth

Cities in themselves are nothing novel. Urban centres where population, cultural activities, and political power are concentrated have been part of human culture for several thousand years. Ancient Mediterranean civilizations, the great Chinese dynasties, and the Mayan and Incan empires all featured sophisticated and powerful urban centres.

What is new in the urban setting of today is the sheer scale of today's metropolitan areas. Human population growth has placed greater numbers of people in towns and cities than ever before. Today, 22 cities are home to more than 10 million residents (**TABLE 20.1**). The greater metropolitan area of the world's most populous city, Tokyo, Japan (defined as the Tokyo–Osaka corridor, an almost continuous urban belt), is home to 36.5 million people. North America's largest metropolises, Mexico City and New York City, each hold about 19 million. However, the majority of urban dwellers in North America live in much smaller cities.

The **mega-cities** of 10 million people or more that now characterize much of the developing world are of a scale that is unfamiliar to most North Americans. For example, even using the broadest possible definition of *metropolitan area*, which bundles everything from Hamilton to Oshawa into one large Toronto-centred economic area called the Golden Horseshoe, the population is still only just over 5.6 million. (This is based on a definition that considers the continuity of urbanized or built-up areas, economic integration, and the location of the workforce in a region.) Some of the large urban centres of the devel-

oping world now host homeless and transient populations that are larger than the entire population of the Golden Horseshoe area.

Most fast-growing cities today are in the developing world. Some of this growth and rural–urban migration is occurring because industrialization is decreasing the need for farm labour and promoting commerce and jobs in cities. Sadly, another reason is that wars, conflict, and ecological degradation are driving millions of people out of the countryside and into cities. Cities like Mumbai (India), Lagos (Nigeria), and Cairo (Egypt) are growing in population even more quickly than North American cities did prior to the 1970s.

Many cities in the developing world are growing at rates of 3–5% per year and even higher. These rates have been matched by some North American cities during their fastest growth, but only for short periods. (For example, Calgary—currently Canada's fastest-growing city—grew by 4% in 2006.) Recall how exponential growth works; on a sustained basis, even these seemingly small growth rates imply doubling times of just 14 to 23 years for many cities in the developing world.

All too often, this is happening without the economic growth and infrastructure development needed to match

Table 20.1 Metropolitan Areas with 10 Million Inhabitants or More	
City, Country	**Millions of people**
Tokyo, Japan	36.5
Delhi, India	21.7
São Paulo, Brazil	20.0
Mumbai (Bombay), India	19.7
Mexico City, Mexico	19.3
New York–Newark, United States	19.3
Shanghai, China	16.3
Calcutta, India	15.3
Dhaka, Bangladesh	14.3
Buenos Aires, Argentina	13.0
Karachi, Pakistan	12.8
Los Angeles–Long Beach–Santa Ana, United States	12.7
Beijing, China	12.2
Rio de Janeiro, Brazil	11.8
Manila, Philippines	11.4
Osaka–Kobe, Japan	11.3
Cairo, Egypt	10.9
Moscow, Russia	10.5
Paris, France	10.4
Istanbul, Turkey	10.4
Lagos, Nigeria	10.2

Source: United Nations Population Division, 2010. World urbanization prospects: The 2009 revision. *New York: UNPD.*

weighing the issues

DEFINING HOMELESSNESS

Definitions of *homelessness* vary dramatically. Are you homeless if your lack of shelter is "voluntary"? What if you are unable to maintain a job and home because of a mental illness or an addiction? Are you homeless if you live in wholly inadequate housing? (What if the "housing" is a cardboard box or a shipping crate?) Are you homeless if you are a transient worker, sleeping each night, for example, at the construction site where you will work the next day?

Are there homeless people in the town or city where you are living? If you think not, look again. Many homeless people are "invisible," either because they prefer to keep a low profile or because we choose not to see them.

Can you think of some ways in which environmental change could cause homelessness, perhaps on a temporary basis? How do environmental change and environmental hazards make life difficult for homeless people? Try to think beyond the borders of the familiar, and consider what life is like for homeless people in the developing world.

the population growth. As a result, many of these cities are facing overcrowding, pollution, and poverty. Nearly three of every four governments of developing nations have enacted policies to discourage the movement of people from the countryside into cities.

Various factors influence the geography of urban areas

Location is vitally important for urban centres. Environmental variables, such as climate, topography, and the configuration of waterways, go a long way toward determining whether a small settlement will become a large city—and successful cities historically have been located in places that give them economic advantages. Think of any major city, and chances are that it is situated along a major river, seacoast, railroad, or highway—some corridor for trade that has driven economic growth (see **FIGURE 20.1**).

Many well-located cities have acted as linchpins in trading networks, funnelling resources from agricultural regions, processing them, manufacturing products, and shipping those products to other markets. Montreal's location at the confluence of two rivers cemented its strategic location for trade and commerce as early as the 1700s. For Calgary and other western towns, it took the arrival of the main line of the Canadian Pacific Railway in the late 1800s to initiate major growth.

All cities, from ancient times to the present day, have supported themselves by drawing in resources from outlying rural areas through trade, persuasion, or conquest. In turn, cities have historically influenced how people use land in surrounding areas. Although city life and country life may seem very different, cities and the rural regions surrounding them have always been linked by tight economic relationships.

Spatial patterns of urbanization can change with changing times. Today, several factors are causing population centres to decentralize in developed nations. For one thing, people now are globally interconnected to an unprecedented degree. Being located on a river or seacoast is no longer as vital to a city's success in our age of global commerce, jet travel, diplomacy, television, cell phones, and the Internet. Globalization has connected distant societies, and businesses and individuals can more easily communicate from locations away from major city centres. Moreover, fossil fuels have enabled the outward spread of cities. By easing long-distance transport, fossil fuels and the proliferation of highway networks have made it easier to commute into and out of cities and to import and export resources, goods, and waste. Such factors have enabled a shift of population from cities to suburbs, particularly in North America.

People have moved to suburbs

By the mid-twentieth century, many cities in North America had accumulated more people than these cities had jobs to offer. Unemployment rose, and crowded inner-city areas began to suffer increasing poverty and crime. As inner cities declined economically from the 1960s onward, many affluent city dwellers chose to move outward to the cleaner, less crowded, and more parklike suburban communities beginning to surround the cities (**FIGURE 20.4**). These people were pursuing more space, better economic opportunities, cheaper real estate, less crime, and better schools for their children.

The development of highway systems and reliable transportation options allowed millions of people to commute by car to their downtown workplaces from new homes in suburban "bedroom communities." The exodus to the suburbs, in turn, hastened the economic decline of central cities, especially in the United States; for example, in the 1960s and 1970s, Chicago's population declined to 80% of its peak because so many residents moved to the suburbs.

In most ways, suburbs have delivered the qualities people sought in them. The wide spacing of houses, with each house on its own plot of land, gives families room and privacy. However, by allotting more space to each person, suburban growth has spread human impact across the landscape. Natural areas have disappeared as housing developments are constructed. We have built extensive road networks to ease travel, but suburbanites now find themselves needing to drive everywhere, since public transit is less feasible and more expensive in

FIGURE 20.4
Suburbs, as illustrated in this aerial photograph have grown because they allow each person to have a bit more individual space and privacy, and a cleaner environment than in the inner city. In recent years, suburbs may have become the victim of their own success, as crowding and sprawl have made the suburbs more and more like the cities their inhabitants sought to avoid in the first place.

areas with low population density. They commute longer distances to work and spend more time in congested traffic. The expanding rings of suburbs surrounding cities have grown larger than the cities themselves, and towns are running into one another. These aspects of suburban growth have inspired a new term: *sprawl*.

Sprawl

The term *sprawl* has become laden with meanings and connotes different things to different people. To some, sprawl is esthetically ugly, environmentally harmful, and economically inefficient. To others, it is the collective outgrowth of reasonable individual desires and decisions in a world of growing human population. We can begin our discussion by giving **sprawl** a simple, nonjudgmental definition: the spread of low-density urban or suburban development outward from an urban centre.

Today's urban areas spread outward

As urban and suburban areas have grown in population, they have also grown spatially. This growth is obvious from maps and satellite images of rapidly spreading cities, such as Las Vegas (**FIGURE 20.5**).

roots

SPRAWL

The term **sprawl is** derived from an Old English word, *spreawlian*, meaning "to move convulsively." This originated from the Scandinavian and Northern Frisian *spraweli*, likely from the Proto-Indo-European *sper*, meaning "to strew." The expression *urban sprawl* was first used in the mid-1950s.

Because suburban growth entails allotting more space per person than does city dwelling, in most cases this outward spatial growth across the landscape has outpaced the growth in numbers of people. According to the 2006 census, the urbanized land area in Canada increased by 2% between 2001 and 2006, whereas the urban population only increased by 0.3% over the same time period. Between 1950 and 1990, the population of 58 major U.S. metropolitan areas rose by 80%, but the land area they covered rose by 305%.

Many researchers thus define *sprawl* simply as the physical spread of development at a rate greater than the rate of population growth. University of Toronto researcher Matthew Turner and colleagues used satellite

(a) Las Vegas, Nevada, 1984

(b) Las Vegas, Nevada, 2009

FIGURE 20.5 Satellite images show the type of rapid urban and suburban expansion that many people have dubbed *sprawl*. Las Vegas, Nevada, is currently one of the fastest-growing cities in North America. Between 1984 **(a)** and 2009 **(b)**, the population increased more than fivefold, and the quantity of developed area rose more than threefold.

imagery to investigate the factors that drive and control sprawl. They found that sprawl varies greatly from one metropolitan area to another, even during periods when the overall extent of sprawl does not change. They also determined that a variety of factors are statistically correlated with sprawl, including temperate climate, decentralized employment, early public transport infrastructure, and the availability of unincorporated land in the urban fringe.[9]

Several types of standard development approaches can result in sprawl (**FIGURE 20.6**). However, to determine whether the growth patterns actually represent sprawl would require examining the nature and density of development within the high-growth areas. The high rate of growth might be indicative of the phenomenon of *in-fill*, in which suburban areas fill in and become more densely populated as people move out of areas that have already reached their optimal densities. Some of the questions a researcher might ask about sprawl include the following:

- Are the peripheral growth areas characterized by low-density development throughout, or are there pockets of higher-density development?
- Does the spread of urbanized land area relative to the growth in urban population necessarily imply that each resident is occupying more land?
- If low-density development is occurring and spreading, will this lead necessarily to a qualitative experience of sprawl by residents of urban areas?
- What characterizes the daily experience of sprawl—longer commuting times, more air pollution, less parking?
- What, if any, will be the environmental impacts?
- What are the causes of sprawl?

(a) Uncentred commercial strip development

(b) Low-density single-use development

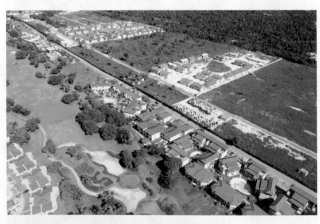

(c) Scattered, or leapfrog, development

(d) Sparse street network

FIGURE 20.6   Several conventional approaches to suburban development can result in sprawl. In uncentred commercial strip development **(a)**, businesses are arrayed in a long strip along a roadway, and no attempt is made to create a centralized community with easy access for consumers. In low-density, single-use residential development **(b)**, homes are located on large lots in residential tracts far away from commercial amenities. In scattered or leapfrog development **(c)**, developments are created at great distances from a city centre and are not integrated. In developments with a sparse street network **(d)**, roads are far enough apart that moderate-sized areas go undeveloped, but not far enough apart for these areas to function as natural areas or sites for recreation. All these development approaches necessitate frequent automobile use.

- What are the factors that control the rate and distribution of sprawl in different cities?
- And finally, can—or should—anything be done to curb sprawl?

Sprawl has several causes

From the preceding discussion it should be clear that there are two main components of sprawl. One is human population growth—there are simply more people alive each year. The other is per capita land consumption—each person takes up more land. In a basic sense, the amount of sprawl is a function of the number of people added to an area times the amount of land the average person occupies.

Highways, widely available automobiles, and technologies, such as telecommunications and the Internet, have fostered movement away from city centres because they free businesses from dependence on the centralized infrastructure a major city provides, and they give workers greater flexibility to live wherever they desire.

The primary reasons for greater per capita land consumption, however, are that most people simply like having some space and privacy and dislike congestion. Furthermore, in the consumption-oriented North American lifestyle that promotes bigger houses, bigger cars, and bigger TVs, having more space to house one's possessions becomes important. Unless there are overriding economic or social disadvantages, most people prefer living in a less congested, more spacious, more affluent community.

Economists, politicians, and city boosters have almost universally encouraged the unbridled spatial expansion of cities and suburbs. The conventional assumption has been that growth is good and that attracting business, industry, and residents will unfailingly increase a community's economic well-being, political power, and cultural influence. Today, however, this assumption is increasingly being challenged. As the negative effects of sprawl on citizens' lifestyles accumulate, growing numbers of people have begun to question the mantra that all growth is good.

What is wrong with sprawl?

Sprawl means different things to different people. To some, the word evokes strip malls, homogenous commercial development, and tracts of cookie-cutter houses encroaching on farmland and ranchland. It may suggest traffic jams, destruction of wildlife habitat, and loss of natural land around cities.

However, for other people, sprawl represents the collective result of choices made by millions of well-meaning individuals trying to make a better life for themselves and their families. In this view, those who decry sprawl are being elitist and fail to appreciate the good things about suburban life. Let us try, then, to leave the emotional debate aside and assess the impacts of sprawl.

Transportation Most studies show that sprawl constrains transportation options, essentially forcing people to drive cars. These constraints include the need to own a vehicle and to drive it most places, the need to drive greater distances or to spend more time in vehicles, a lack of available mass transit options, and more traffic accidents. An automobile-oriented culture also increases dependence on nonrenewable petroleum, with its attendant economic and environmental consequences.

Pollution Sprawl's effects on transportation give rise, in turn, to increased pollution. Carbon dioxide emissions from vehicles cause global climate change, while nitrogen- and sulphur-containing air pollutants contribute to tropospheric ozone, urban smog, and acid precipitation. Motor oil and road salt from roads and parking lots pollute waterways, posing risks to ecosystems and human health. Runoff of polluted water from paved areas is estimated to be about 16 times as great as from naturally vegetated areas.

Health Aside from the health impacts of pollution, some research suggests that sprawl promotes physical inactivity because driving cars largely takes the place of walking during daily errands. Physical inactivity increases obesity and high blood pressure, which can in turn lead to other ailments. A 2003 study found that people from the most-sprawling areas weigh 2.7 kg more for their height than people from the least-sprawling metropolitan areas, although a cause-and-effect relationship has not been established.

Land use The spread of low-density development means that more land is developed while less is left as forests, fields, farmland, or ranchland. At the current rate of development around the city of Toronto, for example, 1070 km^2 of rural land will be newly urbanized by 2021. Most of this land—about 92% of it—is prime agricultural land. When farmland, forests, and grasslands are converted to suburban development, their ecosystem services are diminished or lost. These services include resource production, esthetic beauty, habitat for wildlife, cleansing of water, places for recreation, and many others.

Economics Sprawl drains tax dollars from existing communities and funnels them into infrastructure for new development on the fringes of those communities. Money that could be spent maintaining and improving weighing the issues

SPRAWL NEAR YOU

Is there sprawl in the area where you live? Are you both-ered by it, or not? Has development in your area had any of the impacts described above? Do you think your city or town should use its resources to encourage outward growth, or should densification be encouraged?

downtown centres is instead spent on extending the road system, water and sewer system, electricity grid, telephone lines, police and fire service, schools, and libraries. Advocates for sprawling development argue that taxes on new development eventually pay back the invest-ment made in infrastructure, but studies have found that in most cases taxpayers continue to subsidize new devel-opment if municipalities do not pass infrastructure costs along to developers.

Creating Liveable Cities

To respond to the challenges that urban and suburban sprawl presents, architects, planners, developers, and policy makers across North America today are trying to restore the vitality of city centres and to plan and manage how urbanizing areas develop.

City and regional planning are means for creating liveable urban areas

Planning is the professional pursuit that attempts to design cities and other human settlements so as to maximize their efficiency, functionality, and beauty. City planners advise policy makers on development options, transportation needs, public parks, and other matters.

City planning in North America came into its own in the early twentieth century (**FIGURE 20.7**) and grew in importance as urban populations expanded and wealthier residents fled to the suburbs. In today's world of sprawling metropolitan areas, regional planning has become just as important. Regional planners deal with the same issues as city planners, but they work on broader geographic scales and must coordinate their work with multiple municipal governments. In some places, regional planning has been institutionalized in formal governmental bodies; the Metro Vancouver is an example of a regional entity.

Zoning is a key tool for planning

One tool that planners use is **zoning**, the practice of clas-sifying areas for different types of development and land use (**FIGURE 20.8**). For instance, to preserve the clean-liness and tranquility of residential neighbourhoods, industrial plants may be kept out of districts zoned for residential use. The specification of zones for different types of development gives planners a powerful means of guiding what gets built where. Zoning can restrict areas to a single use, as is often done with suburban residential tracts in so-called bedroom communities. Or zoning can allow the type of mixed use—residential and commercial, for instance—that some planners say can reinvigorate urban neighbourhoods. Zoning also gives home buyers and business owners security; they know in advance what types of development can and cannot be located nearby.

Zoning involves government restriction on the use of private land and represents a top-down constraint on personal property rights. However, many people feel that government has a proper role in setting certain limita-tions on property rights for the good of the community. Similar debates arise with endangered species manage-ment and other environmental issues. For the most part, people have supported zoning over the years because the common good it produces for communities is widely felt to outweigh the restrictions on private use.

Urban growth boundaries and greenbelts are now widely used

The state of Oregon in the northwestern United States took a forward-thinking step in the early 1970s, requiring

weighing the issues

ZONING AND DEVELOPMENT

Imagine you own a 5-ha parcel of land that you want to sell for housing development—but the local zoning board rezones the land so as to prohibit the develop-ment. How would you respond?

Now imagine that you live next to someone else's undeveloped 5-ha parcel. You enjoy the privacy it pro-vides—but the local zoning board rezones the land so that it can be developed into a dense housing subdivision. How would you respond?

What factors do you think members of a zoning board should take into consideration when deciding how to zone or rezone land in a community?

(a) Broughton, Nova Scotia (1905)

FIGURE 20.7
Most cities in Canada were "planned," especially the newer towns of the West, although many originated on the sites of preexisting settlements. The town of Broughton, Nova Scotia **(a)**, was a planned community that failed when the nearby mining operation was abandoned. Mount Royal, Québec **(b)**, was planned by the Canadian Northern Railway Company, which purchased land for the settlement and constructed an underground rail tunnel to the site from Montreal in 1912.

(b) Mount Royal, Québec (1913)

every city and county to draw up a comprehensive land use plan in line with statewide guidelines. As part of the land use plan, each metropolitan area had to establish an **urban growth boundary (UGB)**, a line intended to separate areas designated to be urban from areas desired to remain rural. Development for housing, commerce, and industry would be encouraged within these UGBs but severely restricted beyond them. The intent was to revitalize city centres, prevent suburban sprawl, and protect farmland, forests, and open landscapes around the edges of urbanized areas.

A number of other cities in the United States and Canada have adopted some form of UGB. In their own ways, all UGBs aim to concentrate development, prevent

sprawl, and preserve working farms, orchards, ranches, and forests. UGBs also appear to reduce the amounts municipalities have to pay for infrastructure, compared with sprawl. However, UGBs also seem to increase housing prices within their boundaries.

In the Portland, Oregon, area, the UGB has restricted development outside the UGB. It has increased the density of new housing inside the UGB by more than 50% as homes are built on smaller lots and as multistorey apartments fulfill a vision of "building up, not out." Downtown employment has risen, and Portland has been able to absorb considerable immigration while avoiding rampant sprawl. However, urbanized area still increased by 101 km^2 in the decade after the UGB was established because

WEST BRANDYWINE

EAST BRANDYWINE

DOWNINGTOWN

VALLEY

WEST BRADFORD

COATESVILLE

EAST FALLOWFIELD

■ Highway commercial	□ Low-density residential	■ Medium- to high-density residential
■ Regional commercial	■ Low- to medium-density residential	■ Preexisting planned residential community
■ Industrial	■ Medium-density residential	■ Thorndale Village

FIGURE 20.8 By zoning areas for different uses, planners guide how a community develops. Zoning restricts what landowners can do with their land, but it is intended to maximize prosperity, efficiency, and quality of life for the community. This sample zoning map shows several patterns common to modern zoning practice. Public and institutional uses are clustered together in a downtown area. Industrial uses are clustered together, away from most residential areas. Commercial uses are clustered along major roadways, and residential zones generally are higher in density toward the centre of town.

146 000 people were added to the population. This suggests that relentless population growth may thwart even the best antisprawl efforts. Indeed, the Portland-area UGB has been enlarged three dozen times, and population projections for the region suggest there will be pressure for still more expansion. Many other locations that have instituted UGBs have chosen to expand them later. Housing and land prices also have risen dramatically within the UGB while declining in areas outside of the boundary. Given the reality of UGB expansions, it must be asked whether UGBs will truly limit sprawl in the long run.

In Canada, UGBs often take the form of greenbelts, rather than a "line on a map." A **greenbelt**, like an urban growth boundary, is a land use or zoning designation that is intended to contain urban development while protecting natural or agricultural lands in surrounding areas. Greenbelts provide additional benefits, including access to natural areas for city dwellers, better air and water quality, and protection for plant and animal habitats. Cities in Canada that have instituted some form of greenbelt policy include Ottawa, Toronto, and Vancouver.

Toronto's greenbelt (**FIGURE 20.9**), established by the provincial government of Ontario, is particularly extensive. It includes much of the land area that overlies the Oak Ridges Moraine, an environmentally important area and a major aquifer that serves as the source region

for many area streams. It also includes the Niagara Escarpment, designated as a UNESCO Biosphere Reserve. The Canadian Institute for Environmental Law and Policy stated that Ontario's greenbelt is "positioned to be the most useful and successful greenbelt in the world"

FIGURE 20.9
Toronto's greenbelt is thought to be one of the "most successful and most useful" greenbelts in the world. It stretches around the western half of Lake Ontario, encompassing the entire urban-commercial Golden Horseshoe district.

in a report comparing international examples of urban development containment boundaries.[10] As with UGBs, however, greenbelts can be controversial. Opponents argue, for example, that homeowners in the "green" area are acting solely on their own behalf, hoping to increase housing prices and maintain their rural lifestyle close to the city.

"Smart growth" aims to counter sprawl

As more people have begun to feel negative effects of sprawl on their everyday lives, efforts to control growth have sprung up throughout North America. Urban growth boundaries and many other ideas from these policies have coalesced under the concept of **smart growth**. Smart growth principles (**TABLE 20.2**) vary in their details from place to place, but they always include a combination of environmental, economic, and social development goals.

Proponents of smart growth want municipalities to manage the rate, placement, and style of development so as to promote healthy neighbourhoods and communities, jobs and economic development, transportation options, and environmental quality. They aim to rejuvenate the older existing communities that so often are drained and impoverished by sprawl. Smart growth means "building up, not out"—focusing development and economic investment in existing urban centres and favouring multi-storey live/work spaces and high-rises. Many initiatives and experiments in smart growth are going on now in municipalities across Canada.

Table 20.2   Ten Principles of "Smart Growth"

1. Mix land uses.
2. Take advantage of compact building design and green buildings.
3. Create a range of housing opportunities and choices.
4. Create walkable neighbourhoods.
5. Foster distinctive, attractive communities with a strong sense of place.
6. Preserve open space, farmland, natural beauty, and critical environmental areas.
7. Strengthen and direct development toward existing communities.
8. Provide a variety of transportation choices.
9. Make development decisions predictable, fair, and cost effective.
10. Encourage community and stakeholder collaboration in development decisions.

Source: Sierra Club, Ontario Chapter (based on U.S. Environmental Protection Agency, 2005).

"New urbanism" and "liveable cities" are in vogue

Greenbelts and smart growth are efforts to envision the city of the future—a more sustainable, more environmentally friendly urban environment. A related movement among many architects, planners, and developers is labelled the **new urbanism**. This approach seeks to design neighbourhoods on a walkable scale, with homes, businesses, schools, and other amenities all close together for convenience. The aim is to create functional neighbourhoods in which most of a family's needs can be met close to home without the use of a car. Greenspaces, trees, a mix of architectural styles, and creative street layouts add to the visual interest and pleasantness of new urbanist developments. By aiming to accommodate diversity in age, ethnicity, and socioeconomic status, these developments mimic the traditional urban neighbourhoods that existed until the advent of suburbs.

One of the greatest advocates for liveable communities and walkable, people-friendly cities was Toronto resident Jane Jacobs (**FIGURE 20.10**), who died in April 2006. An activist and co-founder of the Energy Probe Research Foundation, Jacobs was widely known as an "urbanist." She was a grassroots activist and an outspoken critic of urban renewal policies that ignored the needs of neighbourhood residents. Although she had no formal training as a planner, Jacobs' various books on cities and urban renewal are highly regarded for their insightful observations on what works and what doesn't work in North American cities. Jacobs' writings and her work in Toronto and New York City (where she spent a significant part of her career) inspired the founders of the Project for Public Spaces, a New York–

FIGURE 20.10
One of the great advocates of the "liveable city" was Jane Jacobs, one of the most important figures in the history of urban planning.

based nonprofit organization that assists city planners in creating vibrant, people-friendly gathering places in downtown areas.

In 2007, Torontonians and New Yorkers honoured Jacobs with "Jane's Walk," a series of coordinated walks through urban neighbourhoods. By 2011, Jane's Walk had already grown to include walks through 511 different neighbourhoods worldwide. As Jacobs herself said about how to make our cities more liveable and people-friendly, "you've got to get out and walk."

Transportation options are vital to liveable cities

A key ingredient in any planner's recipe for improving the quality of urban life is making multiple transportation options available to citizens. These options include public buses, trains and subways, and light rail (smaller rail systems powered by electricity). As long as an urban centre is large enough to support the infrastructure necessary, these mass transit options are cheaper, more energy-efficient, and cleaner than roadways choked with cars (**FIGURE 20.11**). They also ease traffic congestion by carrying passengers who would otherwise be driving cars. Mass transit rail systems take up less space than road networks and emit less pollution than cars. The fuel and productivity lost on roadways to traffic jams have been estimated to cost billions of dollars each year.

In Canada, subway train systems in Montreal and Toronto enjoy heavy use on a daily basis. The most-used train systems in the United States are the extensive heavy-rail subway systems in New York, Washington, D.C., Boston, and San Francisco. Major cities internationally from Moscow to Paris to Tokyo have large and heavily utilized subway systems. Some cities with severe traffic problems—such as Bangkok, Shanghai, and Athens—have recently opened new rail systems that carry hundreds of thousands of commuters a day. Light rail use is increasing in Europe, and ridership is now rising faster than is the rate of new car drivers. Most countries have bus systems that are far more accessible to citizens than are those of Canada or the United States.

One city famous for its efficient transportation system is Curitiba, Brazil (**FIGURE 20.12**). Faced with a heavy influx of immigrants from outlying farms in the 1970s, visionary city leaders led by Mayor Jaime Lerner decided to pursue an aggressive planning process so that they could direct growth rather than being overwhelmed by it. They reconfigured Curitiba's road system to maximize the efficiency of a large fleet of public buses. Today, this

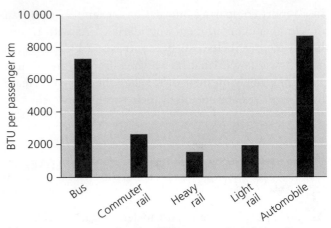

(a) Energy consumption for different modes of transit

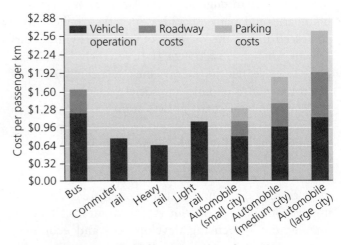

(b) Operating costs for different modes of transit

FIGURE 20.11
Rail transit consumes far less energy per passenger kilometre **(a)** than bus or automobile transit. Rail transit involves fewer costs per passenger kilometre **(b)** than bus or automobile transit.
Source: Based on data from Litman, T. 2005. *Rail Transit in America: A Comprehensive Evaluation of Benefits.* Victoria, BC: Victoria Transport Policy Institute.

metropolis of 2.5 million people has an outstanding bus system that is used each day by three-quarters of the population. The 340 bus routes, 250 terminals, and 1900 buses accompany measures to encourage bicycles and pedestrians. All of this has resulted in a steep drop in car use, despite the city's rapidly growing population.

Establishing mass transit is not always easy, however. Once a road system has been developed and businesses and homes are built alongside roads, it can be difficult and expensive to replace or complement the road system with a mass transit system. In addition, modes of mass transit differ in their effectiveness (see "The Science Behind the Story: Assessing the Benefits of Rail Travel"), depending on city size, size of the transit system, and other factors. To make urban transportation more efficient, governments can raise fuel taxes, tax inefficient modes of transport,

FIGURE 20.12
The rail and bus transit system in Curitiba, a planned community in Brazil, is one of the most efficient urban transportation systems in the world.

reward carpoolers with carpool lanes, encourage bicycle use and bus ridership, and charge trucks for road damage. They can choose to minimize investment in infrastructure that encourages sprawl and to stimulate investment in renewed urban centres.

Parks and open space are key elements of liveable cities

City dwellers often desire some sense of escape from the noise, commotion, and stress of urban life. Natural lands, public parks, and open space provide greenery, scenic beauty, freedom of movement, and places for recreation. These lands also keep ecological processes functioning by regulating climate, producing oxygen, filtering air and water pollutants, and providing habitat for wildlife. The animals and plants of urban parks and natural lands also serve to satisfy *biophilia*, our natural affinity for contact with other organisms.

Protecting natural lands and establishing public parks become more important as our societies become more urbanized because many urban dwellers come to feel increasingly isolated and disconnected from nature. In the wake of urbanization and sprawl, people of every industrialized society in the world today have, to some degree, chosen to conserve land in public parks.

City parks were widely established at the turn of the last century

At the turn of the twentieth century, civic improvement was garnering interest and support as politicians and citizens alike yearned for ways to make their crowded and dirty cities more liveable. In the late 1800s, urban public parks began to be established, using esthetic ideals borrowed from European parks, gardens, and royal hunting grounds. The lawns, shaded groves, curved pathways, and pastoral vistas we see today in many city parks and cemeteries originated with these European ideals. One of the preeminent park designers of the era was the American landscape architect Frederick Law Olmsted, who designed New York's Central Park in 1853 and a host of urban park systems afterward (**FIGURE 20.13**). Olmsted also designed Mount Royal Park in Montreal, although the park that was eventually built followed few of his suggestions.

FIGURE 20.13
City parks were developed in many urban areas in the late nineteenth century to provide citizens esthetic pleasure, recreation, and relief from the stresses of the city. Central Park in New York City, shown here, was one of the first, designed by the famous landscape architect Frederick Law Olmsted.

THE SCIENCE BEHIND THE STORY

Assessing the Benefits of Rail Transit

These subway riders are on a busy commute.

Most urban planning experts see benefits in public mass transit and in making transit systems readily accessible to citizens. But building a mass transit system—and then maintaining and expanding it—can be an expensive undertaking. Thus, planners and policy makers value quantitative information on the costs and benefits of different types of transit systems and on how extensive a given transit system should be to produce the benefits they desire.

For this reason, researcher Todd Litman of the nonprofit Victoria Transport Policy Institute in British Columbia conducted a comprehensive evaluation of the benefits of rail transit. Focusing on cities in the United States, Litman first divided the cities into three categories. "Bus-only" cities have bus service but no rail service; "small-rail" cities have rail systems serving fewer than 12% of daily commuters; "large-rail" cities feature rail service as a major component of the transportation system, serving up to 48% of daily commuters.

Litman compared these three groups of cities for a number of variables. Several key results are summarized in the accompanying figure. Compared with bus-only cities, large-rail cities had 36% fewer per capita traffic deaths each year. Residents of large-rail cities drove 21% fewer kilometres yearly than those of bus-only cities. Large-rail city residents also saved money on transportation, spending 14% less than bus-only city residents on transportation—equivalent to annual savings of $448. Transportation costs took up

only 12% of their household budgets, compared with 14.9% of those of bus-only city residents.

The analysis also revealed benefits of large-rail systems for municipalities running the systems. For example, large-rail cities paid less in operating costs per kilometre travelled and recovered far more of their costs than bus-only cities (38% cost recovery versus 24%).

Small-rail cities were intermediate in traffic deaths and vehicle mileage, as might be expected. However, they performed no better than bus-only cities in terms of operating costs per passenger kilometre or transit cost recovery. And residents of small-rail cities fared slightly worse than residents of bus-only cities in annual transport expenditures and proportion of income spent on transportation. These results suggest that not all benefits of rail transit begin to accrue with small systems. Rather, for many factors, a rail system has to be large enough or accommodate enough riders to gain the economy of scale needed to provide benefits.

A similar pattern was found for annual per capita costs caused by traffic congestion. For bus-only and small-rail cities, congestion costs increased with city size. But for large-rail cities, congestion costs did not vary with size and were lower than in comparably sized cities.

Litman also found that each year governments spend billions of dollars on rail transit systems that they do not get back in revenues from fares, but this is outweighed by the monetary benefits of rail systems. Each year, rail systems save billions of dollars in congestion costs, consumer transportation costs, roadway maintenance costs, parking costs, and accident costs, not to mention indirect savings because of enhanced environmental quality.

A number of studies have critiqued rail transit and portrayed it as ineffective. The Litman study indicates that although not all rail systems are cost-effective, rail systems become more beneficial as they become larger and carry a greater proportion of a city's commuters, thanks to the economy of scale.

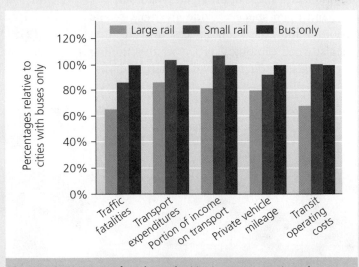

Large-rail cities outperform bus-only cities in transport-oriented variables, but the benefits of rail are not so clear-cut for small-rail cities. *Source: Adapted from Litman, T. 2005. Rail Transit in America: A Comprehensive Evaluation of Benefits. Victoria, BC: Victoria Transport Policy Institute.*

FIGURE 20.14
Riverwood Conservancy is a 60-ha, multiuse urban park in Mississauga, Ontario. Two-thirds of the property is designated to remain in its natural state (or be restored as such); the remainder is designated for a variety of uses by artists, hikers, fishers, bicyclists, school groups, and others.

Two sometimes conflicting goals motivated the establishment and design of early city parks in North America. On the one hand, the parks were meant to be "pleasure grounds" for the wealthy, who helped support their establishment financially and who would ride the parks' winding roadways in carriages. On the other hand, parks were meant to alleviate congestion for poverty-stricken immigrants, and these park users were more interested in active recreation, such as ballgames, than in carriage rides.

At times during the historical development of urban parks, the esthetic interests of the educated elite, the recreational interests of the broader citizenry, and the ecological interests of urban wildlands came into conflict—a friction that survives today in debates over recreation in city parks. For example, Riverwood Conservancy is a 60-ha urban park located in the middle of Mississauga, Ontario (**FIGURE 20.14**). Park planners had to balance many competing interests in designing the park, including the interests of naturalists, artists, mountain bikers, fishers, historians (interested in the heritage buildings on site), schoolchildren, seniors, residents, students and teachers, and the park's wildlife and natural vegetation.

Smaller public spaces are also important

Large city parks are a key component of a healthy urban environment, but even small spaces can make a big difference. Playgrounds provide places where children can be active outdoors and interact with their peers. Community gardens allow people to grow their own vegetables and flowers in a neighbourhood setting (**FIGURE 20.15**).

Vancouver offers gardeners access to 10 community gardens scattered throughout the city, and many other cities across North America now feature thriving community gardens.

Greenways or *corridors*, strips of land that connect parks or neighbourhoods, are often located along rivers, streams, or canals, and they may provide access to networks of walking trails. (Compare this use of "corridor" with the concept of habitat and migration corridors for wildlife.) They can protect water quality, boost property values, and serve as corridors for the movement of birds and wildlife. The Rails-to-Trails Conservancy has spearheaded the conversion of abandoned railroad rights-of-way into trails for walking, jogging, and biking. To date, nearly 24 000 km of 1200 rail lines have been converted across North America.

Besides creating new types of urban spaces, many cities are working to enhance the "naturalness" of their parks through ecological restoration, the practice of

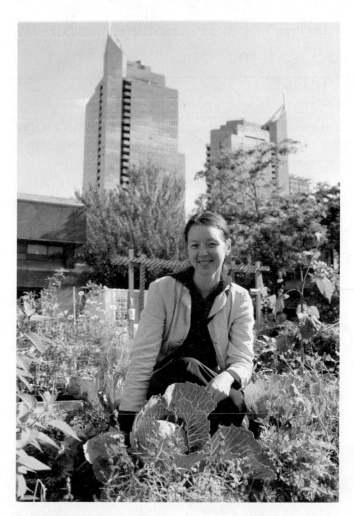

FIGURE 20.15
Urban community gardens like this one provide city residents with a place to grow vegetables. They also serve as greenspaces that beautify cities.

restoring native communities. In Mississauga's Riverwood Conservancy, for example, volunteer teams gather periodically to remove garlic mustard, an invasive plant that smothers native plants on the forest floor. In Vancouver's Hastings Park, restoration activities have included tearing down a number of old park buildings and establishing a 4-ha natural area with a pond. On Vancouver Island, extensive restoration activities have been undertaken to reestablish degraded Garry oak ecosystems. At some Chicago-area forest preserves, scientists and volunteers have used prescribed burns to restore prairie grasses native to the region.

Urban Sustainability

Urbanization and urban centres exert both positive and negative environmental impacts. These impacts depend strongly on how we utilize resources, produce goods, transport materials, and deal with waste.

Urban resource consumption brings a mix of environmental impacts

Most of us might guess that urban living has a greater environmental impact than rural living. However, the picture is not so simple; instead, urbanization brings a complex mix of consequences.

Resource sinks   Cities and towns are sinks for resources, having to import from beyond their borders nearly everything they need to feed, clothe, and house their inhabitants. In other words, the ecological footprints of cities tend to be very large. Urban and suburban areas rely on large expanses of land elsewhere to supply food and other crops, as well as natural resources, such as water, timber, metal ores, and mined fuels. Urban centres also need areas of natural land to provide ecosystem services, including purification of water and air, nutrient cycling, and waste treatment. Major cities, such as New York, depend for their day-to-day survival on water they pump in from faraway watersheds. The city has gone to lengths to acquire, protect, and manage watershed land to minimize pollution of these water sources. When confronted in 1989 with an order by the U.S. Environmental Protection Agency to build a $6 billion filtration plant to protect its citizens against waterborne disease, the city opted instead to purchase and better protect watershed land, for a fraction of the cost.

As cities have grown, and as the material wealth of most societies has risen, the inexorable pull of resources from the countryside to the cities has become stronger. And as urban areas extend their reach, it becomes increasingly hard for urban residents isolated from natural lands to have a tangible demonstration of the environmental impacts of their choices.

The long-distance transportation of resources and goods requires a great deal of fossil fuel use, which has significant environmental impacts. This is of particular concern in Canada because of the great distances from shore to shore to shore. Because of pollution, waste, and other environmental impacts, the centralization of resource use that urbanization entails may seem a bad thing for the environment. However, imagine that all the world's 3.5 billion urban residents were instead spread evenly across the landscape. What would the transportation requirements be, then, to move all those resources and goods around to all those people? A world without cities would likely require *more* transportation to provide people with the same level of access to resources and goods.

Efficiency   Once resources have arrived at an urban centre where people are densely concentrated, however, cities can help minimize per capita consumption by maximizing the efficiency of resource use and delivery of goods and services. For instance, providing electricity from a power plant for urban houses close together is more efficient than providing electricity to far-flung homes in the countryside. The density of cities facilitates the provision of many social services that improve quality of life, including medical services, education, water and sewer systems, waste disposal, and public transportation. This is called *economy of proximity*—it is simpler and cheaper to deliver goods and services to people who are clustered together, and it generates fewer environmental impacts, as well.

More consumption   Because cities draw resources from afar, as mentioned above, their ecological footprints are much greater than their actual land areas. For instance, urban scholar Herbert Girardet calculated that the ecological footprint of London, England, extends 125 times as large as the city's actual area. By another estimate, cities take up only 2% of the world's land surface but consume more than 75% of its resources.

In 2005, the City of Calgary participated in an urban ecological footprint study by the Federation of Canadian Municipalities. The city's footprint team identified energy as the main component of Calgary's ecological footprint (**FIGURE 20.16**), and this continues to be the case today (at 71%). In 2010 they calculated an ecological footprint of 8.59 *global hectares* (*gha*) per capita, the highest of any city in Canada; this compares with a

Calgary's Ecological Footprint, 2010

Built Area (1%)
Forest (14%)
Fishing (3%)
Pasture (3%)
Cropland (8%)
Energy (71%)

Components of footprint

Food 5%
Housing 17%
Mobility 18%
Goods 13%
Services 10%
Government 8%

FIGURE 20.16
In 2010, Calgary's ecological footprint team found that energy use accounted for 71% of the city's ecological footprint.

Canadian average of about 7 gha and a global average of 1.9 gha. The global hectare is a unit that can be used in ecological footprint calculations to describe both the area of biologically productive land or water and the demand on it. Different land types have different productivities. This means that a global hectare of, for example, agricultural land would be physically smaller than a global hectare of pasture land, which is much less biologically productive. In other words, more pasture would be needed to provide the same productivity as one hectare of agricultural land.

The City of Calgary is using the ecological footprint exercise as a guide for both citizens and city planners in making decisions that will affect the city's future. They have made reducing the city's ecological footprint a priority through initiatives such as ImagineCALGARY, a 100-year vision for the city, which includes 30-year targets and strategies for urban sustainability.[11]

However, the ecological footprint concept is most meaningful when used on a per capita basis. So, in asking whether urbanization causes increased resource consumption, we must ask whether the average urban dweller has a larger footprint than the average rural dweller. The answer is yes, but urban and suburban residents also tend to be wealthier than rural residents, and wealth correlates with resource consumption. Thus, although urban citizens tend to consume more than rural ones, the reason could be simply that they are wealthier.

Urban intensification preserves land

The ecological footprints of urban areas are large, but because people are packed densely together in cities, more land outside cities is left undeveloped. Indeed, this is the idea behind urban growth boundaries. If cities did

not exist, and if instead all 7 billion of us were evenly spread across the planet's land area, we would have much less room for agriculture, wilderness, biodiversity, or privacy. There would be no large blocks of land left uninhabited by people or of unfragmented habitat for wildlife. The fact that half the human population is concentrated in discrete locations helps allow room for natural ecosystems to maintain themselves, continue functioning, and provide the ecosystem services on which all of us, urban and rural, depend.

Urban centres suffer and export pollution

Just as cities import resources, they export wastes, either passively through pollution or actively through trade. In so doing, urban centres transfer the costs of their activities to other regions—and mask the costs from their own residents. Citizens of Toronto may not recognize that pollution from coal-fired power plants in their region worsens acid precipitation hundreds of kilometres to the east. Fossil fuel combustion releases primary carbon dioxide and other pollutants, causing climate change and poor air quality. Citizens of New York City may not realize how much garbage their city produces if it is shipped to other states or nations for disposal.

However, not all waste and pollution leaves the city. Urban residents are exposed to heavy metals, industrial compounds, and chemicals from manufactured products that accumulate in soil and water. Airborne pollutants cause photochemical smog, industrial smog, and acid precipitation. These may accumulate as a result of air circulation patterns over the city.

Cities often have ambient temperatures that are several degrees higher than the surrounding suburbs and rural areas. This is called the **urban heat island effect**, and it results from the concentration of heat-generating buildings, cars, factories, and people in the city centre. Tall buildings and paved surfaces are important contributors to the urban heat island effect by absorbing heat and releasing it slowly and by interfering with the convective circulation of air that would otherwise cool the city. When heated air becomes trapped over the city, the smog and particulate air pollution it carries become trapped as well; this can lead to a phenomenon called a **dust dome**. If you drive toward a large city on a hot, hazy summer day—especially if the city is located in a basin or a valley—you will likely see the trapped smog hovering like a brown or blue-grey cloud over the city skyline.

Urban residents also suffer noise pollution and light pollution. **Noise pollution** consists of undesired ambient sound. Excess noise degrades one's surroundings esthetically, can induce stress, and at intense levels (such as with prolonged exposure to the sounds of leaf blowers, lawnmowers, and jackhammers) can harm hearing. The glow of **light pollution** from city lights obscures the night sky, impeding the visibility of stars and disorienting birds, which die by the thousands each year as a result of crashing into illuminated buildings.

These various forms of pollution and the health threats they pose are not evenly shared among urban residents. Those who bear the brunt of the pollution are often those who are too poor to live in cleaner areas. Environmental justice concerns centre on the fact that a disproportionate number of people living near, downstream from, or downwind from factories, power plants, and other polluting facilities are people who are poor and, often, people of racial minorities.

Urban centres foster innovation and offer cultural resources

One of the greatest impacts of urbanization on environmental quality is also one of the most indirect and intangible. Cities promote a flourishing cultural life and, by mixing together diverse people and influences, spark innovation and creativity. The urban environment can promote education and scientific research, and cities have long been viewed as engines of technological and artistic inventiveness. This inventiveness can lead to solutions to societal problems, including ways to reduce environmental impacts.

For instance, research into renewable energy sources is helping us develop ways to replace fossil fuels. Technological advances have helped us reduce pollution. Wealthy and educated urban populations provide markets for low-impact goods, such as organic produce.

FIGURE 20.17
Urban and suburban children take part in environmental education programs that foster awareness and practical training for children and adults interested in learning about and protecting nature in the urban environment. Although natural land is rare in urbanized areas, the education and innovation that urbanization often promotes can lead to solutions that reduce environmental impact.

Recycling programs help reduce the solid waste stream. Environmental education is helping people choose their own ways to live cleaner, healthier, lower-impact lives.

All these phenomena grow from the education, innovation, science, and technology that are part of urban culture. EcoSpark is an example of an urban-based program in Toronto that offers activities for those who are interested in learning about and protecting the natural environment in the urban setting (**FIGURE 20.17**). For example, the Toronto Lichen Count (TLC) is an EcoSpark program in which participants are trained to count lichen colonies, which can be indicators of changes in air quality. The TLC monitoring sites are all located next to subway stations in the downtown Toronto area, for easy access by public transit.

Some seek sustainability for cities

Modern cities that import all their resources and export all their wastes have a linear, one-way metabolism. Such linear models of production and consumption tend to destabilize environmental systems and are not sustainable. Proponents of sustainability for cities stress the need to develop circular systems, akin to systems found in nature, which recycle materials and use renewable sources of energy.

Researchers in the field of **urban ecology** hold that cities can be viewed explicitly as ecosystems and that the fundamentals of ecosystem ecology and systems science apply to urban areas. To help cities improve their

CANADIAN ENVIRONMENTAL PERSPECTIVES

Nola-Kate Seymoar

Nola-Kate Seymoar has devoted her life and career to supporting sustainable communities.

- **President** and **CEO**, International Centre for Sustainable Cities (retired)
- **Advisor** on community economic development, empowerment, and capacity-building
- **Lead developer**, Sustainable Cities International Network

"We are a *do-tank*, not a *think tank*,"[12] says Nola-Kate Seymoar, recently retired CEO of the International Centre for Sustainable Cities, which helps cities resolve problems related to urban growth. The participatory, consultative approach that characterizes the organization may be a holdover from Seymoar's very first job as a recreation director for underprivileged children in Edmonton, a job that she credits with teaching her the value of working cooperatively to achieve shared goals.[13]

Seymoar's academic background is as varied as her career has been since those early days on the playground. She has earned three interdisciplinary degrees: a B.A. in recreation administration, an M.A. in community development, and a Ph.D. in social psychology, with research interests focusing on communities and empowerment. She has since applied these credentials across a spectrum of private, public, and nonprofit organizations and in the academic sector. She was even an entrepreneur early in her career, starting three successful businesses in film, video, and interior design.

Throughout it all, Seymoar's main focus has been on communities, sustainability, and advocacy for youth and local-level empowerment. This is reflected, for example, in her work for the Alberta Department of Youth, the Arctic Children and Youth Foundation, and Sustainable Cities' new Youth Led Development Program. She has served on advisory committees and boards for many organizations and events, including the advisory committee for the World Urban Forum and the World Peace Forum, both held in Vancouver in 2006. She received a Global Citizen Award in 1995 and the Queen's Golden Jubilee Medal in 2002. She currently chairs Simon Fraser University's Urban Studies Advisory Council.

Seymoar was part of the multidisciplinary Vancouver team that won the Gold Prize in the 2003 International Gas Union's cities*PLUS* competition, profiled in the Central Case. After the competition, determined to maintain the momentum, Seymoar conceived and launched the Sustainable Cities International Network, which connects cities around the world that are engaged in long-term planning for sustainability. The network promotes city-to-city peer dialogue, enabling member communities to learn from one another's successes and setbacks. Seymoar continues to lead the Network.

Her connections with cities around the world led Seymoar into new project areas, such as her role as senior adviser to a two-year capacity-building project in Sri Lanka, called *Centering Women in Reconstruction and Governance*, working with a local organization, Sevanatha. The project was funded by the Canadian International Development Agency, GROOTS (Grass Roots Organizations Operating Together in Sisterhood), Beedie Construction, and local municipalities. It involved the participatory design and construction of community resource centres in Matara and Moratuwa, Sri Lanka. The centres are up and running and serve as community focal points for women-led activities.

She has worked on urban greening, urban waste management, community resiliency, and neighbourhood rehabilitation projects from Thailand to Turkey, China to South Africa, Poland to the Philippines. Nola-Kate Seymoar seems tireless in her commitment to community-level sustainability in the urban centres of the world. Our chances for urban sustainability and quality of life in cities are no doubt greater because of her efforts.

"Sustainability is about the future—the quality of life that will be possible for our grandchildren."—**Nola-Kate Seymoar**

Thinking About Environmental Perspectives

Thinking about the city nearest to where you live, what advice do you think this city could offer to, say, Beijing or Bangkok or Dar es Salaam with regard to sustainability, quality of life, and urban liveability? What kinds of advice from cities elsewhere in the world might be of benefit to your home city?

---

standards of living while reducing their environmental impacts, urban sustainability advocates suggest that cities follow an ecosystem-centred model by striving to

- Maximize efficient use of resources
- Recycle as much as possible
- Develop environmentally friendly technologies

- Account fully for external costs
- Offer tax incentives to encourage sustainable practices
- Use locally produced resources
- Use organic waste and wastewater to restore soil fertility
- Encourage urban agriculture

More and more cities are adopting these strategies. For instance, urban agriculture is a growing pursuit in many urban areas, from Cuba to Japan. Singapore produces all of its meat and 25% of its vegetable needs within its city limits. In Berlin, Germany, 80 000 people grow food in community gardens, and 16 000 more are on waiting lists.

Curitiba, Brazil, shows the kind of success that can result when a city invests in well-planned infrastructure. Besides the highly effective bus transportation network described earlier, the city provides recycling, environmental education, job training for the poor, and free health care. Surveys show that its citizens are unusually happy and better off economically than people living in other Brazilian cities.

In general, experts advise that developed countries should invest in resource-efficient technologies to reduce their impacts and enhance their economies, whereas developing countries should invest in basic infrastructure to improve health and living conditions. Successes in places from Vancouver to Curitiba suggest that cities need not be unsustainable. Indeed, because they affect the environment in some positive ways and have the potential for efficient resource use, cities can and should be a key element in achieving progress toward global sustainability.

Conclusion

As half the human population has shifted from rural to urban lifestyles in the relatively recent past, the nature of our impact on the environment has changed. As urban and suburban dwellers, our impacts are less direct but often more far-reaching. Resources must be delivered to us over long distances, requiring the use of still more resources. Limiting the waste of those resources by making our urban and suburban areas more sustainable will be vital for the future. Fortunately, the innovative cultural environment that cities foster has helped us develop solutions to alleviate impact and promote sustainability.

Part of seeking urban sustainability lies in making urban areas better places to live. One key component of these efforts involves expanding transportation options to relieve congestion and make cities run more efficiently. Another lies in ensuring access to adequate parklands and green spaces near and within our urban centres, to keep us from becoming wholly isolated from nature. Accomplishments in city and regional planning have made many cities more liveable than they once were, and we should be encouraged by such progress. Proponents of smart growth and the new urbanism believe they have solutions to the challenges posed by urban and suburban sprawl.

Continuing experimentation in cities from British Columbia to Brazil will help us determine how best to ensure that urban growth improves our quality of life and does not degrade the quality of our environment. With the continued urbanization of the world's population, it is important that we learn how to make cities work for both people and the environment.

REVIEWING OBJECTIVES

You should now be able to:

Describe the scale of urbanization

- The world's population is becoming predominantly urban.
- The shift from rural to urban living is driven largely by industrialization and is proceeding fastest now in the developing world.
- Nearly all future population growth will be in cities of the developing world.
- The geography of urban areas is changing as cities decentralize and suburbs grow and expand.

Assess urban and suburban sprawl

- Sprawl covers large areas of land with low-density development. Both population growth and increased per capita land use contribute to sprawl.
- Sprawl has resulted from the home-buying choices of individuals who prefer suburbs to cities, and it has been facilitated by government policy and technological developments.
- Sprawl may lead to negative impacts involving transportation, pollution, health, land use, natural habitat, and economics.

Outline city and regional planning and land use strategies

- City and regional planning and zoning are key tools for improving the quality of urban life.
- "Smart growth," urban growth boundaries, greenbelts, and the "new urbanism" attempt to recreate compact and vibrant urban spaces.

Evaluate transportation options

- Mass transit systems can enhance the efficiency of urban areas, but bus and train systems of different sizes bring different benefits.

Describe the roles of urban parks

- Urban parklands are vital for providing active recreation, soothing the stress of urban life, and keeping people in touch with natural areas.

Analyze environmental impacts and advantages of urban centres

- Cities are resource sinks with high per capita resource consumption. However, cities also allow natural lands to be preserved.
- Urban centres can maximize efficiency and help foster innovation that can lead to solutions for environmental problems.

Assess the pursuit of sustainable cities

- The linear mode of consumption and production is unsustainable, and more circular modes will be needed to create sustainable cities.

TESTING YOUR COMPREHENSION

1. What factors lie behind the shift of population from rural areas to urban areas? What types of cities and countries are experiencing the fastest urban growth today, and why?
2. Why have so many city dwellers in Canada, the United States, and other developed nations moved into suburbs?
3. Give two definitions of *sprawl*. Describe five negative impacts that have been suggested to result from sprawl.
4. What are city planning and regional planning? Contrast planning with zoning.
5. How are some people trying to prevent or slow sprawl? Describe some key elements of "smart growth." What effects, positive and negative, do urban growth boundaries tend to have?
6. Describe several apparent benefits of rail transit systems. What is a potential drawback?
7. How are city parks thought to make urban areas more liveable? What types of smaller spaces in cities can serve some of the functions of parks?
8. Why do urban dwellers tend to consume more resources per capita than rural dwellers?
9. Describe the connection between urban ecology and sustainable cities. List three actions a city can take to enhance its sustainability.
10. Name two positive effects of urban centres and intensification on the natural environment.

THINKING IT THROUGH

1. Assess the reasons that urban populations are increasing and that rural populations are stable or declining. Do you think these trends will continue in the future, or might they change for some reason?
2. Evaluate the causes of the spread of suburbs and of the environmental, social, and economic impacts of sprawl. Overall, do you think the spread of urban and suburban development that many people label *sprawl* is predominantly a good thing or a bad thing? Do you think it is inevitable? Give reasons for your answers.
3. Would you personally want to live in a neighbourhood developed in the style of the new urbanism? Would you like to live in a city or region with an urban growth boundary? Why or why not?

4. All things considered, do you feel that cities have a positive or a negative effect on environmental quality? How much do you feel we may be able to improve the sustainability of our urban areas?

5. Let's say that you are a person who aims to live in the most ecologically sustainable way you can. Which of the following places would you choose to live: in a high-rise apartment in a big city or on a 30-ha ranch abutting a national forest? Why? What considerations will you factor into your decision?

6. Imagine that after you graduate you are offered three equally desirable jobs, in three very different locations. If you take the first, you will live in the midst of a highly diverse but densely populated city. If you accept the second, you will live in a suburb where you have more space but where development and sprawl may soon surround you. If you select the third, you will live in a rural area with plenty of space and a beautiful natural environment, but you will have a long commute and few cultural amenities. Where would you choose to live? Why?

INTERPRETING GRAPHS AND DATA

In the accompanying graph, urban population density is used as an indicator of sprawl (lower density = more sprawl), and carbon emissions per capita provide some measure of the environmental impact of the transportation system on preferences for each of the cities represented.

1. Describe the relationship between urban density and carbon emissions, as shown in the graph.

2. Assuming that the standard of living is similar in these cities, to what might you attribute the relationship described in your answer to Question 1?

3. If zoning ordinances slowed urban sprawl and resulted in a doubling of urban population density in a city like Houston, Texas, how would you predict that carbon emissions per capita in that city might change? What about in Vancouver?

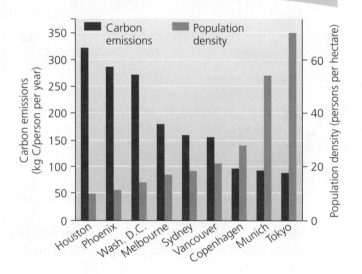

Population density versus carbon emissions from transportation in 1990.

Source: Data from Kenworthy, J., et al. (1999). An International Sourcebook of Automobile Dependence in Cities. Boulder, CO: University Press of Colorado, as cited by Sheehan, M. O. (2002). What Will It Take to Halt Sprawl? Washington, DC: Worldwatch Institute.

CHAPTER ENDNOTES

1. *The Economist*, Where the grass is greener: Cities in Australia and Canada are rated the most liveable in the world, August 22, 2007, www.economist.com/markets/rankings/displaystory.cfm?story_id=8908454&CFID=16415879&CFTOKEN=94552766

2. Vancouver Working Group of Western Economic Diversification Canada Discussion Paper, www.wdgc.ca/rpts/research/livable/2a_e.asp

3. Sustainable Cities International Network, http://sustainablecities.net/citiesnetwork

4. Vancouver Convention Centre, www.vancouverconventioncenter.com

5. UNFPA, *State of world population: Unleashing the potential of urban growth*, 2007, www.unfpa.org/swp/2007/english/introduction.html

6. Statistics Canada (2006) Census, *Summary Tables*, www40.statcan.ca/l01/cst01/demo62a.htm

7. Statistics Canada (2006) Census, *Summary Tables*, www40.statcan.ca/l01/cst01/demo05a.htm

8. Statistics Canada (2006) *Census Dictionary*, www12. statcan.ca/english/census06/reference/dictionary/index.cfm

9. Burchfield, Marcy, Henry G. Overman, Diego Puga, and Matthew A. Turner (2005) *Causes of sprawl: A portrait from space*, Working Paper, http://diegopuga. org/papers/sprawl.pdf

10. Carter-Whitney, Maureen (2008) *Ontario's Greenbelt in an international context: Comparing Ontario's greenbelt to its counterparts in Europe and North America*. Friends of the Greenbelt Foundation Occasional Paper Series. Toronto: Friends of the Greenbelt Foundation, p. 1, www.ourgreenbelt.ca/sites/ourgreenbelt.ca/files/CIELAPsmallerfile.pdf

11. City of Calgary (2008) *Toward a preferred future: Understanding Calgary's ecological footprint*, www. calgary.ca/docgallery/bu/environmental_management/ecological_footprint/towards_preferred_future.pdf

12. From Kowal, Jaime (2006) *Waking up the West: Healers and visionaries*. Vancouver: Catalyst Publications.

13. Tse, Catherine (2006) Swing shift: Nola-Kate Seymoar, International Centre for Sustainable Cities, *Shared Vision: Dialogue for Change*, August, www. shared-vision.com/20060817/swing_shift

MyEnvironmentPlace

Go to **www.myenvironmentplace.ca** where you will find quizzes, animations, your Pearson e text, and more.

Environmental Ethics and Economics: Values and Choices

21

This is an aerial view of Diavik Diamond Mine, Northwest Territories.

Upon successfully completing this chapter, you will be able to

- Characterize the influences of culture and world view on the choices people make

- Outline the nature, evolution, and expansion of environmental ethics in Western cultures

- Describe some basic precepts of economic theory and summarize their implications for the environment

- Compare the concepts of economic growth, economic health, and sustainability

- Explain the fundamentals of environmental economics, ecological economics, and natural resource accounting

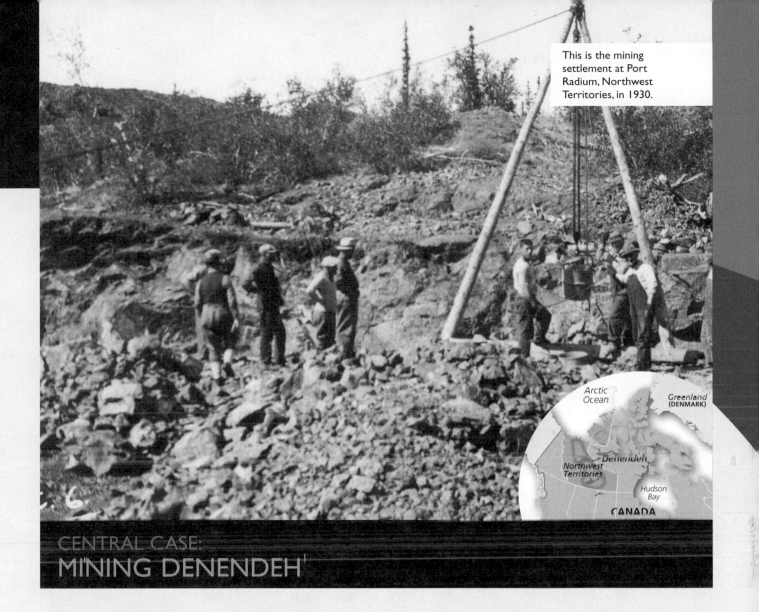

This is the mining settlement at Port Radium, Northwest Territories, in 1930.

Arctic Ocean

Greenland (DENMARK)

Denendeh

Northwest Territories

Hudson Bay

CANADA

CENTRAL CASE:
MINING DENENDEH[1]

"This forest is where our people have fished and trapped for generations—so we have this responsibility to take care of it, and that responsibility came from the elders, our ancestors, who told us to do whatever we have to do to protect the land."

—SOPHIA RABLIAUSKAS, GOLDMAN ENVIRONMENT PRIZE WINNER; POPLAR RIVER FIRST NATION COMMUNITY

"Let us not forget that, in the end, all economies, whether new or old, are built on foundations of access to land, natural wealth and resources."

—MATTHEW COON COME, FORMER GRAND CHIEF OF THE CREE NATION AND NATIONAL CHIEF OF THE ASSEMBLY OF FIRST NATIONS

The traditional lands of the Dene and Métis form the Northwest Territories of Canada, known as *Denendeh*. The people of Denendeh have mined, manufactured, and traded metals—especially copper—since long before the arrival of Europeans.

Industrial-scale mining has played a significant role in the history and development of the Northwest Territories since 1930, when the first modern mining operation, Eldorado uranium mine, was established at Port Radium on Great Bear Lake (*Sahtu*, in the Dene language; see map and photo). The Con and Giant gold mines, which began production at Yellowknife in 1938 and 1948, respectively, were important to the economy of the area for more than 50 years. Mining continues today in the North but the emphasis has shifted to diamonds, with the development of new mines like Ekati and Diavik, the first diamond mines in Canada.

Recent staking rushes in the Northwest Territories, particularly for diamonds, have generated concerns over unsettled land claims. For example, the public hearings of the Mackenzie Valley Environmental Impact Review Board for Wool Bay and Drybones Bay in 2003 centred

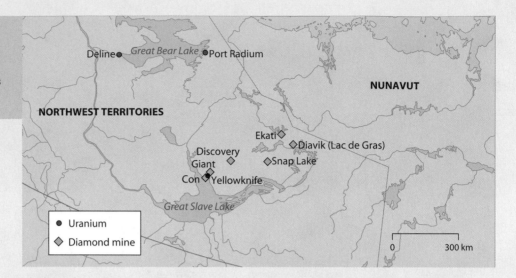

Great Bear Lake in the Northwest Territories was the site of uranium mining at the Eldorado Mine in Port Radium from 1930 until the 1960s. More recent diamond mining centres on an area to the northeast of Yellowknife.

on conflicts between unresolved Aboriginal land claims and mineral claims made by exploration companies. The environmental impact assessments halted exploration. The Dene claimed that their spiritual and cultural use of the land was in jeopardy. This included many practical issues, such as the locations of gravesites, as well as improperly managed waste materials from exploration. In this case, the Aboriginal rights and title to the land were given precedence over mining exploration.

The environmental, social, and economic impacts of past mining development in the North have been considerable, including contamination of land and water; devastating economic boom-and-bust cycles; influxes of large numbers of non-native temporary workers; and persistent health issues for workers and residents. An early case in the Aboriginal rights movement involved Eldorado's alleged discrimination against Dene workers, discussed later in this chapter, which came to light when former mine workers developed health problems that may have resulted from inadequate protection against radiation.

Mines can leave a legacy of contamination, and Canada's North is strewn with closed and abandoned mines. Discovery gold mine, 80 km northeast of Yellowknife (see map), began production in 1944 and closed in 1969. Left behind were uncontrolled tailings and waste rock piles, mercury and cyanide contamination of the nearby lake, and an abandoned and crumbling town site that was finally demolished in 2005.

Mining also can cause profound social and economic changes. The inability to maintain traditional food systems and cultural practices can undermine community health and wellness; impacts can include substance abuse and family breakdown. When Giant closed, the economic impacts on Yellowknife were devastating, causing housing prices to plummet. The recent diamond rush has created a new economic boom in Yellowknife and a construction push to house incoming workers, with the result that rents and housing prices are now some of the highest in Canada.

Today the life cycle of a mine, and the involvement of a mining company with a site and its people, no longer ends when the supply/demand for metal and minerals is depleted. Today, greater care is legally required when new mines are developed, to ensure that they will have minimal environmental, social, and health impacts. Mitigation, closure, and restoration plans, and financing for those plans, must be in place before a mine even begins production. The decision to transform an area into a mine comes with the responsibility of post-operational management and remediation, and a commitment to ongoing quality of life for workers and the community.

The new diamond mines at Ekati, Diavik, and Snap Lake have been designed so that, once mining is finished, the land will be reclaimed and restored. There will be no town, no permanent roads, no waste rock or tailings left behind. The new mines also distinguish themselves in the consideration they give to traditional knowledge, including learning from elders about environmental conditions, and applying this knowledge to construction, aquatic monitoring, and other aspects of mine management.

There is no single perspective or consensus on mining among Dene people today. Some call for greater involvement of Dene leaders in mine development. Some wish for a greater share of economic benefits and reduced risks. Others are concerned about the preservation of their land and culture. Decisions about mining in Canada's North must be based not only on scientific assessments but on social and cultural concerns as well. Mining in Denendeh provides an example of how values, beliefs, lifestyles, and traditions interact with economic interests to influence decisions about how to live within our environment.

Culture, World View, and the Environment

The Dene have an opportunity to gain substantial economic benefits by allowing mining to proceed on their lands, but they are cognizant of the long history of environmental and cultural damage associated with mining in Canada's North. Trade-offs in which economic benefits and social or ethical concerns appear to be in conflict crop up frequently in environmental issues. In this chapter we will examine some of the underlying causes of such conflicts, how they may be resolved, and how they influence the environmental choices we all make every day.

Culture, world view, and values influence our understanding of the environment

Environmental science examines Earth's natural systems, how they affect humans, and how humans affect them. To address environmental problems, however, requires input from disciplines beyond the natural sciences. It is necessary to understand how people perceive their environment, how they relate to it philosophically and pragmatically, and how they value its elements. Ethics and economics are quite different disciplines, but each deals with questions of what we value and how those values influence our decisions and actions. Anyone trying to address an environmental problem must try to understand not only how natural systems work but also how values shape human behaviour. Every action we take affects our environment. Growing food requires soil, cultivation, and irrigation. Building homes requires land, lumber, and metal. Manufacturing and fuelling vehicles require metal, plastic, glass, and petroleum. From nutrition to housing to transportation, we meet our needs by withdrawing resources and altering our surroundings. Decisions about how we manipulate and exploit our environment to meet our needs depend in part on rational assessments of costs and benefits.

Our decisions are also heavily influenced by the culture of which we are a part, and by our particular world view. Culture—the ensemble of knowledge, beliefs, values, and learned ways of life shared by a group of people—together with personal experience, influences each person's perception of the world and his or her place within it, something described as the person's world view. A world view reflects a person's (or group's) beliefs about the meaning, operation, and essence of the world.

People with different world views can study the same situation and review identical data yet draw dramatically different conclusions. For example, many well-meaning people support mining in Canada's North, while many other well-meaning people oppose it. The officers, employees, and shareholders of the mining companies, and the government officials who support mining, view it as a source of jobs, income, energy, and economic growth. They believe mining will benefit the North in general and the Dene in particular. Opponents, in contrast, foresee environmental problems and negative social consequences. They recognize that mining disturbs the landscape and can pollute air and water, while community disruption, substance abuse, and crime can accompany mining booms.

In Australia, too, there have been conflicts between corporations seeking to develop mining operations and Aboriginal people trying to maintain their traditional culture. One such group is the Mirrar Clan (see "The Science Behind the Story: The Mirrar Clan Confronts the Jabiluka Uranium Mine").

Uranium mining is a key contributor to Australia's economy; however, many of Australia's uranium deposits occur on Aboriginal lands in the remote region of Kakadu. When a company proposed to open a new uranium mine on their land, the Mirrar fought back. They saw the mine as a threat not only to their health and the integrity of the environment but also to their culture and religion, which are deeply tied to the landscape. The proposed mine site is near traditional hunting and gathering sites, in the floodplain of a river that provides the clan with food and water. Like many other Aborigines, the Mirrar hold the landscape to be sacred, and they depend on its resources for their daily needs.

The Mirrar Clan Confronts the Jabiluka Uranium Mine

These protestors rallied against the proposed Jabiluka uranium mine.

"The Jabiluka uranium mine will improve the quality of the environment."—Michael Darby, Australian political commentator

"My country is in danger."—Yvonne Margarula, senior traditional land owner, Mirrar Clan and Goldman Environment Prize winner; to the U.N. World Heritage Committee, 1998

The remote Kakadu region of Australia's Northern Territory is home to several groups of **Aborigines**, the native or **indigenous** people who lived there before British colonization. The region features Kakadu National Park (see photo), a World Heritage Site recognized by the United Nations for its irreplaceable natural and cultural resources. The land also holds uranium, a naturally occurring radioactive metal valued for its use in nuclear power plants, nuclear weapons, and medical and industrial tools. Uranium mining is a key contributor to the Australian national economy, accounting for 7% of Australia's economic output.

The occurrence of uranium deposits on Aboriginal land has led to conflicts between corporations seeking to develop mining operations and Aboriginal people trying to maintain their traditional culture. One such group is the Mirrar Clan, an extended family of Kakadu-area Aborigines. The Mirrar have been living with the region's first uranium mine, the Ranger mine, since the Australian government approved its development on their land in 1978.

When the corporate owners of Ranger proposed to open another uranium mine, Jabiluka, on their land, the Mirrar launched into an environmental battle that would rage over a number of years and several continents. The Mirrar viewed Jabiluka as a threat to their health and to the integrity of their environment, particularly given repeated radioactive spills at the Ranger mine. Many feared that contaminated water would be released into area creeks and that radioactive radon gas would emanate from stored waste materials. Moreover, mindful of geologic faults in the area, the Mirrar worried that dams holding mine waste could fail catastrophically in an earthquake. "We are talking about a uranium mine inside our largest national park," said Peter Robertson, coordinator of the Environment Centre of the Northern Territory at the time. "This is not a place to cut corners."[2]

Environmental activists worldwide joined the Mirrar's struggle. In 1998 nearly 3000 people travelled to the Kakadu region to protest Jabiluka. In late 2002 their efforts finally succeeded. Sir Robert Wilson, chief executive officer of Rio Tinto, the corporation holding rights to the ore body, announced the cancellation of mining plans at Jabiluka, citing economic factors (declining world uranium prices) and ethical factors (concerns about developing the mine without Mirrar consent). The company agreed to rehabilitate the site and restore damage done during exploration and assessment.

Since that time, the price of uranium has risen on the world market. The corporation's plans are now in a holding pattern as it waits and hopes that the Mirrar will one day give their consent. In 2007 the new CEO of Rio Tinto, Tom Albanese, reiterated the company's intention not to pressure the government for approval to develop Jabiluka without the prior informed consent of the traditional landowners.[3] **Prior informed consent**, one of the hallmark principles of modern environmental ethics, means that consent or acceptance of an activity (such as land development or waste disposal) is not legally valid unless the consenting person or group has been properly and adequately informed *and* can be shown to have a reasonable understanding of all potential impacts before giving consent.

The Mirrar opposed the mine development despite the economic benefits promised to them in the form of jobs, income, development, and a higher material standard of living. The decision to bypass these economic incentives was not easy; indeed, other Aboriginal groups in the Kakadu region supported the mine development. In formulating their approaches to the mining proposal, they had to weigh economic, social, cultural, and philosophical questions as well as scientific ones.

This is Kakadu National Park, Australia, where Aboriginal residents, environmentalists, and mining companies have battled over mining rights.

weighing the issues

ECOIMPERIALISM?

The Mirrar Clan opposed the development of the Jabiluka uranium mine on their land, in spite of potential economic benefits. They were supported by an extensive international network of environmentalists. How do you think those environmentalists would have reacted if the Mirrar, having gained self-determination over their land, had changed their position and opted to approve the mine? Do you believe that the right to self-determination *obliges* Aboriginal people to retain their traditional way of life and preserve the integrity of their ancestral lands?

(a) Ranger Uranium Mine, Kakadu region, Australia

(b) Voisey's Bay Nickel Mine, northern Labrador, Canada

FIGURE 21.1
The Ranger mine **(a)**, located on Australian Aboriginal lands amid sacred sites, caused enough environmental impacts to spark fierce opposition to the proposed Jabiluka mine nearby. **(b)** The Voisey's Bay mine and concentrator site in northern Labrador faced similar challenges from both Innu Nation and Nunatsiavut Government. The mine's owner, Vale, negotiated special agreements with the two Aboriginal groups prior to the opening of the mine, dealing with land rights, social and economic considerations, and numerous environmental concerns.[5]

Many factors shape our world views and perception of the environment

The traditional culture and world view of the Mirrar Clan helped shape its response to the proposed Jabiluka mine. Australian Aborigines view the landscape around them as the physical embodiment of stories that express the beliefs and values central to their culture. The landscape to them is a sacred text. They believe that spirit ancestors travelled routes called "dreaming tracks," leaving signs and lessons in the landscape. By explaining the origins of specific landscape features, dreaming-track stories assign meaning to notable landmarks and help Aborigines construct detailed mental maps of their surroundings. The stories also teach lessons concerning family relations, hunting, food gathering, and conflict resolution. The Mirrar who opposed the Jabiluka uranium mine believed that it would desecrate sacred sites and compromise their culture (**FIGURE 21.1**).

Similarly, many Aboriginal people of Canada's North, including the Dene and Innu, believe that the landscape is inhabited by spirits, both benevolent and malevolent, and thus must be honoured and protected.[4] They worry that mining may have negative impacts on their lands, traditional hunting routes, water sources, or resource-gathering sites. There is also concern that noise, disruption, and emissions from such operations might cause harm to sacred animals or to sites that have spiritual or cultural significance.

Religion and spiritual beliefs are among many factors that can shape people's world views and perception of the environment. A community may also share a particular view of the environment if its members have lived through similar experiences. For example, European Christian settlers in both Australia and North America viewed their environment as a hostile force because inclement weather, wild animals, and other natural forces frequently destroyed crops, killed livestock, and took settlers' lives. Such experiences were shared in stories and in songs and helped shape social attitudes in frontier communities. The view of nature as a hostile force and an adversary to be overcome passed from one generation to the next and still influences the way many North Americans and Australians view their surroundings.

Political ideology also shapes a person's worldview and attitude toward the environment. For instance, one's

weighing the issues

MINING IN MECCA . . . ?

Suppose a mining company discovered uranium near the Sacred Mosque at Mecca—or the site in Bethlehem believed to be the birthplace of Jesus, or the Wailing Wall in Jerusalem. What do you think would happen if the company announced plans to develop a mine close to one of these sacred locations, assuring the public that environmental impacts would be minimal and that the mine would create jobs and stimulate economic growth? Which aspects of these unlikely situations resemble that of the Jabiluka case, and which are different?

views on the role of government will influence whether or not one wants government to intervene in a market economy to protect environmental quality. Economic factors also sway how people perceive their environment and make decisions. An individual with a strong interest in the outcome of a decision that may result in his or her private gain or loss is said to have a *vested interest*. Mining company executives and shareholders have a vested interest in a decision to open an area to mining because a new mine can increase profits. Vested interests may lead people to view a proposed mine as a source of economic gain, while minimizing (whether consciously or subconsciously) the potential for negative environmental impacts.

There are many ways to understand the environment

An interesting aspect of the relationship of indigenous peoples with their local environment is **traditional ecological knowledge (TEK)**, or *indigenous ecological knowledge,* intimate knowledge of a particular environment possessed and passed along by those who have inhabited an area for many generations.[6] Examples include knowledge of the medicinal properties of local plants; wintering-over or migration habits of local animals; local geographic and microclimatic variations; or the sequence of tasks required to carry out a traditional task, such as trapping and butchering a large animal. Such a deep understanding is gained through generations of hunters, fishers, gatherers, and harvesters sharing their knowledge of the natural world, usually by way of oral teachings, songs, and storytelling.

In some circumstances, TEK can be assigned a market value. For example, indigenous knowledge of local plants might be extremely valuable to a pharmaceutical company searching for plants with modern medicinal applications. In recent years the value of TEK has become more widely recognized, acknowledged, and remunerated by governments and industry. The Nunavut Wildlife Management Board, which meets annually to set limits on the annual polar bear hunt for Inuit traditional hunters, receives and weighs information from government scientists and from the hunters themselves as part of the decision-making process.

Throughout this book you have encountered scientific data regarding the environmental impacts of our choices (where to make our homes, how to make a living, what to wear, what to eat, how to travel, how to spend our leisure time, and so on). Culture, world views, and values play critical roles in such choices and even can influence the interpretation of scientific data. Thus, acquiring a foundation of scientific understanding is only one part of the search for solutions to environmental problems. Attention to ethics and economics helps us understand why and how we value those things we value.

Environmental Ethics

The field of **ethics** is a branch of philosophy that involves the study of good and bad, right and wrong. The term *ethics* can also refer to the set of moral principles or values held by a person or a society. Ethicists help clarify how people judge right from wrong by elucidating the criteria, standards, or rules that people use in making these judgments. Such criteria are grounded in values— for instance, promoting human welfare, maximizing individual freedom, or minimizing pain and suffering.

People of different cultures or with different world views may differ in their fundamental values and thus may differ in the specific actions they consider to be right or wrong. Ethical standards help differentiate right

roots

ETHICS

The word **ethics**, referring to the study of good and bad, as well as to an individual's or society's set of morals, is thought to derive from the Greek *ethike philosophia,* "moral philosophy." Related words are the Greek *ethikos,* meaning "customs," and *ethos* or *thos,* meaning "character."

weighing the issues

THE ATLANTIC SEAL HUNT

No environmental issue identified with Canada is more emotionally charged than the Atlantic seal hunt. Each year environmentalists and animal activists mobilize to try to stop the hunt, arguing that too many seals are killed, and that the methods used are inhumane. The hunters and supporters counter that they are continuing a way of life that has been practised by Aboriginal people in Canada for at least 4000 years, that it is their right to practise their traditional ways, and that the hunt is vital for the economic well-being and survival of their communities.

What do you think? Who should decide which of these sets of values—animal rights or Aboriginal self-determination—should take precedence?

---

from wrong across different cultures and situations. One classic ethical standard is the *categorical imperative* proposed by philosopher Immanuel Kant, which roughly approximates the "golden rule" common to many of the world's great religions. For example, Hindus learn that they should "not do to others what would cause pain if done to you"; a central tenet of Buddhism is to "hurt not others in ways that you yourself would find hurtful"; and Christians are encouraged to "do unto others as you would have others do unto you." The universality of the golden rule or categorical imperative makes it a fundamental ethical standard.

Another ethical standard is the principle of *utility*, elaborated by British philosopher John Stuart Mill, among others. The **utilitarian principle** holds that something is right when it produces the greatest practical benefits for the most people. For example, a utilitarian might argue that forest biodiversity should be conserved because the possibility exists that a cure for cancer might be found there among the naturally occurring biological compounds. The argument that forest species should be preserved because they have an *intrinsic value*, or an inherent right to exist, would be much less convincing to a utilitarian. This is particularly true in the context of marine protected areas, which are often justified on the basis of utilitarian ends.

Environmental ethics pertains to humans and the environment

The application of ethical standards to relationships between humans and nonhuman entities is known as **environmental ethics.** This branch of ethics arose once people began to perceive environmental changes brought about by industrialization. Human interactions with the environment frequently give rise to ethical questions that can be difficult to resolve. Consider some examples:

1. Does the present generation have an obligation to conserve resources for future generations? If so, how should this influence our decision making, and how much are we obligated to sacrifice?
2. Are there situations that justify exposing some communities to a disproportionate share of pollution? If not, what actions are warranted in preventing this problem? By extension, if a certain community stands to gain the most from a particular activity, should that community be expected to take on most of the risk associated with the activity?
3. Are humans justified in driving species to extinction? Are we justified in causing other permanent changes in ecological systems? If destroying a forest would drive extinct an insect species few people have heard of, but would create jobs for 10 000 people, would that action be ethically admissible? What if it were an owl species, or an ape, or a whale? What if only 100 jobs would be created? What if it were a species that is harmful to humans, such as mosquitoes? What about a bacterium or a virus?

The intergenerational question—whether we owe consideration to those who will live on this planet and make use of its resources years from now—is of particular interest. The most common definition of **sustainable development** says that we must meet our current needs without compromising the availability of natural resources or the quality of life for future generations. But how can we tell what future generations may need or want, or what they will value or hold sacred?

In 2007 and 2008 construction crews began digging trenches for the laying of an oil pipeline extension through pristine wilderness areas of Jasper National Park and Mount Robson Provincial Park in the Canadian Rockies. The extension, which will allow for the movement of an extra 40 000 barrels of oil each day from Alberta to markets in the United States, was approved in 1952. If the pipeline extension had been requested today, it is highly unlikely that it would have been approved because of the environmental disruption involved. Would it have been possible to know, in 1952, how this decision would be viewed more than 50 years later? And how can we determine how the environmental decisions that we make today will be viewed 50 years into the future?

We extend ethical consideration to non-human entities

Answers to questions like those above depend partly on what ethical standard(s) a person chooses to use. They also depend on the breadth and inclusiveness of the person's domain of ethical concern. A person who feels responsibility for the welfare of insects would answer the third question very differently from a person whose domain of ethical concern ends with humans. Most of us feel moral obligations to some entities in the world but by no means to all.

Throughout the history of Western cultures, people have gradually enlarged the array of entities they feel deserve ethical consideration. The enslavement of human beings by other human beings was common in many societies until recently, for instance. Women were not allowed to vote in Canada until 1916 (even then, only in Manitoba), and many still receive lower pay for equal work. Consider, too, how little ethical consideration citizens of one nation generally extend to those of another on which their government has declared war. Human societies are only now beginning to embrace the principle that all people should be granted equal ethical consideration.

Our expanding domain of ethical concern has begun to include nonhuman entities as well. Mahatma Gandhi reportedly said, "The greatness of a nation and its moral progress can be judged by the way its animals are treated." Concern for the welfare of domesticated animals is evident today in humane societies and in the way many people provide for their pets. Animal-rights activists voice concern for animals that are hunted or used in laboratory testing. Most people now accept that wild animals (at least obviously sentient animals, such as primates and other large vertebrates, with which we share similarities) merit ethical consideration.

Today many environmentalists are concerned not only with certain animals but also with the well-being of whole natural communities. Some have gone still further, suggesting that all of nature—living and nonliving things, even rocks—should be ethically represented (**FIGURE 21.2**). If you think this is a silly idea, consider how you might react if someone put a fast-food restaurant on the top of Mt. Everest, or if a multinational corporation decided to paint a gigantic corporate logo on the Moon. Do the unique landmarks of the natural environment deserve ethical consideration? Do they have any inherent value, or the "right" to exist unaltered? Is their value distinct from the services they may render to humans, or inseparable from human interests? These questions are all worth considering.

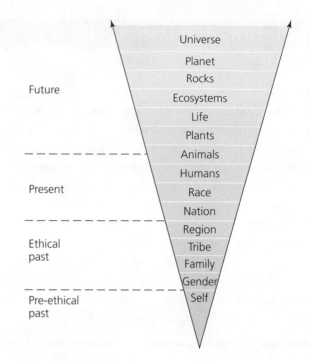

FIGURE 21.2
Through time, people in Western cultures have broadened the scope of their ethical consideration for others. We can view ethics progressing through time in a generalized way outward from the self.

What is behind this ongoing expansion of ethical consideration? Rising economic prosperity in Western cultures, as people became less anxious about their day-to-day survival, has helped enlarge our ethical domain. Science has also played a role in demonstrating that humans do not stand apart from nature but rather are part of it. Ecology, as it has developed over the past 75 years, has made clear that all organisms are interconnected, and what affects plants, animals, and ecosystems can in turn affect humans. Evolutionary biology has shown that humans are merely one species out of millions and have evolved subject to the same pressures as other organisms.

For many non-Western cultures, expansive ethical domains are nothing new. Many traditional cultures have long granted ethical standing to nonhuman entities. Aborigines, like the Mirrar, Innu, and Dene, who view their landscape as sacred and alive, are a case in point. However, it is worthwhile to examine Western ethical expansion because it underlies so many of modern secular society's beliefs and actions regarding the environment. We can simplify the continuum of attitudes toward the natural world by dividing it into three ethical perspectives: anthropocentrism, biocentrism, and ecocentrism.

Anthropocentrism   **Anthropocentrism** takes a human-centred view of our relationship with the environment. An anthropocentrist denies or ignores the notion that nonhuman entities can have rights, and measures the costs and benefits of actions solely according to their impact on people (**FIGURE 21.3**). To evaluate an action that affects the environment, an anthropocentrist might use such criteria as impacts on human health, economic costs and benefits, and aesthetic concerns.

For example, if a mine provides a net economic benefit while doing no harm to human health and having little aesthetic impact, the anthropocentrist would conclude it was a worthwhile venture, even if it might drive some native species extinct. If protecting the area would provide spiritual, economic, or other benefits to humans now or in the future, an anthropocentrist might favour its protection. In the anthropocentric perspective, anything not providing benefit to people is considered to be of negligible value.

Biocentrism   In contrast to anthropocentrism, **biocentrism** ascribes values to actions, entities, or properties on the basis of their effects on all living things or on the integrity of the biotic realm in general (see **FIGURE 21.3**). In this perspective, all life has ethical standing. A biocentrist evaluates actions in terms of their overall impact on living things, including—but not exclusively focusing on—human beings. In the case of a mine proposal, a biocentrist might oppose the mine if it posed a serious threat to the abundance and variety of living things in the area, even if it would create jobs, generate economic growth, and pose no threat to human health. Some biocentrists advocate equal consideration of all living things, whereas others advocate that some types of organisms should receive more than others.

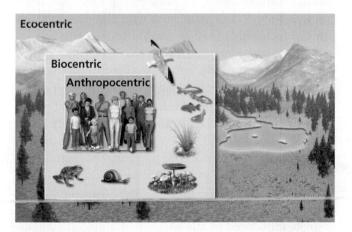

FIGURE 21.3
An anthropocentrist extends ethical standing only to humans and judges actions in terms of their effects on humans. A biocentrist values and considers all living things, human and otherwise. An ecocentrist extends ethical consideration to living and nonliving components of the environment. The ecocentrist also takes a holistic view of the connections among these components, valuing the larger functional systems of which they are a part.

Ecocentrism   **Ecocentrism** judges actions in terms of their benefit or harm to the integrity of whole ecological systems, which consist of biotic and abiotic elements and the relationships among them (see **FIGURE 21.3**). An ecocentrist would value the well-being of entire species, communities, or ecosystems over the welfare of a given individual. Implicit in this view is that the preservation of larger systems generally protects their components, whereas selective protection of the components may not always safeguard the entire system. Ecocentrism is a *holistic* perspective. Not only does it encompass a wide variety of entities, but it also stresses preserving the connections that tie the entities together into functional systems.

Environmental ethics has ancient roots

Environmental ethics arose as an academic discipline in the early 1970s, but people have contemplated our relationship with nature for thousands of years. Ancient Aboriginal oral traditions and dreaming-track stories treat the environment as a source of sacred teachings, worthy of contemplation and protection. In the Jain Dharma, one of the oldest religious traditions in the world, compassion for all life—human and nonhuman— is a core belief. Jains are typically vegetarian or vegan and try to avoid foods obtained with unnecessary cruelty; for some, this even involves refusing to eat root vegetables (such as potatoes and onions) to avoid killing the plant from which they were obtained. In the Western tradition, the ancient Greek philosopher Plato expressed what he considered humans' moral obligation to the environment, writing, "The land is our ancestral home and we must cherish it even more than children cherish their mother."

Some ethicists and theologians have pointed to the religious traditions of Christianity, Judaism, and Islam as sources of anthropocentric hostility toward the environment. They point out biblical passages such as, "Be fruitful and multiply, and fill the earth and subdue it; and have dominion over the fish of the sea and over the birds of the air and over every living thing that moves upon the earth." Such wording has justified and encouraged separation from and animosity toward nature over the centuries, some scholars say. Others emphasize sacred texts that encourage benevolent human stewardship over nature. Consider the directive, "You shall not defile the land in which you live. . . ." Although people have held differing views of their ethical relationship with the environment for millennia, environmental impacts that became apparent during the Industrial Revolution intensified debate about our relationship with the environment.

The Industrial Revolution inspired environmental philosophers

As the Industrial Revolution spread from Great Britain throughout Europe and elsewhere, its technological advances and resultant population growth amplified human impacts on the environment. In this period of social and economic transformation, agricultural economies became industrialized, machines enhanced or replaced human and animal labour, and much of the rural population moved into cities. Consumption of natural resources accelerated, and pollution increased dramatically as coal combustion fuelled railroads, steamships, ironworks, and factories.

Many writers and philosophers of the time criticized industrialization. British critic John Ruskin (1819–1900) called cities "little more than laboratories for the distillation into heaven of venomous smokes and smells." He complained that people prized the material benefits that nature could provide, but no longer appreciated its spiritual and aesthetic benefits. A number of citizens' groups sprang up in nineteenth-century England that could be considered some of the first environmental organizations. These included the Commons Preservation Society, the Coal Smoke Abatement Society, and the Selborne League, dedicated to the protection of rare plants, birds, and landscapes.

During the 1840s, a philosophical movement called *transcendentalism* flourished, espoused by American philosophers Ralph Waldo Emerson and Henry David Thoreau and poet Walt Whitman. The transcendentalists viewed nature as a direct manifestation of the divine, emphasizing the soul's oneness with nature and God. They objected to what they saw as their fellow citizens' obsession with material things. Through their writings the transcendentalists promoted a holistic view of nature. They identified a need to experience wild nature and portrayed natural entities as symbols or messengers of a deeper truth. Thoreau viewed nature as divine, but he also observed the natural world closely, in the manner of a scientist; he was in many ways one of the first ecologists. His book *Walden*, in which he recorded his observations and thoughts while he lived at Walden Pond away from the bustle of urban Massachusetts, is a classic of philosophical and environmental literature.

Conservation and preservation arose at the start of the twentieth century

One admirer of Emerson and Thoreau was John Muir (1838–1914), a Scottish immigrant who eventually settled in California and made the Yosemite Valley his wilder-

FIGURE 21.4

A pioneering advocate of the preservation ethic, John Muir is remembered for his efforts to protect the Sierra Nevada from development and for his role in founding the Sierra Club. Muir (right) is shown with President Theodore Roosevelt in Yosemite National Park. After his 1903 wilderness camping trip with Muir, the president instructed his interior secretary to increase protected areas in the Sierra Nevada.

ness home. Although Muir chose to live in isolation in his beloved Sierra Nevada for long stretches of time, he nonetheless became politically active and won fame as a tireless advocate for the preservation of wilderness (**FIGURE 21.4**).

Muir was motivated by the rapid deforestation and environmental degradation he witnessed throughout North America and by his belief that the natural world should be treated with the same respect that cathedrals receive. Today he is associated with the **preservation ethic**, which holds that we should protect the natural environment in a pristine, unaltered state. Muir argued that nature deserved protection for its own inherent value (an ecocentrist argument), but he also maintained that nature played a large role in human happiness and fulfillment (an anthropocentrist argument). "Everybody needs beauty as well as bread," he wrote in his 1912 work *The Yosemite*, "places to play in and pray in, where nature may heal and give strength to body and soul alike."

Canadian James Bernard Harkin (1875–1955) also believed in preserving the beauty of nature. He was strongly influenced by the writings of Muir, his contemporary. Harkin was the first commissioner of Dominion Parks (which eventually became Parks Canada) and is credited with saving vast areas of Canadian wilderness from development (**FIGURE 21.5**). He believed in the spiritual, healing, and restorative power of nature. He was drawn to mountains, which, he said, "elevate the mind and purify the spirit." Harkin believed that setting aside land

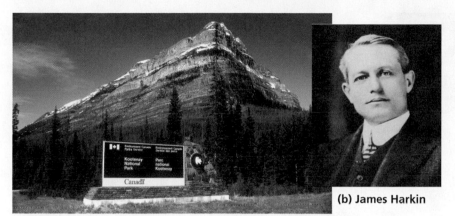

FIGURE 21.5
Kootenay National Park **(a)** was designated as a national park in 1920. It was one of 11 national parks designated during the tenure of James Harkin **(b)** as Canada's commissioner of Dominion Parks. Mount Harkin in the Mitchell Range is named in his honour.

(b) James Harkin

(a) Kootenay National Park

as national parks was only the beginning of preservation; the real challenge would be to maintain them as wilderness. Resource extraction and even some vehicle use were limited in national parks during his service, and he came to be known as the "Father of National Parks" of Canada.[7]

Some of the factors that motivated Muir and Harkin also inspired American forester Gifford Pinchot (1865–1946), who opposed rapid deforestation and unregulated economic development of land. However, Pinchot took a more anthropocentric view of how and why nature should be valued. He is today the person most closely associated with the **conservation ethic**, which holds that humans should put natural resources to use but also that we have a responsibility to manage them wisely. Whereas preservation aims to preserve nature for its own sake, conservation promotes the prudent, efficient, and sustainable extraction and use of natural resources for the benefit of present and future generations. The conservation ethic uses a utilitarian standard, stating that in using resources, humans should attempt to provide the greatest good to the greatest number of people for the longest time.

Pinchot's counterpart in Canada was Clifford Sifton (1861–1929), a controversial politician and conservationist. As minister of the interior, Sifton aggressively lured immigrants to settle and farm in the West; he was deeply committed to the agricultural development of land as Canada's principal natural resource—not an obvious conservationist position. However, Sifton was also a "champion" of Canada's natural resources, and was particularly devoted to forest conservation and reforestation. He was the first chairman of the Commission for the Conservation of Natural Resources, which undertook detailed inventories of Canadian natural resources.[8]

Conservation and preservation are rooted in fundamentally different ethical approaches, which often meant that advocates were pitted against one another on policy issues of the day. Nonetheless, both branches represented reactions against the prevailing "frontier development ethic," which held that humans should be masters of nature, and which promoted economic development without regard to its negative consequences. Those who led the conservation and preservation movements in the nineteenth and early twentieth centuries left legacies that reverberate today in our ethical approaches to the environment.

The land ethic and deep ecology enlarged ethical boundaries

As a young forester and wildlife manager, Aldo Leopold (1887–1949) **(FIGURE 21.6)** began his career as a conservationist. At first, he embraced the government policy of shooting predators, such as wolves, to increase populations of deer and other game animals. At the same time, however, Leopold was following the development of ecological science. He eventually ceased to view certain species as "good" or "bad" and instead came to see that healthy ecological systems depend on the protection of all their interacting parts, including predators as well as prey. Drawing an analogy to mechanical maintenance, he wrote, "to keep every cog and wheel is the first precaution of intelligent tinkering."

Leopold argued that humans should view themselves and "the land" as members of the same community, and that people are obliged to treat the land in an ethical manner based on mutual respect. In his 1949 essay "The Land Ethic," he wrote:

> All ethics so far evolved rest upon a single premise: that the individual is a member of a community of interdependent parts . . . The land ethic simply enlarges the boundaries of the community to include soils, waters, plants, and animals, or collectively: the land . . . A land ethic changes the role of Homo sapiens from conqueror of the land-community to plain member and citizen of it.[9]

FIGURE 21.6
Aldo Leopold, wildlife manager and pioneering environmental philosopher, articulated a new relationship between people and the environment. In his essay "The Land Ethic," he called on people to include the environment in their ethical framework.

Leopold intended that the land ethic would help guide decision making. "A thing is right," he wrote in his 1949 book *A Sand County Almanac*, "when it tends to preserve the integrity, stability, and beauty of the biotic community. It is wrong when it tends otherwise." Many today view Aldo Leopold as the most eloquent and important philosopher of environmental ethics.

One philosophical perspective that goes beyond even ecocentrism is **deep ecology**, which emerged in the 1970s. Proponents describe the movement as resting on principles of "self-realization" and biocentric equality. They define self-realization as the awareness that humans are inseparable from nature and that the air we breathe, the water we drink, and the foods we consume are both products of the environment and integral parts of us. Biocentric equality is the concept that all living beings have equal value and that because we are truly inseparable from our environment, we should protect all living things as we would protect ourselves.

Ecofeminists see parallels between the oppression of nature and of women

As deep ecology and mainstream environmentalism were extending people's ethical domains during the 1960s and 1970s, major social movements, such as the civil rights movement and the feminist movement, were gaining prominence. A number of feminist scholars saw parallels in human behaviour toward nature and men's behaviour toward women. The degradation of nature and the social oppression of women shared common roots, these scholars asserted.

Ecofeminism argues that the patriarchal (male-dominated) structure of society—which traditionally grants more power and prestige to men than to women—is a root cause of both social and environmental problems. Ecofeminists hold that a world view traditionally associated with women, which interprets the world in terms of interrelationships and cooperation, is more compatible with nature than a world view traditionally associated with men, which interprets the world in terms of hierarchies and competition. Ecofeminists maintain that a tendency to try to dominate and conquer has historically been exercised against both women and the natural environment.

One of the most interesting environmental movements of our time is Chipko Andolan, which had its philosophical grounding in the principles of Gandhian nonviolent resistance, grassroots social activism, and ecofeminism.[10] Chipko emerged in the early 1970s in the northern Uttarakhand region of India, as an effort to stop clear-cutting from decimating the vast forests of northern India. The movement came to a climax in 1973, when government workers turned up unannounced to cut trees but were met by a group of village women who refused to allow the work to proceed (**FIGURE 21.7A**). Leader Gaura Devi reportedly stated, "The forest is like our mother. You will have to shoot us before you can cut it down." The women stood watch over the forest, wrapping their arms around the trees. Eventually, after considerable negotiation, the government declared the region to be an environmentally "sensitive" area. Today, Chipko is an international icon of grassroots environmentalism.

roots

CHIPKO

The name **Chipko Andolan** ("Chipko Movement") comes from the Hindi root word *chipka*, "stick" or "cling" or "embrace" (related to *chipku*, "hanger-on"). *Andolan* is Hindi for a "movement" or "campaign." Its use by the women of northern Uttarakhand in their nonviolent resistance against logging may have been the origin of the term *tree-hugger*, commonly used (often condescendingly) in reference to environmentalists.

(a) Villagers placed their bodies between the trees and the contractor's axes.

(b) Wangari Maathai

FIGURE 21.7 In the early 1970s, grassroots resistance efforts by village women led to the establishment of the Chipko Movement, dedicated to preventing deforestation in northern India's Himalayan foothills **(a)**. The founder of Kenya's Green Belt Movement, Professor Wangari Maathai **(b)** was awarded the Nobel Peace Prize in 2004 for her work to empower women and fight deforestation; she died in 2011.

Another movement rooted in ecofeminism and the empowerment of the poor is the Green Belt Movement of Kenya. This organization, which began by paying impoverished village women to plant tree seedlings, was founded in 1977. The Nobel Peace Prize was awarded to Green Belt's founder, Wangari Maathai, in 2004 (**FIGURE 21.7B**).[11]

Environmental justice seeks equitable access to resources and protection from environmental degradation

Our society's domain of ethical concern has been expanding from rich to poor and from majority races and ethnic groups to minority ones. This ethical expansion involves applying a standard of fairness and equality and has given rise to the environmental justice movement. **Environmental justice** is based on the principle that all people—regardless of race, colour, national origin, or income—have the right to live and work in a clean, healthy environment; to receive protection from the risks and impacts of environmental degradation, and to

be compensated for having suffered such impacts; and to have equitable access to environmental resources of high quality.

The environmental justice movement is fuelled by the fact that the poor and minorities tend to be exposed to a greater share of pollution, hazards, and environmental degradation than are richer people and whites. This has been supported by scientific research (**FIGURE 21.8**). For example, studies have found the percentage of minorities in areas with toxic waste sites to be twice that in areas without toxic waste sites. Researchers in many parts of the world who study air pollution, lead poisoning, pesticide exposure, and workplace hazards have found similar patterns.

A protest in the early 1980s by African Americans in Warren County, North Carolina, against a toxic waste dump in their community is widely seen as the beginning of the movement in North America. The state had chosen to site the dump in the county with the highest percentage of blacks, prompting residents to suspect "environmental racism." Environmental justice grew in prominence as more people began fighting environmental hazards in their communities.

The early environmental justice movement—like the Chipko and Green Belt movements internationally but

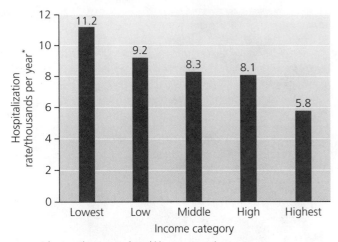

FIGURE 21.8

Many studies have demonstrated links between exposure to pollution and socioeconomic status. This is demonstrated by a graph comparing incidences of hospitalization for respiratory illnesses—a common health impact of exposure to environmental pollutants—among children of different income levels in Toronto.

in contrast to early environmental movements in North America—was made up largely of low-income people and minorities. Today the movement has broadened to encompass worker health and safety; education and financial services for preparation for, response to, and recovery from natural disasters; and access to land, water, and other environmental resources worldwide.

There are two basic ways that environmental injustice is manifested. First, a community or group can be denied equitable access to environmental resources. This often occurs where poverty is common, or where land of high quality is scarce. For example, in many developing countries rich landowners control the best agricultural land, while poor subsistence farmers are left to scratch out a living on small patches of unsuitable land. In North America we may see this inequity expressed as expensive beachfront or mountain-view properties that are available only to the wealthiest few, or as limited access to an expensive diet rich in vitamins and nutrients.

Second, a community or group can be subjected to environmental injustice by having disproportionate risks or costs of pollution or degradation transferred to them, as in the example (above) of toxic waste dumps sited in communities of racial or ethnic minorities. In less economically developed parts of the world, the poor and other marginalized groups are directly dependent on the environment for survival and therefore suffer the harshest and most immediate impacts of environmental degradation. Cultural differences also can lead to disproportionate exposure of specific groups to the effects of environmental degradation. For example, the traditional diet of many

of Canada's Aboriginal people is heavily reliant on fish and marine mammals, which tend to have high concentrations of harmful pollutants, such as mercury.

Aboriginal groups struggling to maintain a traditional lifestyle have been linked with the environmental justice movement. Many such struggles originate not as environmental causes but as social justice causes. The rubbertappers or *seringueiros* of the Brazilian Amazon are representative of causes that originate at this intersection of environmental justice and social justice. The *seringueiros* and their leader, Chico Mendes (**FIGURE 21.9**), caught the world's attention when it became apparent that the battle to save their traditional economy—based on the sustainable extraction of latex and other forest resources—was intimately connected with efforts to stop deforestation of the Amazonian rainforest for ranching.

The *seringueiros* forged a partnership with indigenous Amazonians, who face many of the same challenges to their traditional lands, resources, and lifestyle. Chico Mendes thought of himself first as a social activist, fighting on behalf of his people and their way of life. Would the international environmental movement have embraced his cause if it had *not* been intimately connected with the rainforest? Sadly, Chico Mendes' iconic status and effectiveness as an activist on behalf of his people and their beloved forests and traditions were dramatically heightened by his assassination, in 1988, by Brazilian ranchers.

FIGURE 21.9

Chico Mendes, seen here shortly before his assassination in 1988, was a social activist on behalf of the traditional lifestyle of his people, but he caught the eye of the world because of his struggle to preserve the Amazon rainforest.

Critics have characterized the attempts of the predominantly white Australian government and uranium mining companies to open mines on traditional lands of the Mirrar as environmental injustice. In North America, as well, uranium mining has been a focus of environmental justice concerns. As discussed in the Central Case, Dene mineworkers from the Northwest Territories and Saskatchewan, as well as Navajo mineworkers from the United States, suffered delayed health effects that may have been caused by working in uranium mines with minimal safeguards.

Dene workers were hired as early as 1930 to haul radioactive uranium ore wrapped in cloth bags at Eldorado. The governments of Canada (then the world's largest supplier of uranium) and the United States (main purchaser of the ore) were aware of the health hazards of dealing with radioactive ores, as documented in government publications from the time.[12] However, these concerns were not communicated to Dene workers, many of whom did not speak English, and protective equipment was not provided. For decades, until the mine was shut down in the 1960s, Dene miners "slept on the ore, ate fish from water contaminated by radioactive tailings and breathed radioactive dust while on the barges, docks and portages," according to the *Calgary Herald*.[13]

The later deaths, from lung cancer, of many Port Radium miners led to the nickname "Village of Widows" for the settlement of Deline, and the Dene Nation called for an official response from the federal government. In 2005 the government of Canada issued the results of its study, which concluded that there was insufficient evidence to link the deaths of the miners with exposure to radiation during mining work at Port Radium. The report acknowledged that the mine had had an impact on soil and water quality in the immediate vicinity of Great Bear Lake and called for the proper decommissioning of the site, with provisions for continued environmental monitoring. Compensation for residents and the remaining miners was not addressed in the report.[14]

Although cases of lung cancer began to appear among uranium mineworkers in the early 1960s, scientific studies of radiation's effects on miners at the time specifically excluded Aboriginal mineworkers. The decision to include only white miners in those studies was attributed to the researchers' desire to study a "homogeneous population." A later generation would perceive this as negligence and discrimination.

In the United States, the *Radiation Exposure Compensation Act* of 1990 compensated Navajo miners who suffered health effects from unprotected work in the mines. Even the compensation process, though, has been controversial; as of 2006, approximately 80% of the $300 million allocated to compensate these miners and their families had been allocated to non-native miners. Many of the Navajo miners lacked the extensive documentation required to apply for compensation, including medical documentation and records of the exact dates and conditions in which they worked. Some Navajo miners also have been denied compensation because they fail to qualify as "nonsmokers" as a result of having participated in traditional native ceremonies involving smoke.[15] Cases like these illustrate the interplay between changing ethical values and resultant policy making.

Economics: Approaches and Environmental Implications

Economics, like ethics, addresses people's values, influences behaviour, and widely informs policy. People who oppose mining and other developments in wilderness areas or on traditional lands typically do so on the basis of ethical concerns and worries over environmental impacts. Few challenge such activities on economic grounds; even opponents generally recognize them as lucrative activities that generate jobs and income. On the other hand, support for mining and other development and resource extraction activities is primarily founded in economic reasoning.

Conflict between ethical and economic motivations is thus a recurrent theme in environmental issues. We often hear it said that environmental protection works in opposition to economic progress. Arguments are made that environmental protection costs too much money, interferes with progress, and leads to job loss. But is this necessarily the case? Growing numbers of economists assert that there need be no such trade-off—that, in fact, environmental protection can be *good* for the economy. The position one takes often depends on whether one thinks in the short term or the long term, and whether one holds to traditional economic schools of thought or to newer ones that view human economies as coupled to the natural environment.

Economics studies the allocation of scarce resources

Like ethics, economics examines factors that guide human behaviour. **Economics** is the study of how people decide to use scarce resources to provide goods and services in the face of demand for them. By this definition, environmental problems are economic problems that can intensify as population and resource consumption increase. For example, pollution may be viewed as depleting the scarce resources of clean air, water, or soil.

roots
ECONOMICS

The word **economics** comes from the Greek words *oikos*, meaning "household," and *oikonomia*, "household management." *Oikos* is the same word from which the term *ecology* is derived (with the suffix *-logia*, "the study of"). Economists have traditionally studied the "household" of the human society, and ecologists study the broader household of all life.

Several types of economies exist today

An **economy** is a social system that converts resources into **goods**, material commodities manufactured for and bought by individuals and businesses; and **services**, work done for others as a form of business. The oldest type of economy is the *subsistence economy*. People in subsistence economies—who still compose much of the human population—meet most or all of their daily needs directly from nature and do not purchase or trade for most of life's necessities.

A second type of economy is the *capitalist market economy*. In this system, buyers and sellers interact to determine which goods and services to produce, how much to produce, and how these should be produced and distributed. Capitalist economies are often contrasted with state socialist economies, or *centrally planned economies*, in which government determines in a top-down manner how to allocate resources.

A utopian pure market economy would operate without any government intervention. In reality, all capitalist market economies today, including that of Canada, are hybrid systems (often called *mixed economies*). In modern market economies, governments intervene for several reasons: (1) to eliminate unfair advantages held by monopoly buyers or sellers; (2) to provide social services, such as national defence, medical care, and education; (3) to provide "safety nets" (for older adults, the unemployed, those with chronic illnesses or disabilities, victims of natural disasters, and so on); (4) to manage commonly owned resources (the "commons"); and (5) to mitigate pollution and other types of environmental damage.

Environment and economy are intricately linked

All human economies exist within the larger environment and depend on it in important ways. Economies receive inputs from the environment, process them in complex ways that enable human society to function, and then discharge outputs of waste from this process into the environment. Economies are thus *open systems* integrated with the larger environmental system of which they are a part. Earth, in turn, is a *closed system*. This means that the material inputs Earth can provide to economies are ultimately finite and so is the waste-absorbing capacity of the planet.

Although the interactions between human economies and the nonhuman environment are readily apparent, traditional economic schools of thought have long overlooked the importance of these connections. Indeed, most conventional economists today still adhere to a world view that largely ignores the environment (**FIGURE 21.10A**), and this world view continues to drive most policy decisions. A conventional economic world view essentially holds that environmental resources (the inputs into the economy) are limitless and free and that wastes (outputs) can be endlessly exported and absorbed by the environment, at no cost. However, modern economists belonging to the fast-growing fields of environmental economics, ecological economics, and natural resource accounting explicitly accept that human economies are subsets of the environment and depend crucially on the environment (**FIGURE 21.10B**).

Economic activity uses resources from the environment. Natural resources are the substances and forces we need to survive: the Sun's energy, fresh water, trees that provide lumber, rocks that provide metals, and fossil fuels and other energy sources that power our machines. We can think of natural resources as "goods" produced by nature. Without Earth's natural resources, there would be no human economies and no human beings.

Environmental systems also function in a manner that naturally supports economies. Earth's ecological systems purify air and water, cycle nutrients, provide for the pollination of plants by animals, and serve as receptacles and recycling systems for the wastes generated by our economic activity. Such essential services, often called **ecosystem services** (**TABLE 21.1**), sustain the life that makes our economic activity possible. Some ecosystem services represent the very nuts-and-bolts of our survival; others enhance our quality of life.

Although the environment allows economic activity to occur by providing ecosystem goods and services, that economic activity can affect the environment in return. When we deplete natural resources or produce pollution, we degrade the ability of ecological systems to function. The *Millennium Ecosystem Assessment* concluded in 2005 that 15 of 24 ecosystem services surveyed globally were being degraded or used unsustainably. The degradation of ecosystem services can in turn negatively affect

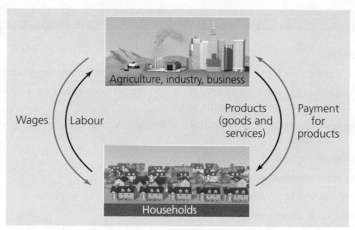

(a) Conventional view of economic activity

FIGURE 21.10
Standard neoclassical economics focuses on processes of production and consumption between households and businesses **(a)**, viewing the environment only as a "factor of production" that helps enable the production of goods. Environmental and ecological economists view the human economy as existing within the natural environment **(b)**, receiving resources from it, discharging waste into it, and interacting with it through ecosystem services.

(b) Economic activity as viewed by environmental and ecological economists

economies. Ecological degradation harms poor people more than wealthy people, the Millennium Ecosystem Assessment found. As a result, restoring ecosystem services is a prime objective for alleviating poverty in much of the world.

These interrelationships have only recently become widely recognized. Let us briefly examine how economic thought has changed over the years, tracing the path that is now beginning to lead economies to become more compatible with natural systems.

Table 21.1   Ecosystem Services

Type of ecosystem service*	Example(s)
Regulation of atmospheric gases	Maintaining the ozone layer; balancing oxygen, carbon dioxide, and other gases
Regulation of climate	Controlling global temperature and precipitation through oceanic and atmospheric currents, greenhouse gases, cloud formation, and so on
Protection and buffering	Providing storm protection, flood control, and drought recovery, mainly through vegetation and shoreline structure
Regulation of water flow	Providing water for agriculture, industry, transportation
Storage of water	Providing water through watersheds, reservoirs, aquifers
Control of erosion	Preventing soil loss from wind or runoff; storing silt in lakes and wetlands
Formation of soil	Weathering rock; accumulating organic material
Cycling of nutrients	Cycling carbon, nitrogen, phosphorus, sulphur, and other nutrients through ecosystems
Waste treatment	Removing toxins, recovering nutrients, controlling pollution
Pollination of plants	Transporting floral gametes by wind or pollinating animals, enabling crops and wild plants to reproduce
Population control	Controlling prey with predators; controlling hosts with parasites; controlling herbivory on crops with predators and parasites
Provision of habitat	Providing ecological settings in which creatures can breed, feed, rest, migrate, winter
Provision of food	Producing fish, game, crops, nuts, and fruits that humans obtain by hunting, gathering, fishing, subsistence farming
Supply of raw materials	Producing lumber, fuel, metals, fodder
Genetic resources	Providing unique biological sources for medicine, materials science, genes for resistance to plant pathogens and crop pests, ornamental species (pets and horticultural plant varieties)
Recreational opportunities	Ecotourism, sport fishing, hiking, birding, kayaking, other outdoor recreation
Noncommercial services	Aesthetic, artistic, educational, spiritual, and/or scientific values of ecosystems

*Ecosystem "goods" are here included in ecosystem services.

Source: Adapted with permission from Costanza, R., et al. 1997. The value of the world's ecosystem services and natural capital. Nature 387:253–260.

Classical economics promoted the free market

Economics shares a common intellectual heritage with ethics, and practitioners of both have long been interested in the relationship between individual action and societal well-being. Some philosophers argued that individuals acting in their own self-interest would harm society (as in the tragedy of the commons). Others believed that such behaviour could benefit society, as long as the behaviour was constrained by the rule of law and private property rights and operated within fairly competitive markets.

The latter view was articulated by Scottish philosopher Adam Smith (1723–1790). Known today as the father of classical economics, Smith believed that when people are free to pursue their own economic self-interest in a competitive marketplace, the marketplace will behave as if guided by "an invisible hand" that ensures their actions will benefit society as a whole. In his 1776 book *Inquiry into the Nature and Causes of the Wealth of Nations*, Smith wrote:

> [Each individual] intends only his own security, only his own gain. And he is led in this by an invisible hand to promote an end which was no part of intention. By pursuing his own interests he frequently promotes that of society more effectually than when he really intends to.[16]

Smith's philosophy remains a pillar of free market thought today, and many credit it for the tremendous gains in material prosperity that industrialized nations have experienced in the past few centuries. Others argue that the policies spawned by free-market thought worsen inequalities between rich and poor and contribute to environmental degradation. Market capitalism, these critics assert, should be constrained and regulated by democratic government.

Neoclassical economics considers price, supply, and demand

Economists subsequently took more quantitative approaches to issues related to price, supply, and demand. Modern neoclassical economics examines the psychological factors underlying consumer choices, explaining market prices in terms of consumer preferences for units of particular commodities. In neoclassical economic theory, buyers desire the lowest possible price, whereas sellers desire the highest possible price. This conflict between buyers and sellers results in a compromise price being reached and the "right" quantity of commodities being bought and sold.

This is often phrased in terms of *supply*, the amount of a product offered for sale at a given price, and *demand*, the amount of a product people will buy at a given price if free to do so. Theoretically, when prices go up, demand drops and supply increases; when prices fall, demand rises and supply decreases. In theory, the market automatically moves toward an equilibrium point, a price at which supply equals demand (**FIGURE 21.11A**). Similar reasoning can be applied to environmental issues, such that economists can determine "optimal" levels of resource use or pollution control (**FIGURE 21.11B**).

Cost–benefit analysis is a useful tool

Neoclassical economists commonly use a method referred to as **cost–benefit analysis**. In this approach, estimated costs for a proposed action are totalled and compared with the sum of benefits anticipated to result from the action. If total benefits exceed costs, the action should be pursued; if costs exceed benefits, it should not. When choosing among multiple alternative actions, the one with the greatest excess of benefits over costs should be chosen.

This reasoning seems eminently logical; however, problems often arise in applying it to environmental situations because not all costs and benefits are easily quantified, or even easily identified. It may be simple to quantify wages paid to uranium miners or the market value of uranium extracted from a mine or even the cost of measures to minimize health risks for miners. But it is much more difficult to assess the cost of a landscape's being scarred by mine development or the cost of radioactive contamination of a stream or the costs in health and emotional well-being to the families of miners who die from mining-related cancers.

Because some costs and benefits cannot easily be assigned monetary values, cost–benefit analysis is often controversial. Moreover, because economic benefits

(a) Classic supply-demand curve

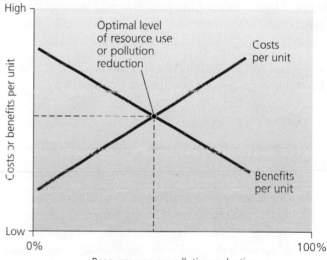

(b) Marginal benefit and cost curves

FIGURE 21.11
This basic supply-and-demand curve **(a)** illustrates the relationship among supply, demand, and market equilibrium, the "balance point" at which demand is equal to supply. We can use a similar graph **(b)** to determine an "optimal" level of resource use or pollution mitigation. In this graph, the cost per unit of resource use or pollution cleanup (blue line) rises as the resource use or pollution cleanup proceeds and it becomes expensive to extract or clean up the remaining amounts. Meanwhile, the benefits per unit of resource use or pollution cleanup (red line) decrease. The point where the lines intersect gives the optimal level.

usually are more easily quantified than environmental costs, economic benefits tend to be overrepresented in traditional cost–benefit analyses. As a result, environmental advocates often feel these analyses are biased in favour of economic development and against environmental protection.

A corollary to cost–benefit analysis has been the development of a variety of mechanisms for understanding, calculating, and defining the value, to society and to individuals, of environmental costs and benefits. In general, **valuation** refers to the attempt to quantify the value of a particular environmental good or service—even if it cannot easily be expressed in monetary terms. We will discuss how different valuation approaches can be used to more accurately represent the environment in cost–benefit analysis and asset accounting, below.

Aspects of neoclassical economics have profound implications for the environment

Today's capitalist market systems have generated unprecedented material wealth, employment, and other desirable outcomes, but they have also contributed to environmental problems. Four of the fundamental assumptions of neoclassical economics have implications for the environment:

1. Resources are infinite or substitutable.
2. Long-term effects should be discounted.
3. Costs and benefits are internal.
4. Growth is good.

Let us critically examine each of these assumptions in turn.

Are resources infinite or substitutable?

Neoclassical economic models generally treat the supply of workers and other resources as being either infinite or largely "substitutable and interchangeable." This implies that once we have depleted a resource—natural, human, or otherwise—we should be able to find a replacement for it. Human resources can substitute for financial resources, for instance, or manufactured resources can substitute for natural resources. Theory allows that the substituted resource may be less efficient or more costly, but some degree of substitutability is generally assumed. In other words, traditional economists have considered environmental goods and services to be so-called free gifts of nature—infinitely abundant and resilient, and ultimately substitutable by human technological ingenuity.

It is true that many resources can be replaced; societies have transitioned from manual labour to animal labour to steam-driven power to fossil fuel power and may yet transition to renewable power sources, like solar energy. However, Earth's material resources are ultimately limited. Nonrenewable resources, such as fossil fuels, can be depleted, and even renewable resources can be used up if we exploit them more quickly than they can be replenished. This has been experienced by many ancient civilizations, including the inhabitants of Rapa Nui, who harvested wood faster than their forests could regrow.

Should long-term effects be discounted?

Although few people would dispute that resources are *ultimately* limited, many assume that their depletion will take place so far in the future that there is no need for current generations to worry. For economists in the neoclassical tradition, an event far in the future counts much less than one in the present; in economic terminology, we say that these future effects are "discounted." In discounting, short-term costs and benefits are granted more importance than long-term costs and benefits. This encourages policy makers to play down long-term consequences of decisions we make today.

For example, a stock of uranium ore in the ground or living trees standing in the forest or fish in a stream represent potential commodities that would have monetary or **market values** if they were extracted or harvested and sold. In cost–benefit analysis, however, such commodities are typically discounted for future use to the extent that they appear to be of economic value only if they can be used up as quickly as possible. Some governments and businesses use a 10% annual discount rate for decisions on resource use. This means that the long-term value of a stand of ancient trees worth $500 000 for the timber it contains would drop by 10% each year; after 10 years of discounting, it would be worth only $174 339.22. By this logic, the more quickly the trees are cut down, the more they are worth.

A related problem is that accounting procedures at the national level typically do not assign an *asset value* to intact natural resources as they would, for example, for a physical asset, such as a factory or a system of roads. This means that an unexploited natural resource has *no discernible value* to the nation that possesses it, providing a powerful incentive for nations to exploit their natural resources to the greatest extent and as quickly as possible.

This was stated eloquently by Robert Repetto, one of the pioneers of **natural resource accounting**, which seeks mechanisms by which to incorporate the economic asset values of natural resources into national accounting systems. According to Repetto:

> *A country can cut down its forests, erode its soils, pollute its aquifers and hunt its wildlife and fisheries to extinction, but its measured income is not affected as its assets disappear . . . By failing to recognize the asset value of natural resources, the accounting framework that underlies the principal tools of economic analysis misrepresents the policy choices nations face.*[17]

To further complicate matters, national accounting systems also fail to incorporate certain categories of activities and expenses into the calculations. For example, an individual or a nation might spend money to prevent future environmental degradation, or to restore a degraded natural environment. This could include, for example, launching a program of pollution abatement, constructing windbreaks to prevent soil erosion, or installing heavy-walled containers in oil tankers to prevent spills. Such costs, which economists call *defensive expenditures*, are calculated only as current expenses; the future value of the resource these activities may be helping to preserve or restore is of no economic value to the system.

Are costs and benefits internal? A third assumption of neoclassical economics is that all costs and benefits associated with a particular exchange of goods or services are borne by individuals engaging directly in the transaction. In other words, it is assumed that the costs and benefits of a transaction are "internal" to the transaction, experienced by the buyer and seller alone, and do not affect other members of society.

However, in many situations this is simply not the case. Pollution from a factory can harm people living nearby. In such cases, someone—often taxpayers not involved in producing the pollution—ends up paying the costs of alleviating it. Market prices do not take the social, environmental, or economic costs of this pollution into account. Costs or benefits of a transaction that involve people other than the buyer or seller are known as **externalities**. A positive externality is a benefit enjoyed by someone not involved in a transaction, and a negative externality, or *external cost*, is a cost borne by someone not involved in a transaction (**FIGURE 21.12**). Negative externalities often harm groups of people or society as a whole, while allowing certain individuals private gain.

External costs commonly include the following:

- Property damage
- Declines in desirable elements of the environment, such as poorer air quality, or fewer fish in a stream
- Aesthetic damage, such as that resulting from air pollution or clear-cutting
- Stress and anxiety experienced by people downstream or downwind from a pollution source
- Declining real estate values resulting from these problems

The Mirrar experienced external costs in the form of pollution from the Ranger mine. In March 2002, radioactive material from the Ranger mine contaminated a stream on Mirrar land with uranium concentrations 4000 times as high as allowed by law. According to an Aboriginal representative, this was the fourth such violation in less than three months. In 2004 the government temporarily shut down the mine and brought the owners to court for these violations.[18] For the Dene of Great Bear Lake the external costs of uranium mining have come in the form of lingering contamination of soil, water, and fish, as well

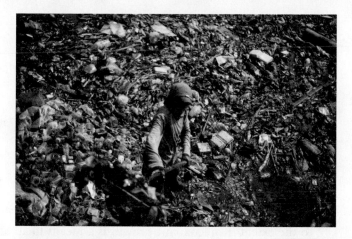

FIGURE 21.12
An Indonesian boy wading in a polluted river suffers external costs, costs that are not borne by the buyer or seller. External costs may include water pollution, aesthetic harm, human health problems, property damage, harm to aquatic life, aesthetic degradation, declining real estate values, and other impacts.

as health impacts on workers and, by extension, economic and psychological impacts on their families.

By ignoring external costs, economies create a false idea of the true and complete costs of particular choices, and unjustly subject people to the consequences of transactions in which they did not participate. External costs are one reason governments develop environmental legislation and regulations. Unfortunately, external costs are difficult to account for and eliminate. It is tough to assign a monetary value to illness, premature death, or degradation of an aesthetically or spiritually significant site.

Is growth good? A fourth assumption of the neoclassical economic approach is that economic growth is required to keep employment high and maintain social order. The argument goes something like this: If the poor view the wealthy as the source of their suffering, they may revolt. Promoting economic growth can defuse this situation by creating opportunities for the poor to become wealthier themselves. By making the overall economic pie larger, everyone's slice becomes larger, even if some people still have much smaller slices than others.

The idea that economic growth is good has been encouraged over the centuries by the concept of material progress, espoused by Western cultures since the Enlightenment. Everywhere, every day in the modern industrialized world we see expressions of the view that "more and bigger" is always better. We hear constantly in business news of increases in an industry's output or percentage growth in a country's economy, with increases touted as good news and decreases, stability, or even a minor drop in the *rate* of growth presented as bad news. Economic growth has become the quantitative ruler by which progress is measured.

Is the growth paradigm good for us?

The rate of economic growth in recent decades is unprecedented in human history. As a result, the world economy is seven times the size it was half a century ago. All measures of economic activity—trade, rates of production, amount and value of goods manufactured—are higher than they have ever been and are still increasing. This growth has brought many people much greater material wealth (although gaps between rich and poor are immense, and growing).

To the extent that economic growth is a means to an end—a tool with which we can achieve greater human happiness—it can be a good thing. However, many observers today worry that growth has become an end in itself and is no longer necessarily the best tool with which to pursue happiness. Critics of the growth paradigm often note that runaway growth resembles the multiplication of cancer cells, which eventually overwhelm and destroy the organism in which they grow. These critics fear that runaway economic growth will likewise destroy the economic system on which we all depend. Resources for growth are ultimately limited, they argue, so nonstop growth is not sustainable and will fail as a long-term strategy.

Defenders of traditional economic approaches reply that critics have been saying for decades that limited resources would doom growth-oriented economies, yet most of these economies are still expanding dramatically. If resources are dwindling, why are we witnessing the most rapid growth of material wealth in human history?

One prime reason is technological innovation. In case after case, improved technology has enabled us to push back the limits on growth, effectively expanding the carrying capacity of the environment. More powerful technology for extracting minerals, fossil fuels, and groundwater has expanded the amounts of these natural resources available to us. Technological developments, such as automated farm machinery, fertilizers, and chemical pesticides, have allowed us to grow more food per unit area of land, boosting agricultural output. Faster, more powerful machines in our factories have enabled us to translate our enhanced resource extraction and agricultural production into faster rates of manufacturing.

Economists disagree on whether economic growth is sustainable

Can we conclude, then, that endless improvements in technology are possible and that we will never run into shortages of resources? At one end of the spectrum are those who believe that technology can solve everything—a philosophy that has greatly influenced economic policy in market economies over the past century.

At the other end of the spectrum, *ecological economists* argue that a couple of centuries is not a very long period of time and that history suggests that civilizations do not, in the long run, overcome their environmental limitations. Ecological economics, which has emerged as a discipline only in the past decade or two, applies the principles of ecology and systems science to the analysis of economic systems. Earth's natural systems generally operate in self-renewing cycles, not in a linear or progressive manner. Ecological economists advocate sustainability in economies and see natural systems as good models.

To evaluate an economy's sustainability, ecological economists take a long-term perspective and ask, "Could we continue this activity forever and be happy with the outcome?" Most ecological economists argue that the growth paradigm will eventually fail and that if nothing is done to rein in population growth and resource consumption, depleted natural systems could plunge our economies into ruin. Many advocate economies that do not grow and do not shrink but rather are stable. Such steady-state economies are intended to mirror natural ecological systems.

Environmental economists tend to agree that economies are unsustainable if population growth is not reduced and resource use is not made more efficient. However, they maintain that we can accomplish these changes and attain sustainability within our current economic systems. By retaining the principles of neoclassical economics but modifying them to address environmental challenges, environmental economists argue that we can keep our economies growing and that technology can continue to improve efficiency. Environmental economists were the first to develop ways to tackle the problems of external costs and discounting, and to weigh the true costs and benefits associated with resource use. They then went farther, proposing that sustainability requires far-reaching changes leading ultimately to a steady-state economy. The idea of a steady-state economy did not originate with the rise of ecological economics. Back in the nineteenth century, British economist John Stuart Mill (1806–1873) hypothesized that as resources became harder to find and extract, economic growth would slow and eventually stabilize. Economies would carry on in a state in which individuals and society subsist on steady flows of natural resources and on savings accrued during occasional productive but finite periods of growth.

Modern proponents of a steady-state global economy, such as the pioneering economist Herman Daly, believe we need to rethink our assumptions and fundamentally change the way we conduct economic transactions. They argue that quality of life can continue to rise under a steady-state economy and, in fact, may be more likely to do so. Technological advances will not cease just because growth stabilizes, they argue, and neither will behavioural changes (such as greater use of recycling) that enhance sustainability. Instead, wealth and human happiness can continue to rise after economic growth has levelled off.

Attaining sustainability will certainly require reforms and may well require fundamental shifts in thinking, values, and behaviour. How can these goals be attained in a world whose economic policies are still largely swayed by a cornucopian world view that barely takes the environment into account? While keeping in mind that ecological and environmental economic approaches are still actively being developed, we will now survey a few strategies for sustainability that have been offered so far.

We can measure economic progress differently

For decades, economists have assessed the economic robustness of a nation by calculating its gross domestic product (GDP), the total monetary value of final goods and services produced in a country each year (**FIGURE 21.13**). GDP is an extremely powerful indicator, used to make financial policy decisions by federal governments worldwide, with fundamental impacts on quality of life and well-being for billions of people.

However, there are problems with using this measure of economic activity to represent a nation's economic well-being. For one, GDP does not account for the nonmarket values of ecosystem goods and services, nor is GDP necessarily an expression of *desirable* economic activity. In fact, GDP can increase, even if the economic activities driving it hurt the environment or society.

For example, a large oil spill would increase GDP because oil spills require cleanups, which cost money and, as a result, increase the production of goods and services. Such activities generate income, and are therefore reflected by a positive change in GDP, but the negative health and ecological costs of disasters like these are typically *not* reflected in the GDP—unless they generate jobs or cash transactions, in which case they may show up as positive changes. A radiation leak at a uranium mine on Mirrar homelands would likely add to the Australian GDP because of the many monetary transactions required for cleanup and medical care. Similarly the $6.7 million in contracts offered by the government of Canada for the cleanup of abandoned uranium mine sites in the Northwest Territories will add to the GDP of Canada. Even Hurricane Katrina—which caused the deaths of almost 2000 people, the loss of tens of thousands

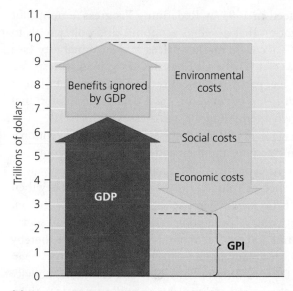

(a) Components of GDP vs. GPI

(b) Change in GDP vs. GPI

FIGURE 21.13

Gross domestic product (GDP; red arrow in **(a)**) sums together all economic activity, whether good or bad. As a result, many researchers today believe that GDP is lacking as an indicator of overall well-being. The genuine progress indicator (GPI) is one example of an alternative indicator of progress and well-being **(b)**. GPI adds to GDP benefits by accounting for the value of activities such as volunteering and parenting (upward-pointing gold arrow). The GPI also subtracts external environmental costs, such as pollution; social costs, such as divorce and crime; and economic costs, such as borrowing and the gap between rich and poor (downward-pointing gold arrow).
Source: Data from Venetoulis, J., and C. Cobb. (2004). The Genuine Progress Indicator, 1950–2002 (2004 Update). Redefining Progress.

of homes and jobs, and the contamination or permanent flooding of millions of square kilometres of coastal marshlands and forests in the United States—generated positive growth in GDP in the third quarter of 2005.

Some economists have attempted to develop economic indicators that differentiate between desirable and undesirable economic activity. Such indicators can function as more accurate guides to nations' welfare. One alternative to the GDP is the genuine progress indicator (GPI), introduced in 1995 by Redefining Progress, a nonprofit organization that develops economic and policy tools to promote accurate market prices and sustainability (see **FIGURE 21.13**). The GPI has not yet gained widespread acceptance, partly because it is tremendously data-intensive, but it has generated a great deal of discussion that has drawn attention to the weaknesses of the GDP.

To calculate GPI, economists begin with conventional economic activity and then add to it all *positive* contributions to the economy that do not have to be paid for with money, such as volunteer work and parenting. They then subtract the *negative* impacts, such as crime, pollution, gaps between rich and poor, and other detrimental social, environmental, and economic factors. The GPI thereby summarizes many more forms of economic activity than does GDP and differentiates between economic activity that increases societal well-being and economic activity that decreases it.

Thus, whereas GDP increases when fossil fuel use increases, GPI declines because of the adverse environmental and social impacts of such consumption, including air and water pollution, increased road congestion and traffic accidents, and global climate change. **FIGURE 21.14** compares changes in per capita GPI and GDP in Alberta from 1961 to 2003. The Pembina Institute in Alberta is a leader in the calculation and application of alternative indicators of economic and overall well-being. The province's GDP has increased greatly as a result of increased economic activity; however, GPI has declined over the same period.

GPI is not the only alternative to GDP. The *Index of Sustainable Economic Welfare (ISEW)* is based on income, wealth distribution, the value of volunteerism, and natural resource depletion. The *Net Economic Welfare (NEW) index* adjusts GDP by deducting the costs of environmental degradation. The United Nations uses a tool called the *Human Development Index*, calculated on the basis of a nation's standard of living, life expectancy, and education. Any of these indices, ecological economists maintain, should give a more accurate portrait of a nation's welfare than GDP, which policy makers currently use so widely.

We can give ecosystem goods and services monetary values

Economies receive from the environment vital resources and ecosystem services. However, any survey of environmental problems today—deforestation, biodiversity loss, pollution, collapsed fisheries, climate change, and so on—makes it immediately apparent that our society often mistreats the very systems that keep it alive and healthy. Furthermore, the values of environmental goods and services are routinely underrepresented in cost–benefit analysis, one of the most powerful tools of economic decision making. Why is this? From the economist's perspective, humans overexploit natural resources and systems because the market assigns them no quantitative monetary value or, at best, assigns values that underestimate their true worth.

Think for a minute about the nature of some of these services. The aesthetic and recreational pleasure we obtain from natural landscapes, whether wildernesses or city parks, is something of real value. Yet this value is hard to quantify and appears in no traditional measures of economic worth. Or consider Earth's water cycle, by which rain fills our reservoirs with drinking water, rivers give us hydropower and flush away our waste, and water evaporates, purifying itself of contaminants and readying itself to fall again as rain. This natural cycle is absolutely vital to our existence, yet because its value is not quantified, markets impose no financial penalties when we interfere with it.

FIGURE 21.14
Although the GDP of Alberta has increased dramatically since 1961, the GPI actually shows a decline over the same period. GPI advocates suggest that this discrepancy means that we are spending more money than ever but that our lives are not that much better.
Source: Data from Pembina Institute, Alberta GPI Accounts, 1961–2003.

Ecosystem services are said to have nonmarket values, values not usually included in the price of a good or service (**TABLE 21.2** and **FIGURE 21.15**). Because the market does not assign value to ecosystem services, debates, such as that over the Jabiluka mine, often involve comparing apples and oranges—in this case, the intangible cultural, ecological, and spiritual arguments of the Mirrar versus the hard numbers of mine proponents.

To partially resolve this dilemma, environmental and ecological economists have sought ways to assign values to ecosystem goods and services. One technique, *contingent valuation*, uses surveys to determine how much people are willing to pay to protect a resource or to restore it after damage has been done.

Such an exercise was conducted with a mining proposal in the Kakadu region in the early 1990s that preceded the Jabiluka proposal. The Kakadu Conservation Zone, a government-owned 50 km² plot of land surrounded by Kakadu National Park, was either to be developed for mining, or to be preserved and added to the park. To determine the degree of public support for environmental protection versus mining, a government commission sponsored a contingent valuation study to

Table 21.2 Values That Modern Market Economies Generally Do Not Address

Nonmarket value	Is the worth we ascribe to things that ...
Use value	We use directly
Option value	We do not use now but might use or find a use for at a later time
Aesthetic value	We appreciate for their beauty or emotional appeal
Cultural value	Sustain or help define our culture
Spiritual value	Are sacred to certain groups, or evoke spiritual, religious, or philosophical responses in us
Scientific value	May be significant as subjects of scientific research
Educational value	May teach us about ourselves and the world
Existence value	Are important or have value simply because they exist, even though we may never experience them directly (e.g., remote wilderness, or endangered species in a far-off place)

FIGURE 21.15
Accounting for nonmarket values, such as those shown here, may help us to make better environmental and economic decisions.

(a) Existence values

(b) Option values

(c) Aesthetic values

(d) Scientific values

(e) Educational values

(f) Cultural values

(g) Use values

determine how much Australian citizens valued keeping the Kakadu Conservation Zone preserved and undeveloped. Researchers interviewed 2034 citizens, asking them how much money they would be willing to pay to stop mine development.

The interviewers presented two scenarios: (1) a "major-impact" scenario based on predictions of environmentalists who held that mining would cause great harm, and (2) a "minor-impact" scenario based on predictions of mining executives who held that development would have few downsides. After presenting both scenarios in detail, complete with photographs, the interviewers asked the respondents how much their households would pay if each scenario, in turn, were to occur. Respondents on average said their households would pay $80 per year to prevent the minor-impact scenario and $143 per year to prevent the major-impact scenario. Multiplying these figures by the number of households in Australia (5.4 million at the time), the researchers found that preservation was "worth" $435 million annually to the Australian population under the minor-impact scenario, and $777 million under the major-impact scenario. Because both of these numbers significantly exceeded the $102 million in annual economic benefits expected from mine development, the researchers concluded that preserving the land in its undeveloped state was worth more than mining it.

Because contingent valuation relies on survey questions, critics complain that in such cases people will volunteer idealistic (inflated) values rather than realistic ones, knowing that they will not actually have to pay the price they name. In part because of such concerns, the

Australian government commission decided not to use the Kakadu contingent valuation study's results. (The mine was stopped, ultimately, but mainly as a result of Aboriginal opposition.)

Whereas contingent valuation measures people's *expressed* preferences, other methods aim to measure people's *revealed* preferences—preferences as revealed by data on actual behaviour. For example, the amount of money, time, or effort people expend to travel to parks for recreation has been used to measure the value people place on parks. Economists have also analyzed housing prices, comparing homes with similar characteristics but different environmental settings to infer the dollar value of landscapes, views, greenspace, and peace and quiet. Another approach assigns environmental amenities value by measuring the cost required to restore natural systems that have been damaged or to mitigate harm from pollution.

In 1997 a research team led by Robert Costanza reviewed ecosystem valuation studies, with the goal of calculating the global economic value of all the services that ecosystems provide (**FIGURE 21.16**). The team identified more than 100 studies that estimated the worth of such ecosystem services as water purification, greenhouse gas regulation, plant pollination, and pollution cleanup. The studies used such methods as contingent valuation to estimate the values of such aspects of natural systems as biodiversity and aesthetics.

To estimate the worth of ecosystem services more accurately, the team reevaluated the data using alternative valuation techniques. One method was to calculate

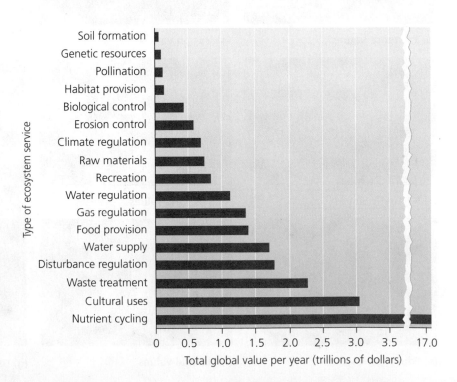

FIGURE 21.16
Costanza and colleagues estimated the total value of the world's ecosystem services at approximately $33 trillion. Shown are subtotals for each major class of ecosystem service. The $33 trillion figure does not include values from some ecosystems, such as deserts and tundra, for which adequate data were unavailable.
Source: Data from Costanza, R., et al. (2007). The value of the world's ecosystem services and natural capital. Nature 387:253–260.

the cost of replacing ecosystem services with technology. For example, marshes protect people from floods and filter out water pollutants. If a marsh were destroyed, the researchers would calculate the value of the services it had provided by measuring the cost of the levees and water-purification technology that would be needed to assume those tasks. The researchers then calculated the global monetary value of such wetlands by multiplying those totals by the global area occupied by the ecosystem. By calculating similar totals from other ecosystems, they arrived at a global value for ecosystem services.[19] The total figure was $33 trillion per year (1997 dollars)—greater than the combined gross domestic products of all nations in the world. A follow-up study in 2002 concluded that the economic benefits of preserving the world's remaining natural areas outweighed the benefits of exploiting them by a factor of 100 to 1. When markets do not reflect the full costs and benefits of actions, they are said to fail. Market failure occurs when markets do not take into account the environment's positive effects on economies (such as ecosystem services) or when they do not reflect the negative effects of economic activity on the environment or on people (external costs).

Traditionally, market failure has been countered by government intervention. Governments can dictate limits on corporate behaviour through laws and regulations. They can institute *green taxes,* which penalize environmentally harmful activities. Or they can design economic incentives that put market mechanisms to work to promote fairness, resource conservation, and economic sustainability.

Corporations are responding to sustainability concerns

As more consumers and investors express preferences for sustainable products and services, more industries, businesses, and corporations are finding that they can make money by "greening" their operations (**FIGURE 21.17**).

Some companies, such as the Body Shop, cultivate eco-conscious images; others donate a portion of their proceeds to environmental and other progressive nonprofit groups. Today, some newer businesses are trying to go even further than these pioneers. The outdoor apparel company Nau manufactures items from materials made of corn biomass and recycled bottles, and helps fund environmental nonprofits. Entrepreneurs are starting thousands of local sustainability-oriented businesses across the world.

In the past few years, corporate sustainability has gone mainstream, and some of the world's largest corporations have joined in, including McDonald's, Starbucks, IKEA, Dow, and British Petroleum. Nike collects millions of used sneakers each year and recycles the materials to create synthetic surfaces for basketball courts, tennis courts, and running tracks. Nike also uses more organic cotton and has developed less-toxic rubber and adhesives. In response to media attention and consumer concern, such corporations as Nike and the Gap are also working to improve labour conditions in their factories overseas.

Of course, corporations exist to make money for their shareholders, so they cannot be expected to pursue goals that are not profitable. Moreover, some corporate greening efforts are more rhetoric than reality, and corporate *greenwashing* may mislead some consumers into thinking that companies are acting more sustainably than they are. However, as consumer preferences turn increasingly to sustainable products and practices, many corporations are seeing the economic wisdom of moving toward a more sustainable model of operation.

Perhaps the most celebrated recent corporate greening is that of Walmart. Environmentalists have long criticized the world's largest retailer for its environmental and social impacts. In 2006 the company began a quest to sell organic and sustainable products, reduce packaging and use recycled materials, enhance fuel efficiency in its truck fleets, reduce energy use in its stores, cut carbon dioxide emissions, and preserve an equivalent area of natural land for every parcel of land developed. Many observers remain skeptical of Walmart's commitment, calling it superficial "greenwashing"; yet, if the company achieves only a fraction of its stated goals, the environmental benefits could be substantial because of the corporation's vast global reach.

FIGURE 21.17
Canada Post now boasts a fleet of "green" fuel-efficient hybrid and all-electric trucks.

CANADIAN ENVIRONMENTAL PERSPECTIVES

Matthew Coon Come

Matthew Coon Come is an advocate for the environmental, social, and political rights of Aboriginal people in Canada.

- ■ **Environmental** and **social activist**
- ■ Former **grand chief** of the Grand Council of the Cree
- ■ Former **national chief** of the Assembly of First Nations

Matthew Coon Come is a politician and activist of Cree descent. He was born in a bush tent on his father's trapline and was taken away at the age of six to attend La Tuque Indian Residential School almost 500 km from his home. He studied law at McGill University and as a young man was elected grand chief of the Grand Council of the Cree. He has since served in many leadership positions on behalf of Aboriginal communities in Canada and around the world. He is a past winner of the Equinox Environmental Award and the Condé Nast Environment Award, among others.[20]

Coon Come is an advocate for his people in a world where environmental rights and social justice collide with economic development. He led the Cree in the late 1980s and early 1990s in opposition to a massive hydroelectric development project, the Great Whale River Phase of Hydro-Québec's James Bay Project, which began in 1971. This phase of the project would have comprised more than 30 dams and 600 dikes, blocking nine major rivers,[21] affecting watersheds with an area the size of France, and creating reservoirs the size of Lake Erie.[22]

Coon Come gathered support from local, national, and international environmental, human rights, and tribal communities, creating a coalition that vocally and visibly opposed the project. As a result of the coalition's efforts, the state of New York cancelled major contracts to purchase electricity from Hydro-Québec,[23] putting the viability of the project in jeopardy. In 1994, the Supreme Court of Canada ruled that federal environmental assessments were required for all Hydro-Québec electricity exports. Shortly after that decision, the premier of Quebec announced the indefinite suspension of work on the Great Whale Project.[24]

For his role in this struggle, Matthew Coon Come was awarded the Goldman Environmental Prize, a prestigious international prize that honours grassroots environmental leaders around the world.

By 2002, though, many Cree had changed their position on the James Bay Project, citing the desperate need for economic development in the North. Cree leaders signed an agreement with the government of Québec that cleared the way for the project to proceed. The next phase, which passed its environmental assessment in 2006, will involve the diversion of about 50% of the water flow of the Rupert River, as well as the construction of two new power stations and four large dams, flooding for a new reservoir, new roads, and worker settlements.

After all these years, the project continues to polarize the Cree Nation. Its supporters argue that the participation of the Cree in this project is a crucial step toward modernization and economic and social stability. Opponents—including residents from the three communities nearest to the project, as well as current grand chief Matthew Mukash, who is pressing instead for the development of wind energy—are concerned that the negative environmental impacts will outweigh any economic benefits.

Meanwhile, Matthew Coon Come became the national chief of the Assembly of First Nations, a position he held until 2003. In 2008 he issued a statement in response to the apology by the government of Canada for the years of abuse suffered by Native children, including Coon Come, in church-run residential schools. The statement, while accepting the government's apology, detailed the damage done to him by the residential school. It said in part, "They told me that my culture, and my people's ways of life, would never sustain me. They lied. I am a son of a hunter, fisherman, and a trapper. My father taught me how to walk the land, and to love and respect the animals and all of creation. I have not lost my culture. Our way of life is thriving."[25]

"Business as usual will not ensure the protection of the land of our children, yet unborn."
—Matthew Coon Come

Thinking About Environmental Perspectives

Put yourself in the place of a Cree community leader like Matthew Coon Come. How would you handle a controversy like the Hydro-Québec James Bay Project? How would you weigh the importance of much-needed jobs and other economic development against the potential for negative environmental impacts like mercury contamination, loss of habitat, or variations in water flow? What do you think of Cree leaders who have changed their positions on this and other projects, first opposing and then supporting them—do you think they are indecisive, or fickle, or are they courageous and forward-thinking?

The bottom line is that corporate actions hinge on consumer behaviour. It is up to all of us as consumers to encourage trends in sustainability by rewarding corporations that truly promote sustainable solutions.

Conclusion

Corporate sustainability, alternative ways of measuring growth, and the valuation of ecosystem goods and services are a few of the recent developments that have brought economic approaches to bear on environmental protection and resource conservation. As economics becomes more environmentally friendly, it renews some of its historic ties to ethics.

Environmental ethics has expanded people's sphere of ethical consideration outward to encompass other societies and cultures, other creatures, and even nonliving entities that were formerly outside the realm of ethical concern. This ethical expansion involves the concept of *distributional equity*, or equal treatment for all, which is the aim of environmental justice. One type of distributional equity is equity among generations. Such concern by current generations for the welfare of future generations is the basis for the notion of sustainability.

Although we tend to think of sustainability as a "modern" idea, it is actually inherent to some of the most basic concepts of neoclassical economics. In his 1939 work *Value and Capital*, Sir John Hicks (1904–1989), one of the most influential economists of the twentieth century, defined income as "the maximum value [a person] can consume during a week, and still expect to be as well off at the end of the week as he was at the beginning." The implication is that *true* income is *sustainable* income—if your spending compromises your resource base and reduces your future ability to produce, then you are depleting your capital. As former World Bank economist Herman E. Daly explains,

> *Why all the fuss about sustainability? Because, contrary to the theoretical definition of income, we are in fact consuming productive capacity and counting it as income in our national accounts. . . . Depletion of natural capital and consequent reduction of its life-sustaining services is the meaning of unsustainability.*[26]

Is sustainability a pragmatic pursuit for us? The answer largely depends on whether we believe that economic well-being and environmental well-being are opposed to each other, or whether we accept that they can work in tandem. Equating economic well-being with economic growth, as most economists traditionally have, suggests that economic welfare entails a trade-off with environmental quality. However, if economic welfare can be enhanced in the absence of growth, we can envision economies and environmental quality benefiting from one another.

REVIEWING OBJECTIVES

You should now be able to:

Characterize the influences of culture and world view on the choices people make

- A person's culture strongly influences his or her world view. Such factors as religion and political ideology are especially influential.

Outline the nature, evolution, and expansion of environmental ethics in Western cultures

- Our society's domain of ethical concern has been expanding, such that we have granted ethical consideration to more and more entities.
- Anthropocentrism values humans above all else, whereas biocentrism values all life and ecocentrism values ecological systems.

- The preservation ethic (preserving natural systems intact) and the conservation ethic (promoting responsible long-term use of resources) have guided branches of the environmental movement during the past century.
- The environmental justice movement, seeking equal treatment for people of all races and income levels, is a recent outgrowth of environmental ethics.

Describe some basic precepts of economic theory and summarize their implications for the environment

- Classical economic theory proposes that individuals acting for their own economic good can benefit society as a whole. This view has provided a philosophical basis for free-market capitalism.

- Neoclassical economics focuses on consumer behaviour and supply and demand as forces that drive economic activity.
- Several assumptions of neoclassical economic theory contribute to environmental impact.

Compare the concepts of economic growth, economic health, and sustainability

- Conventional economic theory has promoted never-ending economic growth, with little regard to possible environmental impact.
- Economic growth is not necessarily required for overall economic well-being.
- In the long run, some economists believe that a steady-state economy will be necessary to achieve sustainability.

Explain the fundamentals of environmental economics, ecological economics, and natural resource accounting

- Environmental economists advocate reforming economic practices to promote sustainability. Key approaches are to identify external costs, assign value to nonmonetary items, find new approaches to measuring growth, and attempt to make market prices reflect real costs and benefits.
- Ecological economists support these efforts and others. Many support developing a steady-state economy.
- Consumer choice in the marketplace can help drive businesses and corporations to pursue sustainability goals.

TESTING YOUR COMPREHENSION

1. What does the study of ethics encompass? Describe the three classic ethical standards. What is environmental ethics?
2. Why in Western cultures have ethical considerations expanded to include non-human entities?
3. Describe the philosophical perspectives of anthropocentrism, biocentrism, and ecocentrism. How would you characterize the perspective of the Mirrar Clan?
4. Differentiate between the preservation ethic and the conservation ethic. Explain the contributions of John Muir, James Harkin, Gifford Pinchot, and Clifford Sifton in the history of environmental ethics.
5. Describe Aldo Leopold's "land ethic." How did Leopold define the "community" to which ethical standards should be applied?
6. Name four key contributions the environment makes to the economy.

7. For each of these basic tenets of neoclassical economics, explain the potential impacts on the environment and provide a hypothetical example:
   - Resources are infinite or substitutable.
   - Long-term effects should be discounted.
   - Costs and benefits are internal.
   - Growth is good.
8. Neoclassical economists have moved away from Adam Smith's original definition of *income* as "economic gains made with no negative impacts on the resource base." What are the environmental implications of straying from this definition of *income*?
9. Compare and contrast the views of neoclassical economists, environmental economists, and ecological economists.
10. What is contingent valuation, and what is one of its weaknesses? Describe an alternative method that addresses this weakness.

THINKING IT THROUGH

1. Do you feel that an introduction to environmental ethics and world views is an important part of a course in environmental science? Should ethics and world views be a component of other science courses? Explain your answers.

2. Describe your world view as it pertains to your relationship with the environment. How do you think your culture has influenced your world view? How do you think your personal experience has influenced it, including your gender and race? Do you feel that you fit into any particular category discussed in this chapter? Why or why not?

3. How would you analyze the case of the Mirrar Clan and the proposed Jabiluka uranium mine from each of the following perspectives? In your description, list two questions that a person of each perspective would likely ask when attempting to decide whether the mine should be developed. Be as specific as possible, and be sure to identify similarities and differences in approaches:

   ■ Preservationist
   ■ Conservationist
   ■ Deep ecologist
   ■ Environmental justice advocate
   ■ Indigenous land rights activist
   ■ Ecofeminist
   ■ Neoclassical economist
   ■ Ecological economist

4. Do you think we should attempt to quantify and assign market values to ecosystem services and other entities that have only nonmarket values? Why or why not? What is a steady-state economy? Do you think this model is a practical alternative to the growth paradigm? Why or why not?

5. A manufacturing facility on a river near your home provides jobs for 200 people in your community and pays $2 million in taxes to the local government each year. Sales taxes from purchases made by plant employees and their families contribute an additional $1 million to local government coffers. However, a recent peer-reviewed study in a well-respected scientific journal revealed that the plant has been discharging large amounts of waste into the river, causing a 25% increase in cancer rates, a 30% reduction in riverfront property values, and a 75% decrease in native fish populations.

   The plant owner says the facility can stay in business only because there are no regulations mandating expensive treatment of waste from the plant. If such regulations were imposed, he says he would close the plant, lay off its employees, and relocate to a more business-friendly community. How would you recommend resolving this situation? What further information would you want to know before making a recommendation? In arriving at your recommendation, how did you weigh the costs and benefits associated with each of the plant's impacts?

6. You are a researcher working for a large pharmaceutical company. You are doing botanical fieldwork, searching for a plant that may offer a new cure for cancer. Some of the indigenous people in the area have a deep understanding of the medicinal properties of local plants, and you would like to ask them some questions. Under what circumstances should you do this? What if you were to make a major discovery on the basis of something you learned from them, with potential earnings of billions of dollars for your company— would the people who passed along the crucial information have a legitimate claim to part of those earnings?

INTERPRETING GRAPHS AND DATA

Economists use various indicators of economic well-being. One that has been used for decades is the gross domestic product (GDP), the total monetary value of final goods and services produced each year. An alternative measure called the genuine progress indicator (GPI) is calculated as follows:

$$\text{GPI} = \text{GDP} + (\text{Benefits Ignored by GDP}) - (\text{Environmental Costs}) - (\text{Social and Economic Costs})$$

Benefits include such things as the value of parenting and volunteer work. Environmental costs include the costs of water, air, and noise pollution; loss of wetlands; depletion of nonrenewable resources; and other environmental damage. Social and economic costs include investment, lending, and borrowing costs; costs of crime, family breakdown, under-employment, commuting, pollution abatement, and automobile accidents; and loss of leisure time.

1. Describe economic growth as measured by GDP for the province of Alberta from 1961 to 2003. Now describe economic growth as measured by GPI over the same time period. To what factors would you attribute the growing difference between these measures?

2. For GPI to grow, one or more things must happen: Either GDP must grow faster, benefits must grow faster, or social, economic, and environmental costs must shrink relative to the other terms. How would you explain the changes in GDP and GPI over the past few decades for the province of Alberta? How do the data in the graph support your answer?

Components of GPI and GDP in Alberta, 1961–2003.
Source: Data from Pembina Institute, Alberta GPI Accounts, 1961–2003.

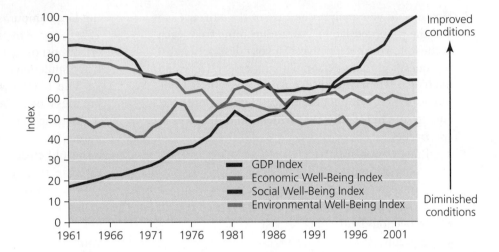

- GDP Index
- Economic Well-Being Index
- Social Well-Being Index
- Environmental Well-Being Index

3. Even with regulations for air and water pollution control, hazardous waste disposal, solid waste management, forestry practices, and species protection, environmental costs continue to increase. Why do you suppose the trend is still in that direction?

4. Alberta in the 2000s is in the midst of a huge economic boom, related largely to the development of the Athabasca and other fossil fuel deposits. How do you think this ongoing resource development will affect Alberta's GDP and GPI for the province over the next few decades? Think about all of the factors—economic, environmental, and social—that will play a role, and whether the impacts will likely be positive or negative.

CHAPTER ENDNOTES

1. This piece is based on a summary of *Mining Denendeh: A Dene Nation Perspective on Community Health Impacts of Mining,* by Chris Paci (Lands and Environment Department, Dene Nation) and Noeline Villebrun, Dene National Chief, prepared for the 2004 Mining Ministers Conference, Coppermine, Nunavut.

2. Regarding the incident of contamination that led to the mine's closure in 2004, as reported by Friends of the Environment, Australia, www.foe.org.au/media-releases/2004-media-releases/mr_24_3_04.htm

3. *The Age,* July 27, 2007, as cited by World Information Service on Energy, www.wise-uranium.org/upjab.html

4. Based partly on information from *Living with the Land: A Manual for Documenting Cultural Landscapes,* NWT Cultural Places Program, Government of NWT, 2007.

5. Voisey's Bay Nickel Mine, Ltd., www.vbnc.com/iba.asp

6. Parts of this paragraph are based on information from *Mining Denendeh: A Dene Nation Perspective on Community Health Impacts of Mining,* by Chris

Paci (Lands and Environment Department, Dene Nation) and Noeline Villebrun, Dene National Chief, prepared for the 2004 Mining Ministers Conference, Coppermine, Nunavut.

7. Based on information from the Canadian Museum of Civilization, James Bernard Harkin, www.civilization.ca/hist/biography/biographi204e.html

8. Based on information from Canadian Museum of Civilization, Clifford Sifton, www.civilization.ca/hist/advertis/ads2-06e.html

9. Leopold, A. *A Sand County Almanac,* Oxford University Press, New York, 1949.

10. Rajiv Rawat (1996, May) *Women of Uttarakhand: On the Frontiers of the Environmental Struggle,* http://uttarakhand.prayaga.org/chipko.html

11. Green Belt Movement, http://eratos.utm.utoronto.ca/research.htm; and other sources.

12. Recall that radioactivity had only been discovered some 30 years earlier, in the late 1890s.

13. Andrew Nikiforuk (1998) "Echoes of the Atomic Age: Cancer kills fourteen aboriginal uranium workers," *Calgary Herald,* Saturday, March 14.

14. World Information Service on Energy, *Decommissioning of Port Radium*, www.wise-uranium.org/-uippra.html#MORE

15. Radiation Exposure Compensation Program www.usdoj.gov/civil/torts/const/reca/; and "Navajo President Joe Shirley, Jr., updates Navajo miners on progress toward getting fair RECA compensation," September 2006.

16. Smith, A., *An Inquiry into the Nature and Causes of the Wealth of Nations* ("The Wealth of Nations"), first published in 1776.

17. Repetto, Robert (1992) Accounting for environment assets, *Scientific American*, June.

18. Environment Centre Northern Territory (Australia), *Mining Archives*, www.ecnt.org/index.html

19. Costanza, R., et al. (1997) The value of the world's ecosystem services and natural capital. *Nature* 387: 253–260.

20. Matthew Coon Come, *Goldman Prize*, www.goldmanprize.org/node/93; and other sources.

21. Matthew Coon Come, *Goldman Prize* www.goldmanprize.org/node/93; and other sources.

22. Government of Canada (2007) *Key Economic Events: 1972–The James Bay Project*, www.canadianeconomy.gc.ca/English/economy/1972James_Bay_Project.html

23. Government of Canada (2007) *Key Economic Events: 1972–The James Bay Project*, www.canadianeconomy.gc.ca/English/economy/1972James_Bay_Project.html

24. Government of Canada (2007) *Key Economic Events: 1972–The James Bay Project*, www.canadianeconomy.gc.ca/English/economy/1972James_Bay_Project.html

25. Nation Talk (2008) *General Statement by Matthew Coon Come*, June 13, www.nationtalk.ca/modules/news/article.php?storyid=10522

26. Daly, Herman E. (2001) Sustainable development and OPEC. Paper invited for the conference OPEC and the Global Energy Balance: Towards a Sustainable Energy Future. Vienna, Austria.

MyEnvironmentPlace

Go to **www.myenvironmentplace.ca** where you will find quizzes, animations, your Pearson eText, and more.

Environmental Policy: Decision Making and Problem Solving

22

Lake Erie has recovered from the worst of its pollution. However, the environmental woes of the lake are far from over.

Upon successfully completing this chapter, you will be able to

- Describe environmental policy and assess its societal context
- Identify the institutions important to Canadian environmental policy
- Recognize major Canadian environmental laws
- List the institutions involved with international environmental policy
- Categorize the different approaches to environmental policy
- Describe how nations handle transboundary issues

In this satellite image, sediment plumes can be seen swirling through the water. Rows of crops surround the lake. The Canada–U.S. international border runs lengthwise along the middle of Lake Erie.

Hudson Bay

CANADA

Lake Erie

UNITED STATES

CENTRAL CASE:
THE DEATH AND REBIRTH OF LAKE ERIE

"We must ask ourselves seriously whether we really wish some future universal historian on another planet to say about us: 'With all their genius and with all their skill, they ran out of foresight and air and food and water and ideas,' or, 'They went on playing politics until their world collapsed around them.'"
—U THANT, FORMER SECRETARY-GENERAL OF THE UNITED NATIONS, 1970

"When you get ready to vote, make sure you know what you're doing."
—BOB HUNTER, JOURNALIST, ACTIVIST, AND CO-FOUNDER OF GREENPEACE

During the 1970s, Lake Erie became infamous when it effectively "died" as a result of pollution. Sewage, fertilizers, phosphate-containing detergents, and other chemicals in runoff combined to result in over-fertilization, algal blooms, eutrophication, and oxygen depletion. The water turned a sickly green colour, and the lake was widely declared to be dead. The water subsequently became so depleted in oxygen that portions of it became crystal clear—not because it was "clean," but because it was incapable of supporting aquatic life.

Lake Erie is the smallest of the Great Lakes in volume and depth, though not in surface area. Erie therefore is lacking the very cold, deep waters that characterize the larger lakes (notably Superior). It is slightly warmer, circulates nutrients more effectively, and is the most biologically productive of the Great Lakes. Erie is surrounded by agricultural land, with significant industrial development and a population that has surged. These factors combined to expose this most sensitive of the Great Lakes to an onslaught of chemicals that overloaded its capacity.

A concentrated international effort brought Lake Erie back from the brink of disaster. After tough legal

Through the *Canada–U.S. Great Lakes Water Quality Agreement (GLWQA)*, Canada and the United States have identified 43 Areas of Concern (AOCs) around the Great Lakes. Each of these has associated with it a Remedial Action Plan, or RAP. There are currently eight AOCs associated with Lake Erie.

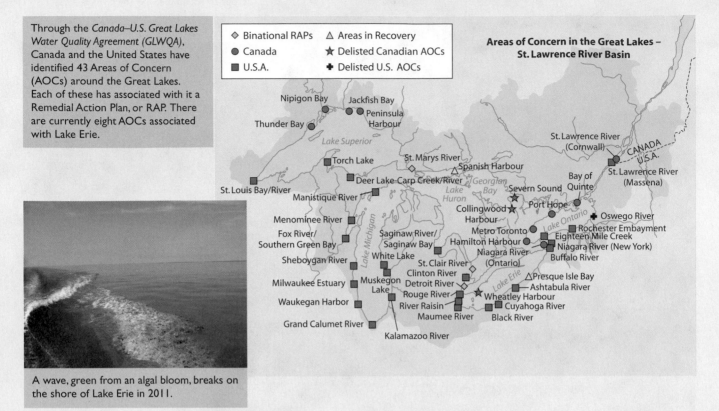

Areas of Concern in the Great Lakes – St. Lawrence River Basin

◇ Binational RAPs   △ Areas in Recovery
● Canada   ★ Delisted Canadian AOCs
■ U.S.A.   ✚ Delisted U.S. AOCs

A wave, green from an algal bloom, breaks on the shore of Lake Erie in 2011.

restrictions on nutrient runoff were implemented on both sides of the border, improvements began to be seen. By the 1980s, nutrient levels in the lake had decreased sufficiently that aquatic populations began to rebound. Achieving this required significant cross-border communication and collaboration on policy and decision making.

The principal binational agreement governing the Great Lakes is the *Canada–U.S. Great Lakes Water Quality Agreement (GLWQA)*. Its precursor was the *Boundary Waters Treaty* of 1909, which set up a mechanism for resolving international disputes over transboundary water resources and established the *International Joint Commission (IJC)* to ensure the respective and common interests of Canada and the United States. Given the significance of the Great Lakes, which contain about 22% of the world's fresh water, with a total surface area of 244 100 km², it is not surprising that this is where much of the work of the IJC has been focused.

In 1972, in response to the "death" of Lake Erie, other pollution crises of the early 1970s, and the increasing environmental awareness of citizens, Canada and the United States signed the *GLWQA*. Its main objective is to restore and maintain the chemical, physical, and biological integrity of the waters of the Great Lakes basin ecosystem, including the St. Lawrence River system.

Under the *GLWQA*, Canada and the United States have designated 43 Areas of Concern (AOCs) in the lakes and connecting channels. Sixteen are in Canada; eight are associated with Lake Erie (see figure). By definition, AOCs are areas in which environmental degradation is pronounced, such that restrictions must be placed on swimming, fishing, and drinking water consumption. Some AOCs, especially those associated with connecting channels, are of particular concern because they contribute to the overall degradation of the Great Lakes. For each AOC, an individually tailored *Remedial Action Plan*, or RAP, has been developed.

The RAPs focus on specific locations, but more holistic *Lakewide Management Plans (LaMPs)* have been created for Erie, Ontario, and Superior. The Lake Erie LaMP involves the province of Ontario, Great Lakes states, and a network of other stakeholders. The goal is to describe the lake's problems, identify the source of the problems, and envision the preferred future state of the resource.[1]

Efforts to cooperate on behalf of the Great Lakes have not been restricted to the two federal governments. The government of Canada has reached an agreement with the province of Ontario, called the *Canada–Ontario Agreement Respecting the Great Lakes Basin Ecosystem (COA)*. Its intention is to promote cooperative action between Canada and Ontario to restore and sustain the environmental quality of the Great Lakes. The Great Lakes states and a number of Tribal Nations in the United States participate in similar agreements.

Lake Erie recovered from the worst of its pollution after the *GLWQA* came into effect. However, the environmental woes of the lake are far from over. For example, phosphate levels in the lake—largely under control since the 1980s—began to increase in the mid-1990s. Invasive species, such as the zebra mussel, are having complex

impacts on native populations. Bioaccumulative toxins in the lake are of concern, as well as recurring algal blooms. The Lake Erie LaMP will attempt to propose solutions for a cleaner, healthier lake.

Who knew that it would take so many decades, so many organizations (and acronyms), and so much effort to get two nations to work together for the good of this crucial resource? The rescue of Lake Erie is one example of how people and organizations work together to achieve environmental goals and how laws and policies directly influence the environment.

Environmental Policy

When a society reaches broad agreement that a problem exists, it may persuade its leaders to try to resolve the problem through the making of policy. *Policy* is a formal set of general plans and principles intended to address problems and guide decision making in specific instances. *Public policy* is policy made by governments, consisting of laws, regulations, orders, incentives, and practices intended to advance societal welfare. **Environmental policy** is policy that pertains to human interactions with the environment. It generally aims to regulate resource

use or reduce pollution to promote human welfare and/or protect natural systems.

Forging effective policy requires input from science, ethics, and economics. Science provides the information and analysis needed to identify and understand environmental problems and devise potential solutions to them. Ethics and economics offer criteria to assess the extent and nature of problems and to help clarify how society might like to address them. Government interacts with individual citizens, organizations, and the private sector in a variety of ways to formulate policy (**FIGURE 22.1**).

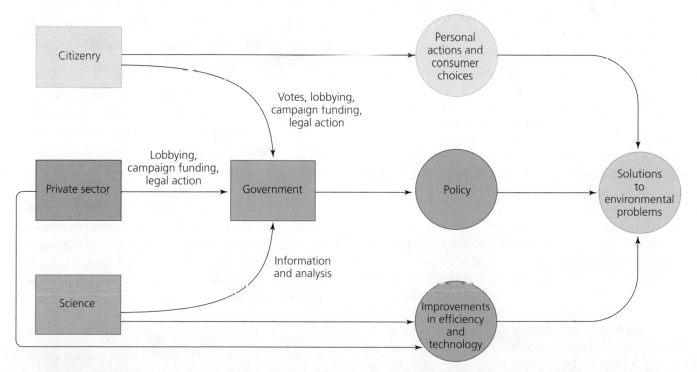

FIGURE 22.1   Policy plays a central role in how we as a society address environmental problems. Voters, the private sector, and groups representing various interests influence government representatives. Scientific research also informs government decisions. Governmental representatives and agencies formulate policy that aims to address social problems, including environmental problems. Public policy—along with improvements in technology and efficiency from the private sector and personal actions and consumer purchasing choices exercised by citizens—can produce lasting solutions to environmental problems.

The problems of Lake Erie show how science, economics, and ethics can inform and motivate policy, both domestically and internationally. Scientific research tells us that agricultural and urban runoff carries potentially harmful pathogens and other contaminants. Science also reveals how excess organic material can radically alter conditions for aquatic and marine life, lowering concentrations of dissolved oxygen and increasing mortality for many species. Pollution and beach closures and impacts on fisheries inflict economic loss by reducing recreation, tourism, and other economic activity associated with clean water and coastal areas. Ethically, water pollution poses problems because pollution from upstream users degrades water quality for downstream users.

Many environmental problems share this combination of impacts—harming human health, altering ecological systems, inflicting economic damage, and creating inequities among people. In the Great Lakes, as in many other environmental systems, all of this takes place in a transboundary, multijurisdictional context, with political pressures from both domestic and international sources.

Environmental policy addresses issues of equity

The economic systems of modern democracies are largely driven by incentives for short-term economic gain rather than long-term social and environmental stability. Market capitalism provides little incentive for businesses or individuals to behave in ways that minimize environmental impact or equalize costs and benefits among parties. Such market failure has traditionally been viewed as justification for government intervention. Environmental policy is one such intervention, which aims to protect environmental quality and natural resources and to promote equity in people's use of resources.

The tragedy of the commons   Policy to protect resources held in common by the public is intended to safeguard these resources from depletion or degradation. As Garrett Hardin explained in his essay "The Tragedy of the Commons,"[2] a resource held in common that is accessible to all and is unregulated will eventually become overused and degraded. Therefore, he argued, it is in our best interest to develop guidelines for the use of such resources. In Hardin's illustrative example of a commonly owned pasture, guidelines might limit the number of animals each individual can graze or might require pasture users to pay to restore and manage the

shared resource. These two concepts—regulation of use and active management—are central to environmental policy today.

The tragedy of the commons does not always play itself out as Hardin predicted. Some traditional societies have devised safeguards against exploitation, and in modern Western societies resource users have occasionally cooperated to prevent overexploitation. Moreover, in many cases Hardin's starting assumptions are not met; resources on public lands may not be equally accessible to everyone but may instead be more accessible to wealthier or more established resource extraction industries. Nonetheless, the threat of overexploiting public resources is real and has been a driving force behind much environmental policy.

Free riders   Another reason to develop policy for publicly held resources is the so-called *free rider* problem. Let us say a community on a river suffers from water pollution that emanates from 10 different factories. The problem could in theory be solved if every factory voluntarily agreed to reduce its own pollution. However, once they all begin reducing their pollution, it becomes tempting for any one of them to stop doing so. Such a factory, by avoiding the sacrifices others are making, would in essence get a "free ride" on the efforts of others. If enough factories take a free ride, the whole effort will collapse.

weighing the issues
PRIVATE VERSUS PUBLIC GOOD

Imagine you have purchased land and plan to clear its forest and build condominiums on it. A local environmental group finds an endangered plant species on the property and petitions the government to prevent development of the land. Should you be allowed to build? If not, should you be financially compensated?

Now imagine that you are a member of the environmental group and a neighbour of the landowner in question. The land holds the last stand of forest in this region. You feel your quality of life and that of your neighbours will be compromised if the development goes ahead. Should you be allowed to claim damages in civil court? Make a case why the landowner should not be allowed to build.

Which argument do you feel has greater merit? What is the best way to balance private property rights with protection of the public good in cases like this?

Because of the free rider problem, private voluntary efforts are often less effective than efforts mandated by public policy. Public policy can prevent free riders and ensure that all parties sacrifice equitably by enforcing compliance with laws and regulations or by taxing parties to attain funds with which to pursue societal goals.

External costs   Environmental policy is also developed to ensure that some parties do not use resources in ways that harm others. One way to promote fairness is by dealing openly with *externalities* and *external costs*, harmful impacts that result from market transactions but are borne by people not involved in the transactions. For example, a factory may reap greater profits by discharging waste freely into a river and avoiding paying for proper waste disposal. Its actions, however, impose external costs (water pollution, decreased fish populations, esthetic degradation, or other problems) on downstream users of the river (**FIGURE 22.2**).

For example, downstream pollution is a problem in the estuary of the St. Lawrence River. The pollution that ends up in the estuary originates far upstream. It comes from the industries, towns, and farms that line the river, all the way upstream to the shores of the Great Lakes. The costs—both economic and ecological—of downstream pollution are passed along to someone else or to society as a whole and are not directly internalized to the activities that generated the pollution in the first place.

These, then, are the fundamental goals of environmental policy: to protect resources and to promote equity by eliminating free riders and addressing external costs.

Many factors hinder implementation of environmental policy

If the goals of environmental policy are seemingly so noble, why is it that environmental laws are so often challenged, environmental regulations frequently derided, and the ideas of environmental activists ignored or rejected by citizens and policy makers?

In North America, most environmental policy has come in the form of laws instituted by government regulators. Some businesses and individuals view these regulations as overly restrictive, bureaucratic, or unresponsive to human needs. For instance, many landowners fear that zoning regulations or protections for endangered species will impose restrictions on their activities or on the use of their land. Developers complain of time and money lost to bureaucracy in obtaining permits; reviews by government agencies; surveys for endangered species; and required environmental controls, monitoring, and mitigation. In the eyes of such property owners and businesspeople, environmental regulation all too often means inconvenience ("red tape") and economic loss.

Another reason people sometimes do not see a need for environmental policy stems from the nature of most environmental problems, which often develop gradually. The degradation of ecosystems and public health caused by human impact on the environment is a long-term process. Human behaviour is geared toward addressing short-term needs, and this tendency is reflected in our social institutions. Businesses usually opt for short-term

FIGURE 22.2
River pollution raises many issues that have been viewed as justification for environmental policy. This woman washing clothes in the river may suffer upstream pollution from factories, and her use of detergents may cause pollution for people living downstream.

economic gain over long-term considerations. The news media have a short attention span based on the daily news cycle, whereby new events are given more coverage than slowly developing long-term trends. Politicians often act out of short-term interest because they depend on reelection every few years. For all these reasons, many environmental policy goals that seem admirable and that attract wide public support in theory may be obstructed in their practical implementation.

Canadian Environmental Law and Policy

Canadians have been leaders in the development of environmental management approaches and policies. However, our approach to environmental management, law, and policy has been inevitably influenced by the United States. This is partly because we are next-door neighbours; it is also because we have economies that are closely linked, as well as a shared history of life on this continent.

Canada's environmental policies are influenced by our neighbour

The United States was a leader in the early development of national-level environmental laws, passing the first comprehensive environmental protection law (*National Environmental Protection Act, NEPA*) in 1970. This led, in turn, to the creation of the Environmental Protection Agency (EPA). Canada followed shortly thereafter, with the establishment of Environment Canada, mandated by the *Department of the Environment Act* in 1971. Most countries in the world have now followed the lead of Canada and the United States in this regard.

Canada is also heavily influenced by the United States in its environmental management approach because of their trading relationship, now governed largely by the North American Free Trade Agreement (NAFTA), which regulates how marketable commodities are handled. This includes things like wood, agricultural crops, and animal products. NAFTA even identifies water resources as a marketable commodity that should not be restricted from export.

Canadian environmental management also is strongly influenced by the sheer extent of the environmental resources we share with our southern neighbour—across the 8891 km of the world's longest undefended border we share countless rivers and watersheds, rock and soil masses, airsheds and weather systems, animal migration paths, and ecosystems. In the past, and still today, human activities on both sides of the border have negatively affected people and ecosystems on the other side. For example, we have previously in this book discussed how agriculture in the Fraser River Valley may be causing nitrate contamination of an aquifer that is shared with the residents of upstate Washington. We also examined how industrial emissions from the central and northeastern states are transported into southern Canada, leading to smog and acid precipitation.

Sometimes Americans and Canadians don't agree on how our shared natural systems and cross-border impacts should be managed. For the most part, however, Canada–U.S. binational management of transboundary pollution and shared environmental resources has been characterized by cooperation and dialogue, and serves as a successful model for international environmental management. We have mentioned a number of these collaborations; an example is the IJC, which was instrumental in the recovery of Lake Erie.

Legal instruments are used to ensure environmental goals are achieved

Government agencies rely on several types of instruments to achieve environmental goals. Acts are laws, or statutes, proposed and voted upon by the Parliament of Canada or the provincial and territorial parliaments. **Regulations** are legal instruments, too, but they are more specific; they are detailed sets of requirements (such as numerical limits, licensing requirements, performance specifications, and exemption criteria) established by governments to allow them to implement, enforce, and achieve the objectives of environmental acts.

Agreements can be either enforceable or voluntary; they are entered into by agencies of government, often with the goal of streamlining, clarifying, or harmonizing the administration of environmental legislation. **Permits** are documents that grant a group or an individual legal permission to carry out an activity that will have environmental impacts, usually within certain limitations and for a specified period of time. Examples at the federal level include permits governing the disposal of substances at sea, import and export of hazardous wastes, and hunting of migratory birds.[3] We will examine agreements, permits, and other types of nonbinding instruments in greater detail later in the chapter.

In Canada there are four basic ways in which individuals and organizations can be required or compelled to obey environmental laws or penalized if they do not obey the law. They are criminal enforcement; penalties or fees; administrative orders to investigate, clean up, or otherwise address an environmental situation of concern; and finally, civil actions, through which an individual or corporation that causes environmental damage to another's property or person may be held responsible for the damage via a lawsuit.[4]

Environmental goals and best practices can be promoted by voluntary initiatives

One alternative to environmental legislation that appeals to many in the private sector is the adoption, by consensus, of *voluntary guidelines* that are sector-based and self-enforced. A familiar example is self-policing by television and music producers for content deemed too violent for children. Some sectors have had success with this approach; others have not. The Canadian mining industry, for example, which is heavily regulated by both federal and provincial environmental legislation, has undertaken some voluntary initiatives and self-imposed guidelines on behalf of the environment. Examples include guidelines on the use of traditional ecological knowledge in mining and best practices for the management of acid drainage at mine sites. The Accelerated Reduction and Elimination of Toxics (ARET) Program was a voluntary initiative that involved industries from a number of sectors, including mining, as well as government agencies and nongovernmental organizations. The program issued a proactive challenge to industry to reduce emissions of toxic substances in advance of legislation and was successful in reaching many of its targets.

An example of voluntary guidelines for environmental practice that have been widely adopted on an international scale is the ISO 14001 standards for environmental management. *ISO* is the *International Organization for Standardization*, a nongovernmental organization with 157 member nations that is headquartered in Geneva, Switzerland. Probably the best-known set of international standards is ISO 9000, aimed at ensuring the consistent use of best practices for quality assurance in industrial processes. The ISO 14000 series was similarly designed to promote consistency and best practices, but in the specific context of environmental management. If a factory, office, government, or other type of organization chooses to become certified under ISO 14001, it voluntarily agrees to meet the standards and follow accepted procedures for environmental management. In turn, it becomes eligible to promote itself as an ISO 14001-certified organization.

It is open to debate whether voluntary initiatives and self-policing are as effective as legislation in achieving environmental goals. Some critics argue that industry is simply seeking to avoid legislation or—more cynically—trying to divert attention from its environmental shortcomings. Even those in industry who favour voluntary initiatives acknowledge that these generally represent the "best practices" of the most proactive, environmentally responsible companies and that legislation is needed in order to avoid free riders that do not follow the voluntary guidelines.

Canadian environmental policy arises from all levels of government

Even with the influence of such a populous nation and heavyweight economy right next door, Canadians have developed our own approach to environmental management and regulation. This approach has tended to make environmental management collaborative, cooperative, and consultative (**FIGURE 22.3**). It is codified in the *Canadian Environmental Protection Act* (1999) that the administration of the act falls to Environment Canada, but all other aspects of its implementation are collaborative. Public consultation also is part of the wording of the act.

In Canada, the federal government shares responsibility for environmental protection with provincial/territorial, Aboriginal, and municipal/local governments. The principal responsibility for the environment falls to the provincial/territorial governments in most situations. This multilevel approach necessitates close collaboration among the levels and agencies of government; sometimes it results in overlapping and redundancies, confusion of jurisdictions, and even contradictions between provincial and federal law.

One way the government attempts to overcome the overlapping of environmental jurisdictions is through the Canadian Council of Ministers of the Environment (CCME), which includes the federal, provincial, and territorial environment ministers. They meet regularly to work on projects of mutual and overlapping interest. For example, the CCME is developing a set of nation-wide standards, the Canadian Environmental Quality Guidelines. The first harmonized standards, for water quality, were signed into accord by the ministers in 1987. Since then, several sets of standards and refinements for water quality (for various uses) and for sediment and soil quality have been added. Similarly, the Natural Ambient Air Quality Objectives (NAAQOs) have established goals, benchmarks, and testing protocols for common air pollutants. The NAAQOs are considered to be a standard, but provinces and territories may nevertheless interpret and implement these standards differently.

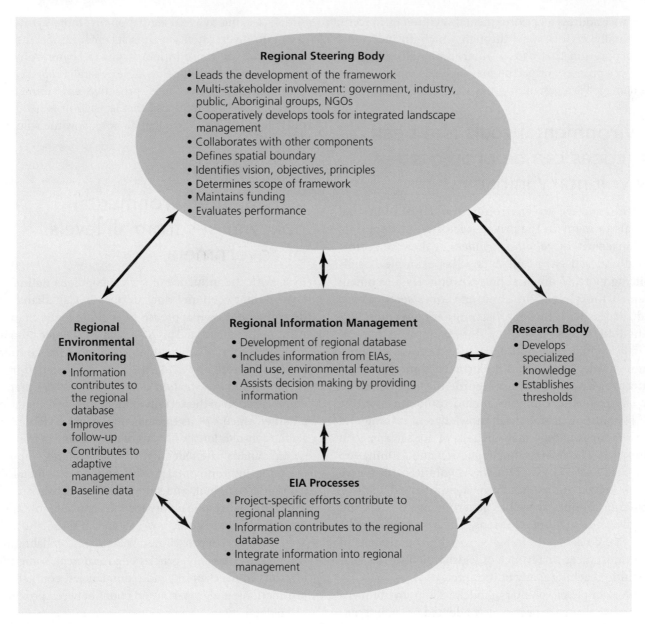

FIGURE 22.3   The Canadian approach to environmental management has always been consultative. The management process shown here, from the Canadian Environmental Assessment Agency, is based on a model for the management of cumulative effects in the region of Cold Lake, Alberta. In this model, stakeholders bring information from a wide variety of sources, to be applied collaboratively to determine a solution to an environmental problem.

Federal government   There are many federal-level laws that affect the environment, some directly and others indirectly. Some of the most important are the following:

■   *Canadian Environmental Protection Act* (CEPA) (1999), the centrepiece of Canada's federal-level environment legislation. CEPA focuses on preventing pollution and protecting the environment and human health. The act gives the government broad enforcement powers and mandates public participation and consultation, giving citizens input into environmental policy decisions.[5]

■   *Canadian Environmental Assessment Act* (1992), which requires any project involving federal funds and lands, Aboriginal lands, or international effects to undertake an **environmental impact assessment (EIA)**, a study of the potential impacts of the project on the environment. The depth or magnitude of the assessment, the specific requirements, and the mitigation efforts that may be required depend on the extent and type of project.

■   *Fisheries Act* (1985), which prohibits the release of "deleterious substances" into any body of water where fish may be present at any time. The Fisheries Act has proven to be one of the most powerful laws that can be brought to bear on the protection of water resources.

- *Transportation of Dangerous Goods Act* (1992), which regulates the transport of hazardous materials in Canada by air, road, rail, or ship, no matter what the purpose or point of origin of the transfer. Hazardous waste materials are also covered under this act.
- *Canadian Wildlife Act* (1985), *Migratory Birds Act* (1994), and *Species at Risk Act* (2002), all of which aim, in various ways, to respect the needs, identify risk factors, and protect organisms in Canada from harm or extinction.

Environment Canada is charged with the administration, implementation, and enforcement of CEPA and several other acts, collaborating in this effort with a wide variety of other federal-level departments. For example, Environment Canada and Health Canada together decide on the allowable levels for various contaminants in drinking water; the regulations are then published by Health Canada. Some other federal-level agencies that commonly work with Environment Canada to set environmental policy and implement environmental legislation are listed in **TABLE 22.1**.

Provincial/territorial governments   The provincial and territorial governments are very active in environmental protection and regulation. The specific details of content and procedure vary from one provincial jurisdiction to the next, but there is some consistency. For example, all of the provincial and territorial governments have some form of legislation that sets limits on the amounts and concentrations of specific harmful or potentially harmful substances that can be released (or *discharged*) into the environment. (The exact limits and the specific lists of controlled substances vary, but the approaches are similar.)

All of the provinces and territories also require organizations and individuals to obtain approvals or permits before undertaking activities that might prove damaging to the environment. For example, the taking of water from aquifers or surface water bodies in amounts over a certain threshold requires a special permit. Construction, dredging, mining, and logging are other examples of activities that are regulated provincially and territorially, and require approval before being undertaken.

In Ontario, citizens are protected by an Environmental Bill of Rights (EBR, 1994), one of the few such laws in the world. The EBR, administered by the appointed Environmental Commissioner of Ontario, establishes that the people of Ontario have as a common goal the protection of the natural environment. It guarantees to all Ontarians the right to a clean, healthy environment and the right to participate in and be made aware of

Table 22.1 Federal Agencies that Influence and Implement Environmental Policy and Natural Resource Management

- **Environment Canada**, which encompasses a number of agencies, including the Canadian Environmental Assessment Agency, Parks Canada, Canadian Wildlife Service, Meteorological Service of Canada, and other agencies and regional offices
- **Health Canada**, which participates in scientific research concerning disease and the health risks of exposure to substances and in the setting of regulatory guidelines for potentially harmful substances in water, air, soil, and food
- **Fisheries and Oceans Canada**, which has the central responsibility for the implementation and enforcement of the Fisheries Act
- **Natural Resources Canada** (including the Office of Energy Efficiency), which promotes the responsible use of Canada's natural resources
- **Agriculture and Agri-Foods Canada**, which provides information, research, technology, policies, and programs for security of the food system, soils, and agricultural lands
- **Natural Sciences and Engineering Research Council (NSERC) of Canada**, which funds scientific research on the environment and related technologies
- **Indian and Northern Affairs**, which (among other roles) promotes the sustainable development of Aboriginal communities and their natural resources
- **Transport Canada**, which regulates the transport of hazardous materials by air, rail, road, and sea in Canada, as well as playing a major role in transportation system design and in Canada's efforts to reduce greenhouse gas emissions
- **Statistics Canada**, which maintains extensive databases on population, patterns of travel, consumption, trade, lifestyle, and other human activities that affect the environment
- Many other agencies, some of which come into play primarily or exclusively when it becomes necessary to respond to an emergency, such as a major flood

government decisions regarding the environment. The EBR mandates the establishment and maintenance of an Environmental Registry whereby any citizen may enter a query against an activity that may be damaging the environment, to which the government and/or industry agents responsible for that activity are required to respond.[6]

Aboriginal governments   Aboriginal governments in Canada participate in environmental governance through a wide variety of mechanisms. In some cases, this involvement stems directly from land claims. For example, Aboriginal governments are extensively involved in decision making about where, when, and under what conditions to allow resource extraction activities, such as mining, forestry, or oil drilling, to proceed on Indian lands. The settlement of land claims and legal establishment of resource rights are central to such activities.

In other cases, involvement stems from the desire to ensure adequate Aboriginal representation in environmental decision making. For example, Aboriginal communities have been represented in all decision making regarding the Mackenzie River Valley natural gas pipeline. Local Aboriginal groups also participate extensively in stakeholder consultations and scientific efforts to document traditional resource use patterns and traditional ecological knowledge of the environment. Modern diamond mining companies in the Northwest Territories depend heavily on collaborations with Aboriginal stakeholders.

Much of Aboriginal involvement in environmental management in Canada is based on ensuring equitable access to natural resources and preventing excessive exposure of Aboriginal communities to environmental degradation. These are the two central concerns of the environmental justice movement. For example, there is an ongoing struggle in Canada to ensure adequate drinking-water quality in Aboriginal communities—a resource that most of the rest of Canada takes for granted.

Municipal/local governments The legal landscape is further complicated by the role taken by municipal governments in environmental regulation and enforcement, a role that is growing in importance. Municipalities in Canada have traditionally taken responsibility for the management of water and sewage systems, noise issues, waste disposal, land-use zoning to regulate development, and local air quality concerns, such as requiring permits for backyard burning of yard wastes. All of these traditional roles have some environmental influence.

Expanding their environmental role, many municipalities have passed bylaws that restrict or prohibit the use of pesticides and herbicides on lawns in urban and suburban areas, even if their use is still approved by the provincial government. Other municipalities have adopted initiatives to deal with sprawl and transportation issues across municipal boundaries (**FIGURE 22.4**). Many urban municipalities are becoming more involved in the documentation, monitoring, and even regulation of brownfields, contaminated sites that may become available for redevelopment once they have been rehabilitated to provincial standards. Some municipalities have even entered into agreements to limit CO_2 emissions—the type of action that traditionally has fallen within the jurisdiction of the federal government.

International agreements In addition to federal, provincial/territorial, and municipal legislation, Canadians (and anyone operating a business within Canada) are also governed by the various international agreements Canada has entered into. For example, it is

Canadian Municipal Pesticide Bylaws

FIGURE 22.4

Many municipalities are expanding their traditional environmental roles in water and waste management to encompass other environmental initiatives, policy, and legislation. This graph shows the increasing number of municipalities in Canada that have enacted bylaws banning the local use of pesticides, effectively bypassing provincial environmental legislation.

Source: Based on data from Coalition for a Healthy Ottawa (2010) Canadian Municipal Pesticide Bylaws, http://www.flora.org/healthyottawa/BylawList.pdf

illegal to import elephant ivory into Canada because Canada is a party to the United Nations Convention on International Trade in Endangered Species. We will discuss the various approaches to international environmental law in greater detail, below.

Government and ENGOs work together on environmental issues

The Canadian approach to environmental management is consultative; in fact, as mentioned above, public participation and consultation are mandated by CEPA. This means that government typically does not undertake

roots

STAKEHOLDER

The word **stakeholder** (*stake* + *holder*) comes from the Old English word *staca*, which referred to a stake that could be driven into the ground and used as a fencepost or property marker. A *holder* is someone who has temporary or permanent ownership of something. Therefore, the *stakeholder* is a person who owns or has a legitimate interest in the property in question.

any major revisions to policy without extensive consultation with stakeholders. A **stakeholder** is any person or group that has an interest in, or might be affected by, the outcome of a particular undertaking. This includes both environmental projects and policies (see **FIGURE 22.3**, for example).

Individual citizen stakeholders in environmental policy development are often represented by **environmental nongovernmental organizations (ENGOs)**. These can be activist groups, such as Greenpeace; or political advocacy groups, like the Sierra Club, Riverkeepers, or the Environmental Defence Fund; or groups with specific mandates, such as the Nature Conservancy, which aims to preserve land, habitat, and ecosystems by acquiring and setting aside land in trust. Stakeholders in the industrial sector may be represented by sector-specific nongovernmental agencies. For example, the Protected Areas Initiative in Manitoba employs an extensive process of public consultation on the environmental impacts of mining, in which the mining industry is represented by the Mining Association of Manitoba and the Mineral Exploration Liaison Committee; the government of Manitoba is represented by staff from the Department of

Conservation and the Manitoba Geological Survey and Mines Branch; and other stakeholders are represented by World Wildlife Fund Canada.

Other types of agencies can be involved in the environmental management process in some circumstances. For example, a Crown corporation called the Ontario Clean Water Agency has been in charge of cleaning up the municipal water supply in the town of Walkerton, Ontario, since the deadly episode of contamination there in 2000.

Another collaborative and consultative vehicle that is commonly used in Canada is the **round table**, a multi-stakeholder working group established to consult on a particular issue, generally within a particular sector or area of concern. Round tables involve representatives from a variety of governmental, nongovernmental, and private-sector organizations. The *National Round Table on the Environment and the Economy (NRTEE)* was established in 1988 as an advisory council to the prime minister. The NRTEE has 25 appointed members, representing a variety of regions, sectors, and disciplines, including business, labour, environmental organizations, academic institutions, and First Nations. They develop recommendations on how best to integrate environmental, economic, and social considerations into decision making.[7]

roots

ROUND TABLE

The term **round table** (or *roundtable*) refers to a gathering in which all participants have equal status (because a round table has no head). Wace, a twelfth-century Anglo-Norman poet, wrote a poetic history of England called *Roman de Brut* in which he described a round table that King Arthur supposedly used in the sixth century to stop quarrelling among his barons.

Different environmental media require different regulatory approaches

The laws governing different environmental media—water, land, forests, mineral resources, and even plants, animals, and air—have built upon different legal precedents. Let us briefly consider how these historical precedents influence the legal landscape today.

For example, water law in Canada has developed from two different historical/legal concepts. The first is called **riparian** law, in reference to the *riparian zone*, or water's edge. In riparian law, anyone who has legal access to the water's edge (such as by owning property on a river bank) has the right to withdraw water from the resource. The second legal concept in water law is **prior appropriation**. This refers to the "first come, first right" principle, in which one's right to withdraw water is established by historical precedent—if you have always withdrawn water from this river, then your right to do so has been established historically.

There are three basic models for water management, depending on whether the resource is public, private, or common property. For public ownership, management of the resource is typically by a government agency.

In private ownership models, resource allocations are primarily controlled and reallocated by market transactions. For common property resources, the management model usually requires users to work cooperatively to establish the rules granting access to the resource. In Canada, the Crown owns all water, and water rights are granted by licence; therefore these distinctions of ownership technically do not apply. However, all three management models are used in water management to greater or lesser degrees, varying somewhat in emphasis and the details of application from province to province.[8]

Many of the environmental problems in natural resource management today were not evident when these historical precedents were set. Groundwater depletion wasn't a problem a hundred years ago, and neither was pollution. These have necessitated some interesting reconsiderations of water law. For example, if you spill a toxic chemical on land that you own, you might not be held liable for any damages; however, if the toxic chemical infiltrates, joins the groundwater, and then migrates in the subsurface into the groundwater in your neighbour's property, contaminating the aquifer and wells there, you would be liable for damages.

The right to govern and allocate water and other natural resources was granted to the provinces by the federal government, which continues to play a role (in the management of fisheries, for example). For the eastern provinces, the transfer of rights to govern and allocate access to natural resources happened at the time of Confederation; for the western provinces, it didn't happen until the *Natural Resources Transfer Act* of 1930. These transfers of jurisdiction over land and natural resources from the federal to the provincial governments happened with little or no regard for the rights of prior Aboriginal inhabitants of the land.

The history of land law and especially mining law in Canada is intricately connected to Aboriginal land claims. There are two categories of Aboriginal land claims in Canada—those for which treaties exist and those for which no treaty exists. Resolving these claims often rests on establishing traditional occupancy and continuous use of lands and resources (**FIGURE 22.5**).

Environmental policy has changed with the society and the economy

Environmental policy in North America has evolved, along with social and economic conditions, in tandem with and influenced by the evolution of environmental ethics. From the 1780s to the late 1800s, environmental law dealt primarily with the management of public

FIGURE 22.5
Aboriginal representatives gathered at to Nelson House, Manitoba, in 1910 for a treaty signing, where the representatives asked many questions about the continuation of their resource rights. The Treaty Commissioner is reported to have assured them that "not for many years to come, probably not in the lifetime of any of them, would their hunting rights be interfered with."
Source (photo): Archives of Manitoba; Source (quote): Frank Tough, Economic Aspects of Aboriginal Title in Northern Manitoba: Treaty 5 Adhesions and Métis Scrip, Manitoba History, 15, Spring 1988.

lands. It grew from early explorations and accompanied the westward expansion of settlers across the continent. This period is associated with a "frontier ethic," characterized by efforts to tame and conquer the wilderness. Environmental laws of this period were intended to promote settlement and the extraction and use of the continent's abundant natural resources.

In the late 1800s, as the continent became more populated and its resources were increasingly exploited, public perception and government policy toward natural resources began to shift. Laws of this period aimed to regulate resource use and mitigate some of the environmental problems associated with westward expansion. Policies were influenced by the emergence of the conservation and preservation ethics. This period saw the opening of the first national parks, including Banff National Park in 1885.

Probably no person is more emblematic of this period in Canada than Clifford Sifton, minister of the interior in the late 1800s and early 1900s. Under Sifton's policies, wave upon wave of immigrants were encouraged to move into Canada's West to settle the Prairie grasslands and convert them into farms. Sifton recognized the value of Canada's natural resources, but unlike some others he also realized that those resources were not unlimited. He saw conservation and reforestation as an economic necessity and created a forestry branch of the department of the interior with the goal of regulating logging (**FIGURE 22.6**) and conserving federal forests. Later he commissioned detailed studies of all Canadian natural resources and came to be known as the "father of conservation" in Canada.

FIGURE 22.6
Early natural resource laws in North America were intended to encourage westward expansion, settlement, land clearing, and resource development. Here, loggers in the late 1800s fell large cedars in British Columbia.
Source: Library and Archives Canada.

Land management policies continued to develop through the twentieth century, targeting soil conservation in the Dust Bowl years, with initiatives like the Prairie Farm Rehabilitation Administration (1935), and extending through the establishment of the National Soil Conservation Program in 1986.

The next wave of environmental policy responded mainly to pollution and environmental crises, and built upon public awareness of the impacts of environmental degradation. During the 1960s and 1970s, several events triggered increased awareness of environmental problems and brought about a shift in public priorities and important changes in public policy. One landmark event was the 1962 publication of *Silent Spring*, by American scientist and writer Rachel Carson (**FIGURE 22.7**). *Silent Spring* awakened the public to the negative ecological and health effects of pesticides and industrial chemicals. (The book's title refers to Carson's warning that pesticides might kill so many birds that few would be left to sing in springtime.)

Several other books brought to the public consciousness environmental issues such as the limitations of resources, the impacts of human activities, and the health implications of environmental degradation. Among these

were *The Limits to Growth* (1972),[9] one of the very first efforts to use computers to develop quantitative models to explore the interplay among population growth, resource use, and resource depletion; *The Population Bomb* (1968),[10] an extreme neo-Malthusian call for action against uncontrolled human population growth; and *Diet for a Small Planet* (1971),[11] probably the first widely read book linking food and vegetarianism with the responsible use of the planet's resources.

The impacts of pollution on surface water bodies also became starkly evident to the average citizen. The "death" of Lake Erie in the early 1970s was a highly publicized environmental disaster. The Cuyahoga River (**FIGURE 22.8**), which flows into Lake Erie, also did its part to bring attention to the hazards of pollution. The Cuyahoga was so polluted with oil and industrial waste that the river actually caught fire near Cleveland, Ohio, more than half a dozen times during the 1950s and 1960s. This spectacle moved the public throughout North America to do more to protect the environment.

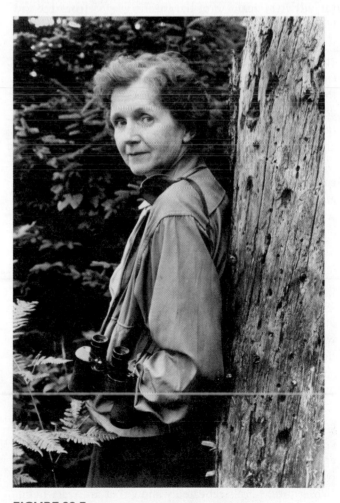

FIGURE 22.7
Scientist, writer, and citizen activist Rachel Carson illuminated the problem of pollution from DDT and other pesticides in her 1962 book *Silent Spring*.

FIGURE 22.8
Ohio's Cuyahoga River caught fire several times in the 1950s and 1960s. The Cuyahoga, which flows into Lake Erie, was so polluted with oil and industrial waste that the river would burn for days at a time.

Other iconic eco-disasters of the 1960s and 1970s included the leakage of hazardous wastes from the old Hooker Chemical waste dump at Love Canal, New York, which led to the first-ever declaration of a federal state of emergency in the United States from an environmental cause; and the complete evacuation and abandonment of the town of Times Beach, Missouri, as a result of dioxin contamination. The Amoco *Cadiz* oil spill off the coast of France in 1978—still one of the largest oil spills ever— also served to raise public awareness.

In response to these events, and armed with unprecedented access to knowledge and information about the environmental and health impacts of pollution, the North American public was moved to action. Several young Canadian activists, including Bob Hunter (quoted at the beginning of this chapter), founded a tiny environmental organization called Greenpeace (**FIGURE 22.9**). Their original intent was to stage daring, high-profile protests against submarine testing of nuclear devices by the United States. They soon branched out into protests against whaling, bottom trawling, and other industrial activities they saw as exploitive and unsustainable. Greenpeace has since grown into one of the most powerful ENGOs in the world, still known for the daring nature of its protests.

Today, largely because of grassroots activism and environmental policies enacted since the 1960s, pesticides are more strictly regulated, and the air and water are considerably cleaner. The public enthusiasm for environmental protection that spurred such advances remains strong today. Polls repeatedly show that an overwhelming majority of Canadians favour environmental protection—even if it means paying more. For example, a 2008

FIGURE 22.9
Jim Bohlen, Greenpeace skipper John Cormack, Erving Stowe, and Paul Cote of the British Columbia branch of the Sierra Club (l-r) at a Vancouver harbour in 1971, prior to setting sail for Amchitka Island where the United States was scheduled to set off an underground nuclear blast.

poll showed that the majority of Canadians want our government to take decisive action against climate change, even in the face of rising oil prices (but would they still say this when it is reflected in soaring prices for gasoline at the pump?).

Such support is evident each year in April, when millions of people worldwide celebrate Earth Day in thousands of locally based events featuring speeches, demonstrations, hikes, bird walks, cleanup parties, and more. Since the first Earth Day, on April 22, 1970, participation in this event has grown and spread to nearly every country in the world (**FIGURE 22.10**).

(a) The first Earth Day, Washington, D.C., 1970

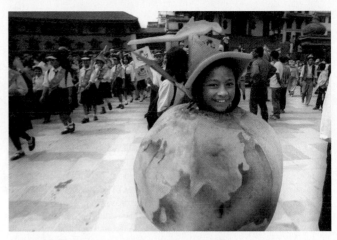

(b) Schoolchildren celebrating Earth Day, Katmandu, Nepal, 2002

(c) Earth Day Canada's familiar logo

FIGURE 22.10
April 22, 1970, saw the first Earth Day celebration **(a)**. This public outpouring of support for environmental protection sparked a wave of environmental policy to address pollution. Decades later, Earth Day is celebrated by millions of people across the world **(b)**, as shown here in Nepal. The familiar Earth Day Canada© logo **(c)** symbolizes leadership in environmental education and action in addition to traditional awareness-raising Earth Day activities. www.earthday.ca

The social context for environmental policy changed over time

Historians have suggested that major advances in environmental policy occurred in the 1960s and 1970s because three factors converged. First, evidence of environmental problems became widely apparent. Second, people could visualize policies to deal with the problems. Third, the political climate was ripe, with a supportive public and leaders who were willing to act.

There was a fourth reason for the advancement in environmental policy: economic confidence. By the 1960s and 1970s, people in North America had reached a point in their economic development where life was reasonably comfortable for more people than ever before. The basic necessities for survival were ensured, and people found themselves willing to make sacrifices—notably financial sacrifices but also behavioural changes—to obtain a cleaner, healthier environment for themselves and their children.

Economists have a name for this change in attitude; it is called a *willingness-to-pay transition* (**FIGURE 22.11**). Most environmental problems (such as lack of sanitation or clean water) improve with increasing economic status of societies, sometimes after an initial stage of worsening while industrial development accelerates (as is the case with air pollution). Until recently, waste generation and carbon emissions were two environmental problems for which there seemed to be no willingness-to-pay threshold—they just continued to increase in severity as incomes rose. In recent years, people in Western nations appear to be more willing to make financial sacrifices and modify their behaviour to address these problems.

During the Industrial Revolution in England and during later industrial development in North America, air pollution from factories and refineries was a huge problem. Financial progress led the more industrially developed nations to invest in technologies to limit air pollution, with the result that air quality has improved dramatically. Developing and rapidly industrializing nations today are facing similar problems, and some of them are reaching their own willingness-to-pay transition.

FIGURE 22.11

This figure shows the theoretical relationship between income and environmental problems. Access to sanitation facilities and clean water generally improves with increasing income in a society undergoing industrial development **(a)**. Air pollution tends to worsen with increasing income early in industrial development **(b)**, which typically involves increased use of fossil fuels. As incomes increase, a willingness-to-pay threshold is eventually reached; pollution control technologies are employed, and air quality improves. Until recently, a willingness-to-pay transition for waste generation and carbon emissions had not been evident **(c)**. These problems traditionally worsen with increasing income. We now seem to be reaching the point where we are willing to alter our behaviour to see some improvements in these two areas.

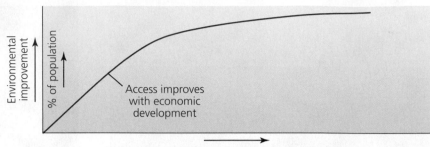

(a) **Access to sanitation and clean water**

(b) **Air quality**

(c) **Waste generation and carbon emissions**

The concept of sustainable development now guides environmental policy

The concept of sustainable development gained popularity as a result of the 1987 report of the United Nations Commission on Environment and Development, led by the (then) prime minister of Norway, Gro Harlem Brundtland. The commission's report, entitled *Our Common Future*, defined **sustainable development** as "development that meets the needs of the present without compromising the ability of future generations to meet their own needs."[12] The concept of sustainable development got a further boost at the 1992 Earth Summit at Río de Janeiro, Brazil. This was the largest international diplomatic conference ever held, drawing representatives from

179 nations and unifying these leaders around the idea of sustainable development.

The idea of sustainable development has not been without controversy. Some people find it too vague. Others find it prone to misuse and misinterpretation, or a contradiction in terms. (Is it "sustainable" development or "sustained" development?) But if nothing else, the concept of sustainable development has led to enthusiastic discussion and debate among the people of the world. An alternative definition that has emerged more recently defines sustainable development as maximizing the co-achievement of economic, environmental, and social goals.

On an international level, sustainable development as a policy approach tries to find ways to safeguard the functionality of natural systems while raising living standards for the world's poorer people (**FIGURE 22.12**). As the world's nations continue to feel the social, economic, and

FIGURE 22.12
At the Barefoot College in Tilonia, India, women construct solar parabolas that track and focus the sun's rays onto cooking pots, to rapidly boil water and other ingredients without the need for firewood. All parts are locally available. Solar cookers made at the College are being set up in remote rural villages and maintained by local women. "Barefoot solutions" like these help both the environment and the economy in the developing world.

ecological effects of environmental degradation, environmental policy will without doubt become a more central part of governance and everyday life in all nations in the years ahead.

Scientific monitoring and reporting helps with environmental policy decisions

All levels of government report to the Canadian public about their activities and any changes, positive or negative, in the condition of the environment within their jurisdiction. **State-of-the-environment reporting (SOER)** refers to the collection, organization, and reporting of information that can be used to measure and monitor changes in the environment and in processes or factors that have impacts on the environment over time. The information is reported by using **indicators**, values that can be measured and in comparison to which changes can be assessed. Some indicators are simple numbers (e.g., number of species on the endangered species list or hectares of forested area). Others are complex, composite, or derived numbers (e.g., the Air Quality Health Index, which combines several indicators into one number).

According to Environment Canada, the purpose of SOER is to answer five key questions:[13]

1. What is happening in the environment (i.e., how are environmental conditions and trends changing)?

2. Why is it happening (i.e., how are human activities and other stresses linked to the issue)?
3. Why is it significant (i.e., what are its ecological and socioeconomic effects)?
4. What is being done about it (i.e., how is society responding to the issues)?
5. Is this response sustainable (i.e., are human actions depleting environmental capital and causing deterioration of ecosystem health)?

The beginning of formal SOER in Canada dates back to *Our Common Future*, the 1987 Report of the United Nations Commission on Environment and Development, when a response was assembled by the Canadian Council of Ministers of the Environment (CCME). Around the same time, several provinces and territories were beginning to develop their own sets of indicators and plans for sustainability (Yukon, Alberta, British Columbia, Nova Scotia, and Saskatchewan were the earliest). Not all provinces and territories have regular programs for comprehensive state-of-the-environment (SOE) or sustainability reporting, though all of them collect and report environmental information in one way or another. It is time-consuming and expensive to collect information on a comprehensive set of indicators and keep the information up-to-date.

Environment Canada takes the lead role in a number of SOER activities. Many other federal-level departments also deliver regular state-of-the-environment reports. These include Agriculture and Agri-Food Canada; Fisheries and Oceans Canada; Health Canada; Natural Resources Canada; Parks Canada; Indian and Northern Affairs Canada; Statistics Canada; Senate of Canada; Transport Canada; and the Treasury Board of Canada Secretariat. Some of these efforts are coordinated; in 1996 the so-called 5NR departments (the five natural resource departments—the first four listed above, plus Environment Canada) produced a coordinated plan and signed a Memorandum of Understanding on SOER.

Regions in Canada that have common environmental concerns sometimes collaborate on the production of SOE reports. Some of these represent Canadian participation in international efforts; an example is the Arctic State of the Environment Report, sponsored by the Circumpolar Council. Others are collaborations among different stakeholders and levels of government; an example is Criteria and Indicators of Sustainable Forest Management in Canada, sponsored by the multistakeholder CCME.

Many municipalities in Canada also produce SOE reports. Municipal-level reports tend to focus more on community-level indicators of well-being of both ecosystems and people. Many corporations, too, have adopted environmental or sustainability reporting as sections or addenda to their annual business reporting framework.

SOER presents organizational challenges

There is so much environmental information that can be measured and reported; what is the most effective way to organize and analyze all of this information? Environment Canada has been a leader in the development of approaches to SOER and was instrumental in the development and early adoption of the **pressure-state-response (PSR) model** for SOER. This organizational framework is based on establishing linkages and causalities (**FIGURE 22.13**). Human activities, such as mining, water extraction, or logging, exert stresses on the environment (shown by the "pressure" box). This affects both the quality of the environment and the quality and quantity of natural resources (shown by the "state" box). Society responds to the changes by adopting environmental and economic policies (shown by the "response" box). The whole system is characterized by cause-and-effect feedback loops.[14]

Another organizational issue in SOER is how to subdivide the information. Most reports are based on geographic or geopolitical boundaries, but these often don't correspond to natural ecosystem boundaries. For example, it is more meaningful to produce a report for the St. Lawrence system as a whole than for any of the provinces or states that border it to produce a report based only on its own jurisdictional boundary. Therefore, some SOE reports focus on a biogeographic feature, such as a specific basin or a location with unique characteristics, such as the Arctic. Others focus on a particular sector, such as the forestry sector; a specific current issue, such as climate change; or a particular environmental medium, such as air, water, or soils.

International Environmental Law and Policy

Natural systems pay no heed to political boundaries, so environmental problems often are not restricted to the confines of particular countries. For instance, most of the world's major rivers straddle or cross international borders, including the

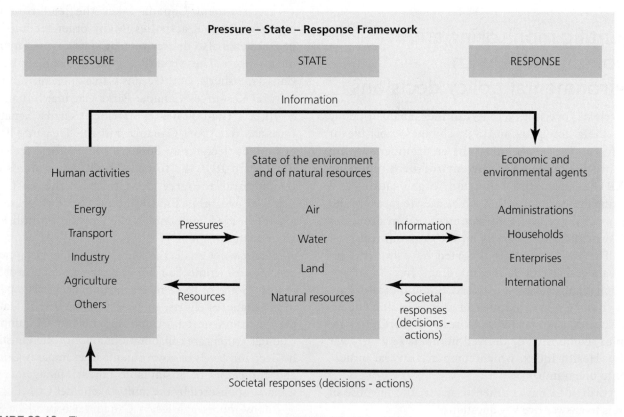

FIGURE 22.13 The pressure–state–response model allows researchers and decision makers to assess linkages and causalities and to assess the effectiveness of responses to environmental change. Activities that cause environmental stress are shown in the "pressure" box; indicators of environmental condition in the "state" box; and human policies in the "response" box. *Source: OECD Environment Monographs, No. 83, OECD Core Set of Indicators for Environmental Performance Reviews: A Synthesis Report by the Group on the State of the Environment, 1993.*

St. Lawrence, the Rhine, the Jordan, the Red River, and many others. Because Canada's laws have no authority in the United States or any other nation outside Canada, international law is vital to solving transboundary problems.

Often nations make progress on international issues not through legislation but through creative bilateral or multilateral agreements hammered out after a lot of hard work and diplomacy. Such was the case with the effort to develop a long-term plan to manage water quality in the Great Lakes through the International Joint Commission. Other examples of important North American environmental agreements, some of which we have mentioned elsewhere in this book, include the Agreement on Air Quality; Migratory Birds Convention; North American Agreement on Environmental Cooperation; Canada–U.S. Agreement on the Transboundary Movement of Hazardous Waste; and Canada–U.S. Joint Marine Pollution Contingency Plan. Because solving transboundary dilemmas requires international cooperation, several principles of international law and a number of international organizations have arisen. International law known as *customary law* arises from long-standing practices, or customs, held in common by most cultures. International law known as *conventional law* arises from conventions or treaties into which nations enter.

The Office of the Auditor General estimates that Canada has entered into more than 100 international environmental agreements (there are some 500 such agreements worldwide).[15] One example is the Montreal Protocol, a 1987 accord among more than 160 nations to reduce the emission of airborne chemicals that deplete the ozone layer. Another example is the Kyoto Protocol, aimed at reducing fossil fuel emissions that contribute to global climate change. (As of 2011, Canada has withdrawn from this agreement.) Some examples of important international environmental laws and agreements are listed in **TABLE 22.2**.

Several organizations shape international environmental policy

Although there is no real mechanism for enforcing international environmental law, a number of international organizations regularly act to influence the behaviour of nations by providing funding, applying peer pressure, and/or directing media attention.

The United Nations   In 1945, representatives of 50 countries founded the United Nations. Headquartered in New York City, this organization's purpose is to maintain international peace and security; to develop friendly relations among nations; to cooperate in solving international economic, social, cultural and humanitarian problems and in promoting respect for human rights and fundamental freedoms; and to be a centre for harmonizing the actions of nations in attaining these ends.[16]

The United Nations has taken an active role in shaping international environmental policy (**FIGURE 22.14**). Of several agencies within it that influence environmental policy, most notable is the **United Nations Environment Programme (UNEP)**, created in 1972, which helps nations understand and solve environmental problems. Based in Nairobi, Kenya, its mission is sustainability, enabling countries and their citizens "to improve their quality of life without compromising that of future generations." UNEP's extensive research and outreach activities provide a wealth of information useful to policy makers and scientists throughout the world.

The European Union   The European Union (EU) seeks to promote Europe's economic and social progress (including environmental protection) and to "assert Europe's role in the world." The EU can sign binding treaties on behalf of its 27 member nations and can enact regulations that have the same authority as national laws in each member nation. It can also issue *directives*, which are more advisory in nature. The EU's European Environment Agency works to address waste management, noise pollution, water pollution, air pollution,

FIGURE 22.14
Many nations are shifting their policies to support sustainable development efforts, trying to increase standards of living while safeguarding the environment. Here, a woman stirs rice on a solar-powered oven at a restaurant made of recycled drink cans, showcased at the U.N. World Summit on Sustainable Development in Johannesburg, South Africa, in 2002.

Table 22.2 Some Important International Environmental Laws and Agreements in Which Canada Is a Party

Air

- Stockholm Convention on Persistent Organic Pollutants (POPs)
- United Nations Framework Convention on Climate Change (UNFCCC)–Kyoto Protocol (Canada withdrew in 2011)
- Vienna Convention for the Protection of the Ozone Layer– Protocol on Substances that Deplete the Ozone Layer (Montreal Protocol)
- Convention of the World Meteorological Organization (WMO)

Biodiversity

- Agreement on the Conservation of Polar Bears
- Convention on Biological Diversity
- Convention on International Trade in Endangered Species of Wild Fauna and Flora (CITES)
- Convention on Wetlands of International Importance (Ramsar)

Ecosystems

- Antarctic Treaty
- Arctic Council

Environmental Cooperation

- UNECE Convention on Environmental Impact Assessment in a Transboundary Context (Espoo Convention)

Hazardous Materials and Wastes

- Basel Convention on the Control of Transboundary Movements of Hazardous Wastes and Their Disposal
- Rotterdam Convention on the Prior Informed Consent (PIC) Procedure for Certain Hazardous Chemicals and Pesticides in International Trade

Lakes and Rivers

- Canada–U.S. Agreement on Great Lakes Water Quality
- Treaty Relating to the Boundary Waters and Questions Arising Along the Border Between the United States and Canada

Oceans

- Convention on the Prevention of Marine Pollution by Dumping of Waste and Other Matter (LC72)
- International Convention for the Prevention of Pollution from Ships (MARPOL 73/78)
- International Convention on Oil Pollution Preparedness, Response, and Cooperation
- United Nations Fish Stocks Agreement
- Northwest Atlantic Fisheries Organization (NAFO)

Source: OECD Environment Monographs, No. 83, OECD Core Set of Indicators for Environmental Performance Reviews: A Synthesis Report by the Group on the State of the Environment, 1993, www.ens.gu.edu.au/AES1161/Topic1/Images/gd93179.pdf

habitat degradation, and natural hazards. The EU also seeks to remove trade barriers among member nations. It has classified some nations' environmental regulations as barriers to trade because some northern European nations have traditionally had more stringent environmental laws that prevent the import and sale of environmentally harmful products from other member nations.

The World Trade Organization Based in Geneva, Switzerland, the World Trade Organization (WTO) was established in 1995, having grown from a 50-year-old international trade agreement. The WTO represents multinational corporations and promotes free trade by reducing obstacles to international commerce and enforcing fairness among nations in trading practices. Whereas the United Nations and the European Union have limited influence over nations' internal affairs, the WTO has real authority to impose financial penalties on nations that do not comply with its directives. These penalties can on occasion play major roles in shaping environmental policy.

Like the EU, the WTO has interpreted some national environmental laws as unfair barriers to trade. For instance, in a well-known example, in 1995 the U.S. EPA issued regulations requiring cleaner-burning gasoline in U.S. cities. Brazil and Venezuela filed a complaint with the WTO, saying the new rules unfairly discriminated against the petroleum they exported to the United States, which did not burn as cleanly. The WTO agreed, ruling that even though the South American gasoline posed a threat to human health in the United States, the EPA rules represented an illegal trade barrier. Not surprisingly, critics have frequently charged that the WTO and trade agreements like NAFTA aggravate environmental problems (see "The Science Behind the Story: The Environment in NAFTA and NAAEC").

The World Bank Established in 1944 and based in Washington, D.C., the World Bank is one of the world's largest sources of funding for economic development. This institution has shaped environmental policy through its funding of dams, irrigation infrastructure, and other major development projects. In fiscal year 2009, the World Bank provided more than $58.8 billion in loans and grants for projects in middle- and low-income countries around the world.

The World Bank has frequently been criticized for funding unsustainable projects that cause more environmental problems than they solve. Providing for the needs of growing human populations in poor nations while minimizing damage to the environmental systems on which people depend can be a tough balancing act. The concept of sustainable development is a guiding principle for such efforts.

THE SCIENCE BEHIND THE STORY

The Environment in NAFTA and NAAEC

The brown cloudy water in this photo is a plume of wastewater being released into the Pacific Ocean, near Tijuana.

In 1992, the United States, Mexico, and Canada signed the North American Free Trade Agreement, better known as NAFTA, a comprehensive trade and investment agreement with aggressive measures to reduce barriers to trade. Since January 1, 2003, virtually all trade among the three countries has been tariff free as a result of NAFTA. Since the signing of NAFTA, however, it has been a major concern of ENGOs and other organizations to determine the impacts—positive or negative—of trade in general, and NAFTA in particular, on the environment.

The critical section of the agreement is the infamous "chapter 11," which aims to prevent the mistreatment of investors by foreign governments. This means, for example, that investors should not have their assets seized (expropriated) by a foreign government and should not be subjected to regulations that give unfair advantages to domestic investors. Chapter 11 provides a dispute settlement mechanism whereby investors may challenge a government's handling of a particular industry or foreign investment.

Canada has participated in a number of disputes; probably the most famous was the softwood lumber dispute, in which the United States claimed that Canada gives unfair advantage to domestic logging companies by subsidizing the forestry industry. The softwood lumber dispute dates back many decades and has been brought to NAFTA and WTO tribunals on numerous occasions. The dispute centred on *stump-*

age fees charged for logging on public lands. The U.S. maintained that stumpage fees were set too low by the Canadian government, giving unfair advantage to domestic loggers. The dispute was settled in 2006 to the satisfaction of the two federal and three provincial governments involved (British Columbia, Ontario, and Québec).

The greatest environmental concern arising from chapter 11 has been the possibility that domestic environmental legislation could be interpreted as a barrier to international free trade, and thus be overruled by NAFTA. An example was the lawsuit brought by Vancouver-based Methanex, the manufacturers of the gasoline additive MTBE, against the state of California. Methanex sought almost $1 billion in damages, claiming that California's ban on the additive amounted to trade protectionism. The Methanex claim was dismissed by a NAFTA tribunal in 2005, but other similar cases remain to be settled.

One major environmental concern has arisen from the establishment of factories in Mexico by Canadian and U.S. companies as a result of free trade. Mexico's federal laws provide strict rules for environmental protection, but the government lacks the financial resources to fully implement them. There has been considerable concern among critics of NAFTA that industries and jobs would migrate from the United States and Canada, where environmental and labour standards are high, to so-called pollution havens in Mexico, where labour is less expensive and environmental standards are less rigorously enforced. This has been labelled the "race to the bottom," referring to the potential for international investors to maximize profits by finding the "lowest common denominator" of environmental protection.

A case in point is the Tijuana River, which winds northwestward through the arid landscape of northern Baja California, Mexico, crossing the U.S. border south of San Diego. The river's watershed covers 4500 km² and is home to 2 million people. It is a transboundary watershed, with approximately 70% of its area in Mexico (see map and photo). On the Mexican side of the border, the river and the *arroyos*, or creeks, that flow into it are lined with farms,

apartments, shanties, and factories, as well as leaky sewage treatment plants and toxic dump sites. Rains wash pollutants from these sources through the arroyos into the Tijuana River and eventually onto U.S. and Mexican beaches. The problem has grown worse in recent years as the region's population has boomed, outstripping the capacity of sewage treatment facilities. Beach closures and pollution advisories have become commonplace, and garbage litters the beaches.

The proliferation of U.S.- and Canadian-owned factories, or *maquiladoras*, on the Mexican side of the border has contributed to the river's pollution, both through direct disposal of industrial waste and by attracting thousands of new workers to the already crowded region. Things are worse on the Mexican side because most Mexican residents of the Tijuana River watershed live in poverty. Close to one-third of Tijuana's homes are not connected to a sewer system, and river pollution directly affects people's day-to-day lives.

To address some of the environmental concerns raised by NAFTA, the three nations reached a corollary agreement called the North American Agreement on Environmental Cooperation (NAAEC, 1993). The objectives are to promote sustainable development, encourage pollution prevention policies and practices, and enhance compliance with environmental laws and regulations. The agreement also promotes transparency and public participation in the development of environmental policies.[17] The agreement mandated the international Commission for Environmental Cooperation, provided a quasi-judicial mechanism for the resolution of disputes, and established a cooperative work plan for the environment among the three nations.[18] The ultimate goal is to ensure that the parties do not lower their environmental standards to attract investment.

Now at the twentieth anniversary of NAFTA, it seems that the agreement has left the North American environment both better and worse off. According to

(Continued)

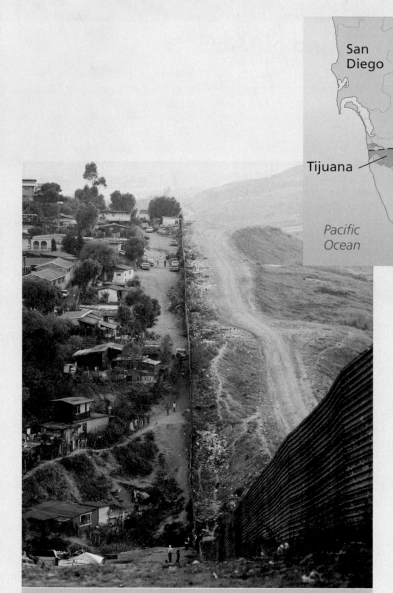

San
Diego

Pacific
Ocean

Tijuana

U.S.
Mexico
Tijuana River
Watershed

Tijuana
River

The Tijuana River winds northwestward from Mexico into California just south of San Diego, draining 4500 km^2 of land in its watershed (coloured green in map). Pollution entering the river affects Mexican residents of the watershed and U.S. citizens on San Diego County beaches, but the situation is much worse on the Mexican side of the border (on the left in the photo), compared with the California side (on the right).

research reported at a symposium on The Environmental Impacts of Free Trade held by the CEC, there has not been one overall or generalized environmental effect of NAFTA; the impacts have been mixed.[19] In his introduction, symposium chair Pierre Marc Johnson commented that:

In the fisheries sector, evidence does not suggest that NAFTA, per se, has had much of an effect, either positive or negative, on sustainable fisheries management. For forest products, on the other hand, the restructuring of the industry has been accompanied by significant changes, including its exposure to contestation from international competition. For freshwater, concerns persist about the possibility of bulk water exports in the face of dwindling water resources and the effects of investor-state challenges under NAFTA's chapter 11. . . . Some air pollution indicators show increases of carbon monoxide and sulfur dioxide (SO_2) levels in the U.S., and of SO_2 in Mexico, and significant reductions of air pollution in the Canadian and Mexican paper

Organization of the Petroleum Exporting Countries (OPEC)   OPEC is an intergovernmental organization of oil-producing and -exporting nations, with 13 members.[20] It was originally founded to protect the interests of its members in the international marketplace, which it has accomplished by controlling the world price of oil. The position of OPEC with regard to recent developments in our understanding of global climate change and

its relationship to fossil fuel use are understandably wary. According to the OPEC website, OPEC "is concerned that some countries may impose environmental and taxation policies that are harmful to those who rely on fossil fuels for a substantial part of their income." It maintains that OPEC functions to supply a stable petroleum market, which is essential for the world economy, and opposes "discriminatory" taxes on fossil fuel use.[21]

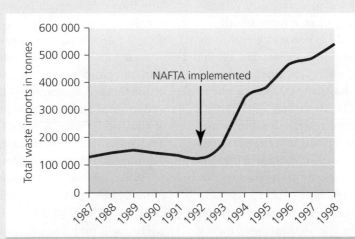

Hazardous waste imports into Canada have increased dramatically since NAFTA was signed. Other areas have seen environmental improvements.
Source: Marisa Jacott, Cyrus Reed, and Mark Winfield, The Generation and Management of Hazardous Wastes and Transboundary Hazardous Waste Shipments Between Mexico, Canada, and the United States, 1990–2000, in North American Symposium on Understanding the Linkages Between Trade and the Environment, Commission on Environmental Cooperation of North America, 2002.

sectors. Data on hazardous waste show a significant increase in hazardous waste generation in some Canadian provinces, along with a decrease in some northern U.S. states. A key finding . . . is that the total amount of trade in hazardous wastes—in particular, waste imported into Canada from the United States—has increased dramatically since NAFTA came into effect.[22]

Johnson continued, addressing the question of the relocation of industries to "pollution havens":

In fact, the evidence suggests that Mexican export specialization has resulted in less and less pollution. In contrast, Canadian export specialization is now much more pollution-prone than Mexico's.[23]

The implications of NAFTA for trade in water are of fundamental importance to Canadians. In a CEC symposium paper, *NAFTA Effects on Water: Testing for NAFTA Effects in the Great Lakes Basin*, Christine Elwell, senior policy analyst for the Sierra Club of Canada, concluded that NAFTA has had clearly demonstrable negative impacts on both water quality and quantity in the Great Lakes, and that without greater attention, future concerns and environmental stresses would arise from the privatization and commodification of water.[24]

With regard to the *maquiladoras* and the impacts of free trade on the environment in northern Mexico, NAFTA opponents maintain that environmental regulations are being ignored, to the profit of the companies that do business there. NAFTA supporters, on the other hand, argue that the savings would be insufficient for a company to consider relocating to Mexico simply to avoid the cost of compliance with environmental regulations.

In his introduction to the CEC symposium, Johnson came to a conclusion that many environmentalists had been waiting to hear when he stated that "environmental concerns need to be addressed during trade negotiations and treaty implementation."[25] Both supporters and opponents of NAFTA should have no trouble agreeing on this point.

International ENGOs   A number of ENGOs have become international in scope and exert influence over international environmental policy. The nature of these advocacy groups is diverse. Some, such as the Nature Conservancy, focus on accomplishing conservation objectives without becoming politically involved. Other groups, including Conservation International, the World Wide Fund for Nature, and many others, attempt to shape policy directly or indirectly through research, education, lobbying, or protest. ENGOs apply more funding and expertise to environmental problems—and conduct more research intended to solve them—than do many national governments. In some Communist and post-Communist countries, nongovernmental organizations that have been illegal or severely restricted are now becoming much more visible and are influencing both awareness and public policy.

This is just a small sampling of the very many organizations that play central roles in determining international environmental policy that affects us all. As globalization proceeds, our world is becoming ever more interconnected. As a result, human societies and Earth's ecological systems are being altered at unprecedented rates. Trade and technology have expanded the global reach of all societies, especially those that, like Canada and the United States, consume resources from across the world. Highly consumptive nations that import goods and resources from far and wide exert extensive impacts on the planet's environmental systems. Multinational corporations operate outside the reach of national laws and rarely have incentive to conserve resources or conduct their business sustainably in the nations where they operate. For all these reasons, in today's globalizing world the organizations and institutions that influence international policy are becoming increasingly vital.

Approaches to Environmental Policy

We have discussed environmental policy so far in this chapter mainly from the regulatory or legislative perspective ("top-down") and from the perspective of public awareness and grassroots environmental activism ("bottom-up"). There are other important approaches that inform environmental policy development and serve to modify both corporate and consumer behaviour. Let us explore some of these.

Science plays a role in policy, but it can be politicized

Ethical values, economic interests, and political ideology influence most policy decisions. However, environmental policy decisions that are effective are generally those informed by scientific research. For instance, when deciding whether and how to regulate a substance that may pose a public health risk, regulatory agencies, such as Health Canada, comb the scientific literature and may commission new studies or have their own scientists carry out studies, seeking to gain as full an understanding of the health risks as science can reasonably provide. When trying to win support for a bill to reduce pollution, a representative may use data from scientific studies to quantify the cost of the pollution or the predicted benefits of its reduction. The more information a policy maker can glean from science, the better the policy he or she will be able to create.

Unfortunately, sometimes policy makers choose to ignore science and instead allow political ideology to determine policy. In past years, some scientists—particularly those working on politically sensitive issues such as climate change or endangered species protection—have occasionally found their work suppressed or discredited, or their jobs threatened. Examples of cases in which the work or opinions of Canadian scientists have been ignored or overlooked by some politicians, who may have been under social and economic pressure, include the collapse of the cod fishery in Atlantic Canada, the connections between asbestos and disease, and recent work on global warming and the potential impacts of climate change.

When scientists are gagged, and when taxpayer-funded science is suppressed or distorted for political ends, we all lose. We cannot simply take for granted that science will play a role in policy. As scientifically literate citizens of a democracy, we all need to make sure our government representatives are making proper use of the tremendous scientific assets we have at our disposal.

Command-and-control policy has improved our lives, but it is not perfect

A great deal of environmental policy has functioned by setting rules or limits and threatening punishment for violating these rules or limits, in what is often called a **command-and-control** approach. Without doubt, our environment would be in far worse shape today were it not for this type of government regulatory intervention.

Most of the major environmental laws of recent decades, and most regulations enforced by agencies today, use the command-and-control approach. This simple and direct approach to policy making has brought citizens of Canada and many other nations cleaner air, cleaner water, safer workplaces, healthier neighbourhoods, and many other improvements in quality of life. The relatively safe, healthy, comfortable lives most of us enjoy today owe much to the environmental policy of the past few decades.

Despite the successes of command-and-control policy, it is not without its drawbacks. Sometimes government actions are well intentioned but not well-enough informed, so they can lead to unforeseen consequences. Policy can also fail if a government does not live up to its responsibilities to protect its citizens or treat them equitably.

Economic tools can be used to achieve environmental goals

The most common critique of command-and-control policy is that it achieves its goals in a more costly and less efficient manner than the free market can. By mandating particular solutions to problems, command-and-control policy fails to take advantage of the fact that private entities competing in the free market can often produce better solutions at lower cost. Many minds that are economically motivated to compete in the market are more likely to innovate and find optimal solutions than a smaller number of policy makers with no such economic incentive.

The most widely developed alternatives to command-and-control policies therefore involve the creative use of economic incentives to encourage desired outcomes, discourage undesired outcomes, and set market dynamics in motion to achieve goals in an economically efficient manner. Policy makers now often try to combine the advantages of government and the private sector. The challenge of crafting economic policy tools is to channel the innovation and economic efficiency of the free market in directions that benefit the public.

Subsidies   One set of economic policy tools aims to encourage industries or activities that are deemed desirable. Governments may give tax breaks to certain types of businesses or individuals, for instance, and national governments commonly provide subsidies to industries they judge to benefit the nation in some way. Subsidies can be used to promote environmentally sustainable activities, but all too often they have been used to prop up unsustainable ones. Some studies suggest that subsidies that are harmful to the environment total roughly $1.45 *trillion* yearly across the globe—an amount larger than the economies of all but five nations.

Although there are many examples of government subsidies in Canada that result—either directly or indirectly—in harm to the environment (subsidies that promote logging in old-growth forests come to mind), perhaps the most controversial are those that support the oil and gas industry (**FIGURE 22.15**). The Sierra Club of Canada estimates that since originally signing the Kyoto Protocol in 1997, Canada has spent $2 in subsidies to support oil and gas industry development for every $1 spent finding ways to meet Kyoto targets.[26]

Advocates of sustainable resource use have long urged governments to subsidize environmentally sustainable activities instead. So far, Canada has lagged behind most other developed nations in subsidizing research into sustainable solutions. For instance, in 2000–2001 less than 5% of federal energy-related investment was devoted to renewable energy research—$12.9 million of a total expenditure of $230.2 million.[27] In the same period, billions of dollars in tax deductions were passed along to the oil, gas, and nuclear industries. We have a long way to go in getting subsidies to work for *both* the economy *and* the environment.

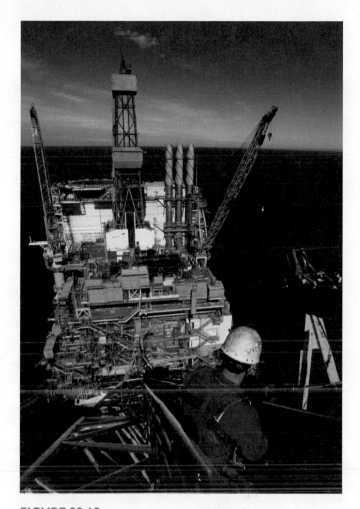

FIGURE 22.15
Subsidies designed to support industry can have a negative impact on the environment, either directly or indirectly. The billions of dollars of subsidies to the oil and gas industry in Canada have so far greatly outweighed investment and subsidies for alternative energy sources.

Green taxes and "polluter pays"   Another economic policy tool—taxation—can be used to discourage undesirable activities. Taxing undesirable activities helps to "internalize" external costs by making them part of the overall cost of doing business. Taxes on environmentally harmful activities and products are called **green taxes**. By taxing activities and products that cause undesirable environmental impacts, a tax becomes a tool for policy as well as simply a way to fund government.

Green taxes have yet to gain widespread support in Canada, although similar "sin taxes" on cigarettes and alcohol are common tools of Canadian social policy. Taxes on pollution have been widely instituted in Europe, where many nations have adopted the **polluter pays principle**. This principle specifies that the price of a good or service should include all its costs, including costs of environmental degradation that would otherwise be passed on as external costs.

Under green taxation, a factory that pollutes a waterway would pay taxes based on the amount of pollution it discharges. The idea is to give companies a financial incentive to reduce pollution, while allowing the polluter the freedom to decide how best to minimize its expenses. One polluter might choose to invest in technologies to reduce its pollution if doing so is less costly than paying the taxes. Another polluter might find abating its pollution more costly and could choose to pay the taxes instead—funds the government might then apply toward mitigating pollution in some other way. Bottle-return programs are an example of the polluter pays principle applied at the consumer end.

Green taxation provides incentive for industry to lower emissions not merely to a level specified in a regulation but to still-lower levels. However, green taxes do have disadvantages. One is that businesses will most likely pass on their tax expenses to consumers, and these increased costs may affect low-income consumers disproportionately more than high-income ones.

Permit trading A different, market-based approach to the management of environmental impacts is permit trading. In a **permit trading** system, the government creates a market in permits for an environmentally harmful activity, and companies, utilities, or industries are allowed to buy, sell, or trade rights to conduct the activity. For instance, to decrease emissions of air pollutants, a government might grant emissions permits and set up an **emissions trading system**. The government first determines the overall amount of pollution it will accept and then issues marketable permits to polluters that allow them each to emit a certain fraction of that amount. Polluters may buy, sell, and trade these permits with other polluters. Each year, the government may reduce the amount of overall emissions allowed.

In such a **cap-and-trade** system, a polluting party that is able to reduce its pollution receives credit for the amount it did not emit and can sell this credit to other parties. Suppose, for example, you are a plant owner with permits to release 10 units of pollution, but you find that you can become more efficient and release only 5 units of pollution instead. You then have a surplus of permits, which might be very valuable to some other plant owner who is having trouble reducing pollution or who wants to expand production. In such a case, you can sell your extra permits. Doing so generates income for you and meets the needs of the other plant, while preventing any increase in the total amount of pollution. Moreover, environmental organizations can buy up surplus permits and "retire" them, thus reducing the overall amount of pollution.

Marketable permits provide companies with an economic incentive to find ways to reduce emissions. If successful, permit trading can end up costing both industry and government much less than a conventional regulatory system. In 2007 the National Round Table on Environment and Economy undertook a major study of emissions reduction goals and market instruments in the Canadian context, in response to a request for advice from the federal government on reducing carbon emissions. They concluded that reaching the government's stated goal of a 65% reduction from 2005 levels by 2050 would require meeting an interim goal of a 20% reduction by 2020, and that this would necessitate the use of an emissions tax, a cap-and-trade system, or a combination of the two (see "Interpreting Graphs and Data").[28]

Ontario has had a capped emissions trading system in place since 2001, covering NO_x and SO_2 emissions. The Ontario Emissions Trading Registry serves as a mechanism for tracking emissions, as well as the transfer and use of allowances and emission-reduction credits, which are issued under the Emissions Trading Regulation. It also provides a forum for public notification and commentary on emissions trading transactions.[29]

Cap-and-trade programs are no panacea. They can reduce pollution overall, but they do allow hotspots of pollution to occur around plants that buy permits to pollute more. Moreover, large firms can hoard permits, deterring smaller new firms from entering the market and thereby suppressing competition. Nevertheless, permit trading has shown promise for safeguarding environmental quality while granting industries the flexibility to lessen their impacts in ways that are economically palatable.

Presently, a market in carbon emissions is operating among European nations as a result of the Kyoto Protocol to address climate change. Under the Kyoto Protocol, nations have targets for reducing their carbon emissions from power plants, automobiles, and other sources that are driving climate change. Each nation participating in the European Union Emission Trading Scheme takes the emissions permits it is allowed and allocates them to its industries according to their emissions at the start of the program. The industries then can trade permits freely, establishing a market whereby the price of a carbon emissions permit fluctuates according to supply and demand.

Unfortunately, European nations allocated too many permits in the program's first phase, destroying industries' financial incentive to cut emissions and causing the permits to become nearly worthless. These nations plan to correct the overallocation when the program enters its next phase.

CANADIAN ENVIRONMENTAL PERSPECTIVES

Maude Barlow

Through her Blue Planet Project, Maude Barlow campaigns for global water justice.

- **Water rights activist** and **author**
- **Co-founder** of The Blue Planet Project
- **National chairperson of the Council of Canadians**

Maude Barlow does not shy away from controversy. When she sees an injustice, she says, "I have to tell people ... I have to do something so that other people will also take action."[30] Barlow comes from a family tradition of concern for social justice issues, and over the years she has taken action in some challenging arenas. She became involved in politics early in her career, serving as Pierre Trudeau's adviser on women's issues in the 1980s. Previously she had worked as the director of equal opportunity for the City of Ottawa and led a campaign to stop violence against women. In 1985 she resigned from political life to start the Council of Canadians, with a

small group of activists that included Farley Mowat. The principal mission of the CofC is to protect Canadian independence.[31] This includes, in part, a goal to "work with Canadians and people around the world to reclaim the global and local commons which are the shared heritage of humanity and of the earth."[32] The CofC is now the largest citizens' organization in Canada; to maintain its ideological independence, it accepts no funding from governments or the private sector.[33]

The first significant undertaking of the organization was to assemble a coalition of labour and social justice organizations opposed to the North American Free Trade Agreement (see "The Science Behind the Story: The Environment in NAFTA and NAAEC"). The organization saw success in its fight against the Multilateral Agreement on Investment (MAI) in the late 1990s. The MAI, an agreement among OECD member countries to standardize investment regulations across international boundaries, would have restricted the ability of governments to limit foreign multinational investments, even if they were seen as potentially harmful. Critics of the agreement felt that it would greatly weaken national sovereignty in the areas of human rights, labour rights, and environmental standards.

More recently, the efforts of both Barlow and the CofC have been focused on fighting the bulk export of Canadian water. Not surprisingly, for Barlow this is more than an environmental issue; it is a social justice issue. In her most recent book, *Blue Covenant*, she pushes for a full U.N.-based international treaty recognizing the right to water. "Finally, the global water justice movement is demanding a change in international law to settle once and for all the question of who controls water. It must be commonly understood that water is not a commercial good,

although of course it has an economic dimension, but rather a human right and a common trust."[34]

For all the controversy that surrounds her, Barlow has been widely recognized for her work. She has received honorary doctorates from 11 Canadian universities and the Canadian Environment Award Citation of Lifetime Achievement. In her acceptance speech for the latter, Barlow highlighted the impacts of the petrochemical industry on the environment and health in Canada.[35] In 2005 she received the Lannan Foundation Cultural Freedom Fellowship and the Right Livelihood Award, which she shared with fellow water rights activist Tony Clarke. Barlow is now the national chairperson of the Council of Canadians and co-founder of the Blue Planet Project, through which she continues to work for international water rights. From 2008–2009, she served as Senior Adviser on Water to the 63rd President of the United Nations General Assembly.

"I am part of a family of activists and environmentalists in Canada and around the world."[36]—**Maude Barlow**

Thinking About Environmental Perspectives

According to the global water justice movement and Maude Barlow, "What is needed now is binding law to codify that states have the obligation to deliver sufficient, safe, accessible, and affordable water to their citizens as a public service."[37] Do you think access to drinking water is a basic human right, like access to air? Or should water be a marketable commodity to be controlled and protected, at least in part, by the private sector? If it is a basic human right, should it be protected by international treaty?

Market incentives are being tried widely on the local level

You may well have already taken part in transactions involving financial incentives as policy tools. For example, many municipalities charge residents for waste disposal according to the amount of waste they generate. Other cities place taxes or disposal fees on items that require costly safe disposal, such as tires and motor oil. Still others give rebates to residents who buy water-efficient toilets and appliances because the rebates can cost the city less than upgrading its sewage treatment system. Power companies sometimes offer discounts to customers who buy high-efficiency light bulbs and appliances because doing so is cheaper for the utilities than expanding the generating capacity of their plants.

ENGOs and even private companies are involved in this process at the local level, too. Many new programs have emerged in the past five years or so, aimed at providing rewards for behavioural changes that will benefit the environment. These include rebate programs for purchasing energy-efficient appliances, vouchers for turning in old, gasoline-guzzling lawnmowers, and financial incentives for businesses that turn down their lighting or air conditioning, among countless other examples.

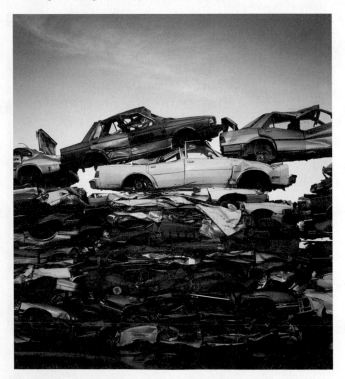

FIGURE 22.16
Car Heaven provides incentives for people to get their old, polluting clunkers off the road. The program ensures that the vehicles (unlike these cars, stacked in a wrecking yard) are recycled and disposed of in an environmentally safe manner, using a three-step program of pretreatment, reuse of parts, and recycling of remaining materials.

"Car Heaven" is one example of a program that helps individual Canadians reduce their impact on the environment by giving them incentives and options for disposing of old, energy-inefficient vehicles. The program was started in Toronto in 2000 under the Clean Air Foundation; it then spread to Edmonton, Calgary, and Vancouver and is now almost nationwide. In addition to retiring high-polluting vehicles from the road, the program ensures that the cars (including all parts and materials, such as mercury switches, tires, residual oil, batteries, and refrigerants) are treated, reused, or recycled, and then disposed of in an environmentally responsible manner (**FIGURE 22.16**).

At all levels, from the local to the international, market-based incentives can reduce environmental impact while minimizing overall costs to industry and easing concerns about the intrusiveness of government regulation. Command-and-control policy is straightforward to implement, easy to monitor, and frequently works. Market-based approaches can be more complicated, but if they work, they can lessen environmental impact at a lower overall cost.

Ecolabelling gives choices to the consumer

More and more, not just in response to legislation but voluntarily, manufacturers are designating on their labels how their products were grown, harvested, or manufactured. This method, called **ecolabelling**, serves to tell consumers which brands use environmentally benign processes. It can also raise consumer awareness of environmental issues, as well as encouraging companies to choose more environmentally friendly production methods. By preferentially buying ecolabelled products, consumers can provide businesses with a powerful incentive to switch to more sustainable processes. One early example was labelling cans of tuna as "dolphin-safe," indicating that the methods used to catch the tuna avoid the accidental capture of dolphins. Other examples include labelling recycled paper, organically grown foods, genetically modified foods (widely done in Europe but not in North America), fair-trade and shade-grown coffee, lumber harvested through sustainable forestry, clothing made from organically grown cotton, and products made from recycled materials (**FIGURE 22.17**).

In a similar vein, individuals who invest their money in the stock market can choose to pursue *socially responsible investing*, which entails investing only in companies that have met certain criteria for environmental or social sustainability.

FIGURE 22.17
Ecolabelling allows businesses to promote products that minimize environmental impacts and gives consumers the opportunity to choose healthier, low-impact products.

Conclusion

Environmental policy is a problem-solving tool that makes use of science, ethics, and economics and that requires an astute understanding of the political process.

Conventional command-and-control approaches of legislation and regulation are the most common approaches to policy making, but various innovative economic policy tools are also being developed. As we have seen in the case of Lake Erie, the Great Lakes, and the St. Lawrence system, environmental issues often overlap political boundaries and require international cooperation. Through the hard work of concerned citizens interacting with their government representatives, the political process eventually produced promising solutions through binational agreements and management plans.

The central focus of this book has been the science behind the pressing environmental issues of our day. In this chapter, we have departed somewhat from this central focus to consider the fundamentals of environmental law and policy, and some of the approaches to environmental management that have been used in the past and are currently emerging in Canada. By understanding these fundamentals and combining them with your understanding of environmental science, you will be well equipped to develop your own creative solutions to many of the challenging problems we will encounter.

REVIEWING OBJECTIVES

You should now be able to:

Describe environmental policy and assess its societal context

- Policy is a tool for decision making and problem solving that makes use of information from science and values from ethics and economics.
- Environmental policy is designed to protect natural resources and environmental amenities from degradation or depletion and to promote equitable treatment of people.

Identify the institutions important to Canadian environmental policy

- Federal, provincial/territorial, Aboriginal, and municipal/local governments, together with administrative agencies, all play roles in Canadian environmental policy.

Recognize major Canadian environmental laws

- Early environmental policy encouraged frontier expansion and resource extraction. Policies of the next period, in the late 1800s and early 1900s, aimed to regulate resource use and mitigate impacts of the first. More recently, in the 1960s and subsequent years, several high-profile pollution events raised public awareness and gave us many of today's major environmental laws.
- Some major Canadian environmental laws include the *Canadian Environmental Protection Act*, the *Fisheries Act*, and the *Canadian Environmental Assessment Act*.

List the institutions involved with international environmental policy

- Institutions such as the United Nations, European Union, World Bank, World Trade Organization, and nongovernmental organizations all play roles in international policy.

Categorize the different approaches to environmental policy

- Science plays a role in policy making, although some policy makers may ignore or distort it for political ends.

- Legislation that comes from a central government agency is referred to as a top-down or command-and-control approach.
- Shortcomings of the command-and-control approach have led many economists to advocate economic policy tools.
- Market-based approaches include subsidies, green taxation, and permit trading.

Describe how nations handle transboundary issues

- Many environmental processes have impacts that cut across jurisdictional and political boundaries.
- Transboundary issues, though often complicated, can be managed through international law and the implementation of bilateral agreements, such as the Canada–U.S. Great Lakes Water Quality Agreement.

TESTING YOUR COMPREHENSION

1. Describe two common justifications for environmental policy, and discuss three problems that environmental policy commonly seeks to address.
2. What are some factors that may hinder the implementation or enforcement of environmental policy?
3. Environmental policy and management in Canada is shared among all levels of government. What does this mean, in practice, and what are some of the most important agencies that work on behalf of the environment at all levels of government?
4. Summarize the evolution of environmental law from the early settling of the West to the present day. What is the approach that appears to characterize the present wave of environmental policy?
5. What are the central goals of the *Canadian Environmental Protection Act*?

6. What is the difference between customary law and conventional law? What special difficulties do transboundary environmental problems present?
7. What are some of the important international environmental agreements to which Canada is a party?
8. Why are environmental regulations sometimes considered to be unfair barriers to trade?
9. Differentiate among a green tax, a subsidy, a tax break, and a marketable emissions permit.
10. Many recent environmental initiatives have focused on giving incentives to individuals and corporations to change their environmental behaviour. Explain what this means, and give some examples of programs that do this.

THINKING IT THROUGH

1. Many free-market advocates maintain that environmental laws and regulations are an unnecessary government intrusion into private affairs. Economist Adam Smith argued that individuals can benefit society by pursuing their own self-interest. Do you agree? Can you describe a situation in which an individual acting in his or her self-interest could harm society by causing an environmental problem? Can you describe how environmental policy might rectify the situation? What are some advantages and disadvantages of instituting environmental laws and regulations versus allowing unfettered exchange of materials and services?

2. Reflect on the causes for the historical transitions from one type of environmental policy to another. Now peer into the future, and think about how life might be different in 25, 50, or 100 years. What would you speculate about the environmental policy of the future? What issues might it address?
3. Compare the roles of the United Nations, the European Union, the World Bank, the World Trade Organization, and nongovernmental organizations. If you could gain the support of just one of these institutions for a policy you favoured, which would you choose? Why?

4. Think of one environmental problem that you would like to see solved. From what you have learned about the policy-making process, describe how you think you could best shepherd your ideas through the process to address this problem.

5. Compare the main approaches to environmental policy—command-and-control and economic or market-based approaches. Can you describe an advantage and a disadvantage of each? Do you think any one approach is most effective? Could we do with just one approach, or does it help to have more than one?

6. You have just been named minister of the environment. New legislation mandates reductions in water pollution from untreated municipal wastewater, chemical discharges from factories, and oil spillage from commercial and recreational boats. The new law mandates a 25% reduction in these pollution sources over 10 years, but it does not specify how these reductions are to be accomplished. What policy approaches would you choose to pursue to carry out the mandates of the legislation? Give reasons for your choices.

7. You are now the prime minister of Canada. You must represent Canada at a meeting of G8 leaders, and they want to know what Canada's position will be on the future of international agreements to limit climate change. What will you say?

INTERPRETING GRAPHS AND DATA

In 2007 the National Round Table on Environment and Economy (NRTEE) undertook a major study of emissions trading in the Canadian context, in response to a request for advice from the federal government on reducing carbon emissions.[38] The federal government's current stated goal is to reduce greenhouse gas emissions to 17% below 2005 levels by 2020, and (prior to withdrawing from the Kyoto accord in 2011) to 65% below 2005 levels by 2050. The NRTEE produced the following graph in its report, showing a business-as-usual scenario (BAU); a downstream cap-and-trade system scenario (DCT), which would mainly target large industrial emitters; and an upstream cap-and-trade system (UCT), which would limit the carbon content of fuels before they even reach the industrial users.

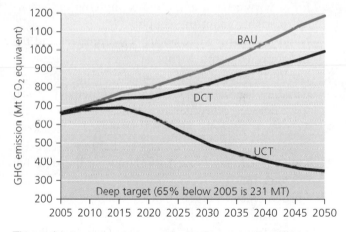

This graph compares emissions reductions over time, based on a business-as-usual scenario (BAU); a downstream cap-and-trade system scenario (DCT), which would mainly target large industrial emitters; and an upstream cap-and-trade (UCT) and/or carbon emissions tax system, which would limit the carbon content of fuels before they even reach the industrial users.

1. Please mark on the graph a point representing the federal government's original emissions target, under the Kyoto agreement, of 461 Mt CO_2 for the year 2012. Why do you think the target has changed?

2. The NRTEE concluded that achieving the government's 2050 emissions targets will require reaching an interim goal of 20% reduction below 2005 levels by 2020. Which of the three scenarios presented in this graph achieves this interim goal?

3. Both the DCT and BAU scenarios end up above the target in 2050. By what percentage do they exceed the target? By what percentage do they exceed 2005 levels?

4. Even the UCT scenario doesn't quite achieve the 2050 target. By how much would the UCT scenario reduce emissions by 2050? By what percentage would emissions still exceed the established target?

CHAPTER ENDNOTES

1. Environment Canada, *Great Lakes Portraits: Lake Erie: A Lake in Flux; Canada–Ontario Agreement Respecting the Great Lakes Basin Ecosystem*, www.on.ec.gc.ca/laws/coa/2001/lake-erie-e.html

2. Hardin, Garrett (1968) "The Tragedy of the Commons." *Science* 162(3859):1243–1248.

3. Environment Canada, *Acts, Regulations, and Agreements*, www.ec.gc.ca/default.asp?lang=En&n=48D356C1-1

4. Based on information from C. W. Daniel Kirby, Radha Curpen, Shawn Denstedt (2006) *Doing Business in Canada: Environmental Law in Canada*, June, www.osler.com/resources.aspx?id=8745

5. CEPA Fact Sheet No. 2: *CEPA 1999 At a Glance: What It Is, What It Does, How It Works*, Government of Canada, October 2005.

6. Based on information from Environmental Commissioner of Ontario, *Environmental Bill of Rights, FAQs*, www.eco.on.ca/eng/index.php/environmental-bill-of-rights/about-the-ebr.php

7. National Round Table on the Environment and the Economy, www.nrtee-trnee.ca

8. Hurlburt, Margot (2007) *Canada's Water Law*, prepared for the National Council of Women of Canada, www.ncwc.ca/pdf/waterlaw.pdf

9. Meadows, Donella H., and Dennis L. Meadows, Jørgen Randers, and William W. Behrens III (1972) *Limits to Growth*. New York: Universe Books, ISBN 0-87663-165-0.

10. Ehrlich, Paul R. (1968) *The Population Bomb*. New York: Ballantine Books.

11. Lappé, Frances Moore (1971) *Diet for a Small Planet*. New York: Ballantine Books, ISBN 0345023781.

12. *Our Common Future: The Report of the United Nations Commission on Environment and Development* (1987). Oxford, UK: Oxford University Press.

13. Bond, Wayne, Dennis O'Farrell, Gary Ironside, Barb Buckland, and Risa Smith, Knowledge Integration Strategies Division, Environmental Reporting Branch, Strategic Information Integration Directorate (2005) *Environmental Indicators and State of the Environment Reporting: An Overview for Canada—Background Paper to an Environmental Indicators and State of the Environment Reporting Strategy, 2004–2009, Environment Canada*. Ottawa: Environment Canada, www.ec.gc.ca/soer-ree/english/resource_network/bg_paper2_e.cfm

14. Environment Canada, International Policy and Cooperation Branch, International Relations Directorate (2002) *Compendium of International Environmental Agreements*, 3rd ed. Ottawa: Environment Canada, www.ec.gc.ca/international/multilat/compendium_e.htm

15. Office of the Auditor General of Canada (2004) Chapter 1: International Environmental Agreements, *Report of the Commissioner of Environment and Sustainable Development*, Ottawa: Office of the Auditor General, www.oag-bvg.gc.ca/internet/english/aud_ch_cesd_2004_1_e_14914.html

16. Excerpt from the Charter of the United Nations (1945) http://www.un.org/en/documents/charter/index.shtml

17. North American Agreement on Environmental Cooperation–Canadian Office, *NAAEC Overview*, www.naaec.gc.ca/eng/agreement/agreement_e.htm

18. Murray, William (1993) *NAFTA and the Environment*. Ottawa: Environment Canada Science and Technology Division, http://dsp-psd.tpsgc.gc.ca/Collection-R/LoPBdP/MR/mr116-e.htm

19. *The Environmental Effects of Free Trade: Papers Presented at the North American Symposium on Assessing the Linkages Between Trade and the Environment, 2000* (2002). Ottawa: Commission for Environmental Cooperation of North America, www.cec.org/files/pdf/ECONOMY/symposium-e.pdf

20. OPEC's members are Algeria, Angola, Ecuador, Indonesia, the Islamic Republic of Iran, Iraq, Kuwait, Libya, Nigeria, Qatar, Saudi Arabia, United Arab Emirates, and Venezuela.

21. OPEC, *Frequently Asked Questions: Does OPEC Support Environmental Policies?* www.opec.org/library/FAQs/aboutOPEC/q17.htm

22. Johnson, Dr. Pierre Marc (symposium chair) (2002) Introduction. *The Environmental Effects of Free Trade: Papers Presented at the North American Symposium on Assessing the Linkages Between Trade and the Environment*. Ottawa: Commission for Environmental Cooperation of North America, www.cec.org/files/pdf/ECONOMY/symposium-e.pdf

23. Johnson, Dr. Pierre Marc (symposium chair) (2002) Introduction. *The Environmental Effects of Free Trade: Papers Presented at the North American Symposium on Assessing the Linkages Between Trade and the Environment*. Ottawa: Commission for

Environmental Cooperation of North America, www.cec.org/files/pdf/ECONOMY/ymposium-e.pdf

24. Elwell, Christine (2002) NAFTA Effects on Water: Testing for NAFTA Effects in the Great Lakes Basin. *The Environmental Effects of Free Trade: Papers Presented at the North American Symposium on Assessing the Linkages Between Trade and the Environment.* Ottawa: Commission for Environmental Cooperation of North America, www.cec.org/files/pdf/ECONOMY/symposium-e.pdf

25. Johnson, Dr. Pierre Marc (symposium chair) (2002) Introduction. *The Environmental Effects of Free Trade: Papers Presented at the North American Symposium on Assessing the Linkages Between Trade and the Environment.* Ottawa: Commission for Environmental Cooperation of North America, www.cec.org/files/pdf/ECONOMY/symposium-e.pdf

26. Ecojustice (2005) *Media Release: Misdirected Spending: Groups Demand Investigation into Billions in Federal Subsidies to Canada's Oil and Gas Industry,* www.ecojustice.ca/media-centre/press-releases/pressrelease.2007-12-03.6697873163

27. Myers, Lynne. *Financial Incentives and Subsidies for Renewable Energy in Canada and the United States,* March 8, 2002.

28. *National Round Table on the Environment and the Economy, Getting to 2050: Canada's Transition to a Low-Emission Future,* www.nrtee-trnee.ca/eng/publications/getting-to-2050/Getting-to-2050-low-res-eng.pdf

29. Ontario Ministry of the Environment (2005) *Emissions Trading: Fact Sheet,* www.ene.gov.on.ca/programs/4346e02.pdf

30. CBC (2001) *Life and Times: Maude Barlow,* www.cbc.ca/lifeandtimes/barlow.html

31. Council of Canadians, *About Us,* www.canadians.org/about/index.html

32. Council of Canadians, *Vision Statement,* www.canadians.org/about/BOD/vision.html

33. Council of Canadians, *About Us,* www.canadians.org/about/index.html

34. Barlow, Maude (2007) *Blue Covenant: The Global Water Crisis and the Coming Battle for the Right to Water,* p. 164, http://canadians.org/about/documents/Blue_Covenant_Excerpt_07.pdf

35. Council of Canadians, *About Us: Maude Barlow,* www.canadians.org/about/Maude_Barlow/

36. On the Road with Maude Barlow (2008) *Canadian Perspectives,* Summer, www.canadians.org/publications/CP/2008/summer/CP_summer_08_Maude.html

37. Barlow, M. (2007) *Global Water Crisis and the Coming Battle for the Right to Water,* http://www.canadians.org/about/documents/Blue_Covenant_Excerpt_07.pdf

38. National Round Table on the Environment and the Economy, *Getting to 2050: Canada's Transition to a Low-Emission Future,* www.nrtee-trnee.ca/eng/publications/getting-to-2050/Getting-to-2050-low-res-eng.pdf

MyEnvironmentPlace

Go to **www.myenvironmentplace.ca** where you will find quizzes, animations, your Pearson eText, and more.

Strategies for Sustainability

23

Mow Down Pollution is a program developed by Summerhill Impact, in which The Home Depot Canada offers rebates to customers who turn in old gas-powered lawn-care equipment for modern, less polluting models.

Upon successfully completing this chapter, you will be able to

- List and describe approaches being taken on college and university campuses to promote sustainability
- Explain the concept of sustainable development
- Discuss how protecting the environment can be compatible with promoting economic welfare
- Describe and assess key approaches to designing sustainable solutions

- Discuss the need for action on behalf of the environment and the tremendous human potential to solve problems
- Name several examples of programs that aim to reduce environmental impacts by changing the behaviour of individuals, corporations, or institutions

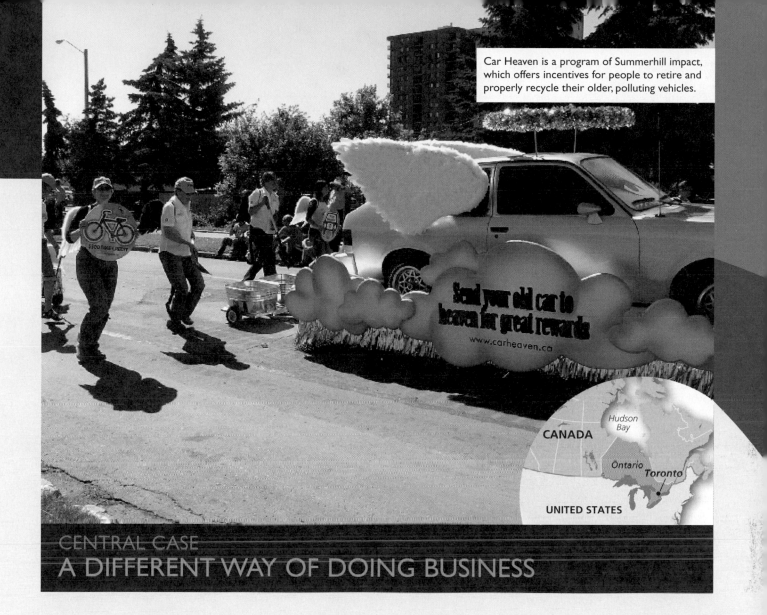

Car Heaven is a program of Summerhill Impact, which offers incentives for people to retire and properly recycle their older, polluting vehicles.

CANADA
Hudson Bay
Ontario
Toronto
UNITED STATES

CENTRAL CASE
A DIFFERENT WAY OF DOING BUSINESS

"We solemnly pledge to the peoples of the world and the generations that will surely inherit this Earth that we are determined to ensure that our collective hope for sustainable development is realized."
—DECLARATION SIGNED BY 193 NATIONS AT THE WORLD SUMMIT, JOHANNESBURG, SOUTH AFRICA, 2002

"We have to move decisively to protect our children's future."
—ELIZABETH MAY, LEADER OF THE GREEN PARTY OF CANADA

The Summerhill Group runs a different kind of business. For one thing, Summerhill is a social enterprise. Definitions of *social enterprise* vary, but they generally focus on the idea that such organizations—whether not-for-profit or for-profit—have, as their core mission, achieving social goals or solving social problems using an entrepreneurial approach.

Summerhill was started as a social enterprise in 2001 by Ian Morton, with the vision of "transforming markets to sustainability." The organization now consists of Summerhill, an environmental consulting company that works with large corporations and other organizations, helping them to design and implement initiatives for sustainability; and Summerhill Impact (formerly the Clean Air Foundation), the not-for-profit arm of the group. Their mission is "to create innovative market-based solutions that generate sustained environmental and social improvements by engaging people and developing partnerships to influence consumer behaviour." The company is fundamentally entrepreneurial and business-oriented, stating in their core values that, "while not perfect, the market is the fastest and most direct method of improving the environment we all share."[1]

At the heart of Summerhill's activities is a fundamentally different way of doing business. It has been traditional to view environmental, social, and economic goals as mutually exclusive. Summerhill makes it their mission to show their large corporate clients (which include The Home Depot Canada, Walmart Canada, and SaskPower) that adopting environmental programs and strategies will, in fact, help them to promote their business, meet their targets, strengthen their brand, engage their customers, and boost the bottom line—all while promoting more environmentally sustainable products and choices. It is an approach that creates economic value in a way that also creates value for society.

The Home Depot Canada discovered the usefulness of this approach through Mow Down Pollution, Go Low Flow, Bright Ideas, and other programs developed by Summerhill (some in conjunction with partners). The programs create a customer experience that builds loyalty, enhances the company's reputation as an environmental leader, and drives sales, all while helping consumers reduce their environmental impacts. For example, the Mow Down Pollution program, which offers rebates to customers who turn in their gas-powered equipment for new, energy-efficient electric models, has retired 45 650 old mowers and trimmers, reducing greenhouse gas and smog-forming emissions by more than 1700 tonnes since its inception in 2001.[2] This is important because, according to Statistics Canada, 70% of Canadian homes own gas-powered lawn equipment, releasing about 80 000 tonnes of polluting emissions every year.[3]

Another successful and longstanding Summerhill Impact program is Car Heaven, which encourages people to turn in their old cars so that they can be safely and properly recycled. So far more than 123 000 vehicles have been recycled through this program, which, in addition to reducing greenhouse gases and smog-causing emissions, has raised over $3 million for affiliated charities.

Programs like these show how small actions by individual people can add up to big changes for the environment. Influencing individual behaviour is at the core of many of Summerhill's programs, which strive to make people aware of easy and effective actions they can take to reduce their impacts on the environment. The opportunity to become engaged doesn't apply just to consumers; the EcoExecutives program gets corporate execs out of the boardroom and into the Toronto Zoo, where they learn about alternative energy, waste management, and climate change and about how these affect the bottom line of their businesses.

Summerhill employees also act as "ambassadors of the improvements we want to see in the world." Summerhill's success in the corporate sector provides hope that we may be moving toward a business model in which social, environmental, and economic goals can be viewed as mutually compatible, rather than mutually exclusive.

Sustainability on Campus

If we are to attain a sustainable civilization, we will need to make efforts at every level, from the individual to the household to the community to the nation to the world. Governments, corporations, and organizations must all encourage and pursue sustainable practices. Among the institutions that can contribute to sustainability efforts are colleges and universities.

We tend to think of colleges and universities as enlightened and progressive institutions that generate benefits for society. However, colleges and universities are also centres of lavish resource consumption. Institutions of higher education feature extensive infrastructure, including classrooms, offices, research labs, and residential housing. Most also have dining establishments, sports arenas, vehicle fleets, and road networks. The ecological footprint of a typical college or university is substantial

(see "The Science Behind the Story: A Campus Ecological Footprint Calculator").

Reducing the size of this footprint is challenging. Colleges and universities tend to be bastions of tradition, where institutional habits are deeply ingrained and where bureaucratic inertia and financial constraints can often block the best intentions for positive change. Nonetheless, faculty, staff, administrators, and especially students are progressing on a variety of fronts to make the operations of educational institutions more sustainable.

In 2008 the Alma Mater Society (AMS), which today represents 45 000 students at UBC Vancouver, created the AMS Lighter Footprint Strategy, based on the ecological footprint concept of William Rees and Mathis Wackernagel.[4] The intent of the strategy was to coordinate and build upon the successes of student-run sustainability initiatives. The strategy defines internal goals that can be achieved by a student organization working on its own and interactive goals that require communication or collaboration with other agencies, both within the university and outside of it. The goals are divided into such categories as food and beverage, communications, transportation, and campus policies. Each category has suggested actions and timeframes, as well as indicators with which progress can be measured. Student-run organizations at other campuses are beginning to adopt some of the actions and principles of the Lighter Footprint Strategy. Even university and college presidents have become involved. The **Talloires Declaration** is a commitment on the part of college and university presidents around the world to pursue and foster sustainability. The declaration provides a ten-point action plan for incorporating sustainability and environmental literacy in teaching, research, operations and outreach at colleges and universities (**TABLE 23.1**). As of 2010, the Talloires Declaration has been signed by 433 presidents and chancellors from 52 nations, including 37 Canadian universities and colleges.[5]

Why strive for campus sustainability?

You enrolled at your college or university to gain an education, not to transform the institution. Why, then, are increasing numbers of students promoting sustainable practices on their campuses? First, reducing the ecological footprint of a campus really can make a difference. The consumptive impact of educating, feeding, and housing hundreds or thousands of students is immense. Second, campus sustainability efforts make students aware of the need to address environmental problems, and students who act to promote campus sustainability serve as models for their peers. Finally, students who engage in sustainability efforts learn and grow as a result. The challenges, successes, and failures that they encounter can serve as valuable preparation for similar efforts in transforming inertia-bound institutions in the broader society.

Support from faculty, staff, and administrators is crucial for success, but students are often the ones who initiate change. Students often feel freer than faculty or staff to express themselves. Students also arrive on campus with new ideas and perspectives, and they generally are less attached to traditional ways of doing things.

Campus efforts may begin with an audit

Campus sustainability efforts often begin with a quantitative assessment of the institution's operations. Such audits provide baseline information on what an institution is doing or how much it is consuming and help set priorities and goals. It is useful in such an **environmental audit** to target items that can lead directly to specific recommendations to reduce impacts and enhance sustainability. Once changes are implemented, the institution can monitor progress by comparing future measurements to the audit's baseline data.

Student auditors at Mount Allison University undertake a comprehensive environmental audit every two years, most recently in 2011. The results of the audits have contributed to the development of a green action plan, which provides ideas for campus groups looking for

Table 23.1 The 10-Step Plan of the Talloires Declaration

1. Raise public, government, industry, foundation, and university awareness by publicly addressing the urgent need to move toward an environmentally sustainable future.
2. Engage in education, research, policy formation, and information exchange on population, environment, and development to move toward a sustainable future.
3. Establish programs to produce expertise in environmental management, sustainable economic development, population, and related fields to ensure that all university graduates are environmentally literate and responsible citizens.
4. Develop the capability of university faculty to teach environmental literacy.
5. Set an example of environmental responsibility by establishing programs of resource conservation, recycling, and waste reduction at the universities.
6. Encourage the involvement of government (at all levels), foundations, and industry in supporting university

research, education, policy formation, and information exchange in environmentally sustainable development. Expand work with nongovernmental organizations to assist in finding solutions to environmental problems.
7. Convene school deans and environmental practitioners to develop research, policy, information exchange programs, and curricula for an environmentally sustainable future.
8. Establish partnerships with primary and secondary schools to help develop the capability of their faculty to teach about population, environment, and sustainable development issues.
9. Work with the U.N. Conference on Environment and Development, the U.N. Environment Programme, and other national and international organizations.
10. Establish a steering committee and a secretariat to continue this momentum and inform and support each other's efforts in carrying out this declaration.

Source: University Leaders for a Sustainable Future, Programs: Talloires Declaration, www.ulsf.org/programs_talloires.html

THE SCIENCE BEHIND THE STORY

A Campus Ecological Footprint Calculator

UTM's ecological footprint project kicked off under the campus "Grow Smart, Grow Green" plan.

Back in the summer of 2004, University of Toronto Mississauga (UTM) undergraduate Greg Bunker worked with Professor Tenley Conway to complete an Ecological Footprint Assessment (EFA) for the UTM campus.[6] The results of the work revealed that the available online calculators, designed for individuals and schools, were ill suited for university campuses. The calculators yielded widely varying results. More importantly, it was discovered that the existing calculators were organized in a manner that made it difficult to collect the required information, and some of the indicators did not accurately reflect the university setting.

For example, when Bunker defined the intercampus shuttle bus as an intercity bus, using the online calculators that were available at the time, fossil fuel consumption was defined as the number of passengers multiplied by the number of kilometres travelled per month. Increasing the number of students using this mode of mass transportation would actually *increase* UTM's footprint, and any improvement in the fuel efficiency of the service would not be considered. This result is counterintuitive, and suggested that the indicator—if calculated in this manner—was not an effective diagnostic tool for resource use at an institution. It became clear that the existing calculators did not accurately reflect the situation of the university campus.

Following up on the recommendations that came out of this early work, undergraduate students Chelsea Dalton and Jennifer Loo worked with Professor Conway in the summer of 2005 to develop the UTM Ecological Footprint Calculator, which is uniquely tailored to the campus setting. The most useful aspect of the calculator is its organizational structure. Rather than being organized by impact categories, as most calculators are, it follows the university's departmental structure. This streamlines the collection of data and

allows the user to easily see which departments on campus should be targeted for footprint reduction strategies.

The calculator has a total of six impact categories: materials and waste, built-up land, water, energy, food, and transportation. The calculator breaks down the footprint by impact category, with the colour-coded results displayed at the bottom of the spreadsheet. As a result of the design of the calculator, the impact categories and departments that have the largest contributions to the campus footprint are clearly indicated. The calculator includes on-campus consumption and commuting only; activities that occur off-campus, such as field trips and at-home consumption by commuter students, are not included. However, these have been the subjects of subsequent student research projects at UTM. In addition, materials used to construct new buildings are not included, because of the difficulty of tracking the weights and exact amounts consumed.

When computed by students Suzana Svadja and Tooba Shakeel in 2009 using the new calculator, UTM's total footprint came out to 10 589.3 ha, or 0.91 ha per full-time equivalent campus community member. Of all the impact categories, energy contributes the most to the footprint, accounting

---

possible activities and serves as a "tool kit" for the environmental issues committee.

Recycling and waste reduction are common campus efforts

Campus sustainability efforts frequently involve waste reduction, recycling, or composting. Waste management initiatives are relatively easy to start and maintain because they offer many opportunities for small-scale improvements and because people generally enjoy recycling and reducing waste. Waste and recycling audits, battery drop-offs, and residence composting programs are popular on Canadian campuses.

Students, faculty, and staff at Concordia University are diverting waste from landfills through recycling and composting initiatives. This includes drop-offs for old computers and other electronic wastes, which are

becoming an increasingly problematic component of municipal waste. In 2007, Concordia became the first university certified under the *Ici on Recycle* program, sponsored by Recyc-Québec and the government of Québec, which recognizes institutions that divert at least 65% of their waste from landfills. McGill University students—inspired by what they saw happening at Concordia and other universities—started Gorilla Composting, a student-run initiative that continues to promote composting on campus (**FIGURE 23.1**).

Students at some campuses run events that promote the reuse of items. At the University of Calgary, the U-Bike program was started when 10 discarded bicycles were salvaged, repaired, and pressed into service. The bikes, painted with bright red and yellow stripes, are available for use free of charge for any university student. Programs similar to this, which apparently originated in the Netherlands in 1998, are springing up at campuses and in cities across North America.

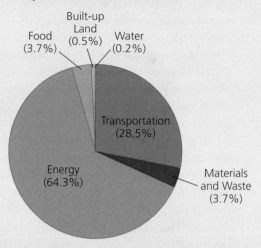

Footprint Breakdown 2008–2009

Food (3.7%)
Built-up Land (0.5%)
Water (0.2%)
Transportation (28.5%)
Energy (64.3%)
Materials and Waste (3.7%)

Energy is by far the largest impact contributor to UTM's campus ecological footprint, at more then 64% of the total.
Source: Data from Ecological Footprint of the University of Toronto, Mississauga 2008–2009: Calculations and Analysis, by S. Svajda and T. Shakeel.

for about 64%, followed by transportation at 28.5%, then food, materials and waste, built-up land, and lastly, water (see figure).

UTM was not the first university to undertake an ecological footprint assessment (EFA). Several other universities and colleges have conducted EFAs of varying scope, with widely differing results. For example, the 2004 EFA for UTM, using two online calculators, determined UTM's footprint to be in excess of 40 000 ha—four times the 2009 result! The completeness of the data affected the calculated footprint size, and differences in methodologies were crucial.

Part of the goal of the UTM Ecological Footprint Project has been to compare how various campus EFA studies have been done and to investigate how the methodologies could be improved and customized for the university setting. Additional goals were to consider the implications of EFAs for sustainability at post-secondary institutions and to propose some ways in which

campus ecological footprints might be reduced.

The Ecological Footprint Project was partly sponsored by the chief executive officer of UTM, who subsequently used some of the results and recommendations to derive strategies for UTM's *Grow Smart, Grow Green* development plan. One aspect of this plan was the establishment of UTM's Centre for Emerging Energy Technologies, whose director is Chris Cheh. The centre has been responsible for a number of initiatives and partnerships on campus, including the acquisition of solar golf carts for grounds maintenance crews and campus tours; a photovoltaic system for supplementary power supply; a solid oxide fuel cell combined heat and power installation for student residences; and a test venue for hydrogen buses.

Goals for the future of the Ecological Footprint Project include expanding the calculator to make it more widely applicable; developing a calculator that allows the user to see the footprint reductions that would result from making certain improvements on campus; and calculating the footprint impacts of various emerging energy technologies that are being used on the UTM campus. Incorporating the project into related course work is another avenue being pursued. This would provide undergraduates with an opportunity to conduct research while contributing in a meaningful way to an ongoing project.

FIGURE 23.1
The mascot of McGill University's student-run Gorilla Composting Team (inset shows the team's logo) introduces new students to on-campus composting.

One very popular initiative on campuses in Canada lately has been Bottled Water Free Day, a partnership among the Canadian Federation of Students, the Polaris Institute, the Sierra Youth Coalition, the Canadian Union of Public Employees, and Development and Peace. The program urges students and staff to pledge not to drink bottled water if tap water is available, with the goal of reducing waste from plastic water bottles. As of 2011, nine campuses in Canada have taken the pledge to ban the sale of plastic water bottles; the University of Winnipeg was first, in early 2009. More than 80 municipalities in Canada have also taken steps to reduce waste from plastic water bottles.[7]

Administrators are more easily convinced to enact institutional changes if they save money. The EcoTrek Project, Canada's largest university energy and water retrofit project, accomplished this at UBC. The project began in the fall of 2002. The objectives were to generate savings, reduce energy use in university buildings by 20%, and reduce water use by 30%; these goals have been met and exceeded. The project is now saving UBC an estimated $2.6 million annually, making the payback period approximately 17 years for the $35 million project. The work involved retrofits to nearly 300 campus buildings, including installing more efficient lighting; weather-stripping nearly 2000 doors; and replacing old steam boilers with energy-efficient burners.[8]

The Renew Project at UBC provided similar savings. This project was aimed at incorporating the full long-term costs—environmental and social, as well as economic— into renovate-versus-replace decisions on campus. As of 2009, the University had avoided $88 million in facilities replacement costs and saved 97 million megajoules of primary energy, 27 million litres of water, and more than 6000 tonnes of greenhouse gas emissions, among others.[9]

Green building design is a key to sustainable campuses

Dozens of campuses now boast "green" buildings that are constructed from sustainable building materials and whose design and technologies encourage energy efficiency, water efficiency, renewable energy, and the reduction of pollution. As with any type of ecolabelling, agreed-upon standards are needed, and for sustainable buildings these are the **Leadership in Energy and Environmental Design (LEED)** standards. Developed and maintained by the nonprofit Green Building Council, LEED standards guide the design and certification of new construction and the renovation of existing structures on campuses and elsewhere.

Buildings earn LEED credits in various categories if they are constructed using materials that were recycled or reused, took little energy to produce, or were locally harvested, produced, or distributed. Other common features are energy-efficient lighting, heating, and appliances, state-of-the-art ventilation systems and paints, adhesives, and carpeting that emit few volatile organic compounds.

Vancouver Island University was an early leader in green buildings and environmental retrofits in Canada. The university adopted a holistic, environmentally sustainable approach to building design in 1990, when it began planning for the Nanaimo campus. Since then, the university has realized millions of dollars in energy savings. The movement for "green buildings" continues to grow. Pavilions Lassonde at the École Polytechnique de Montréal was the first LEED-certified building in Canada, achieving its gold status in October 2005, followed closely by the Life Sciences Centre at UBC in December 2005 and the University of Victoria Medical Sciences Centre in August 2006. Only a handful of buildings in Canada have earned platinum LEED certification; these include the Centre for Child Development at the University of Calgary, certified in 2007 (**FIGURE 23.2**).

Sustainable architecture doesn't stop at the walls of a building. Careful design of campus landscaping can create liveable spaces that promote social interaction, where plantings supply shade, prevent soil erosion, create attractive settings, and provide wildlife habitat. It has been said, in fact, that groundskeepers are more vital to schools' recruiting efforts than are vice-presidents.

The University of Victoria, known for the beauty of its 160-ha campus grounds, protects certain areas from development and has made a commitment to restoration and monitoring of naturalized areas. The university

FIGURE 23.2
The Centre for Child Development at the University of Calgary is Canada's largest platinum LEED-certified building.

has adopted the concept of "naturescaping," a landscaping approach that emphasizes restoring, preserving, and enhancing wildlife habitat in urban and rural areas. The intent is to create new habitats, utilize native plant species, reduce the need for watering, and eliminate chemical pesticides and herbicides. There are several natural landscaping projects on campus, including the Native Plant Study Garden and the Lorene Kennedy Memorial Native Plant Garden (**FIGURE 23.3**).[10]

Efficient water use is important

Managing water efficiently is a key element of sustainable campuses. Simon Fraser University was recently recognized with an Earth Award from the Building Owners and Managers Association (BOMA) of British Columbia, for the new Arts and Social Sciences Complex. The building has many energy-saving features, as well as a cistern under the inner courtyard that can store more than 227 000 L of rainwater, to be used for landscape irri-

gation purposes.[11] The building has also won engineering and architectural design awards; it is certified under the BOMA-sponsored Go Green program, a green building certification program similar to LEED. Simon Fraser University was the first post-secondary institution in North America to have 26 core campus buildings certified under Go Green.

The Living with the Lakes Centre at Laurentian University demonstrates another approach to water management integrated with green building design. This project, which will house the university's aquatic ecology programs, will be completely integrated into its lakeside setting, featuring a flow-through aquatic laboratory with natural lake water. A green roof will store and filter rainwater, and two constructed wetlands, one outdoors and one indoors, will treat and purify stormwater. The building and site are designed to improve the quality of water entering Ramsay Lake, a drinking water reservoir.[12]

Water conservation is just as important indoors. Water-saving technologies, such as waterless urinals and "living machines" to treat wastewater, are being installed at a number of campuses. UBC's EcoTrek program reduced water use on campus by 35% each year.[13] A study by the sustainability office of the University of Toronto found that urinals in some buildings on the downtown campus were set to flush automatically at timed intervals, 24 hours a day, seven days a week, resulting in what the study called an "astronomical" waste of water. The problem was resolved by installing motion sensor flush systems in 15 washrooms, resulting in estimated savings of 7 million litres of water and $10 000 per year.[14]

Energy conservation is achievable

Students are finding many ways to conserve energy on campus. Campuses can realize large energy savings simply by not powering unused buildings. How many times have you walked through a classroom building at night or in the summer when it was totally empty, yet found that all the lights were on and the heating or air conditioning was running full blast? Large buildings are expensive to heat, cool, and light, so powering them down when not in use saves a great deal of energy, money, and greenhouse gas emissions.

One successful on-campus energy conservation program is the University of Toronto's ReWire Project, which aims to help students, staff, and faculty reduce their energy consumption through behavioural changes. Components of the project include sustainability pledges, environmental education initiatives, and "toolkits" that provide information, resources, and strategies to users.

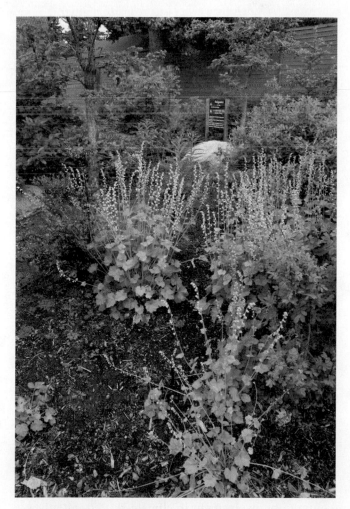

FIGURE 23.3
The Lorene Kennedy Memorial Native Plant Garden is one of a number of "naturescaping" projects at the University of Victoria.

The toolkits contain an assortment of "action tools" that allow users to pass along information to promote sustainable behaviour. The toolkits are designed for use in specific campus settings, such as residence rooms, common areas, and offices. The project has received financial support from a number of sources outside the university, including the Toronto Atmospheric Fund, the Better Buildings Partnership, and the Ontario Power Authority.[15]

Students can promote renewable energy

Campuses can reduce energy consumption and greenhouse emissions by altering the types of energy they use. Student initiatives on campus can also influence the types of energy we use in our society. Every two years, teams of students from 20 universities compete in the Solar Decathlon, which includes teams from Germany, China, Puerto Rico, and Spain, as well as Canada and the United States. In this remarkable event, teams of students travel to Washington, D.C., bringing material for the solar-powered homes they have spent months designing. They erect their homes on the National Mall in Washington, where the buildings stand for three weeks. The homes are judged on 10 criteria, and prizes are awarded to winners in each category. In 2011, Canada was represented by a team from the University of Calgary, which produced a solar-powered house they called *Technological Residence, Traditional Living*. The building celebrated diversity in its design, which was tailored to Alberta's Aboriginal communities (**FIGURE 23.4**).[16]

Solar and wind power and other alternative energy sources play roles on many campuses. Since the 1980s, Carleton University has made use of geothermal energy for space heating, through underground thermal energy storage (UTES) technologies. UTES systems use underground reservoirs to store heat during the summer and provide heat during the winter. Heat is withdrawn from and returned to the reservoir, as needed, by pumping fluids through a system of underground pipes.

Trent University, located on the fast-flowing Otanabe River, has its own hydroelectric power plant, the Stan Adamson Powerhouse, which houses three turbine generators. The plant supplies about 75–80% of the total electricity used on campus in a given year, and excess power from low-use times is exported to the power grid. The power plant technology dates from the original construction in the late 1800s, but Trent plans to start a major upgrade of the facility, which should allow the campus to be 100% self-sufficient on a source of energy that is associated with virtually no pollutants or emissions.[17]

FIGURE 23.4
Teams from colleges and universities around the world compete in the biennial Solar Decathlon in Washington, D.C. Each team erects an entire house, of the students' own design, fully powered by solar energy. In the 2011 event Canada was represented by the University of Calgary. Their solar-powered entry, called *Technological Residence, Traditional Living*, was designed for Alberta's Aboriginal communities.

Carbon neutrality is a new goal

Now that global climate change has vaulted to the forefront of society's concerns, reducing greenhouse gas emissions from fossil fuel combustion has become a top priority for campus sustainability proponents. Today many campuses are aiming to become carbon neutral.

As of 2011, 67 university presidents in the United States had signed on to the American College and University Presidents Climate Commitment (including a few from Canada). This pledge to reduce campus greenhouse emissions commits presidents to undertake inventory of emissions, set target dates for becoming carbon neutral, and take immediate steps to lower emissions with short-term actions, while also integrating sustainability into the curriculum.[18] In March 2008, a similar Climate Change Statement of Action was signed by university and college presidents across British Columbia. The statement commits each institution to initiate a comprehensive plan to reduce greenhouse gases.

Student pressure and petitions at many campuses have nudged administrators and trustees to set targets for reducing greenhouse emissions, and to strive to do more to counteract climate change than they do to contribute to it. Common Energy is a network of students, faculty, staff, and community stakeholders working to encourage their universities to move beyond climate neutrality, by providing resources and undertaking actions to promote community involvement in climate-related initiatives.[19] Go Beyond is a project of the B.C. Campus Climate Network, a partnership among high school, college, and university sustainability organizations. Go Beyond, which supports students in implementing climate action on their campuses, states as its objective to "move beyond climate-neutral step by step together."[20]

Dining services and campus gardens let students eat sustainably

Campus food service operations can promote sustainable practices by buying organic produce, composting food scraps, and purchasing food in bulk or with less packaging. Buying locally grown or produced food supports local economies and cuts down on fuel use from long-distance transportation. At the University of Waterloo, students and the University Food Services teamed up to start an on-campus Farm Market to promote local foods. The market features 100% local produce, preserves and honeys made in Waterloo County, and fresh baked goods made right on campus. McGill University's Organic Campus is a student-run nonprofit organization that delivers local organic fruits and vegetables on campus.

Some college campuses even have community gardens where students can grow food. McGill's Campus Crops is a student-run urban gardening cooperative (**FIGURE 23.5**). Faced with a shortage of community garden plots, the students are aiming to identify unused spaces on the McGill campus that could support urban agriculture. McGill also has a vegan food collective (The Midnight Kitchen).

Institutional purchasing matters

The kinds of purchasing decisions made in dining halls favouring local food, organic food, and biodegradable products can be applied across the entire spectrum of a campus's needs. When campus purchasing departments buy recycled paper, certified sustainable wood, energy-efficient appliances, goods with less packaging, and other ecolabelled products, they send signals to manufacturers and increase the demand for such items. Students are working with campus bookstores to carry, promote, and sell more environmentally and socially sustainable books, paper products, and school supplies.

The University of Guelph in Ontario is one of a number of universities that have undertaken green purchasing policies for their computing services departments, with a pledge to take into consideration the entire life cycle of electronic products. "Green computing" considers everything from "cradle" (the materials and processes used in the manufacturing and shipping of the product), through operational use (the energy efficiency of the product), to "grave" (the effective recycling and disposal of the product).

At Chatham College in Pennsylvania, students chose to honour their school's best-known alumnus, Rachel Carson, by seeking to eliminate toxic chemicals on campus. Administrators agreed to this effort, provided that alternative products to replace the toxic ones worked just as well and were not more expensive. Students brought in the CEO of a company that produces nontoxic cleaning products, who demonstrated to the janitorial staff that his company's products

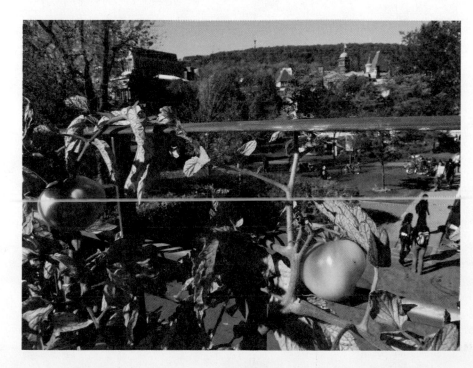

FIGURE 23.5
A number of campuses now include gardens where students can grow organic vegetables that are used for meals in dining halls. This is a view from a garden run by McGill University's Campus Crops Initiative.

were superior. The university switched to the nontoxic products, which were also cheaper, and proceeded to save $10 000 per year. Chatham students then found a company offering paint without volatile organic compounds and negotiated with it for a free paint job and discounted prices on later purchases. Students also worked with grounds staff to eliminate herbicides and fertilizers used on campus lawns and to find alternative treatments.

Transportation alternatives are many

Many campuses struggle with traffic congestion, parking shortages, commuting delays, and pollution from vehicle exhaust. Some are addressing these issues by establishing or expanding bus and shuttle systems; encouraging bicycling, walking, and carpooling; and introducing alternative vehicles to university fleets (**FIGURE 23.6**). The *Allégo* program at Concordia University makes sustainable transportation choices available to those who are commuting to and from the campus, offering a free rideshare board, bicycle safety and maintenance workshops, and a Guaranteed Ride Home program for carpoolers.[21]

The University of British Columbia is also a leader in transportation efforts. For less than $25 a month, UBC's U'Pass program provides students with biking programs and facilities, expanded campus bus and shuttle services, unlimited use of some city transit systems, rides home in emergencies, merchant discounts, and priority parking spaces and ride-matching services for carpoolers. The

program has boosted transit ridership to campus and decreased single-person car use.

Campuses are restoring native plants, habitats, and landscapes

No campus sustainability program would be complete without some attempt to enhance the campus's natural environment, such as on the University of Victoria campus, described above. Such efforts remove invasive species, restore native plants and communities, improve habitat for wildlife, enhance soil and water quality, reduce pesticide use, and create healthier, more attractive surroundings.

The University of Saskatchewan College of Education has constructed a Prairie Habitat Garden with native grasses, shrubs, and wildflowers. The garden helps preserve the natural heritage and habitat of prairie grasslands while acting as an educational resource (**FIGURE 23.7**).

In a unique partnership, the University of Toronto Mississauga joined with Evergreen Foundation's Learning Grounds program for a major campus greening initiative. The partnership has won local environmental awards. Regular volunteer plantings of native shrubs and flowers have contributed to the naturalization of many areas of the campus. Students, staff, faculty, and neighbours routinely turn out for the events. Besides providing wildlife habitat, the restored areas reduce runoff, erosion, and maintenance costs, and provide opportunities for research and education. For example, student researchers have assessed Jefferson salamander populations and habitat conditions at the campus. These studies will provide information

FIGURE 23.6
The Sustainable Concordia *Allégo* program holds free bike tune-up events for students, staff, and faculty.

FIGURE 23.7
Many schools have embarked on habitat restoration projects to beautify their campuses, provide wildlife habitat, restore native plants, and filter water runoff. These flowers are in the University of Saskatchewan's Prairie Habitat Garden.

on the threatened salamander's breeding ponds and terrestrial habitat, educate the university community about the significance of the species, and determine whether habitat restoration actions are required. The university also undertook a controlled burn to restore native vegetation on a small area of the campus, planting experimental plots of native plants to study ecological patterns in the wake of the restoration.

Sustainability efforts include curricular changes

Campus sustainability activities provide students with active, hands-on ways to influence how their campuses function. Sustainability concerns are also transforming academic curricula and course offerings. The course for which you are using this book right now likely did not exist a generation ago. As our society comes to appreciate the looming challenge of sustainability, colleges and universities are attempting to train students to confront this challenge more effectively.

Almost all universities and colleges in Canada now offer courses and programs on environment and sustainability issues. Trent University in Peterborough, Ontario, has offered courses in environmental and resource management since 1975. The university now partners with Fleming College to offer a practical, field-based program in ecological restoration. Faculty at Queen's University have received awards for excellence in education for the promotion of sustainable practices, in recognition of their contributions to sustainability education.[22]

Some universities specialize within the general fields of environment and sustainability. For example, McMaster University is widely recognized for excellence in the field of environmental health. The Institute of Island Studies at Prince Edward Island University emphasizes the study of the culture, environment, and economy of small islands. The institute's associates undertake studies on environmental policy, water quality, land use, and other topics from the particular perspective of island economies, and partner with other island researchers from around the world.

Besides offering new courses and programs, schools are incorporating sustainability issues into established courses across many disciplines. UBC, for example, now offers more than 350 courses with sustainability-related themes. Many of these are also *interdisciplinary* courses and programs, meaning that they integrate knowledge from a variety of different disciplines. An example of an interdisciplinary research program is the National First Nations Environmental Contaminants Program (NFN–ECP), a collaborative program among the First Nations University of Canada, the Assembly of First Nations, and Health Canada. The goal of NFN–ECP is to support research on environmental contaminant exposure and the potential for risks to the health and well-being of First Nations people in Canada.[23]

Sustainability courses and programs often have a practical slant. For example, the University of Waterloo's ERS250 "Greening the Campus" course and the University of Toronto's ENV421 "Environmental Research" course both offer students the opportunity to carry out practical research on campus for course credits. Often the results of student research are used in developing campus policies; examples of past ENV421 projects have included "Recommendations for Reducing Energy Consumption" and "The Natural Step and the University of Toronto: A Value Added Approach to Energy Efficiency Planning."[24]

weighing the issues

SUSTAINABILITY ON YOUR CAMPUS

Find out what sustainability efforts are being made on your campus. What results have these achieved so far? What further efforts would you like to see pursued on your campus? Do you foresee any obstacles to these efforts? How could these obstacles be overcome? How could you become involved? Are there opportunities for you to undertake research or project work for course credits?

The UBC SEEDS program links students, staff, and faculty to research projects that enhance sustainability on campus, and allows students to get course credits for their projects. SEEDS projects have benefited the campus through a number of research projects that have led to policy changes and/or initiatives, including these:

■ A biodiesel project that led UBC's Vancouver Plant Operations to use 20% biodiesel fuel in its diesel fleet vehicles
■ Research that led to UBC's becoming a pesticide-free campus
■ A reassessment of landscape techniques to reduce heavy metal contaminants in stormwater
■ Research that led to new seafood purchasing policies[25]

In the best tradition of colleges and universities, classroom learning and real-world learning go hand in hand in SEEDS and similar programs on campuses across Canada.

Organizations are available to assist campus efforts

Many campus sustainability initiatives are supported by organizations, such as the Sierra Youth Coalition Campus Sustainability Project; University Leaders for a Sustainable Future; the Association for the Advancement of Sus-tainability in Higher Education; and the National Wildlife Federation's Campus Ecology program. These organizations act as information clearinghouses for campus sustainability efforts. With the assistance of these organizations, it is easier than ever to start sustainability efforts on your own campus and obtain the support to carry them through to completion.

The Sierra Youth Coalition (www.syc-cjs.org) offers a framework for sustainability assessments, which has provided a starting point for many initiatives on

roots

SUSTAINABILITY

Sustainability, from the word *sustainable*, originates from a late-thirteenth-century Old French verb, *sustenir* (modern *soutenir*), originally from Latin words meaning "to hold up" or "to endure." The suffix *-ability* adds the meaning "capacity" or "fitness." Therefore, *sustainability* is "the capacity to hold up or endure." *Sustainability* and *sustainable development* were used in the modern environmental context prior to the publication of *Our Common Future* in 1987, but that book popularized both terms.

campuses across Canada (**FIGURE 23.8**). The framework incorporates indicators of both human and ecosystem well-being.

Sustainability and Sustainable Development

Efforts toward sustainability on college and university campuses parallel efforts in the world at large. As more people come to appreciate Earth's limited capacity to accommodate our rising population and consumption, they are voicing concern that we will need to modify our behaviours, institutions, and technologies if we wish to sustain our civilization and the natural environment on which it depends. In the quest for sustainability, the strategies pursued on campuses reflect those pursued in the wider society, and they also can serve as models.

When people speak of **sustainability**, what precisely do they mean to sustain? Generally they mean to sustain human institutions in a healthy and functional state—and also to sustain ecological systems in a healthy and functional state. The contributions of biodiversity and

FIGURE 23.8 The Sierra Youth Coalition's Sustainability Assessment Framework has served as a starting point for many campus initiatives across Canada.

ecosystem goods and services to human welfare are tremendous. Indeed, they are so fundamental (some would say infinitely valuable, thus literally priceless) that we have long taken them for granted.

Sustainable development aims to achieve a triple bottom line

The United Nations has defined **sustainable development** as: "Development that meets the needs of the present without compromising the ability of future generations to meet their own needs."[26] Today, it is widely recognized that sustainability does not mean simply protecting the environment against the ravages of human development. Instead, it means finding ways to promote social justice, economic well-being, and environmental quality at the same time. Meeting this **triple bottom line** is the goal of modern sustainable development (**FIGURE 23.9**). Achieving this goal is most pressing in nations of the developing world, but it is a vital need everywhere. It is our primary challenge for this century and likely for the rest of our species' time on Earth.

"Environmental sustainability" is one of the United Nations' Millennium Development Goals set by the international community at the turn of this century, and the drive for sustainability overall meshes with all eight goals. In the past few years, the Millennium Project and the Millennium Ecosystem Assessment have determined the following:

- Environmental degradation is a major barrier to achieving the Millennium Development Goals.
- Investing in environmental assets and management is vital to relieving poverty, hunger, and disease.
- Reaching environmental goals requires progress in eradicating poverty.

The many actions being taken today on campuses and by governments, businesses, industries, organizations, and individuals across the globe are giving people optimism that achieving these goals and developing in sustainable ways are within reach. Moving businesses toward sustainability is the central goal of the Summerhill Group, as you saw in "Central Case: A Different Way of Doing Business."

Environmental protection can enhance economic opportunity

Reducing resource consumption and waste often saves money, as many colleges and universities discover when they embark on sustainability initiatives. Sometimes savings accrue immediately, and other times an up-front investment brings long-term savings.

For society as a whole, attention to environmental quality can enhance economic opportunity by providing new types of employment. This reality contrasts with the common perception that environmental protection hurts the economy by costing people jobs. In the controversy over logging of old-growth forest in the Pacific Northwest, protection for the endangered northern spotted owl (**FIGURE 23.10**), whose natural habitat ranges from Northern California to British Columbia, set limits on timber extraction. Proponents of logging claim that such restrictions cost local loggers their jobs. However, loggers' jobs are far more at risk when timber companies cut trees at unsustainable rates and then leave a region, seeking mature forests elsewhere, as has happened in region after region throughout history.

The jobs-versus-environment debate frequently overlooks the fact that as some industries decline, others spring up to take their place. As jobs in logging, mining, and manufacturing have disappeared in developed

(a) Sustainability as intersecting goals

(b) Sustainability as "nested" system

FIGURE 23.9 Modern conceptions of sustainable development hold that sustainability occurs at the intersection among three sets of goals: social, economic, and environmental **(a)**, or as a "nested" system in which both the economy and society are supported by the environment **(b)**.

FIGURE 23.10
The northern spotted owl (*Strix occidentalis occidentalis*) has become a symbol of the "jobs-versus-environment" debate. This bird of the Pacific rainforest is considered endangered because of the logging of mature forests. Proponents of logging argue that laws protecting endangered species cause economic harm and job loss. Advocates of endangered species protection argue that unsustainable logging practices pose a larger risk of job loss.

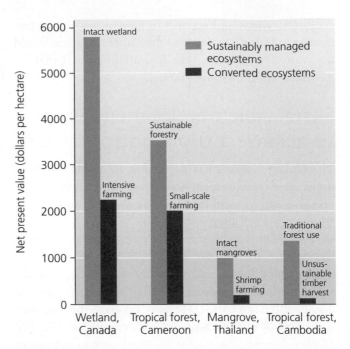

FIGURE 23.11
Once external costs and benefits are factored in, the economic value of sustainably managed ecosystems generally exceeds the economic value of ecosystems that have been converted for intensive private resource harvesting. Shown are land values calculated by researchers in four such comparisons from sites around the world.
Source: Data from Millennium Ecosystem Assessment, 2005.

nations over the past few decades (some, such as logging jobs, as a direct result of mechanization of the industry), jobs have proliferated in service occupations and high-technology sectors. As we decrease our dependence on fossil fuels, jobs and investment opportunities are opening up in renewable energy sectors, such as wind power and fuel cell technology.

Will the alternative energy technology industry provide jobs for all displaced Ontario workers? Not singlehandedly, and certainly not right away. However, environmental protection need not lead to economic stagnation, but instead can enhance economic opportunity. This connection is also suggested by the fact that global economies have expanded rapidly in the past 30 years, the very period during which environmental protection measures have proliferated.

Moreover, if we look beyond conventional economic accounting (which measures only private economic gain and loss) and instead include external costs and benefits that affect people at large, then environmental protection becomes still more valuable. Take several studies reviewed by the Millennium Ecosystem Assessment: They each show how overall economic value is maximized by conserving natural resources rather than exploiting them for short-term private gain (**FIGURE 23.11**).

Although people desire private monetary gain, they also desire to live in areas that have clean air, clean water,

intact forests, and parks and open space. Environmental protection increases a region's attractiveness, drawing more residents and increasing property values and the tax revenues that help fund social services. As a result, those regions that act to protect their environments are generally the ones that retain and increase their wealth and quality of life.

Humans are not separate from the environment

It is common to hear "humans and the environment" or "people and nature" being set in contrast, as though they were separate. Some philosophers venture to say that the perceived dichotomy between humans and nature is the root of all our environmental problems.

On a day-to-day basis, it is easy to feel disconnected from the natural environment, particularly in industrialized nations and large cities. We live inside houses, work in shuttered buildings, travel in enclosed vehicles, and generally know little about the plants and animals around us. Millions of urban citizens have never set foot in an undeveloped area. Just a few centuries or even decades ago, most of the world's people were able to name and describe the habits of the plants and animals that lived nearby. They knew exactly where their food,

FIGURE 23.12

A banana split consists of ingredients from around the world, whose production has impacts on the environments of many distant locations. Ice cream requires milk from dairy cows that graze pastures or are raised in feedlots on grain grown in industrial monocultures. Ice cream is sweetened with sugar from sugar beet farms or sugarcane plantations. The banana was shipped thousands of kilometres by oil-fuelled transport from a tropical country, where it grew on a plantation that displaced rainforest and where it was liberally treated with fertilizers and fungicides. Fruits and nuts grown in California's Central Valley were irrigated generously with water piped in from elsewhere. The spoon originated with metal ores mined along with thousands of tons of soil and processed into stainless steel by using energy from fossil fuels. Transport of the products to the marketplace further contributed greenhouse gases and other emissions to the atmosphere.

Maraschino cherry
Royal Ann cherry from Washington, treated with food colouring, lemon juice, brine, alum, and almond extract from many other locales

Walnuts
Grown in California's Central Valley

Chocolate sauce
Cocoa grown in Latin America or West Africa, with butter, sugars, salt, milk, and extract from many other locales

Strawberries
Grown in coastal California

Banana
Grown in Ecuador or Panama

Spoon
Stainless steel, a complex alloy of metals mined in the U.S., Canada, South Africa, and Asia (or plastic from petroleum from Saudi Arabia or Venezuela)

Ice cream
Milk from dairy cows in Vermont or Wisconsin; sugar from sugarcane in Florida or Hawaii; eggs from hens in Indiana or Georgia; vanilla extract from Mexico or Tahiti

Bowl
Glass, from silica sand, soda ash, limestone, etc., from U.S. Midwest

water, and clothing came from. Today it seems that water comes from the faucet, clothing from the mall, and food from the grocery store. It is not surprising that we have lost track of the connections that tie us to our natural environment.

However, this doesn't make our connections to the environment any less real. Consider a thoroughly un-"natural" invention of the human species: the banana split (**FIGURE 23.12**), in which each and every element has ties to the resources of the natural environment, and each exerts environmental impacts.

Once we learn to consider where the things we use and value each day actually come from, it becomes easier to see how people are part of the environment. And once we reestablish this connection, it becomes readily apparent that our own interests are best served by preservation or responsible stewardship of the natural systems around us. Because what is good for the environment can also be good for people, win–win solutions are very much within reach, if we learn from what science can teach us, think creatively, and act on our ideas. Sustainable solutions to environmental problems are numerous, and we have seen specific examples throughout this book. The challenges lie in being imaginative enough to think of solutions and being shrewd and dogged enough to overcome political or economic obstacles that may lie in the path of their implementation. We will now summarize several broad strategies or approaches that can spawn sustainable solutions (**TABLE 23.2**).

We can refine our ideas about economic growth and quality of life

It is conventional among economists and policy makers to speak of economic growth as an ultimate goal. Many politicians view nurturing an expanding economy as their prime responsibility while in office. Yet economic growth is merely a tool with which we try to attain the real goal of maximizing human happiness. If economic growth depends on an ever-increasing consumption and depletion of nonrenewable resources, then we will

Table 23.2   Some Approaches to Sustainability

- Refine our ideas about economic growth and quality of life.
- Reduce unnecessary consumption.
- Limit population growth.
- Encourage green technologies.
- Mimic natural systems by promoting closed loop industrial processes.
- Think in the long term.
- Enhance local self-sufficiency, and embrace some aspects of globalization.
- Be politically active.
- Vote with our wallets.
- Promote research and education.

not be able to attain long-term happiness by endlessly expanding the size of our economy. We begin by taking our approach, as the Summerhill Group has done, to think of economic, social, and environmental goals as being mutually supportive.

We may also want to incorporate external costs into the market prices of goods and services. Currently, goods and services are priced as though pollution and resource extraction involved no costs to society. If we can make our accounting practices reflect indirect consequences to the public, then we can provide a clearer view of the full costs and benefits of any given action or product. In that case, the free market could become the optimal tool for improving environmental quality, our economy, and our quality of life. Moreover, implementing green taxes and phasing out harmful subsidies could hasten our attainment of prosperous and sustainable economies. The political obstacles to this are considerable, and such changes will require educated citizens to push for them and courageous policy makers to implement them.

We can consume less

Economic growth is driven by consumption: the purchase of material goods and services (and thus the use of resources involved in their manufacture) by consumers (**FIGURE 23.13**). Our tendency to believe that more, bigger, and faster are always better is reinforced by advertisers seeking to sell more goods more quickly. Consumption has grown tremendously, with the wealthiest nations leading the way. Our houses are larger than ever, sport-utility vehicles and mini-vans are among the most popular automobiles, and many citizens have more

material belongings than they know what to do with. We think nothing today of having home computers with high-speed Internet access, let alone the televisions, telephones, refrigerators, and dishwashers that were marvels just decades ago.

Because many of Earth's natural resources are limited and nonrenewable, consumption cannot continue growing forever. Eventually, if we do not shift to sustainable resource use, per capita consumption will drop for rich and poor alike as resources dwindle. Cornucopian critics often scoff at the notion that resources are limited, but we must remember that our perspective in time is limited and that our consumption is taking place within an extraordinarily brief slice of time in the long course of history (**FIGURE 23.14**). Our lavishly consumptive lifestyles are a brand-new phenomenon on Earth. We are enjoying the greatest material prosperity in all of history, but if we do not find ways to make our wealth sustainable, the party may not last much longer.

Fortunately, material consumption alone does not reflect a person's quality of life. For many people in industrialized nations, the accumulation of possessions has not brought contentment. Observing how affluent people often fail to find happiness in their material wealth, social critics have given this phenomenon a name like a dread disease: "**affluenza**." Whether or not it is a disease, scientific research does back up the contention that money cannot buy nearly as much happiness as people typically believe (**FIGURE 23.15**). Although economic growth is generally equated with "progress," true progress consists of an increase in human happiness. In the end we are, one would hope, more than just the sum of what we buy.

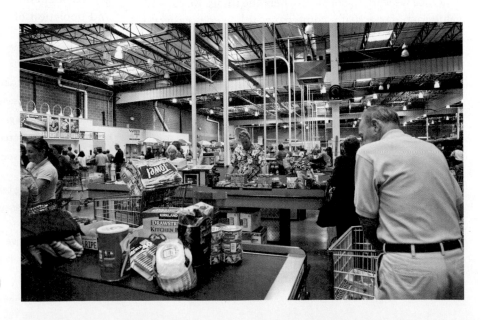

FIGURE 23.13

Citizens of Canada consume more than the people of any other nation, with the exception (but only marginally) of the United States. Unless we find ways to increase the sustainability of our manufacturing processes, this rate of consumption cannot be maintained in the long run.

FIGURE 23.14

By viewing Earth's 4.6-billion-year history as a 12-hour clock, we can gain a better understanding of relative time scales across the immense span of geologic time. *Homo sapiens*, as a species, has come into existence only during the final one or two seconds, around 11:59:59. The Agricultural and Industrial Revolutions that have so greatly increased our environmental impacts have taken up only a minuscule fraction of a second.

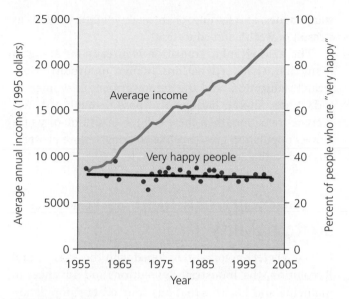

FIGURE 23.15

Although average income of North Americans has risen steadily in the past half-century, the percentage of people reporting themselves as being "very happy" has remained stable or declined slightly. When asked how much a fivefold increase in income improves a person's mood day to day, respondents guessed on average that such an increase would improve mood by 32%, but the actual improvement, from respondents' self-reporting, is only 12%.
Source: Data from Myers, D. G. (2000). The American Paradox: Spiritual Hunger in an Age of Plenty. New Haven, CT: Yale University Press; Gardner, G., and E. Assadourian, (2004). Rethinking the good life, pp. 164–179 in State of the World 2004, Worldwatch Institute; and Kahneman, D., et al. (2006). Would you be happier if you were richer? A focusing illusion. Science 312:1908–1910.

We can reduce our consumption while enhancing our quality of life—squeezing more from less—in at least three ways. One way is to improve the technology of materials and the efficiency of manufacturing processes, so that industry produces goods using fewer natural resources. Another way is to develop a sustainable manufacturing system—one that is circular and based on recycling, in which the waste from a process becomes raw material for input into that process or others. A third way is to modify our behaviour, attitudes, and lifestyles to minimize consumption.

At the outset, such choices may seem like sacrifices, but people who have slowed down the pace of their busy lives and freed themselves of an attachment to material possessions say it can feel tremendously liberating. Fans of local foods, homegrown foods, and the "slow-food" movement (**FIGURE 23.16**) feel that they are helping themselves as much as they are helping the environment.

Population growth must eventually cease

Just as continued growth in consumption is not sustainable, neither is growth in the human population. We have seen that populations may grow exponentially for a time but eventually encounter limiting factors and decline or level off. We have used technology to increase Earth's carrying capacity for our species, but our population cannot continue growing forever; sooner or later, human population growth will end. The question is how: through

FIGURE 23.16

The homegrown, local food, and slow-food movements are growing, all over North America. "Kitchen gardens," like the one shown here, are becoming more and more popular, especially in urban areas.

war, plagues, and famine, or through voluntary means as a result of wealth and education?

The demographic transition is already far along in many industrialized nations thanks to urbanization, wealth, education, and the empowerment of women. If today's developing nations also pass through a demographic transition, then there is hope that humanity may halt its population growth while creating a more prosperous and equitable society.

Technology can help us toward sustainability

It is largely technology—developed with the Agricultural Revolution, the Industrial Revolution, and advances in medicine and health—that has spurred our population increase. Technology has magnified our impact on Earth's environmental systems, yet it can also give us ways to reduce our impact. Recall the IPAT equation, which summarizes human environmental impact (I) as the interaction of population (P), consumption or affluence (A), and technology (T). Technology can exert either a positive or negative value in this equation. The shortsighted use of technology may have gotten us into this mess, but wiser use of environmentally friendly, or "green," technology can help get us out.

In recent years, technology has intensified environmental impact in developing countries as industrial technologies from the developed world have been exported to poorer nations eager to industrialize. In developed nations, meanwhile, green technologies have begun mitigating our environmental impact. Catalytic converters on cars have reduced emissions (**FIGURE 23.17**), as have scrubbers on industrial smokestacks. Recycling technology and advances in wastewater treatment are helping reduce our waste output. Solar, wind, and geothermal energy technologies are producing cleaner renewable energy. Countless technological advances such as these are one reason that people of North America and Western Europe today enjoy cleaner environments—although they consume far more—than people of Eastern Europe or rapidly industrializing nations, such as China.

Industry can mimic natural systems

As industries seek to develop green technologies and sustainable practices, they have an excellent model: nature itself. As you have learned, environmental systems tend to operate in cycles consisting of feedback loops and the circular flow of materials. In natural systems, output is recycled into input. In contrast, human manufactur-

2 Inside the housing of the converter are honeycomb-like masses designed to maximize surface area for contact with the gases

Stainless steel housing for converter

Carbon dioxide (CO₂)
Water vapour (H₂O)
Nitrogen gas (N₂)

5 These less harmful gases are then expelled as exhaust from the vehicle's tailpipe

1 Raw exhaust from a vehicle's engine includes hydrocarbons, carbon monoxide, and nitrogen oxides, and these gases flow into the body of the catalytic converter

Hydrocarbons
Carbon monoxide (CO)
Nitrogen oxides (NO$_x$)

4 These metals and other trace chemicals act as catalysts driving several chemical reactions, which in the presence of heat and oxygen, convert the input gases into carbon dioxide, water vapour, and nitrogen gas

3 The metal or ceramic substrate of this honeycomb structure is covered with a washcoat of aluminum oxide and a thin layer of the metals palladium, rhodium, and platinum

Main chemical reactions
$2CO + O_2 \quad 2CO_2$
$C_2H_4 + 3O_2 \quad 2CO_2 + 2H_2O$
$CO + NO_x \quad CO_2 + N_2$

Catalytic metals
(Pd, Rh, Pt)

Substrate
(metal or ceramic)

Washcoat (Al₂O₃)

FIGURE 23.17 The catalytic converter is a classic example of green technology. This device filters air pollutants from vehicle exhaust and has helped to improve air quality in Canada and many other nations.

ing processes traditionally run on a linear model in which raw materials are input and processed to create a product, while by-products and waste are generated and discarded.

Some forward-thinking industrialists are making their processes more sustainable by transforming linear pathways into closed cycles in which waste is recovered, recycled, and reused. For instance, several companies now produce carpets that can be retrieved from the consumer when they wear out, and these materials are then recycled to create new carpeting. Some automobile manufacturers are planning cars that can be disassembled and recycled into new cars. Proponents of this industrial model see little reason why virtually all appliances and other products cannot be recycled, given the right technology. Their ultimate vision is to create truly closed loop industrial processes, generating almost no waste.

We can think in the long term

To be sustainable, a solution must work in the long term. Often the best long term solution is not the best short term solution, which explains why much of what we currently do is not sustainable. Policy makers in democracies often act for short-term good because they aim to produce immediate, positive results so that they will be reelected. This poses a major hurdle for addressing environmental dilemmas, many of which are cumulative, worsen gradually, and can be resolved only over long periods. Often the costs of addressing an environmental problem are short-term, whereas the benefits are long-term, giving politicians little incentive to tackle the problem. In such a situation, citizen pressure on policy makers is especially vital, because policy is an essential tool for pursuing sustainability (see "The Science Behind the Story: Rating the Environmental Performance of Nations").

Businesses may act according to either long-term or short-term interests. A business committed to operating in a particular community for a long time has incentive to sustain environmental quality. However, a business merely attempting to make a profit and move on has little incentive to invest in environmental protection measures that involve short-term costs.

We can promote local self-sufficiency and embrace some aspects of globalization

As our societies become more globally interconnected, we experience a diversity of impacts, positive and negative. To many people, encouraging local self-sufficiency is an important element of building sustainable societies.

When people feel closely tied to the area in which they live, they tend to value the area and seek to sustain its environment and human communities. This line of reasoning is frequently made in relation to locally based organic or sustainable agriculture.

Many advocates of local self-sufficiency criticize globalization. However, as ecological economist Herman Daly has explained, globalization means different things to different people. Those who view it as a positive phenomenon generally focus on how people of the world's diverse cultures are increasingly communicating and learning about one another. Books, airplanes, television, and the Internet have made us more aware of one another's cultures and more likely to respect and celebrate—rather than fear—differences among cultures.

Those who view globalization in a negative light generally cite the homogenization of the world's cultures, by which a few cultures and world views displace many others. For instance, the world's many languages are going extinct with astonishing speed. Traditional ways of life in many areas are being abandoned as more people take up the material and cultural trappings of a few dominant Western cultures.

In recent years, many people have reacted against this homogenization and the growing power of large multinational corporations. In France, farm activist Jose Bove became a popular hero when he wrecked a McDonald's restaurant with his tractor to protest what many French farmers view as a threat to local French cuisine. In Québec in 2003, hundreds of protesters picketed a meeting of the World Trade Organization, which they viewed as a symbol of Western market capitalism. Since then, protesters have picketed every WTO meeting (**FIGURE 23.18**).

FIGURE 23.18
Protesters picketed the World Trade Organization's meeting in Québec in 2003, criticizing the homogenizing effects of globalization, as well as relaxations in labour and environmental protections brought about by free trade.

THE SCIENCE BEHIND THE STORY

Rating the Environmental Performance of Nations

Top-Ranked Nations, 2010 EPI[27]	
Nation	EPI Score
Iceland	93.5
Switzerland	89.1
Costa Rica	86.4
Sweden	86.0
Norway	81.1
Mauritius	80.6
France	78.2
Austria	78.1
Cuba	78.1
Colombia	76.8

Bottom-Ranked Nations, 2010 EPI	
Nation	EPI Score
Benin	39.6
Haiti	39.5
Mali	39.4
Turkmenistan	38.4
Niger	37.6
Togo	36.4
Angola	36.3
Mauritania	33.7
Central African Republic	33.3
Sierra Leone	32.1

The Environmental Performance Index is a weighted composite indicator that can be used to measure the progress of nations and their relative standings in environmental sustainability.

To measure the progress of nations toward environmental sustainability, researchers devised the Environmental Performance Index (EPI), which rates countries using data from 25 indicators of environmental conditions for which governments can be held accountable. A report detailing the results was produced and published online in 2006 and updated in 2008 and 2010, by Daniel Esty and colleagues at the Yale Center for Environmental Law and Policy and Columbia University's Center for International Earth Science Information Network, in collaboration with the World Economic Forum and the Joint Research Centre of the European Commission. At http://epi.yale.edu you will find an interactive map showing the details of the EPI for all of the 163 nations included in the 2010 study.

The U.N.'s Millennium Development Goals did not define how to quantify progress on environmental measures. The lack of quantitative measures, these researchers said, had stymied progress on how to implement effective environmental policy. To address this problem, the researchers aimed to track the performance of environmental policy with the same quantitative rigour as statistics are tracked for health, poverty reduction, and other development goals. Giving nations scores and ranking them would reveal "leaders and laggards," showing which nations are on the right track and which are not.

The researchers gathered internationally available data from the U.N. and other sources on 10 indicators, subdivided into two main categories:

- Ecosystem health, consisting of
  - Environmental burden of disease
  - Air pollution (effects on humans)
  - Water (effects on humans)
- Ecosystem vitality, consisting of
  - Climate change
  - Agriculture
  - Fisheries
  - Forestry
  - Biodiversity and habitat
  - Air pollution (effects on ecosystems)
  - Water (effects on ecosystems)

Nations were scored on their performance in each category, with overall scores based 50% on their environmental health score and 50% on seven ecosystem vitality scores. Scores for each category ranged from zero to 100, with 100 representing a target value established by international consensus.

The researchers included 163 nations in the 2010 report; some nations could not be included because of lack of data.

The main pattern in the results was conspicuous: Nations with the highest scores (see the first table) are mostly wealthy, industrialized nations with the capacity to commit substantial resources toward environmental protection. Nations

---

We explored the complex relationship between free trade and the environment in "The Science Behind the Story: The Environment in NAFTA and NAAEC."

Daly and others argue that globalization entails a process in which multinational corporations attain greater and greater power over global trade while governments retain less and less. Most critics of globalization consider corporations less likely than governments to support environmental protection, so they feel that globalization will hinder progress toward sustainability. Moreover, market capitalism, almost by definition, promotes a high-consumption lifestyle, which does indeed threaten efforts to attain sustainable solutions.

On the positive side, globalization may foster sustainability because Western democracy, as imperfect as it is, serves as a model for people living under repressive governments. Open societies allow for entrepreneurship and the flowering of creativity in business, research, and academia. Millions of free minds thinking about issues are more likely to come up with sustainable solutions with the lowest scores (see the second table) are largely developing nations with few resources to invest. They include countries with dense populations and stressed ecosystems that are trying to industrialize, those with arid environments and limited natural resources, and those facing extreme poverty.

The correlation between economic vitality and environmental protection was expected, but the researchers were more interested in the variation around this trend. For any given level of income or development, some nations vastly outperformed others. The researchers say this demonstrates that other factors are at work—namely, the political choices national leaders make. Indeed, their data show a strong correlation between EPI scores and "good governance," which involves aspects such as rule of law, open political debate, and lack of corruption.

These interpretations touched sensitive nerves in nations that did not rank as highly as they would have liked. For example, the United States placed 61st, and Canada 46th with a score of 66.4 (far below our 2008 ranking of 12th, with an EPI score of 86.6). Critics say the rankings have little meaning because only certain data sets were measured, and these were then weighted subjectively. Supporters counter that although no one will ever agree on exact numbers, the EPI provides a useful tool for evaluating actions and investments, highlighting policies that work, and identifying future priorities.

Conversely, poorer nations tended to score low on environmental health

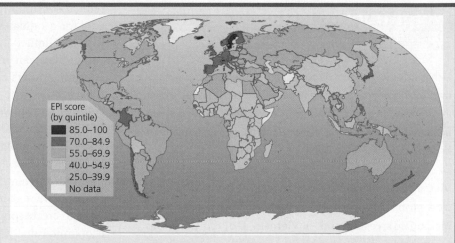

For the Environmental Performance Index, researchers scored nations for their performance in approaching environmental sustainability goals. Higher EPI values (red on the map) indicate better performance. EPI scores for a number of countries, including Canada, have declined since the study was initiated.
Source: Data from Environmental Performance Index, 2010, http://www.epi.yale.edu/Countries

and higher on indicators that reflected the availability of remaining unexploited natural resources. Overall across all nations, performance was worst for the indicators of renewable energy and wilderness protection.

The EPI scores are only as solid as the data that go into them, and not every nation provides reliably accurate data. Moreover, Esty's group acknowledges that there are ways in which the formulas might be improved in the future. Nonetheless, the Environmental Performance Index provides a unique means of assessing what is working in environmental policy. As the methodology is refined year by year, the EPI promises to become a more accurate performance indicator and a more helpful policy tool.

Whereas controversy generated by the overall rankings drew media attention, other trends were apparent for those who examined the data more deeply. For instance, wealthy industrialized nations tended to score highest in environmental health and lowest in ecosystem vitality indicators, especially biodiversity and habitat. This is presumably because they possess money to invest in protecting the health of their citizens but achieved economic development by exploiting their natural resources and degrading their natural environment.

than the minds of a few holding authoritarian power. Politically open democracies offer a compelling route for pursuing sustainability: the power of the vote. Many of the changes needed to attain sustainable solutions require policy making, and individually and collectively we can guide our political leaders to enact policies for sustainability. Policy makers respond to whoever exerts influence. Corporations and interest groups employ lobbyists to influence politicians all the time. Citizens in a democratic republic have the same power, *if* they

choose to exercise it. You can exercise your power at the polling station, by attending public hearings, by donating to advocacy groups that promote ideas you favour, and by writing letters and making phone calls to officeholders. You might be surprised how little input policy makers receive from the public; sometimes a single letter or phone call can make a big difference.

Today's environmental laws came about because citizens pressured their governmental representatives to tackle environmental problems. The raft of environmental

weighing the issues

GLOBALIZATION

What advantages and disadvantages do you see in globalization? Have you personally benefited or been hurt by it in any way? In what ways might promoting local self-sufficiency be helpful for the pursuit of global sustainability? In what ways might it not?

Now consider this: Many people enjoy eating at Vietnamese restaurants in Canada, yet many who criticize globalization would frown on the presence of McDonald's restaurants in Vietnam. Do you think this represents a double standard, or are there reasons the two are not comparable?

legislation enacted in the 1970s in North America might never have come about had ordinary citizens not stepped up and demanded action. We owe it to our children to be engaged and to act responsibly now so that they have a better world in which to live.

Consumers vote with their wallets

Expressing one's preferences through the political system is important, but we also wield influence through the choices we make as consumers. When products produced sustainably are ecolabelled, consumers can "vote with their wallets" by purchasing these products. Consumer choice has helped drive sales of everything from recycled paper to organic produce to "dolphin-safe" tuna.

Individuals can multiply their own influence by promoting "green" purchasing habits at their school or workplace. We saw how purchasing power at colleges and universities has spurred sales of certified sustainable wood, organic food, energy-efficient appliances, and more. Employees in businesses and government agencies can promote change within those institutions by voicing their preferences in purchasing decisions. As Dr. Seuss wrote in the children's classic *The Lorax*, "Unless someone like you cares a whole awful lot, nothing is going to get better. It's not."

Promoting research and education is vital

None of these approaches will succeed fully if the public is not aware of its importance. An individual's decision to reduce consumption, purchase ecolabelled products, or vote for candidates who support sustainable approaches will have limited impact unless many others do the same. Individuals can influence large numbers of people by educating others and by serving as role models through their actions. The campus sustainability efforts at many colleges and universities accomplish both approaches. Moreover, the discipline of environmental science plays a key role in providing information that people can use to make wise decisions about environmental issues. By promoting scientific research, by raising the awareness of decision makers, by exerting pressure on corporations to create social and environmental value along with economic value, and by educating the public about environmental science, we can all assist in the pursuit of sustainable solutions.

Precious Time

The pace of our lives is getting faster, and life's commotion can make it hard to give attention to problems we don't need to deal with on a daily basis. The world's sheer load of environmental dilemmas can feel overwhelming, and even the best intentioned among us may feel we have little time to devote to saving the planet.

The systems we depend on are changing

However, the natural systems we depend on are changing quickly. Many human impacts continue to intensify, including deforestation, overfishing, land clearing, wetlands draining, and resource extraction. Our window of opportunity for turning some of these trends around is shrinking. Even if we can visualize sustainable solutions to our many problems, how can we possibly find the time to implement them before we do irreparable damage to our environment and our own future?

Today, humanity faces a challenge more important than any previous one—the challenge to achieve sustainability. Attaining sustainability will be a larger and more complex process, but it is one to which every single person on Earth can contribute; in which government, industry, and citizens can all cooperate; and toward which all nations can work together. Human ingenuity is capable of it; we merely need to rally public resolve and engage our governments, institutions, and entrepreneurs in the race. However, we must be realistic about the challenges that lie ahead. As we deplete the natural capital we can draw on, we give ourselves, and the rest of the world's creatures, less room to manoeuvre. Until we implement sustainable solutions, we will be squeezing ourselves through a

CANADIAN ENVIRONMENTAL PERSPECTIVES

Keleigh Annau

Keleigh Annau, now a student at Mount Allison University, had the idea for Lights Out Canada when she was a high school student in Parksville, B.C.

- ■ **Youth environmental activist**
- ■ **Toyota Earth Day Scholarship** and **Bell Scholarship winner**
- ■ **Founder** of Lights Out Canada
- ■ **Musician** and **dancer**

When you read about Keleigh Annau, three words that keep popping up are "inspiration," "passion," and "tenacity." Annau—now an inspiration to others— was first inspired to act by a conference on climate change that she attended at the age of 16. The conference opened her eyes to the potential impacts of climate change on her generation. She returned home to Parksville, British Columbia, with the idea for Lights Out Canada—a simple way to "turn off the lights and switch on education about global warming."[28]

Instead of thinking about all of the obstacles in her way, Annau shared her idea with several friends and with mentor Dev Aujla from the organization DreamNow. Together they launched a successful pilot event in December 2005. The first full-fledged Lights Out event took place in May 2006, with about 50 000 students participating in events to raise awareness about climate change in schools across Canada. By the sixth annual event in April 2011, more than 170 000 students participated in what had now become Lights Out World.

Annau and her international network of young environmental activists—many of whom she connected with as a student at United World College of the Adriatic, in Italy—are working to expand Lights Out Canada & Lights Out World. Now a student in International Relations at Mount Allison University in New Brunswick, Annau is focusing her attention on applying for grants, and hopes to expand Lights Out from an annual event into a full-time program. Her plan involves training student representatives to give Lights Out presentations in their schools, acquiring specific commitments from participants, and working with university campuses.

Annau is keenly aware that turning out the lights once a year won't have a significant impact, in itself. However, she recognizes that the impacts on the personal awareness, decisions, and behaviours among youth participants can be much more far-reaching.

"The youth of today will be designating policy and managing the industrial, business, and agricultural sectors in the future. It is my hope that by instilling awareness about the importance of living sustainably in the youth that participate in Lights Out Canada, this will plant a seed and encourage them to make green practices a priority when they make life and career choices in the future."

This is where the "passion" and "tenacity" come in. Annau still points to Lights Out as her central passion, and the process of building it as a transformative experience in her life. "My experience with Lights Out has changed my life, not only in how I feel about environmental issues or what my career goals are, but also because I feel empowered." In the meantime, her tenacity has allowed Annau to keep taking the small steps required to move forward, and to build a little idea into a big force for change. You can follow Keleigh Annau on Twitter @KeleighA.

"Small changes add up to make a big difference."—**Keleigh Annau**

Thinking About Environmental Perspectives

What do *you* think is the most pressing environmental issue facing your generation? Can you think of a way that you might be able to raise the awareness of other students concerning this issue?

---

progressively tighter space, like being forced through the neck of a bottle. The key question for the future of our species and our planet is whether we can make it safely through this bottleneck. Biologist Edward O. Wilson has written eloquently of this view:

> *At best, an environmental bottleneck is coming in the twenty-first century. It will cause the unfolding of a new kind of history driven by environmental change. Or perhaps an unfolding on a global scale of more of the old kind of history, which saw the collapse of regional civilizations [in] Mesopotamia, and subsequently Egypt, then the Mayan and many others ... Somehow humanity must find a way to squeeze through the bottleneck without destroying the environments on which the rest of life depends.*

We must think of Earth as an island

We began this book with the vision of Earth as an island, and indeed that is what it is (**FIGURE 23.19**). Islands can be paradise, as Rapa Nui (Easter Island) likely was when the Polynesians first reached it. But when Europeans arrived at Easter Island, they witnessed the aftermath of a civilization that had depleted its island's resources, degraded its environment, and collapsed as a result. For the few people who remained of the once-mighty culture, life was difficult and unrewarding. They had lost even the knowledge of the history of their ancestors, who had cut trees unsustainably, kicking the base out from beneath their prosperous civilization.

FIGURE 23.19
We end as we began the book, with a photo of Earth from space. This photograph of Earth and Earth's Moon, taken by the spacecraft *Voyager* as it sped away from home, shows our planet as it truly is—an island in space. Everything we know, need, love, and value comes from and resides on this small sphere, so we had best treat it well.

As Easter Island's trees disappeared, some individuals must have spoken out for conservation and for finding ways to live sustainably amid dwindling resources. Likely Easter Island's cornucopians ignored those calls and went on extracting more than the land could bear, assuming that somehow things would turn out all right. Indeed, whoever cut the last tree atop the most remote mountaintop could have looked out across the island and seen that it was the last tree. And yet that person cut it down.

It would be tragic folly to let such a fate befall our planet as a whole. By recognizing this, by deciding to shift our individual behaviour and our cultural institutions in ways that encourage sustainable practices, and by employing science to help us achieve these ends, we may yet be able to live happily and sustainably on our wondrous island, Earth.

Conclusion

In any society facing dwindling resources and environmental degradation, there will be those who raise alarms and those who ignore them. Fortunately, in our global society today we have many thousands of scientists who study Earth's processes and resources. For this reason, we are amassing a detailed knowledge and an ever-developing understanding of our dynamic planet, what it offers us, and what impacts it can bear. The challenge for our global society today, our one-world island of humanity, is to support that science so that we may judge false alarms from real problems and distinguish legitimate concerns from thoughtless denial. This science, this study of Earth and of ourselves, offers us hope for our future.

Unless someone like you cares a whole awful lot, nothing is going to get better. It's not.—**from The Lorax, by Dr. Seuss (1971, Random House)**

REVIEWING OBJECTIVES

You should now be able to:

List and describe approaches being taken on college and university campuses to promote sustainability

- Audits produce baseline data on how much a campus consumes and pollutes.
- The most common campus sustainability efforts involve recycling and waste reduction.
- Green buildings are being constructed on a growing number of campuses.
- There are many ways to reduce water use, and these efforts often save money.
- Students have many feasible ways to conserve energy and promote renewable energy sources.

- A current drive is to make campuses carbon neutral and responsive to concerns about climate change.
- Dining services can help sustainability efforts by providing local food and reducing waste.
- Colleges and universities can favour sustainable products in institutional purchasing.
- Campuses can use alternative fuels and vehicles and encourage bicycling, walking, and public transportation.
- Habitat restoration is one of the most popular campus sustainability activities.
- Curricula are adding issues of sustainability and enabling students to earn course credits while working on campus and community sustainability projects.

Explain the concept of sustainable development

- Sustainable development entails environmental protection, economic development, and social justice.
- Proponents of sustainable development feel that economic development and environmental quality can enhance one another.

Discuss how protecting the environment can be compatible with promoting economic welfare

- Environmental protection and green technologies and industries can create rich sources of new jobs.
- Protecting environmental quality enhances a community's desirability and economy.
- We can think of economic, social, and environmental goals as being mutually supportive.

Describe and assess key approaches to designing sustainable solutions

- Approaches that can inspire sustainable solutions include refining our ideas about quality of life; reducing unnecessary consumption; limiting population growth; encouraging green technologies; mimicking natural systems; thinking long-term; enhancing local self-sufficiency; being politically active; voting with our wallets; and promoting research and education.
- Growth in population and per capita consumption will likely need to be halted if we are to create a sustainable society.

Technology has traditionally increased environmental impact, but new "green" technologies can help reduce impact.

Discuss the need for action on behalf of the environment and the tremendous human potential to solve problems

- Time for turning around our increasing environmental impacts is running short.
- Canada and other nations have met tremendous challenges before, so we have reason to hope that we will be able to attain a sustainable society.

Name several examples of programs that aim to reduce environmental impacts by changing the behaviour of individuals, corporations, or institutions

- There are many ways that individuals can reduce their own impacts on the environment. By combining efforts, people can make a significant difference. By making their wishes known, consumers can influence the behaviour of corporations and governments.
- Programs aimed at changing the behaviour of individuals and organizations include UBC's Lighter Footprint Strategy, Summerhill's Car Heaven program, BOMA's Go Green program, the LEED certification program, McGill University's Gorilla Composting, Lights Out Canada, and many others.

TESTING YOUR COMPREHENSION

1. In what ways are campus sustainability efforts relevant to sustainability efforts in the broader society?
2. Name one way in which campus sustainability proponents have addressed each of the following areas:
   (a) Recycling and waste reduction
   (b) "Green" buildings
   (c) Water conservation
   (d) Energy efficiency
   (e) Renewable energy
   (f) Global climate change
3. Name one way in which campus sustainability proponents have addressed each of the following areas:
   (a) Dining services
   (b) Institutional purchasing
   (c) Transportation
   (d) Habitat restoration
   (e) Curricula
4. What do environmental scientists mean by *sustainable development*?

5. Describe three ways in which environmental protection can enhance economic well-being.
6. Why are many people now living at the highest level of material prosperity in history? Is this level of consumption sustainable? How can it feel good to consume less?
7. In what ways can technology help us achieve sustainability? How do natural processes provide good models of sustainability for manufacturing? Provide examples.
8. Why do many people feel that local self-sufficiency is important? What consequences of globalization may threaten sustainability? How can open democratic societies help to promote sustainability?
9. Explain Edward O. Wilson's metaphor of the "environmental bottleneck."
10. How can thinking of Earth as an island help prevent us from repeating the mistakes of previous civilizations?

THINKING IT THROUGH

1. What sustainability initiatives would you like to see attempted on your campus? If you were to take the lead in promoting such initiatives, how would you go about it? What obstacles would you expect to face, and how would you deal with them?

2. Choose one item or product that you enjoy, and consider how it came to be. Think of as many components of the item or product as you can, and determine how each of them was obtained or created. Now refer to **FIGURE 23.12**. What steps were involved in creating your item's components, and where did the raw materials come from? How was your item manufactured? How was it delivered to you?

3. Do you think that we can increase our quality of life through development while also protecting the integrity of the environment? Discuss examples from your course or from other chapters of this book that illustrate possible win–win solutions. Are you familiar with any cases in your community or at your college that bear on this issue? Describe such a case, and state what lessons you would draw from it.

4. Reflect on the experiences of prior human civilizations and how they came to an end. What is your prognosis for our current human civilization? Do you see a vast world of independent cultures all individually responsible for themselves, or do you consider human civilization to be one great entity? If we accept

that all people depend on the same environmental systems for sustenance, what resources and strategies do we have to ensure that the actions of a few do not determine the outcome for all and that sustainable solutions are a common global goal?

5. You have been elected president of your student government, and your school's administrators promise to be responsive to student concerns. Many of your fellow students are asking you to promote sustainability initiatives on your campus. Consider the many approaches and activities pursued by the colleges and universities mentioned in this chapter, and now think about your own school. Which of these approaches and activities are most needed at your school? Which might be most effective? What ideas would you prioritize and promote during your term as president?

6. In our final "Think It Through" question, you are . . . *you!* In this chapter and throughout this book, you have encountered a diversity of ideas for sustainable solutions to environmental problems. Many of these are approaches you can pursue in your own life. Name at least five ways in which you think you can make a difference—and would most like to make a difference—in helping to attain a more sustainable society. For each approach, describe one specific thing you could do today or tomorrow or next week to begin.

INTERPRETING GRAPHS AND DATA

As we have seen throughout this book, individuals can contribute to sustainable solutions for our society and our planet in many ways. Some of these involve advocating for change at high levels of government or business or academia. But plenty of others involve the countless small choices we make in how we live our lives day to day. Where we live, what we buy, how we travel—these types of choices we each make as citizens, consumers, and human beings determine how we affect the environment and the people around us. As you know, such personal choices are summarized (crudely, but usefully) in an ecological footprint.

Visit an online ecological footprint calculator and calculate your personal ecological footprint. Examples

of sites with online footprint calculators include www.myfootprint.org and www.footprintnetwork.org.

1. Enter your current footprint, as determined by the online calculator, in the table. What changes have you made in your lifestyle since beginning this course that influence your environmental impact?

2. How does your personal footprint compare with the average footprint of a Canadian resident? How does it compare with that of the average person in the world? What do you think would be an admirable yet realistic goal for you to set as a target value for your own footprint?

3. Now think of three changes in your lifestyle that would decrease your footprint. These should be

changes that you would like to make and that you believe you could reasonably make. Take the footprint quiz again, incorporating these three changes. Enter the resulting footprint in the table.

4. Now set a goal of reducing your footprint by 25%, and experiment by changing various answers in your footprint quiz. What changes would allow you to attain a 25% reduction in your footprint? What types of activities is your footprint the most sensitive to, and which changes make the biggest difference in reducing your footprint? What changes would be needed to reduce your footprint to the hypothetical target value you set in Question 2?

	Footprint value* (hectares per person)
World average	2.7
Canadian average	7.0
Your footprint	
Your footprint with three changes	

*These numbers vary widely depending on which calculator is used. The numbers given here are Global Footprint Network's 2010 edition (www.footprintnetwork.org).

CHAPTER ENDNOTES

1. Summerhill Group, www.summerhillgroup.ca/careers.php

2. Mow Down Pollution Event, www.mowdownpollution.ca/eng/facts-and-info.php

3. http://news.ontario.ca/mri/en/2008/05/cut-emissions-when-you-cut-your-grass.html

4. AMS Lighter Footprint Strategy, 2008, www.amsubc.ca/uploads/government/AMS_Lighter_Footprint_Strategy.pdf

5. University Leaders for a Sustainable Future, Talloires Declaration, http://www.ulsf.org/programs_talloires.html

6. UTM Ecological Footprint and Campus Sustainability Assessment Project, http://geog.utm.utoronto.ca/ecofootprint/

7. Bottled Water Free Day, www.bottledwaterfreeday.ca

8. UBC Campus Sustainability Office, ECOTREK Project Complete, *Sustainable Energy Management Program*, www.ecotrek.ubc.ca

9. Funding Models for Facilities Renewal, UBC Renew and EcoTrek Programs, 2009. http://caubo.ca/fedora/repository/caubo:42/OBJ/Jun16_315pm_4_John_Metras.pdf

10. University of Victoria, *Sustainability in Planning, Buildings, and Land Use*, http://web.uvic.ca/sustainability/buildings.php

11. Simon Fraser University, www.sfu.ca/sfunews/Stories/sfunews071008019.shtml

12. Laurentian University, Cooperative Freshwater Ecology Unit, *Living with the Lakes Centre: The Facility*, www.laurentian.ca/Laurentian/Home/Departments/Cooperative+Freshwater+Ecology+Unit/Living+with+Lakes+Centre/The+Facility.htm

13. UBC EcoTrek http://www.sustain.ubc.ca/campus-sustainability/greening-the-campus/ecotrek

14. University of Toronto Sustainability Office, *Projects: Buildings and Infrastructure*, www.sustainability.utoronto.ca:81/projects/projects/buildings-infrastructure

15. University of Toronto Sustainability Office, *ReWire Project*, http://rewire.utoronto.ca

16. University of Calgary Solar Decathlon Team http://www.solardecathlon.ca

17. Trent University, *Physical Resources, Powerhouse*, www.trentu.ca/physicalresources/powerhouse.php

18. American College and University Presidents' Climate Commitment, www.presidentsclimatecommitment.org

19. Common Energy, www.commonenergy.org

20. B.C. Campus Climate Network, *Go Beyond Project*, www.campusclimatenetwork.org/wiki/Go_Beyond_Project

21. Sustainable Concordia, *Allégo: Smarter transport for a more sustainable future*, http://sustainable.concordia.ca/ourinitiatives/allego/

22. Queen's University Faculty of Applied Science, http://appsci.queensu.ca/news/2005-2006/index.php?article=31@amp@view=print

23. First Nations University of Canada, *Academic Programs, Department of Science*, www.firstnationsuniversity.ca/default.aspx?page=30

24. University of Toronto Sustainability Office, *Education and Awareness*, www.sustainability.utoronto.ca:81/course-research/education-awareness

25. *UBC Sustainability Report: SEEDS,* www.sustain.ubc.ca/

26. *Our Common Future* (1987). Report of the World Commission on Environment and Development, Oxford University Press.

27. *2010 Environmental Performance Index,* Yale Center for Environmental Law and Policy and the Center for International Earth Science Information Network of Columbia University in collaboration with the World Economic Forum and the Joint Research Centre of the European Commission, http://www.epi.yale.edu/countries

28. Lights Out Canada, www.lightsoutcanada.org

MyEnvironmentPlace

Go to **www.myenvironmentplace.ca** where you will find quizzes, animations, your Pearson eText, and more.

APPENDICES

Appendix A   Some Basics on Graphs

Presenting data in ways that help make trends and patterns visually apparent is a vital part of the scientific endeavour. For scientists, businesspeople, and others, the primary tool for expressing patterns in data is the graph. Thus, the ability to interpret graphs is a skill that you will want to cultivate. This appendix guides you in how to read graphs, introduces a few vital conceptual points, and surveys the most common types of graphs, giving rationales for their use.

Navigating a Graph

A graph is a diagram that shows relationships among *variables,* which are factors that can change in value. The most common types of graphs relate values of a *dependent variable* to those of an *independent variable*. A dependent variable is so named because its values "depend on" the values of an independent variable. In other words, as the values of an independent variable change, the values of the dependent variable change in response. In a manipulative experiment, changes that a researcher specifies in the value of the independent variable *cause* changes in the value of the dependent variable. In observational studies, there may be no causal relationship, and scientists may plot a correlation. In either case, the values of the independent variable are known or specified, and the values of the dependent variable are unknown and are what we are interested in observing or measuring.

By convention, independent variables are generally represented on the horizontal axis, or *x*-axis, of a graph, while dependent variables are represented on the vertical axis, or *y*-axis. Numerical values of variables generally become larger as one proceeds rightward on the *x*-axis or upward on the *y*-axis. In many cases, independent variables are not numerical at all, but categorical. For example, in a graph presenting population sizes of several nations, the nations comprise a categorical independent variable, whereas population size is a numerical dependent variable.

As a simple example, **FIGURE A.1** shows data from a scientist who ran an experiment to test the effects on laboratory mice of the chemical bisphenol-A. The *x*-axis shows values of her independent variable, the dose of bisphenol-A given to the mice. The values are expressed in units of nanograms per gram of water (ng/g). The researcher was interested in what proportion of mice developed chromosomal problems as a result. Thus, her dependent variable, presented on the *y*-axis, is the percentage of mice found to develop chromosomal problems. For each of four doses of bisphenol-A she supplied in her experiment, a data point on the graph is plotted to show the corresponding percentage of mice with chromosomal problems.

Now that you're familiar with the basic building blocks of a graph, let's survey the most common types of graphs you'll see, and examine a few vital concepts in graphing.

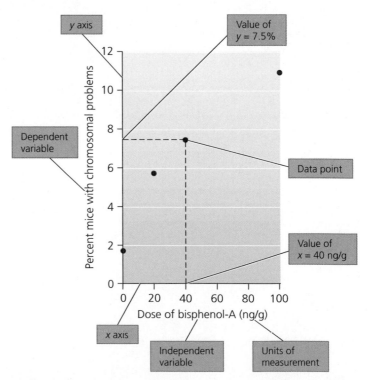

FIGURE A.1   Frequency of chromosomal problems relative to dose of bisphenol-A.

GRAPH TYPE: Line Graph

A line graph is drawn when a data set involves a sequence of some kind, such as a series of values that occur one by one and change through time or across distance (**FIGURE A.2**). Line graphs are most appropriate when the y-axis expresses a continuous numerical variable and the x-axis expresses either continuous numerical data or discrete sequential categories (such as years).

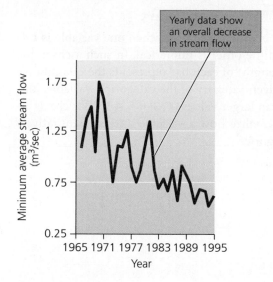

Yearly data show an overall decrease in stream flow

FIGURE A.2 Minimum stream flow.

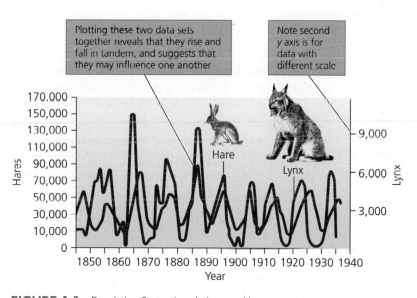

Plotting these two data sets together reveals that they rise and fall in tandem, and suggests that they may influence one another

Note second y axis is for data with different scale

FIGURE A.3 Population fluctuations in hare and lynx.

One useful technique is to plot two or more data sets together on the same graph (**FIGURE A.3**). This allows us to compare trends in the data sets to see whether and how they may be related.

KEY CONCEPT: Projections

Besides showing observed data, we can use graphs to show data that is predicted for the future, based on models, simulations, or extrapolations from past data. Often, projected future data on a line graph are shown with dashed lines, as in **FIGURE A.4**, to indicate that they are less certain than data that have already been observed.

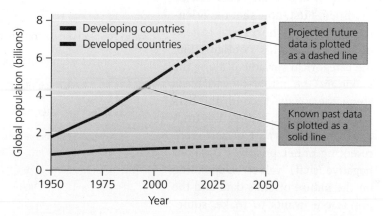

Projected future data is plotted as a dashed line

Known past data is plotted as a solid line

FIGURE A.4 Past and projected population growth for developing and developed countries.

GRAPH TYPE: Bar Chart

A bar chart is most often used when one variable is categorical and the other is numerical. In such a chart, the height (or length) of each bar represents the quantitative value of a given category of the categorical variable; longer bars mean larger values (**FIGURE A.5**). Bar charts allow us to visualize how a variable differs quantitatively among categories.

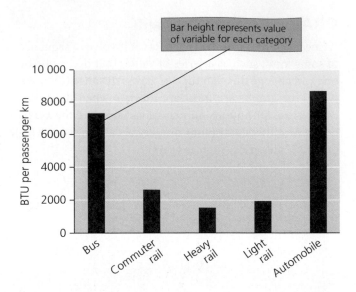

FIGURE A.5 Energy consumption for different modes of transit.

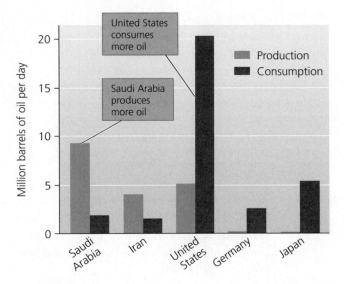

FIGURE A.6 Oil production and consumption by selected nations.

It is often instructive to graph two or more data sets together to reveal patterns and relationships. A bar chart, such as **FIGURE A.6**, allows us to compare two data sets (oil production and oil consumption) both within and among nations. A graph that does double duty in this way allows for higher-level analysis (in this case, suggesting which nations depend on others for petroleum imports). Most bar charts in this book illustrate multiple types of information at once in this manner.

FIGURE A.7 illustrates two ways in which a bar chart can be modified. First, note that the orientation of bars is horizontal instead of vertical. In this configuration, the categorical variable is along the *y*-axis and the numerical variable is along the *x*-axis. Second, the bars can extend in either direction from a central *x*-axis value of zero, representing either positive (right) or negative (left) values. Depending on the nature of one's data and the points one wants to make, sometimes such arrangements can make for a clearer presentation.

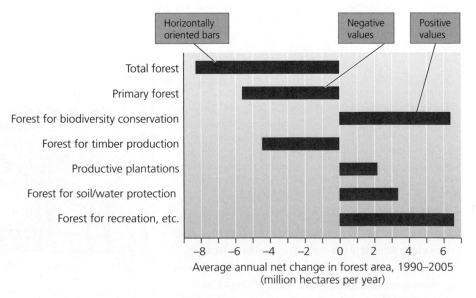

FIGURE A.7 Loss or gain of forests, by type.

One special type of horizontally oriented bar chart is the age pyramid used by demographers (**FIGURE A.8**). Age categories are displayed on the *y*-axis, with bars representing the population size of each age group varying in their horizontal length.

KEY CONCEPT: Statistical Uncertainty

Most data sets involve some degree of uncertainty. Sometimes exact measurements are impossible, so the researcher estimates the likely range of measurement error around the data point. Other times, data points represent the *mean* (average) of many measurements, and the researcher may want to show the degree to which the data vary around this mean. Mathematical techniques are used to obtain precise statistical probabilities for degrees of variation. Results from such analyses are represented in

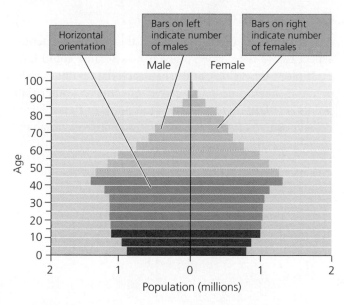

FIGURE A.8   Age structure of Canada, 2005.

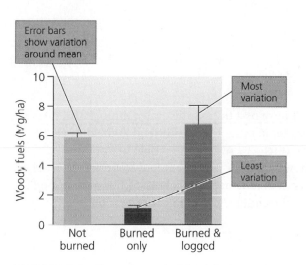

FIGURE A.9   Fine-scale woody debris left after treatments in salvage logging study.

bar charts, such as **FIGURE A.9**, as thin black lines called *error bars*. These bars extend past and within the end of each bar, representing the degree of variation around the bar's value. Longer error bars indicate more uncertainty or variation, whereas short error bars mean we can have high confidence in the value.

The statistical analysis of data is critically important in science. In this book we provide a broad and streamlined introduction to many topics, so we often omit error bars from our graphs and details of statistical significance from our discussions. This is for clarity of presentation only; the research we discuss analyzes its data in far more depth than any textbook could possibly cover.

KEY CONCEPT: Logarithmic Scales

When data span a large range of values, it can help to change the scale on a graph from the standard linear scale to a logarithmic scale. In a logarithmic scale, each equal unit of distance on an axis corresponds to a ratio of values rather than an additive increase in values. Most often, logarithmic scales advance by factors of 10. **FIGURE A.10** uses a logarithmic scale on its *y*-axis for a graph in which we also show a linear scale using white horizontal lines crossing the graph space. The choice of scale does not affect data values, but does drastically affect the appearance of lines or bars on a graph.

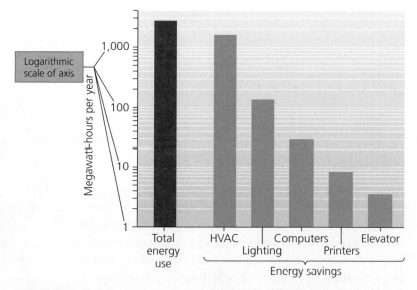

FIGURE A.10   Annual energy use and savings from a campus sustainability study.

GRAPH TYPE: Scatter Plot

A scatter plot is often used when there is no sequential aspect to the data, when a given *x*-axis value could have multiple *y*-axis values, and when each data point is independent, having no particular connection to other data points (**FIGURE A.11**). Scatter plots allow us to visualize a broad positive or negative correlation between variables.

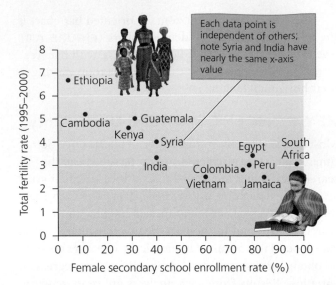

FIGURE A.11   Fertility rate and female education.

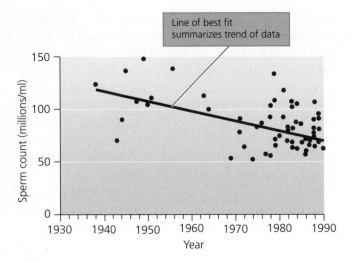

FIGURE A.12   Declining sperm count in men across the world.

A "line of best fit" may be drawn through the data of a scatter plot in order to make a trend in the data clearer to the eye (**FIGURE A.12**). These lines are not drawn casually, however; their placement and slope are determined by precise mathematical analysis of the data through a statistical technique called linear regression.

GRAPH TYPE: Pie Chart

A pie chart is used when we wish to compare the proportions of some whole that are taken up by each of several categories (**FIGURE A.13**). A pie chart is appropriate when one variable is categorical and one is numerical. Each category is represented visually like a slice from a pie, with the size of the slice reflecting the percentage of the whole that is taken up by that category.

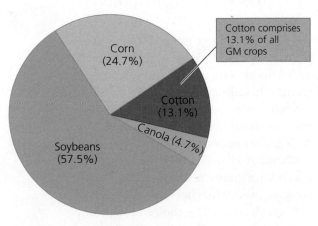

FIGURE A.13   Genetically modified crops grown worldwide, by type.

Appendix B   Units and Conversions

Measurement	Unit and abbreviation	Metric equivalent	Metric to English conversion factor	English to metric conversion factor
Length	1 kilometre (km)	$= 1000\ (10^3)$ metres	1 km = 0.62 miles	1 mile = 1.61 km
	1 metre (m)	$= 100\ (10^2)$ centimetres	1 m = 1.09 yards	1 yard = 0.914 m
		= 1000 millimetres	1 m = 3.28 feet	1 foot = 0.305 m
			1 m = 39.37 inches	
	1 centimetre (cm)	$= 0.01\ (10^{-2})$ metres	1 cm = 0.394 inches	1 foot = 30.5 cm
				1 inch = 2.54 cm
	1 millimetre (mm)	$= 0.001\ (10^{-3})$ metres	1 mm = 0.039 inches	
Area	1 square metre (m^2)	= 10 000 square centimetres	1 m^2 = 1.1960 square yards	1 square yard = 0.8361 m^2
			1 m^2 = 10.764 square feet	1 square foot = 0.0929 m^2
	1 square centimetre (cm^2)	= 100 square millimetres	1 cm^2 = 0.155 square inches	1 square inch = 6.4516 cm^2
	1 hectare (ha)	= 0.01 square kilometres	1 ha = 2.471 acres	1 acre = 0.40469 ha
Mass	1 metric tonne (t)	= 1000 kilograms	1 t = 1.103 tons	1 ton = 0.907 t
	1 kilogram (kg)	= 1000 grams	1 kg = 2.205 pounds	1 pound = 0.4536 kg
	1 gram (g)	= 1000 milligrams	1 g = 0.0353 ounces	1 ounce = 28.35 g
	1 milligram (mg)	= 0.001 grams		
Volume (solids)	1 cubic metre (m^3)	= 1 000 000 cubic centimetres	1 m^3 = 1.3080 cubic yards	1 cubic yard = 0.7646 m^3
			1 m^3 = 35.315 cubic feet	1 cubic foot = 0.0283 m^3
	1 cubic centimetre (cm^3 or cc)	= 0.000 001 cubic metres = 1 millilitre	1 cm^3 = 0.0610 cubic inches	1 cubic inch = 16.387 cm^3
	1 cubic millimetre (mm^3)	= 0.000 000 001 cubic metres		
Volume (liquids and gases)	1 kilolitre (kL)	= 1000 litres	1 kL = 264.17 gallons	1 gallon = 3.785 L
	1 litre (L)	= 1000 millilitres	1 L = 0.264 gallons	1 quart = 0.946 L
			1 L = 1.057 quarts	
	1 millilitre (ml)	= 0.001 litres	1 ml = 0.034 fluid ounces	1 quart = 946 mL
		= 1 cubic centimetre	1 ml = approximately 0.25 teaspoons	1 pint = 473 mL
				1 fluid ounce = 29.57 mL
				1 teaspoon = approx. 5 mL
Time	1 millisecond (ms)	= 0.001 seconds		
Temperature	Degrees Celsius (°C)		$°C = \frac{5}{9}(°F - 32)$	$°F = \frac{9}{5}°C + 32$
Energy and power	1 kilowatt-hour	= 34 113 BTU = 860 421 calories		
	1 watt	= 3.413 BTU/h		
		= 14.34 calories/min		
	1 calorie	= the amount of heat necessary to raise the temperature of 1 g (1 cm^3) of water 1C°		
	1 horsepower	$= 7.457 \times 10^2$ watts		
	1 joule	$= 9.481 \times 10^{-4}$ BTU		
		= 0.239 calories		
		$= 2.778 \times 10^{-7}$ kilowatt-hours		
Pressure	1 pound per square inch (psi)	= 6894.757 pascals (Pa)		
		= 0.068 045 961 atmospheres (atm)		
		= 51.714 93 millimetres of mercury (mm hg = Torr)		
		= 68.947 57 millibars (mbar)		
		= 6.8947 57 kilopascals (kPa)		
	1 atmosphere (atm)	= 101.325 kilopascals (kPa)		

Representative (main group) elements

Period	IA	IIA	IIIB	IVB	VB	VIB	VIIB	VIIIB			IB	IIB	IIIA	IVA	VA	VIA	VIIA	VIIIA
1	1 H 1.0079 Hydrogen																	2 He 4.003 Helium
2	3 Li 6.941 Lithium	4 Be 9.012 Beryllium											5 B 10.811 Boron	6 C 12.011 Carbon	7 N 14.007 Nitrogen	8 O 15.999 Oxygen	9 F 18.998 Fluorine	10 Ne 20.180 Neon
3	11 Na 22.990 Sodium	12 Mg 24.305 Magnesium											13 Al 26.982 Aluminum	14 Si 28.086 Silicon	15 P 30.974 Phosphorus	16 S 32.066 Sulfur	17 Cl 35.453 Chlorine	18 Ar 39.948 Argon
4	19 K 39.098 Potassium	20 Ca 40.078 Calcium	21 Sc 44.956 Scandium	22 Ti 47.88 Titanium	23 V 50.942 Vanadium	24 Cr 51.996 Chromium	25 Mn 54.938 Manganese	26 Fe 55.845 Iron	27 Co 58.933 Cobalt	28 Ni 58.69 Nickel	29 Cu 63.546 Copper	30 Zn 65.39 Zinc	31 Ga 69.723 Gallium	32 Ge 72.61 Germanium	33 As 74.922 Arsenic	34 Se 78.96 Selenium	35 Br 79.904 Bromine	36 Kr 83.8 Krypton
5	37 Rb 85.468 Rubidium	38 Sr 87.62 Strontium	39 Y 88.906 Yttrium	40 Zr 91.224 Zirconium	41 Nb 92.906 Niobium	42 Mo 95.94 Molybdenum	43 Tc 98 Technetium	44 Ru 101.07 Ruthenium	45 Rh 102.906 Rhodium	46 Pd 106.42 Palladium	47 Ag 107.868 Silver	48 Cd 112.411 Cadmium	49 In 114.82 Indium	50 Sn 118.71 Tin	51 Sb 121.76 Antimony	52 Te 127.60 Tellurium	53 I 126.905 Iodine	54 Xe 131.29 Xenon
6	55 Cs 132.905 Cesium	56 Ba 137.327 Barium	57 La 138.906 Lanthanum	72 Hf 178.49 Hafnium	73 Ta 180.948 Tantalum	74 W 183.84 Tungsten	75 Re 186.207 Rhenium	76 Os 190.23 Osmium	77 Ir 192.22 Iridium	78 Pt 195.08 Platinum	79 Au 196.967 Gold	80 Hg 200.59 Mercury	81 Tl 204.383 Thallium	82 Pb 207.2 Lead	83 Bi 208.980 Bismuth	84 Po 209 Polonium	85 At 210 Astatine	86 Rn 222 Radon
7	87 Fr 223 Francium	88 Ra 226.025 Radium	89 Ac 227.028 Actinium	104 Rf 261 Unnilquadium	105 Db 262 Unnilpentium	106 Sg 263 Unnilhexium	107 Bh 262 Unnilseptium	108 Hs 265 Unniloctium	109 Mt 266 Unnilennium	110 Uun 269 Ununnilium	111 Uuu 272 Unununium	112 Uub 277 Ununbium		114		116		

Transition metals

Lanthanides (Rare earth elements)

58 Ce 140.115 Cerium	59 Pr 140.908 Praseodymium	60 Nd 144.24 Neodymium	61 Pm 145 Promethium	62 Sm 150.36 Samarium	63 Eu 151.964 Europium	64 Gd 157.25 Gadolinium	65 Tb 158.925 Terbium	66 Dy 162.5 Dysprosium	67 Ho 164.93 Holmium	68 Er 167.26 Erbium	69 Tm 168.934 Thulium	70 Yb 173.04 Ytterbium	71 Lu 174.967 Lutetium

Actinides

90 Th 232.038 Thorium	91 Pa 231.036 Protactinium	92 U 238.029 Uranium	93 Np 237.048 Neptunium	94 Pu 244 Plutonium	95 Am 243 Americium	96 Cm 247 Curium	97 Bk 247 Berkelium	98 Cf 251 Californium	99 Es 252 Einsteinium	100 Fm 257 Fermium	101 Md 258 Mendelevium	102 No 259 Nobelium	103 Lr 262 Lawrencium

The periodic table arranges elements according to atomic number and atomic weight into horizontal rows called periods and vertical columns called groups.

Elements of each group in Class A have similar chemical and physical properties. This reflects the fact that members of a particular group have the same number of valence shell electrons, which is indicated by the group's number. For example, group IA elements have one valence shell electron, group IIA elements have two, and group VA elements have five. In contrast, as you progress across a period from left to right, properties of the elements change, varying from the very metallic properties of groups IA and IIA to the nonmetallic properties of group VIIA to the inert elements (noble gases) in group VIIIA. This reflects changes in the number of valence shell electrons.

Class B elements, or transition elements, are metals and generally have one or two valence shell electrons. In these elements, some electrons occupy more distant electron shells before the deeper shells are filled.

In this periodic table, elements with symbols printed in black exist as solids under standard conditions (25°C and 1 atm of pressure), while elements in red exist as gases and those in dark blue as liquids. Elements with symbols in green do not exist in nature and must be created by some type of nuclear reaction.

Glossary

abiotic Refers to any nonliving component of the environment. Compare *biotic*.

Aborigine A person who has resided in a particular area since earliest times; an indigenous person.

abyssal plain The flat, mostly topographically featureless ocean floor.

acid drainage (acid mine drainage) A process in which sulphide minerals in newly exposed rock surfaces react with oxygen and rainwater to produce sulphuric acid, which causes chemical runoff as it leaches metals from the rocks. Although acid drainage can be a natural phenomenon, mining can greatly accelerate its rate by exposing many new rock surfaces at once.

acidic deposition The deposition of acidic or acid-forming pollutants from the atmosphere onto Earth's surface by precipitation, by fog, by gases, or by settling of dry particles.

acidic precipitation See *acidic deposition*.

acid rain Acidic precipitation deposited in the form of rain.

act Laws or statutes. Compare *regulation*.

active solar (energy collection) An approach in which technological devices are used to focus, move, or store solar energy. Compare *passive solar energy collection*.

acute exposure Exposure to a toxicant occurring in high amounts for short periods of time. Compare *chronic exposure*.

adaptation A responsive strategy in which it is accepted that an event with potential impacts (such as climatic change) is going to occur, and plans are made to adjust to the impacts. Compare *intervention; mitigation*.

adaptive management The systematic, scientific testing of different management approaches to improve methods over time.

adaptive trait (or adaptation) A trait that confers greater likelihood that an individual will reproduce.

aerobic Occurring in an environment where oxygen is present. For example, the decay of a rotting log proceeds by aerobic decomposition. Compare *anaerobic*.

aerosols Very fine liquid droplets or solid particles aloft in the atmosphere.

"affluenza" Term coined by social critics to describe the failure of material goods to bring happiness to people who have the financial means to afford them.

afforestation Planting of trees where the land has not been forested for a long time.

age distribution The relative numbers of organisms of each age within a population, often displayed on an age structure diagram or age pyramid.

age structure See *age distribution*.

aggregate Unconsolidated or crushed stone or gravel used in construction.

age structure diagram (or age pyramid) A diagram that shows the breakdown of a population in terms of gender and age cohorts. Compare *age distribution*.

agreement An instrument for environmental regulatory purposes, that can be either enforceable or voluntary; they are entered into by agencies of government, often with the goal of streamlining, clarifying, or harmonizing the administration of environmental legislation. Compare *act, regulation*.

Agricultural Revolution The shift around 10 000 years ago from a hunter-gatherer lifestyle to an agricultural way of life in which people began to grow their own crops and raise domesticated animals; this much more intensive, manipulative way of producing and extracting resources marked a permanent change in the relationship of people to the natural environment. Also called *Neolithic Revolution*. Compare *Industrial Revolution; Medical-Technological Revolution*.

agriculture The practice of cultivating soil, producing crops, and raising livestock for human use and consumption.

agroforestry Planting of trees in conjunction with crops. The trees benefit the crops by aiding in the biogeochemical cycling of nutrients and water, by contributing organic material to the soil, and by providing shade. The trees can also provide harvestable products, such as fruits and nuts.

A horizon A layer of soil found in a typical soil profile. It forms the top layer or lies below the O horizon (if one exists). It consists of mostly inorganic mineral components such as weathered substrate, with some organic matter and humus from above mixed in. Often referred to as *topsoil*. Compare *B horizon; C horizon; R horizon*.

air pollution The act of contaminating the air, or the condition of being contaminated by air pollutants.

Air Quality Health Index (AQHI) A standardized, national-level index that quantifies the level of air pollution (from 1 = very low to 10+ = very high) and associated health risks.

airshed The geographical area associated with a particular air mass.

albedo The reflectivity of a surface.

allergen A toxicant that overactivates the immune system, causing an immune response when one is not necessary.

alpine tundra Tundra that occurs at high altitudes.

amensalism A relationship between members of different species in which one organism is harmed and the other is unaffected. Compare *commensalism*.

ammonia (NH$_3$) A colourless gas with a pungent smell; an important precursor component of terrestrial plant nutrients.

anaerobic Occurring in an environment that has little or no oxygen. The conversion of organic matter to fossil fuels (crude oil, coal, natural gas) at the bottom of a deep lake, swamp, or shallow sea is an example of anaerobic decomposition. Compare *aerobic*.

Antarctic Bottom Water (or AABW) The deep portion of the thermohaline circulation in the Southern Ocean. Compare *North Atlantic Deep Water (NADW)*.

anthropocentrism A human-centred view of our relationship with the environment. Compare *biocentrism; ecocentrism*.

anthropogenic Human-generated.

anthroposphere The human sphere, and the built environment; the environment as modified by human actions.

aphotic zone A zone (usually in a water body) that is lacking in light, or where light does not penetrate. Compare *photic zone*.

aquaculture The raising of aquatic organisms for food in controlled environments.

aquifer An underground water reservoir.

arable Used in reference to land or soil that is suitable for growing crops.

artesian aquifer See *confined aquifer*.

artificial selection Trait selection conducted under human direction. Examples include selective breeding of crop plants, pets, and livestock.

artificial wetland See *constructed wetland*.

asbestos Any of several types of mineral that form long, thin microscopic fibres—a structure that gives asbestos the capacity to insulate for heat, muffle sound, and resist fire. When inhaled and lodged in lung tissue, asbestos scars the tissue and may eventually lead to lung cancer or asbestosis.

atmosphere The thin layer of gases surrounding planet Earth. Compare *biosphere; hydrosphere; lithosphere*.

atmospheric deposition The wet or dry deposition on land of a wide variety of pollutants, including mercury, nitrates, organochlorides, and others. Acidic deposition is one type of atmospheric deposition.

atmospheric pressure The weight per unit area produced by a column of air.

atom The smallest component of an element that maintains the chemical properties of that element.

autotroph (or primary producer) An organism that can use the energy from sunlight to produce its own food. Includes green plants, algae, and cyanobacteria.

bedrock The continuous mass of solid rock that makes up Earth's crust.

benthic Of, relating to, or living on the bottom of a water body. Compare *pelagic*.

benthic zone The bottom layer of water body. Compare *littoral zone; limnetic zone; profundal zone*.

B horizon The layer of soil that lies below the A horizon and above the C horizon. Minerals that leach out of the A horizon are carried down into the B horizon (or subsoil) and accumulate there. Sometimes called the subsoil, zone of accumulation, or zone of deposition. Compare *O horizon; R horizon*.

bioaccumulation The buildup of toxicants in the tissues of an animal.

biocentrism A philosophy that ascribes relative values to actions, entities, or properties on the basis of their effects on all living things or on the integrity of the biotic realm in general. The biocentrist evaluates an action in terms of its overall impact on living things, including—but not exclusively focusing on—human beings. Compare *anthropocentrism; ecocentrism*.

biodiesel Diesel fuel produced by mixing vegetable oil, used cooking grease, or animal fat with small amounts of ethanol or methanol (wood alcohol) in the presence of a chemical catalyst.

biodiversity (or **biological diversity**) The sum total of all organisms in an area, taking into account the diversity of species, their genes, their populations, and their communities.

biodiversity hot spot An area that supports an especially great diversity of species, particularly species that are endemic to the area.

biofuel Fuel produced from biomass energy sources and used primarily to power automobiles.

biogeochemical cycle See *nutrient cycle*.

biological control (biocontrol) The attempt to battle pests and weeds with organisms that prey on or parasitize them, rather than by using pesticides.

biological diversity See *biodiversity*.

biological hazard Human health hazards that result from ecological interactions among organisms. These include parasitism by viruses, bacteria, or other pathogens. Compare *chemical hazard; cultural hazard; physical hazard*.

biological weathering Weathering that occurs when living organisms break down parent material, either by physical or chemical means. Compare *chemical weathering; physical weathering*.

biomagnification The magnification of the concentration of toxicants in an organism caused by its consumption of other organisms in which toxicants have bioaccumulated. Also called *food chain concentration*.

biomass Biological material; consists of living and recently deceased organic matter.

biomass energy Energy harnessed from plant and animal matter, including wood from trees, charcoal from burned wood, and combustible animal waste products, such as cattle manure. Fossil fuels are not considered biomass energy sources because their organic matter has not been part of living organisms for millions of years and has undergone considerable chemical alteration since that time.

biome A major regional complex of similar plant communities; a large ecological unit defined by its dominant plant type and vegetation structure. Compare *ecoregion*.

biophilia The concept that human beings subconsciously seek a connection with the rest of life.

biopower The burning of biomass energy sources to generate electricity.

biosphere The sum total of all the planet's living organisms and the abiotic portions of the environment with which they interact. Compare *atmosphere; hydrosphere; lithosphere*.

biotechnology The material application of biological science to create products derived from organisms. The creation of transgenic organisms is one type of biotechnology.

biotic Refers to any living component of the environment. Compare *abiotic*.

biotic potential An organism's capacity to produce offspring.

bitumen A thick and heavy form of petroleum rich in carbon and poor in hydrogen.

bog A type of wetland in which a pond is thoroughly covered with a thick, floating mat of vegetation. Compare *marsh; swamp*.

bond A chemical-physical connection between two or more atoms; an electrical force linking two atoms together.

boreal forest A biome of northern coniferous forest that stretches in a broad band across much of Canada, Alaska, Russia, and Scandinavia. Also known as taiga, boreal forest consists of a limited number of species of evergreen trees, such as black spruce, that dominate large regions of forests interspersed with occasional bogs and lakes.

breakdown product A compound that results from the degradation of a toxicant.

breeder reactor A nuclear reactor that generates fissile material at a rate that is faster than the rate at which it is consumed.

brownfield Sites that have been contaminated by hazardous materials but that have the potential to be cleaned up and remediated for other purposes.

by-catch That portion of a commercial fishing catch consisting of animals caught unintentionally. By-catch kills many thousands of fish, sharks, marine mammals, and birds each year.

Canadian Environmental Protection Act (1999) The centrepiece of Canadian environmental legislation.

canopy (of a forest) The more or less continuous upper level of leaves and branches defined by the tree tops. Forests can have closed or open canopies.

cap-and-trade system A permit trading system in which government determines an acceptable level of pollution and then issues polluting parties permits to pollute. A company receives credit for amounts it does not emit and can then sell this credit to other companies. Compare *emissions trading system*.

captive breeding The practice of capturing members of threatened and endangered species so that their young can be bred and raised in controlled environments and subsequently reintroduced into the wild.

carbohydrate An organic compound consisting of atoms of carbon, hydrogen, and oxygen.

carbon (C) The chemical element with six protons and six neutrons. A key element in organic compounds.

carbon capture and storage (CCS) Technologies or approaches that remove carbon dioxide from power plant or other emissions and sequester it, in an effort to mitigate global climate change.

carbon cycle A major nutrient cycle consisting of the routes that carbon atoms take through the nested networks of environmental systems.

carbon dioxide (CO_2) A colourless gas used in photosynthesis, given off by respiration, and released by burning fossil fuels. A primary greenhouse gas whose buildup contributes to global climate change.

carbon footprint The cumulative amount of carbon, or carbon dioxide equivalent, that a person or institution emits, and is indirectly responsible for emitting, into the atmosphere, contributing to global climate change. Compare *ecological footprint*.

carbon monoxide (CO) A colourless, odourless gas produced primarily by the incomplete combustion of fuel. A criteria pollutant.

carbon neutrality The state in which an individual, business, or institution emits no net carbon to the atmosphere. This may be achieved by reducing carbon emissions and/or employing carbon offsets to offset emissions.

carcinogen A chemical or type of radiation that causes cancer.

carnivore An organism that consumes animals. Compare *detritivore; herbivore; omnivore*.

carrying capacity The maximum population size that a given environment can sustain.

cell The most basic organizational unit of organisms.

cellular respiration The process by which a cell uses the chemical reactivity of oxygen to split glucose into its constituent parts, water and carbon dioxide, and thereby release chemical energy that can be used to form chemical bonds or to perform other tasks within the cell. Compare *photosynthesis*.

channelization Modification of a river's channel or banks by straightening, widening, or concrete-lining, usually for the purposes of navigation, flood control, or diversion for irrigation or water supply.

chemical hazard Chemicals that pose human health hazards. These include toxins produced naturally, as well as many anthropogenic chemicals, including some disinfectants, pesticides, and other synthetic chemicals. Compare *biological hazard; cultural hazard; physical hazard*.

chemical weathering Weathering that results when water or other substances chemically interact with parent material. Compare *biological weathering*; *physical weathering*.

chemosynthesis The process by which bacteria in hydrothermal vents use the chemical energy of hydrogen sulphide (H_2S) to transform inorganic carbon into organic compounds. Compare *photosynthesis*.

chlorofluorocarbon (CFC) One of a group of human-made organic compounds derived from simple hydrocarbons, such as ethane and methane, in which hydrogen atoms are replaced by chlorine, bromine, or fluorine. CFCs deplete the protective ozone layer in the stratosphere.

C horizon The layer of soil that lies below the B horizon and above the R horizon. It contains rock particles that are larger and less weathered than the layers above. It consists of parent material that has been altered only slightly or not at all by the process of soil formation. Compare *A horizon; O horizon*.

chronic exposure Exposure for long periods of time to a toxicant occurring in low amounts. Compare *acute exposure*.

clay Sediment consisting of particles less than 0.002 mm in diameter. Compare *sand; silt*.

clean coal Term used to describe technologies and approaches that seek to reduce the generation and release of sulphur and other pollutants before, during, or after coal is burned for power.

clear-cutting The harvesting of timber by cutting all the trees in an area, leaving only stumps. Although it is the most cost-efficient method, clear-cutting is also the most damaging to the environment.

climate The pattern of atmospheric conditions found across large geographic regions over long periods of time. Compare *weather*.

climate model See *global climate model*.

climatograph (climate diagram) A visual representation of a region's average monthly temperature and precipitation.

climax community In the traditional view of ecological succession, a community that remains in place with little modification until disturbance restarts the successional process. Today, ecologists recognize that community change is more variable and less predictable than originally thought, and that assemblages of species may instead form complex mosaics in space and time.

closed canopy (of a forest) A forest canopy that has very few openings where light can penetrate to the forest floor.

closed system A system that is self-contained with regard to exchanges of matter (but not energy) with its surroundings. Scientists may treat a system as closed to simplify some question they are investigating, but no natural system is truly closed. Compare *open system*.

coal A fossil fuel composed of organic matter that was compressed under high pressure to form a dense, carbon-rich solid material.

coevolution The circumstance in which two species, separated from one another geographically, independently evolve the expression of similar characteristics as a result of adaptation to similar environmental pressures.

cogeneration A practice in which the extra heat generated in the production of electricity is captured and put to use heating workplaces and homes, as well as producing other kinds of power.

cold front The boundary where a mass of cold air displaces a mass of warmer air. Compare *warm front*.

command-and-control An approach to protecting the environment that sets strict legal limits and threatens punishment for violations of those limits.

commensalism A relationship between members of different species in which one organism benefits and the other is unaffected. Compare *amensalism*.

community A group of populations of organisms that live in the same place at the same time.

community-supported agriculture (CSA) A practice in which consumers pay farmers in advance for a share of their yield, usually in the form of weekly deliveries of produce.

compaction (of soil) A decrease in the volume of soil and collapse of the soil structure, which can occur when fluids are withdrawn or when the soil is too heavily tilled, dries out as a result of the removal of vegetation, or bears too much weight.

competition A relationship in which multiple organisms seek the same limited resource.

competitive exclusion An outcome of interspecific competition in which one species excludes another species from resource use entirely.

composting The conversion of organic waste into mulch or humus by encouraging, in a controlled manner, the natural biological processes of decomposition.

compound A molecule whose atoms are composed of two or more elements.

confined aquifer A water-bearing, porous layer of rock, sand, or gravel that is trapped between an upper and lower layer of less permeable substrate, such as clay. The water in a confined aquifer (also called *artesian aquifer*) is under pressure because it is trapped between two impermeable layers. Compare *unconfined aquifer*.

coniferous Refers to trees that are "evergreen," that is, they do not lose their leaves in the fall. Coniferous trees produce cones to host their seeds, and typically have needles rather than broad, flat leaves. Compare *deciduous*.

conservation biology A scientific discipline devoted to understanding the factors, forces, and processes that influence the loss, protection, and restoration of biological diversity within and among ecosystems.

conservation ethic An ethical position, holding that humans should put natural resources to use but also have a responsibility to manage them wisely. Compare *preservation ethic*.

constructed wetland A wetland that is built, usually for the purpose of stormwater runoff management or wastewater management. Also called *artificial wetland*.

consumer See *heterotroph*.

continental collision A convergent boundary between tectonic plates, both of which carry continental crust, leading to the formation of a continental collision zone, rock deformation and metamorphism, and uplift of high mountain chains.

continental shelf The very gently sloping underwater edge of a continent, varying in width from 100 m to 1300 km. At the shelf-slope break, the continental shelf gives way to the steeper continental slope, which leads down to the ocean floor or abyssal plain.

continental slope The relatively steep offshore slope that extends downward from the continental shelf to the continental rise, which connects it to the abyssal plain of the ocean.

control The portion of an experiment in which a variable has been left unmanipulated or untreated.

controlled burn See *prescribed burn*.

convergent plate boundary A boundary along which tectonic plates are moving toward one another. Can result in subduction or collision, and mountain range formation.

convergent evolution The process whereby two completely separate and distinct species evolve similar traits, generally as a result of adaptation to selective pressures from similar environments or habitats.

coral bleaching The loss of the coloured symbiotic algae that normally inhabit corals; possibly caused by stress due to increased water temperature or turbidity.

coral reef A mass of calcium carbonate composed of the skeletons of tiny colonial marine organisms.

core (1) The innermost zone of Earth, made up mostly of iron, that lies beneath the crust and mantle. (2) The part of a forest or reserve that is isolated from the surrounding area by a transitional or buffer zone. Compare *edge*.

Coriolis effect The apparent deflection of north–south air currents to a partly east–west direction, caused by the Coriolis force, which results from the faster spin of regions near the equator than of regions near the poles as a result of Earth's rotation.

corridor A passageway of protected land established to allow animals to travel between islands of protected habitat.

corrosive Substances that corrode (gradually erode, or eat away) metals. One criterion for defining hazardous waste.

cost-benefit analysis A method commonly used by neoclassical economists, in which estimated costs for a proposed action are totalled and then compared to the sum of benefits estimated to result from the action.

criteria (air) contaminants (CACs) (or criteria pollutants) Six air pollutants—carbon monoxide, sulphur dioxide, nitrogen dioxide, tropospheric ozone, particulate matter, and lead—for which maximum allowable concentrations have been established for ambient outdoor air because of the threats they pose to human health.

cropland Land that humans use to raise plants for food and fibre.

crude birth rate The number of births per 1000 individuals for a given time period. Compare *crude death rate*.

crude death rate The number of deaths per 1000 individuals for a given time period. Compare *crude birth rate*.

crude oil (petroleum) A fossil fuel produced by the conversion of organic compounds by heat and pressure. Crude oil is a mixture of hundreds of different types of hydrocarbon molecules characterized by carbon chains of different length.

crust The relatively low-density outer layer of Earth, consisting of rock that floats atop the malleable mantle, which in turn surrounds a mostly iron core.

cryosphere The temporarily and perennially frozen parts of the hydrosphere, including snow, sea ice, lake and river ice, glaciers, and ice caps and sheets. Compare *hydrosphere*.

cultivate Preparing and using soil for the purpose of raising crops (domesticated plants, or *cultivars*).

cultural hazard Human health hazards that result from the place we live, our socioeconomic status, our occupation, or our behavioural choices. These include choosing to smoke cigarettes, or living or working with people who do. Also called *lifestyle hazard*. Compare *biological hazard; chemical hazard; physical hazard*.

current The flow of a liquid (or gas, such as air) in a certain direction.

cycle Flows of elements, compounds, and energy from reservoir to reservoir through the Earth system.

dam Any obstruction placed in a river or stream to block the flow of water so that water can be stored in a reservoir. Dams are built to prevent floods, provide drinking water, facilitate irrigation, and generate electricity.

data Information, generally quantitative information.

deciduous Refers to trees, usually broad-leafed, that lose their leaves each fall and remain dormant during the winter. Compare *coniferous*.

decommissioning The process by which an industrial facility is permanently removed from service and the land on which it resides is reclaimed, remediated, or stabilized.

decomposer Organisms, mainly fungi and bacteria, that break down leaf litter and other nonliving matter into simpler constituents that can then be taken up and used as nutrients by plants.

deep ecology A philosophy established in the 1970s based on principles of self-realization (the awareness that humans are inseparable from nature) and biocentric equality (the precept that all living beings have equal value). Holds that because we are truly inseparable from our environment, we must protect all other living things as we would protect ourselves.

deep-well injection A hazardous waste disposal method in which a well is drilled deep beneath an area's water table into porous rock below an impervious soil layer. Wastes are then injected into the well, so that they will be absorbed into the porous rock and remain deep underground, isolated from groundwater and human contact. Compare *surface impoundment*.

deforestation The loss of forested land.

demographic transition A theoretical model of economic and cultural change that explains the declining death rates and birth rates that occurred in Western nations as they became industrialized. The model holds that industrialization caused these rates to fall naturally by decreasing mortality and by lessening the need for large families.

demography A social science that applies the principles of population ecology to the study of statistical change in human populations.

denitrification A multi-step chemical process in which nitrates in soil are reduced by denitrifying bacteria, and ultimately released to the atmosphere.

deoxyribonucleic acid (DNA) A molecule that directs the production of proteins; self-replicating material that is the main constituent of chromosomes in almost all living organisms. Compare *ribonucleic acid (RNA)*.

deposition The arrival of transported material at a new location. For example, eroded sediment is deposited in streams, and wind-borne particulates are deposited on the surfaces of land and water bodies.

desalination (or desalinization) The removal of salt from seawater.

desert The driest biome on Earth, with annual precipitation of less than 25 cm. Because deserts have relatively little vegetation to insulate them from temperature extremes, sunlight readily heats them in the daytime, but daytime heat is quickly lost at night, so temperatures vary widely from day to night and in different seasons.

desertification A loss of more than 10% of a land's productivity due to erosion, soil compaction, forest removal, overgrazing, drought, salination, climate change, depletion of water sources, or other factors. Severe desertification can result in the expansion of desert areas or creation of new deserts in areas that once supported fertile land.

detritivore Animals such as millipedes and soil insects, which scavenge the waste products or the dead bodies of other community members.

dike A long, raised mound of earth erected along a river bank to protect against floods by holding rising water in the main channel.

directional selection Mode of natural selection in which selection drives a feature in one direction rather than another—for example, toward larger or smaller, or faster or slower. Compare *disruptive selection; stabilizing selection*.

discharge zone An area where groundwater emerges from the subsurface and flows out on the surface to become or join a surface water body.

disruptive selection Mode of natural selection in which a trait diverges from its starting condition in two or more directions. Compare *directional selection; stabilizing selection*.

divergent evolution The process whereby two species with a common genetic ancestor (or two populations of the same species, which have become geographically separated or reproductively isolated) evolve different traits over time as a result of adaptation to selective pressures from different environments or habitats. Divergent evolution of two populations may be expected eventually to result in speciation—that is, the characteristics of the populations eventually become so different that they are no longer of the same species.

divergent plate boundary A boundary along which tectonic plates are moving apart from one another. In some cases, magma surging upward to the surface divides the plates and pushes them apart, forming new crust as the magma cools in the rift. An example is the Mid-Atlantic ridge. Compare *transform plate boundary* and *convergent plate boundary*.

diversion (of water) Removing water from a river system or changing its flow for use in another location.

domesticated Animals bred and raised in captivity, for human use. Crops are domesticated plants.

dose The amount of toxicant a test animal receives in a dose-response test. Also, the amount of toxicant ingested, absorbed, or otherwise taken in by an organism. Compare *response*.

dose-response curve A curve that plots the response of test animals to different doses of a toxicant. The response is generally quantified by measuring the proportion of animals exhibiting negative effects.

downwelling In the ocean, the flow of warm surface water toward the ocean floor. Downwelling occurs where surface currents converge. Compare *upwelling*.

drainage basin Land area where all precipitation that falls drains off through a particular river channel. Compare *watershed*.

driftnet An enormous net that stretches across many kilometres of water, used for commercial industrialized fishing.

dryland An area with generally low precipitation but not so arid as to be classified as a desert; grasslands, savannahs, and shrublands are typical dryland biomes.

dust dome A phenomenon in which smog and particulate air pollution become trapped in a layer overlying an urban centre. Can be exacerbated by the urban heat island effect.

dynamic equilibrium The state reached when processes within a system are moving in opposing directions at equivalent rates so that their effects balance out.

earthquake Ground shaking associated with the sudden release of strain energy stored in rock. The release of stored energy generates seismic waves that travel outward in all directions from the earthquake's focus.

ecocentrism A philosophy that considers actions in terms of their damage or benefit to the integrity of whole ecological systems, including both biotic and abiotic elements. For an ecocentrist, the well-being of an individual organism—human or otherwise—is less important than the long-term well-being of a larger integrated ecological system. Compare *biocentrism*; *anthropocentrism*.

ecofeminism A philosophy holding that the patriarchal structure of society is a root cause of both social and environmental problems. Ecofeminists hold that a worldview traditionally associated with women, which interprets the world in terms of interrelationships and cooperation, is more in tune with nature than a worldview traditionally associated with men, which interprets the world in terms of hierarchies and competition.

ecolabelling The practice of designating on a product's label how the product was grown, harvested, or manufactured, so that consumers buying it are aware of the processes involved and can differentiate between brands that use processes believed to be environmentally beneficial (or less harmful than others) and those that do not.

ecological economics A developing school of economics that applies the principles of ecology and systems thinking to the description and analysis of economies. Compare *environmental economics*.

ecological footprint The cumulative amount of land and water required to provide the raw materials a person or population consumes and to dispose of or recycle the waste that is produced.

ecological restoration Efforts to reverse the effects of human disruption of ecological systems and to restore communities to their "natural" state. Compare *restoration ecology*.

ecology The science that deals with the distribution and abundance of organisms, the interactions among them, and the interactions between organisms and their abiotic environments.

economics The study of how we decide to use scarce resources to satisfy the demand for goods and services.

economy A social system that converts resources into goods and services.

ecoregion A large area of land or water that contains a geographically distinct assemblage of natural communities that share a large majority of their species and ecological dynamics; share similar environmental conditions; and interact ecologically in ways that are critical for their long-term persistence. Compare *biome*.

ecosystem All organisms that occur and interact with each other and with the abiotic environment in a particular area at the same time.

ecosystem-based management The attempt to manage the harvesting of resources in ways that minimize impact on the ecosystems and ecological processes that provide the resources.

ecosystem diversity The number and variety of ecosystems in a particular area. One way to express biodiversity. Related concepts consider the geographic arrangement of habitats, communities, or ecosystems at the landscape level, including the sizes, shapes, and interconnectedness of patches of these entities.

ecosystem ecology The study of how the living and nonliving components of ecosystems interact and transfer energy among themselves.

ecosystem service An essential service an ecosystem provides that supports life and makes economic activity possible. For example, ecosystems naturally purify air and water, cycle nutrients, provide for plants to be pollinated by animals, and serve as receptacles and recycling systems for the waste generated by our economic activity.

ecotone A transitional zone where ecosystems meet.

ecotourism Visitation of natural areas for tourism and recreation. Most often involves tourism by more-affluent people, which may generate economic benefits for less-affluent communities near natural areas and thus provide economic incentives for conservation of natural areas.

ED_{50} (effective dose–50%) The amount of a toxicant it takes to affect 50% of a population of test animals. Compare *threshold dose*; *LD_{50}*.

edge The part of a forest that is immediately adjacent to the surrounding area, and is separated from the forest core by a transitional or buffer zone.

effluent Water that flows out of a facility such as a wastewater treatment plant, mine, or power plant.

electrolysis A process in which electrical current is passed through a compound to release ions. Electrolysis offers one way to produce hydrogen for use as fuel: Electrical current is passed through water, splitting the water molecules into hydrogen and oxygen atoms.

electronic waste (or e-waste) Discarded electronic products such as computers, monitors, printers, DVD players, cell phones, and other devices. Heavy metals in these products mean that this waste may require treatment as hazardous waste.

element A fundamental type of matter; a chemical substance with a given set of properties, which cannot be broken down into substances with other properties. Chemists currently recognize 92 elements that occur in nature, as well as more than 20 others that have been artificially created.

El Niño An exceptionally strong warming of the eastern Pacific Ocean and weakness or even reversal of the trade winds; occurs every 2 to 7 years, affects regional weather systems by distorting the jet streams, and depresses local fish and bird populations by altering the marine food web in the area. Compare *La Niña*.

El Niño – Southern Oscillation (ENSO) A systematic shift in atmospheric pressure, sea-surface temperature, and ocean circulation in the tropical Pacific Ocean. ENSO cycles give rise to El Niño and La Niña conditions.

emergent property A characteristic that is not evident in a system's components individually.

emigration The departure of individuals from a population.

emissions trading system A permit trading system for emissions in which a government issues marketable emissions permits to conduct environmentally harmful activities. Under a cap-and-trade system, the government determines an acceptable level of pollution and then issues permits to pollute. A company receives credit for amounts it does not emit and can then sell this credit to other companies. Compare *cap-and-trade*.

endangered Categorization of a species in danger of extirpation or extinction. Compare *threatened*; *vulnerable*.

endemic Native or restricted to a particular geographic region. An endemic species occurs in one area and nowhere else on Earth.

endocrine disruptor A toxicant that interferes with the endocrine (hormone) system.

"end-of-pipe" A response to pollution that deals only with effluents as they emerge from the "end of the pipe," rather than reducing or eliminating the pollution at its source.

energy An intangible phenomenon that can change the position, physical composition, or temperature of matter.

energy conservation The practice of reducing energy use as a way of extending the lifetime of our fossil fuel supplies, of being less wasteful, and of reducing our impact on the environment.

environment The sum total of our surroundings, including all of the living things and nonliving things with which we interact.

Environment Canada The department of the federal government that is mandated to preserve and enhance the quality of the natural environment; conserve Canada's renewable natural resources; conserve and protect Canada's water resources; forecast weather and environmental change; enforce rules relating to boundary waters; and coordinate environmental policies and programs; created in 1971 by the Department of the Environment Act.

environmental audit An assessment undertaken to determine whether a facility's operations are in compliance with environmental regulations, and/or whether there are changes that could be made to reduce the environmental impacts or enhance the sustainability of the operation.

environmental economics A developing school of economics that modifies the principles of neoclassical economics to address environmental challenges. An environmental economist believes that we can attain sustainability within our current economic systems. Compare *ecological economics*.

environmental ethics The application of ethical standards to environmental questions.

environmental health Environmental factors that influence human health and quality of life and the health of ecological systems essential to environmental quality and long-term human well-being.

environmental impact assessment (EIA) A multi-faceted, multi-stakeholder assessment of the possible impacts, both positive and negative, that a proposed project might have on the environment; the outcome of an EIA is an environmental impact statement.

environmental justice The principle that all people (sometimes extended to all beings) have the right to a clean, healthy environment, and should therefore have equal access to environmental resources and protection from the impacts of environmental degradation.

environmental nongovernmental organization (ENGO) An environmental organization that is not a government or a private-sector agency. Well-known examples include the Sierra Club, Conservation International, and Greenpeace.

environmental policy Public policy that pertains to human interactions with the environment. It generally aims to regulate resource use or reduce pollution to promote human welfare and/or protect natural systems.

environmental refugee A person who has been driven from his or her homeland by natural disasters, resource shortages, or environmental change.

environmental science The study of how the natural world works and how humans and the environment interact.

environmentalism A social movement dedicated to protecting the natural world.

epidemiology A field of study that involves large-scale comparisons among groups of people, usually contrasting a group known to have been exposed to some toxicant and a group that has not.

EROI (Energy Returned on Investment) The ratio determined by dividing the quantity of energy returned from a process by the quantity of energy invested in the process. Higher EROI ratios mean that more energy is produced from each unit of energy invested.

erosion The removal of material from one place and its transport to another by the action of wind or water.

estuary An area where a river flows into the ocean, mixing fresh water with salt water.

ethanol Alcohol produced as a biofuel by fermenting biomass, generally from carbohydrate-rich crops such as corn.

ethics The study of good and bad, right and wrong. The term can also refer to the set of moral principles or values of a group or an individual.

eutrophic Term describing a water body that has high-nutrient and low-oxygen conditions. Compare *oligotrophic*.

eutrophication The process of nutrient enrichment, increased production of organic matter, and subsequent ecosystem degradation.

evaporation The conversion of a substance from a liquid to a gaseous form.

even-aged Condition of timber plantations—generally monocultures of a single species—in which all trees are of the same age. Most ecologists view plantations of even-aged stands more as crop agriculture than as ecologically functional forests. Compare *uneven-aged*.

evenness See *relative abundance*.

evolution Genetically based change in the appearance, functioning, and/or behaviour of organisms across generations, often by the process of natural selection.

e-waste See *electronic waste*.

Exclusive Economic Zone (EEZ) The area of ocean under the jurisdiction of the bordering nation, which extends to 200 nautical miles from the shore, as per the United Nations' *Convention on the Law of the Sea*.

exotic A species that is non-native to an area; alien. Compare *invasive species*.

experiment An activity designed to test the validity of a hypothesis by manipulating variables.

exponential growth The increase of a population (or of anything) by a fixed percentage each year; geometric growth. Contrast with *linear growth*.

extensification Increasing resource productivity by bringing more land into production. Compare *intensification*.

externality A cost or benefit of a transaction that affects people other than the buyer or seller. Examples of negative externalities or external costs include harm to citizens from water pollution or air pollution discharged by nearby factories.

extinction The disappearance of an entire species. Compare *extirpation*.

extirpation The disappearance of a particular population from a given area, but not the entire species globally. Compare *extinction*.

fault A fracture in rock, along which some movement has occurred.

feedback loop (or feedback cycle) A circular process in which a system's output serves as input to that same system. See *negative feedback loop; positive feedback loop*.

feedlot A huge barn or outdoor pen designed to deliver energy-rich food to animals living at extremely high densities. Also called a "factory farm" or *concentrated animal feeding operation (CAFO)*.

Ferrel cell One of a pair of cells of convective circulation between 30 and 60 degrees north and south latitude that influence global climate patterns. Compare *Hadley cell; polar cell*.

fertilizer A substance that promotes plant growth by supplying essential nutrients such as nitrogen or phosphorus.

fission A reaction in which a nucleus splits into two smaller nuclei, with an accompanying release of energy. Compare *fusion*.

flammable Substances that easily catch fire. One criterion for defining hazardous waste.

flat-plate solar collectors See *solar panels*.

floodplain The region of land over which a river has historically wandered, and which is periodically inundated.

floor (of a forest) The lowest level of a forest, consisting of the topsoil, organic litter, and humus.

flux The movement of materials (or energy) among pools or reservoirs in a cycle.

food chain A simple relationship in which primary producers are eaten by primary consumers, who are, in turn, eaten by secondary consumers, and so on. A significant amount of energy is typically lost in moving from the bottom of the food chain to higher levels, in turn.

food security An adequate, reliable, and available food supply to all people at all times.

food web A visual representation of feeding interactions within an ecological community that shows an array of relationships between organisms at different trophic levels.

forest A densely wooded area.

forestry The scientific study and professional management of forests.

fossil The remains, impression, or trace of an animal or plant of past geological ages that has been preserved in rock or sediments.

fossil record The cumulative body of fossils worldwide, which palaeontologists study to infer the history of past life on Earth.

fossil fuel Naturally occurring hydrocarbon fuels, including but not limited to oil (petroleum), natural gas, and coal.

fresh water Water that is relatively pure, holding very few dissolved salts.

front The boundary between air masses that differ in temperature and moisture (and therefore density). See *warm front; cold front*.

fuel cell A technology that produces energy from a chemical reaction similar to that in a battery, without combustion of the fuel.

fundamental niche The full niche of a species. Compare *realized niche*.

fusion A reaction in which two nuclei combine to form a single, more massive nucleus, with an accompanying release of energy. Compare *fission*.

gangue Waste rock and commercially non-valuable minerals that occur with ore.

gene A stretch of DNA that represents a unit of hereditary information.

gene bank See *seed bank*.

generalist A species that can survive in a wide array of habitats or use a wide array of resources. Compare *specialist*.

genetically modified (GM) organism An organism that has been genetically engineered using a technique called recombinant DNA technology.

genetic bottleneck An event in which a significant portion of the population of a species is killed or otherwise prevented from reproducing, leading to a decrease in genetic diversity in subsequent generations.

genetic diversity A measurement of the differences in DNA composition among individuals within a given species.

genetic engineering Any process scientists use to manipulate an organism's genetic material in the lab by adding, deleting, or changing segments of its DNA.

geo-engineering Any of a number of approaches to the artificial manipulation of the global climate system.

geographic information system (GIS) Computer software that takes multiple types of data (for instance, on geology, hydrology, vegetation, animal species, and human development) and overlays them on a common set of spatial coordinates; a common tool of geographers, landscape ecologists, resource managers, and conservation biologists.

geological isolation An approach to waste disposal that makes use of the natural buffering and containment properties of rocks and minerals to hold, absorb, and isolate the waste from contact with the hydrosphere and biosphere. Mainly used for hazardous or radioactive wastes.

geosphere The solid Earth; sometimes the word lithosphere is used with this connotation, but technically it has a distinct meaning. Compare *lithosphere*.

geothermal energy Renewable energy derived from heat generated deep within Earth. The radioactive decay of elements at depth generates heat that rises to the surface in magma, through heat flow by conduction, and through fissures and cracks. Can be synonymous with *terrestrial energy*.

glaciation The process of extension of ice sheets from the polar regions far into Earth's temperate zones during cold periods of Earth's history; also, a period during which this process occurred in the past. Compare *interglaciation*.

global climate change A change in planetary-scale aspects of Earth's climate, such as average temperature, precipitation, and storm activity. Generally refers to the current warming trend in global temperatures and associated climatic changes, which are at least partly of anthropogenic origin.

global climate model (GCM) Quantitative, computer-based models designed to link processes in the atmosphere, hydrosphere, biosphere, and geosphere in three spatial dimensions, on a detailed geographical grid. Such models allow for the study of interrelationships and feedbacks among the processes that control the global climate system, and changes in these processes over time, including projecting possible future changes.

global warming An increase in Earth's average surface temperature. The term is most frequently used in reference to the warming trend of recent years and decades. Global warming is one aspect of global climate change, and in turn drives other components of climate change.

global warming potential A quantity that specifies the ability of one molecule of a given greenhouse gas to contribute to atmospheric warming, relative to carbon dioxide.

goods Something material (such as a resource or a product) that has economic utility.

grassland An area of land in which grasses are the dominant plant species.

greenbelt A protected natural area that is intended to function like an urban growth boundary, restricting the spread of urban development.

greenhouse effect The warming of Earth's surface and atmosphere (especially the troposphere) caused by the energy emitted by greenhouse gases.

greenhouse gas (GHG) A gas that absorbs infrared radiation released by Earth's surface and then warms the surface and troposphere by emitting energy, thus giving rise to the greenhouse effect. Greenhouse gases include carbon dioxide (CO_2), water vapour, ozone (O_3), nitrous oxide (N_2O), halocarbon gases, and methane (CH_4). Compare *radiatively active gas*.

Green Revolution An intensification of the industrialization of agriculture in the latter half of the twentieth century, which has led to dramatically increased crop yields per unit area of farmland. Practices include devoting large areas to monocultures of crops specially bred for high yields and rapid growth; heavy use of fertilizers, pesticides, and irrigation water; and sowing and harvesting on the same piece of land more than once per year or per season.

green tax A levy on environmentally harmful activities and products aimed at providing a market-based incentive to correct for market failure.

gross primary production (GPP) The energy that results when autotrophs convert solar energy (sunlight) to energy of chemical bonds in sugars through photosynthesis. Autotrophs use a portion of this production to power their own metabolism, which entails oxidizing organic compounds by cellular respiration. Compare *net primary production; secondary production*.

ground-source heat pump A pump that harnesses geothermal energy from near-surface sources of earth and water, and that can help heat residences.

groundwater Water held in aquifers underground. Abbreviated *GHSP*.

gyre A rotating oceanic current, or vortex, that forms as a result of complex interactions involving wind, ocean water, currents, friction, and the Coriolis force.

habitat The specific environment in which an organism lives, including both biotic and abiotic factors.

habitat fragmentation The process by which large expanses of habitat are broken up into smaller, isolated pieces. The size of contiguous habitat is an issue for some large animals, but the character of the habitat can be an issue even for smaller animals; smaller habitat fragments have a greater proportion of edge, and the characteristics of core and edge habitat can differ substantially.

Hadley cell One of a pair of cells of convective circulation between the equator and 30 degrees north and south latitude that influence global climate patterns. Compare *Ferrel cell; polar cell*.

half-life The amount of time it takes for one-half the atoms of a radioisotope to emit radiation and decay. Different radioisotopes have different half-lives, ranging from fractions of a second to billions of years.

hardwood Wood derived from broad-leafed, deciduous trees. Compare *softwood*.

harvesting Gathering, withdrawal, capture, or other method of removal of product from the stock of a resource.

hazardous waste Waste that is toxic, chemically reactive, flammable, or corrosive. Compare *industrial solid waste; municipal solid waste*.

heavy metals A metallic element with relatively high density or atomic mass. Some of these, such as lead, mercury, and arsenic, are neurotoxins and thus are of concern from a public health and environmental perspective.

herbivore An organism that consumes plants. Compare *carnivore; omnivore*.

herbivory The consumption of plants by animals.

heterotroph (consumer) An organism that consumes other organisms. Includes most animals, as well as fungi and microbes that decompose organic matter.

high-pressure system An air mass with elevated atmospheric pressure, containing air that descends, typically bringing fair weather. Compare *low-pressure system*.

homeostasis The characteristic whereby a system tends to maintain constant or stable internal conditions.

horizon A distinct layer of soil. See *A horizon; B horizon; C horizon; E horizon; O horizon, R horizon*.

host The organism in a parasitic relationship that suffers harm while providing the parasite with nourishment or some other benefit.

Hubbert's peak The peak in production of crude oil in the United States, which occurred in 1970 as Shell Oil geologist M. King Hubbert predicted in 1956.

humus A dark, spongy, crumbly material in the soil, composed of complex organic compounds, resulting from the partial decomposition of organic matter.

hydrocarbon An organic compound consisting solely of hydrogen and carbon atoms.

hydroelectric power (hydropower) The generation of electricity using the kinetic energy of moving water.

hydrologic cycle The flow of water—in liquid, gaseous, and solid forms—through our biotic and abiotic environment.

hydropower See *hydroelectric power*.

hydrosphere Earth's water—salt or fresh, liquid, ice, or vapour—that resides in surface bodies, underground, and in the atmosphere. Compare *biosphere; lithosphere*.

hypothesis An educated guess that explains a phenomenon or answers a scientific question. Compare *theory*.

hypoxia A state of oxygen deficiency.

igneous rock One of the three main categories of rock. Formed from the cooling and solidification of magma. Granite and basalt are examples of igneous rock. Compare *metamorphic rock; sedimentary rock*.

immigration The arrival of individuals from outside a population.

incineration A controlled process of burning solid waste for disposal in which mixed garbage is combusted at very high temperatures. Compare *sanitary landfill*.

indicator A fact or piece of data or information that reveals the status or level of something.

indigenous Originating in or native to a particular place.

industrial ecology A holistic approach to industry that integrates principles from engineering, chemistry, ecology, economics, and other disciplines and seeks to redesign industrial systems in order to reduce resource inputs and minimize inefficiency.

industrialized agriculture A form of agriculture that uses large-scale mechanization and fossil fuel combustion, enabling farmers to replace horses and oxen with faster and more powerful means of cultivating, harvesting, transporting, and processing crops. Other aspects include irrigation and the use of inorganic fertilizers. Use of chemical herbicides and pesticides reduces competition from weeds and herbivory by insects. Compare *traditional agriculture*.

Industrial Revolution The dramatic shift in the mid-1700s from rural life, animal-powered agriculture, and manufacturing by craftsmen to an urban society powered by fossil fuels such as coal and crude oil. The Industrial Revolution led to rapid industrialization and urbanization, with related economic and social changes in population, health, transportation, agricultural productivity, and environmental quality. Compare *Agricultural Revolution; Medical-Technological Revolution*.

industrial smog Gray-air smog caused by the incomplete combustion of coal or oil when burned. Compare *photochemical smog*.

industrial solid waste Nonliquid waste that is not especially hazardous and that comes from production of consumer goods, mining, petroleum extraction and refining, and agriculture. Compare *hazardous waste; municipal solid waste*.

infrared radiation Electromagnetic radiation with wavelengths longer than visible red.

inorganic compound Chemical compounds that are of mineral (rather than biological) origin. Inorganic compounds may contain carbon—the element that characterizes organic compounds—but lack the carbon–carbon bonds that are typical of organic compounds.

inorganic fertilizer A fertilizer that consists of mined or synthetically manufactured mineral supplements. Inorganic fertilizers are generally more susceptible than organic fertilizers to leaching and runoff and may be more likely to cause unintended off-site impacts.

insolation Solar radiation that reaches Earth's surface.

integrated pest management (IPM) The use of multiple techniques in combination to achieve long-term suppression of pests, including biocontrol, use of pesticides, close monitoring of populations, habitat alteration, crop rotation, transgenic crops, alternative tillage methods, and mechanical pest removal.

intensification Increasing the resource productivity of a given unit of land, usually by applying new technologies to enhance productivity. Compare *extensification*.

interdisciplinary field A field that borrows techniques from several more traditional fields of study and brings together research results from these fields into a broad synthesis.

interglaciation A period of global warming, between glaciations. Compare *glaciation*.

Intergovernmental Panel on Climate Change (IPCC) An international panel of atmospheric scientists, climate experts, and government officials established in 1988 by the United Nations Environment Programme and the World Meteorological Organization, whose mission is to assess information relevant to questions of human-induced global climate change. The IPCC's reports summarize current and probable future global trends and represent the consensus of atmospheric scientists around the world.

intertidal Of, relating to, or living along shorelines between the highest reach of the highest tide and the lowest reach of the lowest tide.

intervention A set of possible actions that could be taken to modify the climate system on a global scale. Compare *adaptation, geo-engineering, mitigation*.

invasive species A species that spreads widely and rapidly becomes dominant in a community, interfering with the community's normal functioning. Compare *exotic*.

ion An electrically charged atom or combination of atoms.

ion exchange Process in which soil exchanges positively-charged ions (cations) and negatively-charged ions (anions) with the soil solution. Negatively-charge soil particles hold (adsorb) positively-charged cations, notably Al^{3+}, Ca^{2+}, Mg^{2+}, K^+, NH_4^+, and Na^+, releasing them to the soil solution where they become available as plant nutrients.

IPAT model A formula that represents how humans' total impact (I) on the environment results from the interaction among three factors: population (P), affluence (A), and technology (T).

irrigation The artificial provision of water to support agriculture.

isotope One of several forms or variants of an element having differing numbers of neutrons in the nucleus of its atoms. Chemically, isotopes of an element behave almost identically, but they have different physical properties because they differ in mass. Compare *stable isotope geochemistry*.

kelp Large brown algae or seaweed that can form underwater "forests," providing habitat for marine organisms.

kerogen A substance derived from deeply buried organic matter that acts as a precursor or source material for both natural gas and crude oil.

keystone species A species that has an especially far-reaching effect on a community.

kinetic energy Energy of motion. Compare *potential energy*.

K-selected (or K-strategist) Term denoting a species with low biotic potential whose members produce a small number of offspring and take a long time to gestate and raise each of their young, but invest heavily in promoting the survival and growth of these few offspring. Populations of K–selected species are generally regulated by density-dependent factors. Compare *r–selected*.

Kyoto Protocol An agreement drafted in 1997 that calls for reducing, by 2012, emissions of six greenhouse gases to levels lower than their levels in 1990. Canada was the 99th country to ratify the agreement, which happened in 2002 , and then become the first nation to withdraw from the agreement, in 2011.

landfill An engineered waste disposal site. Compare *sanitary landfill, secure landfill*.

landfill gas A mix of gases that consists of roughly half methane produced by anaerobic decomposition deep inside landfills, and which can be captured and used as a source of energy.

landslide A type of mass wasting in which a mass of rock or sediment moves downslope, often as a relatively coherent block.

land trust Local or regional organization that preserves lands valued by its members. In most cases, land trusts purchase land outright with the aim of preserving it in its natural condition. The Nature Conservancy may be considered the world's largest land trust.

landscape ecology An approach to the study of organisms and their environments at the landscape scale, focusing on geographic areas that include multiple ecosystems.

La Niña An exceptionally strong cooling of surface water in the equatorial Pacific Ocean that occurs every 2 to 7 years and has widespread climatic consequences. Compare *El Niño*.

lava Magma that is released from the lithosphere and flows or spatters across Earth's surface.

LD$_{50}$ (lethal dose–50%) The amount of a toxicant it takes to kill 50% of a population of test animals. Compare *ED$_{50}$; threshold dose*.

leachate Liquids that seep through liners of a sanitary landfill and leach into the soil underneath.

leaching The process by which solid materials such as minerals are dissolved in a liquid (usually water) and transported to another location.

Leadership in Energy and Environmental Design (LEED) A widely used set of standards for sustainable building.

lichen A mutualistic aggregate of fungi and algae in which the algal component provides food and energy via photosynthesis, while the fungal component takes a firm hold on rock and captures moisture.

life-cycle analysis In industrial ecology, the examination of the entire life cycle of a given product—from its origins in raw materials, through its manufacturing, to its use, and finally its disposal—in an attempt to identify ways to make the process more ecologically efficient.

life expectancy The average number of years that individuals in particular age groups are likely to continue to live.

lifestyle hazard See *cultural hazard*.

light pollution Pollution from city lights that obscures the night sky.

limiting factor A physical, chemical, or biological characteristic of the environment that restrains population growth.

limnetic zone In a water body, the layer of open water through which sunlight penetrates. Compare *littoral zone; benthic zone; profundal zone.*

linear growth The increase of a population (or of anything) by a fixed amount each year; arithmetic growth. Contrast with *exponential growth.*

lipid One of a chemically diverse group of large, biologically important molecules that are classified together because they do not dissolve in water. Lipids include fats, phospholipids, waxes, pigments, and steroids.

lithosphere The solid part of Earth, including the rocks, sediment, and soil at the surface and extending down many kilometres underground; technically, the crust and the outer portion of the mantle. Compare *atmosphere; biosphere; hydrosphere.*

litter Leaves, twigs, and other organic refuse that accumulates on the land surface, especially in forested areas.

littoral See *intertidal.*

littoral zone The region ringing the edge of a water body. Compare *benthic zone; limnetic zone; profundal zone.*

loam Soil with a relatively even mixture of clay-, silt-, and sand-sized particles.

logistic growth curve A plot that shows how the initial exponential growth of a population is slowed and finally brought to a standstill by limiting factors, yielding an S-shaped or sigmoidal growth curve.

low-pressure system An air mass in which the air moves toward the low atmospheric pressure at the centre of the system and spirals upward, typically bringing clouds and precipitation. Compare *high-pressure system.*

macronutrient A nutrient that organisms require in relatively large amounts. Compare *micronutrient.*

magma Molten, liquid rock.

malnutrition The condition of lacking nutrients the body needs, including a complete complement of vitamins and minerals.

mangrove A tree with a unique type of roots that curve upward to obtain oxygen, which is lacking in the mud in which they grow, and that serve as stilts to support the tree in changing water levels. Mangrove forests grow on the coastlines of the tropics and subtropics.

mantle The layer of rock that lies beneath Earth's crust and surrounds a mostly iron core.

marine protected area (MPA) An area of the ocean set aside to protect marine life from fishing pressures. An MPA may be protected from some human activities but be open to others. Compare *marine reserve.*

marine reserve An area of the ocean designated as a "no-fishing" zone, allowing no extractive activities. Compare *marine protected area.*

market value (of natural resources) The monetary value that would be achievable by placing a natural resource for sale on the open market. It is relatively straightforward to quantify the potential market value of a resource (such as a standing forest, or an ore deposit) that is already represented in the market as a traded commodity (timber, or minerals); it is much more challenging to quantify the market value of an environmental good or service with no existing analogy in the marketplace, such as the value of a particular habitat, or a beautiful view, or the natural filtering function of groundwater. Compare *valuation.*

marsh A type of wetland.

mass extinction (event) The extinction of a large proportion of the world's species in a very short time period due to some extreme and rapid change or catastrophic event. Earth has seen five mass extinction events in the past half-billion years.

mass wasting The downslope movement of Earth material (such as rock or soil) under the influence of gravity.

matter Any material that has mass and occupies space.

maximum sustainable yield (MSY) The maximal harvest of a particular renewable natural resource that can be accomplished while still keeping the resource available for the future.

mechanical weathering See *physical weathering.*

Medical-Technological Revolution The modern era of medicine, public health innovations, and technological advances, including the shift to modern agriculture through what is known as the Green Revolu-

tion. Compare *Agricultural Revolution; Industrial Revolution; Green Revolution.*

Mediterranean A biome typical of the Mediterranean climate zone, which is characterized by warm, dry summers and mild, wet winters. Chapparal is one example of a Mediterranean-type biome.

"mega-city" A city of enormous size, generally with a population greater than 10 million.

meltdown The accidental melting of the uranium fuel rods inside the core of a nuclear reactor, causing the release of radiation.

mesosphere The atmospheric layer above the stratosphere, extending 50–80 km above sea level. (The term mesosphere also applies to part of Earth's mantle.)

metal An element or an alloy of elements which displays properties that typically include malleability, ductility, shiny (metallic) lustre, and good electrical conductivity.

metamorphic rock One of the three main categories of rock. Formed by great heat and/or pressure that reshapes crystals within the rock and changes its appearance and physical properties. Common metamorphic rocks include marble and slate. Compare *igneous rock; sedimentary rock.*

methane (CH_4) The simplest hydrocarbon compound; the key component of natural gas, and a naturally occurring greenhouse gas.

methane hydrate An ice-like solid consisting of molecules of methane (CH_4) embedded in a crystal lattice of water molecules called a clathrate structure. Methane hydrates are being investigated as a potential new source of energy from fossil fuels. Also called *methane ice.*

microclimate Variations in weather and climate that occur on an extremely local scale, such as from one side of a hill to the other.

micronutrient A nutrient that organisms require in relatively small amounts. Compare *macronutrient.*

Milankovitch cycle One of three types of variations in Earth's rotation and orbit around the sun that result in slight changes in the relative amount of solar radiation reaching Earth's surface at different latitudes. As the cycles proceed, they change the way solar radiation is distributed over Earth's surface and contribute to changes in atmospheric heating and circulation that have triggered the ice ages and other climate changes.

mineral A naturally occurring, solid, crystalline, inorganic compound; the building blocks of rocks.

mining The extraction of mineral resources and other valuable Earth materials.

mitigation A responsive strategy in which efforts are made to forestall or minimize the anticipated impacts of environmental change. Compare *adaptation; intervention.*

model A simplified representation of a natural process. Models can be physical, graphical, or quantitative and computer-based. They allow scientists to study natural systems and processes that are highly complex or unwieldy in their spatial or temporal scale. They also can be used to predict future behaviour in complex systems.

molecule A combination of two or more atoms.

monoculture The uniform planting of a single crop over a large area. Characterizes modern industrialized agriculture.

Montreal Protocol International treaty ratified in 1987, in which the (now 197) signatory nations agreed to restrict production of chlorofluorocarbons (CFCs) in order to forestall stratospheric ozone depletion.

mortality Deaths within a population.

mountaintop removal A surface mining process in which the entire top part of a mountain is removed in order to extract the material of interest, commonly coal.

multiple-barrier approach (to waste containment) An approach to hazardous waste disposal and management that places as many impediments as possible in the way of any escaping waste, leachate, effluents, or other harmful emissions from waste (such as radioactivity), including both manufactured and natural barriers.

multiple-use A principle that has nominally guided management policy for national forests over the past half century. The multiple-use principle specifies that the forests be managed for recreation, wildlife habitat, mineral extraction, and various other uses.

municipal solid waste Nonliquid waste that is not especially hazardous and that comes from homes, institutions, and small businesses. Compare *hazardous waste; industrial solid waste.*

mutagen A toxicant that causes mutations in the DNA of organisms.

mutation An accidental change in DNA that may range in magnitude from the deletion, substitution, or addition of a single nucleotide to a change affecting entire sets of chromosomes. Mutations provide the raw material for evolutionary change.

mutualism A relationship in which all participating organisms benefit from their interaction. Compare *parasitism.*

natality Births within a population.

natural gas A fossil fuel composed primarily of methane (CH_4), produced as a by-product when bacteria decompose organic material under anaerobic conditions.

natural rate of population growth The rate of change in a population's size resulting from birth and death rates alone, excluding migration.

natural resource Any of the various substances and energy sources we need in order to survive.

natural resource accounting A discipline that has the goal of adjusting national accounts and indicators, such as GDP, to reflect the true costs of economic production, including the costs of depleting natural resources and damaging the environment.

natural selection The process by which traits that enhance survival and reproduction are passed on more frequently to future generations of organisms than those that do not, thus altering the genetic makeup of populations through time. Natural selection acts on genetic variation and is a primary driver of evolution.

negative feedback loop (or **cycle**) A feedback loop in which output of one type acts as input that moves the system in the opposite direction. The input and output essentially neutralize each other's effects, stabilizing the system. Compare *positive feedback loop.*

nekton Marine animals that actively swim. Compare *plankton.*

net energy The quantitative difference between energy returned from a process and energy invested in the process. Positive net energy values mean that a process produces more energy than is invested. See also *EROI.*

net metering Process by which owners of houses with photovoltaic systems can sell their excess solar energy to their local power utility.

net primary production (NPP) The energy or biomass that remains in an ecosystem after autotrophs have metabolized enough for their own maintenance through cellular respiration. Net primary production is the energy or biomass available for consumption by heterotrophs. Compare *gross primary production; secondary production.*

neurotoxin A toxicant that assaults the nervous system. Neurotoxins include heavy metals, pesticides, and some chemical weapons developed for use in war.

new forestry A set of ecosystem-based management approaches for harvesting timber that explicitly mimic natural disturbances. For instance, "sloppy clear-cuts" that leave a variety of trees standing mimics the changes a forest might experience if hit by a severe windstorm.

new urbanism A school of thought among architects, planners, and developers that seeks to design neighbourhoods in which homes, businesses, schools, and other amenities are within walking distance of one another. In a direct rebuttal to sprawl, proponents of new urbanism aim to create functional neighbourhoods in which families can meet most of their needs close to home without the use of a car.

niche The functional role of a species in a community. See *fundamental niche; realized niche.*

nitrification The conversion by bacteria of ammonium ions (NH_4^+) first into nitrite ions (NO_2^-) and then into nitrate ions (NO_3^-).

nitrogen (N) The chemical element with seven protons and seven neutrons. The most abundant element in the atmosphere, a key element in macromolecules, and a crucial plant nutrient.

nitrogen cycle A major nutrient cycle consisting of the routes that nitrogen atoms take through the nested networks of environmental systems.

nitrogen dioxide (NO_2) A criteria air contaminant and a common by-product of internal combustion engines.

nitrogen fixation The process by which inert nitrogen gas combines with hydrogen to form ammonium ions (NH_4^+), which are chemically and biologically active and can be taken up by plants.

nitrous oxides (NO_x or NOX) Various gaseous compounds, including NO_2 and NO_3, which commonly result from industrial processes involving combustion.

noise pollution Ambient sound that is undesirable or unhealthy.

non-point source A diffuse source of pollutants, often consisting of many small sources. Compare *point source.*

nonrenewable natural resource A natural resource that is in limited supply and is formed much more slowly than we use it. Compare *renewable natural resource.*

North Atlantic Deep Water (NADW) The deep portion of the thermohaline circulation in the northern Atlantic Ocean. Compare *Antarctic Bottom Water (AABW).*

not-in-my-backyard ("NIMBY") A common reaction by homeowners to proposals for waste disposal facilities, wind farms, or other installations.

nuclear power Power derived from the energy released during the splitting of an atom (fission) in a nuclear reactor.

nuclear reactor A facility within a nuclear power plant that initiates and controls the process of nuclear fission in order to generate electricity.

nucleic acid A molecule that directs the production of proteins. Includes DNA and RNA.

nutrient An element or compound that organisms consume and require for survival.

nutrient cycle The comprehensive set of cyclical pathways by which a given nutrient moves through the environment.

ocean acidification The process whereby ocean waters becomes more acidic (lower pH), which can happen when the flux of atmospheric carbon dioxide into surface ocean water increases. Ocean acidification poses a threat to many marine organisms.

ocean thermal energy conversion (OTEC) A potential energy source that involves harnessing the solar radiation absorbed by tropical oceans in the tropics.

O horizon The top layer of soil in some soil profiles, made up of organic matter, such as decomposing branches, leaves, crop residue, and animal waste. Compare *A horizon; B horizon; C horizon; R horizon.*

oil See *crude oil.*

oil sands (or **tar sands**) Deposits that can be mined from the ground, consisting of moist sand and clay containing 1–20% bitumen, that some envision as a replacement for crude oil as this resource is depleted. Oil sands represent crude oil deposits that have been degraded and chemically altered by water erosion and bacterial decomposition.

oil shale Sedimentary rock filled with kerogen that can be processed to produce liquid petroleum. Oil shale is formed by the same processes that form crude oil but occurs when kerogen was not buried deeply enough or subjected to enough heat and pressure to form oil. Compare *shale gas.*

old-growth forest A complex, primary forest in which the trees are generally at least 200 years old.

oligotrophic Term describing a water body that has low-nutrient and high-oxygen conditions. Compare *eutrophic.*

omnivore An organism that consumes both plants and animals. Compare *carnivore; herbivore.*

open canopy (of a forest) A forest canopy with many openings that allow light to pass through to the forest floor.

open system A system that allow both energy and matter to cross its boundaries. Compare *closed system.*

open-pit mining Mining of rock or mineral resources through extraction at the surface from a large, open pit or hole.

open system A system that exchanges energy, matter, and information with other systems. Compare *closed system.*

ore Naturally occurring rock or mineral from which an economically valuable material can be profitably extracted, using current extraction and processing technologies.

organic agriculture Agriculture that uses no synthetic fertilizers or pesticides but instead relies on biological approaches such as composting and biocontrol.

organic compound A compound made up of carbon atoms (and, generally, hydrogen atoms) joined by covalent bonding and sometimes including other elements, such as nitrogen, oxygen, sulphur, or phosphorus. The unusual ability of carbon to build elaborate molecules has resulted in millions of different organic compounds showing various degrees of complexity. Compare *inorganic compound.*

organic fertilizer A fertilizer made up of natural materials (largely the remains or wastes of organisms), including animal manure, crop residues, fresh vegetation, and compost. Compare *inorganic fertilizer.*

ozone (O_3) A molecule consisting of three atoms of oxygen. Absorbs ultraviolet radiation in the stratosphere. Compare *ozone layer; tropospheric ozone.*

ozone hole Term popularly used to describe the annual depletion of the stratospheric ozone layer as a result of chemical interactions with anthropogenic pollutants such as chlorofluorocarbons.

ozone layer A portion of the stratosphere, roughly 17–30 km above sea level, that contains most of the ozone in the atmosphere.

paleoclimate A climate of Earth's ancient past.

parasite The organism in a parasitic relationship that extracts nourishment or some other benefit from the host.

parasitism A relationship in which one organism, the parasite, depends on another, the host, for nourishment or some other benefit while simultaneously doing the host harm. Compare *mutualism.*

parent material The base geological material in a particular location.

particulate matter (PM) Solid and (sometimes) liquid particles small enough to be suspended in the atmosphere and able to damage respiratory tissues when inhaled. Includes primary pollutants such as dust and soot, as well as secondary pollutants such as sulphates and nitrates. A criteria air contaminant, abbreviated PM.

passive solar (energy collection) An approach in which buildings are designed and building materials are chosen to maximize their direct absorption of sunlight in winter, even as they keep the interior cool in the summer. Compare *active solar energy collection.*

pathogen A microbe that causes disease.

peak oil Term used to describe the point of maximum production of petroleum in the world (or for a given nation), after which oil production declines. This is also expected to be roughly the midway point of extraction of the world's oil supplies. The term is generally used in contexts suggesting that our society will face tremendous challenges once the peak has been passed. Compare *Hubbert's peak.*

peat An organic rich soil; a precursor stage to coal, produced when organic material that is broken down by anaerobic decomposition remains wet, near the surface, and not well compressed.

peer review The process by which a manuscript submitted for publication in an academic journal is examined by other specialists in the field, who provide comments and criticism (generally anonymously), and judge whether the work merits publication in the journal.

pelagic Of, relating to, or living between the surface and floor of the ocean. Compare *benthic.*

permafrost Permanently frozen ground; a layer of perennially frozen water under the surface, essentially the W horizon in an arctic soil.

permeability A measure of the interconnectedness of pore spaces in a rock, sediment, or soil. Compare *porosity.*

permit A document that grants a group or individual legal permission to carry out an activity that will have environmental impacts, usually within certain limitations and for a specified period of time. Compare *act, regulation, agreement.*

permit trading The practice of buying and selling government-issued marketable emissions permits to conduct environmentally harmful activities. Under such a system, the government determines an acceptable level of pollution and then issues permits to pollute. A company receives credit for amounts it does not emit and can then sell this credit to other companies.

persistent A chemical that does not break down, degrade, or decompose easily, and that consequently may have a long residence time in a given environmental reservoir.

pest A species—typically, but not always, a non-native or alien invasive species—that has more harmful than beneficial impacts on an ecosystem or community (or on human interests, such as human health or crop health).

pesticide An artificial chemical used to kill insects (insecticide), plants (herbicide), or fungi (fungicide).

petroleum See *crude oil.*

pH A measure of the concentration of hydrogen ions in a solution. The pH scale ranges from 0 to 14: Solution with pH of 7 are neutral; solutions with pH below 7 are acidic, and those with pH higher than 7 are basic. Because the pH scale is logarithmic, each step on the scale represents a tenfold difference in hydrogen ion concentration.

phosphorus (P) The chemical element with 15 protons and 15 neutrons. An abundant element in the lithosphere, a key element in macromolecules, and a crucial plant nutrient.

phosphorus cycle A major nutrient cycle consisting of the routes that phosphorus atoms take through the nested networks of environmental systems.

photic zone In the ocean or a freshwater body, the well-lit top layer of water where photosynthesis occurs. Compare *aphotic zone.*

photochemical smog Brown-air smog caused by light-driven reactions of primary pollutants with normal atmospheric compounds that produce a mix of over 100 different chemicals, ground-level ozone often being the most abundant among them. Compare *industrial smog.*

photosynthesis The process by which autotrophs produce their own food. Sunlight powers a series of chemical reactions that convert carbon dioxide and water into sugar (glucose), thus transforming low-quality energy from the sun into high-quality energy the organism can use. Compare *cellular respiration.*

photovoltaic (PV) cell A device designed to collect sunlight and convert it to electrical energy directly by making use of the photoelectric effect.

phylogenetic tree A treelike diagram that represents the history of divergence of species or other taxonomic groups of organisms.

physical hazard Physical processes that occur naturally in our environment and pose human health hazards. These include discrete events such as earthquakes, volcanic eruptions, fires, floods, blizzards, landslides, hurricanes, and droughts, as well as ongoing natural phenomena such as ultraviolet radiation from sunlight. Compare *biological hazard; chemical hazard; cultural hazard.*

physical weathering Weathering that breaks down rock without triggering a chemical change in the parent material. Wind and rain are two main forces. Compare *biological weathering; chemical weathering.*

phytoplankton Microscopic floating plants and protists, mainly algae. Compare *plankton, zooplankton.*

pioneer species A species that arrives earliest, beginning the ecological process of succession in a terrestrial or aquatic community.

placer mining Mining of ore that has been concentrated by alluvial processes, that is, by the action of running water or waves.

plankton Microscopic aquatic organisms that float (rather than swim). Compare *phytoplankton, zooplankton, nekton.*

planning The professional pursuit that attempts to design cities in such a way as to maximize their efficiency, functionality, and beauty.

plastic A synthetic polymer material, mostly derived from the hydrocarbons in petroleum.

plate tectonics The process by which Earth's surface is shaped by the extremely slow movement of tectonic plates—large fragments of lithosphere. Earth's surface includes about 15 major tectonic plates. Their interactions give rise to processes that build mountains, cause earthquakes and volcanic eruptions, and otherwise influence the landscape.

point source A specific spot—such as a factory's smokestacks—where large quantities of pollutants are discharged. Compare *non-point source.*

polar cell One of a pair of cells of convective circulation between the poles and 60 degrees north and south latitudes that influence global climate patterns. Compare *Ferrel cell; Hadley cell.*

pollination An interaction in which one organism (for example, bees) transfers pollen (male sex cells) from one flower to the ova (female cells) of another, fertilizing the female flower, which subsequently grows into a fruit.

polluter-pays principle Principle in which the party that produces pollution pays the costs of cleaning up or mitigating the pollution.

pollution Any matter or energy released into the environment that causes undesirable impacts on the health and well-being of humans or other organisms. Pollution can be physical, chemical, or biological, and can affect water, air, or soil.

pollution prevention (P2) strategies Industrial strategies that aim to prevent pollution or mitigate pollution-generating processes beforehand, rather than having to clean up after the pollution has been generated.

population A group of organisms of the same species that live in the same area. Species are often composed of multiple populations.

population density The number of individuals within a population per unit area. Compare *population size*.

population dispersion See *population distribution*.

population distribution The spatial arrangement of organisms within a particular area. Also called *population dispersion*.

population growth rate An increase in the size of a population, or group of individuals of a particular species in a given location, in a given unit of time.

population pyramid A graph that represents the age cohorts and gender breakdown of a particular population at a given time.

population size The number of individual organisms present at a given time.

porosity The proportion of open pore space in a rock, sediment, or soil. Compare *permeability*.

positive feedback loop (or cycle) A feedback loop in which output of one type acts as input that moves the system in the same direction. The input and output drive the system further toward one extreme or another. Compare *negative feedback loop*.

potential energy Energy of position. Compare *kinetic energy*.

precautionary principle The idea that one should not undertake a new action until the ramifications of that action are well understood.

precipitation Water that condenses out of the atmosphere and falls to Earth in droplets or crystals.

predation The process in which one species (the predator) hunts, tracks, captures, and ultimately kills its prey.

predator An organism that hunts, captures, kills, and consumes individuals of another species, the prey.

prediction A specific statement, generally arising from a hypothesis, that can be tested directly and unequivocally.

prescribed (controlled) burns The practice of burning areas of forest or grassland under carefully controlled conditions to improve the health of ecosystems, return them to a more natural state, and help prevent uncontrolled catastrophic fires.

preservation ethic An ethical position, holding that we should protect the natural environment in a pristine, unaltered state. Compare *conservation ethic*.

pressure-state-response (PSR) model A framework for environmental monitoring and reporting, which considers activities and processes that cause pressure or stress on the environment, the resulting state or condition of the environment, and the effectiveness of human responses to the management of these stresses.

prey An organism that is killed and consumed by a predator.

primary consumer An organism that consumes producers and feeds at the second trophic level.

primary extraction The initial drilling and pumping of available crude oil. Compare *secondary extraction*.

primary forest Forest uncut by people. Compare *second-growth*.

primary pollutant A hazardous substance, such as soot or carbon monoxide, that is emitted into the troposphere in a form that is directly harmful. Compare *secondary pollutant*.

primary producer See *autotroph*.

primary succession A series of changes that theoretically would be expected to occur as an ecological community develops over time, beginning with a lifeless substrate. In terrestrial systems, primary succession begins when a bare expanse of rock, sand, or sediment becomes newly exposed to the atmosphere and pioneer species arrive. Compare *secondary succession*.

prior appropriation A concept of water law in which a user who can demonstrate a history of earlier use is entitled to have access to the resource.

prior informed consent The ethical and legal principle that consent or acceptance of an activity (such as land development or waste disposal) is not legally valid unless the consenting person or group has been properly and adequately informed and can be shown to have a reasonable understanding of all potential impacts before giving consent.

producer See *autotroph*.

productivity The rate at which plants convert solar energy (sunlight) to biomass. Ecosystems whose plants convert solar energy to biomass rapidly are said to have high productivity. See *gross primary production; net primary production*.

profundal zone In a water body, the volume of open water that sunlight does not reach. Compare *littoral zone; benthic zone; limnetic zone*.

protein A large molecule made up of long chains of amino acids.

proxy indicator Indirect evidence, such as pollen from sediment cores and air bubbles from ice cores, of the climate of the past.

quarry An open pit or hole from which rock, gravel, or other Earth materials are extracted.

radiative forcing The amount of change in energy that a given factor (such as aerosols, albedo, or greenhouse gases) exerts over Earth's energy balance. By convention, positive radiative forcing warms the surface, whereas negative radiative forcing cools it.

radiatively active gas Greenhouse gas. A gas in the atmosphere that is effective at absorbing infrared radiation.

radioactive The quality by which some isotopes decay, changing their chemical identity as they spontaneously shed atomic particles and emit high-energy radiation.

radioactive isotope (or radioisotope) An isotope that emits subatomic particles and high-energy radiation as it decays into progressively lighter isotopes until becoming stable.

radon A radioactive gas that occurs naturally in soil gas; can be hazardous when it accumulates as an indoor air pollutant.

rainforest A forest biome that is characterized by high annual rainfall and, in general, aseasonality.

rangeland Land used for grazing livestock.

reactive Materials that are chemically unstable and readily able to react with other compounds, often explosively or by producing noxious fumes. One criterion for defining hazardous waste.

realized niche The portion of the fundamental niche that is fully realized (used) by a species.

recharge zone An area where precipitation falls and infiltrates the ground, percolating downward to eventually join and replenish groundwater in an aquifer.

reclamation The process of remediating land degraded by mining, industrial pollution, desertification, or other damaging processes, to make it suitable once again for agriculture, habitation, or recreational use.

recycling The collection of materials that can be broken down and reprocessed to manufacture new items.

Red List A list of species facing unusually high risks of extinction. The list is maintained by the World Conservation Union (IUCN).

red tide A harmful algal bloom consisting of algae that produce reddish pigments that discolour surface waters.

refining Process of separating the molecules of the various hydrocarbons in crude oil into different-sized classes and transforming them into various fuels and other petrochemical products.

reforestation Planting or replanting of trees in a previously forested area from which the trees had been removed by logging, fire, or some other cause.

regulation A specific rule or set of criteria issued by an administrative agency, based on the more broadly written statutory law or act.

relative abundance The extent to which numbers of individuals of different species are equal or skewed. One way to express species diversity. See *evenness*; compare *species richness*.

relative humidity The ratio of the water vapour contained in a given volume of air to the maximum amount the air could contain, for a given temperature.

remote sensing The collection of information about a target, from a distance. Most commonly refers to the collection of information about the near-surface Earth environment by instruments carried on satellites.

renewable natural resource A natural resource that is virtually unlimited or that is replenished by the environment over relatively short periods of hours to weeks to years. Compare *nonrenewable natural resource*.

replacement fertility The total fertility rate (TFR) that maintains a stable population size.

reserve That portion of a resource that is known with a high degree of certainty, and is profitably extractable using present extraction and refining technologies.

reservoir A location where materials in a cycle remain for a period of time, before moving to another reservoir. Also called a *pool*. Compare *flux*.

residence time The amount of time a material in a cycle remains in a given pool or reservoir before moving to another reservoir. Compare *flux, turnover time*.

resilience The ability of an ecological community to change in response to disturbance but later return to its original state. Compare *resistance*.

resistance The ability of an ecological community to remain stable in the presence of a disturbance. Compare *resilience*.

resource management Strategic decision making about who should extract resources and in what ways, so that resources are used wisely and not wasted.

resource partitioning The process by which species adapt to competition by evolving to use slightly different resources, or to use their shared resources in different ways, thus minimizing interference with one another.

response The type or magnitude of negative effects an animal exhibits in response to a dose of toxicant in a dose-response test. Compare *dose*.

restoration ecology The study of the historical conditions of ecological communities as they existed before humans altered them. Compare *ecological restoration*.

R horizon The bottommost layer of soil in a typical soil profile. Also called *bedrock*. Compare *A horizon; B horizon; C horizon; O horizon*.

ribonucleic acid (RNA) (DNA) A nucleic acid molecule that is involved in protein synthesis and sometimes in the transmission of genetic information. Compare *deoxyribonucleic acid (DNA)*.

riparian Relating to a river or the area along a river.

risk The mathematical probability that some harmful outcome (for instance, injury, death, environmental damage, or economic loss) will result from a given action, event, or substance.

risk assessment The quantitative measurement of risk, together with the comparison of risks involved in different activities or substances.

risk management The process of considering information from scientific risk assessment in light of economic, social, and political needs and values, in order to make decisions and design strategies to minimize risk.

rock Durable Earth material made principally of minerals.

rock cycle The very slow process in which rocks and the minerals that make them up are heated, melted, cooled, broken, and reassembled, forming igneous, sedimentary, and metamorphic rocks.

round table An approach to decision making in which stakeholders with differing views meet, exchange ideas, and seek consensus. An example is the National Round Table on the Environment and the Economy (NRTEE).

r-selected (or **-strategist**) Term denoting a species with high biotic potential whose members produce a large number of offspring in a relatively short time but do not care for their young after birth. Populations of r-selected species are generally regulated by density-independent factors. Compare *K-selected*.

runoff The water from precipitation that flows into streams, rivers, lakes, and ponds, and (in many cases) eventually to the ocean.

run-of-river Any of several methods used to generate hydroelectric power without greatly disrupting the flow of river water. Run-of-river approaches eliminate much of the environmental impact of large dams. Compare *storage*.

salination (or **salinization**) The buildup of salts in surface soil layers.

salinity Saltiness; the concentration of dissolved salts in water.

salt marsh Flat land that is intermittently flooded by the ocean where the tide reaches inland. Salt marshes occur along temperate coastlines and are thickly vegetated with grasses, rushes, shrubs, and other herbaceous plants.

salvage logging The removal of dead trees following a natural disturbance. Although it may be economically beneficial, salvage logging can be ecologically destructive, because the dead trees provide food and shelter for a variety of insects and wildlife and because removing timber from recently burned land can cause severe erosion and damage to soil.

sand Sediment consisting of particles 0.005–2.0 mm in diameter. Compare *clay; silt*.

sanitary landfill A site at which solid waste is buried in the ground or piled up in large mounds for disposal, designed to prevent the waste from contaminating the environment. Compare *incineration; secure landfill*.

savannah A biome characterized by grassland interspersed with clusters of acacias and other trees. Savannah is found across parts of Africa (where it was the ancestral home of our species), South America, Australia, India, and other dry tropical regions.

science A systematic process for learning about the world and testing our understanding of it.

scientific method A formalized method for testing ideas with observations that involves several assumptions and a more or less consistent series of interrelated steps.

scrubber Technology used to chemically treat gases produced in combustion to remove hazardous components and neutralize acidic gases, such as sulphur dioxide and hydrochloric acid, turning them into water and salt, in order to reduce smokestack emissions.

secondary consumer An organism that consumes primary consumers and feeds at the third trophic level.

secondary extraction The extraction of crude oil remaining after primary extraction by using solvents or by flushing underground rocks with water or steam. Compare *primary extraction*.

secondary pollutant A hazardous substance produced through the reaction of substances added to the atmosphere with chemicals normally found in the atmosphere. Compare *primary pollutant*.

secondary production The total biomass that heterotrophs generate by consuming autotrophs. Compare *gross primary production; net primary production*.

secondary succession A series of changes that would theoretically be expected to occur as an ecological community develops over time, beginning when some event disrupts or dramatically alters an existing community. Compare *primary succession*.

second-growth Term describing trees that have sprouted and grown to partial maturity after virgin timber has been cut.

secure landfill A landfill that is especially engineered to receive and effectively isolate hazardous wastes. Compare *sanitary landfill*.

sediment Loose particles, mainly of weathered rock.

sedimentary rock One of the three main categories of rock. Formed when dissolved minerals seep through sediment layers and act as a kind of glue, crystallizing and binding sediment particles together. Sandstone and shale are examples of sedimentary rock. Compare *igneous rock; metamorphic rock*.

seed bank A storehouse for samples of the world's crop diversity.

selection systems (for forest harvesting) Timber harvesting approaches in which some trees are cut and others are selectively allowed to remain standing.

selective breeding See *artificial selection*.

septic system A wastewater disposal method, common in rural areas, consisting of an underground tank and series of drainpipes. Wastewater runs from the house to the tank, where solids precipitate out. The water proceeds downhill to a drain field of perforated pipes laid horizontally in gravel-filled trenches, where microbes decompose the remaining waste.

sequestration Isolation; very long-term storage in a *reservoir*.

services Something that is of economic value, but is not a tangible or material product; in economics, the intangible equivalent of goods.

sex ratio The ratio of males to females in a population.

shale gas Natural gas produced from shale. Compare *oil shale*.

shelterbelt A row of trees or other tall perennial plants that are planted along the edges of farm fields to break the wind and thereby minimize wind erosion.

shrubland An area of open woodland, characterized by low, bushy vegetation and occasional taller trees.

sick-building syndrome An illness produced by indoor air pollution of which the specific cause is not identifiable.

silt Sediment consisting of particles 0.002–0.005 mm in diameter. Compare *clay; sand*.

silviculture See *forestry*.

sink In a cycle, a reservoir that takes in more material that it releases. Compare *flux, source*.

sinkhole An area where the ground has given way with little warning as a result of subsidence caused by depletion of water from an aquifer.

SLOSS ("Single Large or Several Small") dilemma The debate over whether it is better to make reserves large in size and few in number or many in number but small in size.

smart growth A planning concept in which a community's growth is managed in ways that limit sprawl and maintain or improve residents' quality of life. It involves guiding the rate, placement, and style of development such that it serves the environment, the economy, and the community.

smelting The extraction of metals by heating and melting of ore.

smog See *industrial smog, photochemical smog.*

softwood Wood derived from coniferous or needle-bearing trees. Compare *hardwood.*

soil A complex plant-supporting system consisting of disintegrated rock, organic matter, air, water, nutrients, and microorganisms.

soil degradation Damage to soils (typically through loss of organic matter or moisture, or through chemical contamination), or loss of soils (typically through erosion).

soil profile The cross-section of a soil as a whole, from the surface to the bedrock.

soil structure A measure of the organization or "clumpiness" of soil.

soil texture A characteristic of soil, which is determined by the relative proportions of clay, sand, and silt particles.

solar energy Energy from the sun. It is perpetually renewable and may be harnessed in several ways.

solar panels Panels generally consisting of dark-coloured, heat-absorbing metal plates mounted in flat boxes covered with glass panes, often installed on rooftops to harness solar energy. Also called *flat-plate solar collectors.*

solution A chemical mixture; most often used in reference to liquids, it can also be applied to solid and gaseous mixtures.

source In a cycle, a reservoir that releases more material than it takes in. Compare *sink; flux.*

source reduction The reduction of the amount of material that enters the waste stream to avoid the costs of disposal and recycling, help conserve resources, minimize pollution, and save money for consumers and businesses.

specialist A species that can survive only in a narrow range of habitats that contain very specific resources. Compare *generalist.*

speciation The process by which new species are generated.

species A population or group of populations of a particular type of organism, whose members share certain characteristics and can breed freely with one another and produce fertile offspring. Different biologists may have different approaches to diagnosing species boundaries.

Species at Risk Act (SARA) Canada's endangered species protection law, enacted in 2002.

species diversity The number and variety of species in the world or in a particular region.

species richness The number of species in a particular region. One way to express species diversity. Compare *evenness; relative abundance.*

sprawl The unrestrained spread of urban or suburban development outward from a city centre and across the landscape.

stabilizing selection Mode of natural selection in which selection produces intermediate traits, in essence preserving the status quo. Compare *directional selection; disruptive selection.*

stable isotope A non-radioactive form of an element.

stable isotope geochemistry The study of the behaviour of isotopes that are not radioactive. Stable isotopes can act as tracers to help scientists unravel the effects of past environmental processes.

stakeholder A party (an individual or organization) that has a specific interest or stake in a proceeding. Stakeholders have specific, legally defined rights and responsibilities in processes such as environmental impact assessments.

state-of-the-environment reporting (SOER) Monitoring and analysis of the conditions of the environment and periodic reporting on the results of the monitoring, usually undertaken by agencies at various levels of government.

steady state A state of dynamic equilibrium or balance in which there is no net change in the system. Compare *homeostasis.*

stock The harvestable portion of a resource.

storm surge A temporary and localized rise in sea level and associated large waves, brought on by the high tides, low atmospheric pressure, and winds associated with storms.

stratosphere The layer of the atmosphere above the troposphere and below the mesosphere; it extends from 11 km to 50 km above sea level.

strip-mining The use of heavy machinery to remove huge amounts of earth to expose coal or ore minerals, which are mined out directly. Compare *subsurface mining.*

subduction The plate tectonic process by which a tectonic plate carrying dense oceanic crust slides beneath a plate carrying lighter continental crust at a convergent plate boundary.

subsistence agriculture The oldest form of traditional agriculture, in which farming families produce only enough food for themselves.

subsurface mining Method of mining underground coal deposits, in which shafts are dug deeply into the ground and networks of tunnels are dug or blasted out to follow coal seams. Compare *strip-mining.*

suburb A smaller community that fringes a city; areas peripheral to and strongly influenced by a city.

succession A stereotypical series of changes in the composition and structure of an ecological community through time. See *primary succession; secondary succession.*

sulphur dioxide (SO$_2$) A criteria air contaminant and a common by-product of the burning of fossil fuels; sometimes grouped with other sulphur oxides as "SOx" or "SOX".

surface impoundment A hazardous waste disposal method in which a shallow depression is dug and lined with impervious material, such as clay. Water containing small amounts of hazardous waste is placed in the pond and allowed to evaporate, leaving a residue of solid hazardous waste on the bottom. Compare *deep-well injection.*

survivorship curve A graph that shows how the likelihood of death for members of a population varies with age.

sustainability A guiding principle of environmental science that requires us to live in such a way as to maintain Earth's systems and its natural resources for the foreseeable future.

sustainable agriculture Agriculture that does not deplete soils faster than they form.

sustainable development Development that satisfies our current needs without compromising the future availability of natural resources or our future quality of life.

sustainable forestry certification A form of ecolabelling that identifies timber products that have been produced using sustainable methods. Several organizations issue such certification.

swamp A type of wetland consisting of shallow water rich with vegetation, occurring in a forested area. Compare *bog; marsh.*

symbiosis A parasitic or mutualistic relationship between different species of organisms that live in close physical proximity.

synergistic effect An interactive effect (for example, of toxicants) that is more than or different from the simple sum of their constituent effects.

system A network of relationships among a group of parts, elements, or components that interact with and influence one another through the exchange of energy, matter, and/or information.

taiga The northern boreal forest biome.

tailings Residual materials that remain after processing of ore. Tailings, which are commonly stored at minesites, often consist of crushed waste rock contaminated with chemicals used in ore processing.

Talloires Declaration A document composed in Talloires, France, in 1990 that commits university leaders to pursue sustainability on their campuses. It has been signed by over 300 university presidents and chancellors from more than 40 nations.

tar sands See *oil sands.*

temperate deciduous forest A biome consisting of midlatitude forests characterized by broad-leafed trees that lose their leaves each fall and remain dormant during winter. These forests occur in areas where precipitation is spread relatively evenly throughout the year: much of Europe, eastern China, and eastern North America.

temperate forest A forest biome in a temperate climate zone, that is, a seasonal climate.

temperate grassland A biome whose vegetation is dominated by grasses and features more extreme temperature differences between winter and summer, and less precipitation than temperate deciduous forests; also known as steppe or prairie.

temperate rainforest A biome consisting of tall coniferous trees, cooler and less species-rich than tropical rainforest and milder and wetter than temperate deciduous forest.

temperature inversion See *thermal inversion*.

teratogen A toxicant that causes harm to the unborn, resulting in birth defects.

theory A widely accepted, well-tested explanation of one or more cause-and-effect relationships that has been extensively validated by a great amount of research. Compare *hypothesis*.

thermal inversion A departure from the normal temperature distribution in the atmosphere, in which a pocket of relatively cold air occurs near the ground, with warmer air above it. The cold air, denser than the air above it, traps pollutants near the ground and causes a buildup of smog. Compare *temperature inversion*.

thermal pollution Heat or heated water released into the environment, which can damage natural ecosystems.

thermocline A zone of the ocean (or large lake) beneath the surface in which temperature decreases rapidly with depth.

thermohaline circulation A worldwide system of ocean currents in which warmer, fresher water moves along the surface and colder, saltier water (which is more dense) moves deep beneath the surface.

thermosphere The atmosphere's top layer, extending upward to an altitude of 500 km.

threatened Categorization of a species at risk; this category encompasses both vulnerable and endangered species.

threshold dose The dose at which a toxicant begins to affect a population of test animals. Compare ED_{50}; LD_{50}.

tidal energy Energy harnessed by erecting a dam across the outlet of a tidal basin. Water flowing with the incoming or outgoing tide through sluices in the dam turns turbines to generate electricity.

tide The periodic rise and fall of the ocean's height at a given location, caused by the gravitational pull of the Moon and Sun.

topsoil That portion of the soil that is most nutritive for plants and is thus of the most direct importance to ecosystems and to agriculture. Also known as the *A horizon*.

total fertility rate (TFR) The average number of children born per female member of a population during her lifetime.

toxic Materials that are poisonous; able to harm health of people or other organisms when a substance is inhaled, ingested, or touched. One criterion for defining hazardous waste. Compare *toxicant*.

toxic air pollutant Air pollutant that is known to cause cancer, reproductive defects, or neurological, developmental, immune system, or respiratory problems in humans, and/or to cause substantial ecological harm by affecting the health of nonhuman animals and plants.

toxicant (toxin or toxic agent) A substance that acts as a poison to humans or wildlife.

toxicity The degree of harm a chemical substance can inflict.

toxicology The scientific field that examines the effects of poisonous chemicals and other agents on humans and other organisms.

toxin See *toxicant*.

trade winds Prevailing winds between the equator and 30 degrees latitude that blow from east to west.

traditional agriculture Biologically powered agriculture, in which human and animal muscle power, along with hand tools and simple machines, perform the work of cultivating, harvesting, storing, and distributing crops. Compare *industrialized agriculture*.

traditional ecological knowledge (TEK) Indigenous ecological knowledge. The intimate knowledge of a particular environment, possessed and passed along by those who have inhabited an area for many generations, typically via an oral tradition of teachings, songs, and storytelling.

tragedy of the commons The scenario in which each individual withdraws whatever benefits are available from an unregulated or poorly regulated common property resource, as quickly as possible, until the resource becomes overused and depleted.

transform plate boundary A boundary along which two tectonic plates are moving past one another in a translational sense. For example, the Pacific Plate and the North American Plate are slipping and grinding past each other along California's San Andreas Fault.

transgenic Term describing an organism that contains DNA from another species.

transpiration The release of water vapour by plants through their leaves.

trawling Fishing method that entails dragging immense cone-shaped nets through the water, with weights at the bottom and floats at the top to keep the nets open.

tributary A smaller river that flows into a larger one.

triple bottom line An approach to sustainability that attempts to meet environmental, economic, and social goals simultaneously.

trophic level Rank in the feeding hierarchy of a food chain. Organisms at higher trophic levels consume those at lower trophic levels.

trophic pyramid A diagram showing the trophic levels in a food chain from bottom to top, with the autotrophs at the bottom, moving up through the various levels of consumers. The diagram is typically pyramid-shaped because biomass, energy, and numbers of individuals decrease upward through the trophic levels.

tropical dry forest A biome that consists of deciduous trees and occurs at tropical and subtropical latitudes where wet and dry seasons each span about half the year. Widespread in India, Africa, South America, and northern Australia.

tropical forest A forest located in a low-latitude region with a tropical climate.

tropical rainforest A biome characterized by year-round rain and uniformly warm temperatures. Found in Central America, South America, Southeast Asia, West Africa, and other tropical regions. Tropical rainforests have dark, damp interiors; lush vegetation; and highly diverse biotic communities.

troposphere The bottommost layer of the atmosphere; it extends to 11 km above sea level. See also *stratosphere*.

tropospheric ozone Ground level ozone, an air pollutant and a component of smog.

tsunami A wave or series of waves produced by the vertical displacement of a large volume of water; also called seismic sea wave. Tsunamis differ from normal waves in their large amplitude, very long wavelength, high velocity of propagation, and potentially large onshore run-up heights.

tundra A biome that is nearly as dry as desert but is located at very high latitudes along the northern edges of Russia, Canada, and Scandinavia. Extremely cold winters with little daylight and moderately cool summers with lengthy days characterize this landscape of lichens and low, scrubby vegetation.

turbine A rotary device that converts the kinetic energy of a moving substance, such as steam, into mechanical energy. Used widely in commercial power generation from various types of energy sources.

turnover time The time it would take for a material to work its way through and out of a reservoir, if all of the sources or fluxes of that material into the reservoir were stopped. Compare *residence time*.

unconfined aquifer A water-bearing, porous layer of rock, sand, or gravel that lies atop a less-permeable substrate. The water in an unconfined aquifer is not under pressure because there is no impermeable upper layer to confine it. Compare *confined aquifer*.

understory (of a forest) The floor and the lowest levels of growth within a forest.

uneven-aged Term describing stands of trees in timber plantations that are of different ages. Uneven-aged stands more closely approximate a natural forest than do even-aged stands.

United Nations Environment Programme (UNEP) The department of the United Nations, headquartered in Nairobi, Kenya, established after the Conference on the Human Environment in 1972 to deal with international environmental concerns and encourage nations to adopt environmentally sound approaches to development. One of several agencies within the United Nations that influence international environmental policy and practice.

upwelling In the ocean, the flow of cold, deep water toward the surface. Upwelling occurs in areas where surface currents diverge. Compare *downwelling*.

urban ecology A scientific field that views cities explicitly as ecosystems. Researchers in this field seek to apply the fundamentals of ecosystem ecology and systems science to urban areas.

urban growth boundary (UGB) In planning, a geographical boundary intended to separate areas desired to be urban from areas desired to remain rural. Development for housing, commerce, and industry are encouraged within urban growth boundaries, but beyond them such development is severely restricted. Compare *greenbelt*.

urban heat island effect A phenomenon in which cities are generally several degrees warmer than surrounding suburbs and rural areas, due to tall buildings that interfere with convective cooling, paved surfaces that absorb heat, and concentrated activities that generate waste heat. The urban heat island effect can contribute to the development of dust domes.

urbanization The shift from rural to city and suburban living.

utilitarian principle The principle that something is right when it produces the greatest practical benefits for the most people.

valuation The attempt to quantify the value of a particular environmental good or service—even if it cannot easily be expressed in monetary terms.

variable In an experiment, a condition that can change.

vector An organism that transfers a pathogen to its host. An example is a mosquito that transfers the malaria pathogen to humans.

volcano A vent through which lava, ash, and other volcanic materials are extruded to the surface.

volatile organic compound (VOC) One of a large group of potentially harmful organic chemicals used in industrial processes.

vulnerable Categorization of a species that is likely to become endangered unless there is improvement in the circumstances threatening its survival or reproduction. Compare *endangered; threatened*.

warm front The boundary where a mass of warm air displaces a mass of colder air. Compare *cold front*.

waste Any unwanted product that results from a human activity or process.

waste exchange A system whereby producers of waste materials are matched with organizations in need of the same materials as inputs into other industrial processes.

waste management Strategic decision making to minimize the amount of waste generated and to dispose of waste safely and effectively.

waste stream The flow of waste as it moves from its sources toward disposal destinations.

waste-to-energy (WTE) facility An incinerator that uses heat from its furnace to boil water to create steam that drives electricity generation or fuels heating systems.

waste water Any water that is used in households, businesses, industries, or public facilities and is drained or flushed down pipes, as well as the polluted runoff from streets and storm drains.

waterlogging The saturation of soil by water, in which the water table is raised to the point that water bathes plant roots. Waterlogging deprives roots of access to gases, essentially suffocating them and eventually damaging or killing the plants.

water quality The suitability of water for various purposes (such as drinking or swimming), as determined by comparing the water's physical, chemical, and biological characteristics with a set of predetermined standards.

watershed The entire area of land from which water drains into a given river.

water table The upper limit of groundwater held in an aquifer.

wave energy Energy harnessed from the motion of wind-driven waves at the ocean's surface. Many designs for machinery to harness wave energy have been invented, but few have been adequately tested.

weather The local physical properties of the troposphere, such as temperature, pressure, humidity, cloudiness, and wind, over relatively short time periods. Compare *climate*.

weathering The physical, chemical, and biological processes that break down rocks and minerals, turning large particles into smaller particles.

weed A plant that competes with crops. The term is defined by economic interest and is not biologically meaningful. Compare *pest*.

wetland A system that combines elements of fresh water and dry land. These biologically productive systems include freshwater marshes, swamps, and bogs.

wildlife refuge An area set aside to serve as a haven for wildlife and also sometimes to encourage hunting, fishing, wildlife observation, photography, environmental education, and other public uses.

wind energy Energy (power) derived from wind.

wind farm A development involving a large group of wind turbines.

wind turbine A mechanical assembly that converts the wind's kinetic energy, or energy of motion, into electrical energy.

woodland Land that is covered with woody vegetation, including trees and shrubs. Compare *forest*.

zoning The practice of classifying areas for different types of development and land use.

zooplankton Very small or microscopic floating animals. Compare *plankton; phytoplankton*.

Credits

Text

Chapter 1 Page 20: Figure 1.10 Data are for 2005 from Global Footprint Network, 2008.; **p. 21:** Table 1.1 (top right) Adapted from Millennium Ecosystem Assessment, 2005. *Ecosystems and human well-being: biodiversity synthesis.* World Resources Institute. Washington, DC. Used with permission.; **p. 25:** Reprinted by permission of David Suzuki.

Chapter 2 Page 31: An excerpt from "Central Case: The Unusual Microbialites of Pavilion Lake" by Darlene Lim & Bernard Laval. Pavillion Lake Research Project: Relevance to Astrobiology and Space Exploration. http://supercritical.civil.ubc.ca/~pavilion/information/relevance.htm © Lim & Laval. Reprinted by permission of the authors.; **p. 33:** Figure 2.1 (bottom left) U.S. Department of Commerce/National Oceanic and Atmospheric Administration/Illustration by Kate Sweeney and Mary Baker; **p. 35:** Source: Leonard I. Wassenaar and Keith A. Hobson, *Natal origins of migratory monarch butterflies at wintering colonies in Mexico: New isotopic evidence* PNAS 1998 95(26) 15436-15439 Fig 3; doi:10.1073/pnas.95.26.15436. Copyright 1998 National Academy of Sciences, USA; **p. 53:** Reprinted by permission of Praveen Saxena; **p. 57:** Data from Lombi, E., et al. 2001. Phytoremediation of heavy metal-contaminated soils: natural hyperaccumulation versus chemically enhanced phytoextraction. *Journal of Environmental Quality* 30(6): 1919–1926.

Chapter 3 Page 67: Figure 3.6a (top) Data in a) Whittaker, R. H. 1975. Communities and ecosystems, 2nd ed. New York: MacMillan., **p. 67:** Figure 3.6b (middle) Map in (b) from satellite data presented by Field, C. D., et al. 1998. Primary production of the biosphere: Integrating terrestrial and oceanic components. *Science* 281: 237–240. DOI:10.1126/science.281.5374.237. Reprinted with permission from AAAS.; **p. 75:** Figure 3.13 Source: Data from Schlesinger, W.H. 1997. *Biogeochemistry: An analysis of global change,* 2nd ed. London: Academic Press. Copyright © 1997, with permission from Elsevier.; **p. 76:** Figure 3.14 Source: Data from Schlesinger, W.H. 1997. *Biogeochemistry: An analysis of global change, 2nd ed.* London: Academic Press. Copyright © 1997, with permission from Elsevier.; **p. 78:** Figure 3.15 (top) Source: Data from Schlesinger, W.H. 1997. *Biogeochemistry: An analysis of global change, 2nd ed.* London: Academic Press. Copyright © 1997, with permission from Elsevier.; **p. 81:** (top) Data from Dr. Nancy Rabalais, LUMCON; **p. 81:** (bottom) Data from Dr. Nancy Rabalais, LUMCON; **p. 83:** Figure 3.18 Source: Data from Schlesinger, W. H. 1997. *Biogeochemistry: An analysis of global change, 2nd ed.* London: Academic Press.); **p. 84:** Reprinted by permission of Robert Bateman.; **p. 86:** Table from *Beluga Whale Population of the Estuary, 2nd ed.* (2009) by Lena Measures, Jean-François Gosselin, and Michel Lebeuf. Table 1. Cat. No. Fs124-7/2009E-PDF. Reproduced with the permission of the Minister of Public Works and Government Services Canada, 2012.; **p. 87:** (left middle) Source: Graph from *Beluga Whale Population of the Estuary, 2nd ed.* (2009) by Lena Measures, Jean-François Gosselin, and Michel Lebeuf. Figure 6. Cat. No. Fs124-7/2009E-PDF. Reproduced with the permission of the Minister of Public Works and Government Services Canada, 2012.; **p. 87:** (bottom right) Source: Pie chart based on studies of 148 whale carcasses; from *Beluga Whale Population of the Estuary, 2nd ed.* (2009) by Lena Measures, Jean-François Gosselin, and Michel Lebeuf. Figure 5. Cat. No. Fs124-7/2009E-PDF. Reproduced with the permission of the Minister of Public Works and Government Services Canada, 2012.

Chapter 4 Page 109: Figure 4.14 (top left) Source: Data from Bennett, K. D. 1983. Postglacial population expansion of forest trees in Norfolk, U.K.
Nature 303: 164–167 (12 May 1983); doi:10.1038/303164a0.; **p. 110:** Figure 4.17a (top left) Source: Data from Pearl, R. 1927. The growth of populations. *The Quarterly Review of Biology* Vol. 2, No. 4 (Dec., 1927), pp. 532–548. Copyright © 1927, The University of Chicago Press.; **p. 110:** Figure 4.17b (bottom left) Source: Data from Huffaker, C.B. 1958. Experimental studies on predation: Dispersion factors and predator-prey oscillations, *Hilgardia* 27(14): 343–383. Fig. 7. (b); **p. 110:** Figure 4.17c (top right) Source: Data from Utida, S. 1967. Damped oscillation of population density at equilibrium, *Researches on Population Ecology* 9(1): 1–9. DOI: 10.1007/BF02521392, (c).; **p. 110:** Figure 4.17d (bottom right) Source: Data from Scheffer, V. C. 1951. Rise and fall of a reindeer herd, *Scientific Monthly* 73: 356–362, (d).; **p. 113:** Adapted from Lips, K.R., et al., 2008. Riding the wave: Reconciling the roles of disease and climate change in amphibian declines. *PLoS Biol* 6(3): 441–454. doi:10.1371/journal.pbio.0060072; **p. 114:** Reprinted by permission of Maydianne Andrade.; **p. 117:** Source: Data from Kiesecker, J. M., et al. 2001. Complex causes of amphibian population declines. *Nature* 410: 681–684 (5 April 2001). doi:10.1038/35070552.

Chapter 5 Page 123: Figure 5.4 (top left) Data from MacInich, D. A. 1937 *Fluctuation in the numbers of varying hare (Lepus americanus).* University of Toronto Studies in Biololgy Ser. No. 43. Toronto: University of Toronto Press.; **p. 133:** Source: Estes, J., et al. 1998. Killer whale predation on sea otters linking oceanic and nearshore ecosystems. *Science* 282(5388): 473-476. DOI. 10.1126/science.282.5388.473. Reprinted with permission from AAAS.; **p. 134:** Figure 5.14b (bottom) Source for (b): Benson, A. J. 2011. USGS. Zebra mussel sightings distribution. Retrieved 7/31/2011 from http://nas.er.usgs.gov/taxgroup/mollusks/zebramussel/zebramussel distribution.aspx. Benson, A. J. 2011. Quagga mussel sightings distribution. Retrieved 1/18/2012 from http://nas.er.usgs.gov/taxgroup/mollusks/zebramussel/quaggamusseldistribution.aspx; **p. 146:** Reprinted by permission of Sable Island Green Horse Society; **p. 149:** Data from Wilmers, C.C., and W.M. Getz. 2005. Gray wolves as climate change buffers in Yellowstone. *PLoS Biology* 3(4):e92. doi:10.1371/journal.pbio.0030092.

Chapter 6 Page 155: Figure 6.2 Data from U.S. Bureau of Census; **p. 156:** Figure 6.3 Data from Population Reference Bureau, 2010. *2010 World population data sheet,* By permission.; **p. 158:** Helmut Haberl; **p. 158:** Data from Haberl, H., et al., 2007. Quantifying and mapping the human appropriation of net primary production in Earth's terrestrial ecosystems. *Proc. Natl. Acad. Sci.* 104:12942-12947.; **p. 159:** Data from Haberl, H., et al., 2007. Quantifying and mapping the human appropriation of net primary production in Earth's terrestrial ecosystems. *Proc. Natl. Acad. Sci.* 104:12942-12947, Fig 1b. © 2007 National Acadamy of Sciences, USA. By permission.; **p. 160:** Figure 6.5a (top) Data from Meadows, D., et al. 2004. *Limits to Growth: The 30-year Update.* White River Junction, VT: Chelsea Green Publishing.; **p. 160:** Figure 6.5b (bottom) Data from Meadows, D., et al. 2004. *Limits to Growth: The 30-year Update.* White River Junction, VT: Chelsea Green Publishing.; **p. 161:** Figure 6.6 Data from Goudies, A. 2000. *The Human Impact.* Cambridge, MA: MIT Press.; **p. 162:** Figure 6.7 (bottom left) Data are projected for mid-2011, based on Population Reference Bureau, 2010. *2010 World population data sheet.*; **p. 162:** Figure 6.8 (top right) Adapted by permission from Population Division of the Department of Economic and Social Affairs of the United Nations Secretariat, 2009. *World population prospects: The 2008 revision,* http://esa.un.org/unpp, Fig 1. © United Nations, 2009; **p. 163:** Figure 6.9 Data are for 2000, from the Center for International Earth Science Information Network (CIESIN), Columbia University; and Centro International de Agricultura Tropical (CIAT). 2005 Gridded Population of the World Version 3 (GPWv3). Palisades, NY: Socioeconomic Data and Applications Center (SEDAC), Columbia

University.; **p. 164:** Figure 6.11 (bottom) Data from United Nations, Department of Economic and Social Affairs of the Secretariat, 2009. *World population prospects: The 2010 revision,* http://esa.un.org/unpd/wpp/index.htm © United Nations, 2010; **p. 165:** Figure 6.12 Data from United Nations, Department of Economic and Social Affairs, Population Division: *World Population Aging,* 2009.; **p. 167:** Figure 6.14 (left) Data from United Nations, Department of Economic and Social Affairs, 2009. *World population prospects: The 2010 revision,* http://esa.un.org/unpd/wpp/index.htm © United Nations, 2010; **p. 167:** Table 6.1 (right) Data from Population Reference Bureau, 2010. *2010 World population data sheet,* By permission.; **p. 168:** Figure 6.15 Data from Kent, M.M, and K.A. Crews. 1990. *World Population: Fundamentals of Growth.* Washington, DC: Population Reference Bureau.; **p. 169:** Figure 6.16 Data from McDonald, M., and D. Nierenberg. 2003. *Linking population, women, and biodiversity. State of the World 2003.* Washington, DC: Worldwatch Institute; **p. 170:** Figure 6.17 Data from Harrison, P. and F. Pearce, 2000. AAAS. *Atlas of population and environment,* edited by the American Association for the Advancement of Science, © 2000 by the American Association for the Advancement of Science. Used by permission of the publisher, University of California Press.; **p. 171:** Figure 6.18 Source: CIA World Fact Book (www.cia.gov); **p. 172:** Figure 6.20 Adapted from WWF International. 2008. *Living Planet Report 2008.* Published in October 2008 by WWF-World Wide Fund for Nature. © 2008 WWF. (panda.org). Zoological Society of London, and Global Footprint Network.; **p. 173:** Figure 6.22 Data from UNAIDS and WHO, 2009. *AIDS epidemic update 2009,* Geneva, Switzerland; **p. 174:** Table 6.2 Source: United Nations. End poverty 2015: Millennium Development Goals. © United Nations. Reproduced with permission.; **p. 175:** Reprinted by permission of William Rees.; **p. 177:** Data from Population Reference Bureau, 2006. *World Population Data Sheet 2006.*

Chapter 7 Page 180: Based on information from Environment Canada, *Clean Air Online,* http://www.ec.gc.ca/cleanair-airpur/Pollutants-WSBCC0B44A-1_En.htm; Centers for Disease Control, Agency for Toxic Substances and Disease Registry, Division of Toxicology ToxFAQs, September 2002, http://www.atsdr.cdc.gov/tfacts35.pdf; & UNEP, *Phasing Lead Out of Gasoline: An Examination of Policy Approaches in Different Countries,* 1999.; **p. 186:** Table 7.2 Source: Table based on Soil Classification Working Group. 1998. *The Canadian System of Soil Classification, 3rd ed.* Ottawa: Agriculture and Agri-Food Canada. Publication 1646, 187 pp. (available online through the National Land and Water Information Service, http://sis2.agr.gc.ca/cansis/taxa/cssc3/index.html).; **p. 190:** Figure 7.9 Data from United Nations Environment Programme (UNEP). 2002. *Global environmental outlook 3.* London: UNEP and Earthscan Publications Limited.; **p. 191:** Figure 7.10a Data from United Nations Environment Programme (UNEP). 2002. *Global environmental outlook 3.* London: UNEP and Earthscan Publications Limited.; **p. 193:** Table 7.3a Source: Table based on material from University of BC, *SoilWeb,* www.landfood.ubc.ca/soil200/soil_mgmt/soil_erosion.htm.; **p. 203:** Johannes Lehmann. 2007. Bio-energy in the black. *Frontiers in Ecology and the Environment* 5: 381–387. Fig. 1. p.382.doi:http://dx.doi.org/10.1890/1540-9295(2007)5[381:BITB]2.0.CO;2; **p. 205:** Reprinted by permission of Myrna Simpson.; **p. 209:** (top) Source: Janzen, H.H. (2004), Carbon cycling in earth systems—a soil science perspective. *Agriculture, Ecosystems and Environment* 104, 399-417, Fig. 2, plotted from values in Goldewijk, K.K. (2001), Estimating global land use change over the past 300 years: the HYDE database. Global Biogeochem. *Cycles* 15 (2), 417-433. Copyright 2004, with permission from Elsevier.; **p. 209:** (bottom) Based on information in Table 1 from Janzen, H.H. (2004), Carbon cycling in earth systems—a soil science perspective. Agriculture, Ecosystems and Environment 104, 399-417.

Chapter 8 Page 215: Figure 8.1 Data from Syntheses in Diamond, J., 1997. *Guns, germs, and steel.* New York: W.W. Norton; and Goudie, A. 2000. *The human impact, 5th ed.* Cambridge, MA: MIT Press.; **p. 216:** Figure 8.3 (bottom right) Data from U.N. Food and Agriculture Organization (FAO); **p. 222:** Table 8.1 *Appendix 3.2 Description of Major Groups of Chemical Pesticides* from http://www2.parl.gc.ca/HousePublications/Publication.aspx?DocID=1031697&Language=E&Mode+1&Parl=36&Ses=2&File=508. This table is excerpted from information available in the Government of Canada report *Pesticides: Making the Right Choice for*

Health and the Environment. Report of the Standing Committee on Environment and Sustainable Development, 2000. http://cmte.parl.gc.ca/cmte/CommitteePublication.aspx?COM=173&Lang=1&SourceId=36396.; **p. 229:** Figure 8.16 Data from International Service for the Acquisition of Agri-Biotech Application (ISAAA), 2004.; **p. 233:** Figure 8.19 Data from Food and Agriculture Organization of the United Nations.; **p. 235:** Figure 8.21 (left) Data from Smil, V. 2001. *Feeding the World: A Challenge for the Twenty-First Century.* Cambridge, MA: MIT Press.; **p. 235:** Figure 8.22 (right) Data from Smil, V. 2001. *Feeding the World: A Challenge for the Twenty-First Century.* Cambridge, MA: MIT Press.; **p. 236:** Figure 8.23 FAO. 2004. *The State of World Fisheries and Aquaculture.* Rome, Italy: Jay Withgott.; **p. 237:** Table 8.2 Source: Modified from Shaxson T.F. 1999. *The Roots of Sustainability Concepts and Practice: Zero tillage in Brazil – Contribution to "ENABLE"* – Newsletter to ABLH Nairobi Kenya and to the World Association for Soil and Water Conservation (WASWC) Newsletter; **p. 239:** Data from Liebig, M. A., and J. W. Doran, 1999. Impact of organic production practices on soil quality indicators, *Journal of Environmental Quality* 28(5): 1601–1609.; **p. 241:** Reprinted by permission Alisa Smith and J.B. MacKinnon.; **p. 241:** Excerpts from *The 100 Mile Diet* Website & Blog by Alisa Smith & J.B. MacKinnon. © 2006 Alisa Smith & J.B. MacKinnon. Reprinted by permission of the authors.; **p. 244:** Data from Food and Agriculture Organization of the United Nations.

Chapter 9 Page 248: Data from U.S. National Snow and Ice Data Center, Fig. 3, "Average monthly Arctic Sea Ice Extent - February 1979 to 2011". http://nsidc.org/arcticseaicenews/2011/030211.html, accessed 18 December 2011.; **p. 253:** Figure 9.4 Data from Groombridge, B., and M. D. Jenkins. 2002. *Global biodiversity: Earth's living resources in the 21st century.* UNEP-World Conservation Monitoring Centre. Cambridge, U.K.: Hoechst Foundation.; **p. 254:** Figure 9.5 Data from Groombridge, B., and M.D. Jenkins. 2002. *Global biodiversity: Earth's living resources in the 21st century.* UNEP-World Conservation Monitoring Centre. Cambridge, U.K.: Hoechst Foundation.; **p. 255:** Figure 9.6 Adapted from Cook, R. E. 1969. Variation in species density in North American birds. *Systematic Zoology* 18 (1): 63-84. doi:10.1093/sysbio/18.1.63; **p. 257:** Figure 9.8 Data from Raup, D. M., and J. J. Sepkoski. 1982. Mass extinctions in the marine fossil record. *Science* 215(4539): 1501–1503. Reprinted with permission from AAAS and the author.; **p. 259:** Figure 9.10 Adapted from Barnosky, A. D., et al. 2004. Assessing the causes of late Pleistocene extinctions on the continents. *Science* 306(5693): 70–75. DOI: 10.1126/science.1101476; and Wilson, E. O. 1992. *The diversity of life.* Cambridge, MA: Belknap Press.; **p. 260:** Figure 9.11 Source: Barnosky, et al., "Has the Earth's Sixth Mass Extinction Already Arrived?" *Nature* 71, 51-57. Fig. 2. doi:10.1038/nature09678; **p. 261:** Figure 9.12 Graphic from p. 20 of the *2010 Living Planet Report* © Text and graphics: 2010 WWF.; **p. 265:** Data from International Union for Conservation of Nature (IUCN), 2008. Global Amphibian Assessment.; **p. 267:** Figure 9.15 (left) Adapted from Wilson, E. O. 1992. *The diversity of life.* Cambridge, MA: Belknap Press.; **p. 267:** Figure 9.16 (right) Adapted from Wilson, E. O. 1992. *The diversity of life.* Cambridge, MA: Belknap Press.; **p. 272:** Figure 9.22 (bottom) Data from MacArthur, R. H., and E. O. Wilson. 1967. *The theory of island biogeography.* Princeton University Press.; **p. 277:** Figure 9.23 Data from Conservation International, 2008.; **p. 281:** Copyright Orangutan Foundation International.; **p. 284:** Data from Hole, D., et al. 2005. Does organic farming benefit biodiversity? *Biological Conservation* 122(1): 113–130. Table 1, p. 122. doi:10.1016/j.biocon.2004.07.018. Copyright 2005, with permission from Elsevier.

Chapter 10 Page 289: Figure 10.1 Data from U.N. Food and Agriculture Organization (FAO), 2005, *Global Forest Resources Assessment 2005* (with updated information from *Global Forest Resources Assessment 2010*).; **p. 293:** Excerpts from *National Forest Strategy 2003-2008. A Sustainable Forest: The Canadian Commitment,* National Forest Strategy Coalition, http://nfsc.ca/strategies/strategy5.html. © 2008 Canadian Council of Forest Ministers. Reprinted by permission of the Canadian Council of Forest Ministers.; **p. 297:** Figure 10.9 Data from U.N. Food and Agriculture Organization (FAO) *Global Forest Resources Assessment 2010, Key Findings,* p. 10.; **p. 301:** Figure 10.14a (top) Canada's Forest Inventory 2001. 2006. Power, K.; Gillis, M.D. Natural Resources Canada, Canadian Forest Service, Pacific Forestry Centre, Victoria BC. *Information Report.* Fig. 10,

p. 16. Cat. No.: BC-X-408E.; **p. 302:** *Changing Climate Stops Pest Outbreaks on Vancouver Island*, http://cfs.nrcan.gc.ca/news/585, Natural Resources Canada, Canadian Forest Service. Reproduced with the permission of the Minister of Public Works and Government Services, 2011.; **p. 304:** Figure 10.16 Data from U.N. Food and Agriculture Organization, *Global Forest Resources Assessment, 2010.*; **p. 307:** Data from U.N. Food and Agriculture Organization (FAO), 2005. *Global Forest Resources Assessment.*; **p. 311:** Reprinted by permission of Tzeporah Berman.; **p. 314:** Data from the Food and Agriculture Organization of the United Nations.

Chapter 11 Page 329: Figure 11.10 Data are for 2009 from U.S. Geological Survey, 2010. *Mineral Commodity Summaries 2010.* USGS, Washington, D.C.; **p. 331:** Adapted with kind permission from Springer Science and Business Media from Tabak, H.H., et al., 2003. Advances in biotreatment of acid mine drainage and biorecovery of metals: 1. Metal precipitation for recovery and recycle. *Biodegradation* 14(6): 423–436. DOI: 10.1023/A:1027332902740; **p. 333:** Table 11.1 Data are for 2005 from U.S. Geological Survey, 2006. *Recycled cell phones—A treasure trove of valuable metals.* USGS Fact Sheet 2006-3097.; **p. 337:** (top) Data for 1990–1993 from U.S. Geological Survey, *Minerals Yearbook (MYB) 1994*, Columbium (Niobium) and Tantalum, by L. D. Cunningham, Table 10; 1994–1997 from USGS MYB 1998, Table 10; 1998–2001 from USGS MYB 2002, p. 21.13; 2002–2003 from USGS MYB 2004, p. 20.13; 2004 from USGS MYB 2008, p. 52.12; 2005–2009 from USGS MYB 2009, p. 52.13, USGS did not report data for other countries owing to data uncertainties.; **p. 337:** (bottom) Source: Fm122/Wikimedia. http://en.wikipedia.org/wiki/File:Global-minedtantalum-production-1990-2009.png. Accessed 22 July 2011.

Chapter 12 Page 342: Figure 12.1 Data from United Nations Environment Programme (UNEP) and World Resources Institute.; **p. 346:** Figure 12.6 Natural Resources Canada, *Groundwater Mapping Program: Overview.* Reproduced by permission of Public Works Government Service of Canada, 2012.; **p. 347:** Figure 12.7 Data from United Nations Environment Programme (UNEP) and World Resources Institute, as presented by Harrison, P. and F. Pearce. 2000. AAAS *Atlas of Population and the Environment.* Berkeley, CA: University of California Press.; **p. 348:** Figure 12.8 (top) Data from Enivronment Canada, *Water Use: Withdrawal Uses* (as of 2006), http://www.cc.gc.ca/cau-water/default. asp?lang=en&n=851B096C-1#municipal. Reproduced with the permission of the Minister of Public Works and Government Services Canada, 2011.; **p. 348:** Figure 12.9 (bottom) Data are based on information from UN Food and Agriculture Organization (FAO, 2000) and from Environment Canada, 2005, The Management of Water: Water Use.; **p. 352:** Figure 12.13 (bottom) Data from Postel, S. 2005. *Liquid assets: The critical need to safeguard freshwater ecosystems.* Fig. 3. p. 170. Washington, DC: Worldwatch Institute. www.worldwatch.org. By permission.; **p. 354:** Figure 12.15 Data from UNESCO, 2006. *Water: A Shared Responsibility. World Water Development Report 2.* Paris and New York: UNESCO and Berghahn Books; **p. 364:** Source: Reproduced by permission of the British Geological Survey. © NERC. All rights reserved. IPR/146-08CT. BGS AND DPHE, 2001. *Arsenic Contamination of Groundwater in Bangladesh.* KINNIBURGH, D G and SMEDLEY, P L (Editors). British Geological Survey Technical Report WC/00/19. British Geological Survey, Keyworth.; **p. 368:** Reprinted by permission of David Schindler.; **p. 371:** Data from Wallace, J.S. Increasing agricultural water use efficiency to meet future food production. *Agriculture, Ecosystems and Environment* 82(1):105-119. doi:10.1016/S0167-8809(00)00220-6. Copyright 2000, with permission from Elsevier.

Chapter 13 Page 377: Figure 13.4 Source: Garrison,T. 2005. *Oceanography, 5th ed.* Belmont, CA: Brooks/Cole.; **p. 379:** Courtesy of Professor G.W.K. Kent Moore; **p. 380:** Figure 13.6 Source: Garrison,T. 2005. *Oceanography, 5th ed.* Belmont, CA: Brooks/Cole.; **p. 381:** Figure 13.7 (top) Adapted from National Oceanic and Atmospheric Administration, *Tropical Atmospheric Ocean Project.*; **p. 382:** Figure 13.9 Adapted from Thurman, H. V. 1990. *Essentials of Oceanography, 4th ed.* New York: Macmillan.; **p. 390:** Figure 13.18a Data in (a) from National Research Council. 2003. *Oil in the Sea III. Inputs, Fates, and Effects.* Washington, DC: National Academies Press.; **p. 391:** Figure 13.20 *The State of World Fisheries and Aquaculture*

2008, FAO Fisheries and Aquaculture Department, Food and Agriculture Organization of the United Nations, Rome, 2009, p. 4. www.fao.org/docrep/011/i0250e/i0250e00.htm; **p. 394:** Figure 13.23a (top) Data in (a) from Millennium Ecosystem Assessment, 2005. *Ecosystems and Human Well-Being: Synthesis.* Figure 11. p. 12. Island Press, Washington, DC. Copyright © 2005 World Resources Institute. Used with permission.; **p. 394:** Figure 13.23b (bottom) Data in (b) from Mayo, R.K.; Terceiro, M., editors. 2005. Assessment of 19 Northeast groundfish stocks through 2004. 2005 Groundfish Assessment Review Meeting (2005 GARM), Fig. A1a. Northeast Fisheries Science Center, Woods Hole, Massachusetts, 15-19 August 2005. U.S. Dep. *Commer., Northeast Fish. Sci. Cent. Ref. Doc.* 0513; **p. 395:** Figure 13.24 Adapted from Myers, R.A. and B. Worm. 2003. Rapid worldwide depletion of predatory fish communities. *Nature* 423:280-283 (15 May 2003) doi:10.1038/nature01610; **p. 397:** Table 13.1 © Monterey Bay Aquarium Foundation; **p. 400:** Profile reprinted by permission of Farley Mowat.; **p. 401:** Figure 13.26 Source: Adapted from Halpern, B.S., and R.R. Warner, 2003. Matching marine reserve design to reserve objectives. *Proceedings of the Royal Society of London* B 270: 1871–1878, Fig 1. Used by permission of The Royal Society and the author.; **p. 403:** Adapted from Rosenberg, A., et al. 2006. Rebuilding U.S. Fisheries: Progress and problems. *Frontiers in Ecology and the Environment* 4(6) 303-308.

Chapter 14 Page 408: Figure 14.1 (left) Data from Ahrens, C.D. 2007. *Meteorology Today, 8th ed.* Belmont, CA: Brooks/Cole.; **p. 408:** Figure 14.2 (right) Adapted from Jacobson, M.Z. 2002. *Atmospheric Pollution: History, Science, and Regulation.* Cambridge: Cambridge University Press; and Parson, E.A. 2003. *Protecting the Ozone Layer: Science and Strategy.* Oxford: Oxford University Press.; **p. 409:** Figure 14.3 Adapted from Ahrens, C.D. 2007. *Meteorology Today, 8th ed.* Belmont, CA: Brooks/Cole.; **p. 421:** Figure 14.13 Adapted from information from Environment Canada, *Clean Air Online*, http://www.ec.gc.ca/cleanair-airpur/Pollutants-WSBCC0B44A-1_En.htm; **p. 422:** Figure 14.14 Based on data from National Air Pollution Surveillance Network, Environment Canada; **p. 426:** Figure 14.19a (top) Data in (a) from Earth System Research Laboratory Global Monitoring Division, NOAA. www.esrl.noaa.gov; **p. 430:** Table 14.1 Source: Adapted from Driscoll, C.T., et al., 2001. *Acid rain revisited.* Hubbard Brook Research Foundation. Copyright © 2001 C.T. Driscoll. Used with permission.; **p. 431:** Figure 14.21 From Environment Canada, 2001, *Acid Rain and Forests*, www.ec.gc.ca/acidrain/images/Exceedance_E.jpg. Reproduced with the permission of the Minister of Public Works and Government Services Canada, 2012.; **p. 432:** Figure 14.22 From *Canadian National Atmospheric Chemistry Database*, Meteorological Service of Canada, Environment Canada, Cat. No.: En85-1/2010E-PDF. pp. 9-10. Reproduced with the permission of the Minister of Public Works and Government Services Canada, 2011; *National Atmospheric Deposition Program (NRSP-3).* 2007. NADP Program Office, Illinois State Water Survey, 2204 Griffith Dr., Champaign, IL 61820.; **p. 433:** Figure 14.23 Source: *State of the Environment Infobase Acid Rain*, Environment Canada, Ontario, Atlantic, and Quebec Regions, adapted by National Indicators and Reporting Office, www.ec.gc.ca; **p. 434:** Data from Likens, G.E. 2004. SOME PERSPECTIVES ON LONG-TERM BIOGEOCHEMICAL RESEARCH FROM THE HUBBARD BROOK ECOSYSTEM STUDY *Ecology* 85(4):2355-2362. doi:http://dx.doi.org/10.1890/03-0243; **p. 436:** Figure 14.26 Source: Natural Resources Canada, *Geoscape Ottawa-Gatineau: Indoor Radon*, www.geoscape.nrcan.gc.ca/ottawa/radon_e.php?p=1. Reproduced with the permission of the Minister of Public Works and Government Services Canada, 2011.; **p. 439:** Excerpts from Meteorological Service of Canada, Environment Canada, David Phillips www.msc-smc.ec.gc.ca/cd/biographies/david_phillips_e. html. & Environment Canada *Envirozone, Issue 78, Canada's Weather Guru: A Chat with David Phillips*, www.ec.gc.ca/EnviorZine/english/issues/78/feature_1_e.cfm. © Government of Canada & David Phillips.; **p. 442:** Source: NOAA, www.cpc.ncep.noaa.gov/products/stratosphere/polar/gif_files/ozone_hole_plot.png.

Chapter 15 Page 448: Figure 15.1 Data from Kiehl, J.T., and K.E. Trenberth. Earth's annual global mean energy budget. Fig. 7, p. 206. *Bulletin of the American Meteorological Society* 78(2):197-208 (February 1997) © American Meteorological Society (AMS).; **p. 449:** Table 15.1 (left) Data are for a 100-year time horizon, from Intergovernmental Panel on Climate

Change, 2007. *Fourth assessment report.* Climate change 2007: The physical science basis.; **p. 449:** Figure 15.2 (right) Data from Intergovernmental Panel on Climate Change, 2007. *Fourth assessment report.*; **p. 450:** Figure 15.3 Adapted from Intergovernmental Panel on Climate Change, 2007. *Fourth assessment report.*; **p. 451:** Figure 15.4 Data from Intergovernmental Panel on Climate Change, 2007. *Fourth assessment report.*; **p. 456:** Figure 15.9 (top) Data from National Oceanic and Atmospheric Administration (NOAA), Earth System Research Laboratory, *Global Monitoring Division, 2010.*; **p. 457:** Figure 15.11 Data from Intergovernmental Panel on Climate Change, 2007. *Fourth assessment report.*; **p. 459:** Leland McInnes/Wikimedia; data sources: (red) EPICA Dome C temperature data: doi:10.1594/PANGAEA.683655; (dark blue) Vostok CO2 data: doi:10.1594/PANGAEA.55501; (steel blue) EPICA DomeC temperature data, 423-391 kybp: doi:10.1594/PANGAEA.472482; (pale blue) EPICA DomeC CO2 data, 650-413 kybp: doi:10.1594/PANGAEA.472481; (cyan) EPICA DomeC CO2 data, 800-650 kybp: doi:10.1594/PANGAEA.710901;current CO2 level: http://en.wikipedia.org/wiki/Carbon_dioxide#Concentrations_of_CO2_in_atmosphere; **p. 461:** Figure 15.12 Data from Intergovernmental Panel on Climate Change, 2007. Fourth assessment report.; **p. 462:** Figure 15.13 Data from Intergovernmental Panel on Climate Change, 2007. *Fourth assessment report* (a); and Intergovernmental Panel on Climate Change, 2001. *Third assessment report (b).*; **p. 462:** Figure 15.14 (bottom) Map data from National Center for Atmospheric Research and National Snow and Ice Data Center. www.nsidc.org; **p. 463:** Figure 15.15 (top) Data from Intergovernmental Panel on Climate Change, 2007. *Fourth assessment report.*; **p. 463:** Figure 15.16 (bottom) Data from Intergovernmental Panel on Climate Change, 2007. *Fourth assessment report.*; **p. 464:** Figure 15.17 (top) Data from Lemke, P., J. Ren, et al., 2007: *Observations: Changes in Snow, Ice and Frozen Ground.* In: Climate Change 2007: The Physical Science Basis. Contribution of Working Group I to the Fourth Assessment Report of the Intergovernmental Panel on Climate Change [Solomon, S., et al. (eds.)]. Cambridge University Press, Cambridge, UK. Figure 4.13.; **p. 464:** Figure 15.18 (bottom) Adapted from Environment Canada, *Canadian Centre for Climate Modelling and Analysis (CCMA),* p. 3. Cat. No.: En56-207/2005. www.cccma.ec.gc.ca/20051116_brochure_e_pgs.pdf. Reproduced with the permission of the Minister of Public Works and Government Services Canada, 2011.; **p. 466:** Figure 15.20 (top) Data from Intergovernmental Panel on Climate Change, 2007. Fourth assessment report. *Climate change 2007: The physical science basis working group.*; **p. 466:** Figure 15.21 (bottom) Data from Intergovernmental Panel on Climate Change, 2007. *Fourth assessment report.*; **p. 467:** Figure 15.22 Source: The Atlas of Canada, NRCan, *Coastal Sensitivity to Sea-Level Rise,* http://atlas.nrcan.gc.ca/site/english/index.html. Reproduced with the permission of the Minister of Public Works and Government Services Canada, 2011.; **p. 470:** Figure 15.24 NASA/JPL-Caltech; **p. 471:** Figure 15.25 Data from Intergovernmental Panel on Climate Change, 2007. *Fourth assessment report.*; **p. 472:** Figure 15.26 (left) Source: *Climate Change and Forest Fires,* http://cfs.nrcan.gc.ca/publications?id=18179, Natural Resources Canada, 2000. Reproduced with the permission of the Minister of Public Works and Government Services Canada, 2012.; **p. 472:** Figure 15.27 (right) Source: Environment Canada, *National Inventory Report 1990-2008: Greenhouse Gas Sources and Sinks in Canada.* (2010). Cat. No.: En81-4/2008E-PDF.; **p. 474:** Figure 15.28 Data from Intergovernmental Panel on Climate Change, 2007. *Fourth assessment report.*; **p. 475:** Figure 15.29 Lawrence Livermore National Laboratory; **p. 478:** Table 15.2 Data from UN Framework Convention on Climate Change, *National Greenhouse Gas Inventory Reports, 2007.*; **p. 479:** Figure 15.32 Source: Environment Canada, *National Inventory Report 1990-2008: Greenhouse Gas Sources and Sinks in Canada.* (2010). Fig. S-1, p. 19. Cat. No.: En81-4/2008E-PDF. www.ec.gc.ca/ges-ghg/default.asp?lang=En&n=83A34A7A-1. Reproduced with the permission of the Minister of Public Works and Government Services Canada, 2011.; **p. 481:** Reprinted by permission of Sheila Watt-Cloutier.; **p. 484:** Based on Environment Canada, *National GHG Inventory,* this graph shows Canada's GHG emissions (CO2) between 1990 and 2002, with projections to 2010 according to a "business-as-usual" scenario and a "Kyoto-based" scenario.

Chapter 16 Page 490: Figure 16.1a (top) Data for (a) from U.S. Engery Information Administration and International Engery Agency.; **p. 490:** Figure 16.1b (bottom) Data for (b) from Natural Resources Canada. 2006.

Report of the National Advisory Panel on Sustainable Energy Science and Techology. p. 76. Catalogue No.: M4-40/2006E. Office of Energy Research and Development.; **p. 491:** Table 16.1 Data from British Petroleum 2010. *Statistical review of world energy 2010.*; **p. 492:** Figure 16.3 Data from British Petroleum 2010. *Statistical review of world energy 2010.*; **p. 493:** Figure 16.4 Data from British Petroleum 2010. *Statistical review of world energy 2010.*; **p. 494:** Table 16.2 Data from British Petroleum 2010. *Statistical review of world energy 2010.*; **p. 497:** Table 16.3 (bottom right) Data from British Petroleum 2010. *Statistical review of world energy 2010.*; **p. 498:** Figure 16.7 (bottom) Energy Resources Conservation Board, *Information Kit: Alberta's Unconventional Oil & Natural Gas,* www.ercb.ca; **p. 499:** Table 16.4 Data from British Petroleum 2010. *Statistical review of world energy 2010.*; **p. 504:** Figure 16.11a (top) Data in (a) from Deffeyes, K.S. 2001. *Hubbert's Peak: The Impending World Oil Shortage.* Princeton, NJ: Princeton University Press; and U.S. Energy Information Administration.; **p. 504:** Figure 16.11b (bottom) Data in (b) from Campbell, C.J., and the Association for the Study of Peak Oil and Gas, 2007.; **p. 505:** Figure 16.13 Data from British Petroleum 2010. *Statistical review of world energy 2010.*; **p. 507:** Figure 16.15 Data are from Boden, T.A., G. Marland, and R.J. Andres (2010) *Global, Regional, and National Fossil-Fuel CO2 Emissions.* Carbon Dioxide Information Analysis Center, Oak Ridge National Laboratory, U.S. Department of Energy, Oak Ridge, Tenn., U.S.A. doi: 10.3334/CDIAC/00001.; **p. 511:** Figure 16.19 (left) Data from U.S. Energy Information Administration, 2007. *Annual Energy Review 2006.* Washington, DC.; **p. 511:** Figure 16.20 (right) Data from U.S. Energy Information Administration; **p. 512:** Figure 16.21 Data from British Petroleum 2010. *Statistical review of world energy 2010.*; **p. 514:** Reprinted by permission of Mary Griffiths.; **p. 517:** Data from Dukes, J. 2003. Buring buried sunshine: Human consumption of ancient solar energy. *Climate Change* 61(1):31-44. DOI: 10.1023/A:1026391317686.

Chapter 17 Page 522: Figure 17.1b (bottom) Source: Energy Information Administration, U.S. Department of Energy, *Country Analysis Briefs: Canada,* http://www.eia.doe.gov/emeu/cabs/Canada/Full.html; **p. 524:** Figure 17.4 (bottom) Data are for 2009, from International Hydropower Association, IHA Activity Report, 2010. Fig. 2. p. 6. © 2011 International Hydropower Association. All rights reserved; **p. 526:** Table 17.1 As of August, 2010. Data from the Nuclear Energy Institute (http://www.nei.org/).; **p. 531:** Figure 17.10 Data from Swiss Agency for Development and Cooperation, Bern, 2005.; **p. 535:** Figure 17.15 Data from Energy Information Administration, U.S. Department of Energy.; **p. 536:** Table 17.2 (top) Data sources: Canadian Wind Energy Association (www.canwea.ca); International Small Hydro Atlas (www.small-hydro.com); Canadian Solar Industries Association (www.cansia.ca); Pembina Institute (www.pembina.org); Centre for Energy (www.centreforenergy.com); Canadian Geothermal Energy Association (www.cangea.ca); Nova Scotia Power (www.nspower.ca).; **p. 536:** Figure 17.16 (bottom) Data from International Energy Agency Statistics, 2007.; **p. 537:** Figure 17.17 Data from Natural Resources Canada. 2006. *Report of the National Advisory Panel on Sustainable Energy Science and Technology.* p. 76. Catalogue No.: M4-40/2006E. Office of Energy Research and Development.; **p. 539:** Figure 17.19 Data from U.S. Environmental Protection Agency.; **p. 545:** Figure 17.25a (left) The Atlas of Canada, 5th ed. 1995. *Solar Radiation - Annual.* Reproduced with the permission of the Minister of Public Works and Government Services, 2012.; **p. 547:** Figure 17.27a *Canadian Wind Energy Atlas.* Environment Canada, 2008. Reproduced with the permission of the Minister of Public Works and Government Services, 2012.; **p. 548:** Figure 17.29 Data from *Power Generation in Canada: A Guide,* Canadian Electricity Association 2006.; **p. 555:** Reprinted by permission of David Keith.

Chapter 18 Page 566: Figure 18.2 Data are for 2004, from Environment Canada, *Waste Management, Municipal Solid Waste.* http://www.ec.gc.ca/gdd-mw/default.asp?lang=En&n=EF0FC6A9-1; **p. 567:** Figure 18.4 Data from Statistics Canada (2010), Table 12.5 *Waste disposal and diversion,* 2002, 2004, and 2006. CANSIM Table 153-0041.; **p. 574:** Table 18.1 (left) Data from U.S. Environmental Protection Agency.; **p. 574:** Table 18.2 (right) Source: Statistics Canada, *Households and the Environment Survey,* 2007.; **p. 580:** Table 18.3 Source: Stewardship Ontario, *Municipal Hazardous or Special Waste, Do What You Can Program;* for more information see "What's Included".; **p. 581:** Table 18.4 Source: Statistics Canada,

Households and the Environment Survey, 2009.; **p. 582:** Figure 18.12b Data from Townsend, T.G., et al. 2004. *RCRA toxicity characterization of computer CPUs and other discarded electronic devices.* July 15, 2004, report to the U.S. EPA.; **p. 587:** Reprinted by permission of Brennain Lloyd.; **p. 590:** Source: Statistics Canada, *Recycling in Canada.* Contributed by Angela McCanny, Statistics Canada resource teacher, Ottawa, ON. www19.statcan. ca/02/02_051-eng.htm

Chapter 19 Page 598: Figure 19.2 The map, from Public Safety Canada, was prepared collaboratively with Natural Resources Canada, the Geological Survey of Canada, The Atlas of Canada, Environment Canada, and Statistics Canada.; **p. 601:** Figure 19.3 Data are for 2004, from World Health Organization (WHO); **p. 604:** Table 19.4 Data from Harrison, P., and F. Pearce. 2000. *AAAS Atlas of Population and Environment.* Berkeley, CA: University of California Press.; **p. 612:** Data from Hunt, P.A., et al. 2003. Bisphenol-A exposure causes meiotic aneuploidy in the female mouse. *Current Biology* 13:546-553.; **p. 619:** Figure 19.13 Data from Cohen, B. 1991. Catalogue of risks extended and updated. *Health Physics* 61(3):317-335. © 1991 Health Physics Society; **p. 620:** Figure 19.14 Source: Treasury Board of Canada Secretariat (March 2000) *Report of the ADM Working Group on Risk Management.* Reproduced by permission of Public Works Government of Canada, 2012.; **p. 622:** Table 19.5 Data from United Nations Environment Programme (UNEP), 2001.; **p. 623:** Reprinted by permission of Wendy Mesley.; **p. 626:** Source: Adpated from Schlumpf, M., et al. In Vitro and in Vivo Estrogenicity of UV Screens. *Environ Health Perspect* 109:239-244. http://dx.doi.org/10.1289/ehp.01109239.

Chapter 20 Page 630: Source: The World Urban Forum 2006, *Vancouver Working Discussion Paper: The Liveable City*, March 2005, Fig. 5, p. 21. www.cscd.gov.bc.ca/lgd/intergov_relations/library/ wuf_the_livable_city. pdf; **p. 632:** Figure 20.2 (top) Data from United Nations, Department of Economic and Social Affairs, 2010. *World urbanization prospects: The 2009 revision*, Fig 3. By permission.; **p. 632:** Figure 20.3 (bottom) Source: Statistics Canada, 2006. *Portrait of the Canadian Population in 2006: Subprovincial population dynamics*, Census Analytical Series, Fig. 5. Cat. No.: 97-550-XWE2006001 www12.statcan.ca/census-recensement/2006/ as-sa/97-550/figures/c5-eng.cfm; **p. 633:** Table 20.1 Source: United Nations Population Division, 2010. *World urbanization prospects: The 2009 revision.* New York: UNPD.; **p. 641:** Table 20.2 Source: Sierra Club, Ontario Chapter (based on U.S. Environmental Protection Agency, 2005).; **p. 642:** Figure 20.11 Based on data from Litman, T. 2005. *Rail Transit in America: A Comprehensive Evaluation of Benefits.* Victoria, BC: Victoria Transport Policy Institute; **p. 644:** Adapted from Litman, T. 2005. *Rail Transit in America: A Comprehensive Evaluation of Benefits.* Victoria, BC: Victoria Transport Policy Institute; **p. 649:** Reprinted by permission of Nola-Kate Seymoar.; **p. 652:** Data from Kenworthy, J., et al. 1999. *An International Sourcebook of Automobile Dependence in Cities.* Boulder, CO: University Press of Colorado, as cited by Sheehan, M.O. 2002. *What Will It Take to Halt Sprawl?* Washington DC: Worldwatch Institute.

Chapter 21 Page 655: Extract from *Mining Denendeh: A Dene Nation Perspective on Community Health Impacts of Mining* by Chris Paci and Noeline Villebrun. Prepared for the 2004 Mining Ministers Conference, Coppermine, Nunavut. Reprinted with the permission of the authors.; **p. 672:** Table 21.1 Source: Adapted by permission from Macmillan Publishers Ltd: Nature, Costanza, R., et al. 1997. The value of the world's ecosystem services and natural capital. *Nature* 387:253–260 (15 May 1997). Copyright 1997.; **p. 677:** Figure 21.13 Data from Venetoulis, J. and C. Cobb (2004). *The Genuine Progress Indicator, 1950-2002 (2004 Update).* Redefining Progress, Oakland, CA.; **p. 678:** Figure 21.14 Data from Pembina Institute, Alberta GPI Accounts, 1961–2003.; **p. 680:** Figure 21.16 Data from Costanza, R., et al., 1997. The value of the world's ecosystem services and natural capital. *Nature* 387 (6630): 253–260 (15 May 1997); **p. 682:** Reprinted by permission of Matthew Coon Come.; **p. 686:** Data from Pembina Institute, Alberta GPI Accounts, 1961–2003.

Chapter 22 Page 696: Figure 22.3 *Regional Cumulative Effects Management Framework for Cold Lake, Alberta*, 2001. Cat. no.: En105-3/82-2004E Figure 13. Reproduced by permission of Public Works Government of Canada, 2012.; **p. 698:** Figure 22.4 Coalition for a Healthy Ottawa, www.flora.org/

healthyottawa/BylawList.pdf; **p. 706:** Figure 22.13 Source: Adpated from OECD Environment Monographs, No. 83, *OECD Core Set of Indicators for Environmental Performance Reviews: A Synthesis Report by the Group on the State of the Environment*, 1993.; **p. 708:** Table 22.2 OECD Environment Monographs, No. 83, *OECD Core Set of Indicators for Environmental Performance Reviews: A synthesis report by the Group on the State of the Environment*, 1993, www.ens.gu.edu.au/AES1161/Topic1/Images/gd93179. pdf; **p. 711:** Marisa Jacott, Cyrus Reed and Mark Winfield, *The Generation and Management of Hazardous Wastes and Transboundary Hazardous Waste Shipments Between Mexico, Canada and the United States, 1990-2000, in North American Symposium on Understanding the Linkages Between Trade and the Environment*, Commission on Environmental Cooperation of North America, 2002. pp. 161-208. Fig. 1. http://www.cec.org/files/ pdf/ECONOMY/symposium-e.pdf. © Commission for Environmental Cooperation, 2002; **p. 715:** Reprinted by permission of Maude Barlow.; **p. 719:** Adapted from National Round Table on Environment and Economy (NRTEE), 2007. *Getting to 2050: Canada's Transition to a Low-emission Future.* http://nrtee-trnee.ca/climate/getting-to-2050.

Chapter 23 Page 725: Table 23.1 Excerpted from the Association of University Leaders for a Sustainable Future, *Talloires Declaration 10 Point Action Plan.* Reprinted by permission of ULSF. Available online at www.ulsf.org/programs_talloires.html.; **p. 727:** Data from S. Svajda and T. Shakeel, 2008-2009, *Ecological Footprint of the University of Toronto (Mississauga): Calculations and Analysis.* Fig. 1, p. 8.; **p. 736:** Figure 23.11 Data from Millennium Ecosystem Assessment, 2005. *Ecosystems and human well-being: biodiversity synthesis.* p. 39. World Resources Institute. Washington, DC. Used with permission.; **p. 739:** Figure 23.15 Data from Myers, D.G., 2000. *The American Paradox: Spiritual Hunger in an Age of Plenty.* New Haven, CT: Yale University Press; Gardner, G., and E. Assadourian, 2004. *Rethinking the good life*, pp. 164-179 in State of the World 2004, Worldwatch Institute; and Kahneman, D., et al. 2006, Would you be happier if you were richer? A focusing illusion. *Science* 312:1908-1910.; **p. 742:** (top) Emerson et al. 2010. *Environmental Performance Index.* New Haven 2010. Yale Center for Environmental Law & Policy; **p. 742:** (bottom) Emerson et al. 2010. *Environmental Performance Index.* New Haven 2010. Yale Center for Environmental Law & Policy; **p. 743:** Emerson et al. 2010. *Environmental Performance Index.* New Haven 2010. Yale Center for Environmental Law & Policy; **p. 745:** Reprinted by permission of Kelcigh Annau.

Photo

Part Openers Photos: Part 1 p. 1: Rolf Hicker/All Canada Photos; **Part 2 p. 151:** Abbie Trayler-Smith/Panos.

Chapter 1 *Page 2:* NASA/Visible Earth; **p. 3:** NASA; **p. 8:** © Izabela Habur/ iStockphot.com; **p. 11:** George Konig/Keystone Features/Getty Images; **p. 12:** (top left) Viktor Gmyria/Shutterstock; **p. 12:** (top right) Alexander Chaikin/Shutterstock; **p. 13:** CP Photo/Sean Kilpatrick; **p. 14:** Courtesy of Jay Withgott; **p. 21:** Nickolay Khoroshkov/Shutterstock; **p. 22:** (top left) Data made available by NASA/GSFC/MITI/ERSDAC/JAROS, and U.S/ Japan ASTER Science Team; **p. 22:** (bottom right) Jacques Descloitres, MODIS Land Rapid Response Team NASA/GSFC; **p. 23:** (bottom left) © Don White/SuperStock; **p. 23:** (top right) © Al Harvey/SlideFarm.com Inc.; **p. 25:** Photograph of David Suzuki. Reprinted by permission of David Suzuki.

Chapter 2 *Page 30:* Boris Gjenero; **p. 31:** Donnie Reid/Pavillion Lake Research Project; **p. 32:** Donnie Reid/Pavillion Lake Research Project; **p. 34:** © Heidi Den Haan; **p. 37:** Bridgetjones/GetStock.com; **p. 41:** (left) Stuart Jenner/Shutterstock; **p. 41:** (right) Val Thoermer/Shutterstock; **p. 43:** (bottom right) © Jim Lane/Alamy; **p. 44:** (bottom left) Neil Rabinowitz/CORBIS; **p. 44:** (top right) B. MURTON/SOUTHAMPTON OCEANOGRAPHY CENTRE/ SCIENCE PHOTO LIBRARY; **p. 44:** (top right) © Ralph White/CORBIS; **p. 49:** (top left) CARL JUSTE/MCT/ Landov; **p. 49:** (right middle) Courtesy of J.D. Griggs/USGS; **p. 51:** (top left) iStockphoto/Thinkstock.com; **p. 51:** (top right) Glow Images/Alamy;

p. 51: (middle left) dbimages/Alamy; **p. 51:** (middle right) iStockphoto/Thinkstock.com; **p. 51:** (bottom left) © Orchidpoet/iStockphoto.com; **p. 52:** Illustration by Peter Sawyer/Smithsonian Institute; **p. 53:** Reprinted by permission of Praveen Saxeena.

Chapter 3 Page 58: Satellite image by GeoEye from SeaWiFS Project, NASA/Goddard Space Flight Center, and ORBIMAGE/GeoEye. Copyright © 2011 GeoEye; **p. 59:** (top) Jonathan Bird/Peter Arnold, Inc./Photolibrary; **p. 59:** (bottom right) Jacques Descloitres, MODIS Land Rapid Response Team, NASA/GSFC; **p. 64:** (top right) © SimplyCreativePhotography; **p. 64:** (bottom left) © Kenneth Wiedemann/iStockphoto.com; **p. 64:** (top left) Vzion/GetStock.com; **p. 64:** (bottom right) © JJRD/iStockphoto.com; **p. 64:** (bottom a) Paha_l/Dreamstime.com/GetStock.com; **p. 64:** (bottom b) Itsajoop/GetStock.com; **p. 64:** (bottom c) Icefields/GetStock.com; **p. 64:** (bottom d) Elnavegante/GetStock.com; **p. 64:** (bottom e) iStockphoto/Thinkstock.com; **p. 64:** (bottom f) Vzion/GetStock.com; **p. 68:** Courtesy of D. W. Schindler; **p. 71:** (top left) COLIN CUTHBERT/NEWCASTLE UNIVERSITY/ SCIENCE PHOTO LIBRARY; **p. 71:** (bottom right) SIMON FRASER/SCIENCE PHOTO LIBRARY; **p. 78:** (bottom left) Custom Medical Stock Photo, Inc.; **p. 78:** (bottom right) Custom Medical Stock Photo, Inc.; **p. 80:** EMILY MICHOT/MCT /Landov; **p. 84:** Photograph of Robert Bateman by Brigit Freybe Bateman. Reprinted by permission of Robert Bateman.

Chapter 4 Page 89: © Focus_on_Nature/iStockphoto.com; **p. 90:** (top) © Michael & Patricia Fogden/CORBIS; **p. 92:** (left) Nicholas Athanas; **p. 92:** (centre left) © Sarah Hodgkins/Alamy; **p. 92:** (centre right) © Premaphotos/Alamy; **p. 92:** (right) Michael Fogden/Oxford Scientific/Getty Images; **p. 94:** (top) © Philippe Clement/naturepl.com; **p. 94:** (bottom) A Jagel/AGE fotostock/MaXx Images; **p. 100:** Colin Keates © Dorling Kindersley, Courtesy of the Natural History Museum, London; **p. 101:** "Hagerman Horse Quarry" by Jay Matternes. © National Museum of Natural History, Smithsonian Institution.; **p. 104:** © SuperStock; **p. 105:** (left) G.I. Bernard/Photo Researchers, Inc.; **p. 105:** (right) Wisconsin Historical Society Asc. No. WHI-25763; **p. 106:** (top) © Getty Images/Thinkstock.com; **p. 106:** (middle) Tom Brakefield/Thinkstock.com; **p. 106:** (bottom) © Doug Perrine/naturepl.com; **p. 112:** (top left) J. Alan Pounds; **p. 114:** © MCB Andrade 2006. Photo: Ken Jones.

Chapter 5 Page 118: © Jim West/Alamy; **p. 119:** © Maximilian Weinzierl/Alamy; **p. 122:** Michael & Patricia Fogden/Corbis; **p. 123:** (left) © Peter Johnson/CORBIS; **p. 123:** (centre) Sari O'Neal/Shutterstock; **p. 123:** (right) Michael & Patricia Fogden/Corbis; **p. 124:** (top left) © ARCO/Reinhard, H/MaXx Images; **p. 124:** (bottom left) PATRICK LANDMANN/SCIENCE PHOTO LIBRARY; **p. 124:** (bottom right) Leroy Simon/Visuals Unlimited, Inc.; **p. 125:** Michael & Patricia Fogden/Corbis; **p. 131:** Charles D. Winters/Photo Researchers, Inc.; **p. 132:** Jim Bodkin; **p. 136:** Michael Wheatley/AllCanadaPhotos.com; **p. 139:** (top left) © Getty Images/Thinkstock.com; **p. 139:** (right) Terry W Ryder/Shutterstock; **p. 140:** Klaus Lang/All Canada Photos; **p. 141:** (left) Philip Gould/CORBIS; **p. 141:** (right) © North Light Images/MaXx Images; **p. 142:** (left) iStockphoto/Thinkstock.com; **p. 142:** (right) © Edd Westmacott/Alamy; **p. 143:** (left) © AfriPics.com/Alamy; **p. 143:** (right) Oleg Znamenskiy/Shutterstock; **p. 144:** Maro Markovic/Shutterstock; **p. 146:** Photograph of Zoe Lucas. Reprinted by permission of Sable Island Green Horse Society.

Chapter 6 Page 152: © Redlink/Corbis; **p. 153:** © Louise Gubb/The Image Works; **p. 155:** © epa/Corbis; **p. 156:** (bottom left) © The Trustees of the British Museum/Art Resource, NY ; **p. 156:** (bottom) © Bettmann/CORBIS; **p. 158:** Courtesy of Helmut Haberl; **p. 165:** KIN CHEUNG/Reuters /Landov; **p. 166:** JEREMIAH KAMAU/Reuters /Landov; **p. 171:** AKINTUNDE AKINLEYE/Reuters /Landov; **p. 172:** (top) Peter Menzel/Peter Menzel Photography; **p. 172:** (bottom) Peter Ginter/Peter Menzel Photography; **p. 175:** Photograph of William Rees. Reprinted by permission of William Rees.

Chapter 7 Page 179: Copyright Robert Williams, 2012; **p. 180:** Landsat imagery courtesy of NASA Goddard Space Flight Center and U.S. Geological Survey; **p. 181:** Nathan Basiliko; **p. 185:** (top left) SHEILA TERRY/SCIENCE PHOTO LIBRARY; **p. 185:** (top right) Scientifica/Visuals Unlimited,

Inc.; **p. 185:** (bottom left) TREVOR CLIFFORD PHOTOGRAPHY/SCIENCE PHOTO LIBRARY; **p. 186:** (bottom right) G. R. 'Dick' Roberts/NSIL/Visuals Unlimited, Inc.; **p. 192:** Ron Gilling/Photolibrary/Getty Images; **p. 194:** (top left) Greg Dale/Getty Images; **p. 194:** (bottom left) © David Cole/Alamy; **p. 194:** (top right) U.S. Department of Agriculture; **p. 194:** (bottom right) U.S. Department of Agriculture; **p. 196:** (top) © Tor Eigeland/Alamy; **p. 196:** (bottom) CP Photo/Library and Archives Canada PA-139645; **p. 198:** (left) © 2012 Michael Grandmaison Photography; **p. 198:** (right) China Photos/Getty Images; **p. 200:** (top left) © Scott Sinklier/Agestockusa/ MaXx Images; **p. 200:** (middle right) © inga spence/Alamy; **p. 200:** (top right) Charlesbolin/GetStock.com; **p. 200:** (middle left) iStockphoto/Thinkstock.com; **p. 200:** (bottom left) Yann Arthus-Bertrand/Corbis; **p. 200:** (bottom right) U.S. Department of Agriculture; **p. 201:** KAJ R. SVENSSON/SCIENCE PHOTO LIBRARY; **p. 202:** (top left) Jason Koski/Cornell University Photography; **p. 202:** (right) Courtesy of Dr. Jocelyn Parry-Jones, www.biocharproject.org; **p. 205:** Photo by Ken Jones. Courtesy of Myrna Simpson.

Chapter 8 Page 211: Paul Austring Photography/Firstlight; **p. 212:** © Stefano Paterna/Alamy; **p. 213:** Photo by John Schmeiser.; **p. 217:** TONY KARUMBA/AFP/Getty Images; **p. 218:** Art Rickerby/Time Life Pictures/Getty Images; **p. 220:** (top left) © kevin miller/iStockphoto.com; **p. 220:** (bottom left) © Carol Cohen/CORBIS; **p. 221:** Merrill Dyck/Shutterstock; **p. 223:** (left) Department of Natural Resources, Queensland, Australia; **p. 223:** (right) Department of Natural Resources, Queensland, Australia; **p. 225:** (top) PhotoDisc/Getty Images; **p. 225:** (bottom) Bob Rowan/Progressive Image/Corbis; **p. 226:** Peggy Greb/United States Department of Agriculture; **p. 231:** AFP/Getty Images; **p. 232:** (top) Native Seeds/SEARCH; **p. 232:** (bottom) Native Seeds/SEARCH; **p. 233:** © mediacolor's/Alamy; **p. 236:** Atlas Press/eyevine; **p. 238:** Courtesy of the Canadian Food Inspection Agency; **p. 239:** Courtesy of Dr. Paul Voroney; **p. 240:** (top) Scott Warren/Aurora Photos; **p. 240:** (bottom) © Fabienne Fossez/Alamy; **p. 241:** Photo of Alisa Smith & J.B. MacKinnon reprinted by permission of Paul Joseph.

Chapter 9 Page 246: © B&C Alexander/ArcticPhoto; **p. 247:** © Russell Millner/Alamy; **p. 248:** © INTERFOTO/MaXx Images; **p. 258:** © LYNN-STONE/MaXx Images; **p. 263:** Konrad Wothe/Getty Images; **p. 264:** TBC - Asanga Ratnaweera and Madhava Meegaskumbura; **p. 264:** (right) Dr. Anil Zachariah; **p. 268:** (top) © Dave Fleetham/MaXx Images; **p. 268:** (bottom) © R Linke/MaXx Images; **p. 269:** (left) Matthias Clamer/Stone/Getty Images; **p. 269:** (right) © Frans Lanting/Corbis; **p. 271:** Joel Sartore/National Geographic Stock; **p. 274:** (top) © Corbis; **p. 274:** (bottom) Wayne Lynch/All Canada Photos; **p. 276:** Tom & Pat Leeson/Photo Researchers, Inc.; **p. 278:** © Andrew Penner; **p. 280:** Russ Heinl /All Canada Photos; **p. 281:** Profile and photograph of Birute Mary Galdikas. Copyright Orangutan Foundation International.

Chapter 10 Page 286: TJ Watt/All Canada Photos; **p. 287:** © Wolfgang Kaehler/CORBIS; **p. 288:** © Dewitt Jones/CORBIS; **p. 293:** John E. Marriott; **p. 294:** (top left) © Robert Fraser/Dreamstime.com; **p. 294:** (middle left) © Tim Ennis/Alamy; **p. 294:** (bottom left) © Perry Mastrovito/Corbis; **p. 295:** © brytta/iStockphoto.com; **p. 297:** © Ian Graham; **p. 299:** (bottom) Courtesy of Weyerhaeuser Company; **p. 299:** (middle left) Studio/GetStock.com; **p. 299:** (centre) Breagen/GetStock.com; **p. 299:** (middle right) Paura/GetStock.com; **p. 300:** Library and Archives Canada, PA-040927; **p. 301:** csp/Shutterstock; **p. 302:** (top left) Dion Manastyrski/Natural Resources Canada. Reproduced with the permission of the Minister of Public Works and Government Services Canada, 2011.; **p. 302:** (bottom right) Tracy Ferrero/GetStock.com; **p. 302:** (bottom) © Keith Douglas/All Canada Photos; **p. 303:** © Pgiam/iStockphoto.com; **p. 305:** (top) A.S. Zain/Shutterstock; **p. 305:** (bottom) Chris Fredriksson/Alamy; **p. 306:** Timothy Epp/Shutterstock; **p. 309:** (top) PhotoSky 4t com/Shutterstock; **p. 309:** (middle) © A. T. Willett/Alamy; **p. 309:** (bottom) George Brits/Getty Images; **p. 310:** (top) TODD KOROL/Reuters /Landov; **p. 310:** (bottom) Paulo Whitaker/REUTERS/Corbis; **p. 311:** © Jaime Kowal.

Chapter 11 Page 316: REUTERS/Hereward Holland/Landov; **p. 317:** © Eric Baccega; **p. 321:** (left) DIRK WIERSMA/SCIENCE PHOTO LIBRARY;

p. 321: (centre) Jim Coon Studio; **p. 321:** (right) Pearson Education/Pearson Science; **p. 324:** Copyright © 2010 Steven Holt/Stockpix.com, All Rights Reserved.; **p. 325:** David R. Frazier/The Image Works; **p. 326:** REUTERS/David Lewis/Landov; **p. 327:** (left) George Steinmetz; **p. 327:** (right) Les Stone Photo; **p. 328:** © Greenshoots Communications/Alamy; **p. 330:** © Montana Stock Photography/Alamy; **p. 333:** Jeff Greenberg/GetStock.com; **p. 334:** © 2012 Robbie McClaran.

Chapter 12 Page 339: © Sebastien Cote; **p. 340:** Courtesy of NASA; **p. 343:** (left) © Peri's Picx/Alamy; **p. 343:** (right) blickwinkel/Wothe/GetStock.com; **p. 351:** (top left) Jjspring/Dreamstime.com; **p. 351:** (bottom left) Ian Berry/Magnum Photos; **p. 351:** (top right) © Hulton-Deutsch Collection/CORBIS; **p. 352:** (top) Courtesy of Canadian Space Agency; **p. 353:** (left) © Vladimir Borodin/Dreamstime.com; **p. 353:** (right) NASA Earth Observatory/NASA Goddard Space Flight Center; **p. 355:** Minden Pictures/SuperStock; **p. 356:** (top) Mike Grandmaison/First Light; **p. 356:** (bottom) AP Photo/CP Photo; **p. 358:** Bettmann/Corbis; **p. 360:** (top) © Tryphosa Ho/Alamy; **p. 360:** (bottom) © Emily Norton/iStockphoto.com; **p. 362:** © SuperStock/SuperStock; **p. 363:** © Earth Gallery Environment/Alamy; **p. 364:** © Shehzad Noorani/MaXx Images; **p. 367:** (top left) CP Photo/Frank Gunn; **p. 367:** (right) © Charles O'Rear/CORBIS; **p. 368:** Photograph of David Schindler. Reprinted by permission of David Schindler.

Chapter 13 Page 373: Jeffrey L. Rotman/CORBIS; **p. 374:** Library and Archives Canada, PA-110814; **p. 379:** (top left) Courtesy of Professor GWK Kent Moore; **p. 383:** (bottom) LAGUNA DESIGN/SCIENCE PHOTO LIBRARY; **p. 383:** (top) David Shale/Nature Picture Library; **p. 384:** (left) © Island Effects/iStockphoto.com; **p. 384:** (top right) Nata Sdobnikova/Shutterstock; **p. 384:** (bottom right) © Stephen Frink/CORBIS; **p. 386:** Copyright Robert Williams, 2012; **p. 387:** © Alberto Pomares/iStockphoto.com; **p. 389:** ©Momatiuk Eastcott/Animals Animals - Earth Scenes—All rights reserved.; **p. 391:** (left) Dr. David Phillips/Visuals Unlimited, Inc.; **p. 391:** (right) © Photoshot Holdings Ltd/Alamy; **p. 393:** (bottom) Peter Auster KRT/Newscom; **p. 398:** Dr. Verena Tunnicliffe, University of Victoria; **p. 400:** Photo by Ted Amsden.

Chapter 14 Page 405: Bettmann/Corbis; **p. 406:** Wikipedia; **p. 407:** Department of Fisheries and Oceans, Canada. "Protecting the Helath of Canada's Lakes: Experimental Lakes Area". Photographer: Dr. Ken Mills. Reproduced by permission of Public Works Government of Canada, 2012.; **p. 412:** Todd Shoemake/Shutterstock; **p. 415:** (top left) NASA Earth Observatory/NASA Goddard Space Flight Center; **p. 415:** (top right) © Nordic Photos/SuperStock; **p. 415:** (bottom left) Noel Hendrickson/Masterfile; **p. 417:** Frederic J. Brown/AFP/Getty Images; **p. 423:** Copyright Pittsburgh Post-Gazette. All rights reserved.; **p. 424:** © M/iStockphoto.com; **p. 426:** (bottom) NASA; **p. 427:** Crispin Halsall © Lancaster University, 2008; **p. 428:** AP photo/Martina Huber; **p. 434:** (top left) Photo by HO Photography. Courtesy of Gene Likens.; **p. 434:** (bottom) © David Turnley/CORBIS; **p. 435:** © Rob & Ann Simpson/Visuals Unlimited/Corbis; **p. 439:** Excerpts from Meteorological Service of Canada, Environment Canada, David Phillips www.msc-smc.ec.gc.ca/cd/biographies/david_phillips_e.html. & Environment Canada Envirozone, Issue 78, Canada's Weather Guru: A Chat with David Phillips, www.ec.gc.ca/EnviorZine/english/issues/78/feature_1_e.cfm. © Government of Canada & David Phillips.

Chapter 15 Page 444: © Scottbeard | Dreamstime.com; **p. 445:** All rights reserved by Redbeard Math Pirate; **p. 446:** (top) H.F. Lambert, Canada. Dept. of Mines and Technical Surveys/Library and Archives Canada/PA-023178; **p. 446:** (bottom) © 2011 Google; Image Parks Canada; © 2012 Cnes/Spot Image; **p. 455:** (top) © George Steinmetz/Corbis; **p. 455:** (bottom) Ted Spiegel/National Geographic/Getty Images; **p. 458:** Pasquale Sorrentino/Photo Researchers, Inc.; **p. 462:** (top left) Lars Johansson/Alamy; **p. 462:** (right) Andrew Bain/Getty Images; **p. 462:** (bottom left) © B&C Alexander/ArcticPhoto; **p. 465:** (top) NASA; **p. 465:** (bottom) NASA; **p. 468:** Rex A. Stucky/National Geographic Stock; **p. 469:** Adrian Baras/Shutterstock; **p. 477:** Colin Mcconnell/ GetStock.com; **p. 481:** Photograph of Sheila Watt-Cloutier. Reprinted by permission of Sheila Watt-Cloutier.

Chapter 16 Page: © Terry A. Parker/All Canada Photos/Corbis; **p. 487:** Raymond K. Gehman/National Geographic/Getty Images; **p. 491:** Photo by Joe Doherty/US Fish and Wildlife Service (USFWS); **p. 496:** Sam Ogden/Photo Researchers, Inc.; **p. 498:** (left) Courtesy of Nathan Schneider, Wikipedia; **p. 499:** Ron Watts/Firstlight.ca; **p. 502:** © JOHN GRESS/Reuters/Corbis; **p. 503:** © Calyx22 | Dreamstime.com; **p. 505:** © Photo 707/Alamy; **p. 507:** (left) CP Photo/Larry MacDougal; **p. 507:** (right) Jordan Verlage/Sun Media; **p. 509:** © Jim West/Alamy; **p. 510:** © Steven Kazlowski; **p. 513:** PASIEKA/SCIENCE PHOTO LIBRARY; **p. 514:** Photograph of Mary Griffiths. Reprinted by permission of Mary Griffiths.

Chapter 17 Page 519: (left) Barrett & MacKay/All Canada Photos; **p. 519:** (right) Barrett & MacKay/All Canada Photos; **p. 520:** CP Photo/Mike Dembeck; **p. 521:** NASA/GSFC/METI/ERSDAC/JAROS; **p. 523:** (left) Copyright © 2012 Ontario Power Generation Inc. All Rights Reserved.; **p. 523:** (right) Tank_bmb/GetStock.com; **p. 527:** Cameco Corporation; **p. 530:** (top) Savintsev Fyodor/ITAR-TASS /Landov ; **p. 530:** (bottom) Gleb Garanich /Reuters/Corbis; **p. 532:** (top left) GAMMA/Gamma-Rapho/Getty Images; **p. 532:** (top right) Roger Ressmeyer/Corbis; **p. 532:** (bottom right) PATRICK LANDMANN/SCIENCE PHOTO LIBRARY; **p.535:** © Arnstein Staverløkk/iStockphoto.com; **p.538:** © Nabokv | GetStock.com; **p. 539:** (top) USDA/ARS/Agricultural Research Service; **p. 539:** (bottom) Imagechina via AP Images; **p. 540:** (top) © Gunter Marx/Alamy; **p. 540:** (bottom) Photo courtesy of Jake Eaton, Director Research & Resource Planning, GreenWood Resources, Inc., www.greenwoodresources.com; **p. 541:** (top right) ROBERT BROOK/SCIENCE PHOTO LIBRARY; **p. 541:** (top right) Courtesy of Ken Hogg, M.Eng; **p. 543:** (top) Centro Gaviotas; **p. 543:** (bottom) George Steinmetz/Corbis; **p. 545:** (right) © David Overall; **p. 547:** (top right) Comstock/JUPITER IMAGES; **p. 547:** (bottom) Courtesy of Yukon Energy Corporation; **p. 549:** (top) Simon Fraser/Photo Researchers, Inc. **p. 551:** Enwave Energy Corporation; **p. 552:** © Lonely Planet Images/Alamy; **p. 555:** Photo of David Keith by University of Calgary. Reprinted by permission of David Keith.

Chapter 18 Page 561: Goodshoot/Thinkstock.com; **p. 562:** Jim Robb, Friends of the Rouge Watershed; **p. 567:** © Environmental Images/ age fotostock/MaXx Images; **p. 569:** Jim Robb, Friends of the Rouge Watershed; **p. 572:** (top left) © Andrew Holbrooke/Corbis; **p. 572:** (bottom) Louie Psihoyos/Getty Images; **p. 576:** (top) City of Edmonton; **p. 576:** (bottom) City of Edmonton; **p. 579:** Bill Sanford/Sun Media; **p. 582:** Bill Hinton Photography/Getty Images; **p. 583:** (bottom) © Visions of America, LLC/Alamy; **p. 583:** (top) ROBERT BROOK/SCIENCE PHOTO LIBRARY; **p. 587:** Photograph of Brennain Lloyd. Reprinted by permission of Brennain Lloyd.

Chapter 19 Page 593: Bill Brooks/Masterfile; **p. 594:** AFP/Getty Images; **p. 595:** (left) PAUL RAPSON/SCIENCE PHOTO LIBRARY; **p. 595:** DR JEREMY BURGESS/SCIENCE PHOTO LIBRARY; **p. 597:** (top left) iStockphoto/Thinkstock; **p. 597:** (top right) SINCLAIR STAMMERS/SCIENCE PHOTO LIBRARY; **p. 597:** (bottom left) © Ivanov_ark | GetStock.com; **p. 597:** (bottom right) Ryan McVay/Thinkstock; **p. 604:** © imagebroker/Alamy; **p. 605:** © Bettmann/CORBIS; **p. 606:** (left) © Bettmann/CORBIS; **p. 606:** (right) James L. Stanfield/National Geographic/ Getty Images; **p. 609:** (top) © Olga_sweet | GetStock.com; **p. 609:** (bottom) David De Lossy/Thinkstock; **p. 612:** (top left) Charles Shuster/New Mexico State University; **p. 612:** (top right) Charles Shuster/New Mexico State University; **p. 616:** John Harrison, Stanford University; **p. 617:** Guillette EA, Meza MM, Aquilar MG, Soto AD, Garcia IE 1998. An anthropological approach to the evaluation of preschool children exposed to pesticides in Mexico. Environ Health Perspect 106:347-353. http://dx.doi.org/10.1289/ehp.98106347; **p. 623:** Photograph of Wendy Mesley. Reprinted by permission of Wendy Mesley and CBC Still Photo Collection.

Chapter 20 Page 628: Gail Mooney/Masterfile ; **p. 629:** Courtesy of Vancouver Convention Centre; **p. 631:** (top) Corbis Premium RF/Alamy; **p. 631:** (bottom) Radius Images/All Canada Photos; **p. 634:** Stockbyte/Thinkstock; **p. 635:** (left) Courtesy of NASA/Earth Observatory; **p. 635:** (right) Courtesy of NASA/Earth Observatory; **p. 636:** (top left) © Pete Mcbride/National Geographic Society/Corbis; **p. 636:** (top right) © Bob Krist/CORBIS; **p. 636:** (bottom left) Hemera/Thinkstock.com; **p. 636:**

(bottom right) Aldo Torelli/Stone/Getty Images; **p. 639:** (top) Nova Scotia Archives: V7/239 Broughton/Neg no. O/S N-70; **p. 639:** (bottom) Plan of the "Model City", Mount Royal, Quebec by MacKenzie, Mann & Co. Ltd for the Canadian Northern Railway May 1913.; **p. 641:** Time & Life Pictures/Getty Images; **p. 643:** (top) © Carlos Cazalis/Corbis; **p. 643:** (bottom) George Grantham Bain Collection/Library of Congress; **p. 644:** Ahchang/GetStock.com; **p. 645:** (top) Dick Hemingway; **p. 645:** (bottom) AFP/Getty Images; **p. 648:** © Sally and Richard Greenhill/Alamy; **p. 649:** Reprinted by permission of Nola-Kate Seymoar.

Chapter 21 Page 654: Photo courtesy of The Diavik Diamond Mine; **p. 655:** Library and Archives Canada, PA-061609; **p. 658:** (top) Courtesy of Australia Department of Lands; **p. 658:** (bottom) GERRY ELLIS/MINDEN PICTURES/National Geographic Stock; **p. 659:** (top) The Gundjehmi Aboriginal Corporation; **p. 659:** (bottom) Courtesy of Vale Archive; **p. 664:** Library of Congress; **p. 665:** (left) NORMA JOSEPH/Alamy; **p. 665:** (right) Library and Archives Canada, PA-121371; **p. 666:** Corbis; **p. 667:** (left) © Right Livelihood Award Foundation. www.rightlivelihood.org; **p. 667:** (right) © Patrick Robert/Corbis; **p. 668:** ANTONIO SCORZA/AFP/ Getty Images; **p. 675:** MAST IRHAM/EPA /Landov; **p. 679:** (top left) Bob Suir/GetStock.com; **p. 679:** (right bottom) iStockphoto.com/Thinkstock; **p. 679:** (top middle) iStockphoto.com/Thinkstock; **p. 679:** (left middle) Tbarrat/GetStock.com; **p. 679:** (middle centre) Frans Lanting/Corbis; **p. 679:** (bottom left) © Sally and Richard Greenhill/Alamy; **p. 679:** (bottom middle) Pgiam/iStockphoto.com; **p. 681:** © Gerry Rousseau/Alamy; **p. 682:** Reprinted by permission of Matthew Coon Come.

Chapter 22 Page 688: © Peter Johnson/CORBIS; **p. 689:** Jeff Schmaltz, MODIS Land Rapid Response Team, NASA GSFC; **p. 690:** NOAA/ Center of Excellence for Great Lakes and Human Health (CEGLHH); **p. 693:** BEAWIHARTA/Reuters /Landov; **p. 699:** Ms Fr 112 f.5 The Round Table and the Holy Grail, from the 'Livre de Messire Lancelot du Lac', 1470 (vellum) by French School (15th century) Bibliotheque Nationale, Paris, France/ The Bridgeman Art Library; **p. 700:** Library and Archives Canada, PA-094969; **p. 701:** (left) Library and Archives Canada, PA-011632; **p. 701:** (right) © Pittsburgh Post-Gazette/ZUMA Press/Corbis; **p. 702:** (top) Bettmann/CORBIS; **p. 702:** (bottom) © Bettmann/CORBIS; **p. 703:** (left) © Santi Visalli/age fotostock/MaXx Images; **p. 703:** (right) AP Photo/ Binod Joshi; **p. 703:** (bottom left) The word mark "Earth Day" and the Earth Day logo are registered trademarks of Earth Day Canada (1991) Inc. Use of these trademarks are for mercantile, promotional and communication purposes are strictly forbidden without the written approval of Earth Day Canada.; **p. 705:** Robert Wallis/Panos; **p. 706:** © Don Boroughs/The Image Works; **p. 709:** Ocean Imaging Inc.; **p. 710:** © Mark Karrass/Corbis; **p. 713:** © Peter Bowater/Alamy; **p. 715:** Photograph of Maude Barlow. Reprinted by permission of Maude Barlow; **p. 716:** Philip Rostron/Masterfile; **p. 717:** © Realimage/Alamy.

Chapter 23 Page 722: Moe Down, Summerhill Impact, www.summerhill-group.ca; **p. 723:** Car Heaven, Summerhill Impact, www.summerhillgroup. ca; **p. 726:** Barbara Murck; **p. 727:** (bottom) Gorilla Composting; **p. 727:** (inset) Gorilla Composting; **p. 728:** Project: Child Development Centre, University of Calgary. Architect: Kasian.; **p. 729:** Don Pierce/UVic Photo Services; **p. 730:** Al Jaugelis - Innotech Windows; **p. 731:** Christopher DeWolf; **p. 732:** Cindy Lopez/The Concordian; **p. 733:** Jay Wilson; **p. 734:** Sierra Youth Coalition; **p. 736:** Galen Rowell/CORBIS; **p. 738:** © Dorothy Alexander/Alamy; **p. 739:** John Howard/Riser/Getty Images; **p. 741:** NORMAND BLOUIN/AFP/Getty Images; **p. 745:** Profile and photograph of Keleigh Annau. Reprinted by permission of Keleigh Annau.; **p. 746:** Courtesy of NASA.

Selected References for Further Reading

Chapter 1

Bahn, Paul, and John Flenley. 1992. *Easter Island, Earth island*. Thames and Hudson, London.

Diamond, Jared. 2005. *Collapse: How societies choose to fail or succeed*. Viking, New York.

Edwards, Andres R. 2005. *The sustainability revolution: Portrait of a paradigm shift*. New Society Publishers, Gabriola Island, British Columbia, Canada.

Ehrlich, Paul. 1968. *The population bomb*, 1997 reprint. Buccaneer Books, Cutchogue, New York.

Global Footprint Network. 2009. *How we can bend the curve: Global Footprint Network annual report*. Oakland, California. www.footprintnetwork.org

Global Footprint Network. 2010. *The ecological wealth of nations*. Oakland, California.

Goudie, Andrew. 2005. *The human impact on the natural environment*, 6th ed. Blackwell Publishing, London.

Hardin, Garrett. 1968. The tragedy of the commons. *Science* 162: 1243–1248.

Hunt, Terry L., and Carl P. Lipo. 2006. Late colonization of Easter Island. *Science* 311: 1603–1606.

Lomborg, Bjorn. 2001. *The skeptical environmentalist: Measuring the real state of the world*. Cambridge University Press, Cambridge.

Malthus, Thomas R. 1983. *An essay on the principle of population*, Penguin USA, New York.

Millennium Ecosystem Assessment. 2005. *Ecosystems and human well-being: General synthesis*. Millennium Ecosystem Assessment and World Resources Institute.

Sagan, Carl. 1997. *The demon-haunted world: Science as a candle in the dark*. Ballantine Books, New York.

U.N. Environment Program. 2007. *Global environment outlook 4 (GEO-4)*. UNEP and Progress Press, Nairobi and Malta.

Venetoulis, Jason, and John Talberth. 2005. *Ecological footprint of nations: 2005 update*. Redefining Progress, Oakland, California.

Wackernagel, Mathis, and William Rees. 1996. *Our ecological footprint: Reducing human impact on the earth*. New Society Publishers, Gabriola Island, British Columbia, Canada.

Wackernagel, Mathis, et al. 2002. Tracking the ecological overshoot of the human economy. *Proceedings of the National Academy of Sciences of the USA* 99: 9266–9271.

Worldwatch Institute. 2010. *Vital signs 2010*. Worldwatch Institute, Washington, D.C. http://vitalsigns.worldwatch.org

WWF–World Wide Fund for Nature. 2010. *Living planet report 2010*. WWF, Gland, Switzerland.

Chapter 2

Berardelli, Phil. 2008. Human-driven plant: Time to make it official? *ScienceNOW*, 24 Jan. 2008. http://sciencenow.sciencemag.org/cgi/content/full/2008/124/1

Berry, R. Stephen. 1991. *Understanding energy: Energy, entropy and thermodynamics for every man*. World Scientific Publishing Co.

Craig, James R., David J. Vaughan, and Brian J. Skinner. 2010. *Earth resources and the environment*, 4th ed. Benjamin Cummings, San Francisco.

Fenchel, Tom. 2003. *Origin and early evolution of life*. Oxford University Press, Oxford.

Fortey, Richard. 1998. *Life: A natural history of the first four billion years of life on Earth*. Alfred Knopf, New York.

Van Ness, H.C. 1983. *Understanding thermodynamics*. Dover Publications, Mineola, New York.

Ward, Peter D., and Donald Brownlee. 2000. *Rare Earth: Why complex life is uncommon in the universe*. Copernicus, New York.

Wassenaar, Leonard I., and Keith A. Hobson. 1998. Natal origins of migratory monarch butterflies at wintering colonies in Mexico: New isotopic evidence. *Proceedings of the National Academy of Sciences of the USA* 95: 15436–15439.

Zalasiewicz, Jan. Are we now living in the Anthropocene? *GSA Today* 18(2): 4-8.

Chapter 3

Appenzeller, Tim. 2004. The case of the missing carbon. *National Geographic*, February 2004: 88–117.

Capra, Fritjof. 1996. *The web of life: A new scientific understanding of living systems*. Anchor Books Doubleday, New York.

Carpenter, Edward J., and Douglas G. Capone, eds. 1983. *Nitrogen in the marine environment*. Academic Press, New York.

Christopherson, Robert W. 2006. *Geosystems*, 6th ed. Prentice Hall, Upper Saddle River, New Jersey.

Diaz, Robert J., and Rutger Rosenberg. 2008. Spreading dead zones and consequences for marine ecosystems. *Science* 321: 926–929.

Ferber, Dan. 2004. Dead zone fix not a dead issue. *Science* 305: 1557.

Gruber, Nicolas, and James N. Galloway. 2008. An Earth-system perspective of the global nitrogen cycle. *Nature* 451: 293–296.

Jacobson, Michael, et al. 2000. *Earth system science from biogeochemical cycles to global changes*. Academic Press, San Diego, California.

Skinner, Brian J., and Stephen C. Porter. 2003. *The dynamic Earth: An introduction to physical geology*, 5th ed. John Wiley and Sons, Hoboken, New Jersey.

Takahashi, Taro. 2004. The fate of industrial carbon dioxide. *Science* 305: 352–353.

Turner, R. Eugene, and Nancy N. Rabalais. 2003. Linking landscape and water quality in the Mississippi River Basin for 200 years. *Bio Science* 53: 563–572.

Vitousek, Peter M., et al. 1997. Human alteration of the global nitrogen cycle: Sources and consequences. *Ecological Applications* 7: 737–750.

Wu, Jianguo, and Richard J. Hobbs, eds. 2007. *Key topics in landscape ecology*. Cambridge University Press, Cambridge.

Chapter 4

Alvarez, Luis W., et al. 1980. Extraterrestrial cause for the Cretaceous-Tertiary extinction. *Science* 208: 1095–1108.

Begon, Michael, Colin R. Townsend, and John L. Harper. 2005. *Ecology: From individuals to ecosystems*, 4th ed. Blackwell Publishing, London.

Campbell, Neil A., and Jane B. Reece. 2005. *Biology*, 7th ed. Benjamin Cummings, San Francisco.

Crump, L. Martha, et al. 1992. Apparent decline of the golden toad: Underground or extinct? *Copeia* 1992: 413–420.

Darwin, Charles. 1859. *The origin of species by means of natural selection*. John Murray, London.

Endler, John A. 1986. *Natural selection in the wild*. Monographs in Population Biology 21, Princeton University Press, Princeton, New Jersey.

Futuyma, Douglas J. 2009. *Evolution*, 2nd ed. Sinauer Associates, Sunderland, Massachusetts.

Krebs, Charles J. 2001. *Ecology: The experimental analysis of distribution and abundance*, 5th ed. Benjamin Cummings, San Francisco.

Molles, Manuel C. 2010. *Ecology: Concepts and applications*, 4th ed. McGraw-Hill, Boston.

Pounds, J. Alan, et al. 2006. Widespread amphibian extinctions from epidemic disease driven by global warming. *Nature* 439: 161–167.

Pounds, J. Alan, and Martha L. Crump. 1994. Amphibian declines and climate disturbance: The case of the golden toad and the harlequin frog. *Conservation Biology* 8: 72–85.

Powell, James L. 1998. *Night comes to the Cretaceous: Dinosaur extinction and the transformation of modern geology*. W. H. Freeman, New York.

Raup, David M. 1991. *Extinction: Bad genes or bad luck?* W. W. Norton, New York.

Rohr, Jason R., et al. 2008. Evaluating the links between climate, disease spread, and amphibian declines. *PNAS* 105: 17436–17441.

Savage, Jay M. 1966. An extraordinary new toad (*Bufo*) from Costa Rica. *Revista de Biologia Tropical* 14: 153–167.

Savage, Jay M. 1998. The "brilliant toad" was telling us something. *Christian Science Monitor*, 14 September 1998.

Wilson, Edward O. 1992. *The diversity of life*. Harvard University Press, Cambridge, Massachusetts.

Chapter 5

Baskin, Yvonne. 2002. *A plague of rats and rubbervines: The growing threat of species invasions*. Island Press, Washington, D.C.

Breckle, Siegmar-Walter. 2002. *Walter's vegetation of the Earth: The ecological systems of the geo-biosphere*, 4th ed. Springer-Verlag, Berlin.

Bright, Chris. 1998. *Life out of bounds: Bioinvasion in a borderless world*. Worldwatch Institute and W. W. Norton, Washington, D.C., and New York.

Bronstein, Judith L. 1994. Our current understanding of mutualism. *Quarterly Journal of Biology* 69: 31–51.

Chase, Jonathan M., et al. 2002. The interaction between predation and competition: A review and synthesis. *Ecology Letters* 5: 302.

Clewell, Andre F., and James Aronson. 2008. *Ecological restoration: Principles, values, and structure of an emerging profession*. Island Press, Washington, D.C.

Connell, Joseph H., and Ralph O. Slatyer. 1977. Mechanisms of succession in natural communities. *American Naturalist* 111: 1119–1144.

Drake, John M., and Jonathan M. Bossenbroek. 2004. The potential distribution of zebra mussels in the United States. *Bio Science* 54: 931–941.

Ewald, Paul W. 1987. Transmission modes and evolution of the parasitism-mutualism continuum. *Annals of the New York Academy of Sciences* 503: 295–306.

Gurevitch, Jessica, and Dianna K. Padilla. 2004. Are invasive species a major cause of extinctions? *Trends in Ecology and Evolution* 19: 470–474.

Hobbs, Richard J., et al. 2006. *Foundations of restoration ecology: The science and practice of ecological restoration*. Island Press, Washington, D.C.

Menge, Bruce A., et al. 1994. The keystone species concept: Variation in interaction strength in a rocky intertidal habitat. *Ecological Monographs* 64: 249–286.

Morin, Peter J. 1999. *Community ecology*. Blackwell, London.

Power, Mary E., et al. 1996. Challenges in the quest for keystones. *Bio Science* 46: 609–620.

Shea, Katriona, and Peter Chesson. 2002. Community ecology theory as a framework for biological invasions. *Trends in Ecology and Evolutionary Biology* 17: 170–176.

Sih, Andrew, et al. 1985. Predation, competition, and prey communities: A review of field experiments. *Annual Review of Ecology and Systematics* 16: 269–311.

Strayer, David L. 2009. Twenty years of zebra mussels: Lessons from the mollusk that made headlines. *Frontiers in Ecology and the Environment* 7: 135–141.

Thompson, John N. 1999. The evolution of species interactions. *Science* 284: 2116–2118.

Van Andel, Jelte, and James Aronson. 2005. *Restoration ecology: The new frontier*. Blackwell Publishing, London.

Woodward, Susan L. 2003. *Biomes of Earth: Terrestrial, aquatic, and human-dominated*. Greenwood Publishing, Westport, Connecticut.

Chapter 6

Ausubel, Jesse H. 1996. Can technology spare the earth? *American Scientist* 84: 166–178.

Ball, Philip. 2008. Where have all the flowers gone? [China's one-child legacy.] *Nature* 454: 374–375.

Balter, Michael. 2006. The baby deficit. *Science* 312: 1894–1897.

Cohen, Joel E. 1995. *How many people can the Earth support?* W. W. Norton, New York.

Cohen, Joel E. 2003. Human population: The next half century. *Science* 302: 1172–1175.

Cohen, Joel E. 2005. Human population grows up. *Scientific American* 293(3): 48–55.

De Souza, Roger-Mark, et al. 2003. Critical links: Population, health, and the environment. *Population Bulletin* 58(3). Population Reference Bureau, Washington, D.C.

Eberstadt, Nicholas. 2000. China's population prospects: Problems ahead. *Problems of Post-Communism* 47: 28.

Ehrlich, Paul R., and Anne H. Ehrlich. 1990. *The population explosion*. Touchstone, New York.

Ehrlich, Paul R., and John P. Holdren. 1971. Impact of population growth: Complacency concerning this component of man's predicament is unjustified and counterproductive. *Science* 171: 1212–1217.

Engelman, Robert, Brian Halweil, and Danielle Nierenberg. 2002. Rethinking population, improving lives. Pp. 127–148 in *State of the world 2002*. Worldwatch Institute and W. W. Norton, Washington, D.C., and New York.

Greenhalgh, Susan. 2001. Fresh winds in Beijing: Chinese feminists speak out on the one-child policy and women's lives. *Signs: Journal of Women in Culture & Society* 26: 847–887.

Harrison, Paul, and Fred Pearce, eds. 2000. *AAAS atlas of population & environment*. University of California Press, Berkeley.

Haub, Carl, and O.P. Sharma. 2006. India's population reality: Reconciling change and tradition. *Population Bulletin* 61(3). Population Reference Bureau, Washington, D.C.

Imhoff, Marc L., et al. 2004. Global patterns in human consumption of net primary production. *Nature* 429: 870–873.

Kent, Mary M., and Carl Haub. 2005. Global demographic divide. *Population Bulletin* 60(4). Population Reference Bureau, Washington, D.C.

Mastny, Lisa, and Richard P. Cincotta. 2005. Examining the connections between population and security. Pp. 22–41 in *State of the world 2005*. Worldwatch Institute and W. W. Norton, Washington, D.C., and New York.

McDonald, Mia, with Danielle Nierenberg. 2003. Linking population, women, and biodiversity. Pp. 38–61 in *State of the world 2003*. Worldwatch Institute and W. W. Norton, Washington D.C., and New York.

Meadows, Donella, Jørgen Randers, and Dennis Meadows. 2004. *Limits to growth: The 30-year update*. Chelsea Green Publishing Co., White River Junction, Vermont.

Notestein, Frank. 1953. Economic problems of population change. Pp. 13–31 in *Proceedings of the Eighth International Conference of Agricultural Economists*. Oxford University Press, London.

Population Reference Bureau. 2010. *2010 world population data sheet*. Population Reference Bureau, Washington, D.C.

United Nations Population Division. 2010. *World population prospects: The 2009 revision*. UNPD, New York.

United Nations Population Fund. 2010. *The Millennium Development Goals report 2010*. UNFPA, New York.

Wackernagel, Mathis, and William Rees. 1996. *Our ecological footprint: Reducing human impact on the earth*. New Society Publishers, Gabriola Island, British Columbia, Canada.

Chapter 7

Ashman, Mark R., and Geeta Puri. 2002. *Essential soil science: A clear and concise introduction to soil science*. Blackwell Publishing, Malden, Massachusetts.

Charman, P.E.V., and Brian W. Murphy. 2000. *Soils: Their properties and management*, 2nd ed. Oxford University Press, South Melbourne, Australia.

Curtin, Charles. 2007. Integrating landscape and ecosystems approaches through science-based collaborative conservation. *Conservation Biology*, 21(4): 1117–1119.

Glanz, James. 1995. *Saving our soil: Solutions for sustaining Earth's vital resource*. Johnson Books, Boulder, Colorado.

Goudie, Andrew. 2000. *The human impact on the natural environment*, 5th ed. MIT Press, Cambridge, Massachusetts.

Harrison, Paul, and Fred Pearce, eds. 2000. *AAAS atlas of population & environment*. University of California Press, Berkeley.

Jenny, Hans. 1941. *Factors of soil formation: A system of quantitative pedology*. McGraw-Hill, New York.

Kaiser, Jocelyn. 2004. Wounding Earth's fragile skin. *Science* 304: 1616–1618.

Larsen, Janet. 2003. Deserts advancing, civilization retreating. *Eco-Economy Update #23*, 27 March 2003. Earth Policy Institute. www.earth-policy.org/Updates/Update23.htm

Millennium Ecosystem Assessment. 2005. *Ecosystems and human wellbeing: Desertification synthesis*. Millennium Ecosystem Assessment and World Resources Institute.

Montgomery, David R. 2007. Soil erosion and agricultural sustainability. *PNAS* 104: 13268–13272.

Morgan, R.P.C. 2005. *Soil erosion and conservation*, 3rd ed. Blackwell, London.

Pierzynski, Gary M., et al. 2005. *Soils and environmental quality*, 3rd ed. CRC Press, Boca Raton, Florida.

Richter, Daniel D., Jr., and Daniel Markewitz. 2001. *Understanding soil change: Soil sustainability over millennia, centuries, and decades*. Cambridge University Press, Cambridge.

Soil Science Society of America. 2001. Internet glossary of soil science terms. www.soils.org/sssagloss

Stocking, M.A. 2003. Tropical soils and food security: The next 50 years. *Science* 302: 1356–1359.

Wilkinson, Bruce H. 2005. Humans as geologic agents: A deep-time perspective. *Geology* 33: 161–164.

Chapter 8

Bazzaz, Fakhri A. 2001. Plant biology in the future. *Proceedings of the National Academy of Sciences of the United States of America* 98: 5441–5445.

Brown, Lester R. 2002. World's rangelands deteriorating under mounting pressure. *Eco-Economy Update #6*, 5 February 2002. Earth Policy Institute. www.earth-policy.org/Updates/Update6.htm

Brown, Lester R. 2004. *Outgrowing the Earth: The food security challenge in an age of falling water tables and rising temperatures*. Earth Policy Institute, Washington, D.C.

Buchmann, Stephen L., and Gary Paul Nabhan. 1996. *The forgotten pollinators*. Island Press/Shearwater Books, Washington, D.C./Covelo, California.

Center for Food Safety. 2005. *Monsanto vs. U.S. farmers*. Center for Food Safety, Washington, D.C.

Commission for Environmental Cooperation. 2004. *Maize and biodiversity: The effects of transgenic maize in Mexico*. CEC Secretariat.

Diamond, Jared. 1999. *Guns, germs, and steel: The fates of human societies*. W. W. Norton, New York.

Diamond, Jared, and Peter Bellwood. 2003. Farmers and their languages: The first expansions. *Science* 300: 597–603.

The Farm Scale Evaluations of spring-sown genetically modified crops. 2003. A themed issue from *Philosophical Transactions of the Royal Society of London B: Biological Sciences* 358(1439), 29 November 2003.

Fedoroff, Nina, and Nancy Marie Brown. 2004. *Mendel in the kitchen: A scientist's view of genetically modified foods*. National Academies Press, Washington, D.C.

Food and Agriculture Organization of the United Nations. 2001. Conservation agriculture: Case studies in Latin America and Africa. *FAO Soils Bulletin No. 78*. FAO, Rome.

Food and Agriculture Organization of the United Nations. 2009. *The state of food insecurity in the world*. FAO, Rome.

Food and Agriculture Organization of the United Nations. 2009. *The state of world fisheries and aquaculture 2008*. FAO Fisheries and Aquaculture Department, Rome.

Gardner, Gary, and Brian Halweil. 2000. *Underfed and overfed: The global epidemic of malnutrition*. Worldwatch Paper #150. Worldwatch Institute, Washington, D.C.

Halweil, Brian. 2004. *Eat here: Reclaiming homegrown pleasures in a global supermarket*. Worldwatch Institute, Washington, D.C.

Halweil, Brian, and Danielle Niereberg. 2004. Watching what we eat. Pp. 68–95 in *State of the world 2004*. Worldwatch Institute and W. W. Norton, Washington, D.C., and New York.

International Food Information Council. 2004. Food biotechnology. IFIC, Washington, D.C. www.ific.org/food/biotechnology/index.cfm

James, Clive. 2010. *Global status of commercialized biotech/GM crops: 2009*. International Service for the Acquisition of Agri-biotech Applications.

Kristiansen, P., A. Taji, and J. Reganold, eds. 2006. *Organic agriculture: A global perspective*. CABI Publishing, Oxfordshire, U.K.

Kuiper, Harry A. 2000. Risks of the release of transgenic herbicide-resistant plants with respect to humans, animals, and the environment. *Crop Protection* 19: 773.

Liebig, Mark A., and John W. Doran. 1999. Impact of organic production practices on soil quality indicators. *Journal of Environmental Quality* 28: 1601–1609.

Losey, John E., Linda S. Raynor, and Maureen E. Carter. 1999. Transgenic pollen harms monarch larvae. *Nature* 399: 214.

Maeder, Paul, et al. 2002. Soil fertility and biodiversity in organic farming. *Science* 296: 1694–1697.

Mann, Charles C. 2002. Transgene data deemed unconvincing. *Science* 296: 236–237.

Manning, Richard. 2000. *Food's frontier: The next green revolution*. North Point Press, New York.

Miller, Henry I., and Gregory Conko. 2004. *The frankenfood myth: How protest and politics threaten the biotech revolution*. Praeger Publishers, Westport, Connecticut.

Nestle, Marion. 2002. *Food politics: How the food industry influences nutrition and health*. University of California–Berkeley Press, Berkeley.

Nierenberg, Danielle. 2005. *Happier meals: Rethinking the global meat industry*. Worldwatch Paper #171. Worldwatch Institute, Washington, D.C.

Nierenberg, Danielle. 2006. Meat consumption and output up. Pp. 24–25 in *Vital signs 2006–2007*. Worldwatch Institute and W. W. Norton, Washington, D.C., and New York.

Nierenberg, Danielle, and Brian Halweil. 2005. Cultivating food security. Pp. 62–79 in *State of the world 2005*. Worldwatch Institute and W. W. Norton, Washington, D.C., and New York.

Norris, Robert F., Edward P. Caswell-Chen, and Marcos Kogan. 2002. *Concepts in integrated pest management*. Prentice Hall, Upper Saddle River, New Jersey.

Pearce, Fred. 2002. The great Mexican maize scandal. *New Scientist* 174(2347): 14.

Pedigo, Larry P., and Marlin E. Rice. 2006. *Entomology and pest management*, 5th ed. Prentice Hall, Upper Saddle River, New Jersey.

Pimentel, David. 1999. Population growth, environmental resources, and the global availability of food. *Social Research*, Spring 1999.

Pinstrup-Andersen, Per, and Ebbe Schioler. 2001. *Seeds of contention: World hunger and the global controversy over GM (genetically modified) crops*. International Food Policy Research Institute, Washington, D.C.

Polak, Paul. 2005. The big potential of small farms. *Scientific American* 293(3): 84–91.

Pretty, Jules, and Rachel Hine. 2001. *Reducing food poverty with sustainable agriculture: A summary of new evidence*. Occasional Paper 2001-2. Center for Environment and Society, University of Essex.

Pringle, Peter. 2003. *Food, Inc.: Mendel to Monsanto—The promises and perils of the biotech harvest*. Simon and Schuster, New York.

Quist, David, and Ignacio H. Chapela. 2001. Transgenic DNA introgressed into traditional maize landraces in Oaxaca, Mexico. *Nature* 414: 541–543.

Ruse, Michael, and David Castle, eds. 2002. *Genetically modified foods: Debating technology*. Prometheus Books, Amherst, New York.

Schmeiser, Percy. 2004. Monsanto vs. Schmeiser. www.percyschmeiser.com

Shiva, Vandana. 2000. *Stolen harvest: The hijacking of the global food supply*. South End Press, Cambridge, Massachusetts.

Smil, Vaclav. 2001. *Feeding the world: A challenge for the twenty-first century*. MIT Press, Cambridge, Massachusetts.

Smith, Alisa, and J.B. MacKinnon. 2007. *The 100-mile diet: A year of local eating*. Random House, Canada.

Stewart, C. Neal. 2004. *Genetically modified planet: Environmental impacts of genetically engineered plants*. Oxford University Press, Oxford.

Teitel, Martin, and Kimberly Wilson. 2001. *Genetically engineered food: Changing the nature of nature*. Park Street Press.

Weasel, Lisa. 2008. *Food fray: Inside the controversy over genetically modified food.* AMACOM Books.

Willer, Helga. 2010. Organic agriculture worldwide. The main results of the FiBL-IFOAM survey 2010. www.fibl.org

Willer, H., and L. Klicher, eds. 2009. *The world of organic agriculture: Statistics and emerging trends 2009.* FiBL and IFOAM, Bonn and Frick.

Chapter 9

Balmford, Andrew, et al. 2002. Economic reasons for conserving wild nature. *Science* 297: 950–953.

Barnosky, Anthony D., et al. 2004. Assessing the causes of late Pleistocene extinctions on the continents. *Science* 306: 70–75.

Baskin, Yvonne. 1997. *The work of nature: How the diversity of life sustains us.* Island Press, Washington, D.C.

Bright, Chris. 1998. *Life out of bounds: Bioinvasion in a borderless world.* Worldwatch Institute and W. W. Norton, Washington D.C., and New York.

CITES Secretariat. Convention on International Trade in Endangered Species of Wild Fauna and Flora. www.cites.org

Convention on Biological Diversity. www.biodiv.org

Daily, Gretchen C., ed. 1997. *Nature's services: Societal dependence on natural ecosystems.* Island Press, Washington, D.C.

Ehrenfeld, David W. 1970. *Biological conservation.* International Thomson Publishing, London.

Gaston, Kevin J., and John I. Spicer. 2004. *Biodiversity: An introduction,* 2nd ed. Blackwell, London.

Groom, Martha J., et al. 2005. *Principles of conservation biology,* 3rd ed. Sinauer Associates, Sunderland, Massachusetts.

Groombridge, Brian, and Martin D. Jenkins. 2002. *Global biodiversity: Earth's living resources in the 21st century.* UNEP, World Conservation Monitoring Centre, and Aventis Foundation; World Conservation Press, Cambridge, U.K.

Groombridge, Brian, and Martin D. Jenkins. 2002. *World atlas of biodiversity: Earth's living resources in the 21st century.* University of California Press, Berkeley.

Harris, Larry D. 1984. *The fragmented forest: Island biogeography theory and the preservation of biotic diversity.* University of Chicago Press, Chicago.

Jenkins, Martin. 2003. Prospects for biodiversity. *Science* 302: 1175–1177.

Louv, Richard. 2005. *Last child in the woods: Saving our children from nature-deficit disorder.* Algonquin Books, Chapel Hill, North Carolina.

Lovejoy, Thomas E., and Lee Hannah, eds. 2006. *Climate change and biodiversity.* Yale University Press, New Haven, Connecticut.

MacArthur, Robert H., and Edward O. Wilson. 1967. *The theory of island biogeography.* Princeton University Press, Princeton, New Jersey.

Maehr, David S., Reed F. Noss, and Jeffrey Larkin, eds. 2001. *Large mammal restoration: Ecological and sociological challenges in the 21st century.* Island Press, Washington, D.C.

Matthiessen, Peter. 2000. *Tigers in the snow.* North Point Press, New York.

Meegaskumbura, Madhava, et al. 2002. Sri Lanka: An amphibian hot spot. *Science* 298: 379.

Millennium Ecosystem Assessment. 2005. *Ecosystems and human wellbeing: Biodiversity synthesis.* Millennium Ecosystem Assessment and World Resources Institute.

Mooney, Harold A., and Richard J. Hobbs, eds. 2000. *Invasive species in a changing world.* Island Press, Washington, D.C.

Newmark, William D. 1987. A land-bridge perspective on mammal extinctions in western North American parks. *Nature* 325: 430.

Pimm, Stuart L., and Clinton Jenkins. 2005. Sustaining the variety of life. *Scientific American* 293(3): 66–73.

Primack, Richard B. 2006. *Essentials of conservation biology,* 4th ed. Sinauer Associates, Sunderland, Massachusetts.

Quammen, David. 1996. *The song of the dodo: Island biogeography in an age of extinction.* Touchstone, New York.

Simberloff, Daniel. 1998. Flagships, umbrellas, and keystones: Is single-species management passé in the landscape era? *Biological Conservation* 83: 247–257.

Simberloff, Daniel S., and Edward O. Wilson. 1969. Experimental zoogeography of islands: The colonization of empty islands. *Ecology* 50: 278–296.

Simberloff, Daniel S., and Edward O. Wilson. 1970. Experimental zoogeography of islands: A two-year record of colonization. *Ecology* 51: 934–937.

Soulé, Michael E. 1986. *Conservation biology: The science of scarcity and diversity.* Sinauer Associates, Sunderland, Massachusetts.

Takacs, David. 1996. *The idea of biodiversity: Philosophies of paradise.* Johns Hopkins University Press, Baltimore, Maryland.

United Nations Environment Programme. 2003. Sustaining life on Earth: How the Convention on Biological Diversity promotes nature and human well-being. www.biodiv.org/doc/publications/guide.asp

Wilson, Edward O. 1984. *Biophilia.* Harvard University Press, Cambridge, Massachusetts.

Wilson, Edward O. 1992. *The diversity of life.* Harvard University Press, Cambridge, Massachusetts.

Wilson, Edward O. 1994. *Naturalist.* Island Press, Shearwater Books, Washington, D.C.

Wilson, Edward O. 2002. *The future of life.* Alfred A. Knopf, New York.

Wilson, Edward O., and Daniel S. Simberloff. 1969. Experimental zoogeography of islands: Defaunation and monitoring techniques. *Ecology* 50: 267–278.

World Conservation Union. IUCN Red List. www.iucnredlist.org

WWF–World Wide Fund for Nature. 2010. *Living planet report 2010.* WWF, Gland, Switzerland.

Chapter 10

British Columbia Ministry of Forests. Introduction to silvicultural systems. British Columbia Ministry of Forests, Victoria, B.C. www.for.gov.bc.ca/hfd/pubs/SSIntroworkbook/index.htm

Canadian Broadcasting Corporation. 1993. A little place called Clayoquot Sound. CBC broadcast, 13 April 1993. http://archives.cbc.ca/IDC-1-75-679-3918/Science_technology/clearcutting/clip6

Donato, Daniel C., et al. 2006. Post-wildfire logging hinders regeneration and increases fire risk. *Science* 311: 352.

Food and Agriculture Organization of the United Nations. 2009. *State of the world's forests 2009.* FAO Forestry Department, Rome.

Food and Agriculture Organization of the United Nations. 2010. *Global forest resources assessment.* FAO Forestry Department, Rome.

Foster, Bryan C., and Peggy Foster. 2002. *Wild logging: A guide to environmentally and economically sustainable forestry.* Mountain Press, Missoula, Montana.

Myers, Norman, and Jennifer Kent. 2001. *Perverse subsidies: How misused tax dollars harm the environment and the economy.* Island Press, Washington, D.C.

Natural Resources Canada. 2006. *The state of Canada's forests, 2005–2006.* Natural Resources Canada, Ottawa.

Singh, Ashbindu, et al. 2001. *An assessment of the status of the world's remaining closed forests.* United Nations Environmental Program, UNEP/DEWA/TR 01–2l, August 2001.

Smith, David M., et al. 1996. *The practice of silviculture: Applied forest ecology,* 9th ed. Wiley, New York.

Stegner, Wallace. 1954. *Beyond the hundredth meridian: John Wesley Powell and the second opening of the West.* Houghton Mifflin, Boston.

Chapter 11

Brugge, Doug, and Rob Goble. 2002. The history of uranium mining and the Navajo people. *American Journal of Public Health* 92(9): 1410–1419.

Cohen, David. 2007. Earth's natural wealth: an audit. *New Scientist* 2605: 34–41.

Craig, James R., David J. Vaughan, and Brian J. Skinner. 2010. *Earth resources and the environment,* 4th ed. Benjamin Cummings, San Francisco.

Essick, Kristi. 2001. Guns, money, and cell phones. *The Industry Standard Magazine,* 11 June 2001.

Gordon, R.B., et al. 2006. Metal stocks and sustainability. *PNAS* 103(5): 1209–1214.

Harden, Blaine. 2001. The dirt in the new machine. *New York Times Magazine,* 12 Aug. 2001.

Keller, Edward A. 2008. *Introduction to environmental geology*, 4th ed. Prentice Hall, Upper Saddle River, N.J.

Mooallem, Jon. 2008. The afterlife of cellphones. *New York Times Magazine*, 13 Jan. 2008.

Rogich, D.G., and G.R. Matos. 2008. *The global flows of metals and minerals: U.S. Geological Survey Open-File Report 2008-1355*, 11 pp. available only online at http://pubs.usgs.gov/of/2008/1355/

Chapter 12

American Rivers. 2002. *The ecology of dam removal: A summary of benefits and impacts.* American Rivers, Washington, D.C.

De Villiers, Marq. 2000. *Water: The fate of our most precious resource.* Mariner Books.

Gleick, Peter H. 2003. Global freshwater resources: Soft-path solutions for the 21st century. *Science* 302: 1524–1527.

Gleick, Peter H., et al. 2006. *The world's water 2006–2007: The biennial report on freshwater resources.* Island Press, Washington, D.C.

Gleick, Peter H., and H.S. Cooley. 2009. Energy implications of bottled water. *Environmental Research Letter* 4: 014009.

Gleick, Peter H., et al. 2009. *The world's water 2008–2009: The biennial report on freshwater resources.* Island Press, Washington, D.C.

Harrison, Paul, and Fred Pearce, eds. 2000. *AAAS atlas of population & environment.* University of California Press, Berkeley.

Millennium Ecosystem Assessment. 2005. *Ecosystems and human well-being: Wetlands and water synthesis.* Millennium Ecosystem Assessment and World Resources Institute.

Pala, Christopher. 2006. Once a terminal case, the North Aral Sea shows new signs of life. *Science* 312: 183.

Postel, Sandra. 2005. *Liquid assets: The critical need to safeguard freshwater ecosystems.* Worldwatch Paper #170. Worldwatch Institute, Washington, D.C.

Postel, Sandra, and Amy Vickers. 2004. Boosting water productivity. Pp. 46–67 in *State of the world 2004.* Worldwatch Institute and W. W. Norton, Washington, D.C., and New York.

Sampat, Payal. 2001. Uncovering groundwater pollution. Pp. 21–42 in *State of the world 2001.* Worldwatch Institute and W. W. Norton, Washington, D.C., and New York.

Stone, Richard. 1999. Coming to grips with the Aral Sea's grim legacy. *Science* 284: 30–33.

United Nations Educational, Scientific and Cultural Organization (UNESCO). 2006. *Water: A shared responsibility.* The United Nations World Water Development Report 2. UNESCO and Berghahn Books, Paris and New York.

United Nations Environment Programme. 2006. *Challenges to international waters: Regional assessments in a global perspective.* UNEP, Nairobi, Kenya.

United Nations Environment Programme. 2007. Water. Pp. 115–156 in *Global environment outlook 4 (GEO-4).* UNEP and Earthscan Publications, Nairobi and London.

United Nations Environment Programme. 2008. *Water quality for ecosystem and human health*, 2nd ed. UNEP Global Environment Monitoring System (GEMS)/Water Programme, Burlington, Ontario.

United Nations World Water Assessment Programme. 2009. *U.N. world water development report: Water in a changing world.* UNESCO and Berghahn Books, Paris, New York, and Oxford.

Wolf, Aaron T., et al. 2005. Managing water conflict and cooperation. Pp. 80–99 in *State of the world 2005.* Worldwatch Institute and W. W. Norton, Washington, D.C., and New York.

World Health Organization. 2000. *Global water supply and sanitation assessment 2000 report.* WHO, Geneva, Switzerland.

Youth, Howard. 2005. Wetlands drying up. Pp. 90–91 in *Vital signs 2005.* Worldwatch Institute and W. W. Norton, Washington, D.C., and New York.

Chapter 13

Bellwood, David R., et al. 2004. Confronting the coral reef crisis. *Nature* 429: 827–833.

Embassy of the People's Republic of China. 2001. Fishing statistics "basically correct," ministry says. Press release, 18 December 2001.

Food and Agriculture Organization of the United Nations. 2002. Fishery statistics: Reliability and policy implications. FAO Fisheries Department, Rome. www.fao.org/docrep/field/006/y3354m/y3354m00.htm

Food and Agriculture Organization of the United Nations. 2007. *The state of world fisheries and aquaculture 2006.* FAO Fisheries and Aquaculture Department, Rome.

Frank, Kenneth T., et al. 2005. Trophic cascades in a formerly cod-dominated ecosystem. *Science* 308: 1621–1623.

Garrison, Tom. 2005. *Oceanography: An invitation to marine science*, 5th ed. Brooks/Cole, San Francisco.

Gell, Fiona R., and Callum M. Roberts. 2003. Benefits beyond boundaries: The fishery effects of marine reserves. *Trends in Ecology and Evolution* 18: 448–455.

Halpern, Benjamin S., and Robert R. Warner. 2002. Marine reserves have rapid and lasting effects. *Ecology Letters* 5: 361–366.

Halpern, Benjamin S., and Robert R. Warner. 2003. Matching marine reserve design to reserve objectives. *Proceedings of the Royal Society of London B*: 270: 1871–1878.

Halweil, Brian. 2006. *Catch of the day: Choosing seafood for healthier oceans.* Worldwatch Paper #172. Worldwatch Institute, Washington, D.C.

Hoegh-Guildberg, O., et al. 2007. Coral reefs under rapid climate change and ocean acidification. *Science* 318: 1737–1742.

Jackson, Jeremy B.C., et al. 2001. Historical overfishing and the recent collapse of coastal ecosystems. *Science* 293: 629–638.

Kurlansky, Mark. 1998. *Cod: A biography of the fish that changed the world.* Penguin Books, New York.

Larsen, Janet. 2005. Wild fish catch hits limits—Oceanic decline offset by increased fish farming eco-economy indicators. Earth Policy Institute. www.earth-policy.org/Indicators/Fish/2005.htm

Lotze, Heike L., et al. 2006. Depletion, degradation, and recovery potential of estuaries and coastal seas. *Science* 312: 1806–1809.

Mastny, Lisa. 2001. World's coral reefs dying off. Pp. 92–93 in *Vital signs 2001.* Worldwatch Institute and W. W. Norton, Washington D.C., and New York.

Norse, Elliott, and Larry B. Crowder, eds. 2005. *Marine conservation biology: The science of maintaining the sea's biodiversity.* Island Press, Washington, D.C.

Nybakken, James W., and Mark D. Bertness. 2004. *Marine biology: An ecological approach*, 6th ed. Benjamin Cummings, San Francisco.

Palumbi, Stephen. 2003. *Marine reserves: A tool for ecosystem management and conservation.* Pew Oceans Commission.

Pauly, Daniel, et al. 2002. Towards sustainability in world fisheries. *Nature* 418: 689–695.

Pauly, Daniel, et al. 2003. The future for fisheries. *Science* 302: 1359–1361.

Pew Oceans Commission. 2003. *America's living oceans: Charting a course for sea change.* A report to the nation. May 2003. Pew Oceans Commission, Arlington, Virginia.

United Nations Environment Programme. 2002. Coastal and marine areas. Pp. 180–209 in *Global environment outlook 3 (GEO-3).* UNEP and Earthscan Publications, Nairobi and London.

Watson, Reginald, Lillian Pang, and Daniel Pauly. 2001. The marine fisheries of China: Development and reported catches. *Fisheries Centre Research Reports* 9(2). Fisheries Centre, University of British Columbia, Canada.

Watson, Reginald, and Daniel Pauly. 2001. Systematic distortions in world fisheries catch trends. *Nature* 414: 534–536.

Worm, Boris, et al. 2006. Impacts of biodiversity loss on ocean ecosystem services. *Science* 314: 787–790.

Chapter 14

Ahrens, C. Donald. 2007. *Meteorology today*, 8th ed. Brooks/Cole, San Francisco.

Akimoto, Hajime. 2003. Global air quality and pollution. *Science* 302: 1716–1719.

Boubel, Richard W., et al., eds. 1994. *Fundamentals of air pollution*, 3rd ed. Academic Press, San Diego, California.

Bruce, Nigel, Rogelio Perez-Padilla, and Rachel Albalak. 2000. Indoor air pollution in developing countries: A major environmental and public health challenge. *Bulletin of the World Health Organization* 78: 1078–1092.

Cooper, C. David, and F.C. Alley. 2002. *Air pollution control*, 3rd ed. Waveland Press.

Davis, Devra. 2002. *When smoke ran like water: Tales of environmental deception and the battle against pollution*. Basic Books, New York.

Davis, Devra L., Michelle L. Bell, and Tony Fletcher. 2002. A look back at the London smog of 1952 and the half century since. *Environmental Health Perspectives* 110: A734.

Driscoll, Charles T., et al. 2001. *Acid rain revisited: Advances in scientific understanding since the passage of the 1970 and 1990 Clean Air Act Amendments*. Hubbard Brook Research Foundation. Science Links™ Publication, vol. 1, no.1.

Godish, Thad. 2003. *Air quality*, 4th ed. CRC Press, Boca Raton, Florida.

Hoffman, Matthew J. 2005. *Ozone depletion and climate change: Constructing a global response*. SUNY Press, New York.

Likens, Gene E. 2004. Some perspectives on long-term biogeochemical research from the Hubbard Brook ecosystem study. *Ecology* 85: 2355–2362.

Lutgens, Frederick K., and Edward J. Tarbuck. 2007. *The atmosphere*. Pearson Prentice Hall. Upper Saddle River, New Jersey.

Molina, Mario J., and F. Sherwood Rowland. 1974. Stratospheric sink for chlorofluoromethanes: Chlorine atom catalyzed destruction of ozone. *Nature* 249: 810–812.

Parson, Edward A. 2003. *Protecting the ozone layer: Science and strategy*. Oxford University Press, Oxford.

United Nations Environment Programme. Montreal Protocol. http://ozone.unep.org/Treaties_and_Ratification/2B_montreal_protocol.shtml

United Nations Environment Programme. 2002. Atmosphere. Pp. 210–239 in *Global environment outlook 3 (GEO-3)*. UNEP and Earthscan Publications, Nairobi and London.

World Health Organization. Indoor air pollution. WHO, Geneva, Switzerland. www.who.int/indoorair/en/index.html

Chapter 15

Allen, M.R., et al. 2009. Warming caused by cumulative carbon emissions towards the trillionth ton. *Nature* 458: 1163–1166.

Alley, Richard B. 2000. *The two-mile time machine: Ice cores, abrupt climate change, and our future*. Princeton University Press, Princeton, New Jersey.

Appenzeller, Tim. 2007. The big thaw. *National Geographic*, June 2007: 56–71.

Arndt, D.S., et al., eds. 2010. State of the climate in 2009. *Bulletin of the American Meteorological Society*. 91(6): S1–S224.

Bloom, Arnold J. 2009. *Global climate change: Convergence of disciplines*. Sinauer Associates, Sunderland, Mass.

Burroughs, William James. 2001. *Climate change: A multidisciplinary approach*. Cambridge University Press, Cambridge.

Caldeira, Kenneth, and Michael E. Wickett. 2003. Anthropogenic carbon and ocean pH. *Nature* 425: 365.

Christopherson, R.W. and M-L. Byrne 2009. *Geosystems*, 2nd Canadian Ed. Prentice Hall.

Drake, Frances. 2000. *Global warming: The science of climate change*. Oxford University Press, Oxford.

Dunn, Seth, and Christopher Flavin. 2002. Moving the climate change agenda forward. Pp. 24–50 in *State of the world 2002*. Worldwatch Institute and W. W. Norton, Washington, D.C., and New York.

Dyer, G. 2008. *Climate wars*. Random House, Toronto.

EPICA community members. 2004. Eight glacial cycles from an Antarctic ice core. *Nature* 429: 623–628.

Fagan, B. 2008. *The great warming: Climate change and the rise and fall of civilizations*. Bloomsbury, New York.

Flannery, Tim. 2005. *The weather makers: The history and future impact of climate change*. Text Publishing, Melbourne, Australia.

Gelbspan, Ross. 1997. *The heat is on: The climate crisis, the cover-up, the prescription*. Perseus Books, New York.

Gelbspan, Ross. 2004. *Boiling point: How politicians, big oil and coal, journalists, and activists are fueling the climate crisis—and what we can do to avert disaster*. Basic Books, New York.

Gettleman, Jeffrey. 2006. Annan faults "frightening lack of leadership" for global warming. *New York Times*, 16 November 2006.

Gore, Al. 2006. *An inconvenient truth: The planetary emergency of global warming and what we can do about it*. Rodale Press and Melcher Media, New York.

Hansen, J.E. 2005. A slippery slope: How much global warming constitutes "dangerous anthropogenic interference"?: An editorial essay. *Climatic Change*, 68(3): 269–279.

Hansen, J.E. 2009. *Storms of my grandchildren*. Bloomsbury, New York.

Hansen, J.E., et al. 2005. Earth's energy imbalance: confirmation and implications. *Science* 308: 1431–1435.

Hansen, J.E., M. Sato, and R. Ruedy. 1997. Radiative forcing and climate response. *Journal of Geophysical Research*, 102(D6), 6831–6864.

Harvey, L.D.D. 2000. *Climate and global environmental change*. Prentice Hall.

Harvey, L.D.D. 2000. *Global warming: The hard science*. Prentice Hall.

Hoggan, J., and R. Littlemore. 2009. *Climate cover-up*. Greystone, Vancouver.

Intergovernmental Panel on Climate Change. 2001. *IPCC third assessment report—Climate change 2001: Synthesis report*. World Meteorological Organization and United Nations Environment Programme.

Intergovernmental Panel on Climate Change. 2007. *Climate change 2007: The physical science basis*. Contribution of Working Group I to the fourth assessment report of the Intergovernmental Panel on Climate Change. World Meteorological Organization and United Nations Environment Programme, Geneva, Switzerland.

Intergovernmental Panel on Climate Change. 2007. *Climate change 2007: Impacts, adaptation, and vulnerability*. Contribution of Working Group II to the fourth assessment report of the Intergovernmental Panel on Climate Change. World Meteorological Organization and United Nations Environment Programme, Geneva, Switzerland.

Intergovernmental Panel on Climate Change. 2007. *Climate change 2007: Mitigation of climate change*. Contribution of Working Group III to the fourth assessment report of the Intergovernmental Panel on Climate Change. World Meteorological Organization and United Nations Environment Programme, Geneva, Switzerland.

Intergovernmental Panel on Climate Change. www.ipcc.ch

Mann, M.E., and L.E. Kump 2009. *Dire predictions: Understanding global warming*. Pearson, New York.

Mayewski, Paul A., and Frank White. 2002. *The ice chronicles: The quest to understand global climate change*. University Press of New England, Hanover, New Hampshire.

Oreskes, N. and E.M. Conway. 2010. *Merchants of doubt*. New York, Bloomsbury Press, New York.

Pacala, Stephen, and Robert Socolow. 2004. Stabilization wedges: Solving the climate problem for the next 50 years with current technologies. *Science* 305: 968–972.

Parmesan, Camille, and Gary Yohe. 2003. A globally coherent fingerprint of climate change impacts across natural systems. *Nature* 421: 37–42.

Pew Center on Global Climate Change. www.pewclimate.org

Rosenzweig, C., D. Karoly, M. Vicarelli, P. Neofotis, Q. Wu, G. Casassa, A. Menzel, T.L. Root, N. Estrella, B. Seguin, P. Tryjanowski, C. Liu, S. Rawlins, and A. Imeson, 2008. Attributing physical and biological impacts to anthropogenic climate change. *Nature* 453: 353–358.

The Royal Society. 2005. *Ocean acidification due to increasing atmospheric carbon dioxide*. The Royal Society, London.

Sawin, Janet L. 2005. Climate change indicators on the rise. Pp. 40–41 in *Vital signs 2005*. Worldwatch Institute and W. W. Norton, Washington, D.C., and New York.

Serreze, M.C., M.M. Holland, and J. Stroeve. 2007. Perspectives on the Arctic's shrinking sea-ice cover. *Science* 315: 1533–1536.

Schiermeier, Quirin. 2006. Climate credits. *Nature* 444: 976–977.

Schneider, Stephen H., and Terry L. Root, eds. 2002. *Wildlife responses to climate change: North American case studies*. Island Press, Washington, D.C.

Siegenthaler, Urs, et al. 2005. Stable carbon cycle–climate relationship during the Late Pleistocene. *Science* 310: 1313–1317.

Simpson, J., M. Jaccard, and N. Rivers. 2007. *Hot air: Meeting Canada's climate change challenge*. McClelland and Stewart, Toronto.

Smil, V. 2008. *Global catastrophes and trends: The next fifty years*. MIT Press, Cambridge, Massachusetts.

Spahni, Renato, et al. 2005. Atmospheric methane and nitrous oxide of the Late Pleistocene from Antarctic ice cores. *Science* 310: 1317–1321.

Stevens, William K. 1999. *The change in the weather: People, weather and the science of climate*. Delta Trade Paperbacks, New York.

Taylor, David. 2003. Small islands threatened by sea level rise. Pp. 84–85 in *Vital signs 2003*. Worldwatch Institute and W. W. Norton, Washington D.C., and New York.

United Nations. United Nations Framework Convention on Climate Change. http://unfccc.int/2860.php

United Nations. Kyoto Protocol. http://unfccc.int/kyoto_protocol/items/2830.php

Weaver, A. 2008. *Keeping Our Cool: Canada in a Warming World*. Penguin, Toronto.

Worldwatch Institute. 2009. *State of the world 2009: Into a warming world*. Worldwatch Institute, Washington, D.C.

Chapter 16

Appenzeller, Tim. The end of cheap oil. *National Geographic*, June 2004: 80–109.

Association for the Study of Peak Oil and Gas. www.peakoil.net

British Petroleum. 2010. *BP statistical review of world energy 2010*. BP, London.

Deffeyes, Kenneth S. 2001. *Hubbert's peak: The impending world oil shortage*. Princeton University Press, Princeton, New Jersey.

Deffeyes, Kenneth S. 2005. *Beyond oil: The view from Hubbert's peak*. Farrar, Straus, and Giroux, New York.

Dunn, Seth. 2001. Decarbonizing the energy economy. Pp. 83–102 in *State of the world 2001*. Worldwatch Institute and W. W. Norton, Washington, D.C., and New York.

Energy Information Administration, U.S. Department of Energy. www.eia.doe.gov

Freese, Barbara. 2003. *Coal: A human history*. Perseus Books, New York.

Goodstein, David. 2004. *Out of gas*. W. W. Norton, New York.

Lovins, Amory B. 2005. More profit with less carbon. *Scientific American* 293(3): 74–83.

Lovins, Amory B., et al. 2004. *Winning the oil endgame: Innovation for profits, jobs, and security*. Rocky Mountain Institute, Snowmass, Colorado.

Prugh, Tom, et al. 2005. Changing the oil economy. Pp. 100–121 in *State of the world 2005*. Worldwatch Institute and W. W. Norton, Washington, D.C., and New York.

Ristinen, Robert A., and Jack J. Kraushaar. 2006. *Energy and the environment*, 2nd ed. John Wiley and Sons, New York.

Roberts, Paul. 2008. Tapped out. *National Geographic*, June 2008, 84–91.

Rottmann, Katja. 2006. Fossil fuel use continues to grow. Pp. 32–33 in *Vital signs 2006–2007*. Worldwatch Institute and W. W. Norton, Washington, D.C., and New York.

Sawin, Janet L. 2004. Making better energy choices. Pp. 24–45 in *State of the world 2004*. Worldwatch Institute and W. W. Norton, Washington, D.C., and New York.

Chapter 17

American Wind Energy Association. 2005. *Global wind energy market report*. AWEA, Washington, D.C.

Ananthaswamy, Anil. 2003. Reality bites for the dream of a hydrogen economy. *New Scientist* 2421: 6–7.

British Petroleum. 2007. *BP statistical review of world energy 2007*. BP, London.

Burkett, Elinor. 2003. A mighty wind. *New York Times Magazine*, 15 June, 2003.

The Chernobyl Forum. 2006. Chernobyl's legacy: Health, environmental and socio-economic impacts and recommendations to the governments of Belarus, the Russian Federation and Ukraine. World Health Organization and International Atomic Energy Agency, Vienna, Austria.

Chow, Jeffrey, et al. 2003. Energy resources and global development. *Science* 302: 1528–1531.

Dunn, Seth. 2000. The hydrogen experiment. *World Watch* 13: 14–25.

Dunn, Seth. 2001. Decarbonizing the energy economy. Pp. 83–102 in *State of the world 2001*. Worldwatch Institute and W. W. Norton, Washington, D.C., and New York.

Energy Information Administration, U.S. Department of Energy. www.eia.doe.gov

European Commission/International Atomic Energy Agency/World Health Organization. 1996. One decade after Chernobyl: Summing up the consequences of the accident. Summary of the conference results. Vienna, Austria, 8–12 April 1996. EC/IAEA/WHO.

Flavin, Christopher. 2008. *Low-carbon energy: A roadmap*. Worldwatch Report #178. Worldwatch Institute, Washington, D.C.

Hunt, Suzanne, and Janet L. Sawin, with Peter Stair. 2006. Cultivating renewable alternatives to oil. Pp. 61–77 in *State of the world 2006*. Worldwatch Institute and W. W. Norton, Washington, D.C., and New York.

Hunt, Suzanne, and Peter Stair. 2006. Biofuels hit a gusher. Pp. 40–41 in *Vital signs 2006–2007*. Worldwatch Institute and W. W. Norton, Washington, D.C., and New York.

International Atomic Energy Agency. *Nuclear power and sustainable development*. IAEA Information Series 02-01574/FS Series 3/01/E/Rev.1. IAEA, Vienna, Austria.

International Atomic Energy Agency. 2006. *Environmental consequences of the Chernobyl accident and their remediation: Twenty years of experience*. Report of the U.N. Chernobyl Forum Expert Group "Environment" IAEA, Vienna, Austria.

International Energy Agency. 2007. *Biomass for power generation and CHP*. IEA Publications, Paris.

International Energy Agency. 2007. *Renewables in global energy supply: An IEA fact sheet*. IEA Publications, Paris.

International Energy Agency. 2009. *World energy outlook 2009*. IEA Publications, Paris.

Knott, Michelle. 2003. Power from the waves. *New Scientist* 2413: 33–35.

Murray, Danielle. 2005. Ethanol's potential: Looking beyond corn. *Eco-economy Update #49*, 5 June 2005. Earth Policy Institute. www.earth-policy.org/Updates/2005/Update49.htm

Nature. 2006. Special report: Chernobyl and the future. *Nature* 440: 982–989.

Organisation for Economic Co-operation and Development. 2000. *Business as usual and nuclear power*. OECD Publications, Paris.

Pearce, Fred. 2006. Fuels gold: Are biofuels really the greenhouse-busting answer to our energy woes? *New Scientist*: 36–41.

REN21 Renewable Energy Policy Network. 2005. *Renewables 2005 global status report*. Worldwatch Institute, Washington, D.C.

Sawin, Janet. 2004. *Mainstreaming renewable energy in the 21st century*. Worldwatch Paper #169. Worldwatch Institute, Washington, D.C.

Sawin, Janet L. 2006. Wind power blowing strong. Pp. 36–37 in *Vital signs 2006–2007*. Worldwatch Institute and W. W. Norton, Washington, D.C., and New York.

Sawin, Janet L. 2006. Solar industry stays hot. Pp. 38–39 in *Vital signs 2006–2007*. Worldwatch Institute and W. W. Norton, Washington, D.C., and New York.

Sawin, Janet L., and William R. Moomaw. 2009. *Renewable revolution: Low-carbon energy by 2030*. Worldwatch Report #182. Worldwatch Institute, Washington, D.C.

Science. 2003. News focus: Rethinking nuclear power. *Science* 309: 1168–1179.

Spadaro, Joseph V., Lucille Langlois, and Bruce Hamilton. 2000. Greenhouse gas emissions of electricity generation chains: Assessing the difference. *IAEA Bulletin* 42(2).

U.N. Food and Agriculture Organization. *Biomass energy in ASEAN member countries*. FAO/ASEAN/EC. FAO Regional Wood Energy Development Programme in Asia, Bangkok, Thailand.

U.S. Environmental Protection Agency. Alternative fuels website. www.epa.gov/otaq/consumer/fuels/altfuels/altfuels.htm

Wald, Matthew L. 2006. The energy challenge: It's free, plentiful, and fickle. *New York Times*, 28 December 2006.

World Alliance for Decentralized Energy. 2005. *World survey of decentralized energy 2005*. WADE, Edinburgh, Scotland.

Chapter 18

Ayres, Robert U., and Leslie W. Ayres. 1996. *Industrial ecology: Towards closing the materials cycle*. Edward Elgar Press, Cheltenham, U.K.

Beede, David N., and David E. Bloom. 1995. The economics of municipal solid waste. *World Bank Research Observer* 10: 113–150.

Diesendorf, Mark, and Clive Hamilton. 1997. *Human ecology, human economy*. Allen and Unwin, St. Leonards.

Douglas, Ed. 2007. Better by design. *New Scientist* 2585: 31–35.

Douglas, Ed. 2009. There's gold in them there landfills. *New Scientist* 2676: 34–36.

Graedel, Thomas E., and Braden R. Allenby. 2002. *Industrial ecology*, 2nd ed. Prentice Hall, Upper Saddle River, New Jersey.

Lilienfeld, Robert, and William Rathje. 1998. *Use less stuff: Environmental solutions for who we really are*. Ballantine, New York.

McDonough, William, and Michael Braungart. 2002. *Cradle to cradle: Remaking the way we make things*. North Point Press, New York.

Rathje, William, and Colleen Murphy. 2001. *Rubbish! The archeology of garbage*. University of Arizona Press.

Socolow, Robert H., et al., eds. 1994. *Industrial ecology and global change*. Cambridge University Press, Cambridge.

United Nations Environment Programme. 2000. *International source book on environmentally sound technologies (ESTs) for municipal solid waste management (MSWM)*. UNEP IETC, Osaka, Japan.

United States Environmental Protection Agency. 2006. *Municipal solid waste generation, recycling, and disposal in the United States: Facts and figures for 2006*. EPA Office of Solid Waste and Emergency Response.

United States Environmental Protection Agency. Municipal solid waste. www.epa.gov/epaoswer/non-hw/muncpl

Chapter 19

Bloom, Barry. 2005. Public health in transition. *Scientific American* 293(3): 92–99.

Cagen, S.Z., et al. 1999. Normal reproductive organ development in wistar rats exposed to bisphenol A in the drinking water. *Regulatory Toxicology and Pharmacology* 30: 130–139.

Carson, Rachel. 1962. *Silent spring*. Houghton Mifflin, Boston.

Crain, D. Andrew, and Louis J. Guillette, Jr. 1998. Reptiles as models of contaminant-induced endocrine disruption. *Animal Reproduction Science* 53: 77–86.

Environmental Defence. 2008. *Toxic baby bottles in Canada*. Environmental Defence, Toronto, Ontario.

Guillette, Louis J., Jr., et al. 2000. Alligators and endocrine disrupting contaminants: A current perspective. *American Zoologist* 40: 438–452.

Landis, Wayne G., and Ming-Ho Yu. 2004. *Introduction to environmental toxicology*, 3rd ed. Lewis Press, Boca Raton, Florida.

Loewenberg, Samuel. 2003. E.U. starts a chemical reaction. *Science* 300: 405.

Manahan, Stanley E. 2004. *Environmental chemistry*, 8th ed. Lewis Publishers, CRC Press, Boca Raton, Florida.

McGinn, Anne Platt. 2000. *Why poison ourselves? A precautionary approach to synthetic chemicals*. Worldwatch Paper #153. Worldwatch Institute, Washington, D.C.

McGinn, Anne Platt. 2002. Reducing our toxic burden. Pp. 75–100 in *State of the world 2002*. Worldwatch Institute and W. W. Norton, Washington, D.C., and New York.

Millennium Ecosystem Assessment. 2005. *Ecosystems and human well-being: Health synthesis*. World Health Organization.

Moeller, Dade. 2004. *Environmental health*, 3rd ed. Harvard University Press.

Myers, Samuel S. 2009. *Global environmental change: The threat to human health*. Worldwatch Report #181. Worldwatch Institute, Washington, D.C.

National Center for Environmental Health, U.S. Centers for Disease Control and Prevention. 2005. *Third national report on human exposure to environmental chemicals*. NCEH Pub. No. 05-0570. NCEH, Atlanta, Georgia.

Rodricks, Joseph V. 1994. *Calculated risks: Understanding the toxicity of chemicals in our environment*. Cambridge University Press, Cambridge.

Smith, Rick, and Bruce Lourie with Sarah Dopp. 2009. *Slow death by rubber duck: How the toxic chemistry of everyday life affects our health*. Alfred A. Knopf Canada.

Stephens, Carolyn, and Peter Stair. 2007. Charting a new course for urban public health. Pp. 134–151 in *State of the world 2007: Our urban future*. Worldwatch Institute and W. W. Norton, Washington, D.C., and New York.

Stockholm Convention on Persistent Organic Pollutants. www.pops.int

Chapter 20

Abbott, Carl. 2002. Planning a sustainable city. Pp. 207–235 in Squires, Gregory D., ed. *Urban sprawl: Causes, consequences, and policy responses*. Urban Institute Press, Washington, D.C.

Beck, Roy, et al. 2003. *Outsmarting smart growth: Population growth, immigration, and the problem of sprawl*. Center for Immigration Studies, Washington, D.C.

Breuste, Jurgen, et al. 1998. *Urban ecology*. Springer-Verlag, Berlin.

Cronon, William. 1991. *Nature's metropolis: Chicago and the great West*. W. W. Norton, New York.

Girardet, Herbert. 2004. *Cities, people, planet: Livable cities for a sustainable world*. Academy Press.

Hall, Kenneth B., and Gerald A. Porterfield. 2001. *Community by design: New urbanism for suburbs and small communities*. McGraw-Hill, New York.

Jacobs, Jane. 1961. *The death and life of great American cities*. Random House, New York.

Kalnay, Eugenia, and Ming Cai. 2003. Impact of urbanization and land-use change on climate. *Nature* 423: 528–531.

Kirdar, Uner, ed. 1997. *Cities fit for people*. United Nations, New York.

New Urbanism. www.newurbanism.org

Pearce, Fred. 2005. Cities lead the way to a greener world. *New Scientist* 2582: 8–9.

Sheehan, Molly O'Meara. 2001. *City limits: Putting the brakes on sprawl*. Worldwatch Paper #156. Worldwatch Institute, Washington, D.C.

Sheehan, Molly O'Meara. 2002. What will it take to halt sprawl? *World Watch* 15(1): 12–23.

Sprawl City. www.sprawlcity.org

Stren, R., et al. 1992. *Sustainable cities: Urbanization and the environment in international perspective*. Westview Press, Boulder, Colorado, and San Francisco.

United Nations Environment Programme. 2002. Urban areas. Pp. 240–269 in *Global environment outlook 3 (GEO-3)*. UNEP and Earthscan Publications, Nairobi and London.

United Nations Population Division. 2010. *World urbanization prospects: The 2009 revision*. UNPD, New York.

Worldwatch Institute. 2007. *State of the world 2007: Our urban future*. Worldwatch Institute and W. W. Norton, Washington, D.C., and New York.

Chapter 21

Balmford, Andrew, et al. 2002. Economic reasons for conserving wild nature. *Science* 297: 950–953.

Barbour, Ian G. 1992. *Ethics in an age of technology*. Harper Collins, San Francisco.

Beddoe, Rachael, et al. 2009. Overcoming systemic roadblocks to sustainability: The evolutionary redesign of worldviews, institutions, and technologies. *PNAS* 106: 2483–2489.

Brown, Lester. 2001. *Eco-economy: Building an economy for the Earth*. Earth Policy Institute and W. W. Norton, New York.

Cole, Luke W., and Sheila R. Foster. 2001. *From the ground up: Environmental racism and the rise of the environmental justice movement*. New York University Press, New York.

Costanza, Robert, et al. 1997. The value of the world's ecosystem services and natural capital. *Nature* 387: 253–260.

Costanza, Robert, et al. 1997. *An introduction to ecological economics*. St. Lucie Press, Boca Raton, Florida.

Daily, Gretchen. 1997. *Nature's services: Societal dependence on natural ecosystems*. Island Press, Washington, D.C.

Daly, Herman E. 1996. *Beyond growth*. Beacon Press, Boston.

Daly, Herman E. 2005. Economics in a full world. *Scientific American* 293(3): 100–107.

De Graaf, John, David Wann, and Thomas Naylor. 2002. *Affluenza: The all-consuming epidemic*. Berrett-Koehler Publishers, San Francisco.

Elliot, Robert, and Arran Gare, eds. 1983. *Environmental philosophy: A collection of readings*. Pennsylvania State University Press, University Park.

Esty, Daniel C., and Andrew S. Winston. 2006. *Green to gold: How smart companies use environmental strategy to innovate, create value, and build competitive advantage*. Yale University Press, New Haven, Connecticut.

Field, Barry C., and Martha K. Field. 2005. *Environmental economics*, 4th ed. McGraw-Hill, New York.

Fox, Stephen. 1985. *The American conservation movement: John Muir and his legacy*. University of Wisconsin Press, Madison.

Gardner, Gary, et al. 2004. The state of consumption today. Pp. 3–23 in *State of the world 2004*. Worldwatch Institute and W. W. Norton, Washington, D.C., and New York.

Gardner, Gary, and Erik Assadourian. 2004. Rethinking the good life. Pp. 164–179 in *State of the world 2004*. Worldwatch Institute and W. W. Norton, Washington, D.C., and New York.

Goodstein, Eban. 1999. *The tradeoff myth: Fact and fiction about jobs and the environment*. Island Press, Washington, D.C.

Goodstein, Eban. 2010. *Economics and the environment*, 6th ed. John Wiley & Sons, Hoboken, N.J.

Hawken, Paul, Amory Lovins, and L. Hunter Lovins. 1999. *Natural capitalism*. Little, Brown, and Co., Boston.

HM Treasury. 2006. *Stern review on the economics of climate change*. HM Treasury and Cambridge University Press, U.K.

Kolstad, Charles D. 2010. *Environmental economics*, 2nd ed. Oxford University Press, Oxford.

Leopold, Aldo. 1949. *A Sand County almanac, and sketches here and there*. Oxford University Press, New York.

Millennium Ecosystem Assessment. 2005. *Ecosystems and human wellbeing: Opportunities and challenges for business and industry*. Millennium Ecosystem Assessment and World Resources Institute.

Nash, Roderick F. 1989. *The rights of nature*. University of Wisconsin Press, Madison.

Nordhaus, William. 2007. Critical assumptions in the Stern Review on Climate Change. *Science* 317: 201–202.

O'Neill, John O., R. Kerry Turner, and Ian J. Bateman, eds. 2002. *Environmental ethics and philosophy*. Edward Elgar, Cheltenham, U.K.

Pearson, Charles S. 2000. *Economics and the global environment*. Cambridge University Press, Cambridge.

Ricketts, Taylor, et al. 2004. Economic value of tropical forest to coffee production. *Proceedings of the National Academy of Sciences of the USA* 101: 12579–12582.

Sachs, Jeffrey. 2005. Can extreme poverty be eliminated? *Scientific American* 293(3): 56–65.

Singer, Peter, ed. 1993. *A companion to ethics*. Blackwell Publishers, Oxford, U.K.

Smith, Adam. 1776. *An inquiry into the nature and causes of the wealth of nations*, 1993 ed. Oxford University Press, Oxford.

Stone, Christopher D. 1972. Should trees have standing? Towards legal rights for natural objects. *Southern California Law Review* 1972: 450–501.

Talberth, John, et al. 2007. *The genuine progress indicator 2006: A tool for sustainable development*. Redefining Progress, Oakland, Calif.

White, Lynn. 1967. The historic roots of our ecologic crisis. *Science* 155: 1203–1207.

Chapter 22

Carpentier, Chantal Line. 2006. NAFTA Commission for Environmental Cooperation: Ongoing assessment of trade liberalization in North America. *Impact Assessment and Project Appraisal* 24: 259–272.

Green Scissors. 2010. *Green Scissors 2010: More than $200 billion in cuts to wasteful and environmentally harmful spending*. Friends of the Earth, Taxpayers for Common Sense, Environment America, and Public Citizen.

Houck, Oliver. 2003. Tales from a troubled marriage: Science and law in environmental policy. *Science* 302: 1926–1928.

Kraft, Michael E. 2003. *Environmental policy and politics*, 3rd ed. Longman, New York.

Kubasek, Nancy K., and Gary S. Silverman. 2004. *Environmental law*, 5th ed. Prentice Hall, Upper Saddle River, New Jersey.

Myers, Norman, and Jennifer Kent. 2001. *Perverse subsidies: How misused tax dollars harm the environment and the economy*. Island Press, Washington, D.C.

Nordhaus, Ted, and Michael Shellenberger. 2007. *Break through: From the death of environmentalism to the politics of possibility*. Houghton Mifflin, Boston.

Percival, Robert V., et al. 2009. *Environmental regulation: Law, science, and policy*, 6th ed. Aspen Publishers, New York.

Renner, Michael. 2008. *Green jobs: Working for people and the environment*. Worldwatch Report #177. Worldwatch Institute, Washington, D.C.

Shellenberger, Michael, and Ted Nordhaus. 2004. *The death of environmentalism: Global warming politics in a post-environmental world*. Presented at the Environmental Grantmakers Association meeting, October 2004.

Steel, Brent S., Richard L. Clinton, and Nicholas P. Lovrich. 2002. *Environmental politics and policy*. McGraw-Hill, New York.

Tietenberg, Tom, and Lynne Lewis. 2010. *Environmental economics and policy*, 6th ed. Prentice Hall, Upper Saddle River, N.J.

Vig, Norman J., and Michael E. Kraft, eds. 2009. *Environmental policy: New directions for the twenty-first century*, 7th ed. CQ Press, Washington, D.C.

Chapter 23

Bartlett, Peggy, and Geoffrey W. Chase, eds. 2004. *Sustainability on campus: Stories and strategies for change*. MIT Press, Cambridge, Massachusetts.

Brower, Michael, and Warren Leon. 1999. *The consumer's guide to effective environmental choices: Practical advice from the Union of Concerned Scientists*. Three Rivers Press, New York.

Brown, Lester. 2001. *Eco-economy: Building an economy for the Earth*. Earth Policy Institute and W. W. Norton, New York.

Brown, Lester. 2009. *Plan B 4.0: Mobilizing to save civilization*. Earth Policy Institute and W. W. Norton, New York.

Campus Ecology. 2008. *Campus environment 2008: A national report card on sustainability in higher education*. Campus Ecology Program of the National Wildlife Federation.

Carlson, Scott. 2006. In search of the sustainable campus: With eyes on the future, universities try to clean up their acts. *Chronicle of Higher Education*, 20 Oct. 2006, vol 53: A10.

Creighton, Sarah Hammond. 1998. *Greening the ivory tower: Improving the environmental track record of universities, colleges, and other institutions*. MIT Press, Cambridge, Massachusetts.

Daly, Herman E. 1996. *Beyond growth*. Beacon Press, Boston.

Dasgupta, Partha, Simon Levin, and Jane Lubchenco. 2000. Economic pathways to ecological sustainability. *Bio Science* 50: 339–345.

Durning, Alan. 1992. *How much is enough? The consumer society and the future of the Earth*. Worldwatch Institute, Washington, D.C.

Erickson, Christina, and David J. Eagan. 2009. *Generation E: Students leading for a sustainable, clean energy future*. Campus Ecology Program of the National Wildlife Federation.

Erickson, Jon D., and John M. Gowdy. 2002. The strange economics of sustainability. *Bio Science* 52: 212.

Esty, Daniel C., et al. 2006. *Pilot 2006 Environmental Performance Index*. Yale Center for Environmental Law & Policy, New Haven, Connecticut.

French, Hilary. 2004. Linking globalization, consumption, and governance. Pp. 144–163 in *State of the world 2004*. Worldwatch Institute and W. W. Norton, Washington, D.C., and New York.

Gardner, Gary. 2001. Accelerating the shift to sustainability. Pp. 189–206 in *State of the world 2001*. Worldwatch Institute and W. W. Norton, Washington, D.C., and New York.

Gardner, Gary, and Erik Assadourian. 2004. Rethinking the good life. Pp. 164–179 in *State of the world 2004*. Worldwatch Institute and W. W. Norton, Washington, D.C., and New York.

Gibbs, W. Wayt. 2005. How should we set priorities? *Scientific American* 293(3): 108–115.

Hawken, Paul. 1994. *The ecology of commerce: A declaration of sustainability*. Harper Business, New York.

Kahneman, Daniel, et al. 2006. Would you be happier if you were richer? A focusing illusion. *Science* 312: 1908–1910.

Keniry, Julian. 1995. *Ecodemia: Campus environmental stewardship at the turn of the 21st century*. National Wildlife Federation, Washington, D.C.

McMichael, A. J., et al. 2003. New visions for addressing sustainability. *Science* 302: 1919–1921.

Meadows, Donella, Jørgen Randers, and Dennis Meadows. 2004. *Limits to growth: The 30-year update*. Chelsea Green Publishing Co., White River Junction, Vermont.

Millennium Ecosystem Assessment. 2005. *Ecosystems and human well-being: Synthesis*. Island Press, Washington, DC. World Resources Institute.

National Wildlife Federation. Campus ecology. www.nwf.org/campusecology

Renner, Michael. 2008. *Green jobs: Working for people and the environment*. Worldwatch Report #177. Worldwatch Institute, Washington, D.C.

Toor, Will, and Spenser W. Havlick. 2004. *Transportation and sustainable campus communities: Issues, examples, solutions*. Island Press, Washington, D.C.

United Nations Department of Economic and Social Affairs. 2006. *The Millennium Development Goals report 2006*. U.N. DESA, New York.

University Leaders for a Sustainable Future. www.ulsf.org

Wilson, Edward O. 1998. *Consilience: The unity of knowledge*. Alfred A. Knopf, New York.

World Commission on Environment and Development. 1987. *Our common future*. Oxford University Press, Oxford.

INDEX